Holt Geometry Features Quicklist
TEXAS EDITION

	SEE PAGE(S)
PROVEN INSTRUCTIONAL DESIGN	
• Consistent lesson format of **Example, Solution, Check It Out** provides a logical instructional approach.	216–218
• Step-by-step examples and color-coded explanations help students become independent learners.	224–226
• Know-it Notes indicate key concepts for students to remember and correspond to entries in the students' **Know-it Notebook**.	224
• Exercises matched to examples mean no homework surprises!	256

	SEE PAGE(S)
COMPREHENSIVE DIFFERENTIATED INSTRUCTION	
• Reaching All Learners includes strategies for adapting the material for all types of learners.	TE 224
• English Language Learners identifies strategies particularly effective with this group of students.	TE 253
• Geometry Labs allow students to explore math concepts through manipulatives.	240–241
• Technology Labs assist students in the use of graphing calculators, spreadsheets, and dynamic geometry software.	250–252
• Reteach, Practice, Challenge, Reading Strategies, and Problem Solving reduced images make selecting worksheets quick and easy.	TE 220–221
• Teaching Tips provide suggestions for addressing various learning styles.	TE 235
• Additional Examples offer more classroom review for struggling students.	TE 232
• Assignment Guide recommends homework assignments based on student ability.	TE 234
• Power Presentations are editable PowerPoint® presentations for every lesson as well as extra examples and quizzes.	TE 237

	SEE PAGE(S)
BUILT-IN ASSESSMENT AND INTERVENTION	
• Are You Ready? at the beginning of each chapter assesses students' prerequisite skills..	213
• Ready to Go On? diagnoses students' skill development within the chapter.	239
• Check It Out and Try This questions enable students to check their understanding after every example and activity.	225, 240
• Questioning Strategies aid on-the-spot intervention with questions crafted to assess student comprehension.	TE 243
• Common Error Alert helps teachers anticipate potential pitfalls for students.	TE 229
• Alternative Assessment provides options to monitor student progress.	TE 249
• Chapter Test assesses students' mastery of concepts and skills.	288

	SEE PAGE(S)
READING AND WRITING MATH FOR COMPREHENSION	
• Reading and Writing Math lessons help students develop strong communication skills as they master math concepts.	215
• Reading Math and Writing Math hints appear throughout each chapter to help students use the language of math.	81, 273
• Write About It exercises require students to explain a math concept or procedure.	220
• Journal suggestions encourage students to write about math.	TE 237
• Think and Discuss questions in every lesson extend and enrich student knowledge.	255
• Graphic Organizers in every lesson help students organize and remember key information.	269
• Glossary contains definitions and illustrations of key mathematical terms in English and Spanish.	S115–160

	SEE PAGE(S)
ENGAGING CONNECTIONS AND APPLICATIONS	
• Links spark student interest by giving them the opportunity to apply math skills to other disciplines and the real world.	220, 248, 271
• On Track for TAKS connects TAKS objectives across grade levels.	266
• Career Path relates math concepts to the real world.	237
• Problem Solving on Location uses word problems set in Texas to develop problem-solving skills.	294–295

	SEE PAGE(S)
INTEGRATED TEST PREP	
• Countdown to TAKS prepares students for state tests with daily practice questions.	C4–C27
• Test Prep and Spiral Review provide daily practice of new and previously taught skills in standardized test format.	230
• TAKS Prep Doctor addresses specific test-taking strategies related to the lesson.	TE 290
• Multi-Step TAKS Prep uses real-world scenarios to develop higher order thinking skills.	229, 238
• TAKS Tackler targets specific test-taking strategies to help students become savvy test-takers.	290–291
• College Entrance Exam Practice provides practice for college entrance exams such as the SAT and ACT.	289
• TAKS Prep provides cumulative assessment in TAKS format.	292–293

	SEE PAGE(S)
STUDENT SUPPORT	
• Study Guide: Preview prepares students for the TEKS they will learn in the chapter and familiarizes them with the chapter's vocabulary.	214
• Student to Student shares advice from other students on how to approach the math in the lesson.	233
• TEKS/TAKS Practice directs students to additional, immediate practice of lesson concepts.	246, S11
• Homework Help Online provides stepped-out solutions and additional practice for students as they work independently.	256
• Study Guide: Review highlights each lesson's vocabulary and key skills and offers additional examples and practice exercises.	284–287
• TEKS for each lesson are written out to help students focus on Texas objectives.	223

TEXAS TEACHER'S EDITION

HOLT
Geometry

Edward B. Burger

David J. Chard

Earlene J. Hall

Paul A. Kennedy

Steven J. Leinwand

Freddie L. Renfro

Dale G. Seymour

Bert K. Waits

HOLT, RINEHART AND WINSTON

A Harcourt Education Company

Orlando • **Austin** • New York • San Diego • London

Geometry Texas Student Edition
Contents in Brief

Student Handbook

ISBN 0-03-041663-9

1 2 3 4 5 048 09 08 07 06

Cover photo: Reunion Tower in Dallas, TX ©johnleepbs/Dreamstime.com

Geometry Texas Teacher's Edition
Contents in Brief

Chapter Teacher Material

Student Handbook

Contributing Authors

Linda Antinone
Fort Worth, TX

Ms. Antinone teaches mathematics at R. L. Paschal High School in Fort Worth, Texas. She has received the Presidential Award for Excellence in Teaching Mathematics and the National Radio Shack Teacher award. She has coauthored several books for Texas Instruments on the use of technology in mathematics.

Carmen Whitman
Pflugerville, TX

Ms. Whitman travels nationally helping districts improve mathematics education. She has been a program coordinator on the mathematics team at the Charles A. Dana Center, and has served as a secondary math specialist for the Austin Independent School District.

Texas Reviewers

Sharon Butler
Adjunct Faculty
Montgomery College of
    The Woodlands
Spring, TX

Carey Carter
Mathematics Teacher
Everman Joe C. Bean High School
Everman, TX

Joan Chrismer-McNatt
Mathematics Teacher
Clear Creek High School
League City, TX

Roy L. Conwell, Jr.
Mathematics Department Chair
Sam Houston High School
Houston, TX

Melinda Crook
Mathematics Teacher
Sachse High School
Sachse, TX

Mohammad Elkhatib
Mathematics Department Chair
Jones High School
Houston Community
    College Instructor
Houston, TX

Roger Fuller
Mathematics Department Chair
Grand Prairie High School
Grand Prairie, TX

Mary Gesino
Mathematics Department Co-Chair
R. L. Turner High School
Carrollton, TX

Lynn Guerra
Mathematics Teacher
Patti Welder M.S.
Victoria, TX

Kathy Henry
Mathematics Teacher
Parkland High School
El Paso, TX

Cynthia Hodges
Mathematics Department Chair
Shoemaker High School
Killeen, TX

Connie Johnsen
Mathematics Teacher
Harker Heights High School
Harker Heights, TX

Diana Johnston
Mathematics Teacher
Tuloso Midway High School
Corpus Christi, TX

Lendy Jones
Algebra Teacher
Liberty Hill Middle School
Killeen, TX

Brenda Lynch
Mathematics Department Chair
Montgomery High School
Montgomery, TX

Vilma Martinez
Algebra Teacher
Nikki Rowe High School
McAllen, TX

Dr. Charlotte May
Mathematics Teacher
Austin ISD
Austin, TX

Mende Mays
Algebra Teacher
Crockett Junior High
Odessa, TX

Saundra Paschal
Mathematics Department Chair
Lake View High School
San Angelo, TX

Sarah Ritch
Mathematics Department Chair
Hebron High School
Carrollton, TX

Terri Salas
Mathematics Consultant
Corpus Christi, TX

Raymond Seymour
Mathematics Department Chair, retired
Kirby Middle School
San Antonio, TX

Caren Sorrells
Mathematics Coordinator
Birdville ISD
Haltom City, TX

Stephanie Turner
Former Mathematics Teacher
Colleyville Heritage High School
Colleyville, TX

Anna Valdez
Geometry Teacher
Nikki Rowe High School
McAllen, TX

Pam Walker
Curriculum Teacher Specialist
Nacogdoches ISD
Nacogdoches, TX

Larry Ward
Mathematics Supervisor, retired
Carrollton-Farmers Branch ISD
Carrollton, TX

Carmen Whitman
Director, Mathematics for All Consulting
Pflugerville, TX

Field Test Participants

Jill Morris
Navasota High School
Navasota, TX

Ruth Stutzman
Jefferson Forest High School
Forest, VA

Carey Carter
Alvarado High School
Alvarado, TX

Walter Babst
Bonita High School
La Verne, CA

Texas *Friendship*

Explanation of Correlation

The following document is a correlation of Holt Geometry to the Texas Essential Knowledge and Skills for Geometry. The format for this correlation follows the same basic format established by the TEKS, modified to accommodate the addition of page references. The correlation provides a cross-reference between the skills in the TEKS and representative page numbers where those skills are taught or assessed.

The references contained in this correlation reflect Holt, Rinehart and Winston's interpretation of the mathematics objectives outlined in the Texas curriculum.

KEY TO REFERENCES	
Prefix	**Explanation**
SE	*Student Edition*

The Geometry Basic Understandings are incorporated throughout the text, so no specific correlations have been provided.

(a) Basic understandings.

(1) **Foundation concepts for high school mathematics.** As presented in Grades K-8, the basic understandings of number, operation, and quantitative reasoning; patterns, relationships, and algebraic thinking; geometry; measurement; and probability and statistics are essential foundations for all work in high school mathematics. Students continue to build on this foundation as they expand their understanding through other mathematical experiences.

(2) **Geometric thinking and symbolic reasoning.** Spatial reasoning plays a critical role in geometry; geometric figures provide powerful ways to represent mathematical situations and to express generalizations about space and spatial relationships. Students use geometric thinking to understand mathematical concepts and the relationships among them.

(3) **Geometric figures and their properties.** Geometry consists of the study of geometric figures of zero, one, two, and three dimensions and the relationships among them. Students study properties and relationships having to do with size, shape, location, direction, and orientation of these figures.

(4) **The relationship between geometry, other mathematics, and other disciplines.** Geometry can be used to model and represent many mathematical and real-world situations. Students perceive the connection between geometry and the real and mathematical worlds and use geometric ideas, relationships, and properties to solve problems.

(5) **Tools for geometric thinking.** Techniques for working with spatial figures and their properties are essential in understanding underlying relationships. Students use a variety of representations (concrete, pictorial, numerical, symbolic, graphical, and verbal), tools, and technology (including, but not limited to, calculators with graphing capabilities, data collection devices, and computers) to solve meaningful problems by representing and transforming figures and analyzing relationships.

(5) **Underlying mathematical processes.** Many processes underlie all content areas in mathematics. As they do mathematics, students continually use problem-solving, language and communication, connections within and outside mathematics, and reasoning (justification and proof). Students also use multiple representations technology, applications and modeling, and numerical fluency in problem solving contexts.

(b) Knowledge and skills.

(G.1) Geometric structure. The student understands the structure of, and relationships within, an axiomatic system.

The student is expected to:

(A)	develop an awareness of the structure of a mathematical system, connecting definitions, postulates, logical reasoning, and theorems;	**SE**	6–11, 20–27, 28–33, 36–41, 43–49, 50–55, 110–116, 117, 118–125, 162–169, 172–178, 216–221, 223–230, 252–259, 260–265, 460–461, 746–754, 756–763, 764–769, 772–779, 782–789, 792–798, 799–805, 808–809
(B)	recognize the historical development of geometric systems and know mathematics is developed for a variety of purposes; and	**SE**	20, 25, 41, 252, 257, 348, 353, 493, 566, 589, 595, 703, 768
(C)	compare and contrast the structures and implications of Euclidean and non-Euclidean geometries.	**SE**	726, 729

Johnson Space Center

(G.2) Geometric structure. The student analyzes geometric relationships in order to make and verify conjectures.

The student is expected to:

(A)	use constructions to explore attributes of geometric figures and to make conjectures about geometric relationships; and	**SE**	12, 14, 22, 23, 27, 56–57, 170–171, 172, 177, 179, 243, 248, 249, 250–251, 253, 258, 282–283, 307, 313, 314, 320, 321, 327, 363, 380–381, 404, 415, 416–417, 424, 426, 435, 468–469, 480, 481, 487, 524, 748, 763, 774, 778, 779, 780–781, 790–791, 824, 829, 831, 836, 839, 844, 872, 878
(B)	make conjectures about angles, lines, polygons, circles, and three-dimensional figures and determine the validity of the conjectures, choosing from a variety of approaches such as coordinate, transformational, or axiomatic.	**SE**	12, 18, 19, 25–27, 30, 31, 33, 56–57, 75–79, 89, 124, 229, 230, 236–237, 271–272, 274, 277–278, 312–313, 319–320, 324–327, 380–381, 387, 390, 396–397, 402–405, 413, 415, 416–417, 421–425, 426, 431, 434, 460–461, 499, 659, 750, 754, 761, 763, 775, 777–778, 780–781, 788, 790–791, 798, 805, 829, 833, 836, 844–845, 846–847, 861

(G.3) Geometric structure. The student applies logical reasoning to justify and prove mathematical statements.

The student is expected to:

(A)	determine the validity of a conditional statement, its converse, inverse, and contrapositive;	**SE**	82–87, 97–101
(B)	construct and justify statements about geometric figures and their properties;	**SE**	12, 13, 15–19, 21–27, 89–93, 97–101, 106–109, 110–116, 117, 242–249, 250–251, 253–259, 268–272, 282–283, 300, 303–306, 308, 310, 312–313, 316–320, 324–327, 334–3??, 341–345, 356, 361, 380–381, 387–388, 390, 394, 396–397, 399–405, 410, 413, 415, 416–417, 420–425, 426, 434, 468–469, 480, 486, 790–791
(C)	use logical reasoning to prove statements are true and find counter examples to disprove statements that are false;	**SE**	82, 84–87, 88–93, 106–108, 110–116, 117, 119–125, 128–129, 159–161, 162, 164–169, 173, 175–178, 192, 194–197, 253–259, 275–279, 332, 336, 338–339, 595–597
(D)	use inductive reasoning to formulate a conjecture; and	**SE**	74–79, 222, 380–381
(E)	use deductive reasoning to prove a statement.	**SE**	88–93, 104–109, 110–116, 117, 118–125, 159–161, 162–169, 173, 175–178, 192, 195–197, 242–249, 253–259, 260–265, 305–306, 332, 336, 338–339, 342–345, 394–397, 400, 402–405, 411–415, 420, 422–425, 434–435, 595–597

(G.4) Geometric structure. The student uses a variety of representations to describe geometric relationships and solve problems.

The student is expected to:

(A)	select an appropriate representation (concrete, pictorial, graphical, verbal, or symbolic) in order to solve problems	**SE**	42, 94–95, 128–129, 222, 240–241, 266, 387–388, 501, 755, 780–781, 801–805

McDonald Observatory

(G.5) Geometric patterns. The student uses a variety of representations to describe geometric relationships and solve problems.

The student is expected to:

(A)	use numeric and geometric patterns to develop algebraic expressions representing geometric properties;	**SE**	222, 322–327, 347, 356–362, 383–388, 460–461, 488–494, 501, 589–597, 598–599, 600–605, 622–627, 670–677, 680–687, 689–696, 697–704, 705–712, 714–721, 780–781, 782–789, 790–791, 792–798, 799–805
(B)	use numeric and geometric patterns to make generalizations about geometric properties, including properties of polygons, ratios in similar figures and solids, and angle relationships in polygons and circles;	**SE**	74–79, 331, 332–339, 348–355, 363, 380–381, 382–388, 454–459, 460–461, 462–467, 470–477, 480, 481–487, 501, 518–523, 524, 525–532, 551–558, 570–571, 622–627, 680–687, 689–696, 697–704, 705–712, 714–721, 772–779, 780–781, 782–789, 846–847
(C)	use properties of transformations and their compositions to make connections between mathematics and the real world, such as tessellations; and	**SE**	50, 52–55, 848–849, 851–853, 856–857, 859–862, 863, 865–868, 870–871, 882–883
(D)	identify and apply patterns from right triangles to solve meaningful problems, including special right triangles (45–45–90 and 30–60–90) and triangles whose sides are Pythagorean triples.	**SE**	348–355, 356–362, 518–523, 525–532, 534–541, 544–549, 550, 551–558

(G.6) Dimensionality and the geometry of location. The student analyzes the relationship between three-dimensional geometric figures and related two-dimensional representations and uses these representations to solve problems.

The student is expected to:

(A)	describe and draw the intersection of a given plane with various three-dimensional geometric figures;	**SE**	656–660
(B)	use nets to represent and construct three-dimensional geometric figures; and	**SE**	655, 657, 660, 669, 680–682, 686–687, 689–690, 695–696
(C)	use orthographic and isometric views of three-dimensional geometric figures to represent and construct three-dimensional geometric figures and solve problems.	**SE**	661–668

Gulf Coast shrimp boats

(G.7) Dimensionality and the geometry of location. The student understands that coordinate systems provide convenient and efficient ways of representing geometric figures and uses them accordingly.

The student is expected to:

(A)	use one- and two-dimensional coordinate systems to represent points, lines, rays, line segments, and figures;	SE	13–19, 42, 43–49, 182–187, 190–197, 261, 263, 265, 303–306, 308–309, 311–313, 315, 319, 330, 361, 387, 393, 395, 397, 400–402, 405, 410, 412, 414, 420–425, 434–435, 501, 536–539, 557–558, 560, 562–565, 567, 570–571, 616–621, 826–830, 832–837, 840–845, 846–847
(B)	use slopes and equations of lines to investigate geometric relationships, including parallel lines, perpendicular lines, and special segments of triangles and other polygons; and	SE	184–187, 188–189, 192–197, 303–306, 308–313, 315–319, 322, 324, 326, 393, 395, 397, 400–402, 405, 410, 412, 414, 420–425, 434–435, 454, 617, 619–620
(C)	derive and use formulas involving length, slope, and midpoint.	SE	13, 15–19, 43–49, 182–187, 190, 194–197, 303–306, 315–319, 354, 393, 395, 400–402, 405, 410, 412, 414, 420–425, 434–435, 454, 457–458, 536–539, 560, 562–567, 671–677

West Texas plowed cotton field

(G.8) Congruence and the geometry of size. The student uses tools to determine measurements of geometric figures and extends measurement concepts to find perimeter, area, and volume in problem situations.

The student is expected to:

(A)	find areas of regular polygons, circles, and composite figures;	SE	36–41, 523, 600–605, 606–612, 613, 616–621, 632–636, 637
(B)	find areas of sectors and arc lengths of circles using proportional reasoning;	SE	764–769
(C)	derive, extend, and use the Pythagorean Theorem; and	SE	45, 47–48, 347, 348–355, 522, 531, 539, 592–595, 604–605, 671, 674–677, 759–763
(D)	find surface areas and volumes of prisms, pyramids, spheres, cones, cylinders, and composites of these figures in problem situations.	SE	680–687, 689–696, 697–704, 705–712, 714–721

(G.9) Congruence and the geometry of size. The student analyzes properties and describes relationships in geometric figures.

The student is expected to:

(A) formulate and test conjectures about the properties of parallel and perpendicular lines based on explorations and concrete models;

SE 154, 159, 160, 168, 170–171, 176–178, 179

(B) formulate and test conjectures about the properties and attributes of polygons and their component parts based on explorations and concrete models;

SE 222, 240–241, 250–251, 253, 271, 321, 327, 331, 347, 380–381, 390, 416–417, 426, 468–469, 480, 481, 498, 499, 524

(C) formulate and test conjectures about the properties and attributes of circles and the lines that intersect them based on explorations and concrete models; and

SE 754, 763, 768, 779, 780–781, 788, 790–791

(D) analyze the characteristics of polyhedra and other three-dimensional figures and their component parts based on explorations and concrete models.

SE 655, 657, 658, 668, 669, 671–672, 674–676, 688

(G.10) Congruence and the geometry of size. The student applies the concept of congruence to justify properties of figures and solve problems.

The student is expected to:

(A)	use congruence transformations to make conjectures and justify properties of geometric figures including figures represented on a coordinate plane; and	**SE**	xxvi, 222, 240–241, 250–251, 282–283, 390, 570–571, 824, 826, 830–831, 833, 837, 839, 841, 844, 845, 846–847, 850, 862
(B)	justify and apply triangle congruence relationships.	**SE**	232–237, 240–241, 242–249, 250–251, 252–259, 260–265, 271–272, 273, 275–279, 300, 305–306, 391, 394–396

Oil pumpjack

(G.11) Similarity and the geometry of shape. The student applies the concepts of similarity to justify properties of figures and solve problems.

The student is expected to:

(A)	use and extend similarity properties and transformations to explore and justify conjectures about geometric figures;	**SE**	462–467, 468–469, 470–477, 481–487, 488–494, 495–500, 501, 518–523, 524, 551–558, 570–571, 846–847, 872–879
(B)	use ratios to solve problems involving similar figures;	**SE**	454–459, 462–467, 470–477, 481–487, 488–494, 501, 518–523, 525–532, 534–541, 550, 872–879
(C)	develop, apply, and justify triangle similarity relationships, such as right triangle ratios, trigonometric ratios, and Pythagorean triples using a variety of methods; and	**SE**	348–355, 518–523, 525–532, 534–541, 544–549, 550, 551–558, 562, 564, 565, 567, 570–571
(D)	describe the effect on perimeter, area, and volume when one or more dimensions of a figure are changed and apply this idea in solving problems.	**SE**	490–494, 622–627, 683–686, 691, 693, 694, 700–703, 708, 710, 716, 718, 719, 722–723, 876–878

Coastal Plains ranching

Texas Assessment of Knowledge and Skills
Grades 9–11 Objectives

The full text of the TAKS objectives for Grades 9–11 are provided below. Correlations to the TAKS objectives are provided in features and exercises throughout the text.

Objective	Description
(1)	The student will describe functional relationships in a variety of ways.
(2)	The student will demonstrate an understanding of the properties and attributes of functions.
(3)	The student will demonstrate an understanding of linear functions.
(4)	The student will formulate and use linear equations and inequalities.
(5)	The student will demonstrate an understanding of quadratic and other nonlinear functions.
(6)	The student will demonstrate an understanding of geometric relationships and spatial reasoning.
(7)	The student will demonstrate an understanding of two- and three-dimensional representations of geometric relationships and shapes.
(8)	The student will demonstrate an understanding of the concepts and uses of measurement and similarity.
(9)	The student will demonstrate an understanding of percents, proportional relationships, probability, and statistics in application problems.
(10)	The student will demonstrate an understanding of the mathematical processes and tools used in problem solving.

PREPARING FOR TAKS

Holt Geometry provides many opportunities for
you to prepare for TAKS.

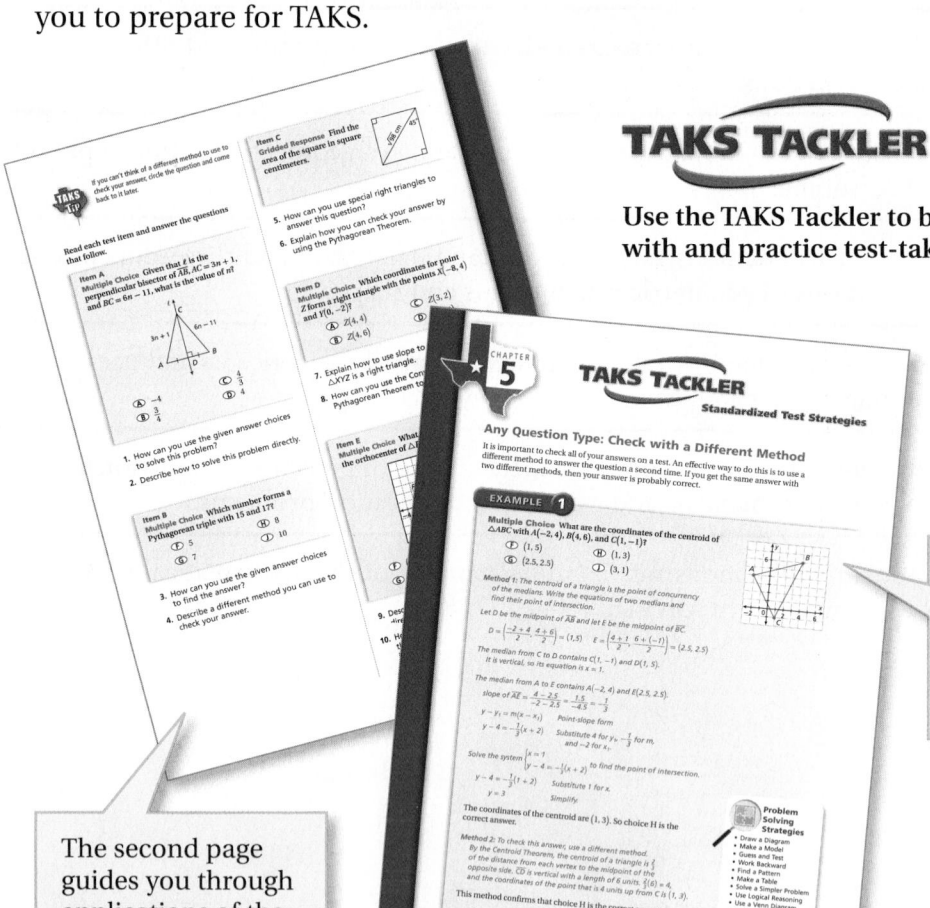

TAKS TACKLER

Use the TAKS Tackler to become familiar
with and practice test-taking strategies.

> The first page
> of this feature
> explains and shows
> an example of a
> test-taking strategy.

> The second page
> guides you through
> applications of the
> test-taking strategy.

TAKS PREP

Use the TAKS Prep to apply
test-taking strategies.

> The TAKS Tip provides
> test-taking tips to help you
> suceed on your tests.

> These pages include practice
> with multiple choice and gridded
> response as seen on the TAKS.
> Also includes short response
> and extended response.

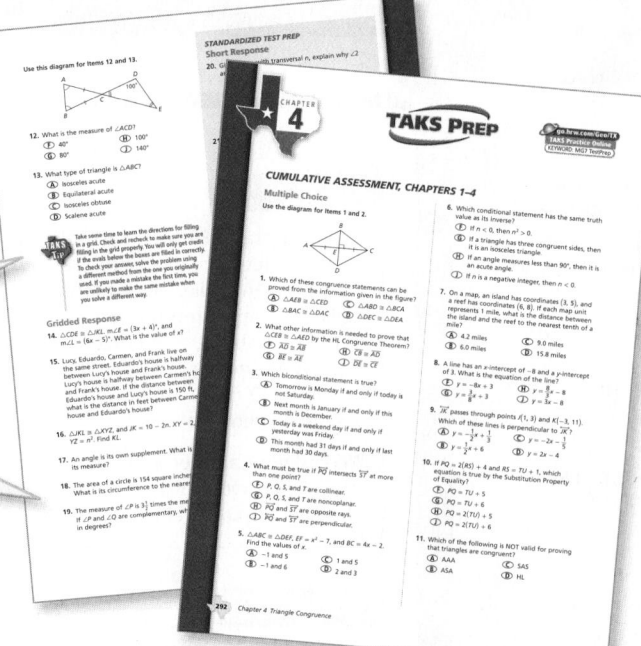

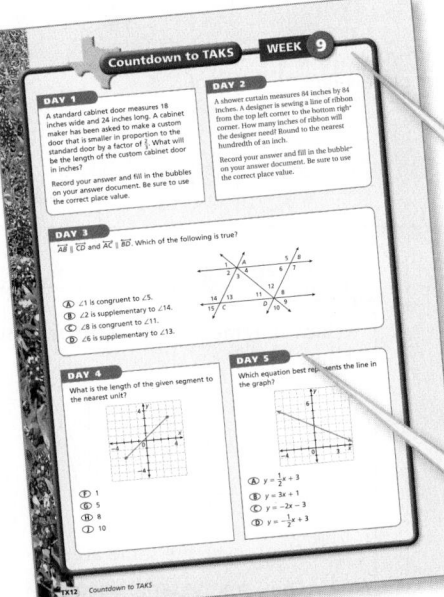

Countdown to TAKS

Use the Countdown to TAKS to practice
for the test every day.

> There are 24 pages of practice for
> TAKS. Each page is designed to be
> used in a week so that all practice will
> be completed before the test is given.

> Each week's page has five
> practice test items, one for
> each day of the week.

Test-Taking Tips

☑ Get plenty of sleep the night before the
test. A rested mind thinks more clearly
and you won't feel like falling asleep
while taking the test.

☑ Draw a figure when one is not provided
with the problem. If a figure is given,
write any details from the problem on
the figure.

☑ Read each problem carefully. As you
finish each problem, read it again to
make sure your answer is reasonable.

☑ Review the formula sheet that will be
supplied with the test. Make sure you
know when to use each formula.

☑ First answer problems that you know
how to solve. If you do not know how to
solve a problem, skip it and come back
to it when you have finished the others.

☑ Use other test-taking strategies that can
be found throughout this book, such
as working backward and eliminating
answer choices.

COUNTDOWN TO TAKS

Each problem on the *Countdown to TAKS* is correlated to the TAKS test by TAKS objective and underlying TEKS. These correlations are shown at the bottom of each page. For the full text of the Geometry TEKS, see pp. TXv–TXxvi. For the TAKS objectives, see p. TXxvii.

DAY 1

A bag contains 88 tiles. Each tile has a different letter on it. There are 16 A tiles, 12 S tiles, 14 O tiles, 18 B tiles, and 10 R tiles. The remaining tiles are U tiles. What is the probability, as a percent, that a person picking a tile out of the bag selects the letter O or U? Round to the nearest whole percent. **36**

Record your answer and fill in the bubbles on your answer document. Be sure to use the correct place value.

DAY 2

If $a = b$ and $b = c$, which statement must be true?

Ⓐ $a > c$

Ⓑ $-a - c = 0$

Ⓒ $a + c = 0$

Ⓓ $a = c$

DAY 3

The width of each square in the grid is 2 centimeters. What is the diameter of the circle in centimeters? **12**

Record your answer and fill in the bubbles on your answer document. Be sure to use the correct place value.

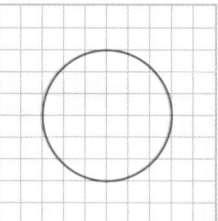

DAY 4

Which shape is NOT included in the figure?

Ⓕ Circle

Ⓖ Square

Ⓗ Triangle

Ⓙ Trapezoid

DAY 5

Which statement best describes these two figures?

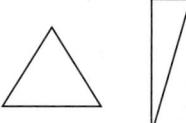

Ⓐ They cover the same area.

Ⓑ They are the same size.

Ⓒ They have the same number of sides.

Ⓓ The distance around each figure is the same.

Day	TEKS ➡ TAKS Grades 9–11
1	Obj. 9, 8.11.A
2	Obj. 10, 8.16.B
3	Obj. 7, G.7.A
4	Obj. 7, G.9.D
5	Obj. 10, 8.15.A

DAY 1

What is the length of $\overline{FD}$?

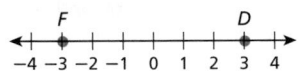

(A) 0

(B) 3

(C) 6

(D) 9

DAY 2

∠ABC is an obtuse angle. Which of these could be the measure of ∠ABC?

(F) 0°

(G) 53°

(H) 90°

(J) 108°

DAY 3

Which point is described by the coordinates $(-2, 3)$?

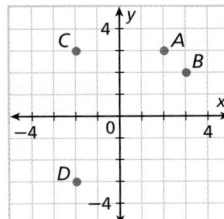

(A) A

(B) B

(C) C

(D) D

DAY 4

An architect is sketching a blueprint of a patio for a new home. On the blueprint, C is the midpoint of $\overline{AD}$, which represents one side of the patio. Point B is the midpoint of $\overline{AC}$. If BC = 8 feet, what is the length of $\overline{AD}$ in feet? **32**

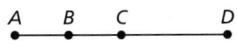

Record your answer and fill in the bubbles on your answer document. Be sure to use the correct place value.

DAY 5

$\overrightarrow{OB}$ bisects ∠AOC, and m∠AOC = 60°. What is m∠BOE in degrees? **150**

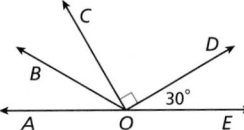

Record your answer and fill in the bubbles on your answer document. Be sure to use the correct place value.

Day	TEKS ➡ TAKS Grades 9–11
1	Obj. 7, G.7.A
2	Obj. 10, 8.16.B
3	Obj. 7, G.7.A
4	Obj. 7, G.7.C
5	Obj. 4, A.7.A

DAY 1

The figure below shows the first three elements in a pattern. The area of the white region in the first element is 8 cm², and the area of the white region in the second element is 16 cm². What will the area of the white region be when an element contains six circles?

  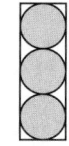

$A_w = 8$ cm² $A_w = 16$ cm² $A_w = 24$ cm²

(A) 36 square centimeters

(B) 48 square centimeters

(C) 144 square centimeters

(D) 168 square centimeters

DAY 2

Jack brought bagels to school. He gave one-fourth of the bagels to the gym teacher and one-sixth of the bagels to his art teacher. The art teacher gave the principal 2 bagels and now has 4 bagels left. How many bagels did Jack bring to school? **36**

Record your answer and fill in the bubbles on your answer document. Be sure to use the correct place value.

DAY 3

Point X is the midpoint of $\overline{HI}$. What is the coordinate of the point X?

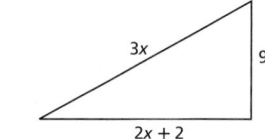

(F) −4

(G) 0

(H) 1

(J) 3

DAY 4

Which expression best represents the perimeter of the figure below?

```
        3x      9

      2x + 2
```

(A) 27x

(B) 5x + 11

(C) 9x + 9

(D) 11x + 5

DAY 5

A line segment is drawn between the points (5, 8) and (−1, 6). What is the y-coordinate of the midpoint of the segment? **7**

Record your answer and fill in the bubbles on your answer document. Be sure to use the correct place value.

Day	TEKS ➡ TAKS Grades 9–11
1	Obj. 6, G.5.B
2	Obj. 10, 8.14.C
3	Obj. 7, G.7.A
4	Obj. 2, A.4.B
5	Obj. 7, G.7.C

DAY 1

What value of x makes the equation
$6x - 12 = 3(5 - x)$ true? **3**

Record your answer and fill in the bubbles
on your answer document. Be sure to use
the correct place value.

DAY 2

Which conjecture best describes a rule for
the pattern below?

(A) Rotate counterclockwise 90°

(B) Rotate clockwise 90°

(C) Rotate counterclockwise 180°

(D) Rotate clockwise 180°

DAY 3

Given: A triangle is a right triangle.

Conclusion: Two of the sides are congruent.

This conclusion—

(F) is true because right triangles have exactly one angle that measures 90°.

(G) is true because all right triangles have two congruent angles.

(H) is false because, for example, the sides of a 30°-60°-90° right triangle have
different lengths.

(J) is false because a right triangle cannot have two congruent angles.

DAY 4

Which of the following best describes the
value of $4n + 1$ when n is an integer?

(A) The value is always negative.

(B) The value is always positive.

(C) The value is always even.

(D) The value is always odd.

DAY 5

Gabby tosses a fair number cube and
flips a coin. What is the probability, as a
percent, that the cube lands on an even
number and the coin lands on heads?
Round to the nearest whole percent. **25**

Record your answer and fill in the bubbles
on your answer document. Be sure to use
the correct place value.

Day	TEKS ⟶ TAKS Grades 9–11
1	Obj. 2, A.7.B
2	Obj. 6, G.10.A
3	Obj. 10, 8.16.B
4	Obj. 2, A.3.B
5	Obj. 9, 8.11.A

DAY 1

Janet is sending a set of documents to her client in an overnight package. The box she uses is 18 inches long, 3 inches tall, and 12.25 inches wide. What is the volume of the box in cubic inches? **661.5**

Record your answer and fill in the bubbles on your answer document. Be sure to use the correct place value.

DAY 2

Which of the following statements is true, based on the figure?

Ⓐ ∠2 and ∠4 are not adjacent but form a linear pair.

Ⓑ ∠2 and ∠4 are adjacent angles that form a linear pair.

Ⓒ ∠1 and ∠3 are adjacent angles and form a linear pair.

Ⓓ ∠1 and ∠3 are not adjacent angles but form a linear pair.

DAY 3

The school board budgets 2.5×10^4 for transportation and 5.85×10^5 for supplies. How many times greater is the supplies budget than the transportation budget? **23.4**

Record your answer and fill in the bubbles on your answer document. Be sure to use the correct place value.

DAY 4

The figure below shows a pattern of right triangles and their areas, *A*. Based on the pattern, what will be the area of a right triangle with a height of 64 units?

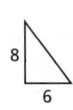

A = 6 square units   A = 24 square units   A = 96 square units

Ⓕ 4 square units

Ⓖ 100 square units

Ⓗ 364 square units

Ⓙ 1536 square units

DAY 5

How many pairs of vertical angles are in the diagram?

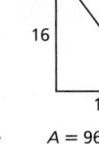

Ⓐ 2

Ⓑ 3

Ⓒ 6

Ⓓ 12

Day	TEKS ▶ TAKS Grades 9–11
1	Obj. 8, G.8.D
2	Obj. 10, 8.15.A
3	Obj. 5, A.11.A
4	Obj. 6, G.5.B
5	Obj. 10, 8.14.C

DAY 1

Rosie has a 25π-square-foot circular area rug. She wants to make a square area rug out of the same carpet as the circular rug. If she uses the radius of the circular rug as the side length of the square rug, what will be the area of the square rug in square feet? **25**

Record your answer and fill in the bubbles on your answer document. Be sure to use the correct place value.

DAY 2

Two angles are labeled in the figure below. Which of the following statements best describes this angle pair?

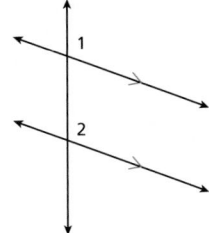

A. They are complementary angles.
Ⓑ They are congruent angles.
C. They are supplementary angles.
D. They are parallel angles.

DAY 3

If line *a* is parallel to line *b*, and m∠8 = 62°, what is m∠1?

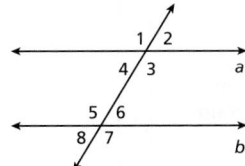

F. 28°
G. 62°
Ⓗ 118°
J. 180°

DAY 4

The area of a circle is about 7 cm². By how many times will the area increase if the radius of the circle is tripled? **9**

Record your answer and fill in the bubbles on your answer document. Be sure to use the correct place value.

DAY 5

B is in the interior of ∠*AOC*. Which of the following statements must be true?

Ⓐ m∠*AOB* + m∠*BOC* = m∠*AOC*
B. m∠*AOB* = m∠*BOC*
C. m∠*AOB* + m∠*AOC* = m∠*BOC*
D. m∠*BOC* + m∠*AOC* = m∠*AOB*

Day	TEKS ➡ TAKS Grades 9–11
1	Obj. 8, G.8.A
2	Obj. 10, 8.15.A
3	Obj. 4, A.7.A
4	Obj. 8, G.8.D
5	Obj. 2, A.3.A

DAY 1

Four rays are drawn from the origin to each of the following points: $S(-2, 5)$, $T(0, 4)$, $U(-1, -3)$, and $V(2, 6)$. Which point is on the ray that forms an acute angle with the ray in the figure?

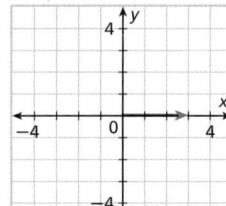

- (A) S
- (B) T
- (C) U
- (D) V ✓

DAY 2

A forest ranger determined that the yearly revenue from his main camp site can be determined by the equation $c = 18.5n$, where n represents the number of campers. If the total revenue last year was $40,718.50, how many campers visited this site? **2201**

Record your answer and fill in the bubbles on your answer document. Be sure to use the correct place value.

DAY 3

Five lines are plotted on a coordinate grid: $y = 2x + 3$, $y = x + 5$, $y = 4x - 6$, $y = 2x - 3$, and $y = 0.5x$. What is the mean value of the slopes? **1.9**

Record your answer and fill in the bubbles on your answer document. Be sure to use the correct place value.

DAY 4

Which expression best represents the perimeter of the rectangle?

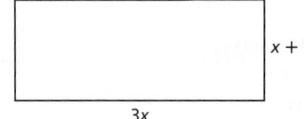

$x + 1$

$3x$

- (F) $4x + 1$
- (G) $6x + 4$
- (H) $8x + 2$ ✓
- (J) $3x^2 + 3x$

DAY 5

Sheena is drawing a line graph to relate the side length of a square to the area of the square. Which of the following best describes the graph?

- (A) steep downward straight line
- (B) steep upward curve ✓
- (C) horizontal line
- (D) upward straight line

Day	TEKS → TAKS Grades 9–11
1	Obj. 7, G.7.A
2	Obj. 2, A.4.A
3	Obj. 3, A.6.A
4	Obj. 2, A.4.B
5	Obj. 5, A.9.D

DAY 1

What is the slope of the given line segment?

- (A) −2
- (B) −$\frac{1}{2}$
- (C) 1
- (D) 2

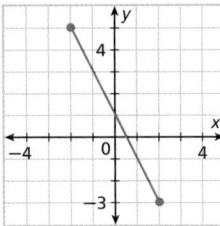

DAY 2

Eric is sketching a blueprint on a coordinate grid. The blueprint includes a wall along the line $y = -2x + 4$. What is the slope of a wall perpendicular to the line on Eric's blueprint? **0.5**

Record your answer and fill in the bubbles on your answer document. Be sure to use the correct place value.

DAY 3

Which of the following is the best classification for the given triangle?

- (F) Equilateral
- (G) Isosceles
- (H) Scalene
- (J) Right

DAY 4

$\triangle SQT$ is an equilateral triangle. $\overline{QR}$ bisects $\angle SQT$. What are the measures of the angles of $\triangle SQR$?

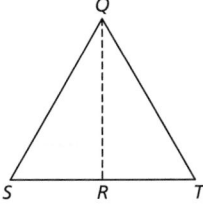

- (A) 30°-30°-30°
- (B) 30°-60°-90°
- (C) 30°-60°-60°
- (D) 60°-60°-60°

DAY 5

Taylor spends 15% of his annual income on utilities, 25% on food, 35% on housing, 15% on his car, and 10% on other expenses. Last year, Taylor earned $63,000. This year, Taylor expects to make $70,000. How many more dollars will he spend on utilities this year than last year? **1050**

Record your answer and fill in the bubbles on your answer document. Be sure to use the correct place value.

TEKS → TAKS
Grades 9–11

Day	
1	Obj. 3, A.6.A
2	Obj. 3, A.6.A
3	Obj. 6, G.4.A
4	Obj. 6, G.5.D
5	Obj. 9, 8.3.B

DAY 1

A standard cabinet door measures 18 inches wide and 24 inches long. A cabinet maker has been asked to make a custom door that is smaller in proportion to the standard door by a factor of $\frac{2}{3}$. What will be the length of the custom cabinet door in inches? **16**

Record your answer and fill in the bubbles on your answer document. Be sure to use the correct place value.

DAY 2

A shower curtain measures 84 inches by 84 inches. A designer is sewing a line of ribbon from the top left corner to the bottom right corner. How many inches of ribbon will the designer need? Round to the nearest hundredth of an inch. **118.79**

Record your answer and fill in the bubbles on your answer document. Be sure to use the correct place value.

DAY 3

$\overleftrightarrow{AB} \parallel \overleftrightarrow{CD}$ and $\overleftrightarrow{AC} \parallel \overleftrightarrow{BD}$. Which of the following is true?

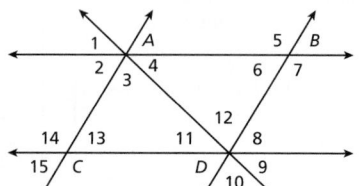

- **(A)** ∠1 is congruent to ∠5.
- **(B)** ∠2 is supplementary to ∠14.
- **(C)** ∠8 is congruent to ∠11.
- **(D)** ∠6 is supplementary to ∠13.

DAY 4

What is the length of the given segment to the nearest unit?

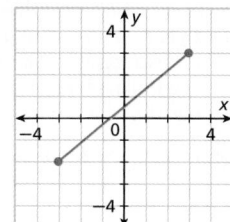

- **(F)** 1
- **(G)** 5
- **(H)** 8
- **(J)** 10

DAY 5

Which equation best represents the line in the graph?

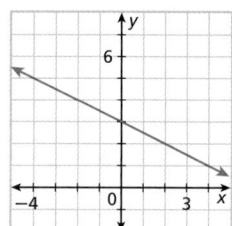

- **(A)** $y = \frac{1}{2}x + 3$
- **(B)** $y = 3x + 1$
- **(C)** $y = -2x - 3$
- **(D)** $y = -\frac{1}{2}x + 3$

Day	TEKS ➡ TAKS Grades 9–11
1	Obj. 8, G.11.B
2	Obj. 6, G.5.D
3	Obj. 10, 8.15.A
4	Obj. 7, G.7.A
5	Obj. 3, A.5.C

DAY 1

Which set of angle measures can be used to conclude that lines *x* and *y* are parallel?

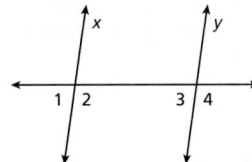

- Ⓐ m∠1 = 87° and m∠3 = 93°
- Ⓑ m∠1 = 82° and m∠4 = 98°
- Ⓒ m∠1 = 80° and m∠2 = 100°
- Ⓓ m∠3 = 88° and m∠4 = 92°

DAY 2

Terrence designed a patio based on the diagram. If $\overline{AB} \parallel \overline{DC}$ and the measure of ∠ADE = 108°, what is the measure of ∠BAD in degrees? **108**

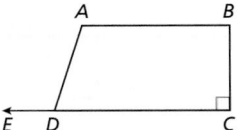

Record your answer and fill in the bubbles on your answer document. Be sure to use the correct place value.

DAY 3

Which of the following conjectures is false?

- Ⓕ The product of an even number and an odd number is even.
- Ⓖ The difference of two negative numbers is a positive number.
- Ⓗ If *x* is negative, then −*x* is positive.
- Ⓙ If *x* is even, then *x* + 1 is odd.

DAY 4

How many line segments can be drawn through four points, no three of which are collinear? **6**

Record your answer and fill in the bubbles on your answer document. Be sure to use the correct place value.

DAY 5

Timothy sketches a sphere with a circle around the middle. He labels the radius of the circle, which is the same as the radius of the sphere. Which problem might he be trying to solve?

- Ⓐ Determining the angle at which Earth tilts
- Ⓑ Calculating the mass of Earth
- Ⓒ Measuring the surface area of Earth
- Ⓓ Finding the distance around the equator

Day	TEKS ⬅ TAKS Grades 9–11
1	Obj. 10, 8.16.B
2	Obj. 6, G.5.B
3	Obj. 10, 8.16.A
4	Obj. 10, 8.16.A
5	Obj. 10, 8.14.A

DAY 1

A cube-shaped box is being used to package little-league football helmets. A larger cube-shaped box is used to package adult-size helmets. The surface area of the smaller box is 864 square inches. The side length of the large box is 6 inches longer than the side length of the smaller box. What is the surface area of the larger box in square inches? **1944**

Record your answer and fill in the bubbles on your answer document. Be sure to use the correct place value.

DAY 2

Jan drew the figure below and claims that line ℓ is parallel to line m. Which of the following proves her statement true?

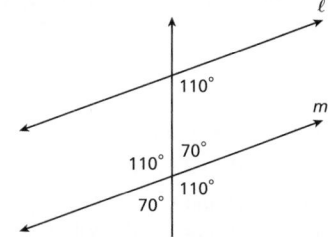

(A) Angles on opposite sides of the transversal are equal.

(B) Corresponding angles on the same side of the transversal are congruent.

(C) More than two angles in the diagram have the same value.

(D) Two straight lines pass through the same transversal.

DAY 3

Which of the following can you use to prove that two angles are complementary?

(F) The sum of their measures is 90°.

(G) The sum of their measures is 180°.

(H) The angles have the same measure.

(J) The measure of one angle is twice the other measure.

DAY 4

Carole purchased a filing cabinet and a fax machine for a total of $127, not including tax. If the price of the filing cabinet is $20 less than one-half the price of the fax machine, how many dollars did the fax machine cost? **98**

Record your answer and fill in the bubbles on your answer document. Be sure to use the correct place value.

DAY 5

$\overrightarrow{OZ}$ is a bisector of $\angle XOY$. Which of the following statements is NOT true?

(A) $2m\angle ZOY = m\angle XOY$

(B) $2m\angle XOZ = m\angle XOY$

(C) $m\angle ZOY = m\angle XOY$

(D) $m\angle XOZ = \frac{1}{2}m\angle XOY$

Day	TEKS ➡ TAKS Grades 9–11
1	Obj. 8, G.11.D
2	Obj. 10, 8.16.B
3	Obj. 10, 8.16.B
4	Obj. 4, A.8.B
5	Obj. 2, A.3.A

DAY 1

The graph shows the height of a tennis ball from the time it is served to the time it hits the ground on the other side of the net. How many seconds elapse while the ball is 7 feet or more above the ground? **0.4**

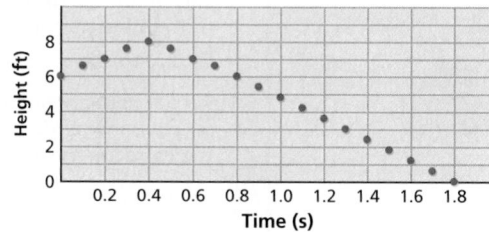

Record your answer and fill in the bubbles on your answer document. Be sure to use the correct place value.

DAY 2

If $x = 7.5$, what is the area of the triangle in square units? **397.5**

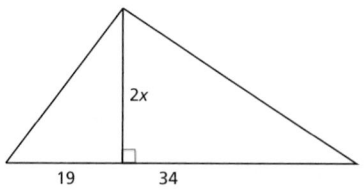

Record your answer and fill in the bubbles on your answer document. Be sure to use the correct place value.

DAY 3

Roberta is attaching wooden trim around a stained glass window. The window is made up of eight congruent isosceles triangles.

What length of trim does Roberta need in order to surround the entire window?

Ⓐ 22 centimeters

Ⓑ 78 centimeters

©Ⓒ 176 centimeters

Ⓓ 624 centimeters

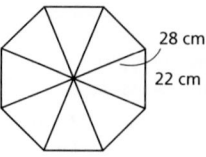

28 cm

22 cm

DAY 4

How many different segments can be created from eight points on a given segment (including the segment's endpoints)?

Ⓕ 8

Ⓖ 13

Ⓗ 28

Ⓙ 36

DAY 5

Which of these conditional statements is true?

Ⓐ If two angles are vertical angles, then they are congruent.

Ⓑ If two angles are congruent, then they are right angles.

Ⓒ If four points are given, then they lie in exactly one plane.

Ⓓ If one angle of a triangle measures 60°, then the triangle is a right triangle.

Day	**TEKS ⬆ TAKS** Grades 9–11
1	Obj. 2, A.2.C
2	Obj. 8, G.8.A
3	Obj. 10, 8.14.B
4	Obj. 10, 8.16.A
5	Obj. 10, 8.16.B

DAY 1

What are the coordinates of point *P*?

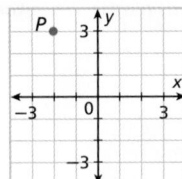

- (A) (3, −2)
- (B) (−2, 3)
- (C) (3, 2)
- (D) (2, −3)

DAY 2

A chemical substance begins with a potency of 64. The sequence below gives the potency of the substance as it changes each hour thereafter. What is the potency of the substance after 7 hours? **0.5**

64, 32, 16, 8, …

Record your answer and fill in the bubbles on your answer document. Be sure to use the correct place value.

DAY 3

Which conjecture is true?

- (F) If a figure is a rectangle, its perimeter is equal to its area.
- (G) If a figure is a triangle, all three sides are congruent.
- (H) If a figure is a quadrilateral, then it has four sides.
- (J) If a figure is a circle, its area is always greater than its circumference.

DAY 4

The layout of a swimming pool is plotted on the coordinate grid below. If each unit on the grid represents 2 meters, what is the length of the pool?

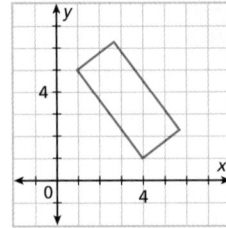

- (A) 5 meters
- (B) 8 meters
- (C) 10 meters
- (D) 25 meters

DAY 5

△*LMN* is shown on the grid. What is the length of $\overline{MN}$? Round to the nearest tenth of a unit. **4.5**

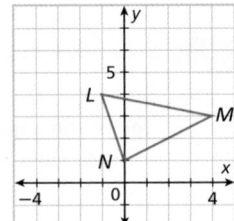

Record your answer and fill in the bubbles on your answer document. Be sure to use the correct place value.

Day	TEKS ➡ TAKS Grades 9–11
1	Obj. 7, G.7.A
2	Obj. 2, A.3.B
3	Obj. 10, 8.16.B
4	Obj. 7, G.7.C
5	Obj. 7, G.7.C

DAY 1

A ceramic tile is in the shape of a 30°-60°-90° triangle. The side across from the 30° angle is 6.25 centimeters long. How long is the hypotenuse of the tile?

Ⓐ 3.125 centimeters

Ⓑ $6.25\sqrt{3}$ centimeters

Ⓒ 12.5 centimeters

Ⓓ 15 centimeters

DAY 2

What is the slope of this line after it is translated 2 units down and 1 unit right? **2**

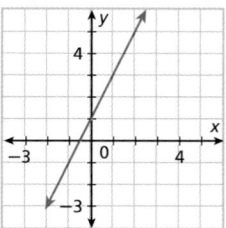

Record your answer and fill in the bubbles on your answer document. Be sure to use the correct place value.

DAY 3

Which equation should Aretha use to find the distance between two points across a river?

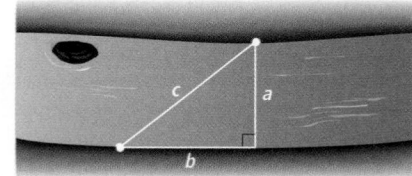

Ⓕ $c = a^2 + b^2$

Ⓖ $c = a + b$

Ⓗ $c^2 = \sqrt{a + b}$

Ⓙ $c = \sqrt{a^2 + b^2}$

DAY 4

The sums of the angle measures of three polygons are given. Based on the pattern, what will be the sum of the measures of a hexagon in degrees? **720**

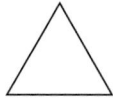 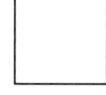 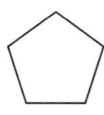

180°   360°   540°

Record your answer and fill in the bubbles on your answer document. Be sure to use the correct place value.

DAY 5

Which line in the graph is described by the equation $y = x + 2$?

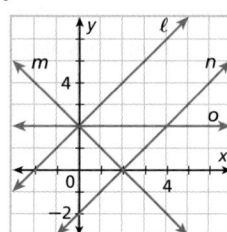

Ⓐ ℓ

Ⓑ m

Ⓒ n

Ⓓ o

Day	TEKS ➡ TAKS Grades 9–11
1	Obj. 6, G.5.D
2	Obj. 6, G.10.A
3	Obj. 8, G.8.C
4	Obj. 6, G.5.B
5	Obj. 3, A.5.C

DAY 1

Three coordinates of □ABCD are A(4, 5), B(10, 5), C(7, 3), and D(1, 3). What is the length of $\overline{DB}$ to the nearest whole unit? 9

Record your answer and fill in the bubbles on your answer document. Be sure to use the correct place value.

DAY 2

A spinner has four equal sections colored red, blue, yellow, and green. Carl spins the spinner 50 times and records that the spinner lands on blue 12 times. What is the experimental probability expressed as a percent of spinning the spinner and having it land on blue? Round to the nearest whole percent. 24

Record your answer and fill in the bubbles on your answer document. Be sure to use the correct place value.

DAY 3

What is the midpoint of $\overline{QR}$?

Ⓐ (1, −2)
Ⓑ (−2, 1)
Ⓒ (1, 2)
Ⓓ (−1, −2)

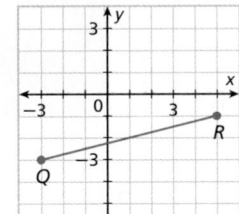

DAY 4

Which of these statements is true?

Ⓕ All quadrilaterals are parallelograms.
Ⓖ Every rectangle is a parallelogram.
Ⓗ Every parallelogram is also a rectangle.
Ⓙ The diagonals of a rhombus are congruent.

DAY 5

Which expression describes the total number of diagonals in a polygon with n sides?

No. of sides	3	4	5	6	7
No. of diagonals	0	2	5	9	14

Ⓐ $\dfrac{n(n-3)}{2}$

Ⓑ $2n$

Ⓒ $\dfrac{3n}{2}$

Ⓓ $\dfrac{2n+6}{3}$

Day	TEKS ⟶ TAKS Grades 9–11
1	Obj. 7, G.7.C
2	Obj. 9, 8.11.B
3	Obj. 7, G.7.C
4	Obj. 7, G.9.D
5	Obj. 6, G.5.A

DAY 1

The coordinates of the vertices of $\triangle ABC$ are (1, 1), (6, 1) and (1, 8). Which of the following could be the coordinates of the vertices of a triangle congruent to $\triangle ABC$?

A (−8, −2), (−3, −2), (−3, −9)

B (4, 1), (6, 2), (8, 10)

C (−2, 5), (−2, −9), (−8, 3)

D (0, 0), (−1, 8), (5, 2)

DAY 2

Natalia is using indirect measurement to find the distance across a pond. Which Pythagorean triple is represented by the triangle?

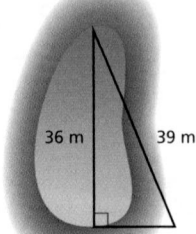

36 m   39 m   15 m

F 3-4-5

G 5-12-13

H 8-15-17

J 7-24-25

DAY 3

Which of the following sets of measurements could represent the side lengths of a right triangle?

A 3, 5, 9

B 4.5, 12, 8.5

C 6, 7, 10

D 2.5, 6, 6.5

DAY 4

Elle is designing a mural for the lobby of an office building. What is the area in square meters of her design? **25**

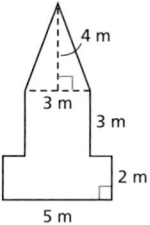

4 m
3 m
3 m
2 m
5 m

Record your answer and fill in the bubbles on your answer document. Be sure to use the correct place value.

DAY 5

What is the measure of ∠3 in degrees in the regular hexagon? **60**

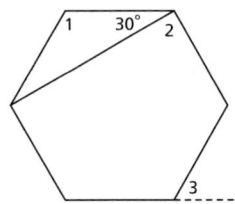

1   30°   2

3

Record your answer and fill in the bubbles on your answer document. Be sure to use the correct place value.

Day	TEKS → TAKS Grades 9–11
1	Obj. 6, G.10.A
2	Obj. 6, G.5.D
3	Obj. 6, G.5.D
4	Obj. 8, G.8.A
5	Obj. 6, G.5.B

DAY 1

Mrs. Euclid asked her students to write two equations that represent perpendicular lines. Which response is correct?

(A) $y = x + 6$ and $y = x - 6$

(B) $y + \frac{2}{3}x = 1$ and $y = \frac{3}{2}x - 4$

(C) $y = \frac{1}{2}x - 2$ and $y = -\frac{1}{2}x + 3$

(D) $y - 2x = 5$ and $y = 2x + 2$

DAY 2

What is the perimeter of the composite figure to the nearest centimeter? **60**

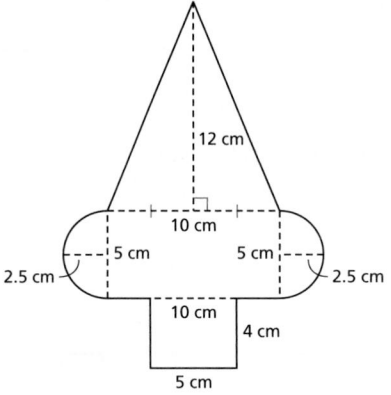

Record your answer and fill in the bubbles on your answer document. Be sure to use the correct place value.

DAY 3

What is the measure of ∠1 in the triangle below?

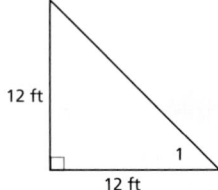

(F) 30°

(G) 45°

(H) 60°

(J) 90°

DAY 4

△ABC has a base of 12 units and a height of 15 units. The base of △EFG is 8 units less than the base of △ABC. If the two triangles are similar, what is the height of △EFG in units? **5**

Record your answer and fill in the bubbles on your answer document. Be sure to use the correct place value.

DAY 5

The vertices of polygon $ABCD$ are $A(1, 5)$, $B(8, 5)$, $C(8, 3)$, and $D(1, 3)$. Which of the following statements about this polygon is true?

(A) It is a square.

(B) Its width is 2 units.

(C) Its perimeter is 6 units.

(D) Its area is 9 square units.

Day	TEKS → TAKS Grades 9–11
1	Obj. 7, G.7.B
2	Obj. 10, 8.14.C
3	Obj. 6, G.5.D
4	Obj. 8, G.11.B
5	Obj. 7, G.7.A

DAY 1

Based on the pattern of similar triangles below, what is the value of *x*?

Ⓐ 2

Ⓑ 4

Ⓒ $4\sqrt{3}$

Ⓓ 8

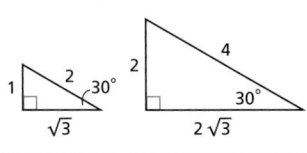
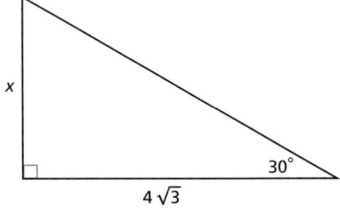

DAY 2

Which Pythagorean triple would be most helpful in finding the value of *a*?

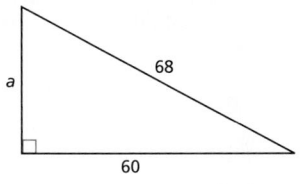

Ⓕ 3-4-5

Ⓖ 5-12-14

Ⓗ 8-15-17

Ⓙ 7-24-25

DAY 3

A forensic scientist collects evidence samples at a crime scene. The samples have the following weights in grams: 0.20, 0.75, 0.18, 0.92, 0.47, and 0.34. What is the mean weight of the samples? Round to the nearest thousandth gram. **0.477**

Record your answer and fill in the bubbles on your answer document. Be sure to use the correct place value.

DAY 4

Natalia plans to install glass doors across the front of her square fireplace opening and then seal the perimeter of the opening with a special caulk that can sustain high temperatures. What is the perimeter of the opening? **24**

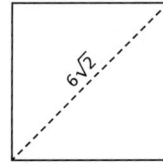

Record your answer and fill in the bubbles on your answer document. Be sure to use the correct place value.

DAY 5

Which conjecture about polygons is NOT true?

Ⓐ The area of a parallelogram is the product of its base and height.

Ⓑ A rhombus has four right angles.

Ⓒ A square has four congruent sides.

Ⓓ A trapezoid has exactly one pair of parallel sides.

Day	TEKS ➡ TAKS Grades 9–11
1	Obj. 6, G.5.B
2	Obj. 6, G.5.D
3	Obj. 10, 8.12.A
4	Obj. 6, G.5.D
5	Obj. 7, G.9.D

DAY 1

Which two line segments are congruent?

Ⓐ $\overline{AB}$ and $\overline{DF}$

Ⓑ $\overline{CE}$ and $\overline{GH}$

Ⓒ $\overline{GH}$ and $\overline{AB}$

Ⓓ $\overline{CD}$ and $\overline{DE}$

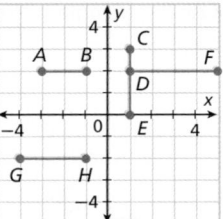

DAY 2

Based on the table, which algebraic expression best represents the number of triangles formed by drawing all of the diagonals from one vertex in a polygon with n sides?

No. of sides	3	4	5	8
No. of triangles formed	1	2	3	6

Ⓕ n

Ⓖ $2n - 1$

Ⓗ $n - 2$

Ⓙ $\dfrac{n + 2}{2}$

DAY 3

At a certain time of the day, a 24-foot tree casts an 18-foot shadow. How long is the shadow cast by a 4-foot mailbox at the same time of day? 3

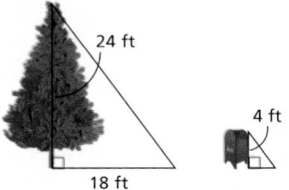

Record your answer and fill in the bubbles on your answer document. Be sure to use the correct place value.

DAY 4

A school increases the width of its rectangular playground from 25 meters to 40 meters and the length from 45 meters to 60 meters. By how much does the perimeter of the playground increase?

Ⓐ 30 meters

Ⓑ 60 meters

Ⓒ 200 meters

Ⓓ 225 meters

DAY 5

Trey is using triangular tiles to floor his bathroom. What is x? 5

Record your answer and fill in the bubbles on your answer document. Be sure to use the correct place value.

Day	TEKS → TAKS Grades 9–11
1	Obj. 7, G.7.A
2	Obj. 6, G.5.A
3	Obj. 8, G.11.B
4	Obj. 6, G.4.A
5	Obj. 6, G.5.D

DAY 1

The figure shows the measure of each interior angle for several regular polygons.

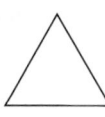 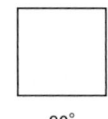 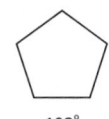 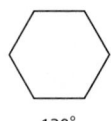

60°   90°   108°   120°

Which algebraic expression best represents the measure of an interior angle of a regular polygon with *n* sides?

(A) $\dfrac{(n-2)180}{n}$

(C) $(n-2)180$

(B) $\dfrac{360n}{n+2}$

(D) $\dfrac{180n}{2}$

DAY 2

Which coordinates represent a vertex of the hexagon?

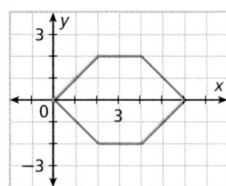

(F) $(0, 2)$

(G) $(4, -2)$

(H) $(3, 2)$

(J) $(-2, 2)$

DAY 3

The two triangles in the figure are similar. What is the length of $\overline{MN}$? **6**

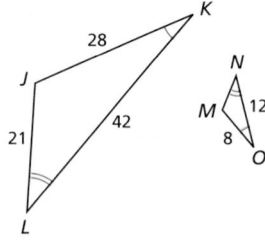

Record your answer and fill in the bubbles on your answer document. Be sure to use the correct place value.

DAY 4

Two regular pentagons have perimeters of 30 and 75 respectively. What scale factor relates the smaller figure to the larger one?

(A) 1 : 2.5

(B) 1 : 6

(C) 1 : 15

(D) 1 : 21

DAY 5

Alissa is painting a diagonal line across a square tile. What is the length of the line in centimeters? Round to the nearest thousandth of a centimeter. **11.314**

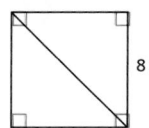

8 cm

Record your answer and fill in the bubbles on your answer document. Be sure to use the correct place value.

Day	TEKS ⟶ TAKS Grades 9–11
1	Obj. 6, G.5.A
2	Obj. 7, G.7.A
3	Obj. 8, G.11.B
4	Obj. 8, G.11.A
5	Obj. 8, G.8.C

DAY 1

The table lists the measure of an exterior angle for the given regular polygon. Which expression best represents the measure of an exterior angle of a regular polygon with n sides?

Figure	Quadrilateral	Pentagon	Decagon
Exterior angle	90°	72°	36°

Ⓐ $\dfrac{360}{n-2}$ Ⓑ $\dfrac{360+n}{2+n}$ Ⓒ $360n$ Ⓓ $\dfrac{360}{n}$

DAY 2

A word game uses a bag of 80 tiles. Forty of the tiles have a consonant on them, and the remaining 40 have a vowel: A, E, I, O, or U. There is an equal number of each vowel tile. What is the probability as a percent that Shelly selects an A tile and then a U tile from the bag without replacement? Round to the nearest hundredth of a percent. **1.01**

Record your answer and fill in the bubbles on your answer document. Be sure to use the correct place value.

DAY 3

When $y = 65$, $x = 8$. If y varies directly with x, what is y when x equals 15? **121.875**

Record your answer and fill in the bubbles on your answer document. Be sure to use the correct place value.

DAY 4

Which equation best describes the line containing the hypotenuse of this triangle?

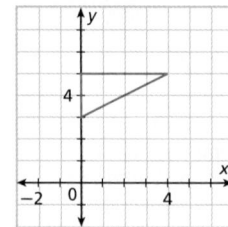

Ⓕ $y = \dfrac{1}{2}x + 3$

Ⓖ $y = 5$

Ⓗ $y = x + 3$

Ⓙ $y = -\dfrac{1}{2}x - 3$

DAY 5

The center of circle C is the midpoint of $\overline{AB}$. What are the coordinates of the midpoint?

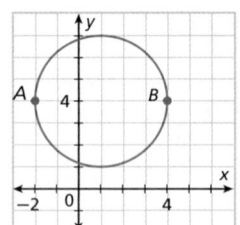

Ⓐ (0, 4)

Ⓑ (1, 4)

Ⓒ (2, 4)

Ⓓ (3, 3)

Day	TEKS ➡ TAKS Grades 9–11
1	Obj. 6, G.5.A
2	Obj. 10, 8.11.A
3	Obj. 3, A.6.G
4	Obj. 3, A.5.C
5	Obj. 7, G.7.C

DAY 1

If this pattern is continued, how many shaded triangles will there be in the fourth element of the pattern?

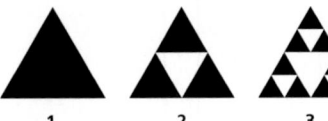

1   2   3

Ⓐ 9   Ⓒ 27

Ⓑ 13   Ⓓ 40

DAY 2

What is the slope of the line?

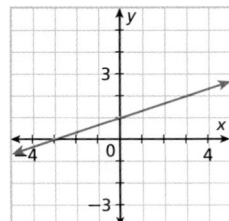

Ⓕ $-\dfrac{1}{2}$

Ⓖ $\dfrac{1}{3}$

Ⓗ $\dfrac{1}{2}$

Ⓙ 3

DAY 3

A delivery truck travels 13.5 mi east and then 18 mi north. How far in miles is the truck from its starting point? **22.5**

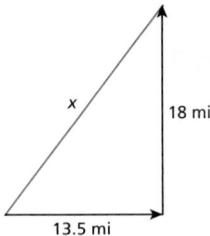

x   18 mi

13.5 mi

Record your answer and fill in the bubbles on your answer document. Be sure to use the correct place value.

DAY 4

What are the side lengths of the triangle?

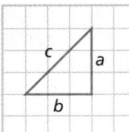

c   a

b

Ⓐ 3, 4, and 5

Ⓑ 2, 3, and 5

Ⓒ 3, 3, and 3

Ⓓ 3, 3, and $3\sqrt{2}$

DAY 5

An 18-foot ladder reaches the top of a building when placed at an angle of 45° with the horizontal. What is the approximate height of the building in feet? Round to the nearest tenth of a foot.

Record your answer and fill in the bubbles on your answer document. Be sure to use the correct place value. **12.7**

Day	TEKS → TAKS Grades 9–11
1	Obj. 10, 8.16.A
2	Obj. 3, A.6.A
3	Obj. 8, G.8.C
4	Obj. 8, G.8.C
5	Obj. 6, G.5.D

DAY 1

$\triangle RST$ is a 30°-60°-90° triangle. What is the y-coordinate of R if $a = -5$ and $c = -2$?

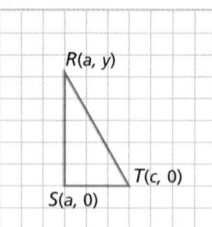

(A) 3

(B) $3\sqrt{2}$

(C) $3\sqrt{3}$

(D) 6

DAY 2

What is x if y is 12.8 and z is 16 in the right triangle below?

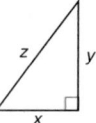

(F) 3.2

(G) 4.0

(H) 9.6

(J) 12.8

DAY 3

How does the slope of the hypotenuse of $\triangle ABC$ compare with that of $\triangle DBC$?

(A) They have the same value and sign.

(B) They have opposite signs.

(C) One is a multiple of the other.

(D) They are reciprocals.

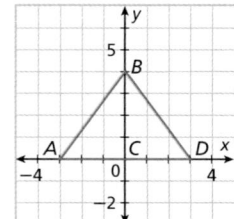

DAY 4

How many sides does a regular polygon have if each interior angle measures 120°?

Record your answer and fill in the bubbles on your answer document. Be sure to use the correct place value. **6**

DAY 5

A piñata in the shape of a basketball is filled with treats for a game during Hanj's birthday party. If the diameter of the piñata is 7 inches, what is the volume of the piñata in cubic inches? Round to the nearest tenth. **179.5**

Record your answer and fill in the bubbles on your answer document. Be sure to use the correct place value.

Day	TEKS ➡ TAKS Grades 9–11
1	Obj. 6, G.5.D
2	Obj. 8, G.8.C
3	Obj. 7, G.7.B
4	Obj. 6, G.5.B
5	Obj. 8, G.8.D

DAY 1

Quadrilaterals *ABCD* and *WXYZ* are similar. What is *XY*?

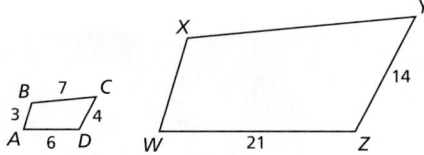

A 3.5
B 21
C 24.5
D 35

DAY 2

The volume of a square pyramid is 108 cubic millimeters. What is the height of the pyramid in millimeters if one side on the base is 4.5 millimeters? **16**

Record your answer and fill in the bubbles on your answer document. Be sure to use the correct place value.

DAY 3

What is the value of *x* in the regular pentagon below?

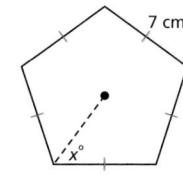

7 cm

F 54°
G 90°
H 108°
J 180°

DAY 4

What is the second term in a proportion in which the first, third, and fourth terms are 3, 9, and 12, respectively? **4**

Record your answer and fill in the bubbles on your answer document. Be sure to use the correct place value.

DAY 5

The endpoints of a segment are *Q*(−2, 6) and *R*(5, −4). What is the length of the segment to the nearest tenth?

A 3.6 units
B 4.1 units
C 8.5 units
D 12.2 units

Day	TEKS ⟶ TAKS Grades 9–11
1	Obj. 8, G.11.B
2	Obj. 8, G.8.D
3	Obj. 6, G.5.B
4	Obj. 2, A.4.A
5	Obj. 7, G.7.C

TEXAS ESSENTIAL KNOWLEDGE AND SKILLS

The Bluebonnet is the state flower.

The state bird is the Mockingbird.

The State Capitol in Austin

Texas wildflowers

Houston skyline

TX28

Texas Essential Knowledge and Skills for Geometry

a Basic understandings.

1 Foundation concepts for high school mathematics. As presented in Grades K–8, the basic understandings of number, operation, and quantitative reasoning; patterns, relationships, and algebraic thinking; geometry; measurement; and probability and statistics are essential foundations for all work in high school mathematics. Students continue to build on this foundation as they expand their understanding through other mathematical experiences.

2 Geometric thinking and spatial reasoning. Spatial reasoning plays a critical role in geometry; geometric figures provide powerful ways to represent mathematical situations and to express generalizations about space and spatial relationships. Students use geometric thinking to understand mathematical concepts and the relationships among them.

3 Geometric figures and their properties. Geometry consists of the study of geometric figures of zero, one, two, and three dimensions and the relationships among them. Students study properties and relationships having to do with size, shape, location, direction, and orientation of these figures.

4 The relationship between geometry, other mathematics, and other disciplines. Geometry can be used to model and represent many mathematical and real-world situations. Students perceive the connection between geometry and the real and mathematical worlds and use geometric ideas, relationships, and properties to solve problems.

5 Tools for geometric thinking. Techniques for working with spatial figures and their properties are essential in understanding underlying relationships. Students use a variety of representations (concrete, pictorial, numerical, symbolic, graphical, and verbal), tools, and technology (including, but not limited to, calculators with graphing capabilities, data collection devices, and computers) to solve meaningful problems by representing and transforming figures and analyzing relationships.

6 Underlying mathematical processes. Many processes underlie all content areas in mathematics. As they do mathematics, students continually use problem-solving, language and communication, connections within and outside mathematics, and reasoning (justification and proof). Students also use multiple representations, technology, applications and modeling, and numerical fluency in problem solving contexts.

Statue of a Texas longhorn

TX29

b Knowledge and skills.

G.1 Geometric structure. The student understands the structure of, and relationships within, an axiomatic system.

The student is expected to:

A develop an awareness of the structure of a mathematical system, connecting definitions, postulates, logical reasoning, and theorems;

B recognize the historical development of geometric systems and know mathematics is developed for a variety of purposes; and

C compare and contrast the structures and implications of Euclidean and non-Euclidean geometries.

G.2 Geometric structure. The student analyzes geometric relationships in order to make and verify conjectures.

The student is expected to:

A use constructions to explore attributes of geometric figures and to make conjectures about geometric relationships; and

B make conjectures about angles, lines, polygons, circles, and three-dimensional figures and determine the validity of the conjectures, choosing from a variety of approaches such as coordinate, transformational, or axiomatic.

G.3 Geometric structure. The student applies logical reasoning to justify and prove mathematical statements.

The student is expected to:

A determine the validity of a conditional statement, its converse, inverse, and contrapositive;

B construct and justify statements about geometric figures and their properties;

C use logical reasoning to prove statements are true and find counter examples to disprove statements that are false;

D use inductive reasoning to formulate a conjecture; and

E use deductive reasoning to prove a statement.

Big Bend National Park

TX30

TX31

West Texas

TX32

G.4 Geometric structure.
The student uses a variety of representations to describe geometric relationships and solve problems.

The student is expected to:

A select an appropriate representation (concrete, pictorial, graphical, verbal, or symbolic) in order to solve problems.

G.5 Geometric patterns.
The student uses a variety of representations to describe geometric relationships and solve problems.

The student is expected to:

A use numeric and geometric patterns to develop algebraic expressions representing geometric properties;

B use numeric and geometric patterns to make generalizations about geometric properties, including properties of polygons, ratios in similar figures and solids, and angle relationships in polygons and circles;

C use properties of transformations and their compositions to make connections between mathematics and the real world, such as tessellations; and

D identify and apply patterns from right triangles to solve meaningful problems, including special right triangles (45-45-90 and 30-60-90) and triangles whose sides are Pythagorean triples.

G.6 Dimensionality and the geometry of location.
The student analyzes the relationship between three-dimensional geometric figures and related two-dimensional representations and uses these representations to solve problems.

The student is expected to:

A describe and draw the intersection of a given plane with various three-dimensional geometric figures;

B use nets to represent and construct three-dimensional geometric figures; and

C use orthographic and isometric views of three-dimensional geometric figures to represent and construct three-dimensional geometric figures and solve problems.

G.7 Dimensionality and the geometry of location.
The student understands that coordinate systems provide convenient and efficient ways of representing geometric figures and uses them accordingly.

The student is expected to:

A use one- and two-dimensional coordinate systems to represent points, lines, rays, line segments, and figures;

B use slopes and equations of lines to investigate geometric relationships, including parallel lines, perpendicular lines, and special segments of triangles and other polygons; and

C derive and use formulas involving length, slope, and midpoint.

SeaWorld

TX33

G.8 Congruence and the geometry of size.
The student uses tools to determine measurements of geometric figures and extends measurement concepts to find perimeter, area, and volume in problem situations.

The student is expected to:

A find areas of regular polygons, circles, and composite figures;

B find areas of sectors and arc lengths of circles using proportional reasoning;

C derive, extend, and use the Pythagorean Theorem; and

D find surface areas and volumes of prisms, pyramids, spheres, cones, cylinders, and composites of these figures in problem situations.

G.9 Congruence and the geometry of size.
The student analyzes properties and describes relationships in geometric figures.

The student is expected to:

A formulate and test conjectures about the properties of parallel and perpendicular lines based on explorations and concrete models;

B formulate and test conjectures about the properties and attributes of polygons and their component parts based on explorations and concrete models;

C formulate and test conjectures about the properties and attributes of circles and the lines that intersect them based on explorations and concrete models; and

D analyze the characteristics of polyhedra and other three-dimensional figures and their component parts based on explorations and concrete models.

G.10 Congruence and the geometry of size.
The student applies the concept of congruence to justify properties of figures and solve problems.

The student is expected to:

A use congruence transformations to make conjectures and justify properties of geometric figures including figures represented on a coordinate plane; and

B justify and apply triangle congruence relationships.

G.11 Similarity and the geometry of shape.
The student applies the concepts of similarity to justify properties of figures and solve problems.

The student is expected to:

A use and extend similarity properties and transformations to explore and justify conjectures about geometric figures;

B use ratios to solve problems involving similar figures;

C develop, apply, and justify triangle similarity relationships, such as right triangle ratios, trigonometric ratios, and Pythagorean triples using a variety of methods; and

D describe the effect on perimeter, area, and volume when one or more dimensions of a figure are changed and apply this idea in solving problems.

Texas State Fair

TX35

TX34

HOLT MATH

You can count on Holt Geometry for

1 Built-in Assessment and Intervention. Prescribe the resources your students need when they need them in order to lead your students to success.

2 Comprehensive Differentiated Instruction. Ensure all students have the opportunity to succeed with strategies designed to reach students of all learning styles and skill levels.

3 Success on the TAKS. Prepare students for success on test day with standards-based test preparation that's embedded into daily lessons.

4 Integrated Technology that Enhances Learning. Motivate your students to excel and manage your classroom with maximum effectiveness using Holt technology.

Program Highlights

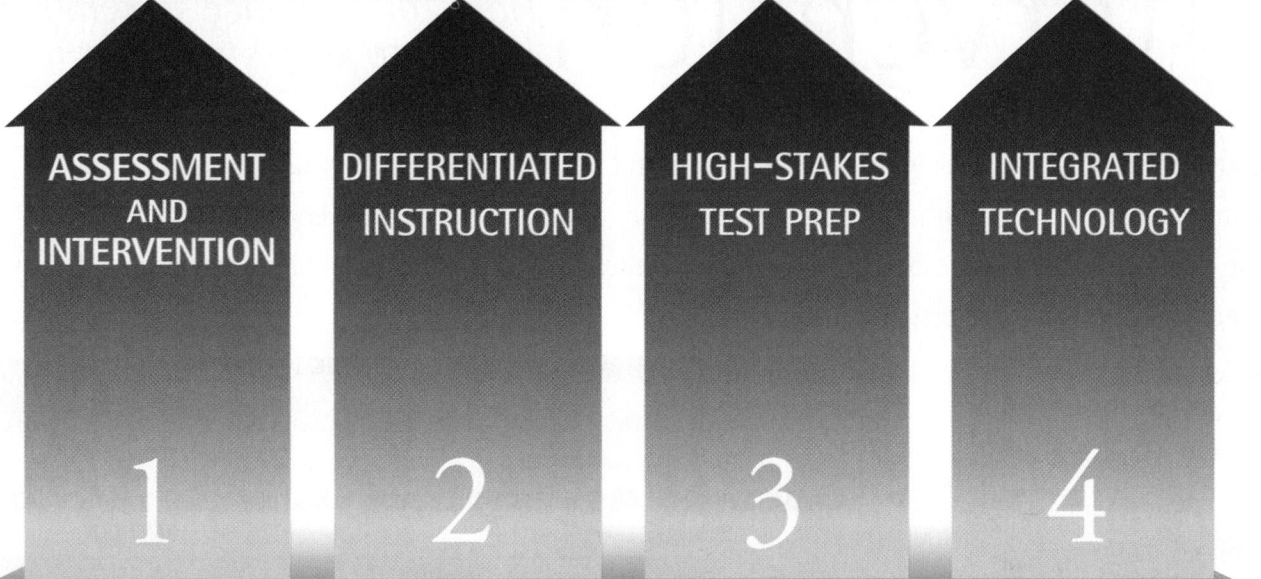

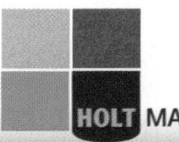 **HOLT** MATH **Student Success**

ASSESSMENT AND INTERVENTION — 1

DIFFERENTIATED INSTRUCTION — 2

HIGH–STAKES TEST PREP — 3

INTEGRATED TECHNOLOGY — 4

GROUNDED IN RESEARCH · BUILT BY EXPERTS · PROVEN IN CLASSROOMS

Built for Student Success... from the Ground Up

Every student is unique with individual strengths and weaknesses. Starting with *Holt Mathematics* for middle school through *Holt Algebra 1, Geometry*, and *Algebra 2*, Holt provides the instruction and resources you need to reach and teach every one of your students. Whether it's an alternative approach to a lesson, a modification for a visual learner, or extra practice with basic skills, Holt has what you need to help all of your students succeed.

> *Deep and abstract ideas are challenging to all, but the **challenge** should be a pleasurable one that students want to conquer.*
>
> **— Dr. Edward B. Burger, Holt author**

Built-in assessment and intervention

Holt's at-a-glance system makes it easy to keep students on track.

You need to know how well your students understand the lesson BEFORE they take the test. With *Holt Geometry*, informal and formal assessment options are given at every stage within the chapter. Intervention resources allow you to reteach or review material without merely sending students back to previous lessons in the book.

- **Assess Prior Knowledge** to make sure all students start the chapter on solid footing.

  Intervene with alternate teaching strategies and basic skills review in **Are You Ready? Intervention and Enrichment.**

- **Formative Assessment** to diagnose skill development within the chapter.

  Intervene with **Ready to Go On?, Lesson Tutorial Videos, Homework Help Online,** and more.

- **Summative Assessment** to allow students to demonstrate their mastery of the concepts.

  Intervene with **Reteach and Lesson Tutorial Videos**.

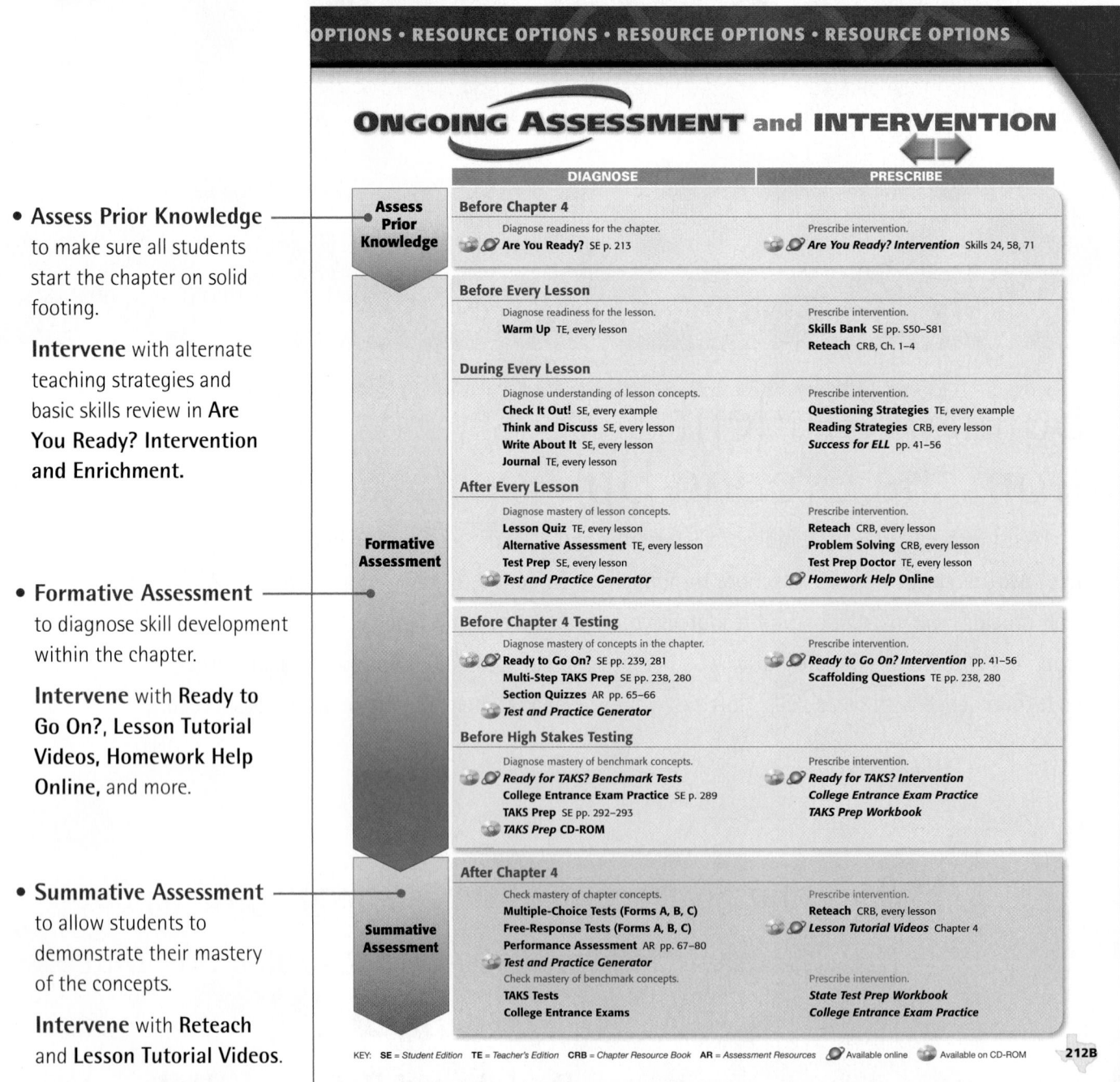

OPTIONS • RESOURCE OPTIONS • RESOURCE OPTIONS • RESOURCE OPTIONS

ONGOING ASSESSMENT and INTERVENTION

DIAGNOSE	PRESCRIBE

Assess Prior Knowledge

Before Chapter 4

Diagnose readiness for the chapter.	Prescribe intervention.
Are You Ready? SE p. 213	**Are You Ready? Intervention** Skills 24, 58, 71

Before Every Lesson

Diagnose readiness for the lesson.	Prescribe intervention.
Warm Up TE, every lesson	**Skills Bank** SE pp. S50–S81
	Reteach CRB, Ch. 1–4

During Every Lesson

Diagnose understanding of lesson concepts.	Prescribe intervention.
Check It Out! SE, every example	**Questioning Strategies** TE, every example
Think and Discuss SE, every lesson	**Reading Strategies** CRB, every lesson
Write About It SE, every lesson	**Success for ELL** pp. 41–56
Journal TE, every lesson	

After Every Lesson

Formative Assessment

Diagnose mastery of lesson concepts.	Prescribe intervention.
Lesson Quiz TE, every lesson	**Reteach** CRB, every lesson
Alternative Assessment TE, every lesson	**Problem Solving** CRB, every lesson
Test Prep SE, every lesson	**Test Prep Doctor** TE, every lesson
Test and Practice Generator	**Homework Help** Online

Before Chapter 4 Testing

Diagnose mastery of concepts in the chapter.	Prescribe intervention.
Ready to Go On? SE pp. 239, 281	**Ready to Go On? Intervention** pp. 41–56
Multi-Step TAKS Prep SE pp. 238, 280	**Scaffolding Questions** TE pp. 238, 280
Section Quizzes AR pp. 65–66	
Test and Practice Generator	

Before High Stakes Testing

Diagnose mastery of benchmark concepts.	Prescribe intervention.
Ready for TAKS? Benchmark Tests	**Ready for TAKS? Intervention**
College Entrance Exam Practice SE p. 289	**College Entrance Exam Practice**
TAKS Prep SE pp. 292–293	**TAKS Prep Workbook**
TAKS Prep CD-ROM	

Summative Assessment

After Chapter 4

Check mastery of chapter concepts.	Prescribe intervention.
Multiple-Choice Tests (Forms A, B, C)	**Reteach** CRB, every lesson
Free-Response Tests (Forms A, B, C)	**Lesson Tutorial Videos** Chapter 4
Performance Assessment AR pp. 67–80	
Test and Practice Generator	
Check mastery of benchmark concepts.	Prescribe intervention.
TAKS Tests	**State Test Prep Workbook**
College Entrance Exams	**College Entrance Exam Practice**

KEY: **SE** = Student Edition **TE** = Teacher's Edition **CRB** = Chapter Resource Book **AR** = Assessment Resources — Available online — Available on CD-ROM

212B

ASSESSMENT AND INTERVENTION

When students are struggling they don't want to keep rereading the same lesson in the hope that eventually it will make sense. They need to try a new approach to the lesson. That's at the core of the assessment and intervention system in *Holt Geometry*.

Are You Ready?
Intervention and Enrichment

- Diagnoses mastery of prerequisite skills
- Strengthens student weaknesses with direct instruction, conceptual models, and scaffolded practice
- Enriches every chapter with critical thinking activities
- Available in print, on CD-ROM, and online

Only from Holt!

Ready to Go On?
Intervention and Enrichment

- Diagnoses mastery of newly taught skills
- Addresses deficiencies with alternative instruction and practice
- Checks student progress with post tests
- Available in print, on CD-ROM, and online

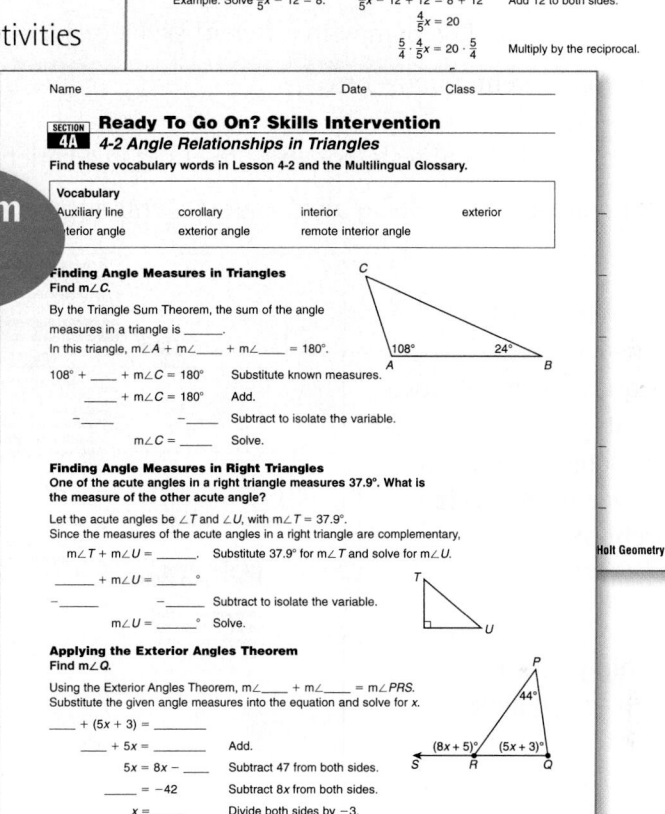

Only from Holt!

Ready for TAKS? Intervention

- Multiple activities with direct instruction for each TEKS
- Questioning strategies for ongoing assessment
- TAKS Mini-Review for each TEKS
- Variety of report templates

> " *Closing the gaps in academic achievement among students from different social divisions (class, ethnicity, gender, language) will require research-based instructional interventions.* "
>
> — **Dr. Earlene J. Hall**, Holt author

Comprehensive differentiated instruction

Reach all learners in your classroom—no matter what their skill levels or learning styles are.

Not all students "get it" at the same time or in the same way. *Holt Geometry* accommodates the students in your classroom with different skill levels and those whose learning styles benefit from different approaches.

With leveled practice and tests, content presented in a variety of media, and teaching strategies built in at point-of-use, helping all of your students succeed has never been easier.

Program Highlights

- **Know-It! Notes** indicate key concepts for students to remember and correspond to entries in the students' **Know It Notebook**.

- **Teaching Tips** make your teaching more adaptable to the range of learning styles in your classroom.

- **Reaching All Learners** recommends alternative approaches to the lesson at point-of-use.

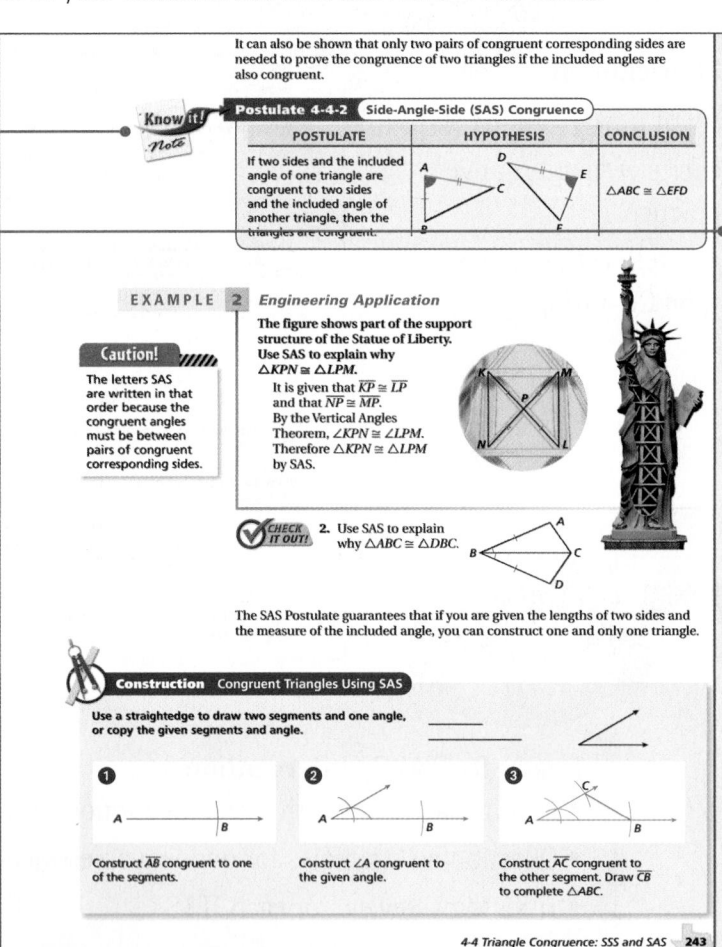

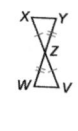

DIFFERENTIATED INSTRUCTION

Professor Edward Burger

180. This is 60. If I subtract 180 minus 60, I see 120 degrees. That's bigger than 90. This is an obtuse triangle. Look how we can classify

KEY OBJECTIVES

■ Classify triangles by their angle measures.

LESSON TUTORIALS
HOLT, RINEHART AND WINSTON

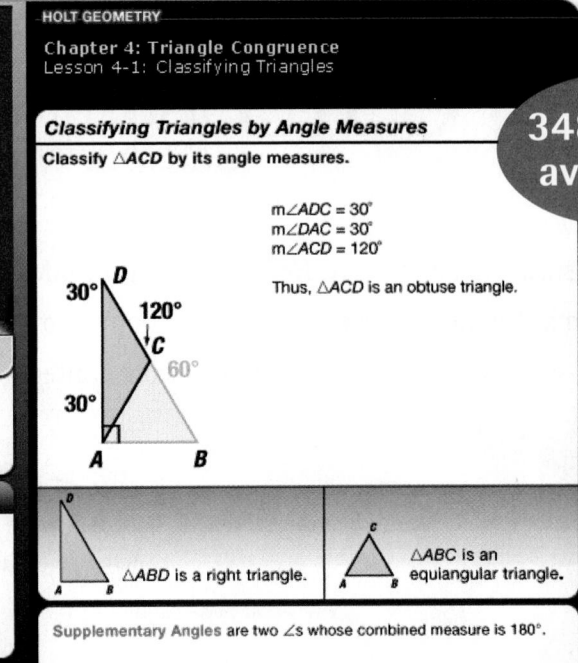

348 videos available!

Lesson Tutorial Videos

• Illustrate every example!

• Your students' personal take-home tutor

• Includes closed captioning in English and Spanish

• Reach your visual and auditory learners

• Available online or on CD-ROM

Program Highlights

Only from Holt!

IDEA Works!
Special Education CD–ROM

• Modified tests, quizzes, and worksheets

• Adapted format for students with special needs

LESSON 1-1 **Practice A**
Variables and Expressions

Write each algebraic expression in words.

> **algebraic expression**
> a mathematical phrase that contains operations, numbers, and/or variables

1. $a + 3$

2. $2x$

_____

3. $5 - y$

4. $\frac{n}{4}$

_____

5. Clint runs c miles.
Brenda runs 2 miles more than Clint.
Write an expression for the number of miles Brenda runs. _____

Evaluate each expression for $a = 2$ and $b = 6$.
The first one has been started for you.

> **evaluate**
> replace the variable with a number

6. $a + b$

7. $b - a$

8. ab

$2 + \quad =$

"*Key to effective instructional design is differentiated levels of support or scaffolding to support student learning when and where they need it.*" — **Dr. David J. Chard, Holt author**

Count on **Holt Geometry** for

Success on High-Stakes Tests

Test prep that covers the basics AND develops higher order thinking

Integrated test prep means no surprises on test day. *Holt Geometry* includes lesson and cumulative review in standardized test format throughout every lesson and chapter to develop student confidence in test-taking skills—without taking time away from core content.

Multi-Step TAKS Prep uses real-world scenarios to develop higher order thinking skills.

TAKS Prep and **Spiral Review** provide daily practice of new and previously taught skills in standardized test format.

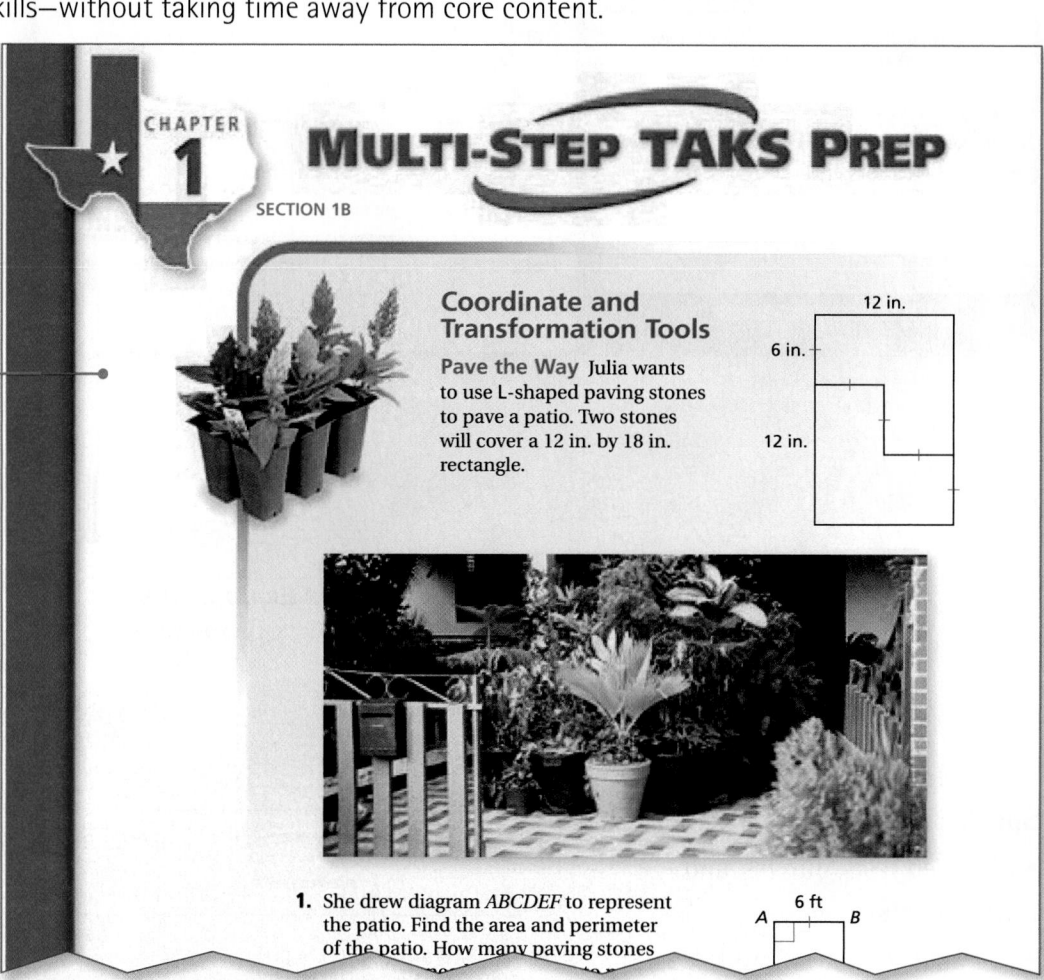

MULTI-STEP TAKS PREP

SECTION 1B

Coordinate and Transformation Tools

Pave the Way Julia wants to use L-shaped paving stones to pave a patio. Two stones will cover a 12 in. by 18 in. rectangle.

1. She drew diagram *ABCDEF* to represent the patio. Find the area and perimeter of the patio. How many paving stones

Only from Holt!

Ready for TAKS? Benchmark Tests
- Includes full-page Pre-Tests and Post-Tests for each TEKS
- TAKS Doctor with complete solutions and error analysis of wrong answers

HOLT MATH

CHAPTER 4

TAKS PREP

go.hrw.com/Geo/TX
TAKS Practice Online
KEYWORD: MG7 TestPrep

CUMULATIVE ASSESSMENT, CHAPTERS 1–4

Multiple Choice

Use the diagram for Items 1 and 2.

[diagram: rhombus A B C D with center E]

1. Which of these congruence statements can be proved from the information given in the [diagram]?

(A) △AEB ≅ △CED   (C) △ABD ≅ △[...]

(B) △BAC ≅ △DAC   (D) △DEC ≅ △D[...]

2. What other information is needed to prove △CEB ≅ △AED by the HL Congruence The[orem]?

(F) $\overline{AD} \cong \overline{AB}$ (H) $\overline{CB} \cong \overline{AD}$

(G) $\overline{BE} \cong \overline{AE}$ (J) $\overline{DE} \cong \overline{CE}$

3. Which biconditional statement is true?

(A) Tomorrow is Monday if and only if to[day is] not Saturday.

(B) Next month is January if and only if t[his] month is December.

(C) Today is a weekend day if and only if yesterday was Friday.

(D) This month had 31 days if and only if [last] month had 30 days.

4. What must be true if $\overrightarrow{PQ}$ intersects $\overleftrightarrow{ST}$ at [more] than one point?

(F) P, Q, S, and T are collinear.

(G) P, Q, S, and T are noncoplanar.

(H) $\overrightarrow{PQ}$ and $\overrightarrow{ST}$ are opposite rays.

(J) $\overrightarrow{PQ}$ and $\overleftrightarrow{ST}$ are perpendicular.

5. △ABC ≅ △DEF, $EF = x^2 - 7$, and $BC = 4x$ [...] Find the values of x.

(A) −1 and 5   (C) 1 and 5

(B) −1 and 6   (D) 2 and 3

6. Which conditional statement has the same truth value as its inverse?

(F) If $n < 0$, then $n^2 > 0$.

(G) If a triangle has three congruent sides, then it is an isosceles triangle.

(H) If an angle measures less than 90°, then it is an acute angle.

(J) If n is a negative integer, then $n < 0$.

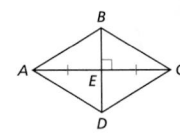

CHAPTER 4

TAKS TACKLER

Standardized Test Strategies

Any Question Type: Identify Key Words and Context Clues

When reading a test item, you should pay attention to key words and context clues given in the problem statement. These clues will guide you in providing a correct response.

EXAMPLE 1

Multiple Choice What is the side length of an equilateral triangle with a perimeter of $42\frac{3}{4}$ cm?

(A) $42\frac{3}{4}$ cm   (C) $21\frac{3}{8}$ cm

(B) $24\frac{3}{7}$ cm   (D) $14\frac{1}{4}$ cm

LOOK for key words and context clues and underline them. Identify what they mean.

What is the side length of an underlined{equilateral triangle} with a underlined{perimeter} of $42\frac{3}{4}$ in.?

equilateral triangle → a triangle with three congruent sides

perimeter → the distance around a figure

perimeter = 3 (length of one side)

$$42\frac{3}{4} = 3(x)$$ *You find the perimeter of an equilateral triangle by multiplying the length of one side of the triangle by three.*

$$\frac{42\frac{3}{4}}{3} = \frac{3(x)}{3}$$

$$\frac{171}{4} \cdot \frac{1}{3} = x$$ *The correct choice is **D** because the length of the side of the equilateral triangle is $14\frac{1}{4}$ cm.*

$$14\frac{1}{4} = x$$

EXAMPLE 2

Gridded Response The vertex angle of an isosceles triangle measures $(5t - 5)°$, and one of the base angles measures $(t + 5)°$. Find t.

isosceles triangle → a triangle with at least two congruent sides

vertex angle → the angle formed by the legs

base angles → The side opposite the vertex angle is called the base, and the base angles are the two angles that have the base as a side.

2(measure of the base angle) + (measure of the vertex angle) = 180°

$$2(t + 5) + (5t - 5) = 180$$
$$2t + 10 + 5t - 5 = 180$$
$$7t + 5 = 180$$
$$t = 25$$ *The correct value for t is 25.*

"*Assessment should enhance mathematics learning. What we assess and how we assess it communicates what we value.*" — **Steven J. Leinwand, Holt author**

Program Highlights

Count on Holt Geometry for

Integrated Technology that enhances learning

Resources help you manage your classroom and motivate students to take learning one step further.

Holt Geometry empowers you with key management and presentation tools that help you meet the needs of a broad range of students.

Interactive Answers and Solutions CD-ROM
allows teachers to create a screen of selected answers and access complete solutions.

Texas One-Stop Planner® CD-ROM with Test and Practice Generator contains everything you need to plan and manage your lessons in one place.
- All print ancillaries
- Customizable lesson plans
- Holt Calendar Planner®
- Holt PuzzlePro®
- ExamView Test and Practice Generator

Transparencies CD-ROM
- Includes **Countdown to Testing Transparencies** and daily **Teaching Transparencies**
- Available in print or on CD-ROM

more than 800 transparencies!

Power Presentations CD-ROM contains colorful, animated, editable presentations for every lesson.

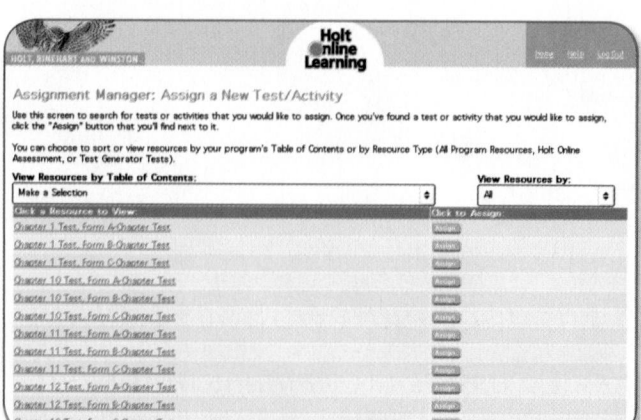

Holt Online Assessment
- Diagnoses individual student performance by standards and textbook objectives
- Automatically assigns resources to strengthen students' skills
- Tracks student progress in one easy-to-manage reporting system

INTEGRATED TECHNOLOGY

With *Holt Geometry* technology, students get all the help they need, any time they need it. Interactive features and online tools make the math more meaningful to deepen student understanding.

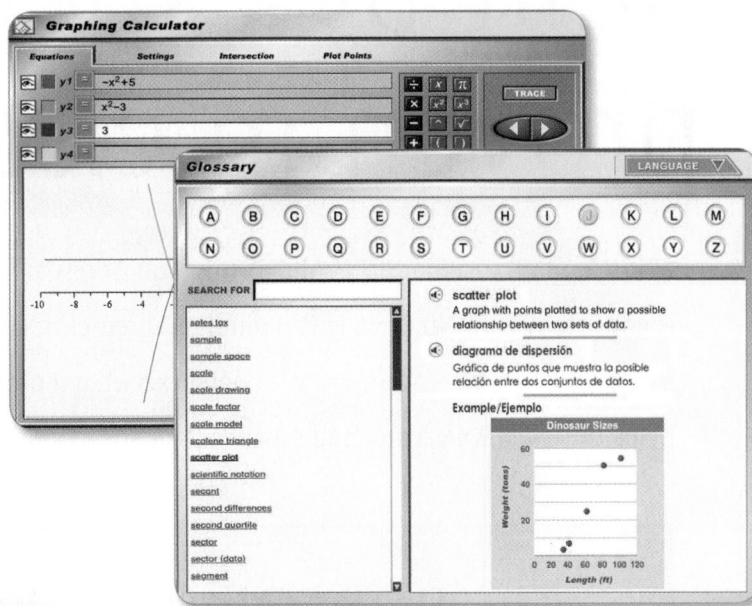

Texas Premier Online Edition makes math come alive!
- Lesson Tutorial Videos
- Interactive practice with feedback
- Online study tools

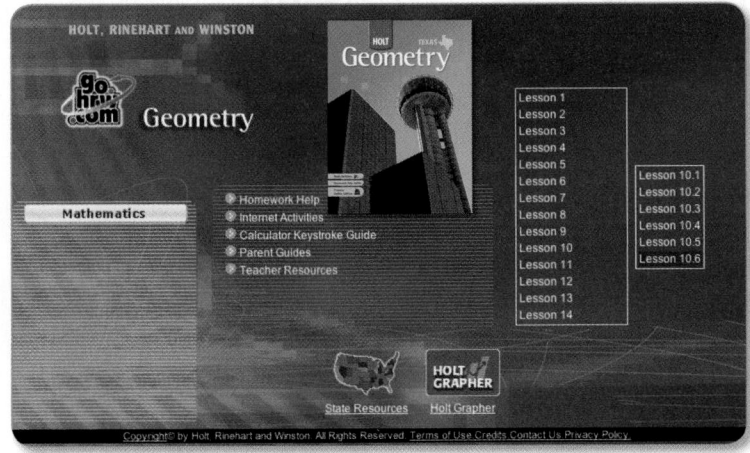

go.hrw.com gives students easy access to lesson resources.
- Homework Help Online
- Intervention and enrichment exercises
- Online games and projects

Texas Student One Stop CD-ROM solves the backpack problem.
- Entire *Student Edition*
- Workbooks
- Intervention and enrichment exercises

> " *Technology, when used appropriately, can improve students' mathematical understanding and problem-solving skills.* "
>
> — **Dr. Bert K. Waits,** Holt author

Program Highlights

Count on **Holt Geometry** to be

Grounded in research, built by experts, proven in classrooms

Holt Geometry is built on a solid foundation of research, proven to work in the classroom, and is consistent with No Child Left Behind requirements. This research is backed by the expertise of a world-class team of authors who have executed a program that makes students *want* to learn, helps them *actually* learn, and ensures their success on high-stakes tests.

The Research Underlying the Program

Holt established a pattern of interaction with the educational community throughout all stages of the program's development.

Needs Assessment
- Teacher Interviews
- University Faculty Interviews
- Federal, State, and Local Agencies
- Advisory Panels
- Task Forces
- Academic Conferences
- Surveys with Teachers, Sales, Administrators

Pedagogical Research
- Thorough
- Effective
- Scientifically-Based

Program Development
- Classroom Observation
- Field Testing of Prototypes
- Reviewed by Program and Field Consultants
- Reviewed by Teachers and Administrators

Program Validation
- User Surveys
- Student and Teacher Appraisals
- Field Consultant and Sales Reports

Program Effectiveness
- Post-Implementation Effectiveness Studies
- Valid and Reliable Tests

HOLT MATH

Edward B. Burger, Ph.D.
Professor of Mathematics and Chair | Williams College, MA

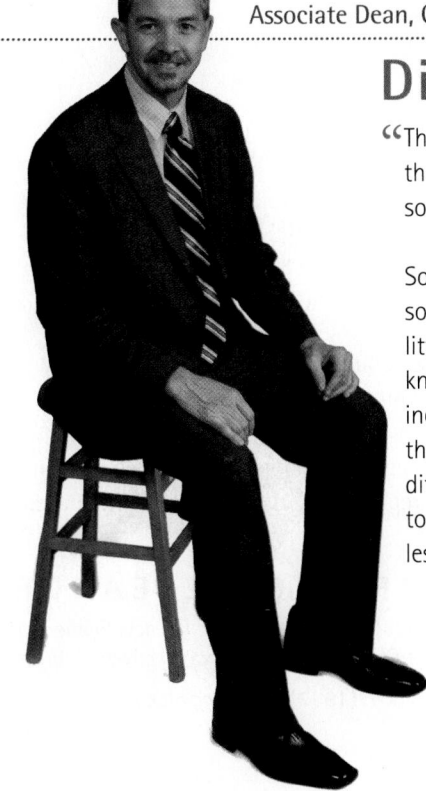

Student Engagement

"Learning should be fun. Deep and abstract ideas are challenging to all, but the challenge should be a pleasurable one that students want to conquer. Thus we offer levity through-out the *Holt Algebra 1/Geometry/Algebra 2* series— jokes for the teachers to share with their students and entertaining antics on the accompanying videos, mixing mathematical insights with laughs. There is no better student than the student who wants to learn. In this program we worked hard to make learning fun so students enjoy the journey and, as a result, attain a deeper understanding of the mathematics they explore.

The mathematics is developed in a meaningful manner with student readers in mind. Questions such as "What would resonate with real high school students today?" were asked at every stage of the writing."

SUPPORTING RESEARCH

Ames, R., & Ames, C. (Eds.). (1984). *Research on motivation in education: Vol. 1. Student motivation.* New York: Academic Press.

Brewster, Cori, and Jennifer Fager. (2000). *Increasing Student Engagement and Motivation: From Time-on-Task to Homework.* Portland, Ore.: Northwest Regional Educational Laboratory.

David J. Chard, Ph.D.
Associate Dean, Curriculum and Academic Programs | University of Oregon

Differentiated Instruction

"The *Holt Algebra 1/Geometry/Algebra 2* series is designed to assist teachers in helping all their students learn conceptual knowledge, skills, and strategies essential to understanding sophisticated mathematics.

Some students often require substantial assistance in developing strategies for problem solving, while others may already have the knowledge necessary to solve problems with little support. In this program, the instructional framework builds the background knowledge essential for ensuring that all students are able to understand and solve increasingly complex problems. Scaffolding in this program takes many forms. For example, the program presents content starting with simple examples and progressing to more difficult content and applications. In addition, the program offers frequent opportunities to review, alternative lessons to help students who did not master content in introductory lessons, and additional examples for extended instruction."

SUPPORTING RESEARCH

Bransford, J. D., Brown, A. L., & Cocking, R. R. (Eds.). (2000). *How people learn: Brain, mind, experience, and school.* Washington, DC: National Research Council.

Gersten, R., Chard, D. J., Baker, S., et al. (2005). *A meta-analysis of research on mathematics instruction for students with learning disabilities.* Signal Hill, CA: Instructional Research Group.

Program Research

Earlene J. Hall, Ed.D
Mathematics Supervisor | Detroit Public Schools

Intervention

"Traditionally, mathematics intervention has been offered in an 'extraction type format'. In this series, Holt has provided teachers a tool kit of strategies that address closing the achievement gap through the use of an innovative intervention system. The *Holt Algebra 1/Geometry/Algebra 2* series provides intervention at the point of misconception. An ongoing assessment and intervention system in each chapter allows the teacher to diagnose, monitor, and assess students' mastery of the mathematical concepts throughout the chapters.

Within each lesson, at each stage of the developing concept, this program offers teachers scaffolding intervention questions and instructional examples that focus on comprehension of the mathematics content by students impacted by language barriers."

SUPPORTING RESEARCH

All Students Reaching The Top : Strategies for Closing Academic Achievement Gaps. A Report of the National Study Group for the Affirmative Development of Academic Ability. (2004)

Resnick, L. B. , & Klopfer, L.E. (1989). *Toward the Thinking Curriculum: Current Cognitive Research.*

Paul A. Kennedy, Ph.D.
Professor, Department of Mathematics | Colorado State University

Algebraic Thinking

" Students learn best when they are provided with opportunities to link present learning to concrete knowledge. This area in which learning occurs, in between the concrete and the abstract, is what Vygotsky calls the "zone of proximal development." Our sequence empowers students to make the transition from concrete to abstract with the notion that "abstractions" become new "concretes" so that they can build on what they know to develop true algebraic thinking.

The *Holt Algebra 1/Geometry/Algebra 2* series focuses on multiple representations—verbal, numerical, graphical, and symbolic. The series provides students with many opportunities to work with multiple representations throughout the program. This allows them to move fluidly among representations, deepening their understanding of algebra. The notion of "doing and undoing," or moving from one representation to another, is integrated throughout the program."

SUPPORTING RESEARCH

Vygotsky, L.S. (1978). *Mind and society: The development of higher mental processes.* Cambridge, MA: Harvard University Press.

Driscoll, Mark J. (1997). *Fostering algebraic thinking.* Portsmouth, NH.; Heinemann.

HOLT MATH

Steven J. Leinwand
Principal Research Analyst, American Institutes for Research | Washington, DC

Assessing Student Understanding

❝As the mathematics curriculum has broadened to encompass communicating and conceptualizing, problem solving and reasoning, so too must our traditional view of assessment broaden. To reflect today's curriculum and more accurately determine students' progress, assessment should be an integral part of the teaching and learning process. Questioning strategies, such as those found in the *Holt Algebra 1/Geometry/Algebra 2* series, can be integral to daily assessment, along with lesson quizzes.

Additionally, assessment should provide opportunities for students to evaluate, reflect upon, and improve their work. The **Are You Ready?** feature allows students to determine if they have the skills to complete the chapter successfully. And more importantly, **Ready to Go On?** provides several opportunities during the course of the chapter for students to see how well they understand the material and to work several times in a chapter to improve their work before the Chapter Test (rather than after).❞

SUPPORTING RESEARCH

NCTM Assessment Standards Working Groups (1995). *Assessment Standards for School Mathematics.* National Council of Teachers of Mathematics. Reston, VA.

National Research Council (1989). *Everybody Counts.* Washington, DC; National Academy Press.

Freddie L. Renfro
Former Director of Mathematics Instruction K–12 | Texas City Independent School District

Differentiated Instruction

❝ Imagine a classroom where diversity in learning is the norm, and the teacher responds to the learners' needs with flexible strategies, open dialogue, and ongoing assessment.

Every child is unique. Finding ways to tailor instruction to meet individual student needs in the classroom can be a manageable task with the right support. In the *Holt Algebra 1/Geometry/Algebra 2* series, we promote differentiated instruction by including activities that address a variety of learning styles: discovery learning, the use of concrete examples, and student interaction, to name a few.

The *Teacher's Edition* offers suggestions for differentiated assessment as well so that students have the opportunity to demonstrate their understanding in a manner that reflects their learning style.❞

SUPPORTING RESEARCH

Tomlinson, C. (1999). *The differentiated classroom: Responding to the needs of all learners.* Alexandria, VA: Association for Supervision and Curriculum Development.

Willis, S. and Mann, Larry. (2000). *Differentiating instruction.* Alexandria, VA: Association for Supervision and Curriculum Development.

Program Research

Program Research

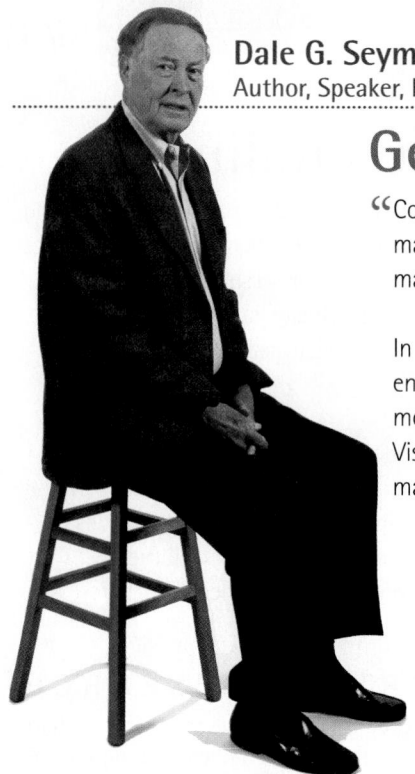

Dale G. Seymour
Author, Speaker, Publisher, and Former Mathematics Teacher | Founder, Creative Publications

Geometry Instructional Design

"Connections in mathematics are key to understanding and appreciating the beauty of mathematics. These connections need to be demonstrated so that students can view mathematics as an integrated whole.

In the *Holt Algebra 1/Geometry/Algebra 2* series we use graphical illustrations to help students envision complex mathematical concepts. Many students can comprehend a difficult concept more quickly if they see it as a whole rather than attempt to understand it as an abstraction. Visualizations in the textbook as well as in the series' accompanying posters enable students to make connections among interrelated ideas. "

SUPPORTING RESEARCH

Fuys, D., Geddes, D., & Tischler, R. (1988). The van Hiele model of thinking in geometry among adolescents. *Journal for Research in Mathematics Education.*

Gagatsis, A. & Patronis, T. (1990, February). Using geometrical models in a process of reflective thinking in learning and teaching mathematics. *Educational Studies in Mathematics, 21, 1, 29-54.*

Bert K. Waits, Ph.D.
Professor Emeritus of Mathematics | The Ohio State University

Technology to Enhance Learning

" Research has demonstrated that technology, when used appropriately, can improve students' mathematical understanding and problem-solving skills. Similarly, technological tools can help teachers challenge students to use and understand mathematics in real-world scenarios.

The *Holt Algebra 1/Geometry/Algebra 2* series presents a balanced approach to learning. We stress that students must utilize all available tools, including mental and paper-and- pencil skills and technology, in the mathematics-learning process. This series uses technology not as an end in itself, but rather as a means for understanding and application. Current research supports this use of computer software including spreadsheets, dynamic geometry software, and graphing calculators. "

SUPPORTING RESEARCH

Graham, A.T., & J.O.J. Thomas. (2000). Building a versatile understanding of algebraic variables with a graphic calculator. *Educational Studies in Mathematics,* 41 (3), 265-282.

Hallar, Jeannie C., & Karen Norwood. (1999). The effects of a graphing-approach intermediate algebra curriculum on students' understanding of function. *Journal for Research in Mathematics Education,* 30 (2), 220-226.

Holt Geometry
Program Components

★ Texas Student Edition
★ Texas Student One Stop CD-ROM
★ Texas Premier Online Edition
★ Texas Teacher's Edition

Assessment and Intervention

Are You Ready? Intervention and Enrichment
Assessment Resources
Ready to Go On? Intervention and Enrichment
★ Ready for TAKS Intervention

Differentiated Instruction

Alternate Openers: Explorations Transparencies
IDEA Works! Special Education CD-ROM
Lesson Tutorial Videos
Manipulatives Kit
Multilingual Glossary
Posters
★ Texas Premier Online Edition
Success for English Language Learners

Workbooks

★ Texas Homework and Practice Workbook
★ Texas Know-It Notebook
★ Texas Problem Solving Workbook
★ TAKS Prep Workbook
★ Texas Lab Manual Workbook

Spanish Resources

Holt Geometry Summary and Review

Anytime, Anyplace
Professional Development:
Building a Community of Learners

High-Stakes Test Prep

★ Countdown to TAKS Transparencies
Holt College Entrance Exam Practice for Mathematics
★ TAKS Prep for Middle School and High School CD-ROM
★ Ready for TAKS Benchmark Tests
★ Ready for TAKS Intervention
End of Course Test Prep
★ TAKS Prep Workbook

Integrated Technology

Are You Ready? Intervention and Enrichment CD-ROM
★ TAKS Prep for Middle School and High School CD-ROM
IDEA Works! Special Education CD-ROM
Interactive Answers and Solutions CD-ROM
Lesson Tutorial Videos CD-ROM
★ Texas One-Stop Planner with Test and Practice Generator and State-Specific Resources CD-ROM
Power Presentations CD-ROM
Quiz Game CD-ROM
★ Texas Premier Online Edition
Ready to Go On? Intervention and Enrichment CD-ROM
★ Texas Student One Stop CD-ROM
Transparencies CD-ROM
★ Ready for TAKS Benchmark Tests and Intervention for Grades 6 through Exit Exam

Teaching Resources

Calendar Planner
Chapter Resource Books
Interactive Answers and Solutions CD-ROM
★ Texas Know-It Notebook Teacher's Guide with Transparencies
★ Texas Lesson Plans
Lesson Transparencies
★ Texas One-Stop Planner with Test and Practice Generator and State-Specific Resources CD-ROM
Power Presentations CD-ROM
Holt PuzzlePro
★ Texas Solutions Key
Transparencies CD-ROM

Foundations for Geometry

go.hrw.com/Geo/TX
Online Resources
KEYWORD: MG7 TOC

Tools for Success

Reading Math 5
Writing Math 10, 18, 26, 33, 40, 48, 54
Vocabulary 3, 4, 9, 17, 24, 31, 38, 47, 53, 60

Know-It Notes 6, 7, 8, 13, 14, 16, 20, 21, 22, 24, 28, 29, 31, 36, 37, 43, 44, 45, 46, 50, 52

Graphic Organizers 8, 16, 24, 31, 37, 46, 52

Homework Help Online 9, 17, 24, 31, 38, 47, 53

Test Prep Exercises 11, 19, 26, 33, 40–41, 49, 55

Multi-Step TAKS Prep 10, 18, 26, 33, 34, 39, 48, 54, 58

College Entrance Exam Practice 65

TAKS Tackler 66

TAKS Prep 68

Geometric Reasoning

Table of Contents

Tools for Success

Reading Math 73

Writing Math 78, 81, 86, 92, 96, 100, 109, 111, 115, 125

Vocabulary 71, 72, 77, 84, 91, 99, 107, 113, 122, 130

Know-It Notes 75, 76, 81, 83, 84, 89, 90, 98, 104, 106, 107, 110, 111, 112, 113, 118, 120, 122, 128

Graphic Organizers 76, 84, 90, 98, 107, 113, 122

Homework Help Online 77, 84, 91, 99, 107, 113, 122

Test Prep Exercises 79, 86, 93, 101, 109, 116, 125

Multi-Step TAKS Prep 78, 85, 92, 100, 102, 109, 115, 124, 126

College Entrance Exam Practice 135

TAKS Tackler 136

TAKS Prep 138

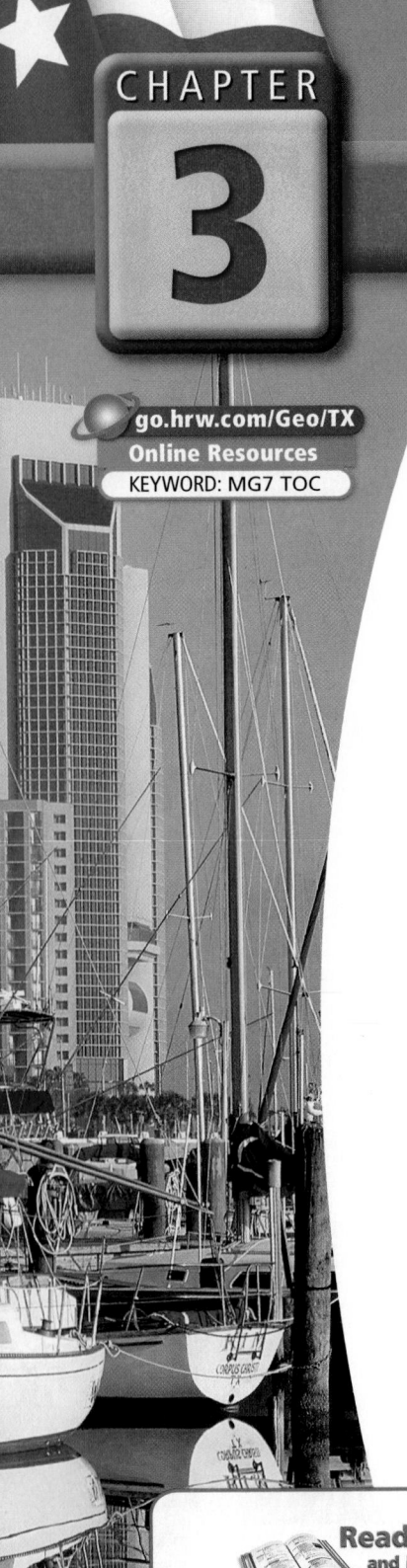

Parallel and Perpendicular Lines

Tools for Success

Reading and Writing Math

Writing Math 150, 160, 168, 177, 186, 196

Vocabulary 143, 144, 148, 175, 185, 194, 202

Study Skills

Study Strategy 145

Know-It Notes 146, 147, 148, 155, 156, 157, 162, 163, 173, 174, 182, 184, 185, 190, 192, 193

Graphic Organizers 148, 157, 165, 174, 185, 193

Homework Help Online 148, 158, 166, 175, 185, 194

TEST PREP

Test Prep Exercises 150–151, 160–161, 168–169, 177–178, 187, 196–197

Multi-Step TAKS Prep 150, 160, 168, 176, 180, 186, 196, 200

College Entrance Exam Practice 207

TAKS Tackler 208

TAKS Prep 210

Triangle Congruence

Tools for Success

Reading Math 215, 273

Writing Math 220, 229, 236, 248, 258, 264, 271, 278

Vocabulary 213, 214, 219, 227, 234, 245, 256, 262, 270, 276, 284

Know-It Notes 216, 217, 218, 223, 224, 225, 226, 231, 233, 242, 243, 245, 252, 254, 255, 262, 267, 269, 273, 274, 275, 276

Graphic Organizers 218, 226, 233, 245, 255, 262, 269, 276

Homework Help Online 219, 227, 234, 245, 256, 262, 270, 276

Test Prep Exercises 221, 230, 236, 248, 258–259, 264–265, 272, 279

Multi-Step TAKS Prep 220, 229, 236, 238, 247, 258, 264, 271, 278, 280

College Entrance Exam Practice 289

TAKS Tackler 290

TAKS Prep 292

CHAPTER 5

go.hrw.com/Geo/TX
Online Resources
KEYWORD: MG7 TOC

Properties and Attributes of Triangles

Tools for Success

Reading Math 299, 300
Writing Math 306, 313, 318, 325, 338, 344, 354, 361
Vocabulary 297, 298, 304, 311, 317, 324, 336, 352, 366

Know-It Notes 300, 301, 303, 307, 309, 310, 314, 317, 323, 324, 333, 334, 335, 340, 342, 350, 351, 352, 356, 358, 359
Graphic Organizers 303, 310, 317, 324, 335, 342, 352, 359
Homework Help Online 304, 311, 317, 324, 336, 343, 352, 360

Test Prep Exercises 306, 313, 319, 326, 339, 345, 355, 362
Multi-Step TAKS Prep 305, 312, 319, 326, 328, 338, 344, 354, 361, 364
College Entrance Exam Practice 371
TAKS Tackler 372
TAKS Prep 374

Polygons and Quadrilaterals

go.hrw.com/Geo/TX
Online Resources
KEYWORD: MG7 TOC

Tools for Success

Reading and Writing Math

Writing Math 379, 388, 397, 404, 414, 424, 434

Vocabulary 377, 378, 386, 395, 412, 432, 438

Study Skills

Know-It Notes 383, 384, 385, 391, 392, 394, 398, 399, 401, 408, 409, 411, 418, 419, 421, 427, 429, 431

Graphic Organizers 385, 394, 401, 411, 421, 431

Homework Help Online 386, 395, 402, 412, 422, 432

TEST PREP

Test Prep Exercises 388, 397, 405, 414–415, 425, 434–435

Multi-Step TAKS Prep 387, 396, 404, 406, 414, 424, 434, 436

College Entrance Exam Practice 443

TAKS Tackler 444

TAKS Prep 446

Similarity

go.hrw.com/Geo/TX
Online Resources
KEYWORD: MG7 TOC

Tools for Success

Reading and Writing Math

Study Skills

TEST PREP

Reading Math 453, 455, 456

Writing Math 459, 463, 466, 476, 486, 493, 499

Vocabulary 451, 452, 457, 465, 491, 498, 504

Know-It Notes 455, 457, 462, 464, 470, 471, 473, 481, 482, 483, 484, 490, 497

Graphic Organizers 457, 464, 473, 484, 490, 497

Homework Help Online 457, 465, 474, 484, 491, 498

Test Prep Exercises 459, 467, 477, 487, 493, 500

Multi-Step TAKS Prep 458, 466, 476, 478, 486, 492, 499, 502

College Entrance Exam Practice 509

TAKS Tackler 510

TAKS Prep 512

Right Triangles and Trigonometry

go.hrw.com/Geo/TX
Online Resources
KEYWORD: MG7 TOC

Tools for Success

Reading Math 517, 534, 570

Writing Math 523, 525, 531, 540, 548, 557, 566, 571

Vocabulary 515, 516, 521, 529, 547, 563, 572

Know-It Notes 518, 519, 520, 525, 528, 537, 546, 552, 553, 554, 561, 563

Graphic Organizers 520, 528, 537, 546, 554, 563

Homework Help Online 521, 529, 537, 547, 555, 563

Test Prep Exercises 523, 532, 540, 549, 558, 567

Multi-Step TAKS Prep 522, 530, 539, 542, 548, 557, 565, 568

College Entrance Exam Practice 577

TAKS Tackler 578

TAKS Prep 580

CHAPTER 9

Extending Perimeter, Circumference, and Area

go.hrw.com/Geo/TX
Online Resources
KEYWORD: MG7 TOC

TEKS

Tools for Success

Reading and Writing Math

Writing Math 596, 605, 611, 620, 626, 635
Vocabulary 585, 586, 603, 609, 633, 640

Study Skills

Study Strategy 587
Know-It Notes 589, 590, 591, 593, 600, 601, 602, 608, 619, 623, 624, 630, 633
Graphic Organizers 593, 602, 608, 619, 624, 633
Homework Help Online 593, 603, 609, 619, 625, 633

TEST PREP

Test Prep Exercises 596–597, 605, 611–612, 621, 627, 636
Multi-Step TAKS Prep 595, 604, 610, 614, 620, 626, 635, 638
College Entrance Exam Practice 645
TAKS Tackler 646
TAKS Prep 648

Spatial Reasoning

go.hrw.com/Geo/TX
Online Resources
KEYWORD: MG7 TOC

Tools for Success

Reading and Writing Math

Writing Math 653, 659, 667, 676, 686, 695, 703, 711, 720

Vocabulary 651, 657, 665, 674, 684, 693, 701, 709, 718, 730

Study Skills

Know-It Notes 654, 656, 664, 670, 671, 672, 673, 680, 681, 683, 689, 690, 692, 697, 699, 700, 705, 707, 708, 714, 716, 717, 726, 727

Graphic Organizers 656, 664, 673, 683, 692, 700, 708, 717

Homework Help Online 657, 665, 674, 684, 693, 701, 709, 718

Test Prep Exercises 659, 667, 677, 687, 695, 703–704, 712, 721

Multi-Step TAKS Prep 658, 666, 675, 678, 686, 695, 703, 711, 720, 724

College Entrance Exam Practice 735

TAKS Tackler 736

TAKS Prep 738

Circles

Tools for Success

Reading and Writing Math

Reading Math 745, 748

Writing Math 754, 756, 762, 769, 778, 788, 797, 804

Vocabulary 743, 744, 751, 760, 767, 776, 810

Study Skills

Know-It Notes 746, 747, 748, 749, 750, 756, 757, 759, 764, 765, 766, 772, 773, 774, 775, 782, 783, 784, 785, 786, 792, 793, 794, 795, 799, 801

Graphic Organizers 750, 759, 766, 775, 786, 795, 801

Homework Help Online 751, 760, 767, 776, 786, 795, 802

 **TEST PREP**

Test Prep Exercises 754, 763, 769, 778, 789, 798, 804

Multi-Step TAKS Prep 753, 762, 768, 770, 777, 788, 797, 803, 806

College Entrance Exam Practice 815

TAKS Tackler 816

TAKS Prep 818

Extending Transformational Geometry

Tools for Success

Writing Math 829, 836, 844, 852, 861, 868, 878, 883

Vocabulary 821, 822, 827, 851, 859, 866, 875, 884

Study Strategy 823

Know-It Notes 825, 826, 832, 833, 840, 841, 848, 849, 850, 856, 857, 858, 866, 873, 874

Graphic Organizers 826, 833, 841, 850, 858, 866, 874

Homework Help Online 827, 834, 842, 851, 859, 866, 875

Test Prep Exercises 829–830, 836–837, 845, 853, 862, 869, 878

Multi-Step TAKS Prep 829, 835, 843, 853, 854, 861, 868, 876, 880

College Entrance Exam Practice 889

TAKS Tackler 890

TAKS Prep 892

WHO USES MATHEMATICS?

The Career Path features are a set of interviews with young adults who are either preparing for or just beginning in different career fields. These people share what math courses they studied in high school, how math is used in their field, and what options the future holds. Also, many exercises throughout the book highlight skills used in various career fields.

Career Path

go.hrw.com/Geo/TX
Career Resources Online
KEYWORD: MG7 Career

Career Applications

ELECTRICIAN *p. 320*

Electricians install and maintain the systems that provide many of the modern-day comforts we rely on, such as climate control, lighting, and technology. Look on page 320 to find out how Alex Peralta got started on this career path.

TECHNICAL WRITER *p. 612*

Have you ever wondered who writes manuals for operating televisions or stereos? A technical writer not only writes manuals for operating electronics, but also documents maintenance procedures for airplanes. Look at the Career Path on page 612 to find out how to become a technical writer.

FURNITURE MAKER *p. 805*

A furniture maker must take precise measurements and be aware of spatial relationships in order to build a quality finished product. The Career Path on page 805 describes the kind of experience needed to be successful as a furniture maker.

WHY LEARN MATHEMATICS?

Links to interesting topics, including some in Texas, may accompany real-world applications in the text. These links help you see how math is used in the real world. For a complete list of all applications in *Holt Geometry,* see page S162 in the Index.

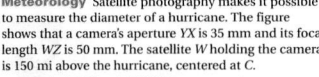

29. Draw and label △PQR and △STU such that $\frac{PQ}{ST} = \frac{QR}{TU}$ but △PQR is NOT similar to △STU.

30. Given: △KNJ is isosceles with ∠N as the vertex angle. ∠H ≅ ∠L
    Prove: △GHJ ~ △MLK

31. **Meteorology** Satellite photography makes it possible to measure the diameter of a hurricane. The figure shows that a camera's aperture YX is 35 mm and its focal length WZ is 50 mm. The satellite W holding the camera is 150 mi above the hurricane, centered at C.
    a. Why is △XYZ ~ △ABZ? What assumption must you make about the position of the camera in order to make this conclusion?
    b. What other triangles in the figure must be similar? Why?
    c. Find the diameter AB of the hurricane.

TEXAS LINK
Meteorology
This satellite image shows Hurricane Lili as it moves across the Gulf of Mexico. In October 2002, an estimated 500,000 people evacuated in advance of Lili's hitting Texas.

Real-World LINKS

Animation 835

LINK
Animation

Each frame of a computer-animated feature represents $\frac{1}{24}$ of a second of film.
Source: www.pixar.com

Archaeology 787
Architecture 159, 220, 695
Astronomy 752
Bicycles 337
Bird-Watching 401
Biology 100, 604
Chemistry 828
Conservation 271
Design 313
Ecology 248
Electronics 692
Engineering 115, 233
Entertainment 149, 683, 803, 833
Fitness 539

Food 195
Geography 626
Geology 86, 804
History 48, 413, 531, 566, 595
Kites 428
Landscaping 607
Marine Biology 698, 720
Math History 41, 78, 257, 318, 493, 611, 703, 768
Measurement 404
Mechanics 434
Meteorology 476, 675, 797
Monument 466
Mosaics 876

TEXAS LINK
Mosaics

This mosaic of the seal of the Republic of Texas is one of six tile mosaics that were installed on the front façade of the Sam Houston Regional Library and Research Center in Liberty, Texas, in fall 2001.

Navigation 278
Oceanography 174
Pets 361
Racing 392
Recreation 92, 674

LINK
Recreation

The Top Thrill Dragster is 420 feet tall and includes a 400-foot vertical drop. It twists 270° as it drops. It is one of 16 roller coasters at Cedar Point amusement park.

Shuffleboard 305
Space Shuttle 548
Sports 19, 530, 635
Surveying 353, 556
Transportation 183
Travel 458

HOW TO STUDY GEOMETRY

This book has many features designed to help you learn and study effectively. Becoming familiar with these features will prepare you for greater success on your exams.

Learn

The **vocabulary** is listed at the beginning of every lesson.

Look for the **Know-It-Note** icons to identify important information.

Study the **examples** to apply new concepts and skills. Examples include stepped out solutions.

Test your understanding of examples by trying the **Check It Out** problems. Check your work in the Selected Answers.

Practice

Use a **graphic organizer** to summarize each lesson.

Refer to the examples from the lesson to solve the **Guided Practice** exercises.

If you get stuck, use the internet for **Homework Help Online**.

Review

Study and review **vocabulary** from the entire chapter.

Use the list on p. S82 to review the **postulates and theorems** found in the chapter.

Test yourself with **practice problems** from every lesson in the chapter.

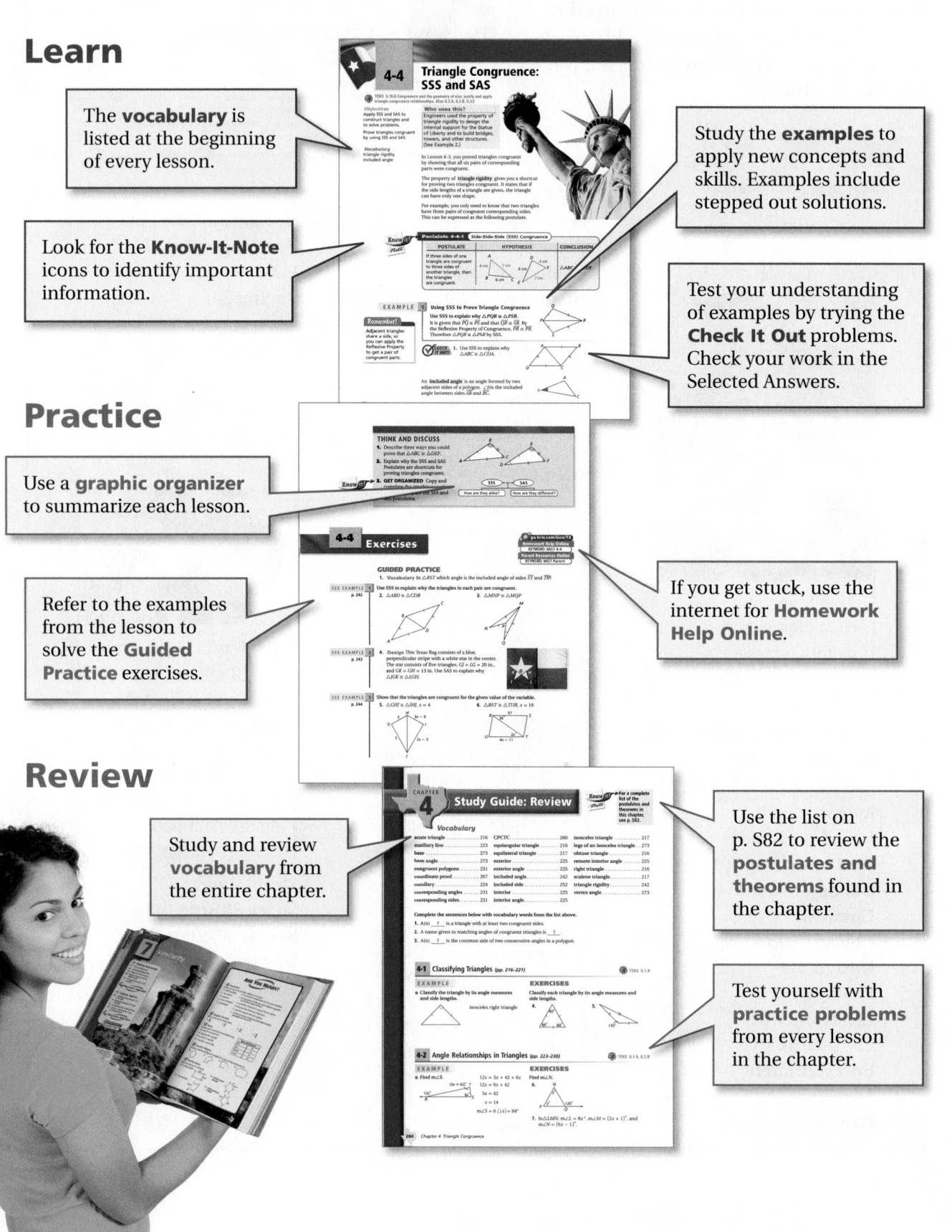

TOOLS OF GEOMETRY

In geometry, it is important to use tools correctly in order to measure accurately and produce accurate figures. One important tool is your pencil. Always use a sharp pencil with a good eraser.

Ruler

The ruler shown has a mark every $\frac{1}{8}$ inch, so the accuracy is to the nearest $\frac{1}{8}$ inch.

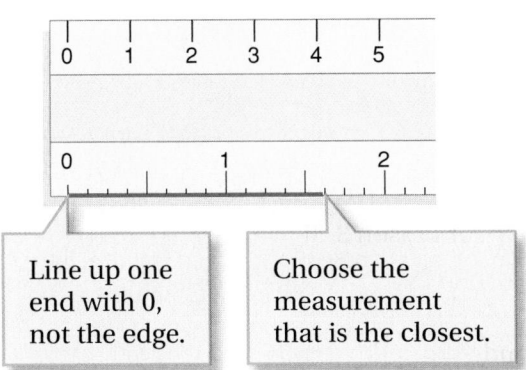

Line up one end with 0, not the edge.

Choose the measurement that is the closest.

Protractor

To use a protractor to measure an angle, you may need to extend the sides of the angle.

For acute angles, use the smaller measurement. For obtuse angles, use the larger measurement.

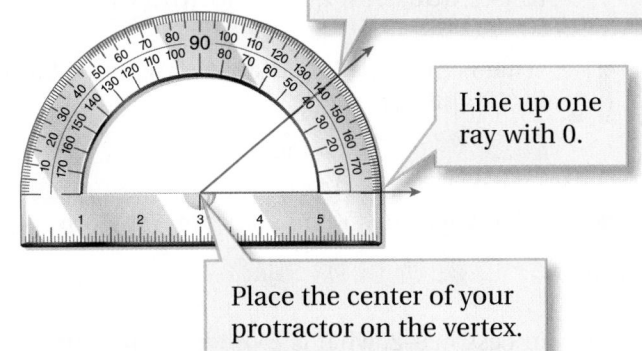

Line up one ray with 0.

Place the center of your protractor on the vertex.

Compass

A compass is used to draw arcs and circles. If you have trouble keeping the point in place, try keeping the compass still and turning the paper.

Keep your wrist flexible. Turn the compass with your index finger and thumb.

Tilt the compass slightly.

Straightedge

A straightedge is used to draw a line through two points. If you use a ruler as a straightedge, do not use the marks on the ruler.

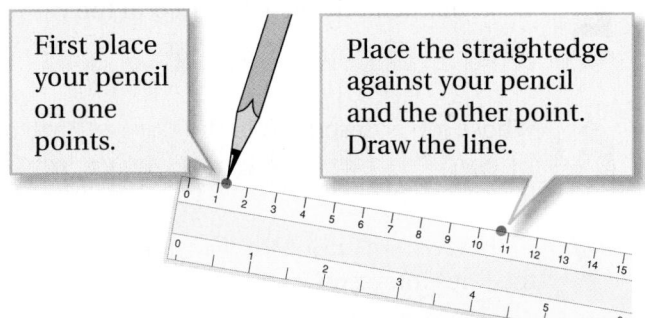

First place your pencil on one points.

Place the straightedge against your pencil and the other point. Draw the line.

Geometry Software

Geometry software can be used to create figures and explore their properties.

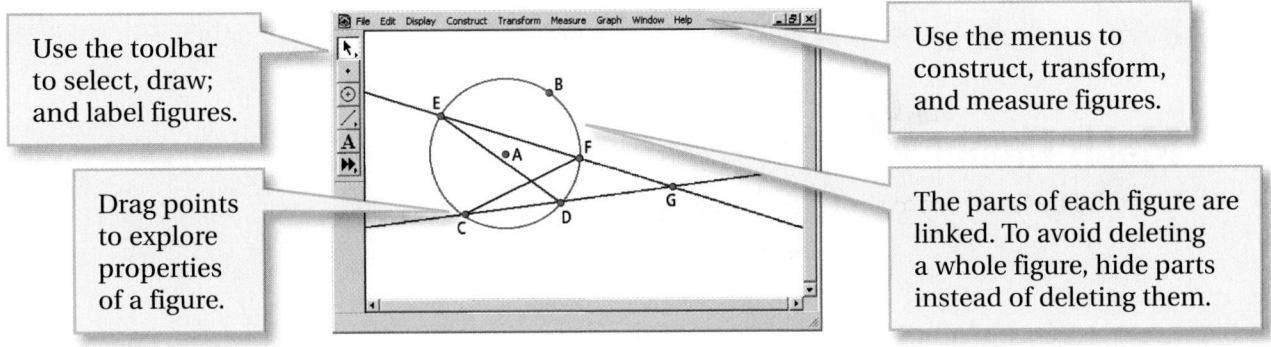

Use the toolbar to select, draw; and label figures.

Drag points to explore properties of a figure.

Use the menus to construct, transform, and measure figures.

The parts of each figure are linked. To avoid deleting a whole figure, hide parts instead of deleting them.

Scavenger Hunt

Use this scavenger hunt to discover a few of the many tools in the Texas Edition of *Holt Geometry* that you can use to become an independent learner.

On a separate sheet of paper, write the answers to each question below. Within each answer, one letter will be in a yellow box. After you have answered every question, identify the letters that would be in yellow boxes and rearrange them to reveal the answer to the question at the bottom of the page.

1. What is the first **Vocabulary** term in the Study Guide: Preview for Chapter 1?

▪▪▪▪▪▫ ANGL**E**

2. What keyword should you enter for **Homework Help** for Lesson 3-3?

▫▪▪▪▪▪ M**A**6 2-1

3. In Lesson 8-2, what is **Example 4** teaching you to find?

▪▪▪▪▫▪▪ LEN**G**THS

4. What theorem are you asked about in the **Know-It Note** on page 352?

▪▫▪▪▪▪▪▪▪▪ P**Y**THAGOREAN

5. What mathematician is featured in the **Math History** link on page 318?

▪▪▫▪▪▪▪▪ ▪▪▪▫ GI**O**VANNI CEVA

6. Whose job is described in the **Career Path** on page 612?

▫▪▪▪▪▪▪▪▪ ▪▪▪▪▪▪ **T**ECHNICAL WRITER

7. In the **Study Guide: Review** for Lesson 11-1, what do the lines intersect?

▪▪▪▪▪▫ CIRCL**E**

8. What advice does Chapter 1's **TAKS Tackler** give about how to answer a multiple choice test item you don't know how to solve?

▪▪▫▪ ▪▪▪▪▪▪▪▪ WO**R**K BACKWARD

Math Humor

What did the little acorn say when it grew up?

▪▪▪▪▪▪▪▪ GEOMETRY

Math Builders

The Math Builders section in the Student Edition uses transparent pages to allow students to learn important concepts through a step-by-step, layered approach. At key points in the text, these pages are referenced in the side margin. The Math Builders are also available on overhead transparencies in *Lesson Transparencies*.

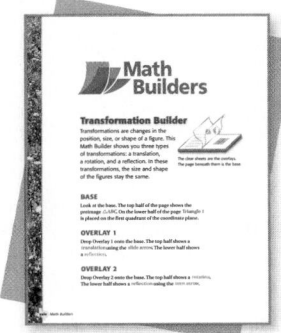

Transformation Builder

Transformations are changes in the position, size, or shape of a figure. This Math Builder shows you three types of transformations: a translation, a rotation, and a reflection. In these transformations, the size and shape of the figures stay the same.

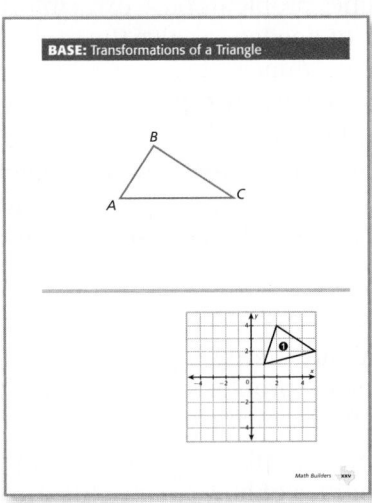

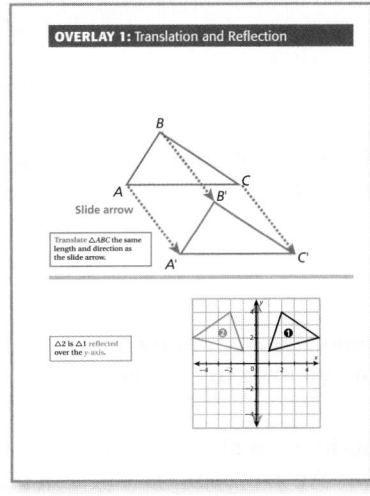

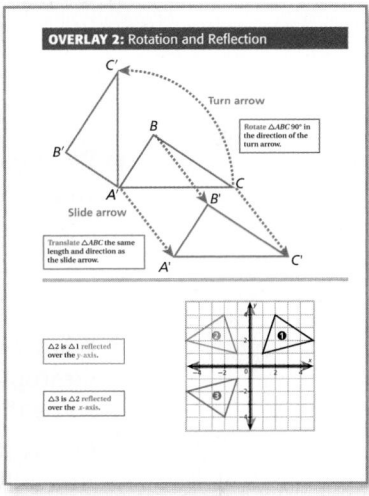

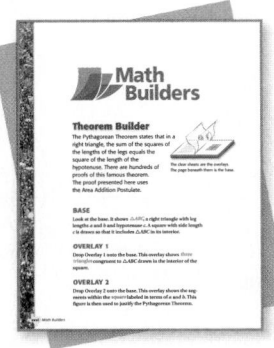

Theorem Builder

The Pythagorean Theorem states that in a right triangle, the sum of the squares of the lengths of the legs equals the square of the length of the hypotenuse. There are hundreds of proofs of this famous theorem. The proof presented here uses the Area Addition Postulate.

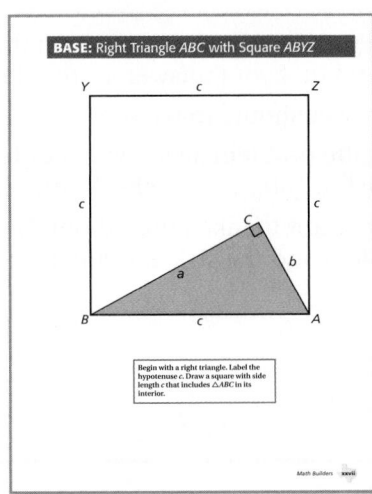

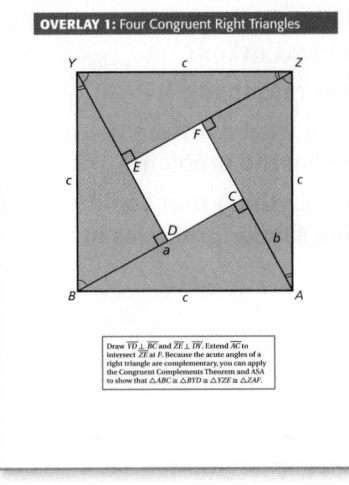

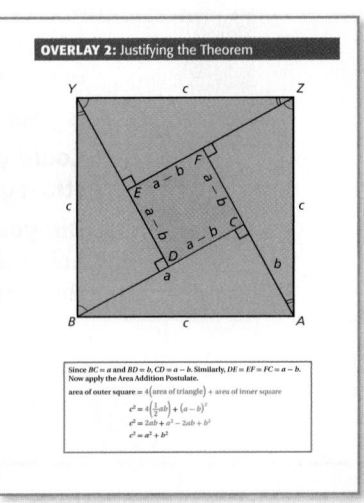

Focus on Problem Solving

The Problem-Solving Plan

To be a good problem solver you need a good problem-solving plan. Using a problem-solving plan along with a problem-solving strategy helps you organize your work and correctly solve the problem. The plan used in this book is outlined below.

UNDERSTAND the Problem

■ **What are you asked to find?**

Make sure you understand exactly what the problem is asking. Restate the problem in your own words.

■ **What information is given in the problem?**

List every piece of information the problem gives you.

■ **Is all the information relevant?**

Sometimes problems have extra information that is not needed to solve the problem. Try to determine what is and is not needed. This helps you stay organized when you are making a plan.

■ **Were you given enough information to solve the problem?**

Sometimes there simply is not enough information to solve the problem. List what else you need to know to solve the problem.

Make a PLAN

■ **What problem-solving strategy or strategies can you use to help you solve the problem?**

Think about strategies you have used in the past to solve problems. Would any of them be helpful in solving this problem?

■ **Create a step-by-step plan of how you will solve the problem.**

Write out your plan in words to help you get a clearer idea of how to solve the problem mathematically.

SOLVE

■ **Use your plan to solve the problem.**

Translate your plan from words to math. Show each step in your solution and write your answer in a complete sentence.

LOOK BACK

■ **Did you completely answer the question that was asked?**

Be sure you answered the question that was asked and that your answer is complete.

■ **Is your answer reasonable?**

Your answer should make sense.

■ **Could you have used a different strategy to solve the problem?**

Solving the problem again with a different strategy is a good way to check your answer.

■ **Did you learn anything that could help you solve similar problems in the future?**

You may want to take notes about this kind of problem and the strategy you used to solve it.

 **Problem Solving on Location**

You can practice using the four-step Problem Solving Plan to solve problems in the Problem Solving on Location feature located at the end of selected chapters. Each page focuses on interesting people, and facts from the Lone Star State.

You can follow the flight path of the hot air balloons in the Great Texas Balloon Race that starts in Longview.

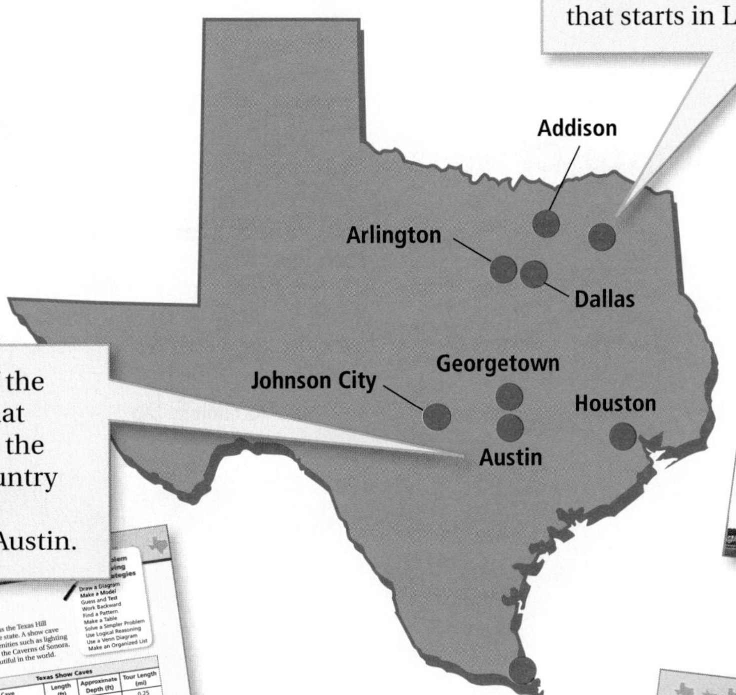

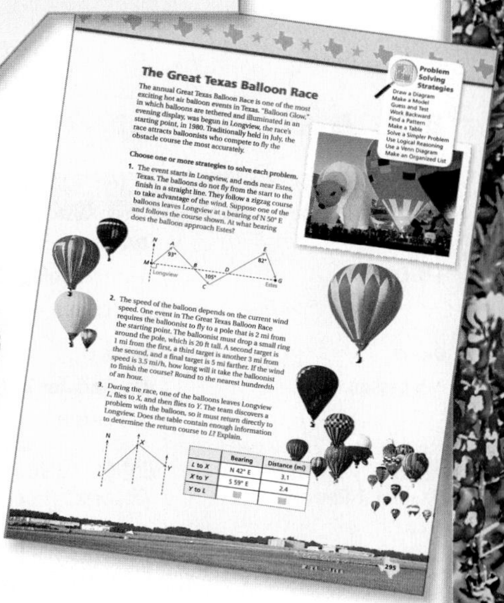

Addison

Arlington

Dallas

Georgetown

Johnson City

Houston

Austin

Take a tour of the show caves that are located in the Texas Hill Country between San Antonio and Austin.

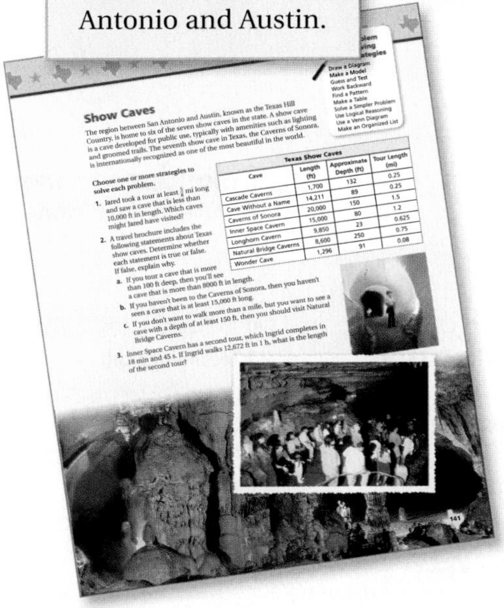

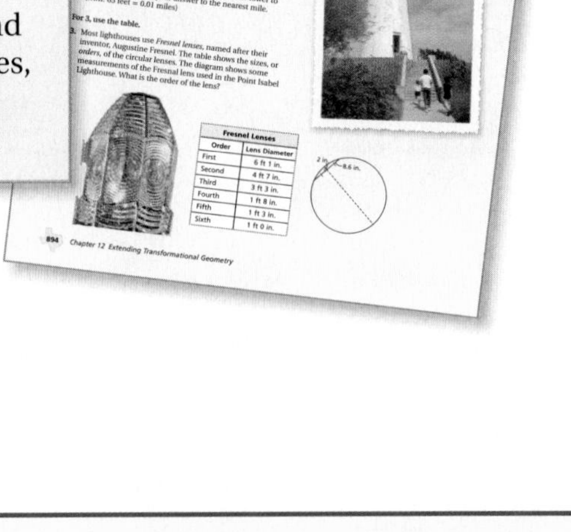

Learn about the sizes and order of lighthouse lenses, such as the one at the Point Isabel Lighthouse.

CHAPTER 1

Foundations for Geometry

Section 1A	Section 1B
Euclidean and Construction Tools	**Coordinate and Transformation Tools**
1-1 Understanding Points, Lines, and Planes	1-5 Using Formulas in Geometry
1-2 Technology Lab Explore Properties Associated with Points	On Track for TAKS Graphing in the Coordinate Plane
1-2 Measuring and Constructing Segments	1-6 Midpoint and Distance in the Coordinate Plane
1-3 Measuring and Constructing Angles	1-7 Transformations in the Coordinate Plane
1-4 Pairs of Angles	1-7 Technology Lab Explore Transformations

Pacing Guide for 45-Minute Classes

Calendar Planner
One-Stop Planner®

Chapter 1

Countdown to TAKS Weeks **1**, **2**

DAY 1	DAY 2	DAY 3	DAY 4	DAY 5
1-1 Lesson	1-2 Technology Lab 1-2 Lesson	1-3 Lesson	1-4 Lesson	Multi-Step TAKS Prep Ready to Go On?
DAY 6	**DAY 7**	**DAY 8**	**DAY 9**	**DAY 10**
1-5 Lesson	On Track for TAKS 1-6 Lesson	1-7 Lesson	1-7 Technology Lab	Multi-Step TAKS Prep Ready to Go On?
DAY 11	**DAY 12**			
Chapter 1 Review	Chapter 1 Test			

Pacing Guide for 90-Minute Classes

Calendar Planner
One-Stop Planner®

Chapter 1

DAY 1	DAY 2	DAY 3	DAY 4	DAY 5
1-1 Lesson 1-2 Technology Lab 1-2 Lesson	1-3 Lesson 1-4 Lesson	Multi-Step TAKS Prep Ready to Go On? 1-5 Lesson	On Track for TAKS 1-6 Lesson 1-7 Lesson	1-7 Technology Lab Multi-Step TAKS Prep Ready to Go On?
DAY 6				
Chapter 1 Review Chapter 1 Test				

ONGOING ASSESSMENT and INTERVENTION

DIAGNOSE	PRESCRIBE

Assess Prior Knowledge

Before Chapter 1

Diagnose readiness for the chapter.	Prescribe intervention.
Are You Ready? SE p. 3	**Are You Ready? Intervention** Skills 20, 57, 60, 79

Formative Assessment

Before Every Lesson

Diagnose readiness for the lesson.	Prescribe intervention.
Warm Up TE, every lesson	**Skills Bank** SE pp. S50–S81
	Reteach CRB, Ch. 1

During Every Lesson

Diagnose understanding of lesson concepts.	Prescribe intervention.
Check It Out! SE, every example	**Questioning Strategies** TE, every example
Think and Discuss SE, every lesson	**Reading Strategies** CRB, every lesson
Write About It SE, every lesson	*Success for ELL* pp. 1–14
Journal TE, every lesson	

After Every Lesson

Diagnose mastery of lesson concepts.	Prescribe intervention.
Lesson Quiz TE, every lesson	**Reteach** CRB, every lesson
Alternative Assessment TE, every lesson	**Problem Solving** CRB, every lesson
Test Prep SE, every lesson	**Test Prep Doctor** TE, every lesson
Test and Practice Generator	*Homework Help* Online

Before Chapter 1 Testing

Diagnose mastery of concepts in the chapter.	Prescribe intervention.
Ready to Go On? SE pp. 35, 59	*Ready to Go On? Intervention* pp. 2–14
Multi-Step TAKS Prep SE pp. 34, 58	**Scaffolding Questions** TE pp. 34, 58
Section Quizzes AR pp. 5–6	
Test and Practice Generator	

Before High Stakes Testing

Diagnose mastery of benchmark concepts.	Prescribe intervention.
Ready for TAKS? Benchmark Tests	*Ready for TAKS? Intervention*
College Entrance Exam Practice SE p. 65	*College Entrance Exam Practice*
TAKS Prep SE pp. 68–69	*TAKS Prep Workbook*
TAKS Prep CD-ROM	

Summative Assessment

After Chapter 1

Check mastery of chapter concepts.	Prescribe intervention.
Multiple-Choice Tests (Forms A, B, C)	**Reteach** CRB, every lesson
Free-Response Tests (Forms A, B, C)	*Lesson Tutorial Videos* Chapter 1
Performance Assessment AR pp. 7–20	
Test and Practice Generator	
Check mastery of benchmark concepts.	Prescribe intervention.
TAKS Tests	*TAKS Prep Workbook*
College Entrance Exams	*College Entrance Exam Practice*

KEY: **SE** = *Student Edition*   **TE** = *Teacher's Edition*   **CRB** = *Chapter Resource Book*   **AR** = *Assessment Resources*   Available online   Available on CD-ROM

2B

CHAPTER

1

Supporting the Teacher

Chapter 1 Resource Book

Practice A, B, C
pp. 3–5, 11–13, 19–21, 27–29, 35–37,
43–45, 51–53

Reading Strategies ELL
pp. 10, 18, 26, 34, 42, 50, 58

Reteach
pp. 6–7, 14–15, 22–23, 30–31, 38–39, 46–47, 54–55

Problem Solving
pp. 9, 17, 25, 33, 41, 49, 57

Challenge
pp. 8, 16, 24, 32, 40, 48, 56

Parent Letter   pp. 1–2

Transparencies

Lesson Transparencies, Volume 1 .... Chapter 1
- Teaching Tools
- Warm Ups
- Teaching Transparencies
- Additional Examples
- Lesson Quizzes

Alternate Openers: Explorations .... pp. 1–7

Countdown to TAKS .... pp. 1–4

Know-It Notebook .... Chapter 1
- Graphic Organizers
- Key Concepts
- Vocabulary
- Chapter Review
- Big Ideas
- Postulates
- Theorems

Teacher Tools

Power Presentations®
Complete PowerPoint® presentations for Chapter 1 lessons

Lesson Tutorial Videos®
Holt authors Ed Burger and Freddie Renfro present tutorials
to support the Chapter 1 lessons.

One-Stop Planner®
Easy access to all Chapter 1 resources and assessments,
as well as software for lesson planning, test generation,
and puzzle creation

IDEA Works!®
Key Chapter 1 resources and assessments modified to address
special learning needs

Lesson Plans .... pp. 1–7

Solutions Key .... p. 1

Geometry Posters .... Chapter 1

TechKeys   **Lab Resources**

Project Teacher Support   **Parent Resources**

Workbooks

Homework and Practice Workbook
Teacher's Guide .... pp. 1–7

Know-It Notebook
Teacher's Guide .... pp. 5–19

Problem Solving Workbook
Teacher's Guide .... pp. 1–7

TAKS Prep Workbook
Teacher's Guide

Technology Highlights for the Teacher

 Power Presentations
Dynamic presentations to engage students.
Complete PowerPoint® presentations for
every lesson in Chapter 1.

 One-Stop Planner
Easy access to Chapter 1 resources and
assessments. Includes lesson-planning, test-
generation, and puzzle-creation software.

Premier Online Edition
Chapter 1 includes Tutorial Videos,
Lesson Activities, Lesson Quizzes,
Homework Help, and Chapter Project.

 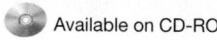

 **Reaching All Learners**

Resources for All Learners

Texas Lab Manual	Chapter 1
Homework and Practice Workbook	pp. 1–7
Know-It Notebook	pp. 5–19
Problem Solving Workbook	pp. 1–7

DEVELOPING LEARNERS

Practice A	CRB, every lesson
Reteach	CRB, every lesson
Inclusion	TE pp. 18, 25, 30, 36, 42, 45, 51
Questioning Strategies	TE, every example
Modified Chapter 1 Resources	*IDEA Works!*
Homework Help Online	

ON-LEVEL LEARNERS

Practice B	CRB, every lesson
Multiple Representations	TE p. 18
Cognitive Strategies	TE pp. 29, 44

ADVANCED LEARNERS

Practice C	CRB, every lesson
Challenge	CRB, every lesson
Reading and Writing Math EXTENSION	TE p. 5
Multi-Step TAKS Prep EXTENSION	TE pp. 34, 58
Critical Thinking	TE p. 14

English Language Learners

Are You Ready? Vocabulary	SE p. 3
Vocabulary Connections	SE p. 4
Lesson Vocabulary	SE, every lesson
Vocabulary Exercises	SE, every exercise set
Vocabulary Review	SE p. 60
English Language Learners	TE pp. 5, 7, 14, 22, 23, 39
Reading Strategies	CRB, every lesson
Success for English Language Learners	pp. 1–14
Multilingual Glossary	

Reaching All Learners Through...

Inclusion	TE pp. 18, 25, 30, 36, 42, 45, 51
Visual Cues	TE pp. 21, 22, 27, 30
Kinesthetic Experience	TE pp. 18, 26
Concrete Manipulatives	TE pp. 14, 51
Multiple Representations	TE p. 18
Cognitive Strategies	TE pp. 29, 44
Cooperative Learning	TE p. 29
Modeling	TE p. 7
Critical Thinking	TE p. 14
Test Prep Doctor	TE pp. 11, 26, 33, 40, 49, 55, 65, 66, 68
Common Error Alerts	TE pp. 15, 19, 21, 23, 25, 29, 39, 45, 49
Scaffolding Questions	TE pp. 34, 58

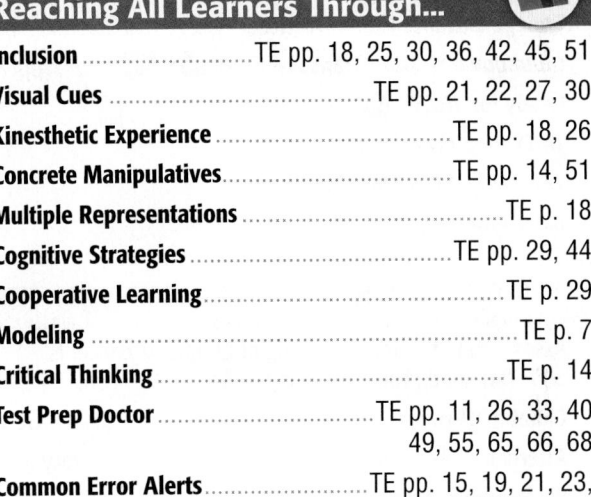

Technology Highlights for Reaching All Learners

Lesson Tutorial Videos

Starring Holt authors Ed Burger and Freddie Renfro! Live tutorials to support every lesson in Chapter 1.

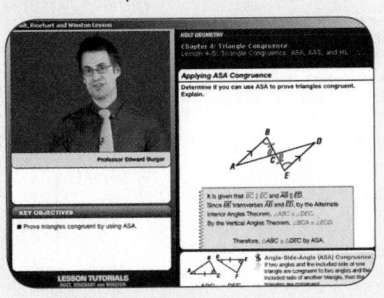

Multilingual Glossary

Searchable glossary includes definitions in English, Spanish, Vietnamese, Chinese, Hmong, Korean, and 4 other languages.

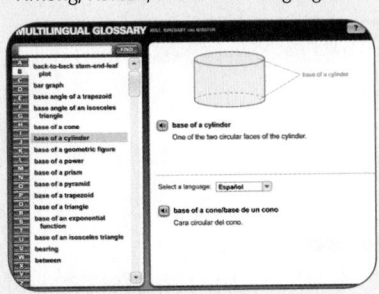

Online Interactivities

Interactive tutorials provide visually engaging alternative opportunities to learn concepts and master skills.

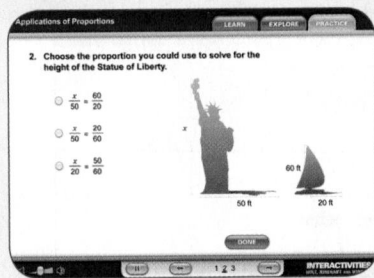

KEY: **SE** = *Student Edition*   **TE** = *Teacher's Edition*   **CRB** = *Chapter Resource Book*    Spanish version available   Available online   Available on CD-ROM

CHAPTER 1

Ongoing Assessment

Assessing Prior Knowledge

Determine whether students have the prerequisite concepts and skills for success in Chapter 1.

Are You Ready?	SE p. 3
Warm Up	TE, every lesson

Test Preparation

Provide review and practice for Chapter 1 and standardized tests.

Multi-Step TAKS Prep	SE pp. 34, 58
Study Guide: Review	SE pp. 60–63
TAKS Tackler	SE pp. 66–67
TAKS Prep	SE pp. 68–69
College Entrance Exam Practice	SE p. 65
Countdown to TAKS **Transparencies** 	pp. 1–4
Ready for TAKS?	
TAKS Prep Workbook	
TAKS Prep **CD-ROM**	
IDEA Works!	

Alternative Assessment

Assess students' understanding of Chapter 1 concepts and combined problem-solving skills.

Chapter 1 Project	SE p. 2
Alternative Assessment	TE, every lesson
Performance Assessment	AR pp. 19–20
Portfolio Assessment	AR p. xxxiv

Daily Assessment

Provide formative assessment for each day of Chapter 1.

Questioning Strategies	TE, every example
Think and Discuss	SE, every lesson
Check It Out! Exercises	SE, every example
Write About It	SE, every lesson
Journal	TE, every lesson
Lesson Quiz 	TE, every lesson
Alternative Assessment	TE, every lesson
Modified Lesson Quizzes	*IDEA Works!*

Weekly Assessment

Provide formative assessment for each week of Chapter 1.

Multi-Step TAKS Prep	SE pp. 34, 58
Ready to Go On?	SE pp. 35, 59
Cumulative Assessment	SE pp. 68–69
Test and Practice Generator SPANISH	*One-Stop Planner*

Formal Assessment

Provide summative assessment of Chapter 1 mastery.

Section Quizzes	AR pp. 5–6
Chapter 1 Test	SE p. 64
Chapter Test (Levels A, B, C)	AR pp. 7–18
• Multiple Choice • Free Response	
Cumulative Test	AR pp. 21–24
Test and Practice Generator SPANISH	*One-Stop Planner*
Modified Chapter 1 Test	*IDEA Works!*

Technology Highlights for Ongoing Assessment

Are You Ready?

Automatically assess readiness and prescribe intervention for Chapter 1 prerequisite skills.

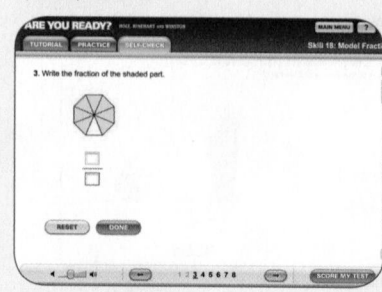

Ready to Go On? SPANISH

Automatically assess understanding of and prescribe intervention for Sections 1A and 1B.

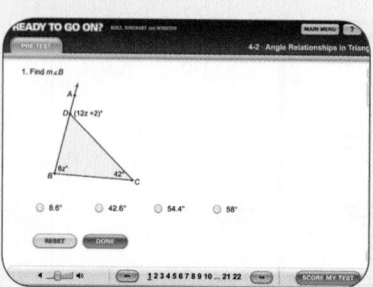

Ready for TAKS? SPANISH

Automatically assess proficiency with and provide intervention for TAKS objectives. Grade 6 through Exit Level.

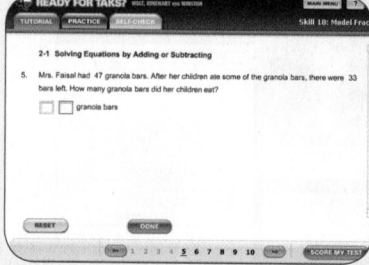

KEY: **SE** = *Student Edition*   **TE** = *Teacher's Edition*   **AR** = *Assessment Resources*   SPANISH Spanish version available   Available online   Available on CD-ROM

Formal Assessment

Three levels (A, B, C) of multiple-choice and free-response chapter tests are available in the *Assessment Resources.*

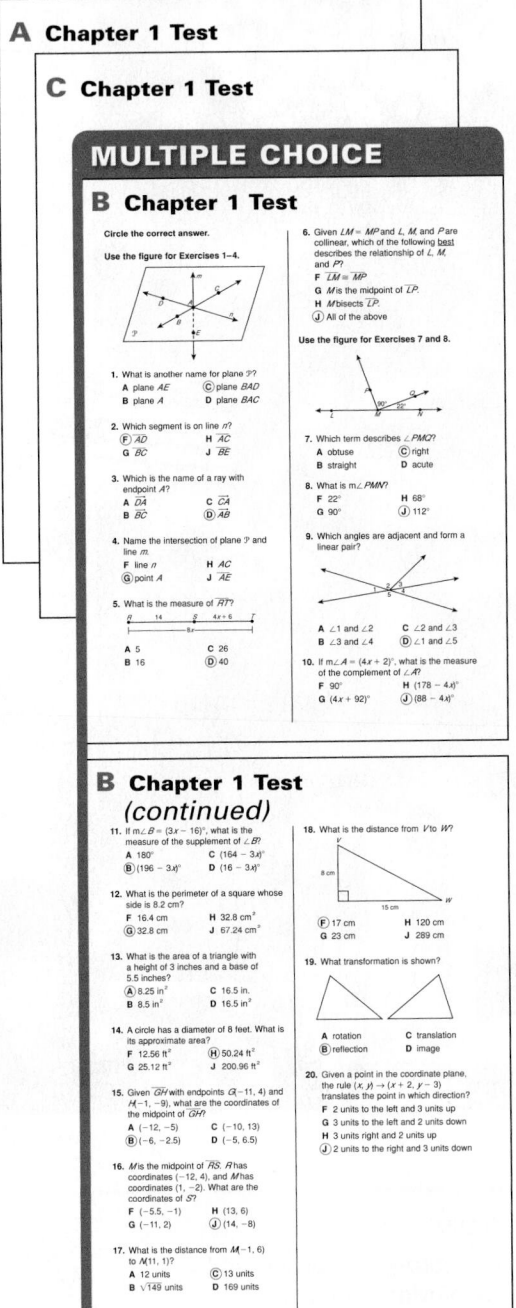

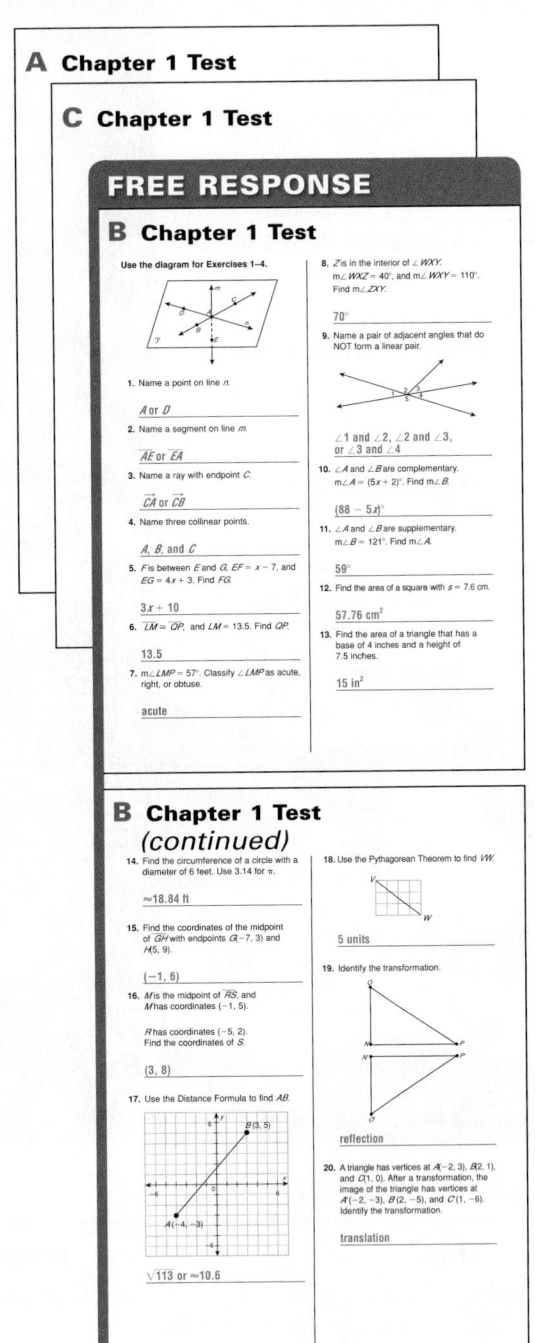

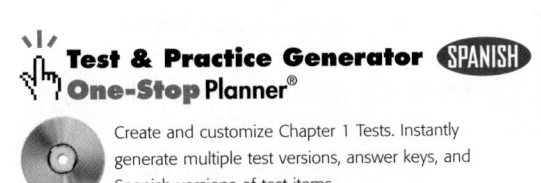

Test & Practice Generator **SPANISH**
One-Stop Planner®

Create and customize Chapter 1 Tests. Instantly generate multiple test versions, answer keys, and Spanish versions of test items.

2F

Foundations for Geometry

SECTION 1A
Euclidean and Construction Tools

 **MULTI-STEP TAKS PREP** On page 34, students analyze a diagram of an archaeological dig by applying definitions, using the distance formula, and classifying angles.

Exercises designed to prepare students for success on the Multi-Step TAKS Prep can be found on pages 10, 18, 26, and 32.

SECTION 1B
Coordinate and Transformation Tools

 **MULTI-STEP TAKS PREP** On page 58, students find the area and perimeter of a patio to determine the total cost of the paving stones used. They use distance, midpoint, and transformations to create the construction plans for the patio.

Exercises designed to prepare students for success on the Multi-Step TAKS Prep can be found on pages 39, 48, and 54.

1A Euclidean and Construction Tools

 **MULTI-STEP TAKS PREP**

1B Coordinate and Transformation Tools

MULTI-STEP TAKS PREP

go.hrw.com/Geo/TX
Chapter Project Online
KEYWORD: MG7 ChProj

The lights encasing the geodesic dome at the top of Reunion Tower are a familiar feature of the Dallas skyline.

Geometry in Texas

Representations of points, lines, and planes can be seen in the Dallas skyline. The buildings resemble vertical planes. Lines are represented by the two miles of green argon tubing that outline the Bank of America Plaza building. Numerous points are represented by the lights on the spherical top of the 50-story Reunion Tower.

About the Project

Picture This

Students begin by using geoboards to explore designs based on line segments. Then they use a compass and paper folding to make star designs. Finally, students use everything they've learned to produce an original piece of string art.

Project Resources

All project resources for teachers and students are provided online.

Materials:
- Activity 1: geoboard, colored rubber bands or colored string
- Activity 2: compass, straightedge
- Activity 3: straightedge
- Activity 4: wooden board, small nails, hammer, colored string or thread

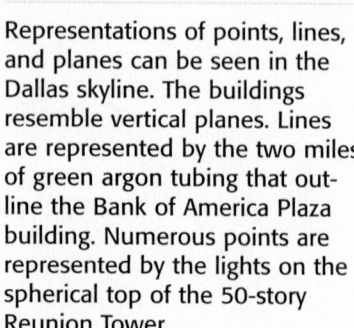

go.hrw.com/Geo/TX
Project Teacher Support
KEYWORD: MG7 ProjectTS

ARE YOU READY?

☑ Vocabulary

Match each term on the left with a definition on the right.

1. coordinate **C**
2. metric system of measurement **E**
3. expression **A**
4. order of operations **D**

A. a mathematical phrase that contains operations, numbers, and/or variables

B. the measurement system often used in the United States

C. one of the numbers of an ordered pair that locates a point on a coordinate graph

D. a list of rules for evaluating expressions

E. a decimal system of weights and measures that is used universally in science and commonly throughout the world

☑ Measure with Customary and Metric Units

For each object tell which is the better measurement.

5. length of an unsharpened pencil $7\frac{1}{2}$ in. or $9\frac{3}{4}$ in. $7\frac{1}{2}$ **in.**

6. the diameter of a quarter 1 m or $2\frac{1}{2}$ cm $2\frac{1}{2}$ **cm**

7. length of a soccer field 100 yd or 40 yd **100 yd**

8. height of a classroom 5 ft or 10 ft **10 ft**

9. height of a student's desk 30 in. or 4 ft **30 in.**

10. length of a dollar bill 15.6 cm or 35.5 cm **15.6 cm**

☑ Combine Like Terms

Simplify each expression.

11. $-y + 3y - 6y + 12y$ **8y**

12. $63 + 2x - 7 - 4x$ **$-2x + 56$**

13. $-5 - 9 - 7x + 6x - x$ **-14**

14. $24 - 3 + y + 7$ **$-2y + 31$**

☑ Evaluate Expressions

Evaluate each expression for the given value of the variable.

15. $x + 3x + 7x$ for $x = -5$ **-55**

16. $5p + 10$ for $p = 78$ **400**

17. $2a - 8a$ for $a = 12$ **-72**

18. $3n - 3$ for $n = 16$ **45**

☑ Ordered Pairs

Write the ordered pair for each point.

19. $A\left(0, 7\right)$
20. $B\left(-5, 4\right)$
21. $C\left(6, 3\right)$
22. $D\left(-8, -2\right)$
23. $E\left(3, -5\right)$
24. $F\left(6, -4\right)$

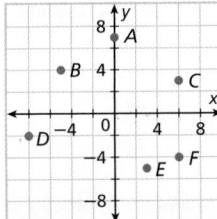

ARE YOU READY?

Organizer

Objective: Assess students' understanding of prerequisite skills.

Prerequisite Skills

Measure with Customary and Metric Units

Combine Like Terms

Evaluate Expressions

Ordered Pairs

Assessing Prior Knowledge

INTERVENTION ◄ ►

Diagnose and Prescribe

Use this page to determine whether intervention is necessary or whether enrichment is appropriate.

Resources

 Are You Ready? Intervention and Enrichment Worksheets

 Are You Ready? CD-ROM

 Are You Ready? Online

my.hrw.com

ARE YOU READY?
Diagnose and Prescribe

NO INTERVENE

YES ENRICH

☑ Prerequisite Skill	☞ Worksheets	💿 CD-ROM	🪐 Online
☑ Measure with Customary and Metric Units	Skill 20	Activity 20	
☑ Combine Like Terms	Skill 57	Activity 57	Diagnose and Prescribe Online
☑ Evaluate Expressions	Skill 60	Activity 60	
☑ Ordered Pairs	Skill 79	Activity 79	

ARE YOU READY? Intervention, Chapter 1

ARE YOU READY? Enrichment, Chapter 1

☞ **Worksheets**

💿 **CD-ROM**

🪐 **Online**

Organizer

Objective: Help students organize the new concepts they will learn in Chapter 1.

Online Edition
Multilingual Glossary

Resources

PuzzlePro
One-Stop Planner®

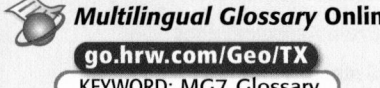
Multilingual Glossary Online
go.hrw.com/Geo/TX
KEYWORD: MG7 Glossary

Answers to Vocabulary Connections

1. An undefined term is a term that is not defined with a word or phrase.

2. A coordinate plane is a flat surface that has numbers on it to describe locations.

3. Possible answer: tip of a sharpened pencil

4. *Transformation* means "to change or move a shape."

Key Vocabulary/Vocabulario

angle	ángulo
area	área
coordinate plane	plano cartesiano
line	línea
perimeter	perímetro
plane	plano
point	punto
transformation	transformación
undefined term	término indefinido

Vocabulary Connections

To become familiar with some of the vocabulary terms in the chapter, consider the following. You may refer to the chapter, the glossary, or a dictionary if you like.

1. A *definition* is a statement that gives the meaning of a word or phrase. What do you think the phrase **undefined term** means?

2. *Coordinates* are numbers used to describe a location. A *plane* is a flat surface. How can you use these meanings to understand the term **coordinate plane** ?

3. A **point** is often represented by a dot. What real-world items could represent points?

4. *Trans-* is a prefix that means "across," as in movement. A *form* is a shape. How can you use these meanings to understand the term **transformation** ?

Geometry TEKS

		Les. 1-1	1-2 Tech. Lab	Les. 1-2	Les. 1-3	Les. 1-4	Les. 1-5	Les. 1-6	Les. 1-7	1-7 Tech. Lab
G.1.A	Geometric structure* develop an awareness of the structure of a mathematical system, connecting definitions, postulates ...	★			★	★	★	★	★	
G.1.B	Geometric structure* recognize the historical development of geometric systems and know mathematics is developed for a variety of purposes				★		★			
G.2.A	Geometric structure* use constructions to explore attributes of geometric figures ...		★	★	★					★
G.2.B	Geometric structure* make conjectures about angles, lines ... and determine the validity of the conjectures, choosing from a variety of approaches such as coordinate, transformational ...		★	★	★	★				★
G.3.B	Geometric structure* construct and justify statements about geometric figures and their properties		★	★	★					
G.5.C	Geometric patterns* use properties of transformations ... to make connections between mathematics and the real world ...								★	
G.7.A	Dimensionality and the geometry of location* use one- and two-dimensional coordinate systems to represent points, lines, rays, line segments ...	★						★		
G.7.C	Dimensionality and the geometry of location* develop and use formulas involving length, slope, and midpoint			★				★		
G.8.A	Congruence and the geometry of size* find areas of regular polygons, circles ...						★			
G.8.C	Congruence and the geometry of size* derive, extend, and use the Pythagorean Theorem							★		

* *Knowledge* and *skills* are written out completely on pages TX28–TX35.

Geometry TEKS—Knowledge and Skills

G.1 Geometric structure The student understands the structure of, and relationships within, an axiomatic system.

G.2 Geometric structure The student analyzes geometric relationships in order to make and verify conjectures.

G.3 Geometric structure The student applies logical reasoning to justify and prove mathematical statements.

G.5 Geometric patterns The student uses a variety of representations to describe geometric relationships and solve problems.

G.7 Dimensionality and the geometry of location The student understands that coordinate systems provide convenient and efficient ways of representing geometric figures and uses them accordingly.

G.8 Congruence and the geometry of size The student uses tools to determine measurements of geometric figures and extends measurement concepts to find perimeter, area, and volume in problem situations.

 **Reading and Writing Math**

Reading Strategy: Use Your Book for Success

Understanding how your textbook is organized will help you locate and use helpful information.

As you read through an example problem, pay attention to the notes in the **margin.** These notes highlight key information about the concept and will help you to avoid common mistakes.

 **Know it! Note**

Writing Math
Writing a similarity statement is like writing a congruen statement—be sur

Helpful Hint
When writing an indirect proof, loo for a contradiction one of the followi

Caution!
Consider all cases when you assume the opposite. If the conclusion is QR >

The **Glossary** is found in the back of your textbook. Use it when you need a definition of an unfamiliar word or phrase.

The **Index** is located at the end of your textbook. If you need to locate the page where a particular concept is explained, use the **Index** to find the corresponding page number.

The **Skills Bank** is located in the back of your textbook. Look in the **Skills Bank** for help with math topics that were taught in previous courses, such as the order of operations.

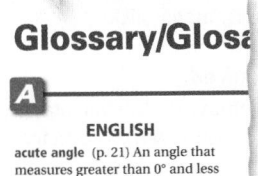 **Glossary/Glosa**

A
ENGLISH
acute angle (p. 21) An angle that measures greater than 0° and less than 90°.

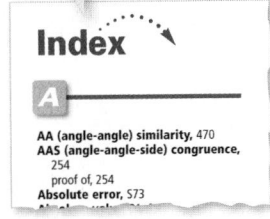 **Index**

A
AA (angle-angle) similarity, 470
AAS (angle-angle-side) congruence, 254
proof of, 254
Absolute error, 573

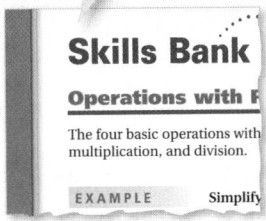 **Skills Bank**

Operations with F

The four basic operations with multiplication, and division.

EXAMPLE Simplify

Try This

Use your textbook for the following problems.

1. Use the index to find the page where *right angle* is defined.

2. What formula does the Know-It Note on the first page of Lesson 1-6 refer to?

3. Use the glossary to find the definition of *congruent segments*.

4. In what part of the textbook can you find help for solving equations?

Organizer

Objective: Help students apply strategies to understand and retain key concepts.

 Online Edition

Resources

 Chapter 1 Resource Book
Reading Strategies

ENGLISH LANGUAGE LEARNERS

Reading Strategy: Use Your Book for Success

Discuss The index, glossary, margin notes, and Skills Bank can provide students with a great deal of useful information as they use this textbook. Have students divide their journal into sections such as research, reflections, constructions, postulates, and so on. Encourage them to use all the resources provided in this book.

Extend Ask students to find a term they do not know and look it up in the glossary. Then ask them to enter the definition in their journal. Challenge the students to use information in the book that was not mentioned. For example, look at the table of contents, highlighted words, words in italics, or words in boldface.

Answers to *Try This*

1. p. 21
2. Mdpt. Formula
3. segs. that have the same length
4. Skills Bank

TAKS Objectives

Grades 9–11

Obj. 2 Properties and Attributes of Functions: A.3.A, A.4.A
Obj. 4 Linear Equations: A.7.A
Obj. 6 Geometric Relationships and Spatial Reasoning: G.5.C, G.10.A
Obj. 7 Two- and Three-Dimensional Representations: G.7.A, G.7.C
Obj. 8 Measurement: G.8.A, G.8.C

Euclidean and Construction Tools

One-Minute Section Planner

Lesson	Lab Resources	Materials
Lesson 1-1 Understanding Points, Lines, and Planes • Identify, name, and draw points, lines, segments, rays, and planes. • Apply basic facts about points, lines, and planes. ☑ Exit Level TAKS ☑ ACT ☑ SAT ☑ SAT Subject Tests		**Required** straightedge (MK) **Optional** raw spaghetti, index cards, straw, clay, gumdrops, toothpicks
1-2 Technology Lab Explore Properties Associated with Points • Use geometry software to measure distances and explore properties of points on segments. ☐ Exit Level TAKS ☑ ACT ☐ SAT ☐ SAT Subject Tests		**Required** geometry software **Optional** ruler (MK)
Lesson 1-2 Measuring and Constructing Segments • Use length and midpoint of a segment. • Construct midpoints and congruent segments. ☑ Exit Level TAKS ☑ ACT ☑ SAT ☐ SAT Subject Tests		**Required** compass (MK), straightedge **Optional** road map, masking tape, butcher paper, small plastic disks, meter stick
Lesson 1-3 Measuring and Constructing Angles • Name and classify angles. • Measure and construct angles and angle bisectors. ☑ Exit Level TAKS ☑ ACT ☑ SAT ☐ SAT Subject Tests		**Required** compass (MK), straightedge, protractor (MK), geometry software **Optional** yarn, index cards, pictures of angles, origami paper, sticky notes, acetate or tracing paper, clock (MK), Mira
Lesson 1-4 Pairs of Angles • Identify adjacent, vertical, complementary, and supplementary angles. • Find measures of pairs of angles. ☑ Exit Level TAKS ☑ ACT ☑ SAT ☐ SAT Subject Tests		**Required** protractor (MK)

MK = *Manipulatives Kit*

Section Overview

Points, Lines, and Planes

Lesson 1-1

Why? Understanding points, lines, planes, and segments is fundamental to the entire geometry course.

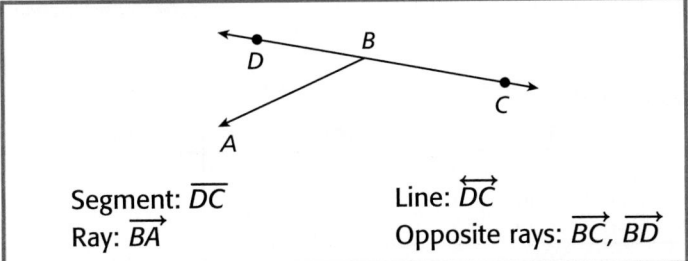

Segment: $\overline{DC}$　　　Line: $\overleftrightarrow{DC}$
Ray: $\overrightarrow{BA}$　　　Opposite rays: $\overrightarrow{BC}, \overrightarrow{BD}$

- The intersection of two lines is a point.
- The intersection of two planes is a line.
- If two points lie in a plane, then the line they determine lies in the plane.

Measuring Segments and Angles

Lessons 1-2, 1-3

Why? Distance and angle measure are important in carpentry, engineering, science, and many other areas.

Congruent Angles

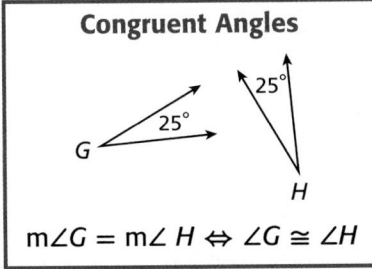

$m\angle G = m\angle H \Leftrightarrow \angle G \cong \angle H$

Congruent Segments

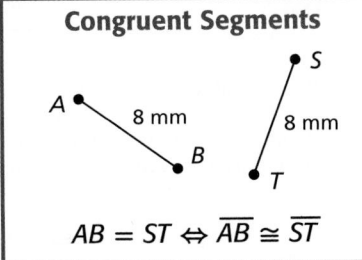

$AB = ST \Leftrightarrow \overline{AB} \cong \overline{ST}$

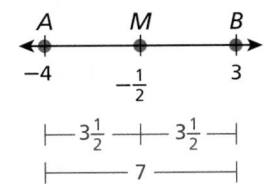

M is the midpoint of $\overline{AB}$.

$AM = \frac{1}{2}AB$　　$MB = \frac{1}{2}AB$

$AM = MB$

Acute Angle　　**Right Angle**　　**Obtuse Angle**

90°

Pairs of Angles

Lesson 1-4

Why? Properties of angle pairs are used in science and engineering.

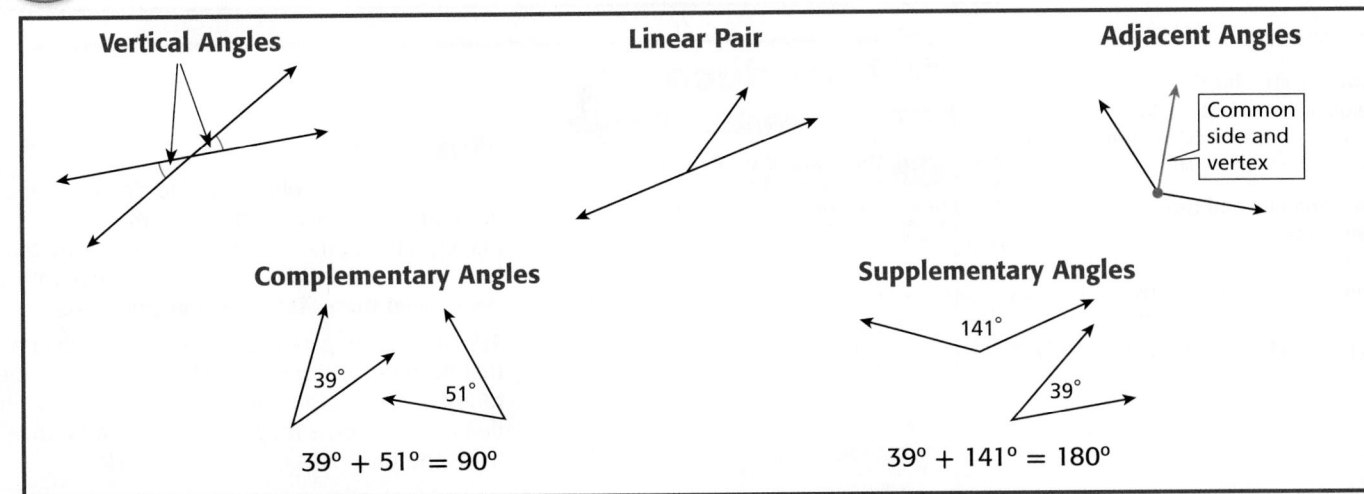

Vertical Angles　　**Linear Pair**　　**Adjacent Angles**

Common side and vertex

Complementary Angles　　**Supplementary Angles**

39°　　51°　　　141°　　39°

39° + 51° = 90°　　　39° + 141° = 180°

Pacing: Traditional 1 day
Block $\frac{1}{2}$ day

Objectives: Identify, name, and draw points, lines, segments, rays, and planes.

Apply basic facts about points, lines, and planes.

Online Edition
Tutorial Videos, Interactivity

Countdown to TAKS Week 1

Power Presentations
with PowerPoint®

Warm Up

Graph each inequality.

1. $x \geq 3$

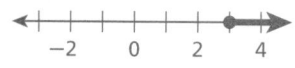
−2　0　2　4

2. $2 \leq x \leq 6$

0　2　4　6

3. $x < 1$ or $x > 0$

0　1

Also available on transparency

Math Humor

Q: What did the little acorn say when it grew up?

A: "Geometry"

⭐ Geometry TEKS

G.1 Geometric structure*
(A) develop an awareness of the structure of a mathematical system, connecting definitions, postulates, …

G.7 Dimensionality and the geometry of location*
(A) use one- and two-dimensional coordinate systems to represent points, lines, rays, line segments, …

* Knowledge and Skills See p. 4.

6 Chapter 1

1-1 Understanding Points, Lines, and Planes

 TEKS G.7.A Dimensionality and the geometry of location: use one- and two-dimensional coordinate systems to represent points, lines, rays, line segments .... Also **G.1.A**

Objectives
Identify, name, and draw points, lines, segments, rays, and planes.

Apply basic facts about points, lines, and planes.

Vocabulary
undefined term
point
line
plane
collinear
coplanar
segment
endpoint
ray
opposite rays
postulate

Who uses this?
Architects use representations of points, lines, and planes to create designs of buildings. Light, color, and geometric shapes are reflected in the design of the Central Library in San Antonio, Texas.

The most basic figures in geometry are **undefined terms**, which cannot be defined by using other figures. The undefined terms *point*, *line*, and *plane* are the building blocks of geometry.

Know it! Note

Undefined Terms

TERM	NAME	DIAGRAM
A **point** names a location and has no size. It is represented by a dot.	A capital letter point *P*	*P* •
A **line** is a straight path that has no thickness and extends forever.	A lowercase letter or two points on the line line ℓ, $\overleftrightarrow{XY}$ or $\overleftrightarrow{YX}$	*X* ────── *Y* ℓ
A **plane** is a flat surface that has no thickness and extends forever.	A script capital letter or three points not on a line plane $\mathcal{R}$ or plane *ABC*	*A* • *C* • $\mathcal{R}$ *B* •

Points that lie on the same line are **collinear**. *K, L,* and *M* are collinear. *K, L,* and *N* are *noncollinear*. Points that lie in the same plane are **coplanar**. Otherwise they are *noncoplanar*.

K　　*L*　*M*
• *N*

EXAMPLE 1 **Naming Points, Lines, and Planes**

Refer to the architectural design of the Central Library building.

A Name four coplanar points.
K, L, M, and *N* all lie in plane $\mathcal{R}$.

B Name three lines.
$\overleftrightarrow{AB}$, $\overleftrightarrow{BC}$, and $\overleftrightarrow{CA}$.

Helpful Hint

A plane may be named by any three noncollinear points on that plane. Plane *ABC* may also be named *BCA, CAB, CBA, ACB,* or *BAC*.

✓ CHECK IT OUT!
1. Use the diagram to name two planes.
Possible answer: plane $\mathcal{R}$ and plane *ABC*

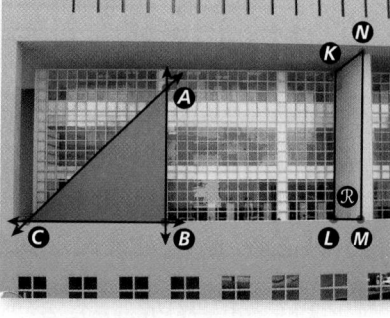

---

1 Introduce

EXPLORATION

1-1 Understanding Points, Lines, and Planes

The following are some of the terms used as the basic building blocks of geometry. Describe a real-world object that is suggested by each term.

1. point　•

2. line　───────

3. plane

4. Tell whether each of the following is most like a point, a line, or a plane.
　a. a desktop
　b. a speck of dust
　c. a jet contrail

THINK AND DISCUSS

5. **Explain** what is represented by the arrowhead at each end of the line in Problem 2.

6. **Discuss** whether the surface of Earth can be an example of a plane.

Motivate

Point out different objects in the classroom that are representations of points, segments, and planes, such as the tips of pushpins on the bulletin board, rulers, and desktops. Discuss with students what these items have in common.

Ask students to give examples of other objects that have these same characteristics and can be found in the world around them, such as the locations of cities on a map, the lines on a football field, and the bases on a baseball field.

Explorations and answers are provided in the *Explorations* binder.

Segments and Rays

DEFINITION	NAME	DIAGRAM
A **segment**, or line segment, is the part of a line consisting of two points and all points between them.	The two endpoints $\overline{AB}$ or $\overline{BA}$	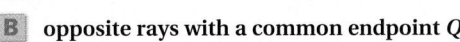 A •———————• B
An **endpoint** is a point at one end of a segment or the starting point of a *ray*.	A capital letter C and D	C • • D
A **ray** is a part of a line that starts at an endpoint and extends forever in one direction.	Its endpoint and any other point on the ray $\overrightarrow{RS}$	
Opposite rays are two rays that have a common endpoint and form a line.	The common endpoint and any other point on each ray $\overrightarrow{EF}$ and $\overrightarrow{EG}$	←•———•———•→ F E G

EXAMPLE 2 Drawing Segments and Rays

Draw and label each of the following.

A a segment with endpoints *U* and *V*   U •———————• V

B opposite rays with a common endpoint *Q*   P • Q • R •

✓ **CHECK IT OUT!** 2. Draw and label a ray with endpoint *M* that contains *N*.
M •———————•→ N

A **postulate**, or *axiom*, is a statement that is accepted as true without proof. Postulates about points, lines, and planes help describe geometric properties.

Postulates Points, Lines, and Planes

1-1-1	Through any two points there is exactly one line.
1-1-2	Through any three noncollinear points there is exactly one plane containing them.
1-1-3	If two points lie in a plane, then the line containing those points lies in the plane.

EXAMPLE 3 Identifying Points and Lines in a Plane

Name a line that passes through two points.

There is exactly one line *n* passing through *G* and *H*.

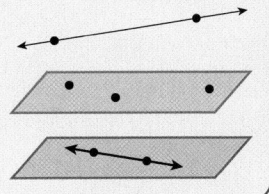

✓ **CHECK IT OUT!** 3. Name a plane that contains three noncollinear points.
Possible answer: plane *GHF*

1-1 Understanding Points, Lines, and Planes **7**

---

2 Teach

Guided Instruction

Show students how to draw a plane. Discuss all the ways to label a line, segment, ray, and plane. Explain that $\overrightarrow{CD}$ and $\overrightarrow{DC}$ are not the same ray.

 Teaching Tip **Visual** Draw a number line. Remind students that the arrows indicate that the numbers go on forever in both directions. Relate this to a geometric line extending forever in both directions. Cover up one end of the number line and relate it to a ray extending forever in one direction.

Reaching All Learners
Through Modeling

Have students work in small groups to use physical models, such as raw spaghetti and index cards, to illustrate Postulates 1-1-3, 1-1-4, and 1-1-5. Use contrasting colors of paper to emphasize the different planes in Postulate 1-1-5.

Additional Examples

Example 1

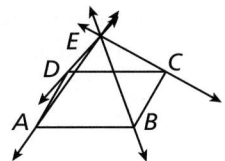

A. Name four coplanar points.
A, B, C, D

B. Name three lines.
Possible answer: $\overleftrightarrow{AE}$, $\overleftrightarrow{BE}$, $\overleftrightarrow{CE}$

Example 2

Draw and label each of the following.

A. segment with endpoints *M* and *N*   M •———• N

B. opposite rays with common endpoint *T*   ←•———•———•→ T

Example 3

Name a line that passes through two points. $\overleftrightarrow{XY}$

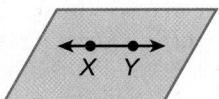

Also available on transparency

Teaching Tip **Reading Math** The phrase "exactly one" means that one exists and it is unique.

ENGLISH LANGUAGE LEARNERS

INTERVENTION
Questioning Strategies

EXAMPLE 1
- What are the different ways you can name the planes represented in the stadium roof?
- How else could you name the lines?

EXAMPLE 2
- What figure is formed by two opposite rays? Is there a way to name the opposite rays? Give an example.

EXAMPLE 3
- Are there other ways to name the line determined by the points in the diagram? Explain.

Lesson 1-1 **7**

INTERVENTION ◀▬▶
Questioning Strategies

EXAMPLE 4

• Must any two planes intersect? Why or why not? Name planes in the classroom that support your answer.

• What would happen if planes were extended? Would they then all intersect?

• If a line lies in a plane, how many points of intersection do the line and the plane have?

Recall that a system of equations is a set of two or more equations containing two or more of the same variables. The coordinates of the solution of the system satisfy all equations in the system. These coordinates also locate the point where all the graphs of the equations in the system *intersect*.

An *intersection* is the set of all points that two or more figures have in common. The next two postulates describe intersections involving lines and planes.

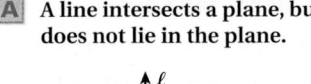

Postulates	Intersection of Lines and Planes

1-1-4 If two lines intersect, then they intersect in exactly one point.

1-1-5 If two planes intersect, then they intersect in exactly one line.

Use a dashed line to show the hidden parts of any figure that you are drawing. A dashed line will indicate the part of the figure that is not seen.

EXAMPLE 4 **Representing Intersections**

Sketch a figure that shows each of the following.

A A line intersects a plane, but does not lie in the plane.

B Two planes intersect in one line.

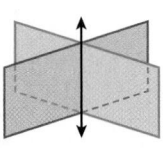

CHECK IT OUT!

4. Sketch a figure that shows two lines intersect in one point in a plane, but only one of the lines lies in the plane.

THINK AND DISCUSS

1. Explain why any two points are collinear.

2. Which postulate explains the fact that two straight roads cannot cross each other more than once?

3. Explain why points and lines may be coplanar even when the plane containing them is not drawn.

4. Name all the possible lines, segments, and rays for the points A and B. Then give the maximum number of planes that can be determined by these points.

5. **GET ORGANIZED** Copy and complete the graphic organizer below. In each box, name, describe, and illustrate one of the undefined terms.

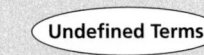

Undefined Terms

---

3 Close

Summarize

Ask students to name the different terms introduced in this lesson and write the notation for each. Give students the postulates with some missing words and ask them to fill in the blanks. Ask students to explain the meaning of the word *postulate*.
to assume or claim as true

ONGOING ASSESSMENT

and INTERVENTION ◀▬▶

Diagnose Before the Lesson
1-1 Warm Up, TE p. 6

Monitor During the Lesson
Check It Out! Exercises, SE pp. 6–8
Questioning Strategies, TE pp. 7–8

Assess After the Lesson
1-1 Lesson Quiz, TE p. 11
Alternative Assessment, TE p. 11

Answers to *Think and Discuss*

Possible answers:

1. By Post. 1-1-1, through any 2 pts. there is a line. Therefore any 2 pts. are collinear.

2. Post. 1-1-4

3. Any 3 noncollinear pts. determine a plane.

4. $\overleftrightarrow{AB}$, $\overline{AB}$, $\overrightarrow{AB}$, $\overrightarrow{BA}$; 0 planes

5. See p. A2.

1-1 **Exercises**

go.hrw.com/Geo/TX
Homework Help Online
KEYWORD: MG7 1-1
Parent Resources Online
KEYWORD: MG7 Parent

1-1 **Exercises**

GUIDED PRACTICE

Vocabulary Apply the vocabulary from this lesson to answer each question.

1. Give an example from your classroom of three *collinear* points.
   Possible answer: the intersection of 2 floor tiles

2. Make use of the fact that *endpoint* is a compound of *end* and *point* and name the *endpoint* of $\overrightarrow{ST}$. **S**

SEE EXAMPLE **1**
p. 6

Use the figure to name each of the following.

3. five points **A, B, C, D, E**

4. two lines Possible answer: $\overleftrightarrow{AC}$, $\overleftrightarrow{BD}$

5. two planes Possible answer: **ABC** and $\mathcal{N}$

6. point on $\overleftrightarrow{BD}$ Possible answer: **B, C, or D**

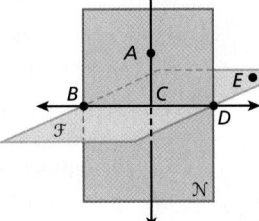

SEE EXAMPLE **2**
p. 7

Draw and label each of the following.

7. a segment with endpoints M and N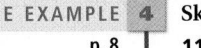

8. a ray with endpoint F that passes through G

SEE EXAMPLE **3**
p. 7

Use the figure to name each of the following.

9. a line that contains A and C Possible answer: $\overleftrightarrow{AB}$

10. a plane that contains A, D, and C
    Possible answer: plane **ABD**

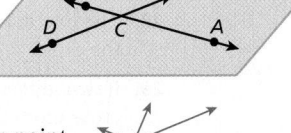

SEE EXAMPLE **4**
p. 8

Sketch a figure that shows each of the following.

11. three coplanar lines that intersect in a common point

12. two lines that do not intersect

PRACTICE AND PROBLEM SOLVING

TEKS ☞ TAKS

Skills Practice p. S4
Application Practice p. S28

Use the figure to name each of the following.

13. three collinear points **B, E, A**

14. four coplanar points Possible answer: **B, C, D, E**

15. a plane containing E
    Possible answer: plane **ABC**

Draw and label each of the following.

16. a line containing X and Y

17. a pair of opposite rays that both contain R

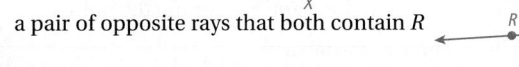

Use the figure to name each of the following.

18. two points and a line that lie in plane $\mathcal{T}$
    Possible answer: G, J, and ℓ

19. two planes that contain ℓ
    Possible answer: planes $\mathcal{T}$ and $\mathcal{S}$

Sketch a figure that shows each of the following.

20. a line that intersects two nonintersecting planes

21. three coplanar lines that intersect in three
    different points

20.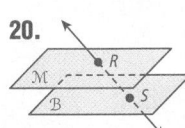

21.

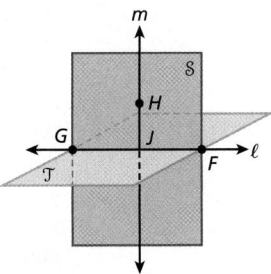

1-1 Understanding Points, Lines, and Planes **9**

1-1 **Exercises**

Assignment Guide

Assign *Guided Practice* exercises as necessary.

If you finished Examples **1–2**
   Basic 13–17, 33
   Average 13–17, 33, 36, 43
   Advanced 13–17, 33, 34, 36, 43–45

If you finished Examples **1–4**
   Basic 13–28, 31–33, 39–42, 47–51
   Average 13–28, 30–33, 35–43, 46–51
   Advanced 14–28 even, 29–51

Homework Quick Check
Quickly check key concepts.
Exercises: 14–20 even, 24, 26, 28, 32

Teaching Tip **Communicating Math** In **Exercises 3–6,** students sometimes forget to place a symbol above the letters that are used to name lines, segments, and rays. Remind students that two letters without a symbol represent a distance.

⬇TAKS Practice

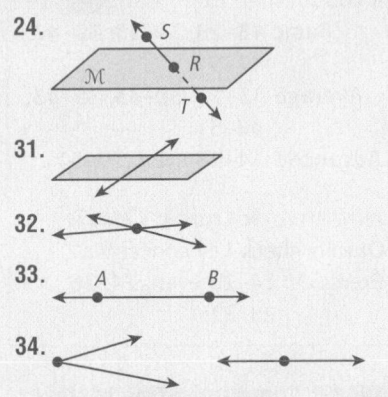
22. Possible answers:
a. tip of a stake
b. string
c. grid formed by string

28. If 2 pts. lie in a plane, then the line containing those pts. lies in the plane.

30. It is not possible. By Post. 1-1-2, any 3 noncollinear pts. are contained in a unique plane. If the 3 pts. are collinear, they are contained in infinitely many planes. In either case, the 3 pts. will be coplanar.

35. Post. 1-1-3

22. This problem will prepare you for the Multi-Step TAKS Prep on page 34. Name an object at the archaeological site shown that is represented by each of the following.

a. a point
b. a segment
c. a plane

Draw each of the following.

23. plane H containing two lines that intersect at M

24. $\overleftrightarrow{ST}$ intersecting plane M at R

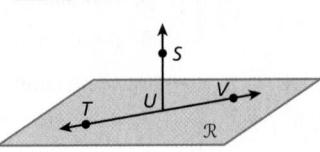

Use the figure to name each of the following.

25. the intersection of $\overleftrightarrow{TV}$ and $\overrightarrow{US}$ **U**

26. the intersection of $\overrightarrow{US}$ and plane R **U**

27. the intersection of $\overleftrightarrow{TU}$ and $\overleftrightarrow{UV}$ **U**

Write the postulate that justifies each statement.

28. The line connecting two dots on a sheet of paper lies on the same sheet of paper as the dots.

29. If two ants are walking in straight lines but in different directions, their paths cannot cross more than once. **If 2 lines intersect, then they intersect in exactly 1 pt.**

30. **Critical Thinking** Is it possible to draw three points that are noncoplanar? Explain.

S   A   N

Tell whether each statement is sometimes, always, or never true. Support your answer with a sketch.

31. If two planes intersect, they intersect in a straight line. **A**

32. If two lines intersect, they intersect at two different points. **N**

33. $\overleftrightarrow{AB}$ is another name for $\overrightarrow{BA}$. **A**

34. If two rays share a common endpoint, then they form a line. **S**

35. **Art** Pointillism is a technique in which tiny dots of complementary colors are combined to form a picture. Which postulate ensures that a line connecting two of these points also lies in the plane containing the points?

36. **Probability** Three of the labeled points are chosen at random. What is the probability that they are collinear? $\frac{1}{4}$

37. Campers often use a cooking stove with three legs. Which postulate explains why they might prefer this design to a stove that has four legs? **Post. 1-1-2**

38. **Write About It** Explain why three coplanar lines may have zero, one, two, or three points of intersection. Support your answer with a sketch.

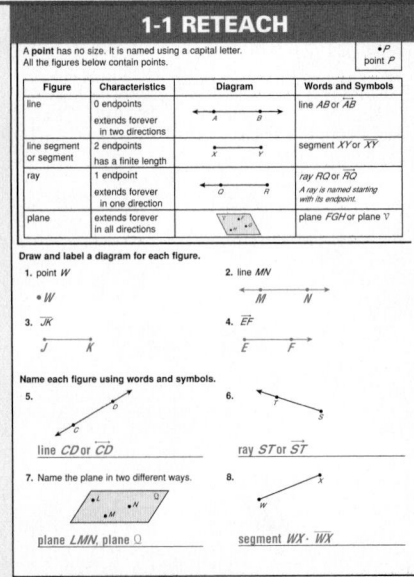

39. Which of the following is a set of noncollinear points?

Ⓐ P, R, T Ⓒ P, Q, R
Ⓑ Q, R, S Ⓓ S, T, U

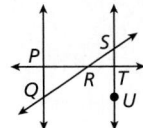

40. What is the greatest number of intersection points four coplanar lines can have?

Ⓕ 6 Ⓗ 2
Ⓖ 4 Ⓙ 0

41. Two flat walls meet in the corner of a classroom. Which postulate best describes this situation?

Ⓐ Through any three noncollinear points there is exactly one plane.

Ⓑ If two points lie in a plane, then the line containing them lies in the plane.

Ⓒ If two lines intersect, then they intersect in exactly one point.

Ⓓ If two planes intersect, then they intersect in exactly one line.

42. Gridded Response What is the greatest number of planes determined by four noncollinear points? 4

CHALLENGE AND EXTEND

Use the table for Exercises 43–45.

Figure	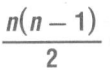	△	⊠
Number of Points	2	3	4
Maximum Number of Segments	1	3	▬

43. What is the maximum number of segments determined by 4 points? 6

44. Multi-Step Extend the table. What is the maximum number of segments determined by 10 points? 45

$\dfrac{n(n-1)}{2}$ **45.** Write a formula for the maximum number of segments determined by n points.

46. Critical Thinking Explain how rescue teams could use two of the postulates from this lesson to locate a distress signal.

SPIRAL REVIEW

47. The combined age of a mother and her twin daughters is 58 years. The mother was 25 years old when the twins were born. Write and solve an equation to find the age of each of the three people. *(Previous course)* **Mother is 36; twins are 11.**

Determine whether each set of ordered pairs is a function. *(Previous course)*

48. $\{(0, 1), (1, -1), (5, -1), (-1, 2)\}$ yes **49.** $\{(3, 8), (10, 6), (9, 8), (10, -6)\}$ no

Find the mean, median, and mode for each set of data. *(Previous course)*

50. 0, 6, 1, 3, 5, 2, 7, 10
mean: 4.25; median: 4; mode: none

51. 0.47, 0.44, 0.4, 0.46, 0.44
mean: 0.44; median: 0.442; mode: 0.44

 students draw three points on a sheet of paper and use the tip of a pencil held perpendicular to the paper for the fourth point. Have a partner hold a sheet of paper up in various ways to determine the planes.

 Teaching Tip
Algebra For **Exercise 45,** tell students not to mutiply $n(n-1)$. This formula would count a line twice.

 *Journal*

Have students draw and label a point, a line, a plane, a ray, opposite rays, 4 coplanar points, and 3 collinear points.

 **ALTERNATIVE ASSESSMENT**

Have students make physical models using straw and clay, or gumdrops and marshmallows with toothpicks, to illustrate the postulates in this lesson. Have them explain their models.

Power Presentations
with PowerPoint®

1-1 Lesson Quiz

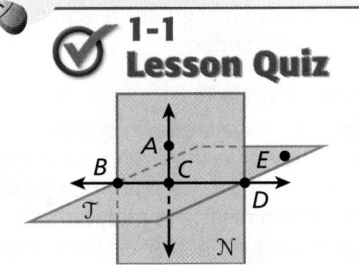

Name each of the following.

1. two opposite rays $\overrightarrow{CB}$ and $\overrightarrow{CD}$

2. a point on $\overrightarrow{BC}$
Possible answer: D

3. the intersection of plane $\mathcal{N}$ and plane $\mathcal{J}$
Possible answer: $\overleftrightarrow{BD}$

4. a plane containing E, D, and B
plane $\mathcal{J}$

Draw each of the following.

5. a line intersecting a plane at one point

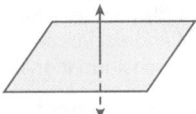

6. a ray with endpoint P that passes through Q

Also available on transparency

1-1 PROBLEM SOLVING

Use the map of part of San Antonio for Exercises 1 and 2.

1. Name a point that appears to be collinear with $\overline{EF}$. Which streets intersect at this point?
Point D, E. Travis St. and Navarro St.

2. Explain why point A is NOT collinear with $\overline{BE}$.
Point A does not lie on the line that contains $\overline{BE}$.

3. Suppose $\overleftrightarrow{UV}$ represents the pencil that you are using to do your homework and plane $\mathcal{P}$ represents the paper that you are writing on. Describe the relationship between $\overleftrightarrow{UV}$ and plane $\mathcal{P}$.
Possible answer: $\overleftrightarrow{UV}$ intersects plane $\mathcal{P}$.

4. Two cyclists start at the same point, but travel along two straight streets in different directions. If they continue, how many times will their paths cross again? Explain.
0 times; If two lines intersect, then they intersect in exactly one point.

Choose the best answer.

5. In a building, planes $\mathcal{W}$, $\mathcal{X}$, and $\mathcal{Y}$ represent each of the three floors; planes $\mathcal{Q}$ and $\mathcal{R}$ represent the front and back of the building; planes $\mathcal{S}$ and $\mathcal{T}$ represent the sides. Which is a true statement?
A Planes $\mathcal{W}$ and $\mathcal{Y}$ intersect in a line.
B Planes $\mathcal{Q}$ and $\mathcal{X}$ intersect in a line.
C Planes $\mathcal{W}$, $\mathcal{X}$, and $\mathcal{T}$ intersect in a point.
D Planes $\mathcal{Q}$, $\mathcal{R}$, and $\mathcal{S}$ intersect in a point.

6. Suppose point G represents a duck flying over a lake, points H and J represent two ducks swimming on the lake, and plane $\mathcal{L}$ represents the lake. Which is a true statement?
F There are two lines through G and J.
G The line containing G and H lies in plane $\mathcal{L}$.
H G, H, and J are noncoplanar.
J There is exactly one plane containing points G, H, and J.

Use the figure for Exercise 7.

7. A frame holding two pictures sits on a table. Which is NOT a true statement?
A The lines containing $\overline{JP}$ and $\overline{KN}$ intersect plane $\mathcal{T}$.
B $\overline{PN}$ and $\overline{NM}$ intersect in a point.
C $\overline{LM}$ and N intersect in a line.
D P and $\overline{NM}$ are coplanar.

Answers

46. Rescue teams can use the principles of Post. 1-1-1 and Post. 1-1-4. A distress signal is received by 2 rescue teams. By Post. 1-1-1, 2 pts. determine a line. So 2 lines are created by the 3 pts., the locations of the rescue teams and the distress signal. By Post. 1-1-4, the intersection of the 2 lines will be the location of the distress signal.

Pacing:
Traditional $\frac{1}{2}$ day
Block $\frac{1}{4}$ day

Objective: Use geometry software to measure distances and explore properties of points on segments.

Materials: geometry software

 Online Edition
TechKeys

 Countdown to TAKS Week 1

Teach

Discuss

Emphasize that there are infinitely many points on a line segment between its endpoints, but only one of these points is the midpoint.

Close

Key Concept

When three points *A*, *B*, and *C* are collinear, then $AB + BC = AC$. The midpoint of a segment is equidistant from each endpoint.

Assessment

Journal Have students summarize how they determine, given three collinear points, if the point between the endpoints is the midpoint. Then have them support their answer with a sketch.

 **Geometry TEKS**

G.2 Geometric structure*
(A) use constructions to explore attributes of geometric figures and to make conjectures about geometric relationships
(B) make conjectures about angles, lines, ... and determine the validity of the conjectures, choosing from a variety of approaches such as coordinate, transformational, ...

G.3 Geometric structure*
(B) construct and justify statements about geometric figures and their properties
* **Knowledge and Skills** See p. 4.

 **1-2**
Technology LAB

Use with Lesson 1-2

Explore Properties Associated with Points

The two endpoints of a segment determine its length. Other points on the segment are *between* the endpoints. Only one of these points is the *midpoint* of the segment. In this lab, you will use geometry software to measure lengths of segments and explore properties of points on segments.

 TEKS G.2.A Geometric structure: use constructions to explore attributes of geometric figures and to make conjectures about geometric relationships. Also G.2.B, G.3.B

go.hrw.com/Geo/TX
Lab Resources Online
KEYWORD: MG7 Lab1

Activity

❶ Construct a segment and label its endpoints *A* and *C*.

❷ Create point *B* on $\overline{AC}$.

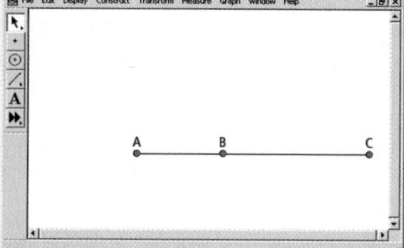

❸ Measure the distances from *A* to *B* and from *B* to *C*. Use the Calculate tool to calculate the sum of *AB* and *BC*.

❹ Measure the length of $\overline{AC}$. What do you notice about this length compared with the measurements found in Step 3?

❺ Drag point *B* along $\overline{AC}$. Drag one of the endpoints of $\overline{AC}$. What relationships do you think are true about the three measurements?

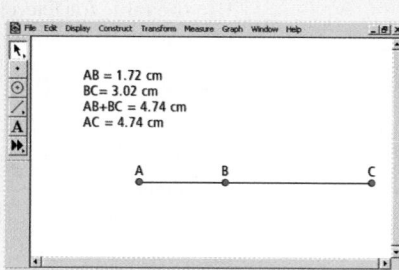

❻ Construct the midpoint of $\overline{AC}$ and label it *M*.

❼ Measure $\overline{AM}$ and $\overline{MC}$. What relationships do you think are true about the lengths of $\overline{AC}$, $\overline{AM}$, and $\overline{MC}$? Use the Calculate tool to confirm your findings.

❽ How many midpoints of $\overline{AC}$ exist?

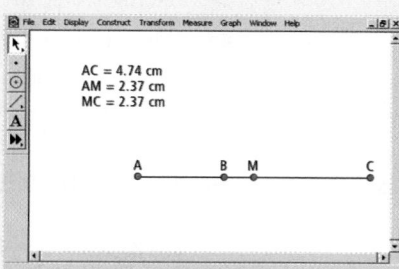

Try This

1. Repeat the activity with a new segment. Drag each of the points in your figure (the endpoints, the point on the segment, and the midpoint). Write down any relationships you observe about the measurements. **Check students' work.**

2. Create a point *D* not on $\overline{AC}$. Measure $\overline{AD}$, $\overline{DC}$, and $\overline{AC}$. Does $AD + DC = AC$? What do you think has to be true about *D* for the relationship to always be true?
No; *D* must be between *A* and *C*.

12 Chapter 1 Foundations for Geometry

Teacher to Teacher

To introduce the concept of midpoint, I like to tell the following riddle to the class.

Q: A hunter walks into the woods and keeps walking in the same direction. At what point does the hunter begin to leave the woods?

A: The midpoint.

Then I can explain to students that once the hunter is half-way through the woods, she is as close to the end as to the beginning. After passing the midpoint, the hunter is going out instead of in. This helps students remember that the midpoint is not just any point between the endpoints, but exactly one point in the middle.

Teresa Salas
Corpus Christi, TX

1-2 Measuring and Constructing Segments

TEKS G.3.B Geometric structure: construct and justify statements about geometric figures and their properties. Also G.2.A, G.2.B, G.7.C

Objectives
Use length and midpoint of a segment.

Construct midpoints and congruent segments.

Vocabulary
coordinate
distance
length
congruent segments
construction
between
midpoint
bisect
segment bisector

Why learn this?
You can measure a segment to calculate the distance between two locations. Maps of a race are used to show the distance between stations on the course. (See Example 4.)

A ruler can be used to measure the distance between two points. A point corresponds to one and only one number on the ruler. This number is called a **coordinate**. The following postulate summarizes this concept.

Know it! Note

Postulate 1-2-1 | **Ruler Postulate**

The points on a line can be put into a one-to-one correspondence with the real numbers.

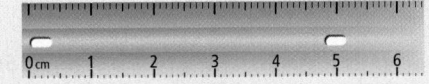

The **distance** between any two points is the absolute value of the difference of the coordinates. If the coordinates of points A and B are a and b, then the distance between A and B is $|a - b|$ or $|b - a|$. The distance between A and B is also called the **length** of $\overline{AB}$, or AB.

$$AB = |a - b| = |b - a|$$

EXAMPLE 1 | **Finding the Length of a Segment**

Find each length.

A DC
$DC = |4.5 - 2|$
$= |2.5|$
$= 2.5$

B EF
$EF = |-4 - (-1)|$
$= |-4 + 1|$
$= |-3|$
$= 3$

Caution!

PQ represents a number, while $\overline{PQ}$ represents a geometric figure. Be sure to use equality for numbers ($PQ = RS$) and congruence for figures ($\overline{PQ} \cong \overline{RS}$).

**CHECK IT OUT!**
Find each length.
1a. XY $3\frac{1}{2}$
1b. XZ $4\frac{1}{2}$

Congruent segments are segments that have the same length. In the diagram, $PQ = RS$, so you can write $\overline{PQ} \cong \overline{RS}$. This is read as "segment PQ is congruent to segment RS." *Tick marks* are used in a figure to show congruent segments.

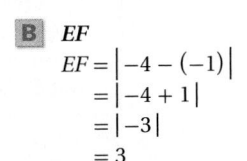
Tick marks

1-2 Organizer

Pacing: Traditional $\frac{1}{2}$ day
Block $\frac{1}{4}$ day

Objectives: Use length and midpoint of a segment.

Construct midpoints and congruent segments.

Online Edition
Tutorial Videos

Countdown to TAKS Week 1

Power Presentations with PowerPoint®

Warm Up

Simplify.
1. $7 - (-3)$ 10
2. $-1 - (-13)$ 12
3. $|-7 - 1|$ 8

Solve each equation.
4. $2x + 3 = 9x - 11$ 2
5. $3x = 4x - 5$ 5
6. How many real numbers are there between $\frac{1}{2}$ and $\frac{3}{4}$?
   infinitely many

Also available on transparency

Math Humor

Carpenter 1: Why did you leave your tape measure in the truck?

Carpenter 2: Because we're entering a construction zone.

⭐ Geometry TEKS

G.2 Geometric structure*
(A) use constructions to explore attributes of geometric figures …
(B) make conjectures about angles, lines, … and determine the validity of the conjectures, choosing from a variety of approaches …

G.3 Geometric structure*
(B) construct and justify statements about geometric figures …

G.7 Dimensionality and the geometry of location*
(C) derive and use formulas involving length, slope, and midpoint
Also G.7.A

* Knowledge and Skills See p. 4.

---

1 Introduce

EXPLORATION

1-2 Measuring and Constructing Segments

Use geometry software or a ruler for the following Exploration.
1. Draw $\overline{AC}$. Then place B on the segment between A and C.

   A ─── B ─── C

2. Measure AB, BC, and AC in inches. Then measure each segment in centimeters and millimeters. Record the lengths in a table like the one shown.

Unit	Length of $\overline{AB}$	Length of $\overline{BC}$	Length of $\overline{AC}$
Inch			
Centimeter			
Millimeter			

THINK AND DISCUSS

3. **Describe** the relationship among the lengths of $\overline{AB}$, $\overline{BC}$, and $\overline{AC}$. Is this relationship the same no matter what measurement unit you use?

4. **Discuss** what would happen if you located D between A and B. What would be the relationship among the lengths of $\overline{AD}$, $\overline{DB}$, $\overline{BC}$, and $\overline{AC}$?

Motivate

Show students a road map. Ask them to locate a place that is midway between two other places. Ask questions about distance between locations on a straight road. "Suppose you are driving to a relative's house. The only place to stop for food is 75 miles from home, and it is $\frac{1}{3}$ of the total trip. How far from the food stop does your relative live?"   150 mi

Explorations and answers are provided in the *Explorations* binder.

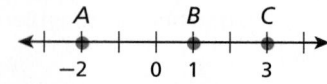

INTERVENTION ◀━▶
Questioning Strategies

EXAMPLE **1**

• To find the length of a segment, why do you subtract the coordinates instead of adding them?

• What equation can you create using *BC*, *AC*, and *AB*?

Construction

Discuss techniques to make an accurate construction, including using a sharp pencil, lining up the compass tip and the pencil tip, and being sure the compass stays the same size.

| Teaching Tip | **Communicating Math** Have students look up the word *between* in the dictionary and compare that definition with the mathematical definition. Emphasize that the mathematical definition of *between* includes collinearity. |

ENGLISH LANGUAGE LEARNERS

| Teaching Tip | **Critical Thinking** Point out that just as there are infinitely many real numbers between any two real numbers, there are infinitely many points between any two points on a line. |

You can make a sketch or measure and draw a segment. These may not be exact. A **construction** is a way of creating a figure that is more precise. One way to make a geometric construction is to use a compass and straightedge.

Construction   Congruent Segment

Construct a segment congruent to $\overline{AB}$.

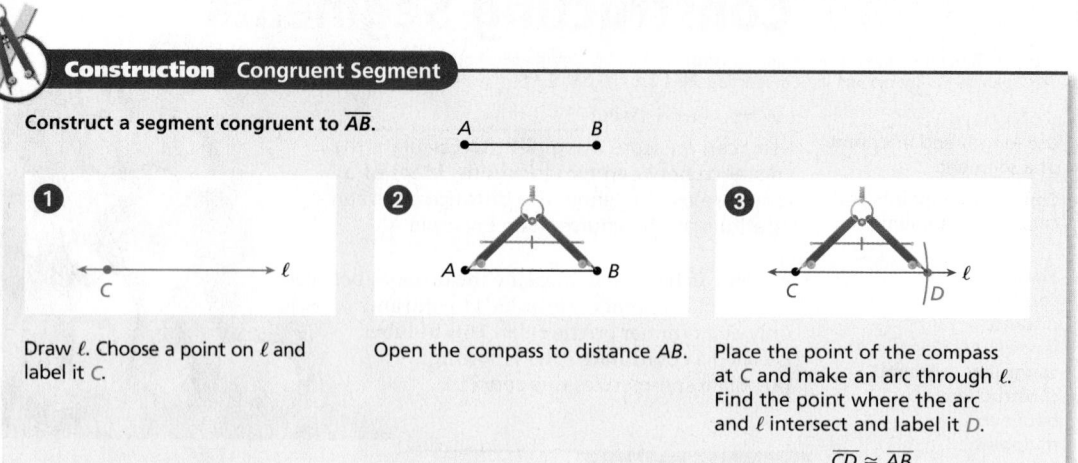

A ●———————● B

1

●————————————→ ℓ
C

Draw ℓ. Choose a point on ℓ and label it C.

2

A ●————● B

Open the compass to distance AB.

3

←————————→ ℓ
  C   D

Place the point of the compass at C and make an arc through ℓ. Find the point where the arc and ℓ intersect and label it D.

$\overline{CD} \cong \overline{AB}$

EXAMPLE **2**   **Copying a Segment**

Sketch, draw, and construct a segment congruent to $\overline{MN}$.

M ●————————● N

Step 1 Estimate and sketch.
Estimate the length of $\overline{MN}$ and sketch $\overline{PQ}$ approximately the same length.

P ●————————● Q

Step 2 Measure and draw.
Use a ruler to measure $\overline{MN}$. MN appears to be 3.1 cm. Use a ruler and draw $\overline{XY}$ to have length 3.1 cm.

X ●————————● Y

Step 3 Construct and compare.
Use a compass and straightedge to construct $\overline{ST}$ congruent to $\overline{MN}$.

A ruler shows that $\overline{PQ}$ and $\overline{XY}$ are approximately the same length as $\overline{MN}$, but $\overline{ST}$ is precisely the same length.

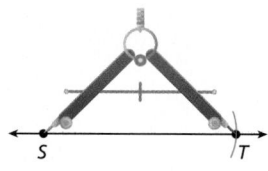

←————————→
  S   T

 **2.** Sketch, draw, and construct a segment congruent to $\overline{JK}$.
Check students' work.

J ●————————● K

In order for you to say that a point *B* is **between** two points *A* and *C*, all three of the points must lie on the same line, and *AB* + *BC* = *AC*.

Know It! Note

Postulate 1-2-2   **Segment Addition Postulate**

If *B* is between *A* and *C*, then *AB* + *BC* = *AC*.

A ●————● B ————————● C

---

2 Teach

Guided Instruction

Discuss how to read PQ, $\overleftrightarrow{PQ}$, and $\overline{PQ}$. Ask students to explain the Ruler Postulate in their own words. Stress that $CD = DC$, and that distances can never be negative. Have students dramatize Postulate 1-2-2. Locate three students as *A*, *B*, and *C* on a line in the classroom. Then ask one of the students to move off the line to illustrate when one point is not *between* the other two. Find distances between points by counting floor tiles or paces, or by using a meterstick.

Reaching All Learners
Through Concrete Manipulatives

Have students use masking tape or draw a long number line, either on their notebook paper or on a long piece of butcher paper taped to the floor. Give them small plastic disks to put on their number lines to represent points. They can then use these to count the spaces between the points.

EXAMPLE 3

Using the Segment Addition Postulate

A *B* is between *A* and *C*, *AC* = 14, and *BC* = 11.4. Find *AB*.

$AC = AB + BC$	*Seg. Add. Post.*
$14 = AB + 11.4$	*Substitute 14 for AC and 11.4 for BC.*
$-11.4 \qquad -11.4$	*Subtract 11.4 from both sides.*
$2.6 = AB$	*Simplify.*

B *S* is between *R* and *T*. Find *RT*.

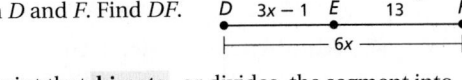

$RT = RS + ST$	*Seg. Add. Post.*
$4x = (2x + 7) + 28$	*Substitute the given values.*
$4x = 2x + 35$	*Simplify.*
$-2x \qquad -2x$	*Subtract 2x from both sides.*
$2x = 35$	*Simplify.*
$\dfrac{2x}{2} = \dfrac{35}{2}$	*Divide both sides by 2.*
$x = \dfrac{35}{2}$, or 17.5	*Simplify.*
$RT = 4x$	
$= 4(17.5) = 70$	*Substitute 17.5 for x.*

CHECK IT OUT!

3a. *Y* is between *X* and *Z*, *XZ* = 3, and $XY = 1\frac{1}{3}$. Find *YZ*. $1\frac{2}{3}$

3b. *E* is between *D* and *F*. Find *DF*. 24

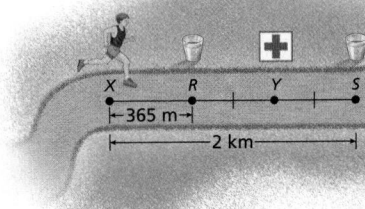

The **midpoint** *M* of $\overline{AB}$ is the point that **bisects**, or divides, the segment into two congruent segments. If *M* is the midpoint of $\overline{AB}$, then $AM = MB$. So if $AB = 6$, then $AM = 3$ and $MB = 3$.

EXAMPLE 4

Recreation Application

x² **Algebra**

The map shows the route for a race. You are 365 m from drink station *R* and 2 km from drink station *S*. The first-aid station is located at the midpoint of the two drink stations. How far are you from the first-aid station?

Let your current location be *X* and the location of the first-aid station be *Y*.

$XR + RS = XS$	*Seg. Add. Post.*
$365 + RS = 2000$	*Substitute 365 for XR and 2000 for XS.*
$-365 \qquad -365$	*Subtract 365 from both sides.*
$RS = 1635$	*Simplify.*
$RY = 817.5$	*Y is the mdpt. of $\overline{RS}$, so $RY = \frac{1}{2}RS$.*
$XY = XR + RY$	
$= 365 + 817.5 = 1182.5$ m	*Substitute 365 for XR and 817.5 for RY.*

You are 1182.5 m from the first-aid station.

CHECK IT OUT!

4. What is the distance to a drink station located at the midpoint between your current location and the first-aid station? 591.25 m

---

When solving equations as in **Examples 3** and **4**, students sometimes forget to do the inverse operation. Review inverse operations if necessary.

Power Presentations with PowerPoint®

Additional Examples

Example 2

Sketch, draw, and construct a segment congruent to $\overline{MN}$.

Check students' drawings and constructions. The segment should be approximately $1\frac{1}{4}$ in.

Example 3

A. *G* is between *F* and *H*, *FG* = 6, and *FH* = 11. Find *GH*. 5

B. *M* is between *N* and *O*. Find *NO*. 27

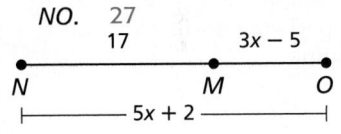

Example 4

The map shows the route for a race. You are at *X*, 6000 ft from the first checkpoint *C*. The second checkpoint *D* is located at the midpoint between *C* and the end of the race *Y*. The total race is 3 miles. How far apart are the 2 checkpoints? 4920 feet

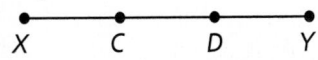

Also available on transparency

INTERVENTION

Questioning Strategies

EXAMPLE 2

• How are drawing and constructing different? How are they alike? Which is more accurate?

EXAMPLE 3

• Do you need to know that one of the points is between the other two? Why or why not?

EXAMPLE 4

• If you are given the midpoint and one endpoint of a segment, what three distances do you know?

Construction

Give each student a ruler. These can be found in the Manipulatives Kit (MK). Use paper other than patty paper and have students bend the line over the ruler. Then fold the paper along the line. Fold the paper end to end to locate the midpoint.

Power Presentations
with PowerPoint®

Additional Examples

Example 5

D is the midpoint of EF, $ED = 4x + 6$, and $DF = 7x - 9$. Find ED, DF, and EF. 26; 26; 52

Also available on transparency

INTERVENTION ◄■►
Questioning Strategies

EXAMPLE 5

• Is it possible for x to be a negative number in this type of problem? Support your answer with an example.

A **segment bisector** is any ray, segment, or line that intersects a segment at its midpoint. It divides the segment into two equal parts at its midpoint.

Construction   Segment Bisector

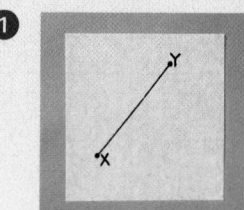

❶ Draw $\overline{XY}$ on a sheet of paper.

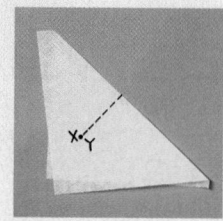

❷ Fold the paper so that Y is on top of X.

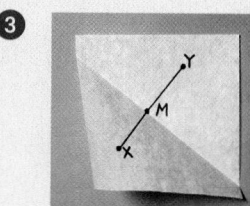

❸ Unfold the paper. The line represented by the crease bisects $\overline{XY}$. Label the midpoint M.
$$XM = MY$$

EXAMPLE 5   Using Midpoints to Find Lengths

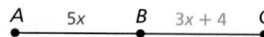
$A \quad 5x \quad B \quad 3x+4 \quad C$

B is the midpoint of $\overline{AC}$, $AB = 5x$, and $BC = 3x + 4$. Find AB, BC, and AC.

✗²ʸ Algebra

Step 1 Solve for x.

$$AB = BC \qquad \text{B is the mdpt. of } \overline{AC}.$$
$$5x = 3x + 4 \qquad \text{Substitute 5x for AB and 3x + 4 for BC.}$$
$$\underline{-3x \quad -3x} \qquad \text{Subtract 3x from both sides.}$$
$$2x = 4 \qquad \text{Simplify.}$$
$$\frac{2x}{2} = \frac{4}{2} \qquad \text{Divide both sides by 2.}$$
$$x = 2 \qquad \text{Simplify.}$$

Step 2 Find AB, BC, and AC.

$$AB = 5x \qquad\qquad BC = 3x + 4 \qquad\qquad AC = AB + BC$$
$$= 5(2) = 10 \qquad = 3(2) + 4 = 10 \qquad = 10 + 10 = 20$$

 **CHECK IT OUT!**   **5.** S is the midpoint of RT, $RS = -2x$, and $ST = -3x - 2$. Find RS, ST, and RT. **RS = 4; ST = 4; RT = 8**

THINK AND DISCUSS

Know it!
Note

1. Suppose R is the midpoint of $\overline{ST}$. Explain how SR and ST are related.

2. GET ORGANIZED Copy and complete the graphic organizer. Make a sketch and write an equation to describe each relationship.

	B is between A and C.	B is the midpoint of $\overline{AC}$.
Sketch		
Equation		

16   Chapter 1 Foundations for Geometry

---

3 Close

Summarize

Review the Segment Addition Postulate, emphasizing that betweenness involves collinearity. Remind students that a segment has exactly one midpoint. Review the steps used to construct a segment congruent to a given segment.

ONGOING ASSESSMENT
and INTERVENTION ◄■►

Diagnose *Before* the Lesson
1-2 Warm Up, TE p. 13

⬇

Monitor *During* the Lesson
Check It Out! Exercises, SE pp. 13–16
Questioning Strategies, TE pp. 14–16

⬇

Assess *After* the Lesson
1-2 Lesson Quiz, TE p. 19
Alternative Assessment, TE p. 19

Answers to *Think and Discuss*

1. Since R is the mdpt. of $\overline{ST}$, you know $SR = RT$. Also, $ST = SR + RT$. By subst., $ST = SR + SR = 2SR$. So ST is twice SR.

2. See p. A2.

1-2 **Exercises**

go.hrw.com/Geo/TX
Homework Help Online
KEYWORD: MG7 1-2
Parent Resources Online
KEYWORD: MG7 Parent

1-2 **Exercises**

GUIDED PRACTICE

Vocabulary Apply the vocabulary from this lesson to answer each question.

1. Line ℓ bisects $\overline{XY}$ at M and divides $\overline{XY}$ into two equal parts. Name a pair of congruent segments. **$\overline{XM}$ and $\overline{MY}$**

2. __?__ is the amount of space between two points on a line. It is always expressed as a nonnegative number. (*distance* or *midpoint*) **distance**

SEE EXAMPLE **1**
p. 13

Find each length.

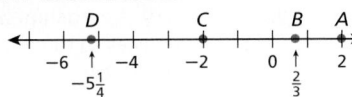

3. AB **3.5**   4. BC **2.5**

SEE EXAMPLE **2**
p. 14

5. Sketch, draw, and construct a segment congruent to $\overline{RS}$. **Check students' work.**

R ———————— S

SEE EXAMPLE **3**
p. 15

6. B is between A and C, $AC = 15.8$, and $AB = 9.9$. Find BC. **5.9**

7. Find MP.
29

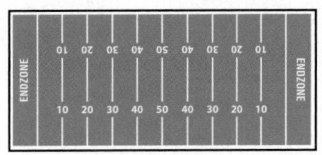

SEE EXAMPLE **4**
p. 15

8. **Travel** If a picnic area is located at the midpoint between Lubbock and Amarillo, find the distance to the picnic area from the sign. **66.5 mi**

Lubbock	5
Plainview	52
Amarillo	128

SEE EXAMPLE **5**
p. 16

9. **Multi-Step** K is the midpoint of $\overline{JL}$, $JL = 4x - 2$, and $JK = 7$. Find x, KL, and JL. **$x = 4$; $KL = 7$; $JL = 14$**

10. E bisects $\overline{DF}$, $DE = 2y$, and $EF = 8y - 3$. Find DE, EF, and DF. **$DE = EF = 1$; $DF = 2$**

PRACTICE AND PROBLEM SOLVING

Independent Practice

For Exercises	See Example
11–12	1
13	2
14–15	3
16	4
17–18	5

TEKS TAKS

Skills Practice p. S4
Application Practice p. S28

Find each length.

11. DB **$5\frac{11}{12}$**   12. CD **$3\frac{1}{4}$**

13. Sketch, draw, and construct a segment twice the length of $\overline{AB}$. **Check students' work.**

14. D is between C and E, $CE = 17.1$, and $DE = 8$. Find CD. **9.1**

15. Find MN. **5**

16. **Sports** During a football game, a quarterback standing at the 9-yard line passes the ball to a receiver at the 24-yard line. The receiver then runs with the ball halfway to the 50-yard line. How many total yards (passing plus running) did the team gain on the play? **28 yd**

17. **Multi-Step** E is the midpoint of $\overline{DF}$, $DE = 2x + 4$, and $EF = 3x - 1$. Find DE, EF, and DF. **$DE = EF = 14$; $DF = 28$**

18. Q bisects $\overline{PR}$, $PQ = 3y$, and $PR = 42$. Find y and QR. **$y = 7$; $QR = 21$**

Assignment Guide

Assign *Guided Practice* exercises as necessary.

If you finished Examples 1–3
Basic 11–15, 20, 24, 26
Average 11–15, 20, 24, 26, 28–30, 35, 36, 43
Advanced 11–15, 20, 24, 26, 28–30, 35, 36, 42–45

If you finished Examples 1–5
Basic 11–20, 22, 27, 28, 31, 34, 35, 37–40, 46–53
Average 11–28, 30–32, 34–41, 43–53
Advanced 12–14, 16–20, 22–30 even, 31, 32, 34–53

Homework Quick Check
Quickly check key concepts.
Exercises: 12–14, 16, 18, 20, 22, 31

Teaching Tip
Algebra For **Exercise 17**, remind students that they have to substitute the value of x into the expressions $2x + 4$ and $3x - 1$ to find DE, EF, and DF.

TAKS Practice

Grades 9–11	Exercises
Obj. 2	31–33, 48, 49
Obj. 7	20–23, 37
Obj. 10	24–26, 28, 34, 42, 43

MULTI-STEP TAKS PREP Exercise 19

involves finding distances between points. This exercise prepares students for the Multi-Step TAKS Prep on page 34.

Teaching Tip — **Kinesthetic** To demonstrate the difference between equal length and congruence in **Exercise 24,** have students place one hand over the other to show how they match for congruence. Then, for equality, have them show 5 fingers on each hand for $5 = 5$.

Teaching Tip — **Inclusion** If students are using a ruler for a straightedge in **Exercise 35,** be sure that they are not using the marks on the ruler to measure distances, and that they show construction arcs.

Teaching Tip — **Multiple Representations** For **Exercise 40,** encourage students to draw and label a diagram with all the given information before attempting to solve the problem.

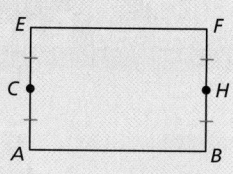

19. This problem will prepare you for the Multi-Step TAKS Prep on page 34. Archaeologists at Valley Forge were eager to find what remained of the winter camp that soldiers led by George Washington called home for several months. The diagram represents one of the restored log cabins.

a. How is C related to $\overline{AE}$? **C is the mdpt. of $\overline{AE}$.**

b. If $AC = 7$ ft, $EF = 2(AC) + 2$, and $AB = 2(EF) - 16$, what are AB and EF? **16**

Use the diagram for Exercises 20–23.

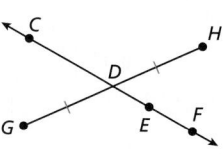

20. $GD = 4\frac{2}{3}$. Find GH. **$9\frac{1}{3}$**

21. $\overline{CD} \cong \overline{DF}$, E bisects $\overline{DF}$, and $CD = 14.2$. Find EF. **7.1**

22. $GH = 4x - 1$, and $DH = 8$. Find x. **4.25**

23. $\overline{GH}$ bisects $\overline{CF}$, $CF = 2y - 2$, and $CD = 3y - 11$. Find CD. **4**

Tell whether each statement is sometimes, always, or never true. Support each of your answers with a sketch.

24. Two segments that have the same length must be congruent. **A;**

25. If M is between A and B, then M bisects $\overline{AB}$. **S;**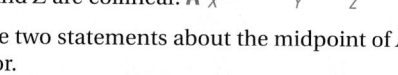

26. If Y is between X and Z, then X, Y, and Z are collinear. **A**

27. $AM \cong MB$ is incorrect. The statement should be written as $\overline{AM} \cong \overline{MB}$, not as 2 distances that are $\cong$.

27. ///ERROR ANALYSIS/// Below are two statements about the midpoint of $\overline{AB}$. Which is incorrect? Explain the error.

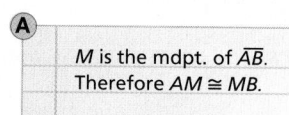
A — M is the mdpt. of $\overline{AB}$. Therefore $AM \cong MB$.

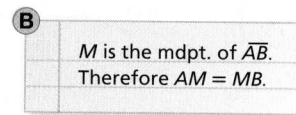
B — M is the mdpt. of $\overline{AB}$. Therefore $AM = MB$.

28. **Carpentry** A carpenter has a wooden dowel that is 72 cm long. She wants to cut it into two pieces so that one piece is 5 times as long as the other. What are the lengths of the two pieces? **60 cm; 12 cm**

29. The coordinate of M is 2.5, and $MN = 4$. What are the possible coordinates for N? **6.5; −1.5**

30.

Possible answer: $\overline{DE} + \overline{EF} = \overline{DF}$

30. Draw three collinear points where E is between D and F. Then write an equation using these points and the Segment Addition Postulate.

Suppose S is between R and T. Use the Segment Addition Postulate to solve for each variable.

31. $RS = 7y - 4$
$ST = y + 5$
$RT = 28$ **3.375**

32. $RS = 3x + 1$
$ST = \frac{1}{2}x + 3$
$RT = 18$ **4**

33. $RS = 2z + 6$
$ST = 4z - 3$
$RT = 5z + 12$ **9**

34. **Write About It** In the diagram, B is not between A and C. Explain. **B is not between A and C, because A, B, and C are not collinear.**

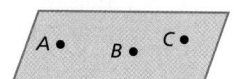

35. **Construction** Use a compass and straightedge to construct a segment whose length is $AB + CD$. **Check students' constructions.**

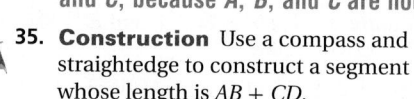
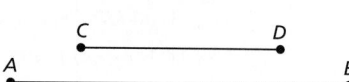

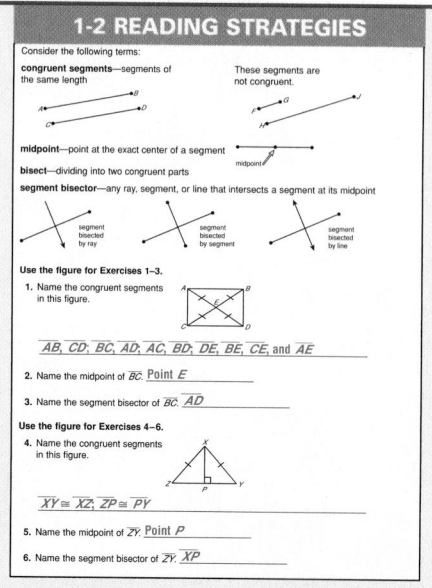

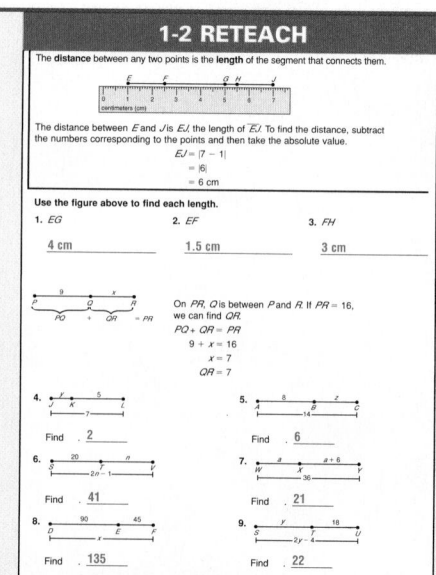

36. Q is between P and R. S is between Q and R, and R is between Q and T. PT = 34, QR = 8, and PQ = SQ = SR. What is the length of $\overline{RT}$?

Ⓐ 9   Ⓑ 10   Ⓒ 18   Ⓓ 22

37. C is the midpoint of $\overline{AD}$. B is the midpoint of $\overline{AC}$. BC = 12. What is the length of $\overline{AD}$?

Ⓕ 12   Ⓖ 24   Ⓗ 36   Ⓙ 48

38. Which expression correctly states that $\overline{XY}$ is congruent to $\overline{VW}$?

Ⓐ XY ≅ VW   Ⓑ $\overline{XY}$ ≅ $\overline{VW}$ Ⓒ $\overline{XY}$ = $\overline{VW}$ Ⓓ XY = VW

39. A, B, C, D, and E are collinear points. AE = 34, BD = 16, and AB = BC = CD. What is the length of $\overline{CE}$?

Ⓕ 10   Ⓖ 16   Ⓗ 18   Ⓙ 24

CHALLENGE AND EXTEND

40. HJ is twice JK. J is between H and K. If HJ = 4x and HK = 78, find JK. **26**

41. A, D, N, and X are collinear points. D is between N and A. NA + AX = NX. Draw a diagram that represents this information.

X   A   D   N

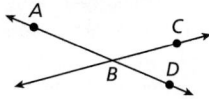

Sports Use the following information for Exercises 42 and 43.

The table shows regulation distances between hurdles in women's and men's races. In both the women's and men's events, the race consists of a straight track with 10 equally spaced hurdles.

Event	Distance of Race	Distance from Start to First Hurdle	Distance Between Hurdles	Distance from Last Hurdle to Finish
Women's	100 m	13.00 m	8.50 m	
Men's	110 m	13.72 m	9.14 m	

42. Find the distance from the last hurdle to the finish line for the women's race. **10.5 m**

43. Find the distance from the last hurdle to the finish line for the men's race. **14.02 m**

44. **Critical Thinking** Given that J, K, and L are collinear and that K is between J and L, is it possible that JK = JL? If so, draw an example. If not, explain.
JK cannot be equal to JL because JK + KL = JL and KL ≠ 0.

SPIRAL REVIEW

Evaluate each expression. (Previous course)

45. |20 − 8| **12**   46. |−9 + 23| **14**   47. −|4 − 27| **−23**

Simplify each expression. (Previous course)

48. 8a − 3(4 + a) − 10 **5a − 22**   49. x + 2(5 − 2x) − (4 + 5x) **−8x + 6**

Use the figure to name each of the following. (Lesson 1-1)

50. two lines that contain B $\overleftrightarrow{AB}$, $\overleftrightarrow{CB}$

51. two segments containing D $\overline{AD}$, $\overline{BD}$

52. three collinear points A, B, D

53. a ray with endpoint C $\overrightarrow{CB}$

1-2 Measuring and Constructing Segments   19

1-2 **Lesson Quiz**

1. M is between N and O, MO = 15, and MN = 7.6. Find NO.   22.6

2. S is the midpoint of $\overline{TV}$, TS = 4x − 7, and SV = 5x − 15. Find TS, SV, and TV.   25, 25, 50

3. Sketch, draw, and construct a segment congruent to $\overline{CD}$.

C   D

Check students' constructions.

4. $\overleftrightarrow{LH}$ bisects $\overline{GK}$ at M. GM = 2x + 6, and GK = 24. Find x.   3

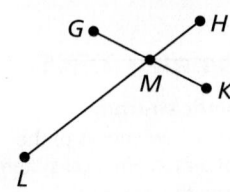
G   H
    M   K
L

5. Tell whether the statement below is sometimes, always, or never true. Support your answer with a sketch. If M is the midpoint of $\overline{KL}$, then M, K, and L are collinear.
A

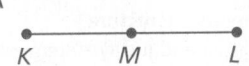
K   M   L

Also available on transparency

Lesson 1-2   **19**

Objectives: Name and classify angles.

Measure and construct angles and angle bisectors.

Online Edition
Tutorial Videos, TechKeys

Countdown to TAKS Week 1

Power Presentations
with PowerPoint®

Warm Up

1. Draw $\overrightarrow{AB}$ and $\overrightarrow{AC}$, where A, B, and C are noncollinear.
Check students' drawings

2. Draw opposite rays $\overrightarrow{DE}$ and $\overrightarrow{DF}$. Check students' drawings

Solve each equation.

3. $2x + 3 + x - 4 + 3x - 5 = 180$ 31

4. $5x + 2 = 8x - 10$ 4

Also available on transparency

Math Humor

Q: What do you call people who are in favor of tractors?

A: Protractors!

⭐ Geometry TEKS

G.1 Geometric structure*
(A) develop an awareness of the structure of a mathematical system, ...
(B) recognize the historical development of geometric systems ...

G.2 Geometric structure*
(A) use constructions to explore attributes of geometric figures ...
(B) make conjectures about angles, ... and determine the validity of conjectures ...

G.3 Geometric structure*
(B) construct and justify statements about geometric figures ...

* Knowledge and Skills See p. 4.

1-3 Measuring and Constructing Angles

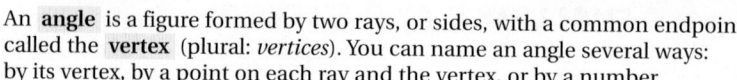

⭐ **TEKS G.3.B** Geometric structure: construct and justify statements about geometric figures and their properties. Also G.1.A, G.1.B, G.2.A, G.2.B

Objectives
Name and classify angles.

Measure and construct angles and angle bisectors.

Vocabulary
angle
vertex
interior of an angle
exterior of an angle
measure
degree
acute angle
right angle
obtuse angle
straight angle
congruent angles
angle bisector

Who uses this?
Surveyors use angles to help them measure and map the earth's surface. (See Exercise 27.)

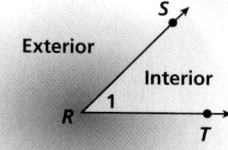

A transit is a tool for measuring angles. It consists of a telescope that swivels horizontally and vertically. Using a transit, a surveyor can measure the *angle* formed by his or her location and two distant points.

An **angle** is a figure formed by two rays, or sides, with a common endpoint called the **vertex** (plural: *vertices*). You can name an angle several ways: by its vertex, by a point on each ray and the vertex, or by a number.

The set of all points between the sides of the angle is the **interior of an angle**. The **exterior of an angle** is the set of all points outside the angle.

Angle Name
∠R, ∠SRT, ∠TRS, or ∠1

You cannot name an angle just by its vertex if the point is the vertex of more than one angle. In this case, you must use all three points to name the angle, and the middle point is always the vertex.

EXAMPLE 1   **Naming Angles**

A surveyor recorded the angles formed by a transit (point T) and three distant points, Q, R, and S. Name three of the angles.

∠QTR, ∠QTS, and ∠RTS

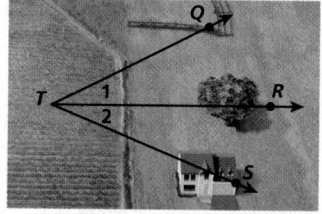

✓ **CHECK IT OUT!**   **1.** Write the different ways you can name the angles in the diagram. ∠RTQ, ∠T, ∠STR, ∠1, ∠2

The **measure** of an angle is usually given in degrees. Since there are 360° in a circle, one **degree** is $\frac{1}{360}$ of a circle. When you use a protractor to measure angles, you are applying the following postulate.

Know it! Note

Postulate 1-3-1   **Protractor Postulate**

Given $\overrightarrow{AB}$ and a point O on $\overrightarrow{AB}$, all rays that can be drawn from O can be put into a one-to-one correspondence with the real numbers from 0 to 180.

1 Introduce

EXPLORATION

1-3 Measuring and Constructing Angles

Use rectangular pieces of paper and a protractor for this Exploration.

1. Fold the paper and make a crease. Then unfold the paper.
2. Fold down the top of the paper so the edge aligns with the crease.
3. Fold up the bottom of the paper so the edge aligns with the crease.
4. Unfold the paper and label the angles as show.

5. Measure ∠ABC, ∠ABD, and ∠DBC. Record the results.
6. Repeat Steps 1 through 5 with a new piece of paper.

THINK AND DISCUSS

7. Describe what you notice about the measure of ∠ABC.
8. Discuss the relationship among the measures of ∠ABC.

Motivate

Point out examples of different types of angles in the classroom, such as the corner of a piece of paper for a right angle, and open scissors to show an acute angle or an obtuse angle. Have students get in groups of three and use a long strand of yarn and three index cards, each labeled with a different letter, to model for the class the different angles that can be formed.

Explorations and answers are provided in the *Explorations* binder.

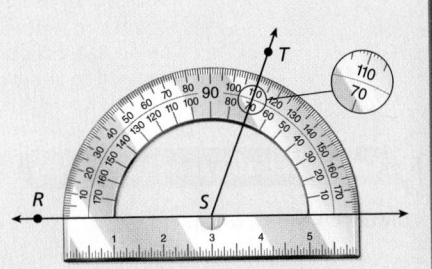
You can use the Protractor Postulate to help you classify angles by their measure. The measure of an angle is the absolute value of the difference of the real numbers that the rays correspond with on a protractor. If $\overrightarrow{OC}$ corresponds with c and $\overrightarrow{OD}$ corresponds with d, m∠DOC = $|d - c|$ or $|c - d|$.

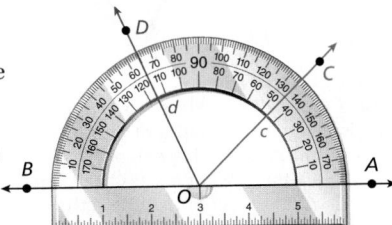

 **Know it!** *Note*

Types of Angles

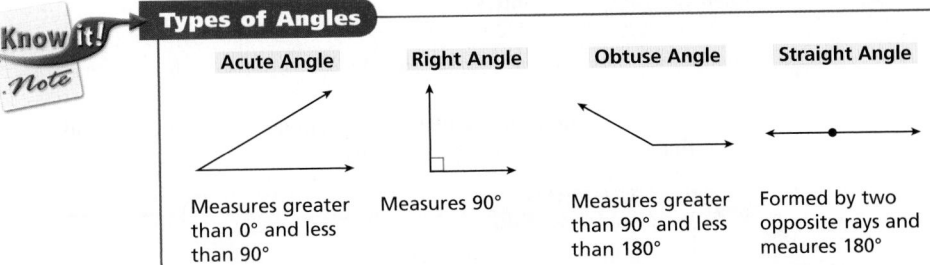

Acute Angle	Right Angle	Obtuse Angle	Straight Angle
Measures greater than 0° and less than 90°	Measures 90°	Measures greater than 90° and less than 180°	Formed by two opposite rays and meaures 180°

EXAMPLE 2 **Measuring and Classifying Angles**

Find the measure of each angle. Then classify each as acute, right, or obtuse.

A ∠AOD
m∠AOD = 165°
∠AOD is obtuse.

B ∠COD
m∠COD = $|165 - 75| = 90°$
∠COD is a right angle.

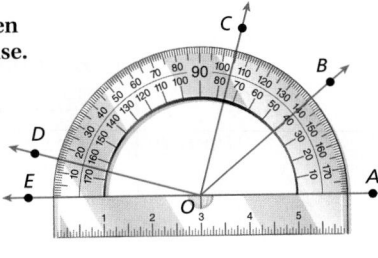

 **CHECK IT OUT!** Use the diagram to find the measure of each angle. Then classify each as acute, right, or obtuse.

2a. ∠BOA
40°; acute

2b. ∠DOB
125°; obtuse

2c. ∠EOC
105°; obtuse

1-3 Measuring and Constructing Angles **21**

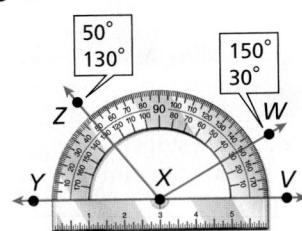

---

2 Teach

Guided Instruction

Discuss how to name angles. The vertex is always the middle letter, or is used as the single letter name. Show students how to use a protractor to measure angles and how to write their measure. Explain that the *measure* of ∠A is written as m∠A. Describe each step of the constructions. Emphasize that congruent angles have equal measures and that an angle bisector divides an angle into two congruent angles.

Reaching All Learners
Through Visual Cues

Use pictures from magazines of angles of different sizes. Ask students to identify the type of angle and estimate the measure. Then have students measure the angles with a protractor. If protractors are not available, they can use index cards or origami paper. The edge is already a 90° angle, and anything greater would be an obtuse angle. A half-fold forms a 45° angle, a tri-fold approximately 30°, and so on. The pictures can be posted by classification and used for reference.

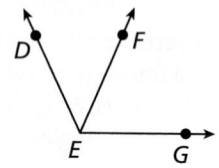

Visual Remind students to show all arcs in their construction. In **Step 4**, they should use the same compass span *BC* when drawing the arcs. Have students practice constructing both acute and obtuse angles.

Teaching Tip

Power Presentations
with PowerPoint®

Additional Examples

Example 3

m∠*DEG* = 115°, and m∠*DEF* = 48°. Find m∠*FEG*.　67°

Also available on transparency

INTERVENTION ⬅➡
Questioning Strategies

EXAMPLE 3

- What is actually being added in the example? Are you adding the angles or the measures of the angles?

Teaching Tip

Reading Math Review the different meanings of m∠*A* = m∠*B* and ∠*A* ≅ ∠*B*. Have students practice reading the symbols aloud.

ENGLISH LANGUAGE LEARNERS

Congruent angles are angles that have the same measure. In the diagram, m∠*ABC* = m∠*DEF*, so you can write ∠*ABC* ≅ ∠*DEF*. This is read as "angle *ABC* is congruent to angle *DEF*." *Arc marks* are used to show that the two angles are congruent.

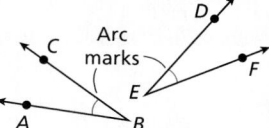

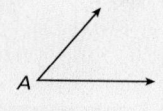

Construction Congruent Angle

Construct an angle congruent to ∠*A*.

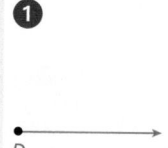 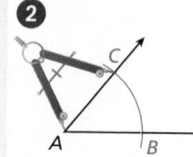 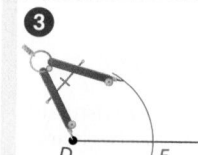 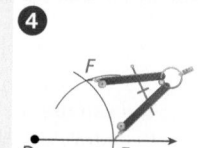 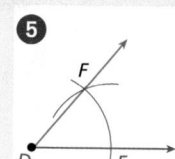

① Use a straightedge to draw a ray with endpoint *D*.

② Place the compass point at *A* and draw an arc that intersects both sides of ∠*A*. Label the intersection points *B* and *C*.

③ Using the same compass setting, place the compass point at *D* and draw an arc that intersects the ray. Label the intersection *E*.

④ Place the compass point at *B* and open it to the distance *BC*. Place the point of the compass at *E* and draw an arc. Label its intersection with the first arc *F*.

⑤ Use a straightedge to draw $\overrightarrow{DF}$.

∠*D* ≅ ∠*A*

The Angle Addition Postulate is very similar to the Segment Addition Postulate that you learned in the previous lesson.

Postulate 1-3-2　**Angle Addition Postulate**

If *S* is in the interior of ∠*PQR*, then
m∠*PQS* + m∠*SQR* = m∠*PQR*.
(∠ Add. Post.)

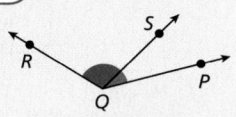

EXAMPLE 3　**Using the Angle Addition Postulate**

x² **Algebra**

m∠*ABD* = 37° and m∠*ABC* = 84°. Find m∠*DBC*.

m∠*ABC* = m∠*ABD* + m∠*DBC*　∠ Add. Post.

84° = 37° + m∠*DBC*　　*Substitute the given values.*

$\underline{-37 \qquad -37}$　　*Subtract 37 from both sides.*

47° = m∠*DBC*　　　　*Simplify.*

 **3.** m∠*XWZ* = 121° and m∠*XWY* = 59°. Find m∠*YWZ*.　62°

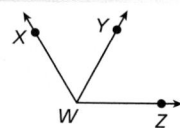

An **angle bisector** is a ray that divides an angle into two congruent angles. $\overrightarrow{JK}$ bisects $\angle LJM$; thus $\angle LJK \cong \angle KJM$.

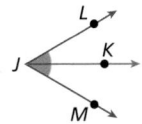

Construction Angle Bisector

Construct the bisector of $\angle A$.

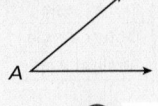

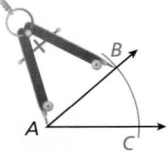 **①**

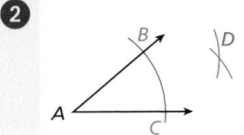 **②**

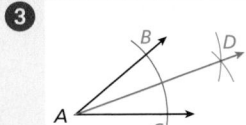 **③**

Place the point of the compass at A and draw an arc. Label its points of intersection with $\angle A$ as B and C.

Without changing the compass setting, draw intersecting arcs from B and C. Label the intersection of the arcs as D.

Use a straightedge to draw $\overrightarrow{AD}$. $\overrightarrow{AD}$ bisects $\angle A$.

EXAMPLE 4

x² Algebra

Finding the Measure of an Angle

$\overrightarrow{BD}$ bisects $\angle ABC$, $m\angle ABD = (6x + 3)^\circ$, and $m\angle DBC = (8x - 7)^\circ$. Find $m\angle ABD$.

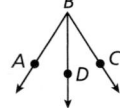

Step 1 Find x.

$m\angle ABD = m\angle DBC$	*Def. of $\angle$ bisector*
$(6x + 3)^\circ = (8x - 7)^\circ$	*Substitute the given values.*
$\underline{+7 \qquad +7}$	*Add 7 to both sides.*
$6x + 10 = 8x$	*Simplify.*
$\underline{-6x \qquad\quad -6x}$	*Subtract 6x from both sides.*
$10 = 2x$	*Simplify.*
$\dfrac{10}{2} = \dfrac{2x}{2}$	*Divide both sides by 2.*
$5 = x$	*Simplify.*

Step 2 Find $m\angle ABD$.

$m\angle ABD = 6x + 3$	
$= 6(5) + 3$	*Substitute 5 for x.*
$= 33^\circ$	*Simplify.*

CHECK IT OUT!

Find the measure of each angle.

4a. $\overrightarrow{QS}$ bisects $\angle PQR$, $m\angle PQS = (5y - 1)^\circ$, and $m\angle PQR = (8y + 12)^\circ$. Find $m\angle PQS$. **34°**

4b. $\overrightarrow{JK}$ bisects $\angle LJM$, $m\angle LJK = (-10x + 3)^\circ$, and $m\angle KJM = (-x + 21)^\circ$. Find $m\angle LJM$. **46°**

Teaching Tip **Reading Math** Explain the *bi* is a prefix meaning "two" and *sect* means "to cut," as into sections. ENGLISH LANGUAGE LEARNERS

Power Presentations with PowerPoint®

Additional Examples

Example 4

$\overrightarrow{KM}$ bisects $\angle JKL$, $m\angle JKM = (4x + 6)^\circ$, and $m\angle MKL = (7x - 12)^\circ$. Find $m\angle JKM$. **30°**

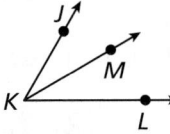

Also available on transparency

INTERVENTION
Questioning Strategies

EXAMPLE 4

• When do you set the angle measures equal to solve for the variable?

• How can you solve for the variable if you are given the measures of the bisected angle and one of the congruent angles?

---

3 Close

Summarize

Review with students the parts of an angle, the names of the types of angles, and how to measure angles. Review the Angle Addition Postulate and how it relates to the bisector of an angle.

ONGOING ASSESSMENT

and INTERVENTION

*Diagnose **Before** the Lesson*
1-3 Warm Up, TE p. 20

*Monitor **During** the Lesson*
Check It Out! Exercises, SE pp. 20–23
Questioning Strategies, TE pp. 21–23

*Assess **After** the Lesson*
1-3 Lesson Quiz, TE p. 27
Alternative Assessment, TE p. 27

1. Two ∡ with the same measure are ≅. All rt. ∡ measure 90°, so any 2 rt. ∡ are ≅.

2. m∠ABD = m∠DBC = ½m∠ABC

3. See p. A2.

THINK AND DISCUSS

1. Explain why any two right angles are congruent.

2. $\overrightarrow{BD}$ bisects ∠ABC. How are m∠ABC, m∠ABD, and m∠DBC related?

3. **GET ORGANIZED** Copy and complete the graphic organizer. In the cells sketch, measure, and name an example of each angle type.

	Diagram	Measure	Name
Acute Angle			
Right Angle			
Obtuse Angle			
Straight Angle			

1-3 Exercises

1-3 Exercises

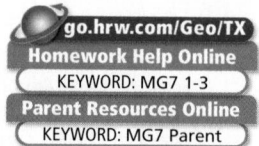

go.hrw.com/Geo/TX
Homework Help Online
KEYWORD: MG7 1-3
Parent Resources Online
KEYWORD: MG7 Parent

Assignment Guide

Assign *Guided Practice* exercises as necessary.

If you finished Examples **1–2**
Basic 11–14, 19–26, 33–35
Average 11–14, 19–27, 32–36
Advanced 11–14, 19–27, 32–36

If you finished Examples **1–4**
Basic 11–26, 29–31, 33–35, 38, 41–45, 51–58
Average 11–37, 39–46, 48–58
Advanced 11, 12–22 even, 23, 26–58

Homework Quick Check
Quickly check key concepts.
Exercises: 11, 12, 16, 18, 20, 26, 30

⬇TAKS Practice

Grades 9–11	Exercises
Obj. 2	32, 41–44, 46, 50
Obj. 4	29–31, 33, 38, 56–58
Obj. 9	34–36, 50, 51
Obj. 10	27, 34–36, 39, 40, 45

GUIDED PRACTICE

Vocabulary Apply the vocabulary from this lesson to answer each question.

3. ∠AOB, ∠BOA, or ∠1; ∠BOC, ∠COB, or ∠2; ∠AOC or ∠COA

1. ∠A is an acute angle. ∠O is an obtuse angle. ∠R is a right angle. Put ∠A, ∠O, and ∠R in order from least to greatest by measure. **∠A, ∠R, ∠O**

2. Which point is the vertex of ∠BCD? Which rays form the sides of ∠BCD? **C; $\overrightarrow{CB}$, $\overrightarrow{CD}$**

SEE EXAMPLE **1**
p. 20

3. **Music** Musicians use a metronome to keep time as they play. The metronome's needle swings back and forth in a fixed amount of time. Name all of the angles in the diagram.

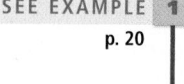

SEE EXAMPLE **2**
p. 21

Use the protractor to find the measure of each angle. Then classify each as acute, right, or obtuse.

4. ∠VXW **15°; acute**

5. ∠TXW **105°; obtuse**

6. ∠RXU **110°; obtuse**

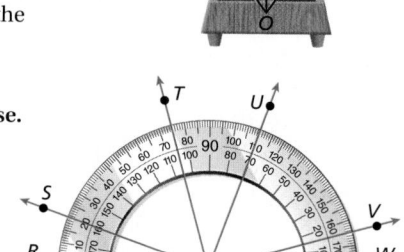

SEE EXAMPLE **3**
p. 22

L is in the interior of ∠JKM. Find each of the following.

7. m∠JKM if m∠JKL = 42° and m∠LKM = 28° **70°**

8. m∠LKM if m∠JKL = 56.4° and m∠JKM = 82.5° **26.1°**

SEE EXAMPLE **4**
p. 23

Multi-Step $\overrightarrow{BD}$ bisects ∠ABC. Find each of the following.

9. m∠ABD if m∠ABD = (6x + 4)° and m∠DBC = (8x − 4)° **28°**

10. m∠ABC if m∠ABD = (5y − 3)° and m∠DBC = (3y + 15)° **84°**

1-3 PRACTICE A

Use the figure for Exercises 1–4.

1. An angle is a figure formed by two rays with a common endpoint called the __vertex__.

2. Name the two rays that form ∠P.
__PQ and PR__

3. Use the angle symbol and three letters to name ∠P in two ways.
__∠QPR and ∠RPQ__

4. Name a point that is in the interior of ∠P.
__point S__

Complete the statement.

5. A tool used to measure and draw angles is called a __protractor__

Find the measure of each angle. Then tell whether each is acute, right, obtuse, or straight.

6. ∠CEA
__90°, right__

7. ∠AEB
__60°, acute__

8. ∠DEA
__180°, straight__

Complete the angle.

9. Use a compass and straightedge to finish constructing ∠IHJ congruent to ∠MLN.

10. Marc doesn't think that the angle of the front seat in his mom's car is very cool, so he tilts the seat back. m∠ZWY = 95° and m∠YWX = 30°.
Find m∠ZWX. __125°__

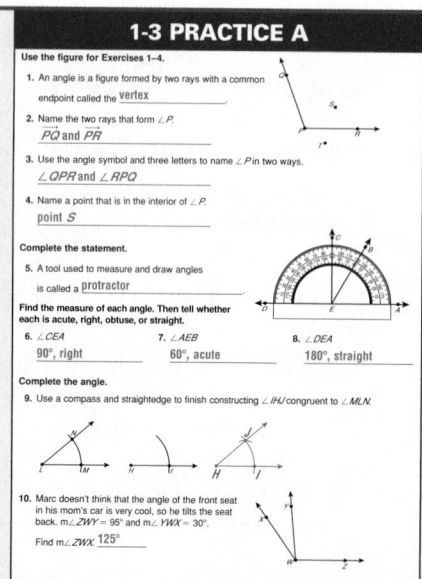

1-3 PRACTICE B

Draw your answer on the figure.

1. Use a compass and straightedge to construct angle bisector $\overrightarrow{DG}$.

2. Name eight different angles in the figure.
__∠A, ∠C, ∠ABC, ∠ABD, ∠ADB,__
__∠ADC, ∠CBD, and ∠CDB__

Find the measure of each angle and classify each as acute, right, obtuse, or straight.

3. ∠YWZ
__90°, right__

4. ∠XWZ
__120°, obtuse__

5. ∠YWX
__30°, acute__

T is in the interior of ∠PQR. Find each of the following.

6. m∠PQT if m∠PQR = 25° and m∠RQT = 11°. __14°__

7. m∠PQR if m∠PQR = (10x − 7)°, and m∠RQT = 5x°, and m∠PQT = (4x + 6)°. __123°__

8. m∠PQR if $\overrightarrow{QT}$ bisects ∠PQR, m∠RQT = (10x − 13)°, and m∠PQT = (6x + 1)°. __44°__

9. Longitude is a measurement of position around the equator of the Earth. Longitude is measured in degrees, minutes, and seconds. Each degree contains 60 minutes, and each minute contains 60 seconds. Minutes are indicated by the symbol ′ and seconds are indicated by the symbol ″. Williamsburg, VA, is located at 76°42′25″. Roanoke, VA, is located at 79°57′30″. Find the difference of their longitudes in degrees, minutes, and seconds. __3°15′05″__

10. To convert minutes and seconds into decimal parts of a degree, divide the number of minutes by 60 and the number of seconds by 3600. Then add the numbers together. Write the location of Roanoke, VA, as a decimal to the nearest thousandths of a degree. __79.958°__

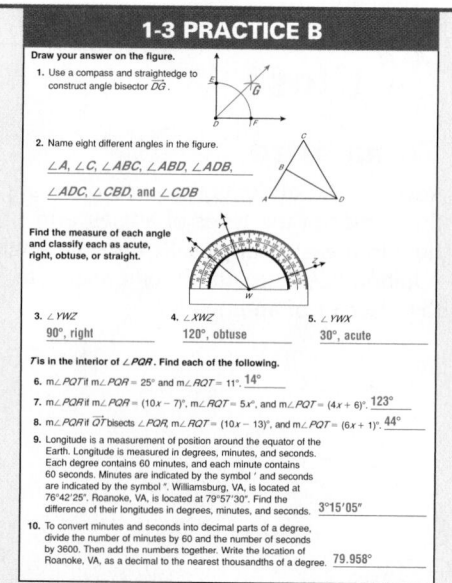

PRACTICE AND PROBLEM SOLVING

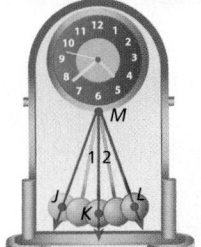

Independent Practice

For Exercises	See Example
11	1
12–14	2
15–16	3
17–18	4

TEKS · TAKS

Skills Practice p. S4

Application Practice p. S28

---

11. Physics Pendulum clocks have been used since 1656 to keep time. The pendulum swings back and forth once or twice per second. Name all of the angles in the diagram.
∠1 or ∠JMK; ∠2 or ∠LMK; ∠M or ∠JML

Use the protractor to find the measure of each angle. Then classify each as acute, right, or obtuse.

12. ∠CGE
90°; rt.

13. ∠BGD
93°; obtuse

14. ∠AGB
20°; acute

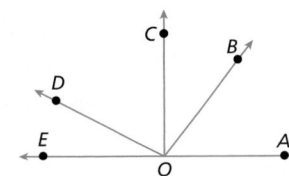

T is in the interior of ∠RSU. Find each of the following.

15. m∠RSU if m∠RST = 38° and m∠TSU = 28.6° **66.6°**

16. m∠RST if m∠TSU = 46.7° and m∠RSU = 83.5°
36.8°

Multi-Step $\overrightarrow{SP}$ bisects ∠RST. Find each of the following.

17. m∠RST if m∠RSP= (3x − 2)° and m∠PST = (9x − 26)° **20°**

18. m∠RSP if m∠RST = $\frac{5}{2}y°$ and m∠PST = $(y + 5)°$ **25°**

Estimation Use the following information for Exercises 19–22.

Assume the corner of a sheet of paper is a right angle. Use the corner to estimate the measure and classify each angle in the diagram.

19. ∠BOA **acute**

20. ∠COA **rt.**

21. ∠EOD **acute**

22. ∠EOB **obtuse**

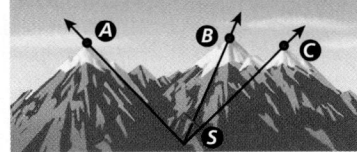

Use a protractor to draw an angle with each of the following measures.

23–26. Check students' drawings.

23. 33° **24.** 142° **25.** 90° **26.** 168°

27. Surveying A surveyor at point *S* discovers that the angle between peaks *A* and *B* is 3 times as large as the angle between peaks *B* and *C*. The surveyor knows that ∠ASC is a right angle. Find m∠ASB and m∠BSC.
67.5°; 22.5°

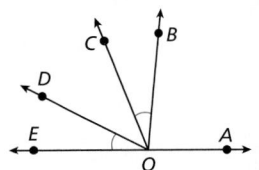

28. Math History As far back as the 5th century B.C., mathematicians have been fascinated by the problem of trisecting an angle. It is possible to construct an angle with $\frac{1}{4}$ the measure of a given angle. Explain how to do this.

Find the value of x.

29. m∠AOC = 7x − 2, m∠DOC = 2x + 8, m∠EOD = 27 **16$\frac{1}{3}$**

30. m∠AOB = 4x − 2, m∠BOC = 5x + 10, m∠COD = 3x − 8 **10**

31. m∠AOB = 6x + 5, m∠BOC = 4x − 2, m∠AOC = 8x + 21 **9**

32. Multi-Step *Q* is in the interior of right ∠PRS. If m∠PRQ is 4 times as large as m∠QRS, what is m∠PRQ? **72°**

1-3 PRACTICE C

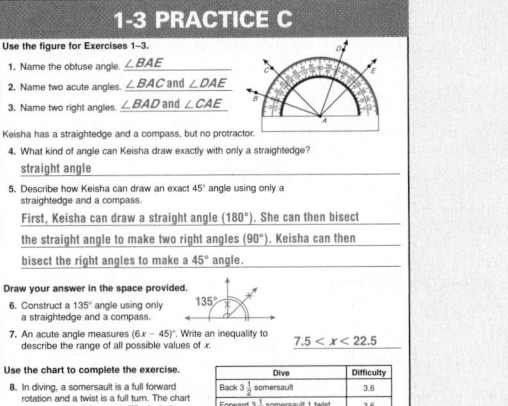

Use the figure for Exercises 1–3.

1. Name the obtuse angle. ∠BAE
2. Name two acute angles. ∠BAC and ∠DAE
3. Name two right angles. ∠BAD and ∠CAE

Keisha has a straightedge and a compass, but no protractor.

4. What kind of angle can Keisha draw exactly with only a straightedge?
straight angle

5. Describe how Keisha can draw an exact 45° angle using only a straightedge and a compass.
First, Keisha can draw a straight angle (180°). She can then bisect the straight angle to make two right angles (90°). Keisha can then bisect the right angles to make a 45° angle.

Draw your answer in the space provided.

6. Construct a 135° angle using only a straightedge and a compass. 135°

7. An acute angle measures (6x − 45)°. Write an inequality to describe the range of all possible values of x. **7.5 < x < 22.5**

Use the chart to complete the exercise.

8. In diving, a somersault is a full forward rotation and a twist is a full turn. The chart names some of the most difficult platform dives according to the International Swimming Federation. Name the dive in which the diver moves through a total of exactly 1800°.
back 2 $\frac{1}{2}$ somersault 2 $\frac{1}{2}$ twists

Dive	Difficulty
Back 3 $\frac{1}{2}$ somersault	3.6
Forward 3 $\frac{1}{2}$ somersault 1 twist	3.6
Reverse 1 $\frac{1}{2}$ somersault 4 $\frac{1}{2}$ twists	3.7
Back 2 $\frac{1}{2}$ somersault 2 $\frac{1}{2}$ twists	3.8

9. $\overrightarrow{HJ}$ bisects ∠IHL, $\overrightarrow{HK}$ bisects ∠JHL, and m∠IHK = 51°. Find m∠IHL. **68°**

10. m∠XWY is twice m∠XWZ. Tell if $\overrightarrow{WZ}$ must be the angle bisector of ∠XWY.
No, $\overrightarrow{WZ}$ does not have to be the angle bisector of ∠XWY.

33. This problem will prepare you for the Multi-Step TAKS Prep on page 34. An archaeologist standing at O looks for clues on where to dig for artifacts.

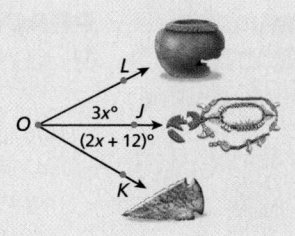

  a. What value of x will make the angle between the pottery and the arrowhead measure 57°? **9**

  b. What value of x makes ∠LOJ ≅ ∠JOK? **12**

  c. What values of x make ∠LOK an acute angle?
    $0 < x < 15.6$

Data Analysis Use the circle graph for Exercises 34–36.

34. Find m∠AOB, m∠BOC, m∠COD, and m∠DOA. Classify each angle as acute, right, or obtuse.

35. m∠COD = 72°; m∠BOC = 90°;

35. **What if…?** Next year, the music store will use some of the shelves currently holding jazz music to double the space for rap. What will m∠COD and m∠BOC be next year?

36. Suppose a fifth type of music, salsa, is added. If the space is divided equally among the five types, what will be the angle measure for each type of music in the circle graph? **72°**

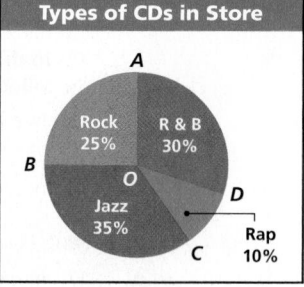

Types of CDs in Store

37. No; an obtuse ∠ measures greater than 90°, so it cannot be ≅ to an acute ∠ (less than 90°).

37. **Critical Thinking** Can an obtuse angle be congruent to an acute angle? Why or why not?

38. The measure of an obtuse angle is $(5x + 45)°$. What is the largest value for x? **27**

39. m∠EFG = m∠EFH + m∠HFG = 2m∠EFH, so m∠EFH = ½m∠EFG

39. **Write About It** $\overrightarrow{FH}$ bisects ∠EFG. Use the Angle Addition Postulate to explain why m∠EFH = ½m∠EFG.

40. **Multi-Step** Use a protractor to draw a 70° angle. Then use a compass and straightedge to bisect the angle. What do you think will be the measure of each angle formed? Use a protractor to support your answer.
Check students' constructions. Each ∠ should be 35°.

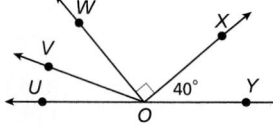

TEST PREP

41. m∠UOW = 50°, and $\overrightarrow{OV}$ bisects ∠UOW. What is m∠VOY?
    Ⓐ 25°   Ⓒ 130°
    Ⓑ 65°   Ⓓ 155°

42. What is m∠UOX?
    Ⓕ 50°   Ⓖ 115°   Ⓗ 140°   Ⓙ 165°

43. $\overrightarrow{BD}$ bisects ∠ABC, m∠ABC = $(4x + 5)°$, and m∠ABD = $(3x − 1)°$. What is the value of x?
    Ⓐ 2.2   Ⓑ 3   Ⓒ 3.5   Ⓓ 7

44. If an angle is bisected and then 30° is added to the measure of the bisected angle, the result is the measure of a right angle. What is the measure of the original angle?
    Ⓕ 30°   Ⓖ 60°   Ⓗ 75°   Ⓙ 120°

45. **Short Response** If an obtuse angle is bisected, are the resulting angles acute or obtuse? Explain. **The ∡ are acute. An obtuse ∠ measures between 90° and 180°. Since ½ of 180 is 90, the resulting ∡ must measure less than 90°.**

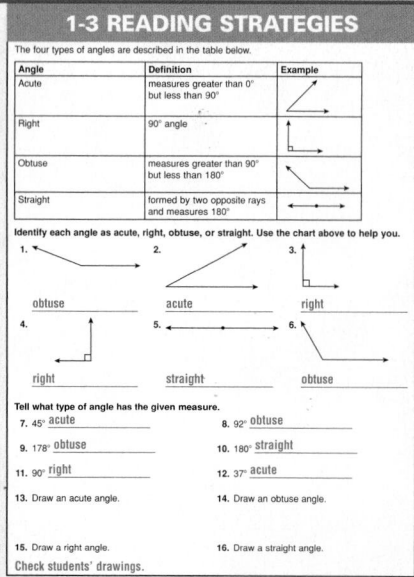

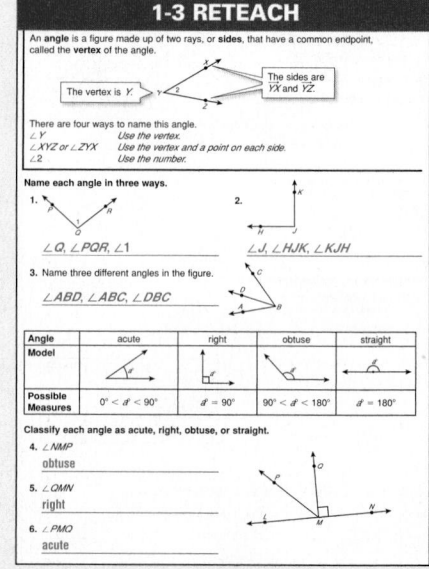

CHALLENGE AND EXTEND

46. Find the measure of the angle formed by the hands of a clock when it is 7:00. **150°**

47. $\overrightarrow{QS}$ bisects $\angle PQR$, $m\angle PQR = (x^2)°$, and $m\angle PQS = (2x + 6)°$. Find all the possible measures for $\angle PQR$. **36° or 4°**

48. For more precise measurements, a degree can be divided into 60 minutes, and each minute can be divided into 60 seconds. An angle measure of 42 degrees, 30 minutes, and 10 seconds is written as 42°30′10″. Subtract this angle measure from the measure 81°24′15″. **38°54′5″**

49. If 1 degree equals 60 minutes and 1 minute equals 60 seconds, how many seconds are in 2.25 degrees? **8100**

50. $\angle ABC \cong \angle DBC$. $m\angle ABC = \left(\frac{3x}{2} + 4\right)°$ and $m\angle DBC = \left(2x - 27\frac{1}{4}\right)°$. Is $\angle ABD$ a straight angle? Explain. **No; $x = 62.5$, and substituting this value into the expressions for the $\angle$ measures gives a sum of 195.5.**

SPIRAL REVIEW

51. What number is 64% of 35? **22.4**

52. What percent of 280 is 33.6? *(Previous course)* **12%**

Sketch a figure that shows each of the following. *(Lesson 1-1)*

53. a line that contains $\overline{AB}$ and $\overrightarrow{CB}$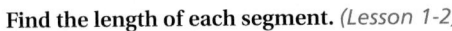

54. two different lines that intersect $\overline{MN}$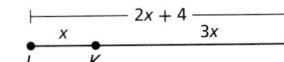

55. a plane and a ray that intersect only at Q

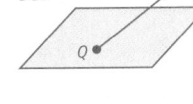

Find the length of each segment. *(Lesson 1-2)*

56. $\overline{JK}$ **2**   **57.** $\overline{KL}$ **6**   **58.** $\overline{JL}$ **8**

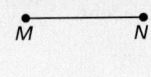

Using Technology — Segment and Angle Bisectors

1. Construct the bisector of $\overline{MN}$.

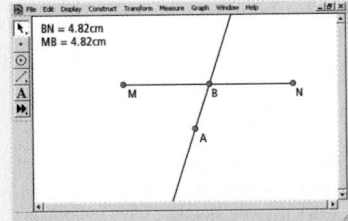

a. Draw $\overline{MN}$ and construct the midpoint B.

b. Construct a point A not on the segment.

c. Construct bisector $\overleftrightarrow{AB}$ and measure $\overline{MB}$ and $\overline{NB}$.

d. Drag M and N and observe MB and NB.

2. Construct the bisector of $\angle BAC$.

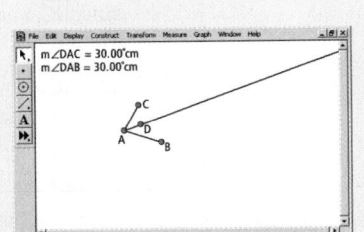

a. Draw $\angle BAC$.

b. Construct the angle bisector $\overrightarrow{AD}$ and measure $\angle DAC$ and $\angle DAB$.

c. Drag the angle and observe $m\angle DAB$ and $m\angle DAC$.

1-3 Measuring and Constructing Angles **27**

1-3 PROBLEM SOLVING

Projection drawings are often used to represent three-dimensional molecules. The projection drawing of a methane molecule is shown below, along with the angles that are formed in the drawing.

Methane Molecule

Projection Drawing	Angles Formed

1. Name five different angles that are formed in the drawing.
Possible answer: $\angle LKG, \angle GKH, \angle HKJ, \angle JKL, \angle LKH$

2. If $m\angle LKH = m\angle JKL + 20°$ and $m\angle HKG = 37°$, what is $m\angle GKL$? **103°**

3. Find $m\angle JKH$. **100°**

The diagram shows the proper way to sit at a computer to avoid straining your back or eyes. Use the figure for Exercises 4 and 5.

4. The *total viewing angle* is $\angle DAB$. If $m\angle DAC = \frac{1}{3}(m\angle ACB)$, what is the measure of the total viewing angle? **65°**

5. The *optimum viewing angle* is 38° below the horizontal. If $\overrightarrow{AV}$ is drawn to form this angle with $\overrightarrow{AB}$, what is the measure of $\angle DAV$? **27°**

Choose the best answer.

6. $\overrightarrow{QR}$ is in the interior of obtuse $\angle PQS$, and $\angle PQR$ is a right angle. Classify $\angle SQR$.
(A) acute   B right   C obtuse   D straight

7. $\overrightarrow{VX}$ bisect $\angle WVY$, $m\angle WVX = (6x)°$, and $m\angle WVY = (16x − 42)°$. What is the value of x?
F $\frac{21}{11}$ G $\frac{42}{13}$ H 4.2   (J) 10.5

1-3 CHALLENGE

A **locus** is the set of all points that satisfy one or more given conditions. The plural of locus is *loci*.

The vertical line that bisects $\overline{XY}$ at the right is an example of a locus. This line can be described as the locus of all points in the plane that are equally distant, or **equidistant**, from the endpoints of the segment.

1. Draw a figure to illustrate a locus of all points in the interior of $\angle EFG$ that are equidistant from the sides of the angle.

2. Name the figure that you drew in Exercise 1.   **angle bisector**

A **central angle** of a circle is an angle that intersects a circle in two points and has its vertex at the center of the circle.

The circle has two cuts through the center, making four congruent angles at the center (central angles). Use the table for Exercises 3–5.

Number of Cuts	Number of Small Congruent Central Angles	Measure of Each Small Central Angle
2	4	90°
3	6	60°
4	8	45°
10	?	?

3. How is the number of congruent small central angles related to the number of cuts?
It is double the number of cuts.

4. For n cuts through the center, the congruent small central angles of a circle have a sum of 360°. Use the pattern in the table to write an expression to find the measure of each small central angle if there are n cuts through the center.
$360 \div (2n)$ or $180 \div n$

5. How many central angles would there be in a circle with 10 cuts? What would be the measure of each central angle in a circle that has 10 cuts?
20; 18°

Teaching Tip **Visual** For **Exercise 46**, use a representation of a clock, such as a paper plate with arrows attached with a brad to represent the hands. Given a measurement, students can show the possible time on the clock. Given a time, students can form and then classify the angle.

Journal

Have students name and give the definition of at least 5 other words that use *bi* to mean "two."

ALTERNATIVE ASSESSMENT

Have students create a diagram containing each type of angle introduced in this lesson. They should identify the angles in their diagram, measure each with their protractor, choose one to copy, and bisect another.

Power Presentations with PowerPoint®

1-3 Lesson Quiz

Classify each angle as acute, right, or obtuse.

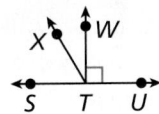

1. $\angle XTS$ acute

2. $\angle WTU$ right

3. K is in the interior of $\angle LMN$, $m\angle LMK = 52°$, and $m\angle KMN = 12°$. Find $m\angle LMN$.   **64°**

4. $\overrightarrow{BD}$ bisects $\angle ABC$, $m\angle ABD = \left(\frac{1}{2}y + 10\right)°$, and $m\angle DBC = (y + 4)°$. Find $m\angle ABC$.   **32°**

5. Use a protractor to draw an angle with a measure of 165°.
Check students' work.

6. $m\angle WYZ = (2x − 5)°$ and $m\angle XYW = (3x + 10)°$. Find the value of x.   **35**

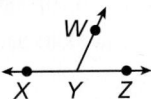

Also available on transparency

Lesson 1-3 **27**

Objectives: Identify adjacent, vertical, complementary, and supplementary angles.

Find measures of pairs of angles.

 Online Edition
Tutorial Videos

 Countdown to TAKS Week 1

Power Presentations
with PowerPoint®

Warm Up

Simplify each expression.

1. $90 - (x + 20)$ $70 - x$

2. $180 - (3x - 10)$ $190 - 3x$

Write an algebraic expression for each of the following.

3. 4 more than twice a number
$2n + 4$

4. 6 less than half a number
$\frac{1}{2}n - 6$

Also available on transparency

Math Humor

Teacher: Today we are going to learn about complementary angles.

Student: Does that mean the angles are nice to each other?

⭐ Geometry TEKS

G.1 Geometric structure*
(A) develop an awareness of the structure of a mathematical system, connecting definitions, postulates, ...

G.2 Geometric structure*
(B) make conjectures about angles, lines, ... and determine the validity of the conjectures, choosing from a variety of approaches such as coordinate, transformational, ...

* Knowledge and Skills See p. 4.

1-4 Pairs of Angles

⭐ **TEKS G.1.A Geometric structure:** develop an awareness of the structure of a mathematical system, connecting definitions, postulates .... Also G.2.B

Objectives
Identify adjacent, vertical, complementary, and supplementary angles.

Find measures of pairs of angles.

Vocabulary
adjacent angles
linear pair
complementary angles
supplementary angles
vertical angles

Who uses this?
Scientists use properties of angle pairs to design fiber-optic cables. (See Example 4.)

A fiber-optic cable is a strand of glass as thin as a human hair. Data can be transmitted over long distances by bouncing light off the inner walls of the cable.

Many pairs of angles have special relationships. Some relationships are because of the measurements of the angles in the pair. Other relationships are because of the positions of the angles in the pair.

Know it!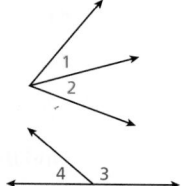
·Note

> ### Pairs of Angles
>
> **Adjacent angles** are two angles in the same plane with a common vertex and a common side, but no common interior points. ∠1 and ∠2 are adjacent angles.
>
> A **linear pair** of angles is a pair of adjacent angles whose noncommon sides are opposite rays. ∠3 and ∠4 form a linear pair.

EXAMPLE 1 **Identifying Angle Pairs**

Tell whether the angles are only adjacent, adjacent and form a linear pair, or not adjacent.

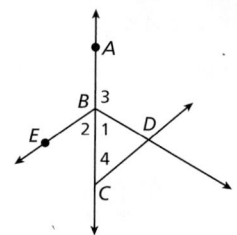

A ∠1 and ∠2

∠1 and ∠2 have a common vertex, B, a common side, $\overrightarrow{BC}$, and no common interior points. Therefore ∠1 and ∠2 are only adjacent angles.

B ∠2 and ∠4

∠2 and ∠4 share $\overline{BC}$ but do not have a common vertex, so ∠2 and ∠4 are not adjacent angles.

C ∠1 and ∠3

∠1 and ∠3 are adjacent angles. Their noncommon sides, $\overrightarrow{BC}$ and $\overrightarrow{BA}$, are opposite rays, so ∠1 and ∠3 also form a linear pair.

CHECK IT OUT! Tell whether the angles are only adjacent, adjacent and form a linear pair, or not adjacent.

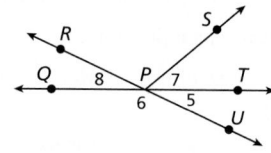

1a. ∠5 and ∠6   adj.; lin. pair
1b. ∠7 and ∠SPU   not adj.
1c. ∠7 and ∠8   not adj.

---

1 Introduce

EXPLORATION

1-4 Pairs of Angles

Use the following figures to help you compare and contrast examples and nonexamples of *adjacent angles*.

Adjacent Angles	Not Adjacent Angles
∠1 and ∠2 ∠2 and ∠3 ∠1 and ∠2	∠1 and ∠3 ∠1 and ∠2
∠1 and ∠2 ∠3 and ∠4	∠1 and ∠ABC ∠2 and ∠ABC

1. List all of the pairs of adjacent angles in the figure.
2. Complete this definition: Adjacent angles are two angles in the same plane with a common __?__ and a common __?__ , but with no common interior points.

Motivate

Angles are used in physics, engineering, art and design. Show students a picture of a quilt pattern with angle pairs in it. Discuss the relationships between different pairs of angles. Ask students what they think the angle measures must be so the pieces will fit together.

Explorations and answers are provided in the *Explorations* binder.

Complementary and Supplementary Angles

Know it! Note

Complementary angles are two angles whose measures have a sum of 90°. ∠A and ∠B are complementary.

Supplementary angles are two angles whose measures have a sum of 180°. ∠A and ∠C are supplementary.

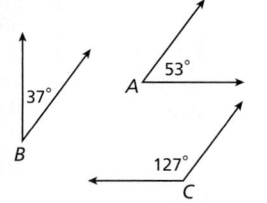

You can find the complement of an angle that measures $x°$ by subtracting its measure from 90°, or $(90 - x)°$. You can find the supplement of an angle that measures $x°$ by subtracting its measure from 180°, or $(180 - x)°$.

EXAMPLE 2 **Finding the Measures of Complements and Supplements**

Find the measure of each of the following.

A complement of ∠M
$(90 - x)°$
$90° - 26.8° = 63.2°$

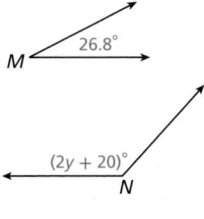

B supplement of ∠N
$(180 - x)°$
$180° - (2y + 20)° = 180° - 2y - 20$
$= (160 - 2y)°$

CHECK IT OUT! Find the measure of each of the following.

2a. complement of ∠E $(102 - 7x)°$

2b. supplement of ∠F $63\frac{1}{2}°$

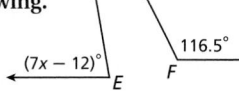

EXAMPLE 3 **Using Complements and Supplements to Solve Problems**

x^2y Algebra

An angle measures 3 degrees less than twice the measure of its complement. Find the measure of its complement.

Step 1 Let m∠A = $x°$. Then ∠B, its complement, measures $(90 - x)°$.

Step 2 Write and solve an equation.

m∠A = 2m∠B − 3

$x = 2(90 - x) - 3$	*Substitute x for m∠A and 90 − x for m∠B.*
$x = 180 - 2x - 3$	*Distrib. Prop.*
$x = 177 - 2x$	*Combine like terms.*
$\underline{+2x \qquad +2x}$	*Add 2x to both sides.*
$3x = 177$	*Simplify.*
$\dfrac{3x}{3} = \dfrac{177}{3}$	*Divide both sides by 3.*
$x = 59$	*Simplify.*

The measure of the complement, ∠B, is $(90 - 59)° = 31°$.

CHECK IT OUT! **3.** An angle's measure is 12° more than $\frac{1}{2}$ the measure of its supplement. Find the measure of the angle. **68°**

1-4 Pairs of Angles **29**

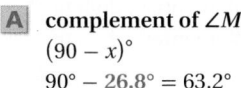

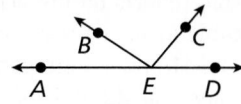

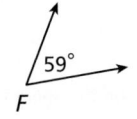

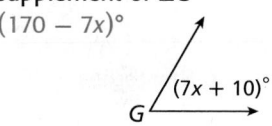

COMMON ERROR ALERT

In **Example 2,** students may not apply the Distributive Property correctly. Stress that in the expression $180 - (2y + 20)$, both $2y$ and 20 must be multiplied by −1 to get $160 - 2y$.

Power Presentations with PowerPoint®

Additional Examples

Example 1

Tell whether the angles are only adjacent, adjacent and form a linear pair, or not adjacent.

A. ∠AEB and ∠BED   lin. pair and adjacent

B. ∠AEB and ∠BEC   only adj.

C. ∠DEC and ∠AEB   not adj.

Example 2

Find the measure of each of the following.

A. complement of ∠F   31°

B. supplement of ∠G
$(170 - 7x)°$

Example 3

An angle is 10° more than 3 times the measure of its complement. Find the measure of the complement.   20°

Also available on transparency

2 Teach

Guided Instruction

Discuss vertical, complementary, supplementary, and adjacent angles and linear pairs. Have students use mental math to find complements and supplements of angles before using variables or expressions.

Teaching Tip **Cognitive Strategies** One way to help students remember that complementary angles add to 90° and that supplementary angles add to 180° is that 90 comes before 180 and C comes before S in the alphabet.

 Reaching All Learners

Through Cooperative Learning

Each student should create a simple puzzle by dividing a square into six regions using segments. Students should measure all of the angles formed and write several hints for the puzzle solver. For example, a hint might be that one corner of the square is made up of a 15° angle and a 75° angle. Students should then exchange puzzles with a partner and try to reassemble the original square.

INTERVENTION

Questioning Strategies

EXAMPLE 1

• What type of angle is formed by a pair of adjacent angles that form a linear pair?

EXAMPLES 2–3

• Do two angles have to be adjacent to be complementary or supplementary?

Visual The following is another way for students to remember which sum is 90 and which is 180: Draw a line along the *C* in complementary to make a 9 for 90, and add a line through the *S* in supplementary to make an 8 for 180.

9 0° MPLEMENTARY

1 8 0° UPPLEMENTARY

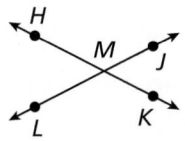

Power Presentations
with PowerPoint®

Additional Examples

Example 4

Light passing through a fiber-optic cable reflects off the walls of the cable in such a way that ∠1 ≅ ∠2, ∠1 and ∠3 are complementary, and ∠2 and ∠4 are complementary. If m∠1 = 47°, find m∠2, m∠3, and m∠4.   47°; 43°; 43°

Example 5

Name the pairs of vertical angles.
∠HML and ∠JMK; ∠HMJ and ∠LMK

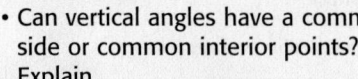

Also available on transparency

INTERVENTION ◄─►
Questioning Strategies

EXAMPLE 4

• How are ∠3 and ∠4 related? Explain.

EXAMPLE 5

• Can vertical angles have a common side or common interior points? Explain.

Inclusion Remind students that the shape of the letter *x* suggests the idea of vertical angles.

EXAMPLE 4

PROBLEM SOLVING

Problem-Solving Application

Light passing through a fiber optic cable reflects off the walls in such a way that ∠1 ≅ ∠2. ∠1 and ∠3 are complementary, and ∠2 and ∠4 are complementary.
If m∠1 = 38°, find m∠2, m∠3, and m∠4.

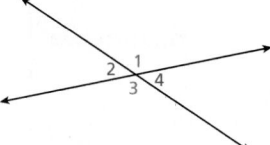

1 **Understand the Problem**

The **answers** are the measures of ∠2, ∠3, and ∠4.
List the important information:
• ∠1 ≅ ∠2
• ∠1 and ∠3 are complementary, and ∠2 and ∠4 are complementary.
• m∠1 = 38°

2 **Make a Plan**

If ∠1 ≅ ∠2, then m∠1 = m∠2.
If ∠3 and ∠1 are complementary, then m∠3 = (90 − 38)°.
If ∠4 and ∠2 are complementary, then m∠4 = (90 − 38)°.

3  **Solve**

By the Transitive Property of Equality, if m∠1 = 38° and m∠1 = m∠2, then m∠2 = 38°. Since ∠3 and ∠1 are complementary, m∠3 = 52°. Similarly, since ∠2 and ∠4 are complementary, m∠4 = 52°.

4  **Look Back**

The answer makes sense because 38° + 52° = 90°, so ∠1 and ∠3 are complementary, and ∠2 and ∠4 are complementary. Thus m∠2 = 38°, m∠3 = 52°, and m∠4 = 52°.

✓ CHECK IT OUT! **4. What if...?** Suppose m∠3 = 27.6°. Find m∠1, m∠2, and m∠4.
m∠1 = m∠2 = 62.4°; m∠4° = 27.6°

Another angle pair relationship exists between two angles whose sides form two pairs of opposite rays. **Vertical angles** are two nonadjacent angles formed by two intersecting lines. ∠1 and ∠3 are vertical angles, as are ∠2 and ∠4.

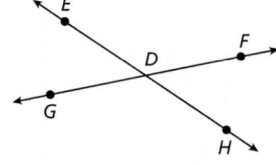

EXAMPLE 5

Identifying Vertical Angles

Name one pair of vertical angles.
Do they appear to have the same measure?
Check by measuring with a protractor.

∠EDF and ∠GDH are vertical angles and appear to have the same measure.

Check m∠EDF ≈ m∠GDH ≈ **135°**.

Possible answer:
∠EDG and ∠FDH;
m∠EDG ≈ m∠FDH
≈ 45°

✓ CHECK IT OUT! **5.** Name another pair of vertical angles. Do they appear to have the same measure? Check by measuring with a protractor.

30 *Chapter 1 Foundations for Geometry*

---

3 **Close**

Summarize

Review the different angle pairs and illustrations in the lesson. Remind students that a linear pair is a pair of adjacent and supplementary angles, but not all complementary and supplementary angles are adjacent. Then have students identify what kind of angle is a complement of an acute angle, a supplement of an obtuse angle, and the supplement of a right angle.
acute, acute, right

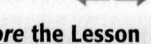

THINK AND DISCUSS

1. Explain why any two right angles are supplementary.

2. Is it possible for a pair of vertical angles to also be adjacent? Explain.

3. GET ORGANIZED Copy and complete the graphic organizer below. In each box, draw a diagram and write a definition of the given angle pair.

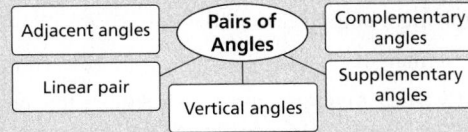

1-4 Exercises

go.hrw.com/Geo/TX
Homework Help Online
KEYWORD: MG7 1-4
Parent Resources Online
KEYWORD: MG7 Parent

1-4 Exercises

GUIDED PRACTICE

Vocabulary Apply the vocabulary from this lesson to answer each question.

$(90 - x)°;$ **1.** An angle measures $x°$. What is the measure of its *complement*? What is the measure
$(180 - x)°$ of its *supplement*?

2. ∠ABC and ∠CBD are *adjacent angles*. Which side do the angles have in common? $\overrightarrow{BC}$

SEE EXAMPLE **1**
p. 28

Tell whether the angles are only adjacent, adjacent and form a linear pair, or not adjacent.

3. ∠1 and ∠2 adj.; **4.** ∠1 and ∠3 not adj.

5. ∠2 and ∠4 lin. pair **6.** ∠2 and ∠3 only adj.
not adj.

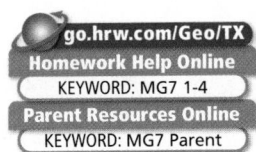

SEE EXAMPLE **2**
p. 29

Find the measure of each of the following.

7. supplement of ∠A 98.8° **8.** complement of ∠A 8.8°

9. supplement of ∠B **10.** complement of ∠B
$(185 - 6x)°$ $(95 - 6x)°$

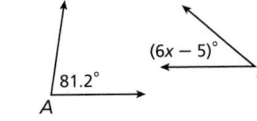

SEE EXAMPLE **3**
p. 29

11. Multi-Step An angle's measure is 6 degrees more than 3 times the measure of its complement. Find the measure of the angle. **69°**

SEE EXAMPLE **4**
p. 30

12. Landscaping A sprinkler swings back and forth between A and B in such a way that ∠1 ≅ ∠2. ∠1 and ∠3 are complementary, and ∠2 and ∠4 are complementary. If m∠1 = 18.5°, find m∠2, m∠3, and m∠4. **m∠2 = 18.5°; m∠3 = m∠4 = 71.5°**

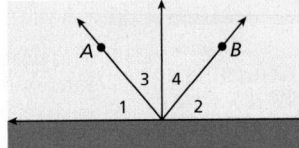

SEE EXAMPLE **5**
p. 30

13. Name each pair of vertical angles.
∠ABE, ∠CBD; ∠ABC, ∠EBD

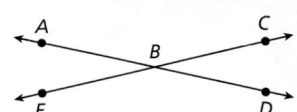

Assignment Guide

Assign *Guided Practice* exercises as necessary.

If you finished Examples **1–3**
Basic 14–22, 25, 27–30, 34
Average 14–22, 25, 27–35
Advanced 14–22, 25, 27–35, 37

If you finished Examples **1–5**
Basic 14–22, 24–30, 33, 34, 37–43, 47–55
Average 14–44, 47–55
Advanced 14–55

Homework Quick Check
Quickly check key concepts.
Exercises: 14, 18, 22, 24, 28, 30, 34

TAKS Practice

Grades 9–11	Exercises
Obj. 2	51–53
Obj. 4	26–31, 40–42, 44–50
Obj. 9	25
Obj. 10	33–38

Answers

33a.

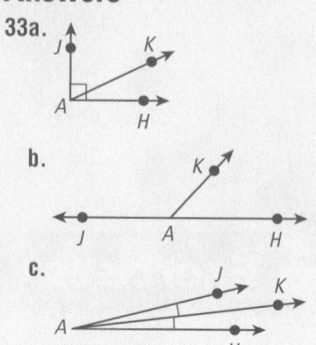

b.

c.

PRACTICE AND PROBLEM SOLVING

Tell whether the angles are only adjacent, adjacent and form a linear pair, or not adjacent.

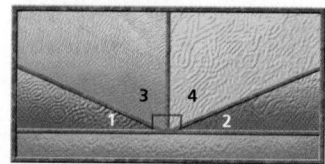

14. ∠1 and ∠4   adj.;
15. ∠2 and ∠3   adj.; lin. pair
   lin. pair
16. ∠3 and ∠4   **17.** ∠3 and ∠1   not adj.
   only adj.

Given m∠A = 56.4° and m∠B = $(2x - 4)°$, find the measure of each of the following.

18. supplement of ∠A **123.6°**   **19.** complement of ∠A **33.6°**

20. supplement of ∠B $(184 - 2x)°$ **21.** complement of ∠B $(94 - 2x)°$

22. Multi-Step An angle's measure is 3 times the measure of its complement. Find the measure of the angle and the measure of its complement. **67.5°; 22.5°**

23. Art In the stained glass pattern, ∠1 ≅ ∠2. ∠1 and ∠3 are complementary, and ∠2 and ∠4 are complementary. If m∠1 = 22.3°, find m∠2, m∠3, and m∠4.
m∠2 = 22.3°; m∠3 = m∠4 = 67.7°

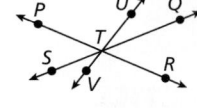

24. Name the pairs of vertical angles.
∠PTU, ∠VTR; ∠UTQ, ∠STV;
∠QTR, ∠PTS; ∠PTQ, ∠STR;
∠UTR, ∠PTV; ∠QTV, ∠UTS

25. Probability The angle measures 30°, 60°, 120°, and 150° are written on slips of paper. You choose two slips of paper at random. What is the probability that the angle measures are supplementary? $\frac{1}{3}$

Multi-Step ∠ABD and ∠BDE are supplementary. Find the measures of both angles.

26. m∠ABD = 5x°, m∠BDE = $(17x - 18)°$ **45°; 135°**

27. m∠ABD = $(3x + 12)°$, m∠BDE = $(7x - 32)°$ **72°; 108°**

28. m∠ABD = $(12x - 12)°$, m∠BDE = $(3x + 48)°$ **103.2°; 76.8°**

Multi-Step ∠ABD and ∠BDC are complementary. Find the measures of both angles.

29. m∠ABD = $(5y + 1)°$, m∠BDC = $(3y - 7)°$ **61°; 29°**

30. m∠ABD = $(4y + 5)°$, m∠BDC = $(4y + 8)°$ **43.5°; 46.5°**

31. m∠ABD = $(y - 30)°$, m∠BDC = $2y°$ **10°; 80°**

32. Critical Thinking Explain why an angle that is supplementary to an acute angle must be an obtuse angle.

32. The measure of an acute ∠ is less than 90°. Therefore the measure of its supp. must be between 90° and 180°, which means the supp. is an obtuse ∠.

MULTI-STEP TAKS PREP

33. This problem will prepare you for the Multi-Step TAKS Prep on page 34. H is in the interior of ∠JAK. m∠JAH = $(3x - 8)°$, and m∠KAH = $(x + 2)°$. Draw a picture of each relationship. Then find the measure of each angle.

   a. ∠JAH and ∠KAH are complementary angles. **m∠JAH = 64°; m∠KAH = 26°**
   b. ∠JAH and ∠KAH form a linear pair. **m∠JAH = 131.5°; m∠KAH = 48.5°**
   c. ∠JAH and ∠KAH are congruent angles. **m∠JAH = m∠KAH = 7°**

Determine whether each statement is true or false. If false, explain why.

34. F; the supp. must be greater than the comp.

34. If an angle is acute, then its complement must be greater than its supplement.

35. A pair of vertical angles may also form a linear pair. F; vert. ∠ cannot be adj. ∠, so they cannot form a lin. pair.

36. If two angles are supplementary and congruent, the measure of each angle is 90°. T

37. If a ray divides an angle into two complementary angles, then the original angle is a right angle. T

38. Write About It Describe a situation in which two angles are both congruent and complementary. Explain. The 2 ∠ must both measure 45°. 45° + 45° = 90°, so the ∠ are comp. and ≅.

39. What is the value of x in the diagram?
- Ⓐ 15
- Ⓒ 45
- Ⓑ 30
- Ⓓ 90

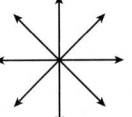

40. The ratio of the measures of two complementary angles is 1:2. What is the measure of the larger angle? (*Hint:* Let x and 2x represent the angle measures.)
- Ⓕ 30°
- Ⓖ 45°
- Ⓗ 60°
- Ⓙ 120°

41. m∠A = 3y, and m∠B = 2m∠A. Which value of y makes ∠A supplementary to ∠B?
- Ⓐ 10
- Ⓑ 18
- Ⓒ 20
- Ⓓ 36

42. The measures of two supplementary angles are in the ratio 7:5. Which value is the measure of the smaller angle? (*Hint:* Let 7x and 5x represent the angle measures.)
- Ⓕ 37.5
- Ⓖ 52.5
- Ⓗ 75
- Ⓙ 105

CHALLENGE AND EXTEND

43. How many pairs of vertical angles are in the diagram? 12

44. The supplement of an angle is 4 more than twice its complement. Find the measure of the angle. 4°

45. An angle's measure is twice the measure of its complement. The larger angle is how many degrees greater than the smaller angle? 30°

46. The supplement of an angle is 36° less than twice the supplement of the complement of the angle. Find the measure of the supplement. 168°

SPIRAL REVIEW

Solve each equation. Check your answer. (*Previous course*)

47. $4x + 10 = 42$ **8**

48. $5m - 9 = m + 4$ **3.25**

49. $2(y + 3) = 12$ **3**

50. $-(d + 4) = 18$ **−22**

Y is between *X* and *Z*, *XY* = 3x + 1, *YZ* = 2x − 2, and *XZ* = 84. Find each of the following. (*Lesson 1-2*)

51. *x* **17**

52. *XY* **52**

53. *YZ* **32**

$\overrightarrow{XY}$ bisects ∠WYZ. Given m∠WYX = 26°, find each of the following. (*Lesson 1-3*)

54. m∠XYZ **26°**

55. m∠WYZ **52°**

1-4 PROBLEM SOLVING

Use the drawing of part of the Eiffel Tower for Exercises 1–5.

1. Name a pair of angles that appear to be complementary.
Possible answer: ∠ALB and ∠BLC

2. Name a pair of supplementary angles.
Possible answer: ∠AML and ∠YML

3. If m∠CSW = 45°, what is m∠JST? How do you know?
45°; They are vertical angles.

4. If m∠FKB = 135°, what is m∠BKL? How do you know?
45°; The angles are supplementary.

5. Name three angles whose measures sum to 180°.
Possible answer: ∠ABM, ∠MBK, and ∠KBC

Choose the best answer.

6. A landscaper uses paving stones for a walkway. Which are possible angle measures for *a°* and *b°* so that the stones do not have space between them?
- A 50°, 100°
- Ⓒ 75°, 105°
- B 45°, 45°
- D 90°, 80°

7. The angle formed by a tree branch and the part of the trunk above it is 68°. What is the measure of the angle that is formed by the branch and the part of the trunk below it?
- F 22°
- H 158°
- Ⓖ 112°
- J 180°

8. ∠R and ∠S are complementary. If m∠R = (7 + 3x)° and m∠S = (2x + 13)°, which is a true statement?
- Ⓐ ∠R is acute.
- C ∠R and ∠S are right angles.
- B ∠R is obtuse.
- D m∠S > m∠R

1-4 CHALLENGE

For greater accuracy in angle measurement, each degree can be divided into sixty equal parts, called **minutes** (1° = 60′). Each minute can be further divided into sixty equal parts, called **seconds** (1′ = 60″).

Given a decimal angle measure, you can convert it to degrees and minutes.	Given an angle measure in degrees and minutes, you can convert it to a decimal measure.
67.2° = 67° + 0.2°	119°51′ = 119° + 51′
= 67° + (0.2 × 60)′	= 119° + (51/60)′
= 67° + 12′, or 67°12′	= 119° + 0.85°, or 119.85°

Find the measure of the complement of each angle using degrees, minutes, and seconds.

1. 37.76°
52°14′24″

2. 84°48′
5°12′

Find the measure of the supplement of each angle using degrees, minutes, and seconds.

3. 152.375°
27°37′30″

4. 115°12′
64°59′48″

Use the diagram for Exercises 5–8.

5. Name a pair of supplementary angles.
Possible answer: ∠KLM and ∠MLN

6. Name a pair of vertical angles whose measures have a sum that is less than 180°.
Possible answer: ∠KLH and ∠MLN

7. If m∠HJK = (3x + 2)°, what is the measure of ∠KJN?
180 − (3x + 2)° or (178 − 3x)°

8. Suppose $\overrightarrow{HQ}$ is drawn on the figure. Name a pair of vertical angles that is formed.
Possible answer: ∠HCK and ∠RCQ

TEST PREP DOCTOR If students chose **F** for **Exercise 40**, they did not substitute the value for x in the expression 2x and find the larger angle. If they chose **D** for **Exercise 41**, they wrote the equation 3y + 2y = 180 instead of multiplying 3y by 2.

Journal
Have students draw and then define vertical angles in their own words. Ask them to give examples of vertical angles used in real-world structures.

ALTERNATIVE ASSESSMENT
Have students name and draw the various pairs of angles introduced in this lesson. Ask them to write and solve a word problem using complementary or supplementary angles on index cards, and then rotate for other students to solve.

Power Presentations with PowerPoint®

1-4 Lesson Quiz

m∠A = 64.1°, and m∠B = (4x − 30)°. **Find the measure of each of the following.**

1. supplement of ∠A   115.9°

2. complement of ∠B (120 − 4x)°

3. Determine whether this statement is true or false. If false, explain why. If two angles are complementary and congruent, then the measure of each is 90°.   False; each is 45°.

m∠XYZ = 2x° and m∠PQR = (8x − 20)°.

4. If ∠XYZ and ∠PQR are supplementary, find the measure of each angle.   40°; 140°

5. If ∠XYZ and ∠PQR are complementary, find the measure of each angle.   22°; 68°

Also available on transparency

MULTI-STEP TAKS PREP

MULTI-STEP
TAKS PREP

Organizer

Objective: Assess students' ability to apply concepts and skills in Lessons 1-1 through 1-4 in a real-world format.

 Online Edition

Resources

 Geometry Assessments

www.mathtekstoolkit.org

Problem	Text Reference
1	Lesson 1-1
2	Lesson 1-2
3	Lesson 1-3
4	Lesson 1-4

Euclidean and Construction Tools

Can You Dig It? A group of college and high school students participated in an archaeological dig. The team discovered four fossils. To organize their search, Sierra used a protractor and ruler to make a diagram of where different members of the group found fossils. She drew the locations based on the location of the campsite. The campsite is located at X on $\overleftrightarrow{XB}$. The four fossils were found at R, T, W, and M.

1. collinear **1.** Are the locations of the campsite at X and the fossils at R and T collinear or noncollinear?

2. mdpt.; 28 ft **2.** How is X related to $\overline{RT}$? If $RX = 10x - 6$ and $XT = 3x + 8$, what is the distance between the locations of the fossils at R and T?

3. m∠$RXM = 23°$; acute;
m∠$RXW = 67°$; acute;
m∠$WXB = 23°$; acute;
m∠$MXW = 44°$; acute;
m∠$RXT = 180°$; straight;
m∠$MXT = 157°$; obtuse;
m∠$WXT = 113°$; obtuse

3. ∠RXB and ∠BXT are right angles. Find the measure of each angle formed by the locations of the fossils and the campsite. Then classify each angle by its measure.

4. Identify the special angle pairs shown in the diagram of the archaeological dig.

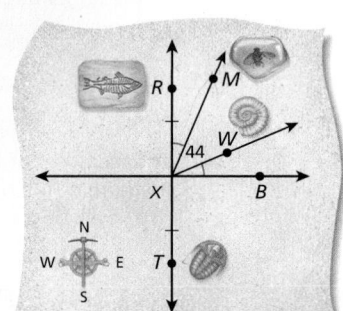

4. adj.; adj. and a lin. pair; supp.; comp.; vert.

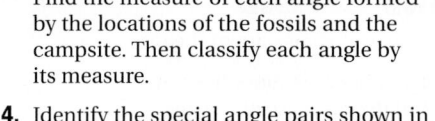 TAKS Practice

Grades 9–11	Problems
Obj. 2	1–4
Obj. 4	2, 3
Obj. 6	3, 4
Obj. 7	1, 2

INTERVENTION

Scaffolding Questions

1. What term describes the placement of and relationship between points? Possible answer: *X, R,* and *T* are collinear.

2. How would you compare the distances between *X* and *R* and between *X* and *T*? The distances are the same.

3. You can assume the measure of which angle? What is the term used to classify the angle? ∠*RXT* = 180°; it is a straight ∠.

4. How are the angle pairs ∠*RXM* and ∠*MXB*, and ∠*RXM* and ∠*MXT* alike?

How are they different? Both ∠ pairs are adj. angles. ∠*RXM* and ∠*MXB* are comp. ∠*RXM* and ∠*MXT* are supp. and a lin. pair.

Extension

What occupations can you name that use angles and directions in a similar manner? Possible answer: Draftspersons use compasses for greater accuracy in their drawings.

READY TO GO ON?

Quiz for Lessons 1-1 Through 1-4

1-1 Understanding Points, Lines, and Planes

Draw and label each of the following.

1. a segment with endpoints X and Y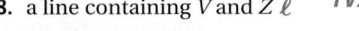
2. a ray with endpoint M that passes through P
3. three coplanar lines intersecting at a point
4. two points and a line that lie in a plane

3.
4.

Use the figure to name each of the following.

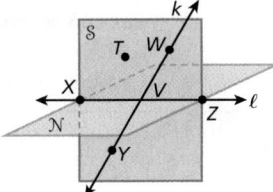

5. three coplanar points **5. Possible**
6. two lines $\overleftrightarrow{XZ}$ and $\overleftrightarrow{WY}$ **answer: T, V, W**
7. a plane containing T, V, and X **plane**
8. a line containing V and Z **ℓ** **TVX**

1-2 Measuring and Constructing Segments

Find the length of each segment.

9. $\overline{SV}$ **6.5** 10. $\overline{TR}$ **6** 11. $\overline{ST}$ **3.5**

12. The diagram represents a straight highway with three towns, Henri, Joaquin, and Kenard. Find the distance from Henri H to Joaquin J. **30**

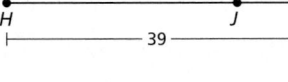

13. Sketch, draw, and construct a segment congruent to $\overline{CD}$. **Check students' work.**

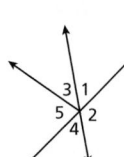

14. Q is the midpoint of $\overline{PR}$, $PQ = 2z$, and $PR = 8z - 12$. Find z, PQ, and PR. **3; 6; 12**

1-3 Measuring and Constructing Angles

15. Name all the angles in the diagram.
$\angle LMN$, $\angle NML$, or $\angle 1$; $\angle NMP$, $\angle PMN$, or $\angle 2$; $\angle LMP$, $\angle PML$

Classify each angle by its measure.

16. $m\angle PVQ = 21°$ **acute** 17. $m\angle RVT = 96°$ **obtuse** 18. $m\angle PVS = 143°$ **obtuse**
19. $\overrightarrow{RS}$ bisects $\angle QRT$, $m\angle QRS = (3x + 8)°$, and $m\angle SRT = (9x - 4)°$. Find $m\angle SRT$. **14°**
20. Use a protractor and straightedge to draw a 130° angle. Then bisect the angle. **Check students' work.**

1-4 Pairs of Angles

Tell whether the angles are only adjacent, adjacent and form a linear pair, or not adjacent.

21. $\angle 1$ and $\angle 2$ 22. $\angle 4$ and $\angle 5$ 23. $\angle 3$ and $\angle 4$
adj.; lin. pair only adj. not adj.

If $m\angle T = (5x - 10)°$, find the measure of each of the following.

24. supplement of $\angle T$ 25. complement of $\angle T$
$(190 - 5x)°$ $(100 - 5x)°$

READY TO GO ON?

Organizer

Objective: Assess students' mastery of concepts and skills in Lessons 1-1 through 1-4.

Resources

Assessment Resources
Section 1A Quiz

Test & Practice Generator
One-Stop Planner®

INTERVENTION ◀▶

Resources

Ready to Go On? Intervention and Enrichment Worksheets

Ready to Go On? CD-ROM

Ready to Go On? Online

my.hrw.com

READY TO GO ON?

Diagnose and Prescribe

NO INTERVENE				YES ENRICH

READY TO GO ON? Intervention, Section 1A			
Ready to Go On? Intervention	*Worksheets*	**CD-ROM**	*Online*
Lesson 1-1	1-1 Intervention	Activity 1-1	Diagnose and Prescribe Online
Lesson 1-2	1-2 Intervention	Activity 1-2	
Lesson 1-3	1-3 Intervention	Activity 1-3	
Lesson 1-4	1-4 Intervention	Activity 1-4	

READY TO GO ON? Enrichment, Section 1A
Worksheets
CD-ROM
Online

Coordinate and Transformation Tools

 One-Minute Section Planner

Lesson	Lab Resources	Materials
Lesson 1-5 Using Formulas in Geometry • Apply formulas for perimeter, area, and circumference. ☑ Exit Level TAKS ☑ ACT ☑ SAT ☑ SAT Subject Tests	***Texas Lab Manual*** 1-5 Geometry Lab (A) 1-5 Geometry Lab (B)	**Optional** quilt patterns
Lesson 1-6 Midpoint and Distance in the Coordinate Plane • Develop and apply the formula for midpoint. • Use the Distance Formula and the Pythagorean Theorem to find the distance between two points. ☑ Exit Level TAKS ☑ ACT ☑ SAT ☐ SAT Subject Tests		**Optional** coordinate grid with points representing a house and a school, graph paper
Lesson 1-7 Transformations in the Coordinate Plane • Identify reflections, rotations, and translations. • Graph transformations in the coordinate plane. ☑ Exit Level TAKS ☑ ACT ☐ SAT ☑ SAT Subject Tests		**Required** graph paper, straightedge **Optional** mirror (MK); examples of tessellations, translations, rotations, and reflections; coordinate grid and cut-out triangle, geometry software
1-7 Technology Lab Explore Transformations • Use geometry software to perform transformations and explore their properties. ☐ Exit Level TAKS ☑ ACT ☐ SAT ☐ SAT Subject Tests		**Required** geometry software

MK = *Manipulatives Kit*

Section Overview

Formulas in Geometry
Lesson 1-5

Why? Finding area and perimeter of figures is an important skill in a variety of occupations.

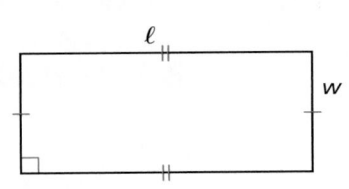

$P = 2\ell + 2w$
$A = \ell w$

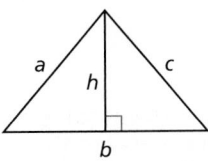

$P = a + b + c$
$A = \frac{1}{2}bh$

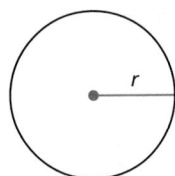

$C = 2\pi r$
$A = \pi r^2$

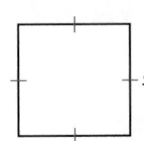

$P = 4s$
$A = s^2$

Midpoint and Distance
Lesson 1-6

Why? Some problems are easier to solve when the figure is drawn on a coordinate plane.

Midpoint Formula
The midpoint of $A(x_1, y_1)$ and $B(x_2, y_2)$ is

$$M\left(\frac{x_1 + x_2}{2}, \frac{y_1 + y_2}{2}\right).$$

Distance Formula
The distance between $A(x_1, y_1)$ and $B(x_2, y_2)$ is

$$AB = \sqrt{(x_2 - x_1) + (y_2 - y_1)}.$$

Given $A(2, 7)$ and $B(-4, 1)$, the midpoint is

$$M\left(\frac{2 + (-4)}{2}, \frac{7 + 1}{2}\right) = \left(\frac{-2}{2}, \frac{8}{2}\right) = (-1, 4).$$

Given $A(2, 7)$ and $B(-4, 1)$, the distance is

$$AB = \sqrt{(-4 - 2)^2 + (1 - 7)^2} = \sqrt{36 + 36} = \sqrt{72} \approx 8.5.$$

Transformations
Lesson 1-7

Why? Patterns are formed by translating, reflecting, and rotating figures.

Reflection

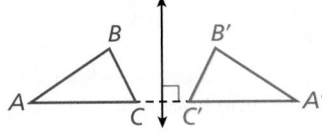

Each point and its image are the same distance from the line of reflection.

Rotation

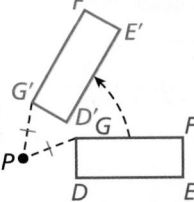

Each point and its image are the same distance from the center of rotation *P*.

Translation

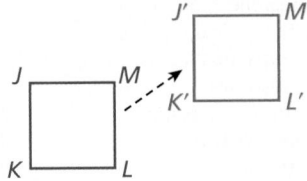

All points of a figure move the same distance in the same direction.

Objectives: Apply formulas for perimeter, area, and circumference.

Geometry Lab
In *Texas Lab Manual*

Online Edition
Tutorial Videos

Countdown to TAKS Week 2

Power Presentations
with PowerPoint®

Warm Up

Evaluate. Round to the nearest hundredth.

1. 12^2 144 **2.** 7.6^2 57.76

3. $\sqrt{64}$ 8 **4.** $\sqrt{54}$ 7.35

5. $3^2(\pi)$ 28.27 **6.** $(3\pi)^2$ 88.83

Also available on transparency

Math Humor

Q: What is the hidden math term?

RO
OT

A: Square root

 Inclusion *Perimeter* contains the word *rim*, which is a single path, so it is one dimension. Area is found by measuring two quantities, so it is two-dimensional.

 Geometry TEKS

G.1 Geometric structure*
(A) develop an awareness of the structure of a mathematical system, connecting definitions, postulates, ...
(B) recognize the historical development of geometric systems and know mathematics is developed for a variety of purposes

G.8 Congruence and the geometry of size*
(A) find areas of regular polygons, circles, ...

* **Knowledge and Skills** See p. 4.

 TEKS G.8.A Congruence and the geometry of size: find areas of regular polygons, circles .... Also G.1.A, G.1.B

Objective
Apply formulas for perimeter, area, and circumference.

Vocabulary
perimeter
area
base
height
diameter
radius
circumference
pi

Why learn this?
Puzzles use geometric-shaped pieces. Formulas help determine the amount of materials needed. (See Exercise 6.)

The **perimeter** *P* of a plane figure is the sum of the side lengths of the figure. The **area** *A* of a plane figure is the number of nonoverlapping square units of a given size that exactly cover the figure.

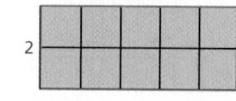

$$\text{area} = 2 \text{ units} \times 5 \text{ units}$$
$$= 10 \text{ square units}$$

Know it!
Note

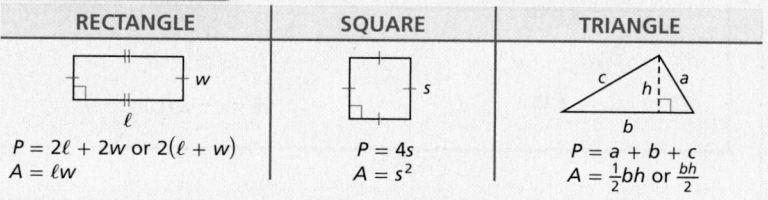

Perimeter and Area		
RECTANGLE	SQUARE	TRIANGLE
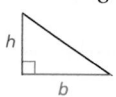	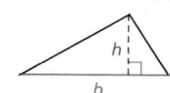	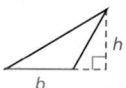
$P = 2\ell + 2w$ or $2(\ell + w)$ $A = \ell w$	$P = 4s$ $A = s^2$	$P = a + b + c$ $A = \frac{1}{2}bh$ or $\frac{bh}{2}$

The **base** *b* can be any side of a triangle. The **height** *h* is a segment from a vertex that forms a right angle with a line containing the base. The height may be a side of the triangle or in the interior or the exterior of the triangle.

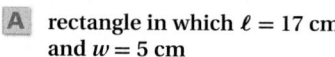

EXAMPLE 1   Finding Perimeter and Area

Find the perimeter and area of each figure.

Remember!
Perimeter is expressed in linear units, such as inches (in.) or meters (m). Area is expressed in square units, such as square centimeters (cm²).

A rectangle in which $\ell = 17$ cm and $w = 5$ cm

$P = 2\ell + 2w$
$= 2(17) + 2(5)$
$= 34 + 10 = 44$ cm

$A = \ell w$
$= (17)(5) = 85$ cm²

B triangle in which $a = 8$, $b = (x + 1)$, $c = 4x$, and $h = 6$

$P = a + b + c$
$= 8 + (x + 1) + 4x$
$= 5x + 9$

$A = \frac{1}{2}bh$
$= \frac{1}{2}(x + 1)(6) = 3x + 3$

 **1.** Find the perimeter and area of a square with $s = 3.5$ in.
$P = 14$ in.; $A = 12.25$ in²

---

1 Introduce

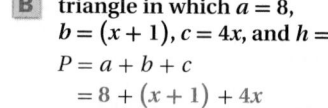

EXPLORATION

1-5 Using Formulas in Geometry

Recall that the area of a rectangle is the product of its length and width. You can use this fact to develop the formula for the area of a triangle.

1. Use a straightedge to draw a triangle. Then cut out the triangle.
2. Trace around the triangle to make a copy of it. Then cut out this second triangle.
3. Arrange the two triangles as shown.
4. Cut off one end of the figure and move it to the other side to make a rectangle.
5. Suppose the original triangle has base *b* and height *h*. What are the length and width of the rectangle in terms of *b* and *h*?

THINK AND DISCUSS
6. Show how you can write the area of the rectangle in terms of *b* and *h*.

Motivate

Discuss buying tile for a room. Ask students how they would determine how much tile they would need to cover a floor. Solicit from them the idea of finding the number of same-sized squares that are needed. Ask them how they could determine the length of baseboard needed to trim the room.

Explorations and answers are provided in the *Explorations* binder.

EXAMPLE  **Crafts Application**

The Texas Treasures quilt block includes 24 purple triangles. The base and height of each triangle are about 3 in. Find the approximate amount of fabric used to make the 24 triangles.

The area of one triangle is

$$A = \frac{1}{2}bh = \frac{1}{2}(3)(3) = 4\frac{1}{2} \text{ in}^2.$$

The total area of the 24 triangles is

$$24\left(4\frac{1}{2}\right) = 108 \text{ in}^2.$$

✓ **CHECK IT OUT!** **2.** Find the amount of fabric used to make the four rectangles. Each rectangle has a length of $6\frac{1}{2}$ in. and a width of $2\frac{1}{2}$ in.
65 in²

In a circle a **diameter** is a segment that passes through the center of the circle and whose endpoints are on the circle. A **radius** of a circle is a segment whose endpoints are the center of the circle and a point on the circle. The **circumference** of a circle is the distance around the circle.

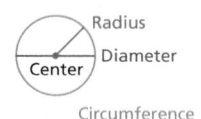

Know it! *Note*

Circumference and Area of a Circle
The circumference C of a circle is given by the formula $C = \pi d$ or $C = 2\pi r$. The area A of a circle is given by the formula $A = \pi r^2$.

The ratio of a circle's circumference to its diameter is the same for all circles. This ratio is represented by the Greek letter π **(pi)**. The value of π is irrational. Pi is often approximated as 3.14 or $\frac{22}{7}$.

EXAMPLE  **Finding the Circumference and Area of a Circle**

Find the circumference and area of the circle.

$$C = 2\pi r \qquad\qquad A = \pi r^2$$
$$= 2\pi(3) = 6\pi \qquad = \pi(3)^2 = 9\pi$$
$$\approx 18.8 \text{ cm} \qquad\quad \approx 28.3 \text{ cm}^2$$

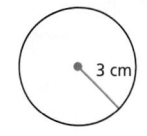

✓ **CHECK IT OUT!** **3.** Find the circumference and area of a circle with radius 14 m.
$C \approx 88.0$ m; $A \approx 615.8$ m²

THINK AND DISCUSS

1. Describe three different figures whose areas are each 16 in².

2. **GET ORGANIZED** Copy and complete the graphic organizer. In each shape, write the formula for its area and perimeter.

 **Know it!** *Note*

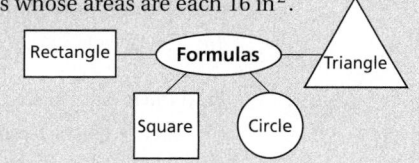

1-5 Using Formulas in Geometry **37**

INTERVENTION ◀▶
Questioning Strategies

EXAMPLES 1–2

• How does knowing the formula for the area of a rectangle help you find the area of a triangle?

EXAMPLE 3

• Compare the results when you multiply 6 by π and multiply 6 by 3.14.

---

2 Teach

Guided Instruction

Review the meanings of *perim*eter, *area*, and *circumference*, and the parts of a circle. Show examples of triangles having interior and exterior heights. Give examples of finding the area and circumference of a circle, leaving answers in terms of π, and rounding. Remind students that the diameter d is twice the radius r or $d = 2r$.

3 Close

Summarize

Review the formulas for finding the area and perimeter (circumference) of a rectangle, triangle, and circle.

Answers to *Think and Discuss*

1. Possible answer: A rect. with length 8 in. and width 2 in.; a square with sides 4 in. long; a △ with base 4 in. and height 8 in.

2. See p. A2.

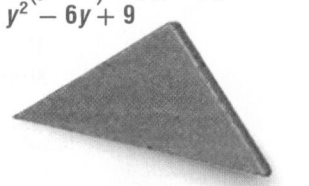
go.hrw.com/Geo/TX
Homework Help Online
KEYWORD: MG7 1-5
Parent Resources Online
KEYWORD: MG7 Parent

Teaching Tip **Math Background**
Exercise 13 involves quilt patterns. Plan ahead and ask students whether their families have quilts they may bring in as examples of different geometric patterns.

GUIDED PRACTICE

Vocabulary Apply the vocabulary from this lesson to answer each question.

1. Explain how the concepts of *perimeter* and *circumference* are related.

1. Both terms refer to the dist. around a figure.

2. For a rectangle, length and width are sometimes used in place of __?__ .
(*base and height* or *radius and diameter*) **base and height**

SEE EXAMPLE **1**
p. 36

Find the perimeter and area of each figure.

3.  4 mm

11 mm

$P = 30$ mm; $A = 44$ mm^2

4. 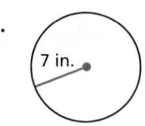 $y - 3$

$P = 4y - 12$;
$A = (y - 3)^2$
$= y^2 - 6y + 9$

5. 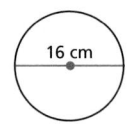 5 m, 4 m, 13 m, 3 m, x m

$P = (x + 21)$ m;
$A = (2x + 6)$ m^2

SEE EXAMPLE **2**
p. 37

6. **Manufacturing** A puzzle contains a triangular piece with a base of 3 in. and a height of 4 in. A manufacturer wants to make 80 puzzles. Find the amount of wood used if each puzzle contains 20 triangular pieces. **9600 in^2**

SEE EXAMPLE **3**
p. 37

Find the circumference and area of each circle. Use the π key on your calculator. Round to the nearest tenth.

7.  2.1 m

$C \approx 13.2$ m; $A \approx 13.9$ m^2

8. 7 in.

$C \approx 44.0$ in.; $A \approx 153.9$ in^2

9. 16 cm

$C \approx 50.3$ cm;
$A \approx 201.1$ cm^2

PRACTICE AND PROBLEM SOLVING

Independent Practice

For Exercises	See Example
10–12	1
13	2
14–16	3

TEKS ➡ TAKS
Skills Practice p. S5
Application Practice p. S28

Find the perimeter and area of each figure.

10. 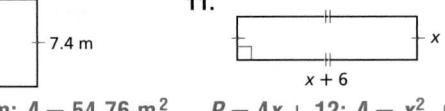 7.4 m

$P = 29.6$ m; $A = 54.76$ m^2

11. x, $x + 6$

$P = 4x + 12$; $A = x^2 + 6x$

12. 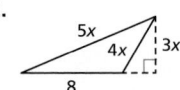 $5x$, $4x$, $3x$, 8

$P = 9x + 8$; $A = 12x$

13. **Crafts** The quilt pattern includes 32 small triangles. Each has a base of 3 in. and a height of 1.5 in. Find the amount of fabric used to make the 32 triangles. **72 in^2**

Find the circumference and area of each circle with the given radius or diameter. Use the π key on your calculator. Round to the nearest tenth.

14. $C \approx 75.4$ m;
$A \approx 452.4$ m^2

15. $C \approx 39.3$ ft;
$A \approx 122.7$ ft^2

16. $C \approx 1.6$ mi;
$A \approx 0.2$ mi^2

14. $r = 12$ m

15. $d = 12.5$ ft

16. $d = \frac{1}{2}$ mi

Find the area of each of the following.

17. square whose sides are 9.1 yd in length **82.81 yd^2**

18. square whose sides are $(x + 1)$ in length **$x^2 + 2x + 1$**

19. triangle whose base is $5\frac{1}{2}$ in. and whose height is $2\frac{1}{4}$ in. **6.1875 in^2**

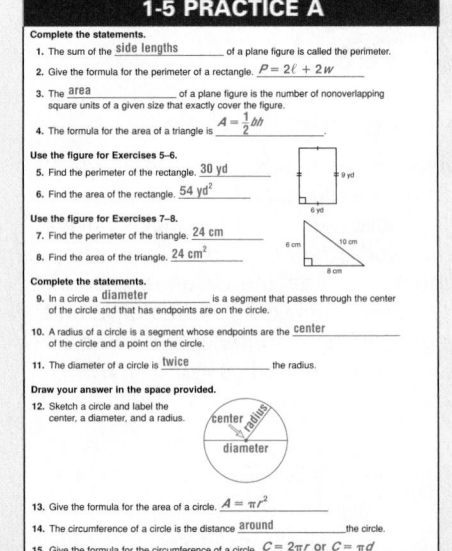

1-5 PRACTICE A

Complete the statements.

1. The sum of the **side lengths** of a plane figure is called the perimeter.

2. Give the formula for the perimeter of a rectangle. **$P = 2\ell + 2w$**

3. The **area** of a plane figure is the number of nonoverlapping square units of a given size that exactly cover the figure.

4. The formula for the area of a triangle is **$A = \frac{1}{2}bh$**.

Use the figure for Exercises 5–6.

5. Find the perimeter of the rectangle. **30 yd**

6. Find the area of the rectangle. **54 yd^2**

Use the figure for Exercises 7–8.

7. Find the perimeter of the triangle. **24 cm**

8. Find the area of the triangle. **24 cm^2**

Complete the statements.

9. In a circle a **diameter** is a segment that passes through the center of the circle and that has endpoints are on the circle.

10. A radius of a circle is a segment whose endpoints are the **center** of the circle and a point on the circle.

11. The diameter of a circle is **twice** the radius.

Draw your answer in the space provided.

12. Sketch a circle and label the center, a diameter, and a radius.

13. Give the formula for the area of a circle. **$A = \pi r^2$**

14. The circumference of a circle is the distance **around** the circle.

15. Give the formula for the circumference of a circle. **$C = 2\pi r$ or $C = \pi d$**

Given the area of each of the following figures, find each unknown measure.

20. The area of a triangle is 6.75 m². If the base of the triangle is 3 m, what is the height of the triangle? **4.5 m**

21. A rectangle has an area of 347.13 cm². If the length is 20.3 cm, what is the width of the rectangle? **17.1 cm**

22. The area of a circle is 64π. Find the radius of the circle. $r = 8$

23. ///ERROR ANALYSIS/// Below are two statements about the area of the circle. Which is incorrect? Explain the error.

8 cm

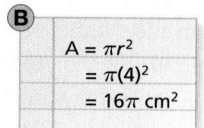
Ⓐ
$A = \pi r^2$
$= \pi (8)^2$
$= 64\pi \text{ cm}^2$

Ⓑ
$A = \pi r^2$
$= \pi (4)^2$
$= 16\pi \text{ cm}^2$

$A = \pi(8)^2$ is incorrect.
The radius is 4, not 8.
$A = \pi r^2 = \pi(4)^2 = 16\pi \text{ cm}^2$

Find the area of each circle. Leave answers in terms of π.

24. circle with a diameter of 28 m $196\pi \text{ m}^2$

25. circle with a radius of $3y$ $9y^2\pi$

26. Geography The radius r of the earth at the equator is approximately 3964 mi. Find the distance around the earth at the equator. Use the π key on your calculator and round to the nearest mile. **24,907 mi**

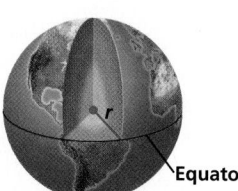
←Equator

27. For a square, the length and width are both s, so $P = 2\ell + 2w = 2s + 2s = 4s$ and $A = \ell w = s(s) = s^2$

27. Critical Thinking Explain how the formulas for the perimeter and area of a square may be derived from the corresponding formulas for a rectangle.

28. $P = 4x - 4$; $A = (x+1)(x-3) = x^2 - 2x - 3$

28. Find the perimeter and area of a rectangle whose length is $(x+1)$ and whose width is $(x-3)$. Express your answer in terms of x.

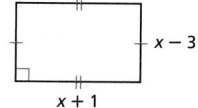
$x - 3$
$x + 1$

29. Multi-Step If the height h of a triangle is 3 inches less than the length of the base b, and the area A of the triangle is 19 times the length of the base, find b and h.
$b = 41$ in.; $h = 38$ in.

30. This problem will prepare you for the Multi-Step TAKS Prep on page 58.

A landscaper is to install edging around a garden. The edging costs $1.39 for each 24-inch-long strip. The landscaper estimates it will take 4 hours to install the edging.

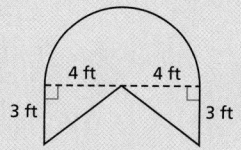
4 ft   4 ft
3 ft   3 ft

a. If the total cost is $120.30, what is the cost of the material purchased? **$20.85**

b. What is the charge for labor? **$99.45**

c. What is the area of the semicircle to the nearest tenth? **25.1 ft²**

d. What is the area of each triangle? **6 ft²**

e. What is the total area of the garden to the nearest foot? **37 ft²**

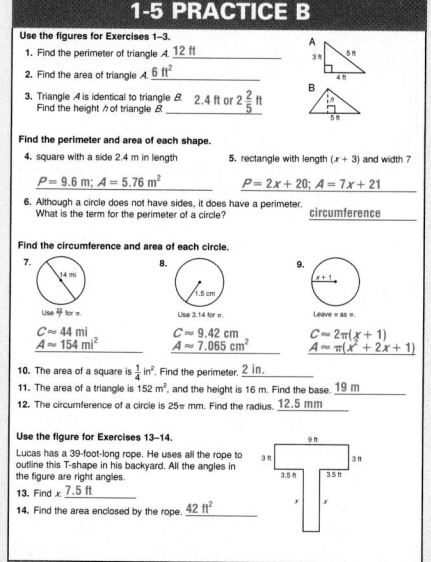

1-5 PRACTICE B

Use the figures for Exercises 1–3.

1. Find the perimeter of triangle A. 12 ft
2. Find the area of triangle A. 6 ft²
3. Triangle A is identical to triangle B. Find the height h of triangle B. 2.4 ft or $2\frac{2}{5}$ ft

Find the perimeter and area of each shape.

4. square with a side 2.4 m in length
   $P = 9.6$ m; $A = 5.76$ m²
5. rectangle with length $(x+3)$ and width 7
   $P = 2x + 20$; $A = 7x + 21$
6. Although a circle does not have sides, it does have a perimeter. What is the term for the perimeter of a circle? circumference

Find the circumference and area of each circle.

7. Use $\frac{22}{7}$ for π.
   $C \approx 44$ mi
   $A \approx 154$ mi²
8. Use 3.14 for π.
   $C \approx 9.42$ cm
   $A \approx 7.065$ cm²
9. Leave π as π.
   $C \approx 2\pi(x+1)$
   $A \approx \pi(x^2 + 2x + 1)$

10. The area of a square is $\frac{1}{4}$ in². Find the perimeter. 2 in.
11. The area of a triangle is 152 m², and the height is 16 m. Find the base. 19 m
12. The circumference of a circle is 25π mm. Find the radius. 12.5 mm

Use the figure for Exercises 13–14.

Lucas has a 39-foot-long rope. He uses all the rope to outline this T-shape in his backyard. All the angles in the figure are right angles.
13. Find x. 7.5 ft
14. Find the area enclosed by the rope. 42 ft²

1-5 PRACTICE C

1. Find the length of the sides of a square whose area and perimeter are the same nonzero number. 4
2. Find the length of the radius of a circle whose area and circumference are the same nonzero number. 2
3. Explain why the area and the perimeter (or the circumference) of a figure can never be equal; they can only have equal numbers.
   Area is measured in square units; perimeter is measured in linear units.

Find the measurements.

4. Faye has 44 feet of fencing to enclose a rectangular garden. She wants to enclose as much area as possible. Use trial-and-error to find the maximum area Faye can enclose with all 44 feet of fence. Name the length and width that give the maximum area.
   $A = 121$ ft²; $\ell = 11$ ft; $w = 11$ ft
5. Explain what the answer to Exercise 4 implies about the relationship of perimeter to area for rectangles.
   For a given perimeter, a rectangle with sides of equal length (a square) encloses the maximum area.
6. Faye decides to use her 44 feet of fencing to enclose a circular garden. Find the area of the garden. (Use $\frac{22}{7}$ for π.) about 154 ft²
7. Find the difference between the area Faye can enclose by a circle and the maximum area she can enclose by a rectangle. about 33 ft²
8. Explain what the answer to Exercise 7 implies about the relationship of perimeter to area for rectangles and circles.
   If a rectangle and a circle have the same perimeter, then the circle has the greater area.
9. A rectangular box of tissues is 9.5 inches long, 4.5 inches wide, and 4 inches high. Find the area of the surface of the box. 197.5 in²
10. A right triangle has two legs with lengths a and b and a hypotenuse with length c. In this triangle, the area and perimeter are the same nonzero number. Find the length a if $b = 6$. (Hint: Use the Pythagorean Theorem, $a^2 + b^2 = c^2$.) $a = 8$

COMMON ERROR
/// **ALERT** \\\

In **Exercises 24** and **25**, students may confuse πr^2 in the area formula and $2\pi r$ in the circumference formula. Remind them that area is measured in square units, so they should use the formula in which r is squared.

Teaching Tip **Reading Math** In **Exercises 24** and **25**, remind students that the direction to leave answers in terms of π means that π is part of the answer.

ENGLISH LANGUAGE LEARNERS

MULTI-STEP TAKS PREP **Exercise 30** involves perimeters of triangles and the circumference of a semicircle. This exercise prepares students for the Multi-Step TAKS Prep on page 58.

 31. Algebra The large rectangle has length $a + b$ and width $c + d$. Therefore, its area is $(a + b)(c + d)$.

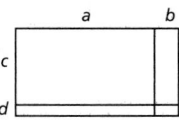

a. Find the area of each of the four small rectangles in the figure. Then find the sum of these areas. Explain why this sum must be equal to the product $(a + b)(c + d)$. $ac + ad + bc + bd$

b. $(a + 1)(c + 1);$ $ac + a + c + 1$

c. $(a + 1)^2;$ $a^2 + 2a + 1$

b. Suppose $b = d = 1$. Write the area of the large rectangle as a product of its length and width. Then find the sum of the areas of the four small rectangles. Explain why this sum must be equal to the product $(a + 1)(c + 1)$.

c. Suppose $b = d = 1$ and $a = c$. Write the area of the large rectangle as a product of its length and width. Then find the sum of the areas of the four small rectangles. Explain why this sum must be equal to the product $(a + 1)^2$.

32. Sports The table shows the minimum and maximum dimensions for rectangular soccer fields used in international matches. Find the difference in area of the largest possible field and the smallest possible field. **1850 m²**

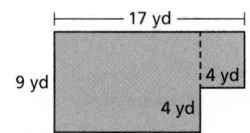

	Minimum	Maximum
Length	100 m	110 m
Width	64 m	75 m

Find the value of each missing measure of a triangle.

33. $b = 2$ ft; $h = $ ■ ft; $A = 28$ ft² **28 ft**

34. $b = $ ■ ft; $h = 22.6$ yd; $A = 282.5$ yd² **25 yd**

Find the area of each rectangle with the given base and height.

35. 9.8 ft; 2.7 ft **26.46 ft²**

36. 4 mi 960 ft; 440 ft **9,715,200 ft², or 0.348 mi²**

37. 3 yd 12 ft; 11 ft **$25\frac{2}{3}$ yd² or 231 ft²**

Find the perimeter of each rectangle with the given base and height.

38. 21.4 in.; 7.8 in. **58.4 in.**

39. 4 ft 6 in.; 6 in. **10 ft**

40. 2 yd 8 ft; 6 ft **13 yd 1 ft**

Find the diameter of the circle with the given measurement. Leave answers in terms of π.

41. $C = 14$ **$\dfrac{14}{\pi}$**

42. $A = 100\pi$ **20**

43. $C = 50\pi$ **50**

45. Measure any side as the base. Then measure the height of the $\triangle$ at a rt. $\angle$ to the base.

44. A skate park consists of a two adjacent rectangular regions as shown. Find the perimeter and area of the park. $P = 52$ ft; $A = 137$ ft²

45. Critical Thinking Explain how you would measure a triangular piece of paper if you wanted to find its area.

46. Write About It A student wrote in her journal, "To find the perimeter of a rectangle, add the length and width together and then double this value." Does her method work? Explain. **The method works because adding the length and width together and doubling the result is $2(\ell + w)$, which is equivalent to $2\ell + 2w$.**

TEST PREP

47. Manda made a circular tabletop that has an area of 452 in². Which is closest to the radius of the tabletop?

  Ⓐ 9 in.   Ⓑ 12 in.   Ⓒ 24 in.   Ⓓ 72 in.

48. A piece of wire 48 m long is bent into the shape of a rectangle whose length is twice its width. Find the length of the rectangle.

  Ⓕ 8 m   Ⓖ 16 m   Ⓗ 24 m   Ⓙ 32 m

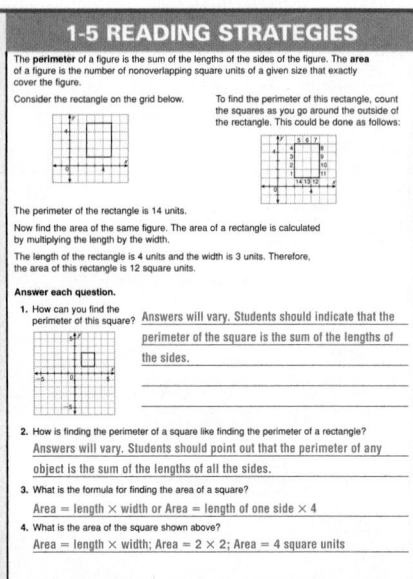

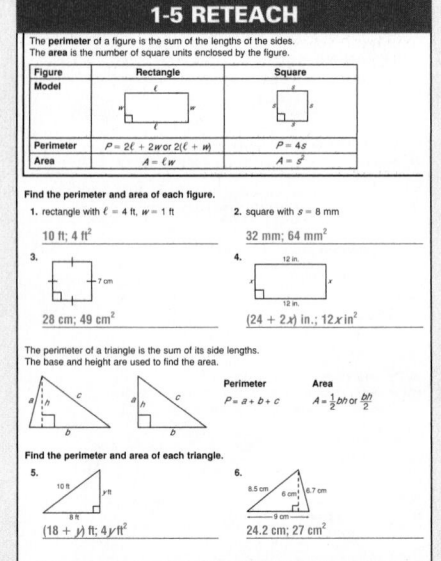

49. Which equation best represents the area A of the triangle?

    Ⓐ $A = 2x^2 + 4x$

    Ⓑ $A = 4x(x + 2)$

    Ⓒ $A = 2x^2 + 2$

    Ⓓ $A = 4x^2 + 8$

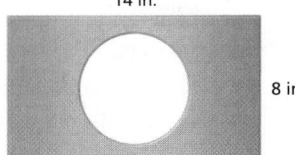

50. Ryan has a 30 ft piece of string. He wants to use the string to lay out the boundary of a new flower bed in his garden. Which of these shapes would use all the string?

    Ⓕ A circle with a radius of about 37.2 in.

    Ⓖ A rectangle with a length of 6 ft and a width of 5 ft

    Ⓗ A triangle with each side 9 ft long

    Ⓙ A square with each side 90 in. long

CHALLENGE AND EXTEND

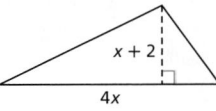

Math History

The Ahmes Papyrus is an ancient Egyptian source of information about mathematics. A page of the Ahmes Papyrus is about 1 foot wide and 18 feet long.
Source: scholars.nus.edu.sg

51. A circle with a 6 in. diameter is stamped out of a rectangular piece of metal as shown. Find the area of the remaining piece of metal. Use the π key on your calculator and round to the nearest tenth. **83.7 in²**

14 in.

8 in.

52. a. Solve $P = 2\ell + 2w$ for w. $w = \dfrac{P - 2\ell}{2}$

    b. Use your result from part **a** to find the width of a rectangle that has a perimeter of 9 ft and a length of 3 ft. **1.5 ft**

53. Find all possible areas of a rectangle whose sides are natural numbers and whose perimeter is 12. **5; 8; 9**

54. Estimation The Ahmes Papyrus dates from approximately 1650 B.C.E. Lacking a precise value for π, the author assumed that the area of a circle with a diameter of 9 units had the same area as a square with a side length of 8 units. By what percent did the author overestimate or underestimate the actual area of the circle? **overestimated by about 0.6%**

55. Multi-Step The width of a painting is $\frac{4}{5}$ the measure of the length of the painting. If the area is 320 in², what are the length and width of the painting?
    width = 16 in.; length = 20 in.

SPIRAL REVIEW

Determine the domain and range of each function. *(Previous course)*

56. $\{(2, 4), (-5, 8), (-3, 4)\}$ **D: {2, −5, −3}; R: {4, 8}**   **57.** $\{(4, -2), (-2, 8), (16, 0)\}$ **D: {4, −2, 16}; R: {−2, 8, 0}**

Name the geometric figure that each item suggests. *(Lesson 1-1)*

58. the wall of a classroom **plane**   **59.** the place where two walls meet **line or segment**

60. Marion has a piece of fabric that is 10 yd long. She wants to cut it into 2 pieces so that one piece is 4 times as long as the other. Find the lengths of the two pieces. *(Lesson 1-2)* **8 yd; 2 yd**

61. Suppose that A, B, and C are collinear points. B is the midpoint of $\overline{AC}$. The coordinate of A is -8, and the coordinate of B is -2.5. What is the coordinate of C? *(Lesson 1-2)* **3**

62. An angle's measure is 9 degrees more than 2 times the measure of its supplement. Find the measure of the angle. *(Lesson 1-4)* **123°**

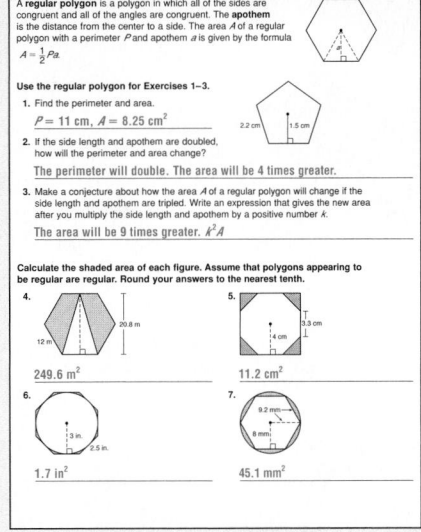

COMMON ERROR ALERT

In **Exercise 51**, some students may attempt to subtract the area of the rectangle from the area of the circle. Explain that they must subtract the smaller area from the larger area, or the result will be a negative number.

Teaching Tip **Algebra** For **Exercise 54**, you might need to review that you find the percent of change by dividing the difference by the original.

Journal

Have students draw a rectangle, a triangle, and a circle on a grid and explain how they would find the area and perimeter (or circumference) of each figure, using their own dimensions.

ALTERNATIVE ASSESSMENT

Give students the area, perimeter, and circumference of three figures. Then ask students to find the dimensions and draw the figures that match the corresponding values.

Power Presentations with PowerPoint®

1-5 Lesson Quiz

Find the area and perimeter of each figure.

1.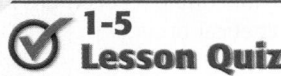
  $x^2 + 4x;\ 4x + 8$

2.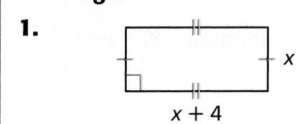
  4.8 cm
  23.04 cm²; 19.2 cm

3.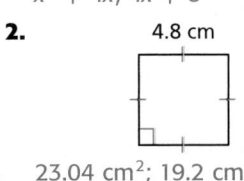
  $3x$ $2x$ $x + 6$ 10
  $10x;\ 4x + 16$

Find the circumference and area of each circle. Leave answers in terms of π.

4. radius 2 cm $4\pi^2$ cm; 4π cm

5. diameter 12 ft $36\pi^2$ ft; 12π ft

6. The area of a rectangle is 74.82 in², and the length is 12.9 in. Find the width. **5.8 in.**

Also available on transparency

Organizer

See Skills Bank page S56

Pacing:
Traditional $\frac{1}{2}$ day
Block $\frac{1}{4}$ day

Objective: Review the coordinate plane.

 Online Edition

 Countdown to TAKS Week 2

Teach

Remember

Students review the parts of the coordinate plane and the associated terms and locate and plot points.

INTERVENTION ◀▬▶ For additional review and practice on plotting points in the coordinate plane, see Skills Bank page S56.

Teaching Tip | **Inclusion** Have students associate the x-coordinate with right/east and left/west direction and the y-coordinate with up/north and down/south direction from the origin. Point out that both of the ordered pairs (x, y) and (horizontal, vertical) are in alphabetical order.

Close

Assess

Have students draw and label a coordinate plane. Then have them make a design. The students can exchange designs and label each others' points.

TAKS *On Track for TAKS* connects TAKS objectives across the grade levels.

Grades 9–11
Obj. 6 Geometric Relationships and Spatial Reasoning 8.7.D locate and name points on a coordinate plane using ordered pairs of rational numbers
Obj. 7 Two-Dimensional and Three-Dimensional Representations G.7.A. use one- and two-dimensional coordinate systems to represent points, …

See Skills Bank page S56

Graphing in the Coordinate Plane

Algebra

The *coordinate plane* is used to name and locate points. Points in the coordinate plane are named by ordered pairs of the form (x, y). The first number is the x-coordinate. The second number is the y-coordinate. The x-axis and y-axis intersect at the origin, forming right angles. The axes separate the coordinate plane into four regions, called quadrants, numbered with Roman numerals placed counterclockwise.

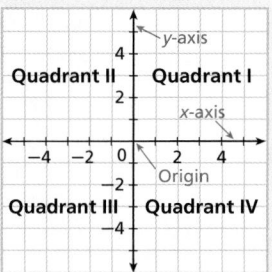

Examples

1 **Name the coordinates of P.**
Starting at the origin $(0, 0)$, you count 1 unit to the right. Then count 3 units up. So the coordinates of P are $(1, 3)$.

2 **Plot and label $H(-2, -4)$ on a coordinate plane. Name the quadrant in which it is located.**
Start at the origin $(0, 0)$ and move 2 units left. Then move 4 units down. Draw a dot and label it H. H is in Quadrant III.

You can also use a coordinate plane to locate places on a map.

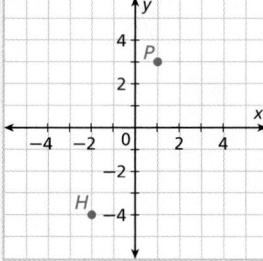

Try This

 TAKS Grades 9–11 Obj. 6, 7

Name the coordinates of the point where the following streets intersect.
1. Chestnut and Plum $(0, 0)$
2. Magnolia and Chestnut $(0, 4)$
3. Oak and Hawthorn $(3, 2)$
4. Plum and Cedar $(-1, 0)$

Name the streets that intersect at the given points.
5. $(-3, -1)$ 6. $(4, -1)$
7. $(1, 3)$ 8. $(-2, 1)$
5. Spruce and Beech
6. Spruce and Hickory
7. Maple and Elm
8. Pine and Birch

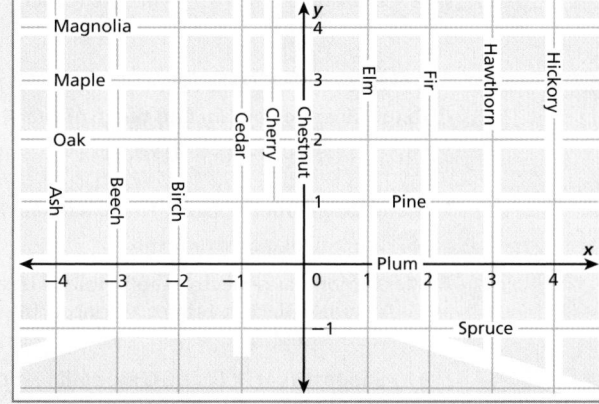

1-6 Midpoint and Distance in the Coordinate Plane

TEKS G.1.A Geometric structure: develop an awareness of the structure of a mathematical system, connecting definitions, postulates, ... Also G.7.A, G.7.C, G.8.C

Objectives
Develop and apply the formula for midpoint.

Use the Distance Formula and the Pythagorean Theorem to find the distance between two points.

Vocabulary
coordinate plane
leg
hypotenuse

Why learn this?
You can use a coordinate plane to help you calculate distances. (See Example 5.)

Major League baseball fields are laid out according to strict guidelines. Once you know the dimensions of a field, you can use a coordinate plane to find the distance between two of the bases.

A **coordinate plane** is a plane that is divided into four regions by a horizontal line (x-axis) and a vertical line (y-axis). The location, or coordinates, of a point are given by an ordered pair (x, y).

Minute Maid Park, Hou...

You can find the midpoint of a segment by using the coordinates of its endpoints. Calculate the average of the x-coordinates and the average of the y-coordinates of the endpoints.

Know it!
Note

Midpoint Formula

The midpoint M of $\overline{AB}$ with endpoints $A(x_1, y_1)$ and $B(x_2, y_2)$ is found by

$$M\left(\frac{x_1 + x_2}{2}, \frac{y_1 + y_2}{2}\right).$$

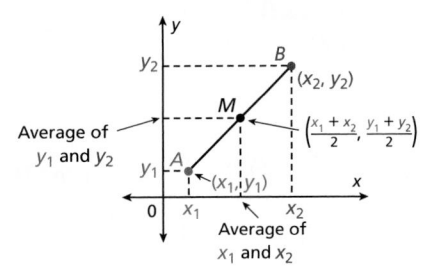

EXAMPLE 1 Finding the Coordinates of a Midpoint

Find the coordinates of the midpoint of $\overline{CD}$ with endpoints $C(-2, -1)$ and $D(4, 2)$.

$$M\left(\frac{x_1 + x_2}{2}, \frac{y_1 + y_2}{2}\right)$$

$$\frac{-2 + 4}{2}, \frac{-1 + 2}{2} = \left(\frac{2}{2}, \frac{1}{2}\right)$$

$$= \left(1, \frac{1}{2}\right)$$

Helpful Hint
To make it easier to picture the problem, plot the segment's endpoints on a coordinate plane.

CHECK IT OUT! 1. Find the coordinates of the midpoint of $\overline{EF}$ with endpoints $E(-2, 3)$ and $F(5, -3)$. $\left(\frac{3}{2}, 0\right)$

1-6 Midpoint and Distance in the Coordinate Plane **43**

1 Introduce

EXPLORATION

1-6 Midpoint and Distance in the Coordinate Plane

The coordinate plane shows graphs of four line segments that are each named $\overline{AB}$. Copy each segment onto a sheet of graph paper.

1. Fold each segment so that A matches up with B. Use the fold to find the midpoint of the segment. In a table, record the coordinates of each segment's endpoints and midpoint.

Segment	Coordinates of A	Coordinates of B	Coordinates of Midpoint
1			
2			
3			
4			

2. For segments 1 and 2, how are the x-coordinates of each segment's midpoint related to the x-coordinates of its endpoints?
3. For segments 3 and 4, how are the y-coordinates of each segment's midpoint related to the y-coordinates of its endpoints?

THINK AND DISCUSS

Motivate
Give students a coordinate graph on which a house and a school have been graphed. Ask them to estimate the distance between the school and the house and to estimate the point that is halfway between these two locations.

Explorations and answers are provided in the *Explorations* binder.

1-6 Organizer

Pacing: Traditional $\frac{1}{2}$ day
Block $\frac{1}{4}$ day

Objectives: Develop and apply the formula for midpoint.

Use the Distance Formula and the Pythagorean Theorem to find the distance between two points.

 Online Edition
Tutorial Videos

 Countdown to TAKS Week 2

Power Presentations with PowerPoint®

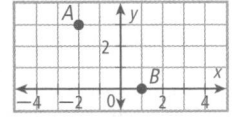

Warm Up
1. Graph $A(-2, 3)$ and $B(1, 0)$.

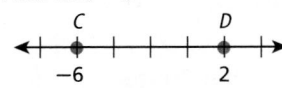

2. Find CD.   8

3. Find the coordinate of the midpoint of $\overline{CD}$. -2

4. Simplify. $\sqrt{\left(3 - (-1)\right)^2}$ 4

Also available on transparency

Math Humor
Q: What keeps a square from moving?
A: Square roots.

Geometry TEKS
G.1 Geometric structure*
(A) develop an awareness of the structure of a mathematical system, ...

G.7 Dimensionality and the geometry of location*
(A) use coordinate systems to represent ... segments, ...
(C) develop and use formulas involving length, slope, and midpoint

G.8 Congruence and the geometry of size*
(C) ... use the Pythagorean Theorem
* **Knowledge and Skills** See p. 4.

Lesson 1-6 **43**

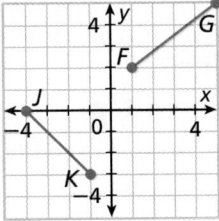

Additional Examples

Example 1

Find the coordinates of the midpoint of $\overline{PQ}$ with endpoints $P(-8, 3)$ and $Q(-2, 7)$. $(-5, 5)$

Example 2

M is the midpoint of $\overline{XY}$. X has coordinates $(2, 7)$, and M has coordinates $(6, 1)$. Find the coordinates of Y. $(10, -5)$

Example 3

Find FG and JK. Then determine whether $\overline{FG} \cong \overline{JK}$. $5; 3\sqrt{2}$; no

Also available on transparency

INTERVENTION
Questioning Strategies

EXAMPLE 1

• Does it matter which point is represented by (x_1, y_1)? Explain.

EXAMPLE 2

• Given the midpoint and one endpoint of a segment, how is the Midpoint Formula used to find the missing endpoint?

EXAMPLE 3

• How do you substitute the coordinates of two points into the Distance Formula?

EXAMPLE 2 Finding the Coordinates of an Endpoint

x²y Algebra

M is the midpoint of $\overline{AB}$. A has coordinates $(2, 2)$, and M has coordinates $(4, -3)$. Find the coordinates of B.

Step 1 Let the coordinates of B equal (x, y).

Step 2 Use the Midpoint Formula: $(4, -3) = \left(\dfrac{2 + x}{2}, \dfrac{2 + y}{2}\right)$.

Step 3 Find the x-coordinate.   Find the y-coordinate.

$4 = \dfrac{2 + x}{2}$	*Set the coordinates equal.*	$-3 = \dfrac{2 + y}{2}$
$2(4) = 2\left(\dfrac{2 + x}{2}\right)$	*Multiply both sides by 2.*	$2(-3) = 2\left(\dfrac{2 + y}{2}\right)$
$8 = 2 + x$	*Simplify.*	$-6 = 2 + y$
$\underline{-2 \quad -2}$	*Subtract 2 from both sides.*	$\underline{-2 \quad -2}$
$6 = x$	*Simplify.*	$-8 = y$

The coordinates of B are $(6, -8)$.

CHECK IT OUT! **2.** S is the midpoint of $\overline{RT}$. R has coordinates $(-6, -1)$, and S has coordinates $(-1, 1)$. Find the coordinates of T. $(4, 3)$

The Ruler Postulate can be used to find the distance between two points on a number line. The Distance Formula is used to calculate the distance between two points in a coordinate plane.

Know it! Note

Distance Formula

In a coordinate plane, the distance d between two points (x_1, y_1) and (x_2, y_2) is

$$d = \sqrt{(x_2 - x_1)^2 + (y_2 - y_1)^2}.$$

EXAMPLE 3 Using the Distance Formula

Find AB and CD. Then determine if $\overline{AB} \cong \overline{CD}$.

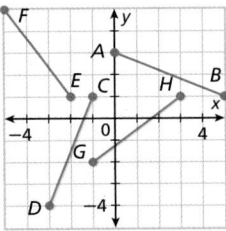

Step 1 Find the coordinates of each point.
$A(0, 3)$, $B(5, 1)$, $C(-1, 1)$, and $D(-3, -4)$

Step 2 Use the Distance Formula.

$d = \sqrt{(x_2 - x_1)^2 + (y_2 - y_1)^2}$

$AB = \sqrt{(5 - 0)^2 + (1 - 3)^2}$ $CD = \sqrt{[-3 - (-1)]^2 + (-4 - 1)^2}$

$\quad = \sqrt{5^2 + (-2)^2}$ $\quad = \sqrt{(-2)^2 + (-5)^2}$

$\quad = \sqrt{25 + 4}$ $\quad = \sqrt{4 + 25}$

$\quad = \sqrt{29}$ $\quad = \sqrt{29}$

Since $AB = CD$, $\overline{AB} \cong \overline{CD}$.

CHECK IT OUT! **3.** Find EF and GH. Then determine if $\overline{EF} \cong \overline{GH}$.
$EF = 5$; $GH = 5$; $\overline{EF} \cong \overline{GH}$

---

2 Teach

Guided Instruction

Before teaching the Midpoint Formula, remind students how to find the average of two numbers. Connect average, a measure of central tendency, to the idea of midpoint. Review how to subtract positive and negative numbers to avoid subtracting errors in the Distance Formula. When finding midpoints and distances on a coordinate plane, relate your instruction to finding distances and midpoints on a number line.

Reaching All Learners
Through Cognitive Strategies

Have students use mental math to estimate the midpoint or distance. Then have them use a calculator to support their answer.

You can also use the Pythagorean Theorem to find the distance between two points in a coordinate plane. You will learn more about the Pythagorean Theorem in Chapter 5.

In a right triangle, the two sides that form the right angle are the **legs**. The side across from the right angle that stretches from one leg to the other is the **hypotenuse**. In the diagram, a and b are the lengths of the shorter sides, or legs, of the right triangle. The longest side is called the hypotenuse and has length c.

Theorem 1-6-1 (**Pythagorean Theorem**)

In a right triangle, the sum of the squares of the lengths of the *legs* is equal to the square of the length of the *hypotenuse*.

$$a^2 + b^2 = c^2$$

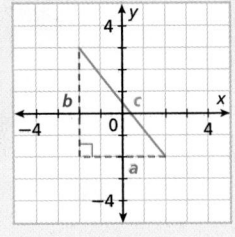

EXAMPLE 4 **Finding Distances in the Coordinate Plane**

Use the Distance Formula and the Pythagorean Theorem to find the distance, to the nearest tenth, from A to B.

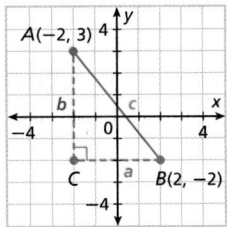

Method 1

Use the Distance Formula. Substitute the values for the coordinates of A and B into the Distance Formula.

$$AB = \sqrt{(x_2 - x_1)^2 + (y_2 - y_1)^2}$$
$$= \sqrt{[2 - (-2)]^2 + (-2 - 3)^2}$$
$$= \sqrt{4^2 + (-5)^2}$$
$$= \sqrt{16 + 25}$$
$$= \sqrt{41}$$
$$\approx 6.4$$

Method 2

Use the Pythagorean Theorem. Count the units for sides a and b.

$a = 4$ and $b = 5$.
$$c^2 = a^2 + b^2$$
$$= 4^2 + 5^2$$
$$= 16 + 25$$
$$= 41$$
$$c = \sqrt{41}$$
$$c \approx 6.4$$

 **CHECK IT OUT!** Use the Distance Formula and the Pythagorean Theorem to find the distance, to the nearest tenth, from R to S.

4a. $R(3, 2)$ and $S(-3, -1)$ **6.7**

4b. $R(-4, 5)$ and $S(2, -1)$ **8.5**

Power Presentations
with PowerPoint®

Additional Examples

Example 4

Use the Distance Formula and the Pythagorean Theorem to find the distance, to the nearest tenth, from $D(3, 4)$ to $E(-2, -5)$. **10.3**

Also available on transparency

INTERVENTION
Questioning Strategies

EXAMPLE 4

• Do you think it is easier to use the Pythagorean Theorem or the Distance Formula to find the distance between two points? Explain.

Teaching Tip **Algebra** Review with students that $\sqrt{3^2 + 4^2} \neq 3 + 4$. They must first square each number and then take the square root of the sum. The answer is 5, not 7.

Teaching Tip **Inclusion** Have students label the coordinates of any two points they are given as (x_1, y_1) and (x_2, y_2) before substituting the numbers into the Midpoint Formula or Distance Formula.

INTERVENTION ◄═►
Questioning Strategies

EXAMPLE 5

• How do you find the coordinates of the endpoints used in the Distance Formula?

• Is the pitcher's mound the midpoint between home plate and second base? Explain.

EXAMPLE 5 *Sports Application*

The four bases on a baseball field form a square with 90 ft sides. When a player throws the ball from home plate to second base, what is the distance of the throw, to the nearest tenth?

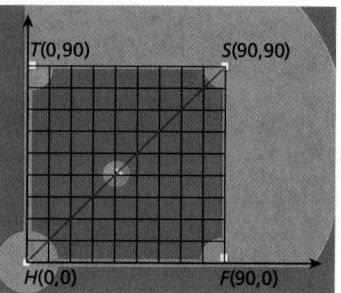

Set up the field on a coordinate plane so that home plate H is at the origin, first base F has coordinates $(90, 0)$, second base S has coordinates $(90, 90)$, and third base T has coordinates $(0, 90)$.

The distance HS from home plate to second base is the length of the hypotenuse of a right triangle.

$$HS = \sqrt{(x_2 - x_1)^2 + (y_2 - y_1)^2}$$
$$= \sqrt{(90 - 0)^2 + (90 - 0)^2}$$
$$= \sqrt{90^2 + 90^2}$$
$$= \sqrt{8100 + 8100}$$
$$= \sqrt{16{,}200}$$
$$\approx 127.3 \text{ ft}$$

 **5.** The center of the pitching mound has coordinates $(42.8, 42.8)$. When a pitcher throws the ball from the center of the mound to home plate, what is the distance of the throw, to the nearest tenth? **60.5 ft**

THINK AND DISCUSS

1. Can you exchange the coordinates (x_1, y_1) and (x_2, y_2) in the Midpoint Formula and still find the correct midpoint? Explain.

2. A right triangle has sides lengths of r, s, and t. Given that $s^2 + t^2 = r^2$, which variables represent the lengths of the legs and which variable represents the length of the hypotenuse?

3. Do you always get the same result using the Distance Formula to find distance as you do when using the Pythagorean Theorem? Explain your answer.

4. Why do you think that most cities are laid out in a rectangular grid instead of a triangular or circular grid?

5. **GET ORGANIZED** Copy and complete the graphic organizer below. In each box, write a formula. Then make a sketch that will illustrate the formula.

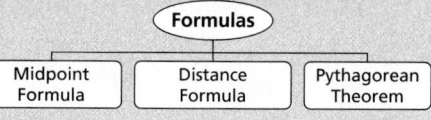

Formulas — Midpoint Formula | Distance Formula | Pythagorean Theorem

---

3 Close

Summarize

Review with students how to use the Midpoint Formula and Distance Formula to find the midpoint of a segment and the distance between two points, given their coordinates.

ONGOING ASSESSMENT
and INTERVENTION ◄═►

Diagnose Before the Lesson
1-6 Warm Up, TE p. 43

Monitor During the Lesson
Check It Out! Exercises, SE pp. 43–46
Questioning Strategies, TE pp. 44–46

Assess After the Lesson
1-6 Lesson Quiz, TE p. 49
Alternative Assessment, TE p. 49

Answers to *Think and Discuss*

1. yes; $\dfrac{x_1 + x_2}{2} = \dfrac{x_2 + x_1}{2}$ and $\dfrac{y_1 + y_2}{2} = \dfrac{y_2 + y_1}{2}$

2. s and t represent the lengths of the legs. r represents the length of the hyp.

3. Yes; you can use either method to find the dist. between 2 pts.

4. Possible answer: to make locating addresses easier

5. See p. A2.

GUIDED PRACTICE

1. **Vocabulary** The ___?___ is the side of a right triangle that is directly across from the right angle. (*hypotenuse* or *leg*) **hypotenuse**

SEE EXAMPLE **1**
p. 43

Find the coordinates of the midpoint of each segment.

2. $\overline{AB}$ with endpoints $A(4, -6)$ and $B(-4, 2)$ $(0, -2)$

3. $\overline{CD}$ with endpoints $C(0, -8)$ and $D(3, 0)$ $\left(1\frac{1}{2}, -4\right)$

SEE EXAMPLE **2**
p. 44

4. M is the midpoint of $\overline{LN}$. L has coordinates $(-3, -1)$, and M has coordinates $(0, 1)$. Find the coordinates of N. $(3, 3)$

5. B is the midpoint of $\overline{AC}$. A has coordinates $(-3, 4)$, and B has coordinates $\left(-1\frac{1}{2}, 1\right)$. Find the coordinates of C. $(0, -2)$

SEE EXAMPLE **3**
p. 44

Multi-Step Find the length of the given segments and determine if they are congruent.

6. $\overline{JK}$ and $\overline{FG}$ $\sqrt{29}$; $\sqrt{29}$; yes 7. $\overline{JK}$ and $\overline{RS}$ $\sqrt{29}$; $3\sqrt{5}$; no

SEE EXAMPLE **4**
p. 45

Use the Distance Formula and the Pythagorean Theorem to find the distance, to the nearest tenth, between each pair of points.

8. $A(1, -2)$ and $B(-4, -4)$ **5.4**

9. $X(-2, 7)$ and $Y(-2, -8)$ **15.0**

10. $V(2, -1)$ and $W(-4, 8)$ **10.8**

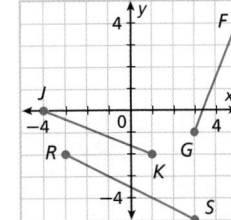

SEE EXAMPLE **5**
p. 46

11. **Architecture** The plan for a rectangular living room shows electrical wiring will be run in a straight line from the entrance E to a light L at the opposite corner of the room. What is the length of the wire to the nearest tenth? **27.2 ft**

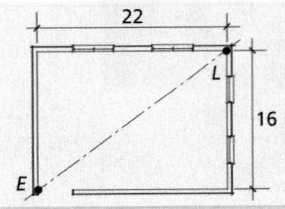

PRACTICE AND PROBLEM SOLVING

Independent Practice

For Exercises	See Example
12–13	1
14–15	2
16–17	3
18–20	4
21	5

Find the coordinates of the midpoint of each segment.

12. $\overline{XY}$ with endpoints $X(-3, -7)$ and $Y(-1, 1)$ $(-2, -3)$

13. $\overline{MN}$ with endpoints $M(12, -7)$ and $N(-5, -2)$ $\left(3\frac{1}{2}, -4\frac{1}{2}\right)$

14. M is the midpoint of $\overline{QR}$. Q has coordinates $(-3, 5)$, and M has coordinates $(7, -9)$. Find the coordinates of R. $(17, -23)$

15. D is the midpoint of $\overline{CE}$. E has coordinates $(-3, -2)$, and D has coordinates $\left(2\frac{1}{2}, 1\right)$. Find the coordinates of C. $(8, 4)$

TEKS ⇒ TAKS

Skills Practice p. S5

Application Practice p. S28

Multi-Step Find the length of the given segments and determine if they are congruent.

16. $\overline{DE}$ and $\overline{FG}$ $2\sqrt{5}$; $2\sqrt{5}$; yes

17. $\overline{DE}$ and $\overline{RS}$ $2\sqrt{5}$; $\sqrt{29}$; no

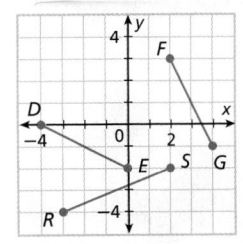

Assignment Guide

Assign *Guided Practice* exercises as necessary.

If you finished Examples **1–3**
  Basic 12–17, 22, 26, 27, 33
  Average 12–17, 22, 24–27, 33, 38
  Advanced 12–17, 22, 24–27, 33, 36, 38

If you finished Examples **1–5**
  Basic 12–23, 26–28, 30, 32–37, 42–50
  Average 12–39, 42–50
  Advanced 12–50

Homework Quick Check
Quickly check key concepts.
Exercises: 12, 14, 16, 18, 21, 26, 30

⊕TAKS Practice

Grades 9–11	Exercises
Obj. 2	42–44
Obj. 7	22, 24–28, 34–40
Obj. 8	23, 28, 30, 31, 38, 41, 48–50
Obj. 10	32, 33

MULTI-STEP TAKS PREP Exercise 33 involves finding the distance between points on a coordinate plane. This exercise prepares students for the Multi-Step TAKS Prep on page 58.

Answers

32. When 2 pts. lie on a horiz. or vert. line, they share a common *x*-coordinate or *y*-coordinate. To find the dist. between the pts., find the difference of the other coordinates.

Use the Distance Formula and the Pythagorean Theorem to find the distance, to the nearest tenth, between each pair of points.

8.9   15.5

10.4 **18.** $U(0, 1)$ and $V(-3, -9)$ **19.** $M(10, -1)$ and $N(2, -5)$ **20.** $P(-10, 1)$ and $Q(5, 5)$

18 in. **21. Consumer Application** Televisions and computer screens are usually advertised based on the length of their diagonals. If the height of a computer screen is 11 in. and the width is 14 in., what is the length of the diagonal? Round to the nearest inch.

$\overline{CD}$, $\overline{EF}$, $\overline{AB}$ **22. Multi-Step** Use the Distance Formula to order $\overline{AB}$, $\overline{CD}$, and $\overline{EF}$ from shortest to longest.

4.47 **23.** Use the Pythagorean Theorem to find the distance from A to E. Round to the nearest hundredth.

$\left(-2a, \frac{3}{2}a\right)$ **24.** X has coordinates $(a, 3a)$, and Y has coordinates $(-5a, 0)$. Find the coordinates of the midpoint of (XY).

Divide each **25.** Describe a shortcut for finding the midpoint of a coord. by 2.   segment when one of its endpoints has coordinates (a, b) and the other endpoint is the origin.

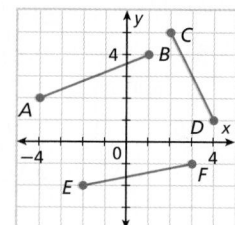

On the map, each square of the grid represents 1 square mile. Find each distance to the nearest tenth of a mile.

TEXAS LINK

History

The Forbidden City of Imperial China is replicated in Katy, Texas. The museum has 6000 miniature terra-cotta soldiers.

Source: www.forbidden-gardens.com

26. Find the distance along Highway 201 from Cedar City to Milltown. **6.1 mi**

27. A car breaks down on Route 1, at the midpoint between Jefferson and Milltown. A tow truck is sent out from Jefferson. How far does the truck travel to reach the car? **2.5 mi**

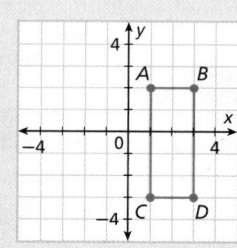

28. History The Forbidden City in Beijing, China, is the world's largest palace complex. Surrounded by a wall and a moat, the rectangular complex is 960 m long and 750 m wide. Find the distance, to the nearest meter, from one corner of the complex to the opposite corner. **1218 m**

29. Critical Thinking Give an example of a line segment with midpoint $(0, 0)$.
Possible answer: seg. with endpts. $(1, 2)$ and $(-1, -2)$

The coordinates of the vertices of $\triangle ABC$ are $A(1, 4)$, $B(-2, -1)$, and $C(-3, -2)$.

30. Find the perimeter of $\triangle ABC$ to the nearest tenth. **14.5**

31. The height h to side $\overline{BC}$ is $\sqrt{2}$, and b is the length of $\overline{BC}$. What is the area of $\triangle ABC$? **1**

32. Write About It Explain why the Distance Formula is not needed to find the distance between two points that lie on a horizontal or a vertical line.

MULTI-STEP TAKS PREP

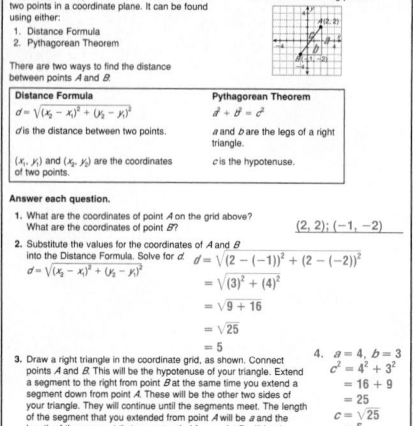

33. This problem will prepare you for the Multi-Step TAKS Prep on page 58. Tania uses a coordinate plane to map out plans for landscaping a rectangular patio area. On the plan, one square represents 2 feet. She plans to plant a tree at the midpoint of $\overline{AC}$. How far from each corner of the patio does she plant the tree? Round to the nearest tenth. **Let M be the mdpt. of $\overline{AC}$; $AM = MC = 5.0$ ft; $MB = MD \approx 6.4$ ft.**

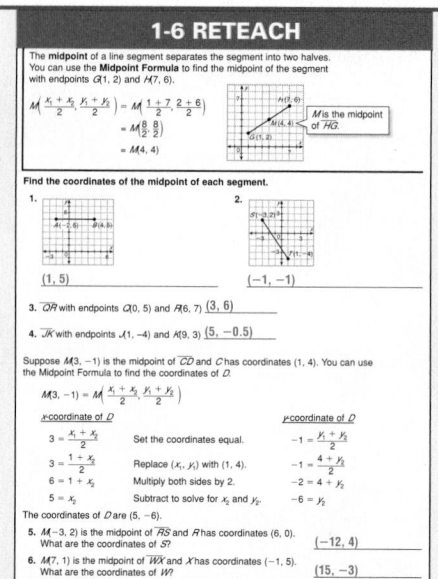

1-6 PRACTICE A

1-6 PRACTICE C

1-6 PRACTICE B

Find the coordinates of the midpoint of each segment.

1. $\overline{TU}$ with endpoints $T(5, -1)$ and $U(1, -5)$ $(3, -3)$

2. $\overline{VW}$ with endpoints $V(-2, -6)$ and $W(x + 2, y + 3)$ $\left(\frac{x}{2}, \frac{y-3}{2}\right)$

3. Y is the midpoint of $\overline{XZ}$. X has coordinates $(2, 4)$, and Y has coordinates $(-1, 1)$. Find the coordinates of Z. $(-4, -2)$

Use the figure for Exercises 4–7.

4. Find AB $\sqrt{26}$

5. Find BC $\sqrt{26}$

6. Find CA $4\sqrt{2}$

7. Name a pair of congruent segments. $\overline{AB}$ and $\overline{BC}$

Find the distances.

8. Use the Distance Formula to find the distance, to the nearest tenth, between $K(-7, -4)$ and $L(-2, 0)$.   6.4

9. Use the Pythagorean Theorem to find the distance, to the nearest tenth, between $R(9, 5)$ and $G(-2, 2)$.   11.4

Use the figure for Exercises 10–11.

Snooker is a kind of pool or billiards played on a 6-foot-by-12-foot table. The side pockets are halfway down the rails (long sides).

10. Find the distance, to the nearest tenth of a foot, diagonally across the table from corner pocket to corner pocket.   13.4 ft

11. Find the distance, to the nearest tenth of an inch, diagonally across the table from corner pocket to side pocket.   101.8 in.

1-6 READING STRATEGIES

There are two ways to find the distance between two points in a coordinate plane. It can be found using either:
1. Distance Formula
2. Pythagorean Theorem

There are two ways to find the distance between points A and B.

Distance Formula	Pythagorean Theorem
$d = \sqrt{(x_2 - x_1)^2 + (y_2 - y_1)^2}$	$a^2 + b^2 = c^2$
d is the distance between two points.	a and b are the legs of a right triangle.
(x_1, y_1) and (x_2, y_2) are the coordinates of two points.	c is the hypotenuse.

Consider the following points:

Answer each question.

1. What are the coordinates of point A on the grid above? What are the coordinates of point B? $(2, 2)$; $(-1, -2)$

2. Substitute the values for the coordinates of A and B into the Distance Formula. Solve for d. $d = \sqrt{(2 - (-1))^2 + (2 - (-2))^2}$
$d = \sqrt{(x_2 - x_1)^2 + (y_2 - y_1)^2}$
$= \sqrt{(3)^2 + (4)^2}$
$= \sqrt{9 + 16}$
$= \sqrt{25}$
$= 5$

3. Draw a right triangle in the coordinate grid, as shown. Connect points A and B. This will be the hypotenuse of your triangle. Extend a segment to the right from point B at the same time you extend a segment down from point A. These will be the other two sides of your triangle. They will continue until the segments meet. The length of the segment that you extended from point A will be a and the length of the segment that you extended from point B will be b.
$a = 4$, $b = 3$
$c^2 = 4^2 + 3^2$
$= 16 + 9$
$= 25$
$c = \sqrt{25}$
$= 5$

4. Use the Pythagorean Theorem to determine the distance between points A and B.

5. Explain the difference between the Pythagorean Theorem and the Distance Formula.
Sample answer: Distance Formula uses a coordinate plane.
Pythagorean Theorem uses known measures of two sides of a triangle.

1-6 RETEACH

The **midpoint** of a line segment separates the segment into two halves. You can use the **Midpoint Formula** to find the midpoint of the segment with endpoints $G(1, 2)$ and $H(7, 6)$.

$M\left(\frac{x_1 + x_2}{2}, \frac{y_1 + y_2}{2}\right) = M\left(\frac{1 + 7}{2}, \frac{2 + 6}{2}\right)$
$= M\left(\frac{8}{2}, \frac{8}{2}\right)$
$= M(4, 4)$

M is the midpoint of $\overline{HG}$.

Find the coordinates of the midpoint of each segment.

1.   2.

3. $\overline{QR}$ with endpoints $Q(0, 5)$ and $R(6, 7)$ $(3, 6)$

4. $\overline{JK}$ with endpoints $J(1, -4)$ and $K(9, 3)$ $(5, -0.5)$

Suppose $M(3, -1)$ is the midpoint of $\overline{CD}$ and C has coordinates $(1, 4)$. You can use the Midpoint Formula to find the coordinates of D.

$M(3, -1) = M\left(\frac{x_1 + x_2}{2}, \frac{y_1 + y_2}{2}\right)$

x-coordinate of D		*y*-coordinate of D
$3 = \frac{x_1 + x_2}{2}$	Set the coordinates equal.	$-1 = \frac{y_1 + y_2}{2}$
$3 = \frac{1 + x_2}{2}$	Replace (x_1, y_1) with $(1, 4)$.	$-1 = \frac{4 + y_2}{2}$
$6 = 1 + x_2$	Multiply both sides by 2.	$-2 = 4 + y_2$
$5 = x_2$	Subtract to solve for x_2 and y_2.	$-6 = y_2$

The coordinates of D are $(5, -6)$.

5. $M(-3, 2)$ is the midpoint of $\overline{RS}$ and R has coordinates $(6, 0)$. What are the coordinates of S? $(-12, 4)$

6. $M(7, 1)$ is the midpoint of $\overline{WX}$ and X has coordinates $(-1, 5)$. What are the coordinates of W? $(15, -3)$

34. Which segment has a length closest to 4 units?

(A) $\overline{EF}$ (C) $\overline{JK}$

(B) $\overline{GH}$ (D) $\overline{LM}$

35. Find the distance, to the nearest tenth, between the midpoints of $\overline{LM}$ and $\overline{JK}$.

(F) 1.8   (H) 4.0

(G) 3.6   (J) 5.3

36. What are the coordinates of the midpoint of a line segment that connects the points $(7, -3)$ and $(-5, 6)$?

(A) $\left(6, -4\frac{1}{2}\right)$ (C) $\left(2, \frac{1}{2}\right)$

(B) $(2, 3)$ (D) $\left(1, 1\frac{1}{2}\right)$

37. A coordinate plane is placed over the map of a town. A library is located at $(-5, 1)$, and a museum is located at $(3, 5)$. What is the distance, to the nearest tenth, from the library to the museum?

(F) 4.5   (G) 5.7   (H) 6.3   (J) 8.9

CHALLENGE AND EXTEND

38. Use the diagram to find the following.

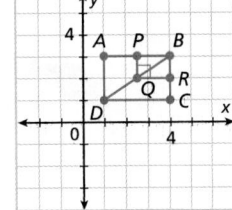

  a. P is the midpoint of $\overline{AB}$, and R is the midpoint of $\overline{BC}$. Find the coordinates of Q. $Q(2.5, 2)$

  b. Find the area of rectangle $PBRQ$. 1.5

  c. Find DB. Round to the nearest tenth. $\sqrt{13} \approx 3.6$

39. The coordinates of X are $(a - 5, -2a)$. The coordinates of Y are $(a + 1, 2a)$. If the distance between X and Y is 10, find the value of a. ± 2

40. Find two points on the y-axis that are a distance of 5 units from $(4, 2)$. $(0, 5); (0, -1)$

41. Given $\angle ACB$ is a right angle of $\triangle ABC$, $AC = x$, and $BC = y$, find AB in terms of x and y. $AB = \sqrt{x^2 + y^2}$

SPIRAL REVIEW

Determine if the ordered pair $(-1, 4)$ satisfies each function. *(Previous course)*

42. $y = 3x - 1$ **43.** $f(x) = 5 - x^2$ **44.** $g(x) = x^2 - x + 2$
    no   yes   yes

$\overrightarrow{BD}$ bisects straight angle ABC, and $\overrightarrow{BE}$ bisects $\angle CBD$. Find the measure of each angle and classify it as acute, right, or obtuse. *(Lesson 1-3)*

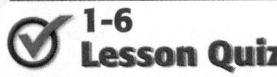

45. $\angle ABD$ **46.** $\angle CBE$ **47.** $\angle ABE$
  90°; rt.   45°; acute   135°; obtuse

Find the area of each of the following. *(Lesson 1-5)*

48. square whose perimeter is 20 in. 25 in^2

49. triangle whose height is 2 ft and whose base is twice its height 4 ft^2

50. rectangle whose length is x and whose width is $(4x + 5)$ $4x^2 + 5x$

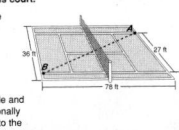

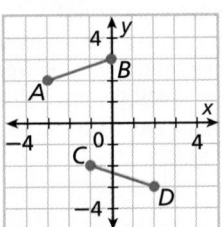

Objectives: Identify reflections, rotations, and translations.

Graph transformations in the coordinate plane.

Online Edition
Tutorial Videos, Interactivity

Countdown to TAKS Week 2

Power Presentations
with PowerPoint®

Warm Up

1. Draw a line that divides a right angle in half.

2. Draw three different squares with (3, 2) as one vertex.
   Check students' drawings.

3. Find the values of x and y if
   $(3, -2) = (x + 1, y - 3)$
   $x = 2; y = 1$

Also available on transparency

Math Humor

Spanish teacher: Why didn't you translate the verb?

Student: I did. I moved it 3 inches right and 2 inches down.

Geometry TEKS

G.1 Geometric structure*
(A) develop an awareness of the structure of a mathematical system, connecting definitions, postulates, ...

G.5 Geometric patterns*
(C) use properties of transformations ... to make connections between mathematics and the real world ...

* **Knowledge and Skills** See p. 4.

★ TEKS G.5.C Geometric patterns: use properties of transformations ... to make connections between mathematics and the real world .... Also G.1.A

Objectives
Identify reflections, rotations, and translations.

Graph transformations in the coordinate plane.

Vocabulary
transformation
preimage
image
reflection
rotation
translation

Who uses this?
Artists use transformations to create decorative patterns. (See Example 4.)

The Alhambra, a 13th-century palace in Grenada, Spain, is famous for the geometric patterns that cover its walls and floors. To create a variety of designs, the builders based the patterns on several different *transformations*.

A **transformation** is a change in the position, size, or shape of a figure. The original figure is called the **preimage**. The resulting figure is called the **image**. A transformation *maps* the preimage to the image. Arrow notation (→) is used to describe a transformation, and primes (′) are used to label the image.

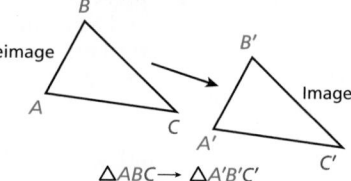

Preimage / Image
$\triangle ABC \rightarrow \triangle A'B'C'$

 Know it! Note

Transformations

REFLECTION	ROTATION	TRANSLATION
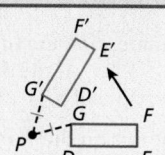	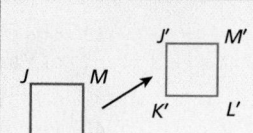	
A **reflection** (or *flip*) is a transformation across a line, called the line of reflection. Each point and its image are the same distance from the line of reflection.	A **rotation** (or *turn*) is a transformation about a point P, called the center of rotation. Each point and its image are the same distance from P.	A **translation** (or *slide*) is a transformation in which all the points of a figure move the same distance in the same direction.

EXAMPLE 1 **Identifying Transformations**

Identify the transformation. Then use arrow notation to describe the transformation.

A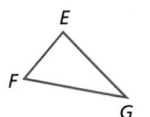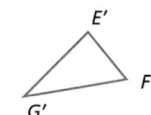

The transformation cannot be a translation because each point and its image are not in the same position.

The transformation is a reflection. $\triangle EFG \rightarrow \triangle E'F'G'$

---

1 Introduce

EXPLORATION

1-7 **Transformations in the Coordinate Plane**

Use geometry software to reflect a triangle across a line segment.

1. Draw $\overline{AB}$. (This will be the line of reflection.)

2. Draw $\triangle RST$ on one side of $\overline{AB}$.

3. Select $\overline{AB}$ and choose Mark Mirror from the Transform menu. Then select $\triangle RST$ and choose Reflect from the Transform menu. Label the new triangle as $\triangle R'S'T'$.

4. Construct $\overline{TT'}$. Then select $\overline{TT'}$ and $\overline{AB}$ and use the Construct menu to construct their intersection X. Measure $\overline{TX}$, $\overline{T'X}$, and $\angle TXB$.

5. Drag T. What do you notice about the measurements as you do so?

Motivate

Show students examples of tessellations, translations, rotations, and reflections in the real world, from magazines or advertisements. Ask students to demonstrate transformations by standing and sliding two steps right and then rotating 90° clockwise.

Explorations and answers are provided in the *Explorations* binder.

Identify the transformation. Then use arrow notation to describe the transformation.

B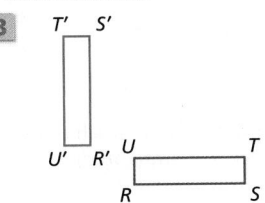

The transformation cannot be a reflection because each point and its image are not the same distance from a line of reflection.

The transformation is a 90° rotation. $RSTU \rightarrow R'S'T'U'$

CHECK IT OUT! Identify each transformation. Then use arrow notation to describe the transformation.

1a.

translation; $MNOP \rightarrow M'N'O'P'$

1b.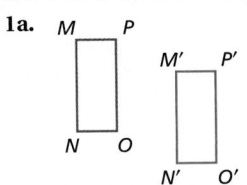

rotation; $\triangle XYZ \rightarrow \triangle X'Y'Z'$

EXAMPLE 2 Drawing and Identifying Transformations

A figure has vertices at $A(-1, 4)$, $B(-1, 1)$, and $C(3, 1)$. After a transformation, the image of the figure has vertices at $A'(-1, -4)$, $B'(-1, -1)$, and $C'(3, -1)$. Draw the preimage and image. Then identify the transformation.

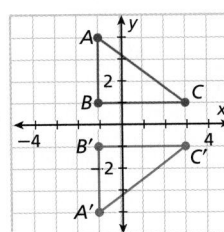

Plot the points. Then use a straightedge to connect the vertices.

The transformation is a reflection across the x-axis because each point and its image are the same distance from the x-axis.

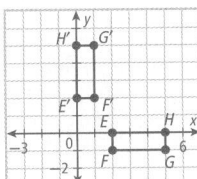

CHECK IT OUT! 2. A figure has vertices at $E(2, 0)$, $F(2, -1)$, $G(5, -1)$, and $H(5, 0)$. After a transformation, the image of the figure has vertices at $E'(0, 2)$, $F'(1, 2)$, $G'(1, 5)$, and $H'(0, 5)$. Draw the preimage and image. Then identify the transformation. **rotation; 90°**

To find coordinates for the image of a figure in a translation, add a to the x-coordinates of the preimage and add b to the y-coordinates of the preimage. Translations can also be described by a rule such as $(x, y) \rightarrow (x + a, y + b)$.

EXAMPLE 3 Translations in the Coordinate Plane

Find the coordinates for the image of $\triangle ABC$ after the translation $(x, y) \rightarrow (x + 3, y - 4)$. Draw the image.

Step 1 Find the coordinates of $\triangle ABC$. The vertices of $\triangle ABC$ are $A(-1, 1)$, $B(-3, 3)$, and $C(-4, 0)$.

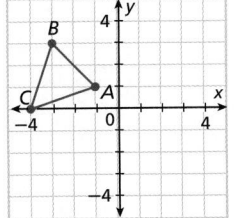

2 Teach

Guided Instruction

Explain the concepts of reflection, rotation, and translation; the terms *preimage* and *image*; and prime notation before using examples on a coordinate plane.

Teaching Tip **Inclusion** Have students look in a mirror (MK). They are the *preimage before* they see themselves in the mirror. The image is their reflection in the mirror.

Reaching All Learners

Through Concrete Manipulatives

Give students a coordinate grid and a cut-out triangle. Have them slide the figure to a new location, rotate it about the origin, and reflect it over a specified line to find the image. Show students why a reflection is not equivalent to a 180° rotation. Use notebook paper with a large *F* marked on one side to show that the image in a rotation is upside down.

Additional Examples

Example 1

Identify the transformation. Then use arrow notation to describe the transformation.

A.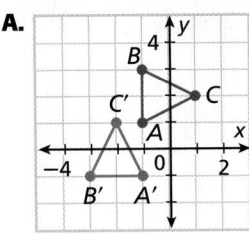

90° rotation, $\triangle ABC \rightarrow \triangle A'B'C'$

B.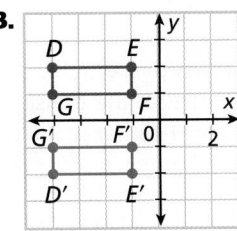

reflection, $DEFG \rightarrow D'E'F'G'$

Example 2

A figure has vertices at $A(1, -1)$, $B(2, 3)$, and $C(4, -2)$. After a transformation, the image of the figure has vertices at $A'(-1, -1)$, $B'(-2, 3)$, and $C'(-4, -2)$. Draw the preimage and image. Then identify the transformation.

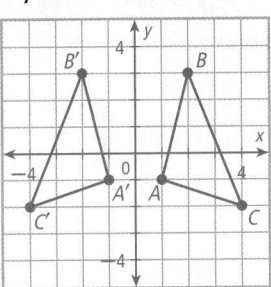

reflection across the y-axis

Also available on transparency

INTERVENTION
Questioning Strategies

EXAMPLE 1
• How would each image in **Example 1A** and **Example 1B** differ if the transformation were a translation?

EXAMPLE 2
• How did you decide what type of transformation this was?

Additional Examples

Example 3

Find the coordinates for the image of △ABC after the translation $(x, y) \rightarrow (x + 2, y - 1)$. Draw the image. $A'(-2, 1)$, $B'(-1, 3)$, $C'(1, 0)$

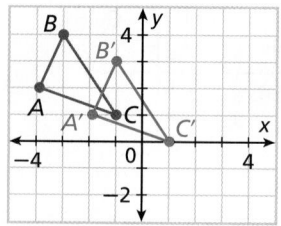

Example 4

The figure shows part of a tile floor. Write a rule for the translation of hexagon 1 to hexagon 2.

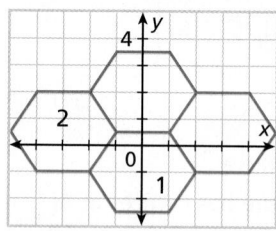

$(x, y) \rightarrow (x - 3, y + 1.5)$

Also available on transparency

INTERVENTION ◀▬▶
Questioning Strategies

EXAMPLE 3

• How would the image differ if the translation were $(x, y) \rightarrow (x - 2, y + 1)$?

EXAMPLE 4

• To write a rule for the translation, does it matter which point on the figure you choose? Why or why not?

Step 2 Apply the rule to find the vertices of the image.
$$A'(-1 + 3, 1 - 4) = A'(2, -3)$$
$$B'(-3 + 3, 3 - 4) = B'(0, -1)$$
$$C'(-4 + 3, 0 - 4) = C'(-1, -4)$$

Step 3 Plot the points. Then finish drawing the image by using a straightedge to connect the vertices.

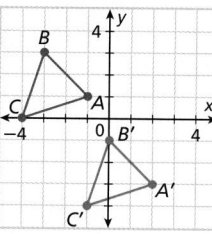

 **3.** Find the coordinates for the image of *JKLM* after the translation $(x, y) \rightarrow (x - 2, y + 4)$. Draw the image. $J'(-1, 5)$; $K'(1, 5)$; $L'(1, 0)$; $M'(-1, 0)$

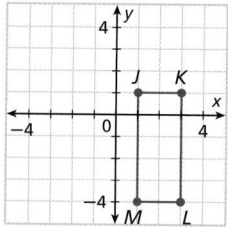

EXAMPLE 4 *Art History Application*

The pattern shown is similar to a pattern on a wall of the Alhambra. Write a rule for the translation of square 1 to square 2.

Step 1 Choose 2 points

Choose a point *A* on the preimage and a corresponding point *A'* on the image. *A* has coordinates $(3, 1)$, and *A'* has coordinates $(1, 3)$.

Step 2 Translate

To translate *A* to *A'*, 2 units are subtracted from the *x*-coordinate and 2 units are added to the *y*-coordinate. Therefore, the translation rule is $(x, y) \rightarrow (x - 2, y + 2)$.

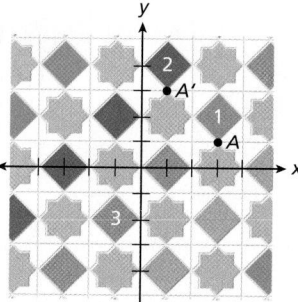

 **4.** Use the diagram to write a rule for the translation of square 1 to square 3. $(x, y) \rightarrow (x - 4, y - 4)$

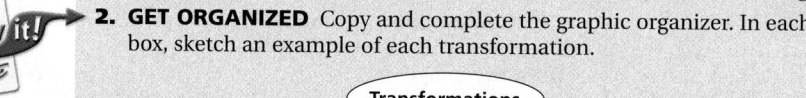

THINK AND DISCUSS

1. Explain how to recognize a reflection when given a figure and its image.

2. GET ORGANIZED Copy and complete the graphic organizer. In each box, sketch an example of each transformation.

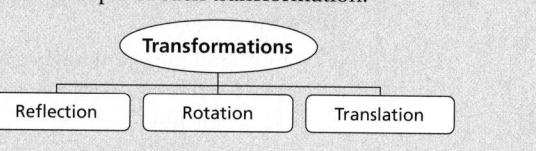

---

3 Close

Summarize

Review the three types of transformations and give an example of each.

ONGOING ASSESSMENT

and INTERVENTION ◀▬▶

Diagnose Before the Lesson
1-7 Warm Up, TE p. 50

Monitor During the Lesson
Check It Out! Exercises, SE pp. 51–52
Questioning Strategies, TE pp. 51–52

Assess After the Lesson
1-7 Lesson Quiz, TE p. 55
Alternative Assessment, TE p. 55

Answers to *Think and Discuss*

Possible answers:

1. The preimage and image will be mirror images of each other.

2. See p. A2.

GUIDED PRACTICE

Vocabulary Apply the vocabulary from this lesson to answer each question.

1. Given the transformation $\triangle XYZ \rightarrow \triangle X'Y'Z'$, name the preimage and image of the transformation. **Preimage is $\triangle XYZ$; image is $\triangle X'Y'Z'$.**

2. The types of transformations of geometric figures in the coordinate plane can be described as a slide, a flip, or a turn. What are the other names used to identify these transformations? **translation; reflection; rotation**

SEE EXAMPLE **1**
p. 50

Identify each transformation. Then use arrow notation to describe the transformation.

3.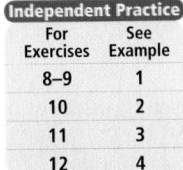
reflection; $\triangle ABC \rightarrow \triangle A'B'C'$

4.
translation; $PQRS \rightarrow P'Q'R'S'$

SEE EXAMPLE **2**
p. 51

5. A figure has vertices at $A(-3, 2)$, $B(-1, -1)$, and $C(-4, -2)$. After a transformation, the image of the figure has vertices at $A'(3, 2)$, $B'(1, -1)$, and $C'(4, -2)$. Draw the preimage and image. Then identify the transformation. **reflection across the y-axis**

SEE EXAMPLE **3**
p. 51

6. $D'(-1, 1)$;
$E'(-2, -1)$;
$F'(1, -2)$

6. **Multi-Step** The coordinates of the vertices of $\triangle DEF$ are $D(2, 3)$, $E(1, 1)$, and $F(4, 0)$. Find the coordinates for the image of $\triangle DEF$ after the translation $(x, y) \rightarrow (x - 3, y - 2)$. Draw the preimage and image.

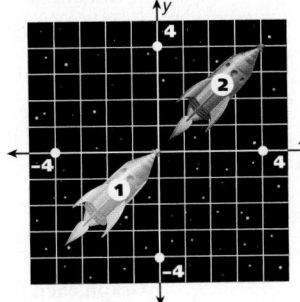

SEE EXAMPLE **4**
p. 52

7. **Animation** In an animated film, a simple scene can be created by translating a figure against a still background. Write a rule for the translation that maps the rocket from position 1 to position 2.
$(x, y) \rightarrow (x + 4, y + 4)$

PRACTICE AND PROBLEM SOLVING

TEKS 🔷 TAKS

Skills Practice p. S5
Application Practice p. S28

Identify each transformation. Then use arrow notation to describe the transformation.

8. 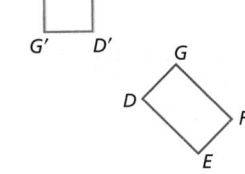 **rotation; $DEFG \rightarrow D'E'F'G'$**

9. **reflection; $WXYZ \rightarrow W'X'Y'Z'$**

10. A figure has vertices at $J(-2, 3)$, $K(0, 3)$, $L(0, 1)$, and $M(-2, 1)$. After a transformation, the image of the figure has vertices at $J'(2, 1)$, $K'(4, 1)$, $L'(4, -1)$, and $M'(2, -1)$. Draw the preimage and image. Then identify the transformation. **translation**

Assignment Guide

Assign *Guided Practice* exercises as necessary.

If you finished Examples **1–2**
  Basic 8–10, 13–15, 17–22
  Average 8–10, 13–15, 17–22
Advanced 8–10, 13–15, 17–22, 34

If you finished Examples **1–4**
  Basic 8–18, 26–32, 38–47
  Average 8–33, 38–47
Advanced 8–47

Homework Quick Check
Quickly check key concepts.
Exercises: 8, 10–12, 14, 18, 26, 28

Answers

5.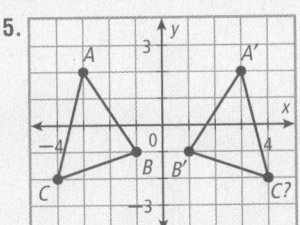

6.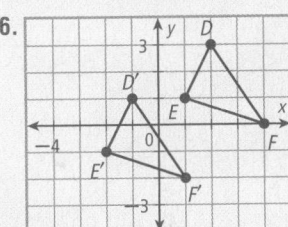

Answers

10.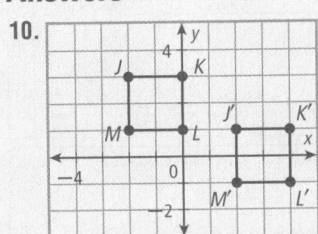

🔶 TAKS Practice

Grades 9–11	Exercises
Obj. 5	38–41
Obj. 6	13–37
Obj. 7	44–47
Obj. 10	13–15, 27, 28

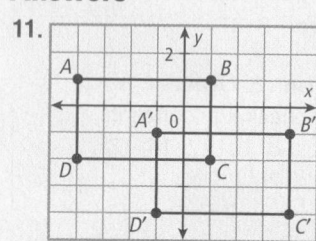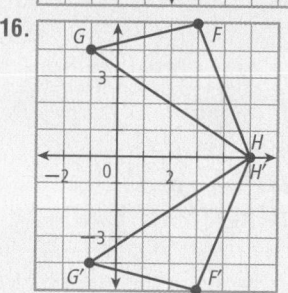
11. $A'(-1, -1)$, $B'(4, -1)$, $C'(4, -4)$, $D'(-1, -4)$

17.

18. $\triangle 1$ to $\triangle 2$:
$(x, y) \rightarrow (x, -y)$
$\triangle 2$ to $\triangle 3$:
$(x, y) \rightarrow (-x, y)$
$\triangle 3$ to $\triangle 4$:
$(x, y) \rightarrow (x, -y)$

11. **Multi-Step** The coordinates of the vertices of rectangle *ABCD* are $A(-4, 1)$, $B(1, 1)$, $C(1, -2)$, and $D(-4, -2)$. Find the coordinates for the image of rectangle *ABCD* after the translation $(x, y) \rightarrow (x + 3, y - 2)$. Draw the preimage and the image.

12. **Travel** Write a rule for the translation that maps the descent of the hot air balloon. $(x, y) \rightarrow (x + 11, y - 4)$

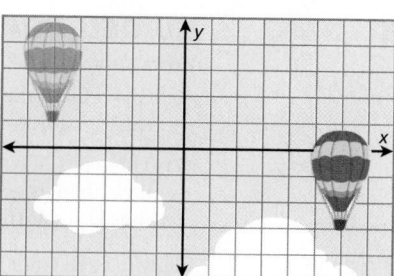

Which transformation is suggested by each of the following?

13. mountain range and its image on a lake **reflection**

14. straight line path of a band marching down a street **translation**

15. wings of a butterfly **reflection**

Given points $F(3, 5)$, $G(-1, 4)$, and $H(5, 0)$, draw $\triangle FGH$ and its reflection across each of the following lines.

16. the *x*-axis   17. the *y*-axis

18. Find the vertices of one of the triangles on the graph. Then use arrow notation to write a rule for translating the other three triangles.

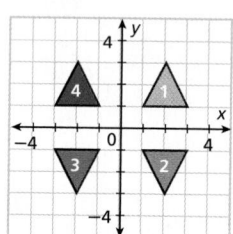

A transformation maps *A* onto *B* and *C* onto *D*.

19. Name the image of *A*. **B**   20. Name the preimage of *B*. **A**

21. Name the image of *C*. **D**   22. Name the preimage of *D*. **C**

23. Find the coordinates for the image of $\triangle RST$ with vertices $R(1, -4)$, $S(-1, -1)$, and $T(-5, 1)$ after the translation $(x, y) \rightarrow (x - 2, y - 8)$. $R'(-1, -12)$; $S'(-3, -9)$; $T'(-7, -7)$

24. **Critical Thinking** Consider the translations $(x, y) \rightarrow (x + 5, y + 3)$ and $(x, y) \rightarrow (x + 10, y + 5)$. Compare the two translations.

Graph each figure and its image after the given translation.

25. $\overline{MN}$ with endpoints $M(2, 8)$ and $N(-3, 4)$ after the translation $(x, y) \rightarrow (x + 2, y - 5)$

26. $\overline{KL}$ with endpoints $K(-1, 1)$ and $L(3, -4)$ after the translation $(x, y) \rightarrow (x - 4, y + 3)$

27. **Write About It** Given a triangle in the coordinate plane, explain how to draw its image after the translation $(x, y) \rightarrow (x + 1, y + 1)$.

MULTI-STEP TAKS PREP

28. This problem will prepare you for the Multi-Step TAKS Prep on page 58. Greg wants to rearrange the triangular pattern of colored stones on his patio. What combination of transformations could he use to transform $\triangle CAE$ to the image on the coordinate plane?
Possible answer: 2 reflections (across the *y*-axis and across $\overleftrightarrow{EC}$)

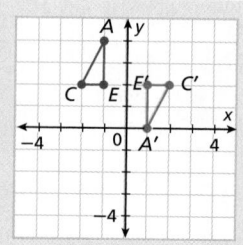

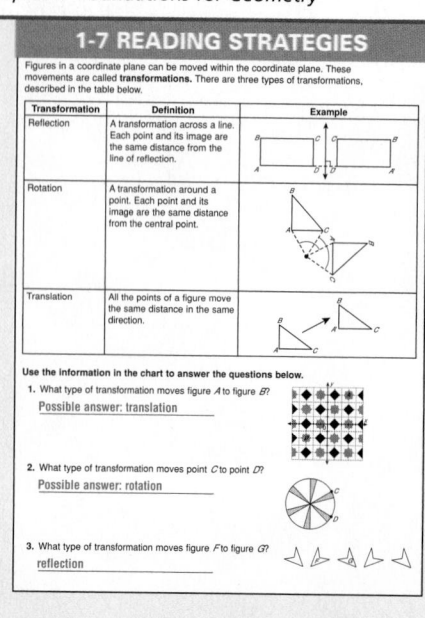

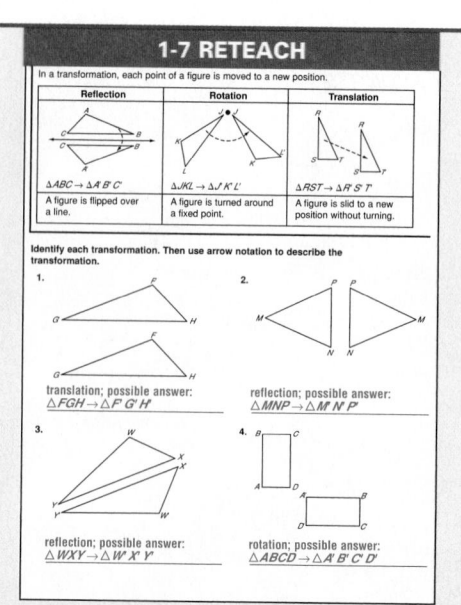

29. Which type of transformation maps △XYZ to △X'Y'Z'?

(A) Reflection (C) Translation
(B) Rotation   (D) Not here

30. △DEF has vertices at $D(-4, 2)$, $E(-3, -3)$, and $F(1, 4)$. Which of these points is a vertex of the image of △DEF after the translation $(x, y) \rightarrow (x - 2, y + 1)$?

(F) $(-2, 1)$ (H) $(-5, -2)$
(G) $(3, 3)$ (J) $(-6, -1)$

31. Consider the translation $(1, 4) \rightarrow (-2, 3)$. What number was added to the x-coordinate?

(A) -3 (B) -1 (C) 1 (D) 7

32. Consider the translation $(-5, -7) \rightarrow (-2, -1)$. What number was added to the y-coordinate?

(F) -3 (G) 3 (H) 6 (J) 8

CHALLENGE AND EXTEND

33. △RST with vertices $R(-2, -2)$, $S(-3, 1)$, and $T(1, 1)$ is translated by $(x, y) \rightarrow (x - 1, y + 3)$. Then the image, △R'S'T', is translated by $(x, y) \rightarrow (x + 4, y - 1)$, resulting in △R"S"T".

a. Find the coordinates for the vertices of △R"S"T". $R''(1, 0)$; $S''(0, 3)$; $T''(4, 3)$

$(x, y) \rightarrow (x + 3, y + 2)$ b. Write a rule for a single translation that maps △RST to △R"S"T".

34. Find the angle through which the minute hand of a clock rotates over a period of 12 minutes. **72°**

35.

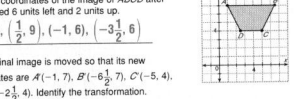

35. A triangle has vertices $A(1, 0)$, $B(5, 0)$, and $C(2, 2)$. The triangle is rotated 90° counterclockwise about the origin. Draw and label the image of the triangle.

Determine the coordinates for the reflection image of any point $A(x, y)$ across the given line.

36. x-axis $(x, -y)$

37. y-axis $(-x, y)$

SPIRAL REVIEW

Use factoring to find the zeros of each function. *(Previous course)*

38. $y = x^2 + 12x + 35$ **−5, −7**

39. $y = x^2 + 3x - 18$ **−6, 3**

40. $y = x^2 - 18x + 81$ **9**

41. $y = x^2 - 3x + 2$ **1, 2**

Given $m\angle A = 76.1°$, find the measure of each of the following. *(Lesson 1-4)*

42. supplement of $\angle A$ **103.9°**

43. complement of $\angle A$ **13.9°**

Use the Distance Formula and the Pythagorean Theorem to find the distance, to the nearest tenth, between each pair of points. *(Lesson 1-6)*

44. $(2, 3)$ and $(4, 6)$ **3.6**

45. $(-1, 4)$ and $(0, 8)$ **4.1**

46. $(-3, 7)$ and $(-6, -2)$ **9.5**

47. $(5, 1)$ and $(-1, 3)$ **6.3**

Journal

Have students explain and give an example on a coordinate plane of a reflection, a translation, and a rotation. Have them write a rule for their translation.

ALTERNATIVE ASSESSMENT

Have students create a figure and its image under a reflection, a rotation, and a translation. Then write rules for each and compare the results.

Power Presentations with PowerPoint®

1-7 Lesson Quiz

1. A figure has vertices at $X(-1, 1)$, $Y(1, 4)$, and $Z(2, 2)$. After a transformation, the image of the figure has vertices at $X'(-3, 2)$, $Y'(-1, 5)$, and $Z'(0, 3)$. Draw the preimage and the image. Identify the transformation.   translation

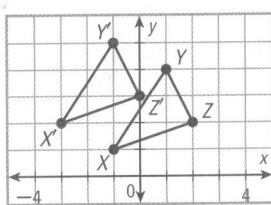

2. What transformation is suggested by the wings of an airplane?   reflection

3. Given points $P(-2, -1)$ and $Q(-1, 3)$, draw $\overline{PQ}$ and its reflection across the y-axis.

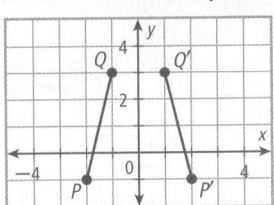

4. Find the coordinates of the image of $F(2, 7)$ after the translation $(x, y) \rightarrow (x + 5, y - 6)$. $(7, 1)$

Also available on transparency

Lesson 1-7 **55**

1-7 PROBLEM SOLVING

Use the diagram of the starting positions of five basketball players for Exercises 1 and 2.

1. After the first step of a play, player 3 is at $(-1.5, 0)$ and player 4 is at $(1, 0.5)$. Write a rule to describe the translations of players 3 and 4 from their starting positions to their new positions.

player 3: $(x, y) \rightarrow (x + 4.5, y - 1)$;

player 4: $(x, y) \rightarrow (x - 4, y + 1)$

2. For the second step of the play, player 3 is to move to a position described by the rule $(x, y) \rightarrow (x - 4, y - 2)$ and player 4 is to move to a position described by the rule $(x, y) \rightarrow (x + 3, y - 2)$. What are the positions of these two players after this step of the play?

player 3: $(-5.5, -2)$; player 4: $(4, -1.5)$

Use the diagram for Exercises 3–5.

3. Find the coordinates of the image of *ABCD* after it is moved 6 units left and 2 units up.

$(-5, 9)$, $\left(\frac{1}{2}, 9\right)$, $(-1, 6)$, $\left(-3\frac{1}{2}, 6\right)$

4. The original image is moved so that its new coordinates are $A'(-1, 7)$, $B'(-6\frac{1}{2}, 7)$, $C'(-5, 4)$, and $D'(-2\frac{1}{2}, 4)$. Identify the transformation.

reflection across the y-axis

5. The original image is translated so that the coordinates of B' are $(11\frac{1}{2}, 17)$. What are the coordinates of the other three vertices of the image after this translation?

$A'(6, 17)$, $C'(10, 14)$, $D'\left(7\frac{1}{2}, 14\right)$

6. Triangle *HJK* has vertices $H(0, -9)$, $J(-1, -5)$, and $K(7, 8)$. What are the coordinates of the vertices after the translation $(x, y) \rightarrow (x - 1, y - 3)$?

A $H'(-1, 12)$, $J'(-2, 8)$, $K'(6, -5)$
B $H'(-1, 12)$, $J'(2, -8)$, $K'(-6, 5)$
C $H'(-1, -12)$, $J'(-2, -8)$, $K'(6, 5)$
D $H'(1, 12)$, $J'(2, 8)$, $K'(-6, -5)$

7. A segment has endpoints at $S(2, 3)$ and $T(-2, 8)$. After a transformation, the image has endpoints at $S'(2, 3)$ and $T'(6, 8)$. Which best describes the transformation?

F reflection across the y-axis
G translation $(x, y) \rightarrow (x + 8, y)$
H rotation about the origin
J rotation about the point $(2, 3)$

1-7 CHALLENGE

In Exercises 1 and 2, each image was the result of more than one transformation of the preimage. Show the steps that you can use to get from the preimage to the image. Graph the intermediate image and describe each step.

1.

Possible answer: first, a reflection across the y-axis.

Then, a translation 3 units right and 5 units down.

2.

Possible answer: first, a reflection across the line $y = 3$.

Then, a translation 8 units left and 4 units down.

Trapezoid *W'X'Y'Z'* resulted after two transformations.

3. Make a conjecture about the coordinates of the vertices of trapezoid *W X Y Z*. Explain.

$W'(-7, -5)$, $X'(-3, -5)$, $Y'(-4, -2)$, $Z'(-6, -2)$; preimage reflected across x-axis; image translated by $(x, y) \rightarrow (x + 8, y + 3)$.

4. Is this the only possible solution for the coordinates of *W X Y Z*? Explain.

No, coordinates could be $W'(1, 8)$, $X'(5, 8)$, $Y'(4, 5)$, $Z'(2, 5)$.

Lesson 1-7 **55**

Objective: Use geometry software to perform transformations and explore their properties.

Materials: geometry software

 Online Edition
TechKeys

 Countdown to TAKS Week 2

Teach

Discuss

Have students measure the sides, angles, and perimeter of both the preimage and the image of △*ABC*. Discuss whether any of these measures change after a translation or a rotation. no Discuss the arrow and prime notation to make sure students understand the difference in naming the preimage and image. Ask students whether the area of the image is affected by either a translation or a rotation. no

 Geometry TEKS

G.2 Geometric structure*

(A) use constructions to explore attributes of geometric figures and to make conjectures about geometric relationships

(B) make conjectures about angles, lines, … and determine the validity of the conjectures, choosing from a variety of approaches such as coordinate, transformational, …

* **Knowledge and Skills** See p. 4.

1-7
Technology **LAB** **Explore Transformations**

A transformation is a movement of a figure from its original position (preimage) to a new position (image). In this lab, you will use geometry software to perform transformations and explore their properties.

Use with Lesson 1-7

 TEKS G.2.A Geometric structure: use constructions to explore attributes of geometric figures and to make conjectures about geometric relationships. **Also G.2.B**

go.hrw.com/Geo/TX
Lab Resources Online
KEYWORD: MG7 Lab1

Activity 1

1 Construct a triangle using the segment tool. Use the text tool to label the vertices *A*, *B*, and *C*.

2 Select points *A* and *B* in that order. Choose Mark Vector from the Transform menu.

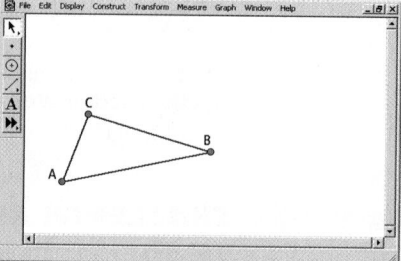

3 Select △*ABC* by clicking on all three segments of the triangle.

4 Choose Translate from the Transform menu, using *Marked* as the translation vector. What do you notice about the relationship between your preimage and its image?
They appear to be ≅.

5 What happens when you drag a vertex or a side of △*ABC*?
The △s move together and stay the same size and shape.

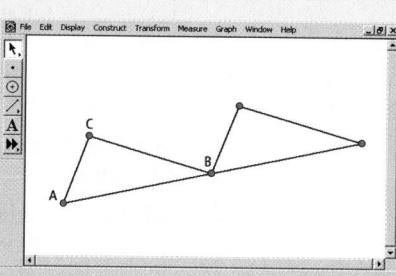

Try This
1. The image of the △ moves in the same direction as the endpt.
2. The △s move together and remain a fixed dist. apart.

For Problems 1 and 2 choose New Sketch from the File menu.

1. Construct a triangle and a segment outside the triangle. Mark this segment as a translation vector as you did in Step 2 of Activity 1. Use Step 4 of Activity 1 to translate the triangle. What happens when you drag an endpoint of the new segment?

2. Instead of translating by a marked vector, use *Rectangular* as the translation vector and translate by a horizontal distance of 1 cm and a vertical distance of 2 cm. Compare this method with the marked vector method. What happens when you drag a side or vertex of the triangle?

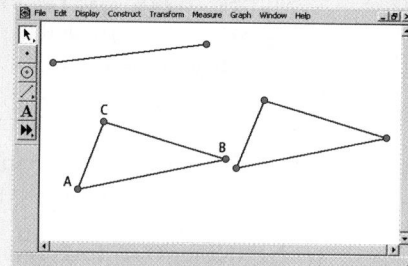

3. Select the angles and sides of the preimage and image triangles. Use the tools in the Measure menu to measure length, angle measure, perimeter, and area. What do you think is true about these two figures? Each measurement is the same for the preimage and image △s. The △s appear to be ≅.

56 Chapter 1 Foundations for Geometry

Activity 2

1 Construct a triangle. Label the vertices G, H, and I.

2 Select point H and choose Mark Center from the Transform menu.

3 Select ∠GHI by selecting points G, H, and I in that order. Choose Mark Angle from the Transform menu.

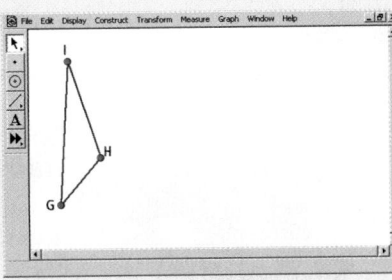

4 Select the entire triangle △GHI by dragging a selection box around the figure.

5 Choose Rotate from the Transform menu, using *Marked Angle* as the angle of rotation.

6 What happens when you drag a vertex or a side of △GHI? **The △ and its image rotate by the same ∠ measure and remain the same size and shape.**

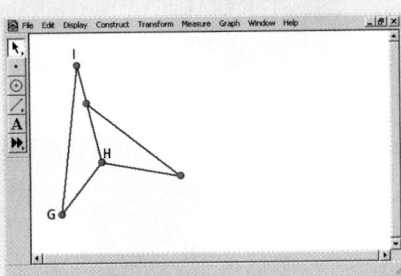

Try This

For Problems 4–6 choose New Sketch from the File menu.

4. Instead of selecting an angle of the triangle as the rotation angle, draw a new angle outside of the triangle. Mark this angle. Mark ∠GHI as Center and rotate the triangle. What happens when you drag one of the points that form the rotation angle? **The image rotates by the same ∠ measure as the marked ∠.**

The △ rotates by the same ∠ measure. When P is inside, the image overlaps the △. When P coincides with a vertex, the image also coincides with the vertex.

5. Construct △QRS, a new rotation angle, and a point P not on the triangle. Mark P as the center and mark the angle. Rotate the triangle. What happens when you drag P outside, inside, or on the preimage triangle?

6. Instead of rotating by a marked angle, use *Fixed Angle* as the rotation method and rotate by a fixed angle measure of 30°. Compare this method with the marked angle method.

7. Using the fixed angle method of rotation, can you find an angle measure that will result in an image figure that exactly covers the preimage figure? **360°**

6. The △ rotated by an ∠ of 30°, not by the measure of the marked ∠.

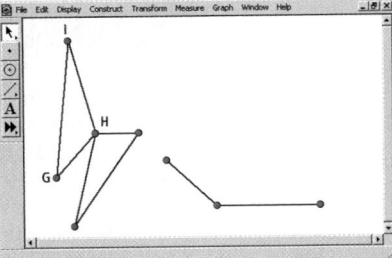

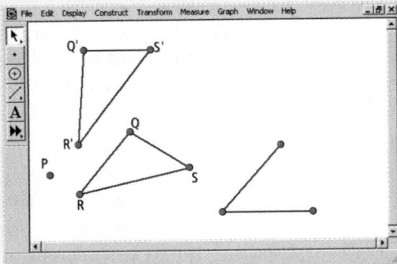

Close

Key Concept

When you translate or rotate a figure, the lengths of sides, angle measures, perimeter, and area do not change. The image is congruent to the preimage.

Assessment

Journal Have students explain how the preimage and image of a figure compare under a translation and a rotation. Have them discuss which properties are preserved.

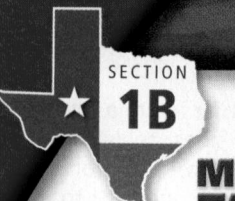

Organizer

Objective: Assess students' ability to apply concepts and skills in Lessons 1-5 through 1-7 in a real-world format.

Online Edition

Resources

Geometry Assessments
www.mathtekstoolkit.org

Problem	Text Reference
1	Lesson 1-5
2	Lesson 1-6
3	Lesson 1-7

Coordinate and Transformation Tools

Pave the Way Julia wants to use L-shaped paving stones to pave a patio. Two stones will cover a 12 in. by 18 in. rectangle.

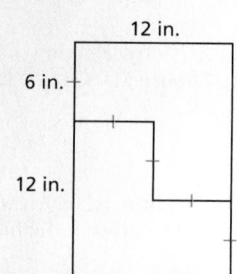

1. $A = 36 + 72$
$= 108$ ft^2; $P = 48$ ft;
She would need 144 stones. Total cost is $324.00.
Explanation: 2 stones make a 12 in. by 18 in. rect.
$12(18) = 216$ in.
$= 1.5$ ft^2. $\frac{108}{1.5} = 72$.
Since 2 stones make up each of the rects., $72(2)$
$= 144$ stones, and
$144(2.25) = 324$.

2. from $B \approx 8.5$ ft; from $C = 6.0$ ft; from $E \approx 13.4$ ft; from $F = 6.0$ ft

3. She used a reflection across $\overline{AB}$. Check students' drawings; possible answers: reflection across $\overline{AF}$; rotation about B; translation from D to F; rotation about E; translation from F to E.

1. She drew diagram *ABCDEF* to represent the patio. Find the area and perimeter of the patio. How many paving stones would Julia need to purchase to pave the patio? If each stone costs $2.25, what is the total cost of the stones for the patio? Describe how you calculated your answer.

2. Julia plans to place a fountain at the midpoint of $\overline{AF}$. How far is the fountain from B, C, E, and F? Round to the nearest tenth.

3. Julia used a pair of paving stones to create another pattern for the patio. Describe the transformation she used to create the pattern. If she uses just one transformation, how many other patterns can she create using two stones? Draw all the possible combinations. Describe the transformation used to create each pattern.

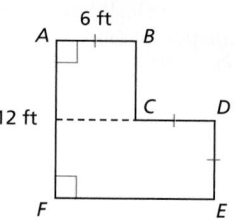

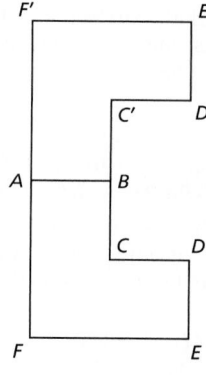

TAKS Practice

Grades 9–11	Problems
Obj. 2	1
Obj. 3	1
Obj. 4	1
Obj. 6	3
Obj. 7	2
Obj. 8	1
Obj. 10	1–3

INTERVENTION

Scaffolding Questions

1. What is the significance of the way the sides of the stones are marked? How can you find the area of this figure? The marks on the sides of the figure mean that these sides are the same length. Right angle marks tell you that $\angle A$ and $\angle F$ measure 90°. You will use the formulas for the area of a rectangle and the area of a square to find the areas of the two parts of the figure. Then add the two areas together.

2. What formulas will you use to find the location of the fountain? First you will find the midpoint of a segment. Then use the Distance Formula to find the distance between the fountain and each point.

3. How can you decide which transformation to use? What is meant by creating different patterns? You can use a reflection, a rotation, or a translation. You just need to be sure that the sides of the figures will touch when you repeat your pattern. Different patterns can be created using the two tiles and one transformation.

Extension

Have students choose a pattern and reproduce it on graph paper. They could also create the tile patterns using geometry software.

READY TO GO ON?

SECTION 1B

Quiz for Lessons 1-5 Through 1-7

1-5 Using Formulas in Geometry

Find the perimeter and area of each figure.

1.
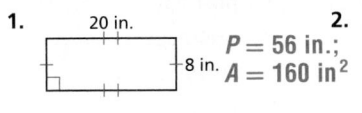
20 in.
8 in.
$P = 56$ in.; $A = 160$ in^2

2.
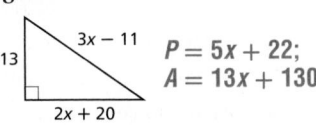
$3x - 11$
13
$2x + 20$
$P = 5x + 22$; $A = 13x + 130$

3.
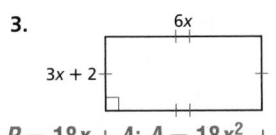
$6x$
$3x + 2$
$P = 18x + 4$; $A = 18x^2 + 12x$

4.
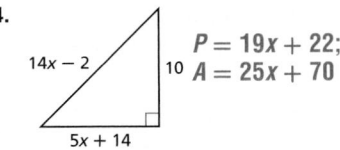
$14x - 2$
10
$5x + 14$
$P = 19x + 22$; $A = 25x + 70$

5. Find the circumference and area of a circle with a radius of 6 m. Use the π key on your calculator and round to the nearest tenth. $C \approx 37.7$ m; $A \approx 113.1$ m^2

1-6 Midpoint and Distance in the Coordinate Plane

6. Find the coordinates for the midpoint of $\overline{XY}$ with endpoints $X(-4, 6)$ and $Y(3, 8)$. $(-0.5, 7)$

7. J is the midpoint of $\overline{HK}$, H has coordinates $(6, -2)$, and J has coordinates $(9, 3)$. Find the coordinates of K. $(12, 8)$

8. Using the Distance Formula, find QR and ST to the nearest tenth. Then determine if $\overline{QR} \cong \overline{ST}$. $QR \approx 7.3$; $ST \approx 7.3$; $\overline{QR} \cong \overline{ST}$

9. Using the Distance Formula and the Pythagorean Theorem, find the distance, to the nearest tenth, from $F(4, 3)$ to $G(-3, -2)$. 8.6

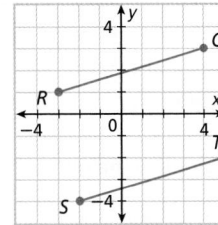

1-7 Transformations in the Coordinate Plane

Identify the transformation. Then use arrow notation to describe the transformation.

10.
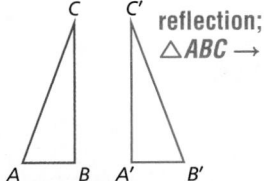
reflection; $\triangle ABC \rightarrow \triangle A'B'C'$

11.

translation; $PQRS \rightarrow P'Q'R'S'$

12. A graphic designer used the translation $(x, y) \rightarrow (x - 3, y + 2)$ to transform square $HJKL$. Find the coordinates and graph the image of square $HJKL$.

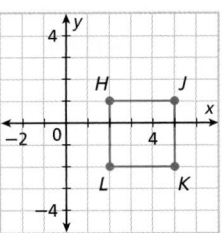

13. A figure has vertices at $X(1, 1)$, $Y(3, 1)$, and $Z(3, 4)$. After a transformation, the image of the figure has vertices at $X'(-1, -1)$, $Y'(-3, -1)$, and $Z'(-3, -4)$. Graph the preimage and image. Then identify the transformation.

12. $H'(-1, 3)$; $J'(2, 3)$; $K'(2, 0)$; $L'(-1, 0)$

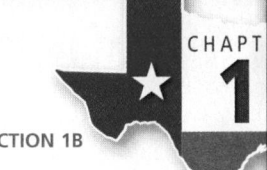

READY TO GO ON?

Organizer

Objective: Assess students' mastery of concepts and skills in Lessons 1-5 through 1-7.

Resources

Assessment Resources
Section 1B Quiz

Test & Practice Generator
One-Stop Planner®

INTERVENTION ⬅➡

Resources

Ready to Go On? Intervention and Enrichment Worksheets

Ready to Go On? CD-ROM

Ready to Go On? Online

my.hrw.com

Answers
12–13. See p. A11.

READY TO GO ON?
Diagnose and Prescribe

NO INTERVENE

YES ENRICH

READY TO GO ON? Intervention, Section 1B			
Ready to Go On? Intervention	**Worksheets**	**CD-ROM**	**Online**
✓ Lesson 1-5	1-5 Intervention	Activity 1-5	Diagnose and Prescribe Online
✓ Lesson 1-6	1-6 Intervention	Activity 1-6	
✓ Lesson 1-7	1-7 Intervention	Activity 1-7	

READY TO GO ON? Enrichment, Section 1B
Worksheets
CD-ROM
Online

Organizer

Objective: Help students organize and review key concepts and skills presented in Chapter 1.

Online Edition
Multilingual Glossary

Resources

PuzzlePro
One-Stop Planner®

Multilingual Glossary Online
go.hrw.com/Geo/TX
KEYWORD: MG7 Glossary

Lesson Tutorial Videos
CD-ROM

Test & Practice Generator
One-Stop Planner®

Answers

1. angle bisector
2. complementary angles
3. hypotenuse
4. *A, F, E, G* or *C, G, D, B*
5. Possible answer: $\overleftrightarrow{GC}$
6. Possible answer: plane *AEG*

 Know it! Note
For a complete list of the postulates and theorems in this chapter, see p. S82.

Vocabulary

acute angle 21	diameter 37	plane 6
adjacent angles 28	distance 13	point 6
angle 20	endpoint 7	postulate 7
angle bisector 23	exterior of an angle 20	preimage 50
area 36	height 36	radius 37
base 36	hypotenuse 45	ray 7
between 14	image 50	reflection 50
bisect 15	interior of an angle 20	right angle 21
circumference 37	leg 45	rotation 50
collinear 6	length 13	segment 7
complementary angles 29	line 6	segment bisector 16
congruent angles 22	linear pair 28	straight angle 21
congruent segments 13	measure 20	supplementary angles 29
construction 14	midpoint 15	transformation 50
coordinate 13	obtuse angle 21	translation 50
coordinate plane 43	opposite rays 7	undefined term 6
coplanar 6	perimeter 36	vertex 20
degree 20	pi 37	vertical angles 30

Complete the sentences below with vocabulary words from the list above.

1. A(n) ___?___ divides an angle into two congruent angles.

2. ___?___ are two angles whose measures have a sum of 90°.

3. The length of the longest side of a right triangle is called the ___?___ .

1-1 Understanding Points, Lines, and Planes (pp. 6–11)

 TEKS G.1.A, G.7.A

EXAMPLES

■ Name the common endpoint of $\overrightarrow{SR}$ and $\overrightarrow{ST}$.

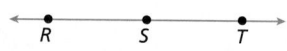
R   S   T

$\overrightarrow{SR}$ and $\overrightarrow{ST}$ are opposite rays with common endpoint *S*.

EXERCISES

Name each of the following.

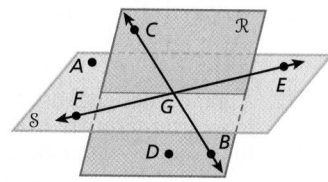

4. four coplanar points

5. line containing *B* and *C*

6. plane that contains *A*, *G*, and *E*

- Draw and label three coplanar lines intersecting in one point.

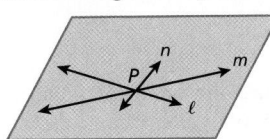

Draw and label each of the following.

7. line containing P and Q

8. pair of opposite rays both containing C

9. $\overleftrightarrow{CD}$ intersecting plane $\mathcal{P}$ at B

 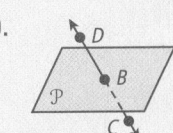
1-2 Measuring and Constructing Segments *(pp. 13–19)*   ⭐ TEKS G.2.A, G.2.B, G.3.B, G.7.C

EXAMPLES

■ Find the length of $\overline{XY}$.

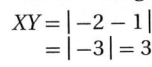

$XY = |-2 - 1|$
$= |-3| = 3$

■ S is between R and T. Find RT.

$RT = RS + ST$
$3x + 2 = 5x - 6 + 2x$
$3x + 2 = 7x - 6$
$x = 2$
$RT = 3(2) + 2 = 8$

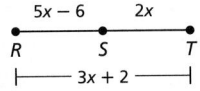

EXERCISES

Find each length.

10. JL **11.** HK

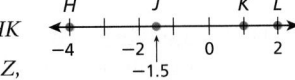

12. Y is between X and Z, $XY = 13.8$, and $XZ = 21.4$. Find YZ.

13. Q is between P and R. Find PR.

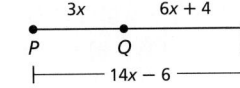

14. U is the midpoint of $\overline{TV}$, $TU = 3x + 4$, and $UV = 5x - 2$. Find TU, UV, and TV.

15. E is the midpoint of $\overline{DF}$, $DE = 9x$, and $EF = 4x + 10$. Find DE, EF, and DF.

1-3 Measuring and Constructing Angles *(pp. 20–27)*   ⭐ TEKS G.1.A, G.1.B, G.2.A, G.2.B, G.3.B

EXAMPLES

■ Classify each angle as acute, right, or obtuse.

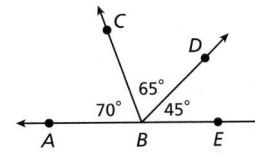

∠ABC acute;
∠CBD acute;
∠ABD obtuse;
∠DBE acute;
∠CBE obtuse

■ $\overrightarrow{KM}$ bisects ∠JKL, m∠JKM = $(3x + 4)°$, and m∠MKL = $(6x - 5)°$. Find m∠JKL.

$3x + 4 = 6x - 5$ *Def. of ∠ bisector*
$3x + 9 = 6x$ *Add 5 to both sides.*
$9 = 3x$ *Subtract 3x from both sides.*
$x = 3$ *Divide both sides by 3.*

m∠JKL = $3x + 4 + 6x - 5$
$= 9x - 1$
$= 9(3) - 1 = 26°$

EXERCISES

16. Classify each angle as acute, right, or obtuse.

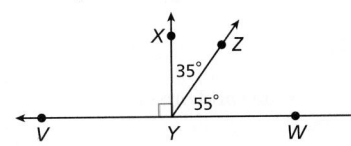

17. m∠HJL = 116°. Find m∠HJK.

18. $\overrightarrow{NP}$ bisects ∠MNQ, m∠MNP = $(6x - 12)°$, and m∠PNQ = $(4x + 8)°$. Find m∠MNQ.

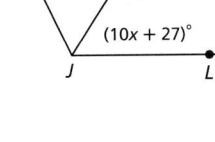

1-4 Pairs of Angles (pp. 28–33)

TEKS G.1.A, G.2.B

EXAMPLES

■ Tell whether the angles are only adjacent, adjacent and form a linear pair, or not adjacent.

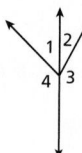

∠1 and ∠2 are only adjacent.

∠2 and ∠4 are not adjacent.

∠2 and ∠3 are adjacent and form a linear pair.

∠1 and ∠4 are adjacent and form a linear pair.

■ Find the measure of the complement and supplement of each angle.

$90 - 67.3 = 22.7°$

$180 - 67.3 = 112.7°$

$90 - (3x - 8) = (98 - 3x)°$

$180 - (3x - 8) = (188 - 3x)°$

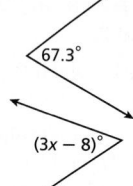

67.3°

$(3x - 8)°$

EXERCISES

Tell whether the angles are only adjacent, adjacent and form a linear pair, or not adjacent.

19. ∠1 and ∠2

20. ∠3 and ∠4

21. ∠2 and ∠5

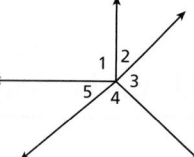

Find the measure of the complement and supplement of each angle.

22.

74.6°

23.

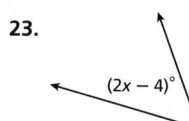

$(2x - 4)°$

24. An angle measures 5 degrees more than 4 times its complement. Find the measure of the angle.

1-5 Using Formulas in Geometry (pp. 36–41)

TEKS G.1.A, G.1.B, G.8.A

EXAMPLES

■ Find the perimeter and area of the triangle.

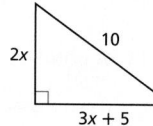

2x

10

$3x + 5$

$P = 2x + 3x + 5 + 10$
$= 5x + 15$

$A = \frac{1}{2}(3x + 5)(2x)$
$= 3x^2 + 5x$

■ Find the circumference and area of the circle to the nearest tenth.

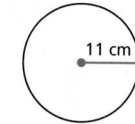

11 cm

$C = 2\pi r$
$= 2\pi(11)$
$= 22\pi$
≈ 69.1 cm

$A = \pi r^2$
$= \pi(11)^2$
$= 121\pi$
≈ 380.1 cm^2

EXERCISES

Find the perimeter and area of each figure.

25.

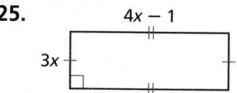

$4x - 1$

3x

26.

$x + 4$

27.

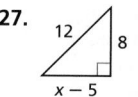

12

8

$x - 5$

28.

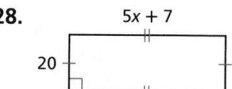

$5x + 7$

20

Find the circumference and area of each circle to the nearest tenth.

29.

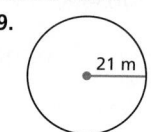

21 m

30.

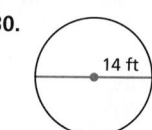

14 ft

31. The area of a triangle is 102 m^2. The base of the triangle is 17 m. What is the height of the triangle?

1-6 Midpoint and Distance in the Coordinate Plane *(pp. 43–49)*  TEKS G.1.A, G.7.A, G.7.C, G.8.C

EXAMPLES

■ X is the midpoint of $\overline{CD}$. C has coordinates $(-4, 1)$, and X has coordinates $(3, -2)$. Find the coordinates of D.

$$(3, -2) = \left(\frac{-4 + x}{2}, \frac{1 + y}{2}\right)$$

$$3 = \frac{-4 + x}{2} \qquad -2 = \frac{1 + y}{2}$$

$$6 = -4 + x \qquad\quad -4 = 1 + y$$

$$10 = x \qquad\qquad -5 = y$$

The coordinates of D are $(10, -5)$.

■ Use the Distance Formula and the Pythagorean Theorem to find the distance, to the nearest tenth, from $(1, 6)$ to $(4, 2)$.

$$d = \sqrt{4 - (1)^2 + 2 - (6)^2} \qquad c^2 = a^2 + b^2$$
$$= \sqrt{3^2 + (-4)^2} \qquad\qquad = 3^2 + 4^2$$
$$= \sqrt{9 + 16} \qquad\qquad = 9 + 16 = 25$$
$$= \sqrt{25} \qquad\qquad\qquad c = \sqrt{25}$$
$$= 5.0 \qquad\qquad\qquad\quad = 5.0$$

EXERCISES

Y is the midpoint of $\overline{AB}$. Find the missing coordinates of each point.

32. $A(3, 2); B(-1, 4); Y(\blacksquare, \blacksquare)$

33. $A(5, 0); B(\blacksquare, \blacksquare); Y(-2, 3)$

34. $A(\blacksquare, \blacksquare); B(-4, 4); Y(-2, 3)$

Use the Distance Formula and the Pythagorean Theorem to find the distance, to the nearest tenth, between each pair of points.

35. $X(-2, 4)$ and $Y(6, 1)$

36. $H(0, 3)$ and $K(-2, -4)$

37. $L(-4, 2)$ and $M(3, -2)$

1-7 Transformations in the Coordinate Plane *(pp. 50–55)*  TEKS G.1.A, G.5.C

EXAMPLES

■ Identify the transformation. Then use arrow notation to describe the transformation.

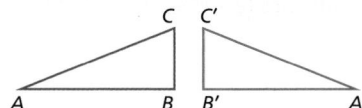

The transformation is a reflection.
$\triangle ABC \rightarrow \triangle A'B'C'$

■ The coordinates of the vertices of rectangle $HJKL$ are $H(2, -1), J(5, -1), K(5, -3)$, and $L(2, -3)$. Find the coordinates of the image of rectangle $HJKL$ after the translation $(x, y) \rightarrow (x - 4, y + 1)$.

$H' = (2 - 4, -1 + 1) = H'(-2, 0)$
$J' = (5 - 4, -1 + 1) = J'(1, 0)$
$K' = (5 - 4, -3 + 1) = K'(1, -2)$
$L' = (2 - 4, -3 + 1) = L'(-2, -2)$

EXERCISES

Identify each transformation. Then use arrow notation to describe the transformation.

38.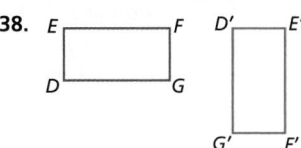

39.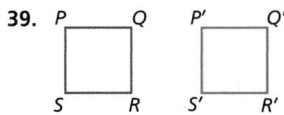

40. The coordinates for the vertices of $\triangle XYZ$ are $X(-5, -4)$, $Y(-3, -1)$, and $Z(-2, -2)$. Find the coordinates for the image of $\triangle XYZ$ after the translation $(x, y) \rightarrow (x + 4, y + 5)$.

Answers

32. $Y(1, 3)$

33. $B(-9, 6)$

34. $A(0, 2)$

35. 8.5

36. 7.3

37. 8.1

38. $90°$ rotation; $DEFG \rightarrow D'E'F'G'$

39. translation; $PQRS \rightarrow P'Q'R'S'$

40. $X'(-1, 1); Y'(1, 4); Z'(2, 3)$

Organizer

Objective: Assess students' mastery of concepts and skills in Chapter 1.

Online Edition

Resources

 Assessment Resources

Chapter 1 Tests

• Free Response
  (Levels A, B, C)

• Multiple Choice
  (Levels A, B, C)

• Performance Assessment

 IDEA Works! CD-ROM

Modified Chapter 1 Test

Test & Practice Generator
One-Stop Planner®

1. Draw and label plane N containing two lines that intersect at B.

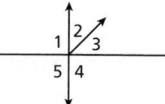

2. Possible answer: D, E, C, A

Use the figure to name each of the following.

3. Possible Answer: $\overleftrightarrow{BE}$

2. four noncoplanar points   **3.** line containing B and E

4. The coordinate of A is −3, and the coordinate of B is 0.5. Find AB. **3.5**

5. E, F, and G represent mile markers along a straight highway. Find EF. **14**

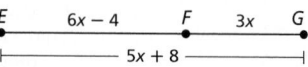

6. J is the midpoint of $\overline{HK}$. Find HJ, JK, and HK.
9; 9; 18

Classify each angle by its measure.

7. m∠LMP = 70° **acute**   **8.** m∠QMN = 90° **rt.**   **9.** m∠PMN = 125° **obtuse**

10. $\overrightarrow{TV}$ bisects ∠RTS. If the m∠RTV = $(16x − 6)°$ and m∠VTS = $(13x + 9)°$, what is the m∠RTV? **74°**

11. An angle's measure is 5 degrees less than 3 times the measure of its supplement. Find the measure of the angle and its supplement. **133.75°; 46.25°**

Tell whether the angles are only adjacent, adjacent and form a linear pair, or not adjacent.

12. ∠2 and ∠3 **only adj.**   **13.** ∠4 and ∠5 **adj. and a lin. pair**   **14.** ∠1 and ∠4 **not adj.**

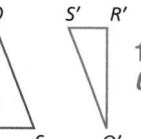

15. Find the perimeter and area of a rectangle with b = 8 ft and h = 4 ft.
P = 24 ft; A = 32 ft²

Find the circumference and area of each circle to the nearest tenth.

16. r = 15 m   **17.** d = 25 ft   **18.** d = 2.8 cm **8.8 cm; 6.2 cm²**   **16. 94.2 m; 706.9 m²**

19. Find the midpoint of the segment with endpoints $(−4, 6)$ and $(3, 2)$. **(−0.5, 4)**   **17. 78.5 ft; 490.9 ft²**

20. M is the midpoint of $\overline{LN}$. M has coordinates $(−5, 1)$, and L has coordinates $(2, 4)$. Find the coordinates of N. **(−12, −2)**

21. Given $A(−5, 1)$, $B(−1, 3)$, $C(1, 4)$, and $D(4, 1)$, is $\overline{AB} \cong \overline{CD}$? Explain. **no; AB ≈ 4.5; CD ≈ 4.2**

Identify each transformation. Then use arrow notation to describe the transformation.

22.

180° rotation;
QRS → Q'R'S'

23.

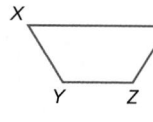 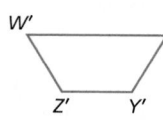

reflection;
WXYZ → W'X'Y'Z'

24. A designer used the translation $(x, y) \rightarrow (x + 3, y − 3)$ to transform a triangular-shaped pin ABC. Find the coordinates and draw the image of △ABC.
$A'(−2, −2)$; $B'(1, 1)$; $C'(2, −2)$

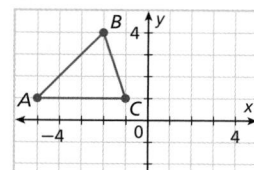 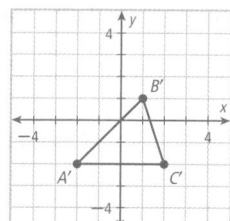

TAKS Practice

Grades 9–11	Items
Obj. 2	4–6, 10, 11
Obj. 3	5, 6, 10, 11
Obj. 4	5, 6, 10, 11
Obj. 6	22–24
Obj. 7	5, 6, 19, 20, 24
Obj. 8	15–18
Obj. 10	24

COLLEGE ENTRANCE EXAM PRACTICE

FOCUS ON SAT

The SAT has three sections: Math, Critical Reading, and Writing. Your SAT scores show how you compare with other students. It can be used by colleges to determine admission and to award merit-based financial aid.

You may want to time yourself as you take this practice test. It should take you about 6 minutes to complete.

On SAT multiple-choice questions, you receive one point for each correct answer, but you lose a fraction of a point for each incorrect response. Guess only when you can eliminate at least one of the answer choices.

---

1. Points D, E, F, and G are on a line, in that order. If $DE = 2$, $FG = 5$, and $DF = 6$, what is the value of $EG(DG)$?

   (A) 13

   (B) 18

   (C) 19

   (D) 42

   (E) 99

2. $\overrightarrow{QS}$ bisects $\angle PQR$, m$\angle PQR = (4x + 2)°$, and m$\angle SQR = (3x - 6)°$. What is the value of x?

   (A) 1

   (B) 4

   (C) 7

   (D) 10

   (E) 19

3. A rectangular garden is enclosed by a brick border. The total length of bricks used to enclose the garden is 42 meters. If the length of the garden is twice the width, what is the area of the garden?

   (A) 7 meters

   (B) 14 meters

   (C) 42 meters

   (D) 42 square meters

   (E) 98 square meters

4. What is the area of the square?

   (A) 16

   (B) 25

   (C) 32

   (D) 36

   (E) 41

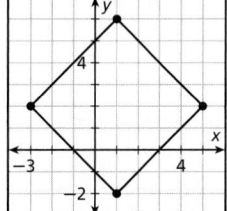

5. If $\angle BFD$ and $\angle AFC$ are right angles and m$\angle CFD = 72°$, what is the value of x?

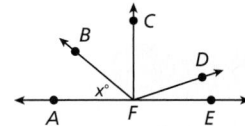

   Note: Figure not drawn to scale.

   (A) 18

   (B) 36

   (C) 72

   (D) 90

   (E) 108

Organizer

Objective: Provide practice for college entrance exams such as the SAT.

 **Online Edition**

Resources

College Entrance Exam Practice

Questions on the SAT represent the following math strands:
Number and Operation, 30–32%
Algebra and Functions, 28–32%
Geometry and Measurement, 27–30%
Data Analysis, Statistics, and Probability, 10–12%

Items on this page focus on:
• Number and Operation
• Algebra and Functions
• Geometry and Measurement

Text References:

Item	1	2	3	4	5
Lesson	1-2	1-3	1-5	1-6	1-3

TEST PREP DOCTOR ✚

1. Students may choose **B** because they have found the incorrect value of *EF*, possibly by subtracting 2 from 5. Remind students to sketch a figure of the situation.

2. Students may choose **A** because they did not do the opposite operation. Also remind students of the definition of *bisect* and the relationship of bisected angles.

3. Students may choose **C** or **D** because they calculated the perimeter of the garden. Remind students to read each test item carefully to determine what question is being asked.

4. Students may choose **A** or **D** because they incorrectly calculated the length of a side of the square. Remind students of the Distance Formula.

5. Students may choose **E** because they assumed the angles were complementary. Remind students that they cannot assume information that is not given in the test item.

Standardized Test Strategies

Organizer

Objective: Provide opportunities to learn and practice common test-taking strategies.

Online Edition

Resources

 TAKS Prep Workbook

 TAKS Prep CD-ROM

 TAKS Practice Online

go.hrw.com/Geo/TX

KEYWORD: MG7 TestPrep

TAKS PREP DOCTOR This TAKS Tackler focuses on how to work backward to obtain an answer to a multiple-choice test item. When faced with a test item they do not know how to solve, students should be encouraged not to skip the item, but to use the answer choices provided in order to make an educated guess. By substituting each answer choice into the test question, students can determine whether the choice makes the test question correct and/or reasonable.

Multiple Choice: Work Backward

When you do not know how to solve a multiple-choice test item, use the answer choices and work the question backward. Plug in the answer choices to see which choice makes the question true.

EXAMPLE 1

T is the midpoint of $\overline{RC}$, $RT = 12x - 8$, and $TC = 28$. What is the value of *x*?

(A) −4   (C) 3

(B) 2   (D) 28

$$\underset{R}{\overset{12x-8}{\rule{0pt}{0pt}}} \qquad \underset{T}{\overset{}{\rule{0pt}{0pt}}} \qquad \underset{C}{\overset{28}{\rule{0pt}{0pt}}}$$

Since T is the midpoint of $\overline{RC}$, then RT = RC, or 12x − 8 = 28.
Find what value of x makes the left side of the equation equal 28.

Try choice A: If x = −4, then 12x − 8 = 12(−4) − 8 = −56.
This choice is not correct because length is always a positive number.

Try choice B: If x = 2, then 12x − 8 = 12(2) − 8 = 16.
Since 16 ≠ 28, choice B is not the answer.

Try choice C: If x = 3, then 12x − 8 = 12(3) − 8 = 28.

Since 28 = 28, the correct answer is C, 3.

EXAMPLE 2

Joel used 6400 feet of fencing to make a rectangular horse pen. The width of the pen is 4 times as long as the length. What is the length of the horse pen?

(F) 25 feet   (H) 640 feet

(G) 480 feet   (J) 1600 feet

Use the formula P = 2ℓ + 2w. P = 6400 and w = 4ℓ. You can work backward to determine which answer choice is the most reasonable.

Try choice J: Use mental math. If ℓ = 1600, then 4ℓ = 6400. This choice is not reasonable because the perimeter of the pen would then be far greater than 6400 feet.

Try choice F: Use mental math. If ℓ = 25, then 4ℓ = 100. This choice is incorrect because the perimeter of the pen is 6400 ft, which is far greater than 2(25) + 2(100).

Try choice H: If ℓ = 640, then 4ℓ = 2560. When you substitute these values into the perimeter formula, it makes a true statement.

The correct answer is H, 640 ft.

Read each test item and answer the questions that follow.

Item A
The measure of an angle is 3 times as great as that of its complement. Which value is the measure of the smaller angle?

(A) 22.5°   (C) 63.5°

(B) 27.5°   (D) 67.5°

1. Are there any definitions that you can use to solve this problem? If so, what are they?

2. Describe how to work backward to find the correct answer.

Item B
In a town's annual relay marathon race, the second runner of each team starts at mile marker 4 and runs to the halfway point of the 26-mile marathon. At that point the second runner passes the relay baton to the third runner of the team. How many total miles does the second runner of each team run?

(F) 4 miles   (H) 9 miles

(G) 6.5 miles   (J) 13 miles

3. Which answer choice should you plug in first? Why?

4. Describe, by working backward, how you know that choices F and G are not correct.

Item C
Consider the translation $(-2, 8) \rightarrow (8, -4)$. What number was added to the x-coordinate?

(A) −12   (C) 4

(B) −6   (D) 10

5. Which answer choice should you plug in first? Why?

6. Explain how to work the test question backward to determine the correct answer.

When you work a test question backward start with choice C. The choices are usually listed in order from least to greatest. If choice C is incorrect because it is too low, you do not need to plug in the smaller numbers.

Item D
△QRS has vertices at $Q(3, 5)$, $R(3, 9)$, and $S(7, 5)$. Which of these points is a vertex of the image of △QRS after the translation $(x, y) \rightarrow (x - 7, y - 6)$?

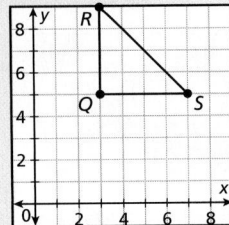

(F) $(-4, 3)$ (H) $(4, 1)$

(G) $(0, 0)$ (J) $(4, -3)$

7. Explain how to use mental math to find an answer that is NOT reasonable.

8. Describe, by working backward, how you can determine the correct answer.

Item E
$\overrightarrow{TS}$ bisects ∠PTR. If m∠PTS = $(9x + 2)°$ and m∠STR = $(x + 18)°$, what is the value of x?

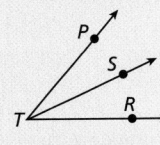

(A) −10   (C) 2

(B) 0   (D) 20

9. Explain how to use mental math to find an answer that is NOT reasonable.

10. Describe how to use the answer choices to work backward to find which answer is reasonable.

Answers

Possible answers:

1. yes; the def. of comp. ∡ and the comp. of an ∠

2. Multiply the ∠ measure given in choice **A** by 3 to get the greater ∠ measure. Then determine whether the sum of the larger ∠ measure and the ∠ measure given in choice **A** equals 90°. Repeat this process with choices **B** and **C**, or until the correct answer is found.

3. Plug in **H** first. If **H** is too high, the answer is **F** or **G**. If **H** is too low, the answer is **J**.

4. One-half of 26 equals 13, and 13 minus 4 does not equal 4, so choice **F** is incorrect; and 13 minus 6.5 does not equal 4, so choice **G** is incorrect.

5. Plug in **C** first. If **C** is too high, the answer is **A** or **B**. If **C** is too low, the answer is **D**.

6. Subtract the value given in each answer choice from 8, the x-coordinate of the translated pt., and see if you get −2, the x-coordinate of the original pt.

7. If you add −7 to the x-coordinate and −6 to the y-coordinate of any of the original pts., you do not get (0, 0). **G** is not a reasonable choice.

8. Add 7 to the x-value of the pt. in choice **F**, and add 6 to the y-value of the pt. in choice **F**. Look to see if this new pt. matches any of the original vertices of the △. If not, repeat this process until the correct answer is found.

Answers to Test Items

A. A

B. H

C. D

D. F

E. C

Answers

Possible answers:

9. If you substitute −10 into $(9x + 2)$, the result is neg. Since an ∠ measure cannot be a neg. value, choice **A** is not reasonable.

10. Substitute the value of x given in choice **B** into both ∠ measures, and simplify. If the resulting values are equivalent, then that value of x is the correct answer. Repeat this process with choices **C** and **D**, or until the correct answer is found.

⚜ TAKS Practice

Grades 9–11	Items
Obj. 2	A–E
Obj. 3	A–E
Obj. 4	A–E
Obj. 6	D
Obj. 7	D
Obj. 10	B

CHAPTER
1
TAKS PREP

CHAPTER
1

TAKS PREP

go.hrw.com/Geo/TX
TAKS Practice Online
KEYWORD: MG7 TestPrep

Organizer

Objective: Provide review and practice for Chapter 1 and standardized tests.

Online Edition

Resources

Assessment Resources
Chapter 1 Cumulative Test

TAKS Prep Workbook

TAKS Prep CD-ROM

TAKS Practice Online
go.hrw.com/Geo/TX
KEYWORD: MG7 TestPrep

TAKS Practice

Grades 9–11	Items
Obj. 1	13, 23, 25, 26
Obj. 2	4, 7, 11–15, 18, 21, 22
Obj. 3	4, 7, 14, 15, 18, 21, 22
Obj. 4	4, 7, 14, 15, 18, 21, 22
Obj. 7	4, 11, 13, 19, 20
Obj. 8	9
Obj. 10	13, 19

CUMULATIVE ASSESSMENT, CHAPTER 1

Multiple Choice

Use the diagram for Items 1–3.

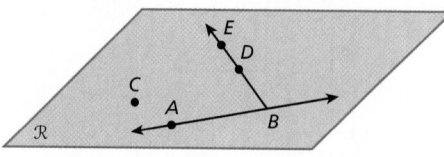

1. Which points are collinear?
- (A) *A*, *B*, and *C*
- (B) *B*, *C*, and *D*
- (C) *A*, *B*, and *E*
- (D) *B*, *D*, and *E*

2. What is another name for plane $\mathcal{R}$?
- (F) Plane $\mathcal{C}$
- (G) Plane *AB*
- (H) Plane *ACE*
- (J) Plane *BDE*

3. Use your protractor to find the approximate measure of $\angle ABD$.
- (A) 123°
- (B) 117°
- (C) 77°
- (D) 63°

4. *S* is between *R* and *T*. The distance between *R* and *T* is 4 times the distance between *S* and *T*. If *RS* = 18, what is *RT*?
- (F) 24
- (G) 22.5
- (H) 14.4
- (J) 6

5. A ray bisects a straight angle into two congruent angles. Which term describes each of the congruent angles that are formed?
- (A) Acute
- (B) Obtuse
- (C) Right
- (D) Straight

6. Which expression states that $\overline{AB}$ is congruent to $\overline{CD}$?
- (F) $AB \cong CD$
- (G) $AB = CD$
- (H) $\overline{AB} = \overline{CD}$
- (J) $\overline{AB} \cong \overline{CD}$

7. The measure of an angle is 35°. What is the measure of its complement?
- (A) 35°
- (B) 45°
- (C) 55°
- (D) 145°

Use the diagram for Items 8–10.

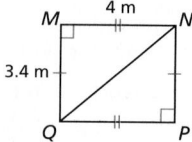

8. Which of these angles is adjacent to $\angle MQN$?
- (F) $\angle QMN$
- (G) $\angle NPQ$
- (H) $\angle QNP$
- (J) $\angle PQN$

9. What is the area of $\triangle NQP$?
- (A) 3.7 square meters
- (B) 6.8 square meters
- (C) 7.4 square meters
- (D) 13.6 square meters

10. Which of the following pairs of angles are complementary?
- (F) $\angle MNQ$ and $\angle QNP$
- (G) $\angle NQP$ and $\angle QPN$
- (H) $\angle MNP$ and $\angle QNP$
- (J) $\angle QMN$ and $\angle NPQ$

11. *K* is the midpoint of $\overline{JL}$. *J* has coordinates (2, −1), and *K* has coordinates (−4, 3). What are the coordinates of *L*?
- (A) (3, −2)
- (B) (1, −1)
- (C) (−1, 1)
- (D) (−10, 7)

12. A circle with a diameter of 10 inches has a circumference equal to the perimeter of a square. To the nearest tenth, what is the length of each side of the square?
- (F) 2.5 inches
- (G) 3.9 inches
- (H) 5.6 inches
- (J) 7.9 inches

13. The map coordinates of a campground are (1, 4), and the coordinates of a fishing pier are (4, 7). Each unit on the map represents 1 kilometer. If Alejandro walks in a straight line from the campground to the pier, how many kilometers, to the nearest tenth, will he walk?
- (A) 3.5 kilometers
- (B) 4.2 kilometers
- (C) 6.0 kilometers
- (D) 12.1 kilometers

68   Chapter 1 Foundations for Geometry

TAKS PREP DOCTOR ✚

For **Item 11,** encourage students to draw a diagram. Students who do not draw a diagram may be more likely to choose answer **A,** which gives the coordinates of the midpoint of $\overline{JK}$, not the coordinates of *L*.

14. m∠R is 57°. What is the measure of its supplement?

- (F) 33°
- (G) 43°
- (H) 123°
- (J) 133°

15. What rule would you use to translate a triangle 4 units to the right?

- (A) $(x, y) \rightarrow (x + 4, y)$
- (B) $(x, y) \rightarrow (x - 4, y)$
- (C) $(x, y) \rightarrow (x, y + 4)$
- (D) $(x, y) \rightarrow (x, y - 4)$

16. If $\overline{WZ}$ bisects ∠XWY, which of the following statements is true?

- (F) m∠XWZ > m∠YWZ
- (G) m∠XWZ < m∠YWZ
- (H) m∠XWZ = m∠YWZ
- (J) m∠XWZ ≅ m∠YWZ

17. The x- and y-axes separate the coordinate plane into four regions, called quadrants. If (c, d) is a point that is not on the axes, such that $c < 0$ and $d < 0$, which quadrant would contain point (c, d)?

- (A) I
- (B) II
- (C) III
- (D) IV

Gridded Response

18. The measure of ∠1 is 4 times the measure of its supplement. What is the measure, in degrees, of ∠1? **144**

19. The exits for Market St. and Finch St. are 3.5 miles apart on a straight highway. The exit for King St. is at the midpoint between these two exits. How many miles apart are the King St. and Finch St. exits? **1.75**

20. R has coordinates $(-4, 9)$. S has coordinates $(4, -6)$. What is RS? **17**

21. If ∠A is a supplement of ∠B and is a right angle, then what is m∠B in degrees? **90**

22. ∠C and ∠D are complementary. m∠C is 4 times m∠D. What is m∠C? **18**

Short Response

23. △ABC has vertices $A(-2, 0)$, $B(0, 0)$, and $C(0, 3)$. The image of △ABC has vertices $A'(1, -4)$, $B'(3, -4)$, and $C'(3, -1)$.

   a. Draw △ABC and its image △A'B'C' on a coordinate plane.

   b. Write a rule for the transformation of △ABC using arrow notation.
$$(x, y) \rightarrow (x + 3, y - 4)$$

24. You are given the measure of ∠4. You also know the following angles are supplementary: ∠1 and ∠2, ∠2 and ∠3, and ∠1 and ∠4.

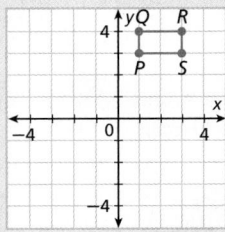

Explain how you can determine the measures of ∠1, ∠2, and ∠3.

25. Marian is making a circular tablecloth from a rectangular piece of fabric that measures 6 yards by 4 yards. What is the area of the largest circular piece that can be cut from the fabric? Leave your answer in terms of π. Show your work or explain in words how you found your answer.

Extended Response

26. Demara is creating a design using a computer illustration program. She begins by drawing the rectangle shown on the coordinate grid.

   a. Demara translates rectangle PQRS using the rule $(x, y) \rightarrow (x - 4, y - 6)$. On a copy of the coordinate grid, draw this translation and label each vertex.

   b. Describe one way that Demara could have moved rectangle PQRS to the same position in part **a** using a reflection and then a translation.

   c. On the same coordinate grid, Demara reflects rectangle PQRS across the x-axis. She draws a figure with vertices at $(1, -3)$, $(3, -3)$, $(3, -5)$, and $(1, -5)$. Did Demara reflect rectangle PQRS correctly? Explain your answer.

26a.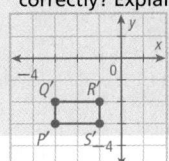

Short-Response Rubric

Items 23–25

2 Points = The student's answer is an accurate and complete execution of the task or tasks.

1 Point = The student's answer contains attributes of an appropriate response but is flawed.

0 Points = The student's answer contains no attributes of an appropriate response.

Extended-Response Rubric

Item 26

4 Points = The student correctly performs the translation on a coordinate grid. Explanations are complete, and work demonstrates a thorough understanding of transformations.

3 Points = The student's translation and explanations are correct but may contain minor flaws. Work demonstrates an understanding of major concepts related to transformation.

2 Points = The student answers correctly, but only part of the problem is answered or explanations are incomplete. Work demonstrates a limited understanding of transformations.

1 Point = The student answers incorrectly but makes a reasonable attempt to show work or offer an explanation.

0 Points = The student does not answer correctly and does not attempt all parts of the problem.

Answers

23a.

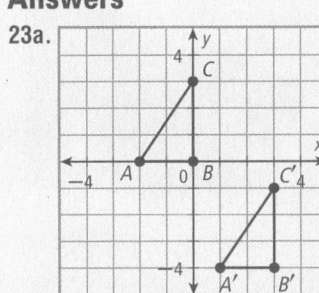

24. Possible answer: ∠1 is supp. to ∠4, so m∠1 = 180° − m∠4. You continue to subtract from 180° to find the measure of each ∠.

25. 4π yd²; possible answer: The largest circular piece can have a diam. no larger than the width of the fabric. The width of the fabric is 4 yd. If the diam. of the circular piece is 4 yd, then its radius is 2 yd and its area is $\pi(2^2) = 4\pi$ yd².

26b. Possible answer: She could have reflected rect. PQRS across the y-axis and then translated it 6 units down.

   c. No; possible answer: a figure and its reflected image should be the same size and shape. Rect. PQRS has a length of 2 units and a width of 1 unit. The image Demara drew is a square with a side length of 2 units.

Because the 2 figures have different shapes, Demara did not perform the reflection correctly.

CHAPTER

2 Geometric Reasoning

Section 2A
Inductive and Deductive Reasoning
2-1 **Using Inductive Reasoning to Make Conjectures**
On Track for TAKS   Venn Diagrams
2-2 **Conditional Statements**
2-3 **Using Deductive Reasoning to Verify Conjectures**
2-3 **Geometry Lab**   Solve Logic Puzzles
2-4 **Biconditional Statements and Definitions**

Section 2B
Mathematical Proof
2-5 **Algebraic Proof**
2-6 **Geometric Proof**
2-6 **Geometry Lab**   Design Plans and Proofs
2-7 **Flowchart and Paragraph Proofs**
EXTENSION **Introduction to Symbolic Logic**

Pacing Guide for 45-Minute Classes

Chapter 2

Countdown to TAKS Weeks ❸, ❹

DAY 1	DAY 2	DAY 3	DAY 4	DAY 5
2-1 Lesson On Track for TAKS	2-2 Lesson	2-3 Lesson	2-3 Geometry Lab	2-4 Lesson
DAY 6	**DAY 7**	**DAY 8**	**DAY 9**	**DAY 10**
Multi-Step TAKS Prep Ready to Go On?	2-5 Lesson	2-6 Lesson	2-6 Lesson	2-6 Geometry Lab
DAY 11	**DAY 12**	**DAY 13**	**DAY 14**	**DAY 15**
2-7 Lesson	Multi-Step TAKS Prep Ready to Go On?	**EXTENSION**	Chapter 2 Review	Chapter 2 Test

Pacing Guide for 90-Minute Classes

Chapter 2

DAY 1	DAY 2	DAY 3	DAY 4	DAY 5
2-1 Lesson On Track for TAKS 2-2 Lesson	2-3 Lesson 2-3 Geometry Lab	2-4 Lesson Multi-Step TAKS Prep Ready to Go On?	2-5 Lesson 2-6 Lesson	2-6 Lesson 2-6 Geometry Lab
DAY 6	**DAY 7**	**DAY 8**		
2-7 Lesson Multi-Step TAKS Prep Ready to Go On?	**EXTENSION** Chapter 2 Review	Chapter 2 Test 3-1 Lesson		

ONGOING ASSESSMENT and INTERVENTION

DIAGNOSE	PRESCRIBE

Assess Prior Knowledge

Before Chapter 2

Diagnose readiness for the chapter.	Prescribe intervention.
Are You Ready? SE p. 71	**Are You Ready? Intervention** Skills 17, 22, 25, 68

Formative Assessment

Before Every Lesson

Diagnose readiness for the lesson.	Prescribe intervention.
Warm Up TE, every lesson	**Skills Bank** SE pp. S50–S81
	Reteach CRB, Ch. 1–2

During Every Lesson

Diagnose understanding of lesson concepts.	Prescribe intervention.
Check It Out! SE, every example	**Questioning Strategies** TE, every example
Think and Discuss SE, every lesson	**Reading Strategies** CRB, every lesson
Write About It SE, every lesson	**Success for ELL** pp. 15–28
Journal TE, every lesson	

After Every Lesson

Diagnose mastery of lesson concepts.	Prescribe intervention.
Lesson Quiz TE, every lesson	**Reteach** CRB, every lesson
Alternative Assessment TE, every lesson	**Problem Solving** CRB, every lesson
Test Prep SE, every lesson	**Test Prep Doctor** TE, every lesson
Test and Practice Generator	**Homework Help** Online

Before Chapter 2 Testing

Diagnose mastery of concepts in the chapter.	Prescribe intervention.
Ready to Go On? SE pp. 103, 127	**Ready to Go On? Intervention** pp. 15–28
Multi-Step TAKS Prep SE pp. 102, 126	**Scaffolding Questions** TE pp. 102, 126
Section Quizzes AR pp. 25–26	
Test and Practice Generator	

Before High Stakes Testing

Diagnose mastery of benchmark concepts.	Prescribe intervention.
Ready for TAKS? Benchmark Tests	**Ready for TAKS? Intervention**
College Entrance Exam Practice SE p. 135	**College Entrance Exam Practice**
TAKS Prep SE pp. 138–139	**TAKS Prep Workbook**
TAKS Prep CD-ROM	

Summative Assessment

After Chapter 2

Check mastery of chapter concepts.	Prescribe intervention.
Multiple-Choice Tests (Forms A, B, C)	**Reteach** CRB, every lesson
Free-Response Tests (Forms A, B, C)	**Lesson Tutorial Videos** Chapter 2
Performance Assessment AR pp. 27–40	
Test and Practice Generator	

Check mastery of benchmark concepts.	Prescribe intervention.
TAKS Tests	**TAKS Prep Workbook**
College Entrance Exams	**College Entrance Exam Practice**

KEY: **SE** = *Student Edition*   **TE** = *Teacher's Edition*   **CRB** = *Chapter Resource Book*   **AR** = *Assessment Resources*   Available online   Available on CD-ROM

CHAPTER 2

Supporting the Teacher

Chapter 2 Resource Book

Practice A, B, C
pp. 3–5, 11–13, 19–21, 27–29, 35–37, 43–45, 51–53

Reading Strategies ELL
pp. 10, 18, 26, 34, 42, 50, 58

Reteach
pp. 6–7, 14–15, 22–23, 30–31, 38–39, 46–47, 54–55

Problem Solving
pp. 9, 17, 25, 33, 41, 49, 57

Challenge
pp. 8, 16, 24, 32, 40, 48, 56

Parent Letter pp. 1–2

Transparencies

Lesson Transparencies, Volume 1 .... Chapter 2
  • Teaching Tools
  • Warm Ups
  • Teaching Transparencies
  • Additional Examples
  • Lesson Quizzes

Alternate Openers: Explorations .... pp. 8–14

Countdown to TAKS .... pp. 5–8

Know-It Notebook .... Chapter 2
  • Graphic Organizers
  • Key Concepts
  • Vocabulary
  • Chapter Review
  • Big Ideas
  • Postulates
  • Theorems

Teacher Tools

Power Presentations®
Complete PowerPoint® presentations for Chapter 2 lessons

Lesson Tutorial Videos®
Holt authors Ed Burger and Freddie Renfro present tutorials to support the Chapter 2 lessons.

One-Stop Planner®
Easy access to all Chapter 2 resources and assessments, as well as software for lesson planning, test generation, and puzzle creation

IDEA Works!®
Key Chapter 2 resources and assessments modified to address special learning needs

Lesson Plans...pp. 8–14

Solutions Key ....p. 83

Geometry Posters .... Chapter 2

TechKeys   **Lab Resources**

Project Teacher Support   **Parent Resources**

Workbooks

Homework and Practice Workbook
  Teacher's Guide ....pp. 8–14

Know-It Notebook
  Teacher's Guide ....pp. 20–34

Problem Solving Workbook
  Teacher's Guide ....pp. 8–14

TAKS Prep Workbook
  Teacher's Guide

Technology Highlights for the Teacher

Power Presentations
Dynamic presentations to engage students. Complete PowerPoint® presentations for every lesson in Chapter 2.

2-1 Solving One-Step Equations

Isolate a variable by using inverse operations which "undo" operations on the variable.

An equation is like a balanced scale. To keep the balance, perform the same operation on both sides.

Inverse Operations	
Operation	**Inverse Operation**
Addition	Subtraction
Subtraction	Addition

One-Stop Planner
Easy access to Chapter 2 resources and assessments. Includes lesson-planning, test-generation, and puzzle-creation software.

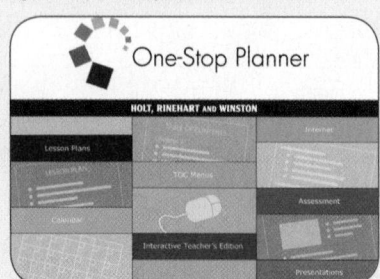

Premier Online Edition
Chapter 2 includes Tutorial Videos, Lesson Activities, Lesson Quizzes, Homework Help, and Chapter Project.

KEY: **SE** = *Student Edition* **TE** = *Teacher's Edition* ELL English Language Learners SPANISH Spanish version available  Available online   Available on CD-ROM

Reaching All Learners

Resources for All Learners

Texas Lab Manual	Chapter 2
Homework and Practice Workbook	pp. 8–14
Know-It Notebook	pp. 20–34
Problem Solving Workbook	pp. 8–14

DEVELOPING LEARNERS

Practice A	CRB, every lesson
Reteach	CRB, every lesson
Inclusion	TE pp. 100, 112
Questioning Strategies	TE, every example
Modified Chapter 2 Resources 	*IDEA Works!*
***Homework Help* Online** 	

ON-LEVEL LEARNERS

Practice B	CRB, every lesson
Cooperative Learning	TE pp. 75, 97
Multiple Representations	TE pp. 82, 119

ADVANCED LEARNERS

Practice C	CRB, every lesson
Challenge	CRB, every lesson
Reading and Writing Math EXTENSION	TE p. 73
Multi-Step TAKS Prep EXTENSION	TE pp. 102, 126
Critical Thinking	TE pp. 82, 111

English Language Learners

ENGLISH LANGUAGE LEARNERS

Are You Ready? Vocabulary	SE p. 71
Vocabulary Connections	SE p. 72
Lesson Vocabulary	SE, every lesson
Vocabulary Exercises	SE, every exercise set
Vocabulary Review	SE p. 130
English Language Learners	TE pp. 73, 78, 82, 97, 98, 108, 129, 141
Reading Strategies	CRB, every lesson
Success for English Language Learners	pp. 15–28
Multilingual Glossary 	

Reaching All Learners Through...

Cooperative Learning	TE pp. 75, 97
Critical Thinking	TE pp. 82, 111
Multiple Representations	TE pp. 82, 119
Visual Cues	TE pp. 82, 87, 105, 119, 128
Auditory	TE pp. 89, 106, 111
Diversity	TE p. 91
Inclusion	TE pp. 100, 112
Kinesthetic Experience	TE pp. 105, 112
Test Prep Doctor	TE pp. 79, 86, 93, 101, 109, 116, 125, 135, 136, 138
Common Error Alerts	TE pp. 75, 79, 83, 87, 101, 105, 111, 121, 129
Scaffolding Questions	TE pp. 102, 126

Technology Highlights for Reaching All Learners

 Lesson Tutorial Videos

Starring Holt authors Ed Burger and Freddie Renfro! Live tutorials to support every lesson in Chapter 2.

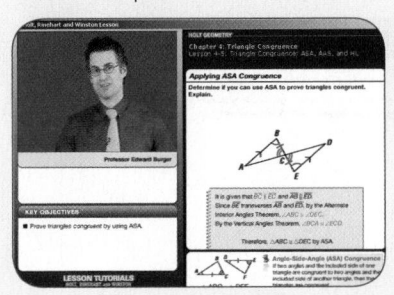

 Multilingual Glossary

Searchable glossary includes definitions in English, Spanish, Vietnamese, Chinese, Hmong, Korean, and 4 other languages.

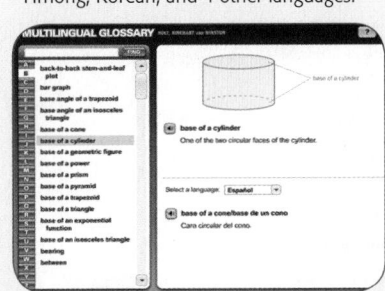

 Online Interactivities

Interactive tutorials provide visually engaging alternative opportunities to learn concepts and master skills.

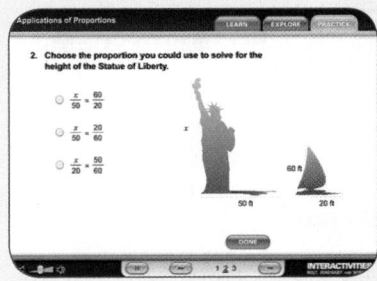

KEY: **SE** = *Student Edition*   **TE** = *Teacher's Edition*   **CRB** = *Chapter Resource Book*   **SPANISH** Spanish version available    Available online    Available on CD-ROM

Ongoing Assessment

Assessing Prior Knowledge

Determine whether students have the prerequisite concepts and skills for success in Chapter 2.

Are You Ready? 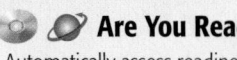 .... SE p. 71
Warm Up .... TE, every lesson

Test Preparation

Provide review and practice for Chapter 2 and standardized tests.

Multi-Step TAKS Prep .... SE pp. 102, 126
Study Guide: Review .... SE pp. 130–133
TAKS Tackler .... SE pp. 136–137
TAKS Prep .... SE pp. 138–139
College Entrance Exam Practice .... SE p. 135
Countdown to TAKS **Transparencies** ....pp. 5–8
Ready for TAKS?
TAKS Prep Workbook
TAKS Prep **CD-ROM**
IDEA Works!

Alternative Assessment

Assess students' understanding of Chapter 2 concepts and combined problem-solving skills.

Chapter 2 Project .... SE p. 70
Alternative Assessment .... TE, every lesson
Performance Assessment .... AR pp. 39–40
Portfolio Assessment .... AR p. xxxiv

Daily Assessment

Provide formative assessment for each day of Chapter 2.

Questioning Strategies .... TE, every example
Think and Discuss .... SE, every lesson
Check It Out! Exercises .... SE, every example
Write About It .... SE, every lesson
Journal .... TE, every lesson
Lesson Quiz .... TE, every lesson
Alternative Assessment .... TE, every lesson
Modified Lesson Quizzes .... *IDEA Works!*

Weekly Assessment

Provide formative assessment for each week of Chapter 2.

Multi-Step TAKS Prep .... SE pp. 102, 126
Ready to Go On? .... SE pp. 103, 127
Cumulative Assessment .... SE pp. 138–139
Test and Practice Generator SPANISH .. *One-Stop Planner*

Formal Assessment

Provide summative assessment of Chapter 2 mastery.

Section Quizzes .... AR pp. 25–26
Chapter 2 Test .... SE p. 134
Chapter Test (Levels A, B, C) .... AR pp. 27–38
      • Multiple Choice   • Free Response
Cumulative Test .... AR pp. 41–44
Test and Practice Generator SPANISH .. *One-Stop Planner*
Modified Chapter 2 Test .... *IDEA Works!*

Technology Highlights for Ongoing Assessment

Are You Ready?

Automatically assess readiness and prescribe intervention for Chapter 2 prerequisite skills.

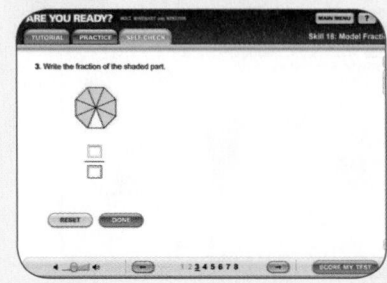

Ready to Go On? SPANISH

Automatically assess understanding of and prescribe intervention for Sections 2A and 2B.

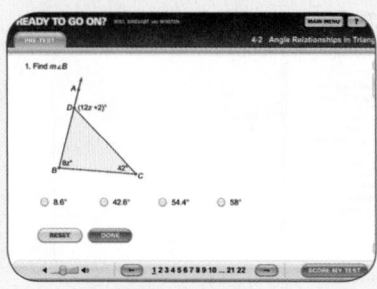

Ready for TAKS? SPANISH

Automatically assess proficiency with and provide intervention for TAKS objectives. Grade 6 through Exit Level.

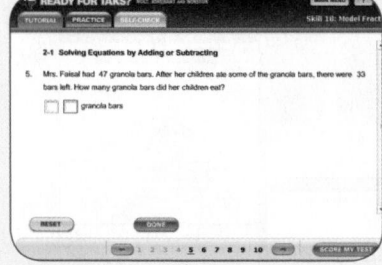

KEY: **SE** = *Student Edition*   **TE** = *Teacher's Edition*   **AR** = *Assessment Resources*   SPANISH Spanish version available   Available online   Available on CD-ROM

CHAPTER
2

Formal Assessment

Three levels (A, B, C) of multiple-choice and free-response chapter tests are available in the *Assessment Resources.*

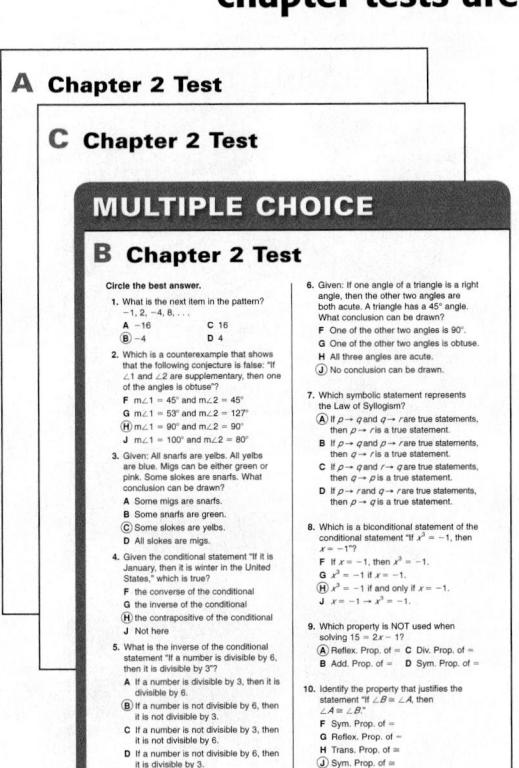

A Chapter 2 Test

C Chapter 2 Test

MULTIPLE CHOICE

B Chapter 2 Test

Circle the best answer.

1. What is the next item in the pattern?
   −1, 2, −4, 8, . . .
   A −16   C 16
   (B) −4   D 4

2. Which is a counterexample that shows that the following conjecture is false: "If ∠1 and ∠2 are supplementary, then one of the angles is obtuse"?
   F m∠1 = 45° and m∠2 = 45°
   G m∠1 = 53° and m∠2 = 127°
   (H) m∠1 = 90° and m∠2 = 90°
   J m∠1 = 100° and m∠2 = 80°

3. Given: All snarfs are yelbs. All yelbs are blue. Migs can be either green or pink. Some slokes are snarfs. What conclusion can be drawn?
   A Some migs are snarfs.
   B Some snarfs are green.
   (C) Some slokes are yelbs.
   D All slokes are migs.

4. Given the conditional statement "If it is January, then it is winter in the United States," which is true?
   F The converse of the conditional
   G The inverse of the conditional
   (H) The contrapositive of the conditional
   J Not here

5. What is the inverse of the conditional statement "If a number is divisible by 6, then it is divisible by 3"?
   A If a number is divisible by 3, then it is divisible by 6.
   (B) If a number is not divisible by 6, then it is not divisible by 3.
   C If a number is not divisible by 3, then it is not divisible by 6.
   D If a number is not divisible by 6, then it is divisible by 3.

6. Given: If one angle of a triangle is a right angle, then the other two angles are both acute. A triangle has a 45° angle. What conclusion can be drawn?
   F One of the other two angles is 90°.
   G One of the other two angles is obtuse.
   H All three angles are acute.
   (J) No conclusion can be drawn.

7. Which symbolic statement represents the Law of Syllogism?
   (A) If p → q and q → r are true statements, then p → r is a true statement.
   B If p → q and p → r are true statements, then q → r is a true statement.
   C If p → q and r → q are true statements, then p → r is a true statement.
   D If p → r and q → r are true statements, then p → q is a true statement.

8. Which is a biconditional statement of the conditional statement "If x³ = −1, then x = −1"?
   F If x = −1, then x³ = −1.
   G x³ = −1 if x = −1.
   (H) x³ = −1 if and only if x = −1.
   J x = −1 → x³ = −1.

9. Which property is NOT used when solving 15 = 2x − 1?
   (A) Reflex. Prop. of =   C Div. Prop. of =
   B Add. Prop. of =   D Sym. Prop. of =

10. Identify the property that justifies the statement "If ∠B = ∠A, then ∠A = ∠B."
    F Sym. Prop. of =
    G Reflex. Prop. of =
    H Trans. Prop. of =
    (J) Sym. Prop. of ≅

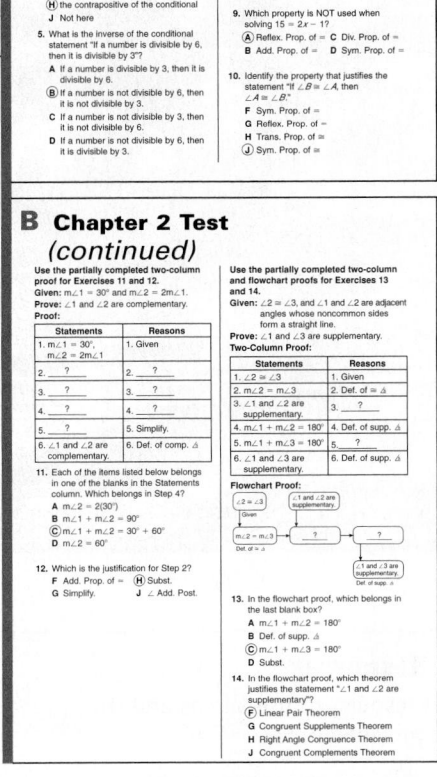

B Chapter 2 Test
(continued)

Use the partially completed two-column proof for Exercises 11 and 12.
Given: m∠1 = 30° and m∠2 = 2m∠1.
Prove: ∠1 and ∠2 are complementary.
Proof:

Statements	Reasons
1. m∠1 = 30°, m∠2 = 2m∠1.	1. Given
2. ?	2. ?
3. ?	3. ?
4. ?	4. ?
5. ?	5. Simplify.
6. ∠1 and ∠2 are complementary.	6. Def. of comp. ∆

11. Each of the items listed below belongs in one of the blanks in the Statements column. Which belongs in Step 4?
    A m∠2 = 2(30°)
    B m∠1 + m∠2 = 90°
    (C) m∠1 + m∠2 = 30° + 60°
    D m∠2 = 60°

12. Which is the justification for Step 2?
    F Add. Prop. of =   (H) Subst.
    G Simplify.   J ≅ Add. Post.

Use the partially completed two-column and flowchart proofs for Exercises 13 and 14.
Given: ∠2 ≅ ∠3, and ∠1 and ∠2 are adjacent angles whose noncommon sides form a straight line.
Prove: ∠1 and ∠3 are supplementary.
Two-Column Proof:

Statements	Reasons
1. ∠2 ≅ ∠3	1. Given
2. m∠2 = m∠3	2. Def. of ≅ ∆
3. ∠1 and ∠2 are supplementary.	3. ?
4. m∠1 + m∠2 = 180°	4. Def. of supp. ∆
5. m∠1 + m∠3 = 180°	5. ?
6. ∠1 and ∠3 are supplementary.	6. Def. of supp. ∆

Flowchart Proof:

∠2 ≅ ∠3 → ∠1 and ∠2 are supplementary.
Given
m∠2 = m∠3 → ? → ?
Def. of ≅ ∆
→ ∠1 and ∠3 are supplementary.
Def. of supp. ∆

13. In the flowchart proof, which belongs in the last blank box?
    A m∠1 + m∠2 = 180°
    B Def. of supp. ∆
    (C) m∠1 + m∠3 = 180°
    D Subst.

14. In the flowchart proof, which theorem justifies the statement "∠1 and ∠2 are supplementary"?
    (F) Linear Pair Theorem
    G Congruent Supplements Theorem
    H Right Angle Congruence Theorem
    J Congruent Complements Theorem

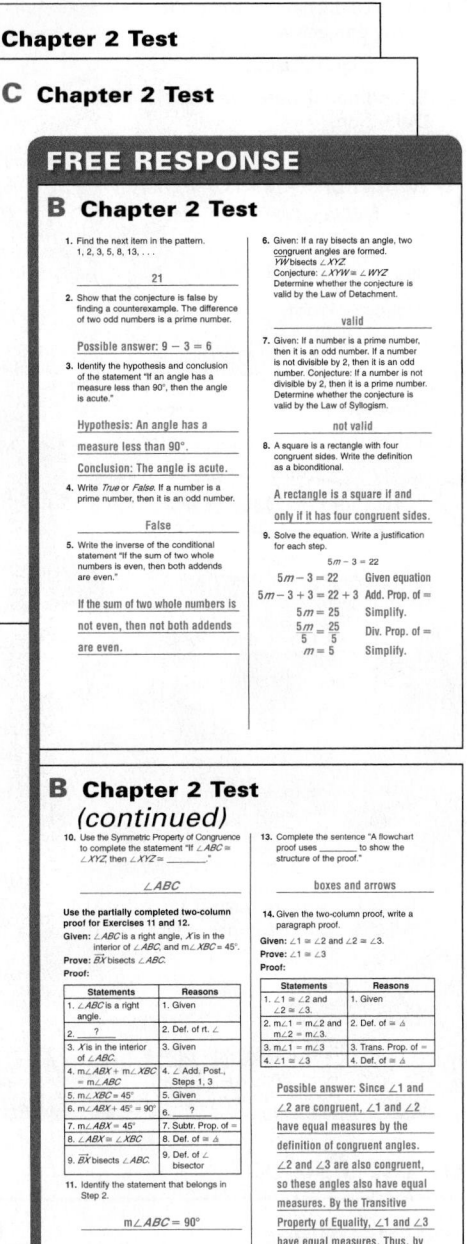

A Chapter 2 Test

C Chapter 2 Test

FREE RESPONSE

B Chapter 2 Test

1. Find the next item in the pattern.
   1, 2, 3, 5, 8, 13, . . .

   _____21_____

2. Show that the conjecture is false by finding a counterexample. The difference of two odd numbers is an even number.

   Possible answer: 9 − 3 = 6

3. Identify the hypothesis and conclusion of the statement "If an angle has a measure less than 90°, then the angle is acute."

   Hypothesis: An angle has a
   measure less than 90°.
   Conclusion: The angle is acute.

4. Write *True* or *False.* If a number is a prime number, then it is an odd number.

   _____False_____

5. Write the inverse of the conditional statement "If the sum of two whole numbers is even, then both addends are even."

   If the sum of two whole numbers is
   not even, then not both addends
   are even.

6. Given: If a ray bisects an angle, two congruent angles are formed.
   YW bisects ∠XYZ.
   Conjecture: ∠XYW ≅ ∠WYZ
   Determine whether the conjecture is valid by the Law of Detachment.

   _____valid_____

7. Given: If a number is a prime number, then it is an odd number. If a number is not divisible by 2, then it is an odd number. Conjecture: If a number is prime, then it is not divisible by 2, then it is a prime number. Determine whether the conjecture is valid by the Law of Syllogism.

   not valid

8. A square is a rectangle with four congruent sides. Write the definition as a biconditional.

   A rectangle is a square if and
   only if it has four congruent sides.

9. Solve the equation. Write a justification for each step.
   $$5m − 3 = 22$$
   5m − 3 = 22   Given equation
   5m − 3 + 3 = 22 + 3   Add. Prop. of =
   5m = 25   Simplify.
   $\frac{5m}{5} = \frac{25}{5}$ Div. Prop. of =
   m = 5   Simplify.

B Chapter 2 Test
(continued)

10. Use the Symmetric Property of Congruence to complete the statement "If ∠ABC ≅ ∠XYZ, then ∠XYZ ≅ _____."

    _____∠ABC_____

Use the partially completed two-column proof for Exercises 11 and 12.
Given: ∠ABC is a right angle, X is in the interior of ∠ABC, and m∠XBC = 45°.
Prove: BX bisects ∠ABC.
Proof:

Statements	Reasons
1. ∠ABC is a right angle.	1. Given
2. ?	2. Def. of rt. ∠
3. X is in the interior of ∠ABC.	3. Given
4. m∠ABX + m∠XBC = m∠ABC	4. ∠ Add. Post., Steps 1, 3
5. m∠XBC = 45°	5. Given
6. m∠ABX + 45° = 90°	6. ?
7. m∠ABX = 45°	7. Subtr. Prop. of =
8. ∠ABX ≅ ∠XBC.	8. Def. of ≅ ∠
9. BX bisects ∠ABC.	9. Def. of ∠ bisector

11. Identify the statement that belongs in Step 2.

    m∠ABC = 90°

12. Identify the justification for Step 6.

    Substitution

13. Complete the sentence "A flowchart proof uses _____ to show the structure of the proof."

    boxes and arrows

14. Given the two-column proof, write a paragraph proof.
    Given: ∠1 ≅ ∠2 and ∠2 ≅ ∠3.
    Prove: ∠1 ≅ ∠3
    Proof:

Statements	Reasons
1. ∠1 ≅ ∠2 and ∠2 ≅ ∠3.	1. Given
2. m∠1 = m∠2 and m∠2 = m∠3.	2. Def. of ≅ ∆
3. m∠1 = m∠3	3. Trans. Prop. of =
4. ∠1 ≅ ∠3	4. Def. of ≅ ∆

Possible answer: Since ∠1 and
∠2 are congruent, ∠1 and ∠2
have equal measures by the
definition of congruent angles.
∠2 and ∠3 are also congruent,
so these angles also have equal
measures. By the Transitive
Property of Equality, ∠1 and ∠3
have equal measures. Thus, by
the definition of congruent
angles, ∠1 ≅ ∠3.

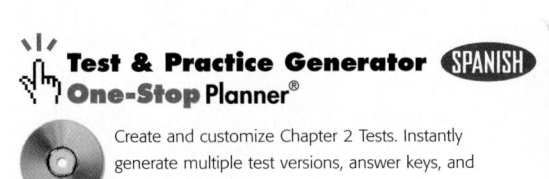

Test & Practice Generator (SPANISH)
One-Stop Planner®

Create and customize Chapter 2 Tests. Instantly generate multiple test versions, answer keys, and Spanish versions of test items.

Geometric Reasoning

go.hrw.com/Geo/TX
Chapter Project Online
KEYWORD: MG7 ChProj

A corn maze from the 7A Ranch near Hondo

About the Project

Winning Strategies

In the Chapter Project, students use logical reasoning to develop strategies for a paper-and-pencil game and to solve a mathematical puzzle.

Project Resources

All project resources for teachers and students are provided online.

go.hrw.com/Geo/TX
Project Teacher Support
KEYWORD: MG7 ProjectTS

Geometry in Texas

Finding your way through the passages of a maze requires strategy and logical thinking.

ARE YOU READY?

ARE YOU READY?

✓ Vocabulary

Match each term on the left with a definition on the right.

1. angle **B**
2. line **A**
3. midpoint **F**
4. plane **C**
5. segment **D**

A. a straight path that has no thickness and extends forever

B. a figure formed by two rays with a common endpoint

C. a flat surface that has no thickness and extends forever

D. a part of a line between two points

E. names a location and has no size

F. a point that divides a segment into two congruent segments

✓ Angle Relationships

Select the best description for each labeled angle pair.

6.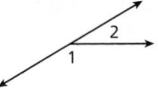

linear pair or
vertical angles
lin. pair

7.

adjacent angles or
vertical angles
vert. ∠

8.

supplementary angles or
complementary angles
comp. ∠

✓ Classify Real Numbers

Tell if each number is a natural number, a whole number, an integer, or a rational number. Give all the names that apply.

9. 6 **natural, whole, integer, rational**
10. −0.8 **rational**
11. −3 **integer, rational**
12. 5.2 **rational**
13. $\frac{3}{8}$ **rational**
14. 0 **whole, integer, rational**

✓ Points, Lines, and Planes

Name each of the following. **15–19. Possible answers:**

15. a point **B**
16. a line **$\overleftrightarrow{BD}$**
17. a ray **$\overrightarrow{CA}$**
18. a segment **$\overline{CD}$**
19. a plane **plane ℱ**

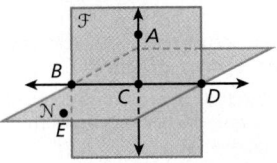

✓ Solve One-Step Equations

Solve.

20. $8 + x = 5$ **−3**
21. $6y = -12$ **−2**
22. $9 = 6s$ **1.5**
23. $p - 7 = 9$ **16**
24. $\frac{z}{5} = 5$ **25**
25. $8.4 = -1.2r$ **−7**

ARE YOU READY?
Diagnose and Prescribe

	ARE YOU READY? Intervention, Chapter 2			
✓ **Prerequisite Skill**	📄 **Worksheets**	💿 **CD-ROM**	🪐 **Online**	
✓ Angle Relationships	Skill 25	Activity 25		
✓ Classify Real Numbers	Skill 17	Activity 17	Diagnose and Prescribe Online	
✓ Points, Lines, and Planes	Skill 22	Activity 22		
✓ Solve One-Step Equations	Skill 68	Activity 68		

ARE YOU READY?
Enrichment, Chapter 2
📄 **Worksheets**
💿 **CD-ROM**
🪐 **Online**

Organizer

Objective: Assess students' understanding of prerequisite skills.

Prerequisite Skills

Angle Relationships

Classify Real Numbers

Points, Lines, and Planes

Solve One-Step Equations

Assessing Prior Knowledge

INTERVENTION ◀▶

Diagnose and Prescribe

Use this page to determine whether intervention is necessary or whether enrichment is appropriate.

Resources

📄 **Are You Ready?**
Intervention and
Enrichment Worksheets

💿 **Are You Ready? CD-ROM**

🪐 **Are You Ready? Online**

my.hrw.com

Organizer

Objective: Help students organize the new concepts they will learn in Chapter 2.

Online Edition
Multilingual Glossary

Resources

PuzzlePro
One-Stop Planner®

Multilingual Glossary Online
go.hrw.com/Geo/TX
KEYWORD: MG7 Glossary

Answers to Vocabulary Connections

1. Possible answer: a number that is not positive, such as −3
2. Possible answer: a general conclusion
3. Possible answer: *Polygon* might mean "a figure with many ∡."

Key Vocabulary/Vocabulario

conjecture	conjetura
counterexample	contraejemplo
deductive reasoning	razonamiento deductivo
inductive reasoning	razonamiento inductivo
polygon	polígono
proof	demostración
quadrilateral	cuadrilátero
theorem	teorema
triangle	triángulo

Vocabulary Connections

To become familiar with some of the vocabulary terms in the chapter, consider the following. You may refer to the chapter, the glossary, or a dictionary if you like.

1. The word **counterexample** is made up of two words: *counter* and *example*. In this case, *counter* means "against." What is a counterexample to the statement "All numbers are positive"?

2. The root of the word **inductive** is *ducere*, which means "to lead." When you are inducted into a club, you are "led into" membership. When you use inductive reasoning in math, you start with specific examples. What do you think inductive reasoning leads you to?

3. In Greek, the word *poly* means "many," and the word *gon* means "angle." How can you use these meanings to understand the term **polygon** ?

⭐ Geometry TEKS

	Les. 2-1	Les. 2-2	Les. 2-3	2-3 Geo. Lab	Les. 2-4	Les. 2-5	Les. 2-6	2-6 Geo. Lab	Les. 2-7	Ext.
G.1.A Geometric structure* develop an awareness of the structure of a mathematical system, connecting definitions, postulates, logical reasoning, and theorems							★	★	★	
G.2.B Geometric structure* make conjectures … and determine the validity of the conjectures, …	★		★						★	
G.3.A Geometric structure* determine the validity of a conditional statement, its converse, inverse, and contrapositive			★		★					
G.3.B Geometric structure* construct and justify statements about geometric figures and their properties			★		★	★	★	★		
G.3.C Geometric structure* use logical reasoning to prove statements are true and find counterexamples to disprove statements that are false		★	★			★	★	★	★	★
G.3.D Geometric structure* use inductive reasoning to formulate a conjecture	★									
G.3.E Geometric structure* use deductive reasoning to prove a statement			★			★	★	★	★	
G.4.A Geometric structure* select an appropriate representation … in order to solve problems				★						★
G.5.B Geometric patterns* use numeric and geometric patterns to make generalizations about geometric properties …	★									

* Knowledge and skills are written out completely on pages TX28–TX35.

⭐ Geometry TEKS—Knowledge and Skills

G.1 Geometric structure The student understands the structure of, and relationships within, an axiomatic system.

G.2 Geometric structure The student analyzes geometric relationships in order to make and verify conjectures.

G.3 Geometric structure The student applies logical reasoning to justify and prove mathematical statements.

G.4 Geometric structure The student uses a variety of representations to describe geometric relationships and solve problems.

G.5 Geometric patterns The student uses a variety of representations to describe geometric relationships and solve problems.

 **Reading and Writing Math**

Reading Strategy: Read and Interpret a Diagram

A diagram is an informational tool. To correctly read a diagram, you must know what you can and cannot assume based on what you see in it.

What You CAN Assume	What You CANNOT Assume
✔ Collinear points	✘ Measures of segments
✔ Betweenness of points	✘ Measures of angles
✔ Coplanar points	✘ Congruent segments
✔ Straight angles and lines	✘ Congruent angles
✔ Adjacent angles	✘ Right angles
✔ Linear pairs of angles	
✔ Vertical angles	

If a diagram includes labeled information, such as an angle measure or a right angle mark, treat this information as given.

What You See

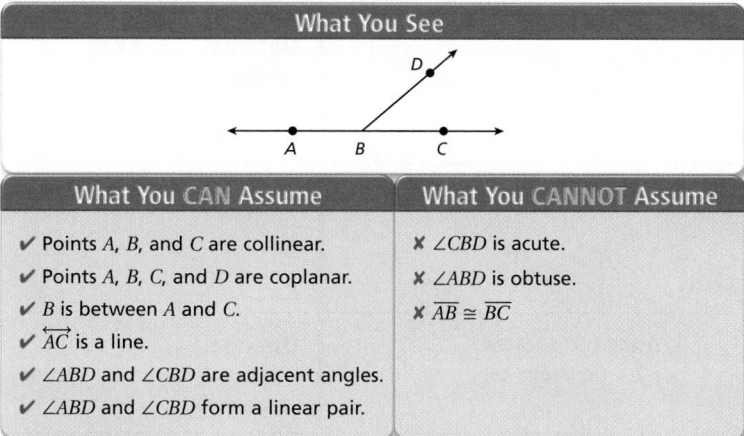

What You CAN Assume	What You CANNOT Assume
✔ Points A, B, and C are collinear.	✘ $\angle CBD$ is acute.
✔ Points A, B, C, and D are coplanar.	✘ $\angle ABD$ is obtuse.
✔ B is between A and C.	✘ $\overline{AB} \cong \overline{BC}$
✔ $\overleftrightarrow{AC}$ is a line.	
✔ $\angle ABD$ and $\angle CBD$ are adjacent angles.	
✔ $\angle ABD$ and $\angle CBD$ form a linear pair.	

Try This

List what you can and cannot assume from each diagram.

1.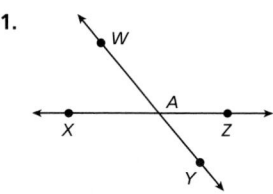

2.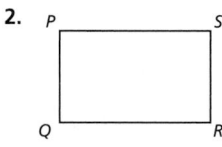

Organizer

Objective: Help students apply strategies to understand and retain key concepts.

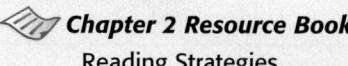 **Online Edition**

Resources

Chapter 2 Resource Book
Reading Strategies

Reading Strategy: Read and Interpret a Diagram
ENGLISH LANGUAGE LEARNERS

Discuss Students will write geometric proofs in Lessons 2-6 and 2-7. Emphasize that knowing what they can and cannot assume from a diagram will be essential to their success in writing proofs and in solving a variety of geometric problems throughout the course.

Extend As students work through the problems in Chapter 2, have them discuss what information can be assumed from the diagrams. Ask them to list the information in their journals and to refer to the list when writing proofs. They might find it helpful to create a separate list of what cannot be assumed.

Answers to *Try This*

1. Possible answer:
   Can assume: W, A, and Y are collinear. X, A, and Z are collinear. All the pts. are coplanar. A is between W and Y. A is between X and Z. $\overleftrightarrow{XZ}$ is a line. $\overleftrightarrow{WY}$ is a line. $\angle XAW$ and $\angle WAZ$ are adj. ∡. $\angle WAZ$ and $\angle ZAY$ are adj. ∡. $\angle ZAY$ and $\angle YAX$ are adj. ∡. $\angle YAX$ and $\angle XAW$ are adj. ∡. $\angle XAW$ and $\angle WAZ$ form a lin. pair. $\angle WAZ$ and $\angle ZAY$ form a lin. pair. $\angle ZAY$ and $\angle YAX$ form a lin. pair. $\angle YAX$ and $\angle XAW$ form a lin. pair. $\angle XAW$ and $\angle ZAY$ are vert. ∡. $\angle WAZ$ and $\angle YAX$ are vert. ∡.
   Cannot assume: anything about the measures of the ∡; anything about the measures of the segs.; $\angle XAW \cong \angle WAZ$; $\angle XAW \ncong \angle WAZ$; $\overline{YA} \cong \overline{AZ}$; $\overline{YA} \ncong \overline{AZ}$.

2. See p. A11.

▼ TAKS Objectives

Grades 9–11

Obj. 1 Functional Relationships: A.1.D

Obj. 2 Properties and Attributes of Functions: A.3.A, A.3.B, A.4.B

Obj. 4 Linear Equations: A.7.A

Obj. 6 Geometric Relationships and Spatial Reasoning: G.5.B

Obj. 10 Mathematical Processes and Tools: 8.14.A, 8.14.B, 8.14.C, 8.15.A, 8.16.A, 8.16.B

Inductive and Deductive Reasoning

 ## One-Minute Section Planner

Lesson	Lab Resources	Materials
Lesson 2-1 Using Inductive Reasoning to Make Conjectures • Use inductive reasoning to identify patterns and make conjectures. • Find counterexamples to disprove conjectures. ☑ Exit Level TAKS ☐ ACT ☑ SAT ☐ SAT Subject Tests		**Optional** toothpicks, science textbook, magazine
Lesson 2-2 Conditional Statements • Identify, write, and analyze the truth value of conditional statements. • Write the inverse, converse, and contrapositive of a conditional statement. ☐ Exit Level TAKS ☐ ACT ☐ SAT ☐ SAT Subject Tests		**Optional** magazine or newspaper advertisements
Lesson 2-3 Using Deductive Reasoning to Verify Conjectures • Apply the Law of Detachment and the Law of Syllogism in logical reasoning. ☐ Exit Level TAKS ☐ ACT ☑ SAT ☐ SAT Subject Tests		**Optional** globe
2-3 Geometry Lab Solve Logic Puzzles • Use tables to solve logic puzzles. • Use networks to solve logic puzzles. ☐ Exit Level TAKS ☐ ACT ☐ SAT ☐ SAT Subject Tests		
Lesson 2-4 Biconditional Statements and Definitions • Write and analyze biconditional statements. ☐ Exit Level TAKS ☐ ACT ☐ SAT ☐ SAT Subject Tests	***Texas Lab Manual*** 2-4 Geometry Lab	**Optional** dictionary, reversible vest or jacket

MK = *Manipulatives Kit*

Section Overview

Inductive Reasoning
Lesson 2-1

 Scientists use inductive reasoning when they form hypotheses to test by experiment.

Inductive reasoning is used to make *conjectures* and continue patterns.

Specific observation → Generalized conclusion

A generalized conclusion is a **conjecture**. To disprove a conjecture, you need only one **counterexample**.

By observing the triangles, you can make a conjecture about the pattern.

Conjecture: The color alternates between red and blue, and the triangle rotates 90° clockwise each time.

Based on the conjecture, the next triangle in the pattern is the following:

Conditionals and Deductive Reasoning
Lessons 2-2, 2-3

 Deductive reasoning is the basis for proof in mathematics. Lawyers use deductive reasoning when presenting cases in court.

Deductive reasoning is the process of using logic to draw conclusions.

A **conditional statement** is an if-then statement. It has a **hypothesis** and a **conclusion**.

If p, then q.
$$p \rightarrow q$$

Conditional:	$p \rightarrow q$
Converse:	$q \rightarrow p$
Inverse:	$\sim p \rightarrow \sim q$
Contrapositive:	$\sim q \rightarrow \sim p$

Logically equivalent

Law of Detachment
If $p \rightarrow q$ is a true statement and p is true, then q is true.

Law of Syllogism
If $p \rightarrow q$ and $q \rightarrow r$ are true statements, then $p \rightarrow r$ is a true statement.

Biconditionals and Definitions
Lesson 2-4

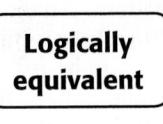 Definitions must be precise in order for people to communicate effectively.

A **biconditional statement** is an if-and-only-if statement.
p if and only if q.
$$p \leftrightarrow q$$
This means both $p \rightarrow q$ and $q \rightarrow p$.

Biconditionals are used to write precise **definitions**.

Pacing: Traditional $\frac{1}{2}$ day
Block $\frac{1}{4}$ day

Objectives: Use inductive reasoning to identify patterns and make conjectures.

Find counterexamples to disprove conjectures.

Online Edition
Tutorial Videos

Countdown to TAKS Week 3

Power Presentations
with PowerPoint®

Warm Up
Complete each sentence.

1. ___?___ points are points that lie on the same line. **Collinear**

2. ___?___ points are points that lie in the same plane. **Coplanar**

3. The sum of the measures of two ___?___ angles is 90°. **complementary**

Also available on transparency

Math Fact !

Some patterns have more than one correct rule. For example, the pattern 1, 2, 4, … can be extended with 8 (by multiplying each term by 2) or 7 (by adding consecutive numbers to each term).

⭐ **Geometry TEKS**

G.2 Geometric structure*
(B) make conjectures about angles, lines, polygons, … and determine the validity of the conjectures, choosing from a variety of approaches such as … axiomatic

G.3 Geometric structure*
(D) use inductive reasoning to formulate a conjecture

G.5 Geometric patterns*
(B) use numeric and geometric patterns to make generalizations about geometric properties …

* Knowledge and Skills See p. 72.

⭐ TEKS G.3.D Geometric structure: use inductive reasoning to formulate a conjecture.
Also G.2.B, G.5.B

Objectives
Use inductive reasoning to identify patterns and make conjectures.

Find counterexamples to disprove conjectures.

Vocabulary
inductive reasoning
conjecture
counterexample

Who uses this?
Biologists use inductive reasoning to develop theories about migration patterns.

Biologists studying the migration patterns of California gray whales developed two theories about the whales' route across Monterey Bay. The whales either swam directly across the bay or followed the shoreline.

EXAMPLE 1 **Identifying a Pattern**

Find the next item in each pattern.

A Monday, Wednesday, Friday, …
Alternating days of the week make up the pattern.
The next day is Sunday.

B 3, 6, 9, 12, 15, …
Multiples of 3 make up the pattern. The next multiple is 18.

C ←, ↖, ↑, …
In this pattern, the figure rotates 45° clockwise each time.
The next figure is ↗.

 1. Find the next item in the pattern 0.4, 0.04, 0.004, … **0.0004**

When several examples form a pattern and you assume the pattern will continue, you are applying *inductive reasoning*. **Inductive reasoning** is the process of reasoning that a rule or statement is true because specific cases are true. You may use inductive reasoning to draw a conclusion from a pattern. A statement you believe to be true based on inductive reasoning is called a **conjecture**.

EXAMPLE 2 **Making a Conjecture**

Complete each conjecture.

A The product of an even number and an odd number is ___?___ .
List some examples and look for a pattern.

$(2)(3) = 6$ $(2)(5) = 10$ $(4)(3) = 12$ $(4)(5) = 20$

The product of an even number and an odd number is even.

---

1 Introduce

EXPLORATION

2-1 Using Inductive Reasoning to Make Conjectures

The figure shows a pattern of squares made from toothpicks. Use the figure to complete the following.

1 × 1   2 × 2   3 × 3   4 × 4

1. Count the number of toothpicks that are needed to make the 1 × 1 square, the 2 × 2 square, the 3 × 3 square, and the 4 × 4 square.

2. Record your results in the table.

Size of Square	1 × 1	2 × 2	3 × 3	4 × 4	5 × 5	…	n × n
Toothpicks							

3. Look for a pattern. Predict the number of toothpicks that are needed to make a 5 × 5 square. Record this value in the table.

Motivate

Ask students to describe a science experiment in which they collected data and formed a hypothesis based on their data. Explain that this kind of reasoning, in which generalizations are based on examples, is called *inductive reasoning*.

Explorations and answers are provided in the *Chapter 2 Resource Book*.

Complete each conjecture.

B The number of segments formed by *n* collinear points is __?__ .

Draw a segment. Mark points on the segment, and count the number of individual segments formed. Be sure to include overlapping segments.

Points	Segments
2	1
3	2 + 1 = 3
4	3 + 2 + 1 = 6
5	4 + 3 + 2 + 1 = 10

The number of segments formed by *n* collinear points is the sum of the whole numbers less than *n*.

 **2.** Complete the conjecture: The product of two odd numbers is __?__ . **odd**

EXAMPLE **3** **Biology Application**

To learn about the migration behavior of California gray whales, biologists observed whales along two routes. For seven days they counted the numbers of whales seen along each route. Make a conjecture based on the data.

Numbers of Whales Each Day

Direct Route	1	3	0	2	1	1	0
Shore Route	7	9	5	8	8	6	7

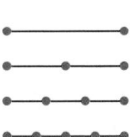

Santa Cruz

Monterey Bay

Monterey
Carmel

North

More whales were seen along the shore route each day. The data supports the conjecture that most California gray whales migrate along the shoreline.

 **3.** Make a conjecture about the lengths of male and female whales based on the data.

Female whales are longer than male whales.

Average Whale Lengths

Length of Female (ft)	49	51	50	48	51	47
Length of Male (ft)	47	45	44	46	48	48

To show that a conjecture is always true, you must prove it. To show that a conjecture is false, you have to find only one example in which the conjecture is not true. This case is called a **counterexample** . A counterexample can be a drawing, a statement, or a number.

Know it!
Note

Inductive Reasoning
1. Look for a pattern
2. Make a conjecture.
3. Prove the conjecture or find a counterexample.

2-1 Using Inductive Reasoning to Make Conjectures **75**

Power Presentations
with PowerPoint®

Additional Examples

Example 1

Find the next item in each pattern.

A. January, March, May, ... July

B. 7, 14, 21, 28, ... 35

C.

Example 2

Complete each conjecture.

A. The sum of two positive numbers is __?__ . positive

B. The number of lines formed by 4 points, no three of which are collinear, is __?__ . 6

Example 3

The cloud of water leaving a whale's blowhole when it exhales is called its *blow*. A biologist observed blue-whale blows of 25 ft, 29 ft, 27 ft, and 24 ft. Another biologist recorded humpback-whale blows of 8 ft, 7 ft, 8 ft, and 9 ft. Make a conjecture based on the data. The height of a blue whale's blow is greater than a humpback whale's.

Also available on transparency

---

2 Teach

Guided Instruction

Many of the examples and exercises in this lesson use the vocabulary learned in Chapter 1. Review terms such as *collinear* and *coplanar,* the different types of angles, linear pairs of angles, and *complementary* and *supplementary* angles.

Teaching Tip **Science** You may want to use a science textbook so you can review the steps of the scientific method. Relate the lesson to students' experiences doing experiments in their science classes.

Reaching All Learners

Through Cooperative Learning

Have students work in small groups. The first student writes a number or draws a shape. The next student writes or draws a second item, beginning a pattern. Have them continue until each student has contributed to the pattern. Then ask the first student to describe a rule for the pattern. Have the groups repeat this activity until each student has gone first.

INTERVENTION ◄■►
Questioning Strategies

EXAMPLE **1**

• Do you have to find a general rule to find the next item in a pattern?

EXAMPLE **2**

• How many examples do you need to look at to complete a conjecture? Explain.

EXAMPLE **3**

• How do you read the data to find what conjecture is supported?

Lesson 2-1 **75**

INTERVENTION ◄─►
Questioning Strategies

EXAMPLE 4

• How do you know which numbers to test when trying to find a counterexample for an algebraic conjecture?

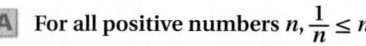

E X A M P L E 4 **Finding a Counterexample**

Show that each conjecture is false by finding a counterexample.

A For all positive numbers n, $\frac{1}{n} \le n$.

Pick positive values for n and substitute them into the equation to see if the conjecture holds.

Let $n = 1$. Since $\frac{1}{n} = 1$ and $1 \le 1$, the conjecture holds.

Let $n = 2$. Since $\frac{1}{n} = \frac{1}{2}$ and $\frac{1}{2} \le 2$, the conjecture holds.

Let $n = \frac{1}{2}$. Since $\frac{1}{n} = \frac{1}{\frac{1}{2}} = 2$ and $2 \nleq \frac{1}{2}$, the conjecture is false.

$n = \frac{1}{2}$ is a counterexample.

B For any three points in a plane, there are three different lines that contain two of the points.

 *Draw three collinear points.*

If the three points are collinear, the conjecture is false.

C The temperature in Abilene, Texas, never exceeds $100°F$ during the spring months (March, April, and May).

Monthly High Temperatures (°F) in Abilene, Texas											
Jan	Feb	Mar	Apr	May	Jun	Jul	Aug	Sep	Oct	Nov	Dec
88	89	97	99	107	109	110	107	106	103	92	89

The temperature in May was $107°F$, so the conjecture is false.

4b. Possible answer:

✓**CHECK IT OUT!** **Show that each conjecture is false by finding a counterexample.**

4a. For any real number x, $x^2 \ge x$. **Possible answer:** $x = \frac{1}{2}$

4b. Supplementary angles are adjacent.

4c. The radius of every planet in the solar system is less than 50,000 km. **Jupiter or Saturn**

Planets' Diameters (km)								
Mercury	Venus	Earth	Mars	Jupiter	Saturn	Uranus	Neptune	Pluto
4880	12,100	12,800	6790	143,000	121,000	51,100	49,500	2300

THINK AND DISCUSS

1. Can you prove a conjecture by giving one example in which the conjecture is true? Explain your reasoning.

2. **GET ORGANIZED** Copy and complete the graphic organizer. In each box, describe the steps of the inductive reasoning process.

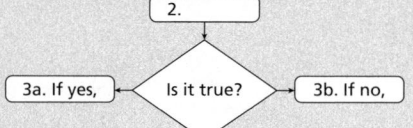

---

3 **Close**

Summarize

Review with students the three steps of the inductive reasoning process:

• Look for a pattern.

• Make a conjecture.

• Prove the conjecture or find a counterexample.

Explain to students that they will learn to prove a conjecture later in the chapter.

ONGOING ASSESSMENT

and INTERVENTION ◄─►

*Diagnose **Before** the Lesson*
2-1 Warm Up, TE p. 74

*Monitor **During** the Lesson*
Check It Out! Exercises, SE pp. 74–76
Questioning Strategies, TE pp. 75–76

*Assess **After** the Lesson*
2-1 Lesson Quiz, TE p. 79
Alternative Assessment, TE p. 79

Answers to *Think and Discuss*

1. No; possible answer: a conjecture cannot be proven true just by giving examples, no matter how many.

2. See p. A2.

go.hrw.com/Geo/TX
Homework Help Online
KEYWORD: MG7 2-1
Parent Resources Online
KEYWORD: MG7 Parent

GUIDED PRACTICE

1. Possible answer: A conjecture is based on observation and is not true until proven true in every case.

1. Vocabulary Explain why a *conjecture* may be true or false.

SEE EXAMPLE **1**
p. 74

Find the next item in each pattern.

2. March, May, July, ...
September

3. $\frac{1}{3}, \frac{2}{4}, \frac{3}{5}, ...$ $\frac{4}{6}$

4. $|\circ|, \frac{\overline{\circ}}{\overline{\circ}}, |\circ|\circ|, ...$ $\frac{\overline{\circ}}{\overline{\circ}}$

SEE EXAMPLE **2**
p. 74

Complete each conjecture.

5. The product of two even numbers is __?__. **even**

6. A rule in terms of n for the sum of the first n odd positive integers is __?__. n^2

SEE EXAMPLE **3**
p. 75

7. Biology A laboratory culture contains 150 bacteria. After twenty minutes, the culture contains 300 bacteria. After one hour, the culture contains 1200 bacteria. Make a conjecture about the rate at which the bacteria increases. **The number of bacteria doubles every 20 minutes.**

SEE EXAMPLE **4**
p. 76

Show that each conjecture is false by finding a counterexample.

9. The 3 pts. are collinear.

8. Kennedy is the youngest U.S. president to be inaugurated. **Roosevelt was inaugurated at age 42.**

9. Three points on a plane always form a triangle.

10. For any real number x, if $x^2 \geq 1$, then $x \geq 1$.
Possible answer: $x = -3$

President	Age at Inauguration
Washington	57
T. Roosevelt	42
Truman	60
Kennedy	43
Clinton	46

PRACTICE AND PROBLEM SOLVING

Independent Practice

For Exercises	See Example
11–13	1
14–15	2
16	3
17–19	4

TEKS ⊷ TAKS
Skills Practice p. S6
Application Practice p. S29

20. Each term is the square of the previous term; 256, 65,536.

21. Possible answer: each term is the previous term multiplied by $\frac{1}{2}$; $\frac{1}{16}$, $\frac{1}{32}$.

22. The terms are multiples of 3 with alternating signs; −15, 18.

Find the next item in each pattern.

11. 8 A.M., 11 A.M., 2 P.M., ...
5 P.M.

12. 75, 64, 53, ...
42

13. △, □, ○, ...
⬡

Complete each conjecture.

14. A rule in terms of n for the sum of the first n even positive integers is __?__. $n(n + 1)$

15. The number of nonoverlapping segments formed by n collinear points is __?__. $n - 1$

16. Industrial Arts About 5% of the students at Lubbock High School usually participate in the robotics competition. There are 526 students in the school this year. Make a conjecture about the number of students who will participate in the robotics competition this year. **About 26 students will participate.**

Show that each conjecture is false by finding a counterexample.

17. If $1 - y > 0$, then $0 < y < 1$. Possible answer: $y = -1$

18. For any real number x, $x^3 \geq x^2$. Possible answer: $x = -1$

19. Every pair of supplementary angles includes one obtuse angle. $m\angle 1 = m\angle 2 = 90°$

Make a conjecture about each pattern. Write the next two items.

20. 2, 4, 16, ...

21. $\frac{1}{2}, \frac{1}{4}, \frac{1}{8}, ...$

22. −3, 6, −9, 12, ...

23. Draw a square of dots. Make a conjecture about the number of dots needed to increase the size of the square from $n \times n$ to $(n + 1) \times (n + 1)$. $2n + 1$

Assignment Guide

Assign *Guided Practice* exercises as necessary.

If you finished Examples **1–2**
Basic 11–15, 20–22, 31–33
Average 11–15, 20–22, 28–33, 41
Advanced 11–15, 20–23, 28–33, 41–43

If you finished Examples **1–4**
Basic 11–27, 31–33, 36–39, 44–53
Average 11–22, 24–29, 31, 32, 34–40, 44–53
Advanced 12, 14, 16, 18, 20–53

Homework Quick Check
Quickly check key concepts.
Exercises: 12, 14, 16, 18, 24, 26, 32

Teaching Tip
Communicating Math
For **Exercises 11–13**, have students describe each pattern in words.

✦TAKS Practice

Grades 9–11	Exercises
Obj. 1	42
Obj. 2	40, 44–47
Obj. 6	23, 52, 53
Obj. 7	52, 53
Obj. 8	48–51
Obj. 9	39
Obj. 10	20–27, 29–34, 40–42

Reading Math In Exercise **34,** some students may have trouble understanding the information given in the text and the table. Explain the concept of "turnaround date" and how this relates to the numbers in the table.

MULTI-STEP TAKS PREP **Exercise 36** involves interpreting text from *Alice's Adventures in Wonderland* and translating these words into a mathematical pattern. This exercise prepares students for the Multi-Step TAKS Prep on page 102.

Answers

26. Possible answer:

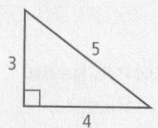

29. $\frac{1}{11} = 0.\overline{09}$, $\frac{2}{11} = 0.\overline{18}$, $\frac{3}{11} = 0.\overline{27}$, …; the fraction pattern is multiples of $\frac{1}{11}$, and the decimal pattern is repeating multiples of 0.09.

30. $6 = 3 + 3$; $8 = 5 + 3$; $10 = 5 + 5$; $12 = 7 + 5$; $14 = 7 + 7$

31. 34, 55, 89; each term is the sum of the 2 previous terms.

32. The middle number is the mean of the other 2 numbers.

35. Possible answer: Even numbers are divisible by 2, but odd numbers are not. So the conjecture, while true for even numbers, does not necessarily hold true for all numbers.

Determine if each conjecture is true. If not, write or draw a counterexample.

24. Points X, Y, and Z are coplanar. **T**

25. If n is an integer, then $-n$ is positive. **F; possible answer:** $n = 2$

26. In a triangle with one right angle, two of the sides are congruent. **F**

27. If $\overrightarrow{BD}$ bisects $\angle ABC$, then m$\angle ABD$ = m$\angle CBD$. **T**

28. **Estimation** The Westside High School band is selling coupon books to raise money for a trip. The table shows the amount of money raised for the first four days of the sale. If the pattern continues, estimate the amount of money raised during the sixth day. **about $400**

Day	Money Raised ($)
1	146.25
2	195.75
3	246.25
4	295.50

29. Write each fraction in the pattern $\frac{1}{11}, \frac{2}{11}, \frac{3}{11}, \dots$ as a repeating decimal. Then write a description of the fraction pattern and the resulting decimal pattern.

30. **Math History** Remember that a prime number is a whole number greater than 1 that has exactly two factors, itself and 1. Goldbach's conjecture states that every even number greater than 2 can be written as the sum of two primes. For example, $4 = 2 + 2$. Write the next five even numbers as the sum of two primes.

31. The pattern 1, 1, 2, 3, 5, 8, 13, 21, … is known as the *Fibonacci sequence*. Find the next three terms in the sequence and write a conjecture for the pattern.

32. Look at a monthly calendar and pick any three squares in a row—across, down, or diagonal. Make a conjecture about the number in the middle.

12	13	14
19	20	21
26	27	28

33. Make a conjecture about the value of $2n - 1$ when n is an integer. **odd**

34. **Critical Thinking** The turnaround date for migrating gray whales occurs when the number of northbound whales exceeds the number of southbound whales. Make a conjecture about the turnaround date, based on the table below. What factors might affect the validity of your conjecture in the future?

Migration Direction of Gray Whales							
	Feb. 16	Feb. 17	Feb. 18	Feb. 19	Feb. 20	Feb. 21	Feb. 22
Southbound	0	2	3	0	1	1	0
Northbound	0	0	2	5	3	2	1

35. **Write About It** Explain why a true conjecture about even numbers does not necessarily hold for all numbers. Give an example to support your answer.

Math History

Goldbach first stated his conjecture in a letter to Leonhard Euler in 1742. Euler, a Swiss mathematician who published over 800 papers, replied, "I consider [the conjecture] a theorem which is quite true, although I cannot demonstrate it."

34. Feb. 19; possible answer: the weather or the whales' health

---

MULTI-STEP TAKS PREP

36. This problem will prepare you for the Multi-Step TAKS Prep on page 102.

a. For how many hours did the Mock Turtle do lessons on the third day? **8**

b. On what day did the Mock Turtle do 1 hour of lessons? **tenth**

"And how many hours a day did you do lessons?" said Alice, in a hurry to change the subject.

"Ten hours the first day," said the Mock Turtle: "nine the next, and so on."

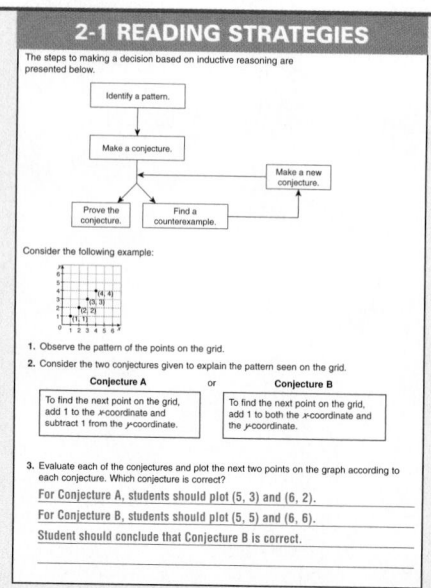

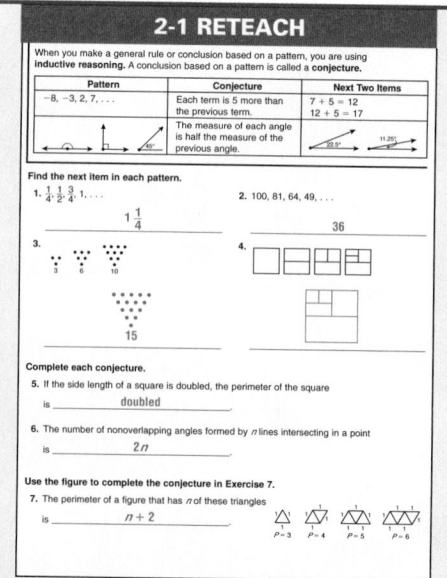

37. Which of the following conjectures is false?

Ⓐ If x is odd, then $x + 1$ is even.

Ⓑ The sum of two odd numbers is even.

Ⓒ The difference of two even numbers is positive.

Ⓓ If x is positive, then $-x$ is negative.

38. A student conjectures that if x is a prime number, then $x + 1$ is not prime. Which of the following is a counterexample?

Ⓕ $x = 11$ Ⓖ $x = 6$ Ⓗ $x = 3$ Ⓙ $x = 2$

39. The class of 2004 holds a reunion each year. In 2005, 87.5% of the 120 graduates attended. In 2006, 90 students went, and in 2007, 75 students went. About how many students do you predict will go to the reunion in 2010?

Ⓐ 12   Ⓑ 15   Ⓒ 24   Ⓓ 30

CHALLENGE AND EXTEND

40. Multi-Step Make a table of values for the rule $x^2 + x + 11$ when x is an integer from 1 to 8. Make a conjecture about the type of number generated by the rule. Continue your table. What value of x generates a counterexample?

41. Political Science Presidential elections are held every four years. U.S. senators are elected to 6-year terms, but only $\frac{1}{3}$ of the Senate is up for election every two years. If $\frac{1}{3}$ of the Senate is elected during a presidential election year, how many years must pass before these same senate seats are up for election during another presidential election year? **12 years**

42. Physical Fitness Rob is training for the President's Challenge physical fitness program. During his first week of training, Rob does 15 sit-ups each day. He will add 20 sit-ups to his daily routine each week. His goal is to reach 150 sit-ups per day.

    a. Make a table of the number of sit-ups Rob does each week from week 1 through week 10.

    b. During which week will Rob reach his goal?

    c. Write a conjecture for the number of sit-ups Rob does during week n.

 43. Construction Draw $\overline{AB}$. Then construct point C so that it is not on $\overline{AB}$ and is the same distance from A and B. Construct $\overline{AC}$ and $\overline{BC}$. Compare m$\angle CAB$ and m$\angle CBA$ and compare AC and CB. Make a conjecture.

SPIRAL REVIEW

Determine if the given point is a solution to $y = 3x - 5$. *(Previous course)*

44. $(1, 8)$ **no**   **45.** $(-2, -11)$ **yes**   **46.** $(3, 4)$ **yes**   **47.** $(-3.5, 0.5)$ **no**

Find the perimeter or circumference of each of the following. Leave answers in terms of x. *(Lesson 1-5)*

48. a square whose area is x^2 **4x**

49. a rectangle with dimensions x and $4x - 3$ **10x − 6**

50. a triangle with side lengths of $x + 2$ **3x + 6**

51. a circle whose area is $9\pi x^2$ **6πx**

52. $(-1, 1), (0, 3),$ and $(4, 2)$

53. $(3, -2), (4, 0),$ and $(8, -1)$

A triangle has vertices $(-1, -1), (0, 1),$ and $(4, 0)$. Find the coordinates for the vertices of the image of the triangle after each transformation. *(Lesson 1-7)*

52. $(x, y) \rightarrow (x, y + 2)$ **53.** $(x, y) \rightarrow (x + 4, y - 1)$

2-1 PROBLEM SOLVING

The table shows the lengths of five green iguanas after birth and then after 1 year.

1. Estimate the length of a green iguana after 1 year if it was 8 inches long when it hatched.

Iguana	Length after Hatching (in.)	Length after 1 Year (in.)
1	10	36
2	9	34
3	11	35
4	12	35
5	10	37

Possible answer: 33 in.

2. Make a conjecture about the average growth of a green iguana during the first year.

Possible answer: The average growth of a green iguana during the first year is about 2 ft.

The times for the first eight matches of the Santa Barbara Open women's volleyball tournament are shown. Show that each conjecture is false by finding a counterexample.

Match	1	2	3	4	5	6	7	8
Time	0:31	0:56	0:51	0:18	0:50	0:34	1:03	0:36

3. Every one of the first eight matches lasted less than one hour.

Match 7 lasted 1 hour 3 minutes.

4. These matches were all longer than a half hour.

Match 4 was 18 minutes long.

Choose the best answer.

5. The table shows the number of cells present during three phases of mitosis. If a sample contained 80 cells during interphase, which is the best prediction for the number of cells present during prophase?

Sample	Number of Cells		
	Interphase	Prophase	Metaphase
1	86	22	5
2	70	28	3
3	76	32	3
4	91	25	5
5	65	16	4
6	89	34	6

A 18 cells   C 40 cells
B 24 cells   D 80 cells

6. About 75% of the students at Jackson High School volunteer to clean up a half-mile stretch of road every year. If there are 408 students in the school this year, about how many are expected to volunteer for the clean-up?

F 102 students   Ⓗ 306 students
G 204 students   J 333 students

7. Mara earned $25, $25, $20, and $28 in the last 4 weeks for walking her neighbor's dogs. If her earnings continue in this way, which is the best estimate for her average weekly earnings for next month?

A $20.50   Ⓒ $24.50
B $23.33   D $25.00

2-1 CHALLENGE

The pattern shown is known as *Pascal's Triangle*.

1. If the pattern is extended, find the terms in row 7.

1, 6, 15, 20, 15, 6, 1

2. Make a conjecture for the pattern.

Each row has 1 as the first and last number. Each of the other numbers is found by adding the two numbers that appear just above it.

row 1					1						
row 2				1		1					
row 3			1		2		1				
row 4		1		3		3		1			
row 5	1		4		6		4		1		
row 6	1	5		10		10		5		1	

3. Make a conjecture about the sum of the terms in each row.

The sum of each row of terms after the first is twice the sum of the terms in the previous row.

Refer to the pattern of figures for Exercises 4 and 5.

Figure 1   Figure 2   Figure 3

4. If the pattern continues, how many black triangles will there be in Figure 4? in Figure 5?   27; 81

5. Write an algebraic expression for the number of black triangles in figure n. 3^{n-1}

Find a counterexample for each statement.

6. For every integer x, $x^2 + 2x - 1$ is divisible by 2.   Possible answer: $x = 2$

7. For every integer n, $n^2 + n$ is prime.   Possible answer: $n = -2$

8. Make a table of values for the expression $4^a - 1$, where a is a positive integer. Make a conjecture about the type of number that is generated by the rule.

a	$4^a - 1$
1	3
2	15
3	63
4	255
5	1023

Possible answer: All values of $4^a - 1$ are divisible by 3.

If students do not recognize the pattern in **Exercise 31**, give them the hint that for each term they should look at the two previous terms.

TEST PREP DOCTOR In **Exercise 38**, point out to students that the hypothesis "if x is a prime number" eliminates choice **G**. They can use the given values of x in choices **F, H,** and **J** to determine whether $x + 1$ is prime.

Answers

40, 42–43. See p. A11.

Journal

Have students write a conjecture about numbers and then use examples to determine whether it is true.

ALTERNATIVE ASSESSMENT

Have students find a pattern in a magazine and describe it in words. Have students make up one conjecture about numbers that is true and one that is false, giving a counterexample to disprove it.

Power Presentations
with **PowerPoint®**

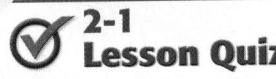
2-1 Lesson Quiz

Find the next item in each pattern.

1. 0.7, 0.07, 0.007, ...   0.0007

2.

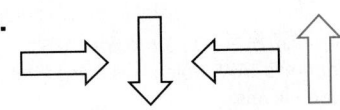

Determine if each conjecture is true. If false, give a counterexample.

3. The quotient of two negative numbers is a positive number.   T

4. Every prime number is odd.   F; 2

5. Two supplementary angles are not congruent.   F; 90° and 90°

6. The square of an odd integer is odd.   T

Also available on transparency

Organizer

See Skills Bank pages S53 and S81

Pacing:
Traditional $\frac{1}{2}$ day
Block $\frac{1}{4}$ day

Objective: Apply reasoning skills to drawing Venn diagrams of number sets.

 **Online Edition**

Teach

Remember

Students review sets of numbers.

INTERVENTION ◄═► For additional review and practice on Venn diagrams, see Skills Bank page S81. For practice with classifying numbers, see Skills Bank page S53.

Teaching Tip **Communicating Math** Show students diagrams of two concentric circles, two overlapping circles, and two circles that do not intersect. Have students describe sets of everyday things, such as animals, for each Venn diagram.

Close

Assess

Have students draw a Venn diagram that shows the relationship between integers and rational numbers.

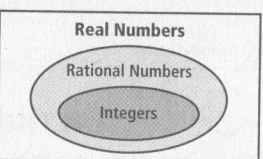

 **TAKS** On Track for TAKS connects TAKS objectives across the grade levels.

Grades 9–11
Obj. 1   Functional Relationships
A.1.D represent relationships among quantities using … diagrams …
Obj. 10 Mathematical Processes and Tools 8.15.A communicate mathematical ideas using … graphical … mathematical models.

Venn Diagrams

Number Theory

See Skills Bank pages S53 and S81

Recall that in a Venn diagram, ovals are used to represent each set. The ovals can overlap if the sets share common elements.

The real number system contains an infinite number of subsets. The following chart shows some of them. Other examples of subsets are even numbers, multiples of 3, and numbers less than 6.

Set	Description	Examples
Natural numbers	The counting numbers	1, 2, 3, 4, 5, …
Whole numbers	The set of natural numbers and 0	0, 1, 2, 3, 4, …
Integers	The set of whole numbers and their opposites	…, −2, −1, 0, 1, 2, …
Rational numbers	The set of numbers that can be written as a ratio of integers	$-\frac{3}{4}, 5, -2, 0.5, 0$
Irrational numbers	The set of numbers that cannot be written as a ratio of integers	$\pi, \sqrt{10}, 8 + \sqrt{2}$

Example

Draw a Venn diagram to show the relationship between the set of even numbers and the set of natural numbers.

The set of even numbers includes all numbers that are divisible by 2. This includes natural numbers such as 2, 4, and 6. But even numbers such as −4 and −10 are not natural numbers.

So the set of even numbers includes some, but not all, elements in the set of natural numbers. Similarly, the set of natural numbers includes some, but not all, even numbers.

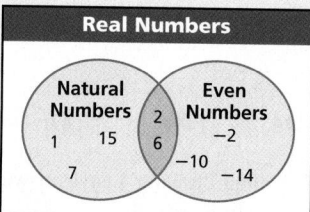

Draw a rectangle to represent all real numbers.

Draw overlapping ovals to represent the sets of even and natural numbers. You may write individual elements in each region.

Try This  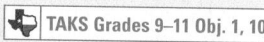 TAKS Grades 9–11 Obj. 1, 10

Draw a Venn diagram to show the relationship between the given sets.

1. natural numbers, whole numbers

2. odd numbers, whole numbers

3. irrational numbers, integers

Answers to *Try This*

1.
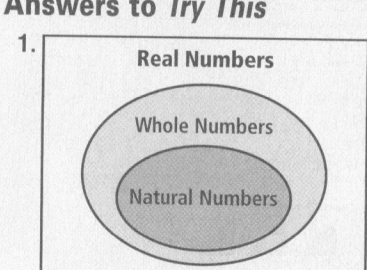

2.
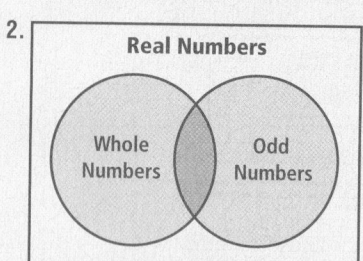

3.
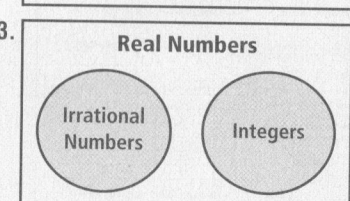

2-2 Conditional Statements

⭐ TEKS G.3.A Geometric structure: determine the validity of a conditional statement, its converse, inverse, and contrapositive. Also G.3.C

Objectives
Identify, write, and analyze the truth value of conditional statements.

Write the inverse, converse, and contrapositive of a conditional statement.

Vocabulary
conditional statement
hypothesis
conclusion
truth value
negation
converse
inverse
contrapositive
logically equivalent statements

Why learn this?
To identify a species of butterfly, you must know what characteristics one butterfly species has that another does not.

It is thought that the viceroy butterfly mimics the bad-tasting monarch butterfly to avoid being eaten by birds. By comparing the appearance of the two butterfly species, you can make the following conjecture:

If a butterfly has a curved black line on its hind wing, then it is a viceroy.

Conditional Statements

DEFINITION	SYMBOLS	VENN DIAGRAM
A **conditional statement** is a statement that can be written in the form "if *p*, then *q*."	$p \rightarrow q$	
The **hypothesis** is the part *p* of a conditional statement following the word *if*.		
The **conclusion** is the part *q* of a conditional statement following the word *then*.		

Know it! .note

By phrasing a conjecture as an if-then statement, you can quickly identify its hypothesis and conclusion.

EXAMPLE 1 Identifying the Parts of a Conditional Statement

Identify the hypothesis and conclusion of each conditional.

A If a butterfly has a curved black line on its hind wing, then it is a viceroy.
Hypothesis: A butterfly has a curved black line on its hind wing.
Conclusion: The butterfly is a Viceroy.

B A number is an integer if it is a natural number.
Hypothesis: A number is a natural number.
Conclusion: The number is an integer.

Writing Math
"If *p*, then *q*" can also be written as "if *p*, *q*," "*q*, if *p*," "*p* implies *q*," and "*p* only if *q*."

✓ CHECK IT OUT!
1. Identify the <u>hypothesis</u> and <u>conclusion</u> of the statement "A number is divisible by 3 if it is divisible by 6."

Many sentences without the words *if* and *then* can be written as conditionals. To do so, identify the sentence's hypothesis and conclusion by figuring out which part of the statement depends on the other.

---

1 Introduce

Motivate
Have students bring in advertisements that promise certain results if you buy a particular product. Ask students to restate the advertising claims in the form "If…, then…." Explain to students that statements of this form are called *conditional statements*.

Explorations and answers are provided in the *Chapter 2 Resource Book*.

2-2 Organizer

Pacing: Traditional 1 day
Block $\frac{1}{2}$ day

Objectives: Identify, write, and analyze the truth value of conditional statements.

Write the inverse, converse, and contrapositive of a conditional statement.

⊕ **Online Edition**
Tutorial Videos, Interactivity

🖥 **Countdown to TAKS Week 3**

Power Presentations with PowerPoint®

Warm Up
Determine if each statement is true or false.

1. The measure of an obtuse angle is less than 90°.   F

2. All perfect-square numbers are positive.   T

3. Every prime number is odd.   F

4. Any three points are coplanar.   T

Also available on transparency

Math Humor

Teacher: Which month has 28 days?
Student: All of them!

⭐ Geometry TEKS

G.3 Geometric structure*
(A) determine the validity of a conditional statement, its converse, inverse, and contrapositive
(C) … find counterexamples to disprove statements that are false

* **Knowledge and Skills** See p. 72.

Additional Examples

Example 1

Identify the <u>hypothesis</u> and <u>conclusion</u> of each conditional.

A. If <u>today is Thanksgiving Day</u>, then <u>today is Thursday</u>.

B. <u>A number is a rational number</u> if <u>it is an integer</u>.

Example 2

Write a conditional statement from each of the following.

A. An obtuse triangle has exactly one obtuse angle. If a triangle is obtuse, then it has exactly one obtuse angle.

B.

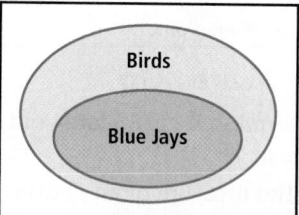

If an animal is a blue jay, then it is a bird.

Also available on transparency

INTERVENTION
Questioning Strategies

EXAMPLE **1**

• When the word *then* does not appear in a conditional statement, how can you tell which part is the conclusion?

EXAMPLE **2**

• If the information is given in a Venn diagram, how can you identify the hypothesis and conclusion?

 Multiple Representations Have students draw Venn diagrams to represent the written conditional statements in **Examples 1** and **2**.

 Critical Thinking Explain to students how to find the negation of statements containing the words *all, some,* or *none.*

EXAMPLE 2 **Writing a Conditional Statement**

Write a conditional statement from each of the following.

A **The midpoint *M* of a segment bisects the segment.**

The midpoint *M* of a segment bisects the segment. *Identify the hypothesis and conclusion.*

Conditional: If *M* is the midpoint of a segment, then *M* bisects the segment.

B

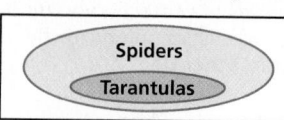

The inner oval represents the **hypothesis**, and the **outer** oval represents the **conclusion**.

Conditional: If an animal is a tarantula, then it is a spider.

 **2.** Write a conditional statement from the sentence "Two angles that are complementary are acute."

If 2 ∠ are comp., then they are acute.

A conditional statement has a **truth value** of either true (T) or false (F). It is false only when the hypothesis is true and the conclusion is false. Consider the conditional "If I get paid, I will take you to the movie." If I don't get paid, I haven't broken my promise. So the statement is still true.

To show that a conditional statement is false, you need to find only one counterexample where the hypothesis is true and the conclusion is false.

EXAMPLE 3 **Analyzing the Truth Value of a Conditional Statement**

Determine if each conditional is true. If false, give a counterexample.

A **If you live in El Paso, then you live in Texas.**

When the hypothesis is true, the conclusion is also true because El Paso is in Texas. So the conditional is true.

B **If an angle is obtuse, then it has a measure of 100°.**

You can draw an obtuse angle whose measure is not 100°. In this case, the hypothesis is true, but the conclusion is false. Since you can find a counterexample, the conditional is false.

C **If an odd number is divisible by 2, then 8 is a perfect square.**

An odd number is never divisible by 2, so the hypothesis is false. The number 8 is not a perfect square, so the conclusion is false. However, the conditional is true because the hypothesis is false.

> **Remember!**
> If the hypothesis is false, the conditional statement is true, regardless of the truth value of the conclusion.

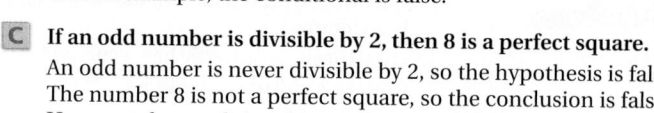

 **3.** Determine if the conditional "If a number is odd, then it is divisible by 3" is true. If false, give a counterexample.

F; possible answer: 7

The **negation** of statement *p* is "not *p*," written as ~*p*. The negation of the statement "*M* is the midpoint of $\overline{AB}$" is "*M* is *not* the midpoint of $\overline{AB}$." The negation of a true statement is false, and the negation of a false statement is true. Negations are used to write related conditional statements.

---

2 Teach

Guided Instruction

Be sure students are able to identify conditional statements in various forms before analyzing their truth values. Explain that to find a counterexample for a conditional, you must find a case in which the hypothesis is true and the conclusion is false. Finally, show students how each related conditional is formed.

Reaching All Learners
Through Visual Cues

When students are first identifying the hypothesis and conclusion in a conditional statement, encourage them to write down the conditional statement and underline or circle the words *if* and *then* wherever they appear. As you discuss conditionals in which these words do not appear, have students insert *if* and *then* where they belong and then rewrite the complete statement in if-then form.

 **Know it!** .Note

Related Conditionals

DEFINITION	SYMBOLS
A conditional is a statement that can be written in the form "If *p*, then *q*."	$p \to q$
The **converse** is the statement formed by exchanging the hypothesis and conclusion.	$q \to p$
The **inverse** is the statement formed by negating the hypothesis and the conclusion.	$\sim p \to \sim q$
The **contrapositive** is the statement formed by both exchanging and negating the hypothesis and conclusion.	$\sim q \to \sim p$

 **COMMON ERROR ALERT**

Many students think that a conditional with a false hypothesis is false. To help students remember when a conditional is false, describe a conditional as a promise, as explained on page 82.

Power Presentations with PowerPoint®

 Additional Examples

Example 3

Determine if each conditional is true. If false, give a counterexample.

A. If this month is August, then next month is September.   T

B. If two angles are acute, then they are congruent.   F; possible answer: 80° and 30°

C. If an even number greater than 2 is prime, then $5 + 4 = 8$.   T

Example 4

Write the converse, inverse, and contrapositive of the conditional statement. Use the Science Fact to find the truth value of each.

If an animal is an adult insect, then it has six legs.

Science Fact
Adult insects have six legs. No other animals have six legs.

Conv.: If an animal has six legs, then it is an adult insect; T. Inv.: If an animal is not an adult insect, then it does not have 6 legs; T. Contra.: If an animal does not have six legs, then it is not an adult insect; T.

Also available on transparency

EXAMPLE 4 *Biology Application*

Write the converse, inverse, and contrapositive of the conditional statement. Use the photos to find the truth value of each.

Moth

> *If an insect is a butterfly, then it has four wings.*
> If an insect is a butterfly, then it has four wings.
> **Converse:** If an insect has four wings, then it is a butterfly.
> A moth also is an insect with four wings. So the converse is false.
> **Inverse:** If an insect is not a butterfly, then it does not have four wings.
> A moth is not a butterfly, but it has four wings. So the inverse is false.
> **Contrapositive:** If an insect does not have four wings, then it is not a butterfly.
> Butterflies must have four wings. So the contrapositive is true.

Butterfly

4. Converse: If an animal has 4 paws, then it is a cat; F. Inverse: If an animal is not a cat, then it does not have 4 paws; F. Contrapositive: If an animal does not have 4 paws, then it is not a cat; T.

 **CHECK IT OUT!** 4. Write the converse, inverse, and contrapositive of the conditional statement "If an animal is a cat, then it has four paws." Find the truth value of each.

Helpful Hint

The logical equivalence of a conditional and its contrapositive is known as the Law of Contrapositive.

In the example above, the conditional statement and its contrapositive are both true, and the converse and inverse are both false. Related conditional statements that have the same truth value are called **logically equivalent statements** . A conditional and its contrapositive are logically equivalent, and so are the converse and inverse.

Statement	Example	Truth Value
Conditional	If m∠A = 95°, then ∠A is obtuse.	T
Converse	If ∠A is obtuse, then m∠A = 95°.	F
Inverse	If m∠A ≠ 95°, then ∠A is not obtuse.	F
Contrapositive	If ∠A is not obtuse, then m∠A ≠ 95°.	T

However, the converse of a true conditional is not necessarily false. All four related conditionals can be true, or all four can be false, depending on the statement.

 **3 Close**

Summarize

Ask students to describe the relationship between a conditional statement and its converse, inverse, and contrapositive. Conv.: Exchange the hypothesis and conclusion. Inv.: Negate the hypothesis and conclusion. Contra.: Exchange and negate the hypothesis and conclusion. Ask "Which pairs of related conditional statements are always logically equivalent?" cond. and contra.; conv. and inv.

ONGOING ASSESSMENT
and INTERVENTION

Diagnose Before the Lesson
2-2 Warm Up, TE p. 81

Monitor During the Lesson
Check It Out! Exercises, SE pp. 81–83
Questioning Strategies, TE pp. 82–83

Assess After the Lesson
2-2 Lesson Quiz, TE p. 87
Alternative Assessment, TE p. 87

INTERVENTION
Questioning Strategies

EXAMPLE 3
• What steps should you take to determine the truth value of a conditional statement?

EXAMPLE 4
• How can you remember the characteristics of the converse, inverse, and contrapositive of a conditional?

Answers to *Think and Discuss*

1. T; F
2. T
3. Yes; possible answer: "If $x = 3$, then $2x = 6$" is true, and so is the conv. "If $2x = 6$, then $x = 3$."
4. See p. A2.

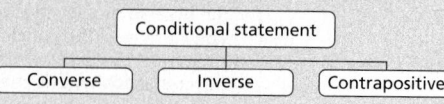

THINK AND DISCUSS

1. If a conditional statement is false, what are the truth values of its hypothesis and conclusion?

2. What is the truth value of a conditional whose hypothesis is false?

3. Can a conditional statement and its converse be logically equivalent? Support your answer with an example.

4. **GET ORGANIZED** Copy and complete the graphic organizer. In each box, write the definition and give an example.

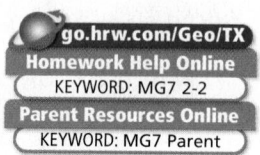

 **Exercises**

2-2 Exercises

go.hrw.com/Geo/TX
Homework Help Online
KEYWORD: MG7 2-2
Parent Resources Online
KEYWORD: MG7 Parent

Assignment Guide

Assign *Guided Practice* exercises as necessary.

If you finished Examples **1–2**
- **Basic** 13–18, 30–33
- **Average** 13–18, 30–36, 54
- **Advanced** 13–18, 30–36, 54–55

If you finished Examples **1–4**
- **Basic** 13–23, 30–37, 42–47, 49–53, 58–66
- **Average** 13–29, 36–55, 58–66
- **Advanced** 13–29, 36–66

Homework Quick Check
Quickly check key concepts.
Exercises: 14, 18, 20, 22, 36, 40

✦TAKS *Practice*

Grades 9–11	Exercises
Obj. 1	58–60
Obj. 6	32, 33, 54, 55
Obj. 10	42–48, 64–66

GUIDED PRACTICE

Vocabulary Apply the vocabulary from this lesson to answer each question.

1. The ___?___ of a *conditional statement* is formed by exchanging the hypothesis and conclusion. (*converse, inverse,* or *contrapositive*) **converse**

2. A *conditional* and its *contrapositive* are ___?___ because they have the same truth value. (*logically equivalent* or *converses*) **logically equivalent**

SEE EXAMPLE 1
p. 81

Identify the hypothesis and conclusion of each conditional.

3. If a person is at least 16 years old, then the person can drive a car.

4. A figure is a parallelogram if it is a rectangle.

5. The statement $a - b < a$ implies that b is a positive number.

SEE EXAMPLE 2
p. 82

Write a conditional statement from each of the following.

6. Eighteen-year-olds are eligible to vote.

7. $\left(\dfrac{a}{b}\right)^2 < \dfrac{a}{b}$ when $0 < a < b$.
If $0 < a < b$, then $\left(\dfrac{a}{b}\right)^2 < \dfrac{a}{b}$.

8. 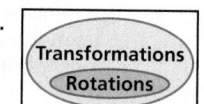 If something is a rotation, then it is a transformation.

SEE EXAMPLE 3
p. 82

Determine if each conditional is true. If false, give a counterexample.

9. If three points form the vertices of a triangle, then they lie in the same plane. **T**

10. If $x > y$, then $|x| > |y|$. **F; possible answer: $x = 2$ and $y = -4$**

11. If the season is spring, then the month is March. **F; possible answer: April**

SEE EXAMPLE 4
p. 83

12. **Travel** Write the converse, inverse, and contrapositive of the following conditional statement. Find the truth value of each.

If Brielle drives at exactly 30 mi/h, then she travels 10 mi in 20 min.

84 *Chapter 2 Geometric Reasoning*

Answers

6. If a person is 18 years old, then that person is eligible to vote.

12. Converse: If Brielle travels 10 mi in 20 min, then she drives at exactly 30 mi/h; F. Inverse: If Brielle does not drive at exactly 30 mi/h, then she does not travel 10 mi in 20 min; F. Contrapositive: If Brielle does not travel 10 mi in 20 min, then she does not drive at exactly 30 mi/h; T.

PRACTICE AND PROBLEM SOLVING

Independent Practice
For Exercises	See Example
13–15	1
16–18	2
19–21	3
22–23	4

TEKS ♦ TAKS

Skills Practice p. S6
Application Practice p. S29

Identify the <u>hypothesis</u> and <u>conclusion</u> of each conditional.

13. If <u>an animal is a tabby</u>, then <u>it is a cat</u>.

14. <u>Four angles are formed</u> if <u>two lines intersect</u>.

15. If <u>8 ounces of cereal cost $2.99</u>, then <u>16 ounces of cereal cost $5.98</u>.

Write a conditional statement from each sentence.

16. You should monitor the heart rate of a patient who is ill.
If a patient is ill, then you should monitor the patient's heart rate.

17. After three strikes, the batter is out.
If the batter makes 3 strikes, then the batter is out.

18. Congruent segments have equal measures.
If segs. are ≅, then they have equal measures.

Determine if each conditional is true. If false, give a counterexample.

19. If you subtract −2 from −6, then the result is −4. T

20. If two planes intersect, then they intersect in exactly one point. F; by Postulate 1-1-5, 2 planes intersect in exactly 1 line.

21. If a cat is a bird, then today is Friday. T

Write the converse, inverse, and contrapositive of each conditional statement. Find the truth value of each.

22. Probability If the probability of an event is 0.1, then the event is unlikely to occur.

23. Meteorology If freezing rain is falling, then the air temperature is 32°F or less. (*Hint:* The freezing point of water is 32°F.)

Find the truth value of each statement.

24. E lies in plane $\mathcal{R}$. T

25. $\overleftrightarrow{CD}$ lies in plane $\mathcal{F}$. T

26. C, E, and D are coplanar. T

27. Plane $\mathcal{F}$ contains $\overrightarrow{ED}$. F

28. B and E are collinear. T

29. $\overleftrightarrow{BC}$ contains $\mathcal{F}$ and $\mathcal{R}$. F

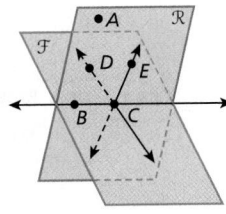

34. If an animal is a dolphin, then it is a mammal.

35. If a person is a Texan, then the person is an American.

36. If $x < -4$, then $x < -1$.

Draw a Venn diagram.

30. All integers are rational numbers.

31. All natural numbers are real.

32. All rectangles are quadrilaterals.

33. Plane is an undefined term.

Write a conditional statement from each Venn diagram.

34.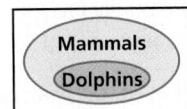

35.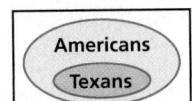

36.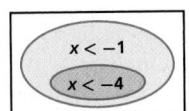

37. This problem will prepare you for the Multi-Step TAKS Prep on page 102.

a. Identify the hypothesis and conclusion in the Duchess's statement.

b. Rewrite the Duchess's claim as a conditional statement.

"Tut, tut, child!" said the Duchess. "Everything's got a moral, if only you can find it." And she squeezed herself up closer to Alice's side as she spoke.

Answers

31.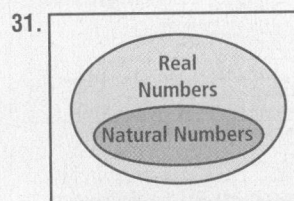

32.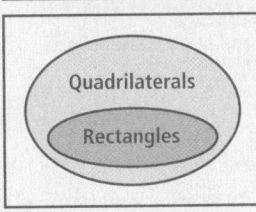

33.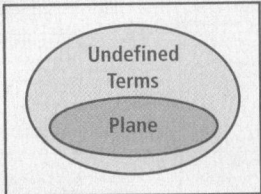

37a. H: Only you can find it. C: Everything's got a moral.

b. If only you can find it, then everything's got a moral.

Teaching Tip **Algebra** If students have difficulty with **Exercise 10**, review the definition of absolute value. If students try only positive numbers for x and y, they may come to the incorrect conclusion that the conditional is true. Remind them to consider all combinations of positive and negative numbers that can be substituted for the variables.

MULTI-STEP TAKS PREP Exercise 37 involves identifying the hypothesis and conclusion in an implied conditional statement. This exercise prepares students for the Multi-Step TAKS Prep on page 102.

Answers

22. Converse: If an event is unlikely to occur, then the probability of the event is 0.1; F. Inverse: If the probability of an event is not 0.1, then the event is likely to occur; F. Contrapositive: If an event is likely to occur, then the probability of the event is not 0.1; T.

23. Converse: If the air temperature is 32°F or less, then freezing rain is falling; F.
Inverse: If freezing rain is not falling, then the air temperature is greater than 32°F; F.
Contrapositive: If the air temperature is greater than 32°F, then freezing rain is not falling; T.

30.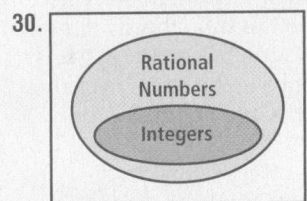

TEST PREP DOCTOR If students answer **Exercise 53** incorrectly, have them write the hypothesis and conclusion of each statement separately and then switch them to form the converse. If the students are unsure of the truth value of any of the statements, review the necessary concepts with them.

Answers

39. Possible answer:

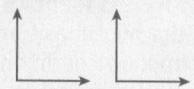

40. Possible answer:

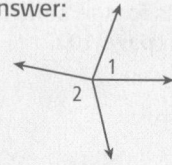

42. If a mineral is calcite, then it has a hardness of 3; T.

43. If a mineral has a hardness less than 5, then it is not apatite; T.

44. If a mineral is not apatite, then it has a hardness less than 5; F.

45. If a mineral is not apatite, then it is calcite; F.

46. If a mineral has a hardness of 3, then it is not apatite; T.

47. If a mineral is calcite, then it has a hardness less than 5; T.

48. Converse: If 2 ⦞ have the same measure, then they are ≅; T. Inverse: If 2 ⦞ are not ≅, then they do not have the same measure; T. Contrapositive: If 2 ⦞ do not have the same measure, then they are not ≅; T.

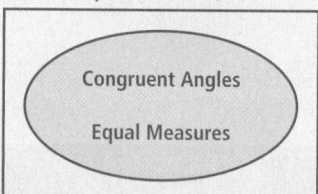

49. Possible answer: A conditional statement is false when its hypothesis is true and its conclusion is false. A conditional statement with a false hypothesis is true because nothing has been guaranteed by the hypothesis.

56a. Possible answer: Figure A is not a rect., so it belongs outside the larger oval in the Venn diagram. It cannot be inside the smaller oval, so it cannot be a square.

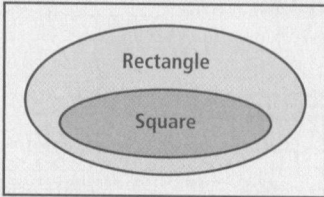

86 Chapter 2

Find a counterexample to show that the converse of each conditional is false.

38. If $x = -5$, then $x^2 = 25$. $x = 5$

39. If two angles are vertical angles, then they are congruent.

40. If two angles are adjacent, then they share a vertex.

41. If you use sunscreen, then you will not get sunburned.
Possible answer: You did not go out in the sun.

Geology

Diamond is four times as hard as the next mineral on Mohs' scale, corundum (ruby and sapphire).

Geology Mohs' scale is used to identify minerals. A mineral with a higher number is harder than a mineral with a lower number.

Use the table and the statements below for Exercises 42–47. Write each conditional and find its truth value.

Mohs' Scale	
Hardness	**Mineral**
1	Talc
2	Gypsum
3	Calcite
4	Fluorite
5	Apatite
6	Orthoclase
7	Quartz
8	Topaz
9	Corundum
10	Diamond

p: calcite   *q*: not apatite

r: a hardness of 3   *s*: a hardness less than 5

42. $p \rightarrow r$ **43.** $s \rightarrow q$ **44.** $q \rightarrow s$

45. $q \rightarrow p$ **46.** $r \rightarrow q$ **47.** $p \rightarrow s$

48. Critical Thinking Consider the conditional "If two angles are congruent, then they have the same measure." Write the converse, inverse, and contrapositive and find the truth value of each. Use the related conditionals to draw a Venn diagram that represents the relationship between congruent angles and their measures.

49. Write About It When is a conditional statement false? Explain why a true conditional statement can have a hypothesis that is false.

TEST PREP

50. What is the inverse of "If it is Saturday, then it is the weekend"?

   (A) If it is the weekend, then it is Saturday.

   (B) If it is not Saturday, then it is the weekend.

   (C) If it is not Saturday, then it is not the weekend.

   (D) If it is not the weekend, then it is not Saturday.

51. Let *a* represent "Two lines are parallel to the same line," and let *b* represent "The two lines are parallel." Which symbolic statement represents the conditional "If two lines are NOT parallel, then they are parallel to the same line"?

   (F) $a \rightarrow b$ (G) $b \rightarrow a$ (H) $\sim b \rightarrow a$ (J) $b \rightarrow \sim a$

52. Which statement is a counterexample for the conditional statement "If $f(x) = \sqrt{25 - x^2}$, then $f(x)$ is positive"?

   (A) $x = 0$ (B) $x = 3$ (C) $x = 4$ (D) $x = 5$

53. Which statement has the same truth value as its converse?

   (F) If a triangle has a right angle, its side lengths are 3 centimeters, 4 centimeters, and 5 centimeters.

   (G) If an angle measures 104°, then the angle is obtuse.

   (H) If a number is an integer, then it is a natural number.

   (J) If an angle measures 90°, then it is an acute angle.

86   *Chapter 2 Geometric Reasoning*

2-2 READING STRATEGIES

Related Conditional Statements

Conditional	Converse	Inverse	Contrapositive
A conditional consists of a hypothesis *h* and a conclusion *c*.	The converse statement is formed by exchanging the hypothesis with the conclusion.	The inverse statement is formed by negating both the hypothesis and the conclusion.	The contrapositive is formed by exchanging and negating the hypothesis and the conclusion.
If ⬚, then ⬚.	If ⬚, then ⬚.	If NOT ⬚, then NOT ⬚.	If NOT ⬚, then NOT ⬚.
EXAMPLE If m∠*Z* = 25°, then ∠*Z* is acute. This statement is TRUE.	EXAMPLE If ∠*Z* is acute, then m∠*Z* = 25°. This statement is FALSE.	EXAMPLE If m∠*Z* ≠ 25°, then ∠*Z* is not acute. This statement is FALSE.	EXAMPLE If ∠*Z* is not acute, then m∠*Z* ≠ 25°. This statement is TRUE.

Determine the converse, inverse, and contrapositive of the conditional statements. Indicate whether each statement is true or false.

1. ⊙̄————⊙̄————⊙̄

Conditional statement: If *R* is the midpoint of $\overline{QS}$, then $\overline{QR} = \overline{RS}$.

Converse: If $\overline{QR} = \overline{RS}$, then *R* is the midpoint of $\overline{QS}$; true

Inverse: If *R* is not the midpoint of $\overline{QS}$, then $\overline{QR} \neq \overline{RS}$; true

Contrapositive: If $\overline{QR} \neq \overline{RS}$, then *R* is not the midpoint of $\overline{QS}$; true

2.

Conditional Statement: If m∠*A* = 140°, then ∠*A* is obtuse.

Converse: If ∠*A* is obtuse, then m∠*A* = 140°; false

Inverse: If m∠*A* ≠ 140°, then ∠*A* is not obtuse; false

Contrapositive: If ∠*A* is not obtuse, then m∠*A* ≠ 140°; true

---

2-2 RETEACH

A **conditional statement** is a statement that can be written as an if-then statement, "if *p*, then *q*."

The **hypothesis** comes after the word *if*.	The **conclusion** comes after the word *then*.

If you buy this cell phone, then you will receive 10 free ringtone downloads.

Sometimes it is necessary to rewrite a conditional statement so that it is in if-then form.

Conditional: A person who practices putting will improve her golf game.
If-Then Form: If a person practices putting, then she will improve her golf game.

For each conditional, underline the hypothesis and double-underline the conclusion.

1. If *x* is an even number, then *x* is divisible by 2.

2. The circumference of a circle is 5π inches if the diameter of the circle is 5 inches.

3. If a line containing the points *J*, *K* and *L* lies in plane *P*, then *J*, *K* and *L* are coplanar.

For Exercises 4–6, write a conditional statement from each given statement.

4. Congruent segments have equal measures.

If segments are congruent, then they have equal measures.

5. On Tuesday, play practice is at 6:00.

If it is Tuesday, then play practice is at 6:00.

6.

Adjacent Angles / Linear Pair

If two angles form a linear pair, then they are adjacent angles.

A conditional statement has a false **truth value** *only* if the hypothesis (H) is true and the conclusion (C) is false.

Determine whether the following conditional is true. If false, give a counterexample.

7. If two angles are supplementary, then they form a linear pair.

False; two supplementary angles need not be adjacent.

CHALLENGE AND EXTEND

54. No lines are pts.
No pts. are lines.

55. Some students are adults. Some adults are students.

56b. If a figure is not a rect., then it is not a square. By the contrapositive, since figure *A* is not a rect., it is not a square.

58. $y = x + 3$

59. $y = 2x + 1$

60. $y = \dfrac{5}{2}x - 4$

For each Venn diagram, write two statements beginning with *Some, All,* or *No.*

54.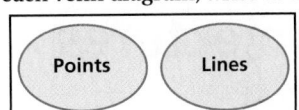

55.

Students	Adults

56. Given: If a figure is a square, then it is a rectangle. Figure *A* is not a rectangle.
Conclusion: Figure *A* is not a square.

  a. Draw a Venn diagram to represent the given conditional statement. Use the Venn diagram to explain why the conclusion is valid.

  b. Write the contrapositive of the given conditional. How can you use the contrapositive to justify the conclusion?

57. Multi-Step How many true conditionals can you write using the statements below?
  p: *n* is an integer.   *q*: *n* is a whole number.   *r*: *n* is a natural number.
  3

SPIRAL REVIEW

Write a rule to describe each relationship. *(Previous course)*

58.

x	−8	4	7	9
y	−5	7	10	12

59.

x	−3	−1	0	4
y	−5	−1	1	9

60.

x	−2	0	4	6
y	−9	−4	6	11

Determine whether each statement is true or false. If false, explain why. *(Lesson 1-4)*

61. If two angles are complementary and congruent, then the measure of each is 45°. **T**

62. A pair of acute angles can be supplementary. **F**

63. A linear pair of angles is also a pair of supplementary angles. **T**

Find the next item in each pattern. *(Lesson 2-1)*

64. 1, 13, 131, 1313, ...
  13,131

65. $2, \dfrac{2}{3}, \dfrac{2}{9}, \dfrac{2}{27}, ... \dfrac{2}{81}$

66. $x, 2x^2, 3x^3, 4x^4, ...$
  $5x^5$

Career Path

go.hrw.com/Geo/TX
Career Resources Online
KEYWORD: MG7 Career

Q: What high school math classes did you take?

A: I took three years of math: Pre-Algebra, Algebra, and Geometry.

Q: What training do you need to be a desktop publisher?

A: Most of my training was done on the job. The computer science and typing classes I took in high school have been helpful.

Q: How do you use math?

A: Part of my job is to make sure all the text, charts, and photographs are formatted to fit the layout of each page. I have to manipulate things by comparing ratios, calculating areas, and using estimation.

Q: What future plans do you have?

A: My goal is to start my own business as a freelance graphic artist.

Stephanie Poulin
Desktop Publisher
Daily Reporter

Answers

62. Possible answer: Acute ∡ measure less than 90°, so the sum of the measures of 2 acute ∡ must be less than 180°. Therefore, 2 acute ∡ cannot be supp.

Objective: Apply the Law of Detachment and the Law of Syllogism in logical reasoning.

PREMIER Online Edition
Tutorial Videos

Countdown to TAKS Week 3

Power Presentations
with PowerPoint®

Warm Up

Identify the hypothesis and conclusion of each conditional.

1. A mapping that is a reflection is a type of transformation.
H: A mapping is a reflection.
C: The mapping is a transformation.

2. The quotient of two negative numbers is positive. H: Two numbers are negative. C: The quotient is positive.

3. Determine if the conditional "If x is a number, then $|x| > 0$" is true. If false, give a counterexample. F; $x = 0$

Also available on transparency

Math Humor

Q: How is a geometry classroom like the United Nations?

A: They both have lots of rulers.

⭐ Geometry TEKS

G.2 Geometric structure*
(B) make conjectures about angles, lines, polygons, ... and determine the validity of the conjectures, ...

G.3 Geometric structure*
(B) construct and justify statements about geometric figures and their properties
(C) use logical reasoning to prove statements are true and find counterexamples to disprove statements that are false
(E) use deductive reasoning to prove a statement

***Knowledge and Skills** See p. 72.

2-3 Using Deductive Reasoning to Verify Conjectures

⭐ **TEKS G.3.E** Geometric structure: use deductive reasoning to prove a statement.
Also **G.2.B, G.3.B, G.3.C**

Objective
Apply the Law of Detachment and the Law of Syllogism in logical reasoning.

Vocabulary
deductive reasoning

Why learn this?
You can use inductive and deductive reasoning to decide whether a common myth is accurate.

You learned in Lesson 2-1 that one counterexample is enough to disprove a conjecture. But to prove that a conjecture is true, you must use *deductive reasoning.* **Deductive reasoning** is the process of using logic to draw conclusions from given facts, definitions, and properties.

EXAMPLE 1 *Media Application*

Urban legends and modern myths spread quickly through the media. Many Web sites and television shows are dedicated to confirming or disproving such myths. Is each conclusion a result of inductive or deductive reasoning?

A There is a myth that toilets and sinks drain in opposite directions in the Southern and Northern Hemispheres. However, if you were to observe sinks draining in the two hemispheres, you would see that this myth is false.

Since the conclusion is based on a pattern of observation, it is a result of inductive reasoning.

B There is a myth that you should not touch a baby bird that has fallen from its nest because the mother bird will disown the baby if she detects human scent. However, biologists have shown that birds cannot detect human scent. Therefore, the myth cannot be true.

The conclusion is based on logical reasoning from scientific research. It is a result of deductive reasoning.

1. There is a myth that an eelskin wallet will demagnetize credit cards because the skin of the electric eels used to make the wallet holds an electric charge. However, eelskin products are not made from electric eels. Therefore, the myth cannot be true. Is this conclusion a result of inductive or deductive reasoning? **deductive reasoning**

In deductive reasoning, if the given facts are true and you apply the correct logic, then the conclusion must be true. The Law of Detachment is one valid form of deductive reasoning.

---

1 Introduce

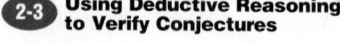

EXPLORATION

2-3 Using Deductive Reasoning to Verify Conjectures

The planet Yercon is full of unusual creatures. Here are some facts about the creatures.

> If you are a zintoid, then you are a quorg.
> If you are a meerk, then you are a ving.
> If you are a quorg, then you are a wiklop.

1. Dorla is a meerk. What else must be true about Dorla?

2. Zim is a quorg. What else must be true about Zim?

3. In general, suppose you know that $p \rightarrow q$ is a true statement and that p is true. What can you conclude?

4. Use the facts about the creatures to write a new conditional statement about zintoids: If you are a zintoid, then   ? .

5. In general, suppose you know that $p \rightarrow q$ and $q \rightarrow r$ are true statements. What can you conclude?

THINK AND DISCUSS

Motivate

Discuss with students the meaning of *myth* (a story of unknown authorship, usually serving to explain some phenomenon of nature, the origin of man, or cultural customs and institutions). Have students recall a myth or legend that they have read or heard. Ask students if the myth is true, and have them explain how they know whether it is true.

Explorations and answers are provided in the *Chapter 2 Resource Book.*

Law of Detachment

If $p \rightarrow q$ is a true statement and p is true, then q is true.

EXAMPLE 2 **Verifying Conjectures by Using the Law of Detachment**

Determine if each conjecture is valid by the Law of Detachment.

A Given: If two segments are congruent, then they have the same length. $\overline{AB} \cong \overline{XY}$.

Conjecture: $AB = XY$

Identify the hypothesis and conclusion in the given conditional.

If two segments are congruent, then they have the same length.

The given statement $\overline{AB} \cong \overline{XY}$ matches the hypothesis of a true conditional. By the Law of Detachment $AB = XY$. The conjecture is valid.

B Given: If you are tardy 3 times, you must go to detention.
Shea is in detention.

Conjecture: Shea was tardy at least 3 times.

Identify the hypothesis and conclusion in the given conditional.

If you are tardy 3 times, you must go to detention.

The given statement "Shea is in detention" matches the conclusion of a true conditional. But this does not mean the hypothesis is true. Shea could be in detention for another reason. The conjecture is not valid.

 **2.** Determine if the conjecture is valid by the Law of Detachment.
Given: If a student passes his classes, the student is eligible to play sports. Ramon passed his classes.
Conjecture: Ramon is eligible to play sports. valid

Another valid form of deductive reasoning is the Law of Syllogism. It allows you to draw conclusions from two conditional statements when the conclusion of one is the hypothesis of the other.

Law of Syllogism

If $p \rightarrow q$ and $q \rightarrow r$ are true statements, then $p \rightarrow r$ is a true statement.

EXAMPLE 3 **Verifying Conjectures by Using the Law of Syllogism**

Determine if each conjecture is valid by the Law of Syllogism.

A Given: If $m\angle A < 90°$, then $\angle A$ is acute. If $\angle A$ is acute, then it is not a right angle.

Conjecture: If $m\angle A < 90°$, then it is not a right angle.

Let p, q, and r represent the following.

p: The measure of an angle is less than 90°.

q: The angle is acute.

r: The angle is not a right angle.

You are given that $p \rightarrow q$ and $q \rightarrow r$. Since q is the conclusion of the first conditional and the hypothesis of the second conditional, you can conclude that $p \rightarrow r$. The conjecture is valid by the Law of Syllogism.

Additional Examples

Example 1

Is each conclusion a result of inductive or deductive reasoning?

A. There is a myth that you can balance an egg on its end only on the spring equinox. A person was able to balance an egg on July 8, September 21, and December 19. Therefore, this myth is false.
inductive reasoning

B. There is a myth that the Great Wall of China is the only man-made object visible from the Moon. The Great Wall is barely visible in photographs taken from 180 miles above Earth. The Moon is about 237,000 miles from Earth. Therefore, the myth cannot be true.
deductive reasoning

Example 2

Determine if each conjecture is valid by the Law of Detachment.

A. Given: If the side lengths of a triangle are 5 cm, 12 cm, and 13 cm, then the area of the triangle is 30 cm². The area of $\triangle PQR$ is 30 cm².

Conjecture: The side lengths of $\triangle PQR$ are 5 cm, 12 cm, and 13 cm. not valid

B. Given: In the World Series, if a team wins four games, then the team wins the series. The Red Sox won four games in the 2004 World Series.

Conjecture: The Red Sox won the 2004 World Series. valid

Also available on transparency

---

2 Teach

Guided Instruction

Review the concept of inductive reasoning, and discuss the differences between inductive and deductive reasoning. Have students give examples of each. Then introduce the Law of Detachment and the Law of Syllogism.

Teaching Tip **Algebra** Show students how the Law of Syllogism is similar to the Transitive Property of Equality used in algebra. Both involve the same term in the middle.

Reaching All Learners
Through Auditory Cues

For each example, read each conditional statement aloud for students. Suggest that they listen for the key words *if* and *then*. Students can then recite back the conditionals in the order needed to apply the Law of Detachment or the Law of Syllogism. Remind students not to worry about the truth value of individual conditionals, but rather to make sure the law is applied correctly.

INTERVENTION ◄►
Questioning Strategies

EXAMPLE 1

• How can you tell the difference between inductive and deductive reasoning?

EXAMPLES 2–3

• How can you recognize when to apply the Law of Detachment versus when to apply the Law of Syllogism?

Additional Examples

Example 3

Determine if each conjecture is valid by the Law of Syllogism.

A. Given: If a figure is a kite, then it is a quadrilateral. If a figure is a quadrilateral, then it is a polygon.

Conjecture: If a figure is a kite, then it is a polygon.   valid

B. Given: If a number is divisible by 2, then it is even. If a number is even, then it is an integer.

Conjecture: If a number is an integer, then it is divisible by 2.   not valid

Example 4

Draw a conclusion from the given information.

A. Given: If $2y = 4$, then $z = -1$. If $x + 3 = 12$, then $2y = 4$. $x + 3 = 12$ $z = -1$

B. If the sum of the measures of two angles is 180°, then the angles are supplementary. If two angles are supplementary, they are not angles of a triangle. $m\angle A = 135°$, and $m\angle B = 45°$. $\angle A$ and $\angle B$ are not angles of a triangle.

Also available on transparency

INTERVENTION ◀━▶
Questioning Strategies

EXAMPLE 4

• When applying the Law of Syllogism, does the order of the conditional statements matter? Explain.

Determine if each conjecture is valid by the Law of Syllogism.

B Given: If a number is divisible by 4, then it is divisible by 2.
If a number is even, then it is divisible by 2.

Conjecture: If a number is divisible by 4, then it is even.

Let x, y, and z represent the following.

x: A number is divisible by 4.
y: A number is divisible by 2.
z: A number is even.

You are given that $x \rightarrow y$ and $z \rightarrow y$. The Law of Syllogism cannot be used to draw a conclusion since y is the conclusion of both conditionals. Even though the conjecture $x \rightarrow z$ is true, the logic used to draw the conclusion is not valid.

Caution! //////
It is possible to arrive at a true conclusion by applying invalid logical reasoning, as in Example 3B.

CHECK IT OUT!
3. Determine if the conjecture is valid by the Law of Syllogism.
Given: If an animal is a mammal, then it has hair.
If an animal is a dog, then it is a mammal.
Conjecture: If an animal is a dog, then it has hair. **valid**

EXAMPLE 4 **Applying the Laws of Deductive Reasoning**

Draw a conclusion from the given information.

A Given: If a team wins 10 games, then they play in the finals. If a team plays in the finals, then they travel to Boston. The Ravens won 10 games.

Conclusion: The Ravens will travel to Boston.

B Given: If two angles form a linear pair, then they are adjacent. If two angles are adjacent, then they share a side. $\angle 1$ and $\angle 2$ form a linear pair.

Conclusion: $\angle 1$ and $\angle 2$ share a side.

CHECK IT OUT!
4. Draw a conclusion from the given information.
Given: If a polygon is a triangle, then it has three sides. If a polygon has three sides, then it is not a quadrilateral. Polygon P is a triangle.
Polygon P is not a quad.

THINK AND DISCUSS

1. Could "A square has exactly two sides" be the conclusion of a valid argument? If so, what do you know about the truth value of the given information?

2. Explain why writing conditional statements as symbols might help you evaluate the validity of an argument.

3. **GET ORGANIZED** Copy and complete the graphic organizer. Write each law in your own words and give an example of each.

Know it!
.Note

```
            Deductive Reasoning
            /                 \
Law of Detachment        Law of Syllogism
```

---

3 Close

Summarize

Remind students of the difference between inductive reasoning (based on patterns) and deductive reasoning (based on logic). Review the Law of Detachment and the Law of Syllogism given on page 89.

ONGOING ASSESSMENT

and INTERVENTION ◀━▶

Diagnose Before the Lesson
2-3 Warm Up, TE p. 88

Monitor During the Lesson
Check It Out! Exercises, SE pp. 88–90
Questioning Strategies, TE pp. 89–90

Assess After the Lesson
2-3 Lesson Quiz, TE p. 93
Alternative Assessment, TE p. 93

Answers to *Think and Discuss*

1. Yes; the given information is false.

2. Possible answer: Using symbols instead of words forces you to look at the validity of the argument itself, without being distracted by the truth value of the individual statements.

3. See p. A2.

go.hrw.com/Geo/TX
Homework Help Online
KEYWORD: MG7 2-3
Parent Resources Online
KEYWORD: MG7 Parent

1. Possible answer: Inductive reasoning is based on a pattern of specific cases. Deductive reasoning is based on logical reasoning.

GUIDED PRACTICE

1. Vocabulary Explain how *deductive reasoning* differs from inductive reasoning.

SEE EXAMPLE **1**
p. 88

Does each conclusion use inductive or deductive reasoning?

2. At Bell High School, students must take Biology before they take Chemistry. Sam is in Chemistry, so Marcia concludes that he has taken Biology.
deductive reasoning

3. A detective learns that his main suspect was out of town the day of the crime. He concludes that the suspect is innocent.
deductive reasoning

SEE EXAMPLE **2**
p. 89

Determine if each conjecture is valid by the Law of Detachment.

4. Given: If you want to go on a field trip, you must have a signed permission slip. Zola has a signed permission slip.
Conjecture: Zola wants to go on a field trip. **invalid**

5. Given: If the side lengths of a rectangle are 3 ft and 4 ft, then its area is 12 ft². A rectangle has side lengths of 3 ft and 4 ft.
Conjecture: The area of the rectangle is 12 ft². **valid**

SEE EXAMPLE **3**
p. 89

Determine if each conjecture is valid by the Law of Syllogism.

6. Given: If you fly from Texas to California, you travel from the central to the Pacific time zone. If you travel from the central to the Pacific time zone, then you gain two hours.
Conjecture: If you fly from Texas to California, you gain two hours. **valid**

7. Given: If a figure is a **square**, then the figure is a **rectangle**. If a figure is a **square**, then it is a **parallelogram**.
Conjecture: If a figure is a **parallelogram**, then it is a **rectangle**. **invalid**

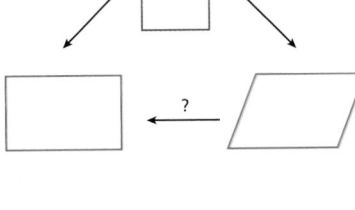

SEE EXAMPLE **4**
p. 90

8. Draw a conclusion from the given information.
Given: If you leave your car lights on overnight, then your car battery will drain. If your battery is drained, your car might not start. Alex left his car lights on last night.
Alex's car might not start.

PRACTICE AND PROBLEM SOLVING

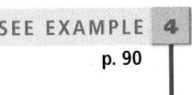

Independent Practice	
For Exercises	See Example
9–10	1
11	2
12	3
13	4

TEKS ⭐ TAKS

Skills Practice p. S6
Application Practice p. S29

Does each conclusion use inductive or deductive reasoning?

9. The sum of the angle measures of a triangle is 180°. Two angles of a triangle measure 40° and 60°, so Kandy concludes that the third angle measures 80°. **deductive reasoning**

10. All of the students in Henry's Geometry class are juniors. Alexander takes Geometry, but has another teacher. Henry concludes that Alexander is also a junior. **inductive reasoning**

11. Determine if the conjecture is valid by the Law of Detachment.
Given: If one integer is odd and another integer is even, their product is even. The product of two integers is 24.
Conjecture: One of the two integers is odd. **invalid**

Assignment Guide

Assign *Guided Practice* exercises as necessary.

If you finished Examples **1–2**
> **Basic** 9–11
> **Average** 9–11, 14
> **Advanced** 9–11, 14

If you finished Examples **1–4**
> **Basic** 9–13, 15–18, 20, 22–25, 29–37
> **Average** 9–14, 16, 18–25, 28–37
> **Advanced** 9–14, 16, 18, 19, 21–37

Homework Quick Check
Quickly check key concepts.
Exercises: 10–13, 16, 18

Teaching Tip
Diversity Some students may not be familiar with time zones. For **Exercise 6,** you may want to use a globe to show how Earth is divided into 24 time zones. Explain that as you travel west, you gain one hour for each time zone you pass through. This accounts for Earth's rotation.

TAKS Practice

Grades 9–11	Exercises
Obj. 2	29–31
Obj. 7	32–34
Obj. 9	14
Obj. 10	14, 26, 28

Answers

21. Possible answers: If Mary goes to the store, then I will go with her. Mary goes to the store. The conclusion "I will go with her" is valid by the Law of Detachment. If Jon goes to the movies, then he will eat popcorn. If Jon eats popcorn, then he needs a drink. The conclusion "If Jon goes to the movies, then he needs a drink" is valid by the Law of Syllogism.

22a. If a creature is a serpent, then it eats eggs.

b. No; possible answer: the Pigeon did not correctly apply the Law of Detachment; "Alice eats eggs" matches the conclusion of the conditional, not the hypothesis.

27a. If you live in San Diego, then you live in the United States.

b. If you do not live in California, then you do not live in San Diego. If you do not live in the United States, then you do not live in California.

c. If you do not live in the United States, then you do not live in San Diego.

d. They are contrapositives of each other.

20. A; comp. ∠ are not necessarily adj., so they may not form a rt. ∠.

---

12. Science Determine if the conjecture is valid by the Law of Syllogism.

Given: If an element is an alkali metal, then it reacts with water. If an element is in the first column of the periodic table, then it is an alkali metal.

Conjecture: If an element is in the first column of the periodic table, then it reacts with water. **valid**

13. Draw a conclusion from the given information.

Given: If Dakota watches the news, she is informed about current events. If Dakota knows about current events, she gets better grades in Social Studies. Dakota watches the news. **Dakota gets better grades in Social Studies.**

14. Technology Joseph downloads a file in 18 minutes with a dial-up modem. How long would it take to download the file with a Cheetah-Net cable modem? **0.24 min or 14.4 s**

CHEETAH-NET CABLE
75 Times As Fast As Dial-Up

Recreation Use the true statements below for Exercises 15–18. Determine whether each conclusion is valid.

I. The Top Thrill Dragster is at Cedar Point amusement park in Sandusky, OH.

II. Carter and Mary go to Cedar Point.

III. The Top Thrill Dragster roller coaster reaches speeds of 120 mi/h.

IV. When Carter goes to an amusement park, he rides all the roller coasters.

15. Carter went to Sandusky, OH. **valid**

16. Mary rode the Top Thrill Dragster. **invalid**

17. Carter rode a roller coaster that travels 120 mi/h. **valid**

18. Mary rode a roller coaster that travels 120 mi/h. **invalid**

19. Critical Thinking Is the argument below a valid application of the Law of Syllogism? Is the conclusion true? Explain your answers.

If $3 - x < 5$, then $x < -2$. If $x < -2$, then $-5x > 10$. Thus, if $3 - x < 5$, then $-5x > 10$. **yes; no; because the first conditional is false**

20. ///**ERROR ANALYSIS**/// Below are two conclusions. Which is incorrect? Explain the error.

If two angles are complementary, their measures add to 90°. If an angle measures 90°, then it is a right angle. ∠A and ∠B are complementary.

A | ∠A and ∠B form a right angle.

B | m∠A + m∠B = 90°

21. Write About It Write one example of a real-life logical argument that uses the Law of Detachment and one that uses the Law of Syllogism. Explain why the conclusions are valid.

Recreation
The Top Thrill Dragster is 420 feet tall and includes a 400-foot vertical drop. It twists 270° as it drops. It is one of 16 roller coasters at Cedar Point amusement park.

MULTI-STEP TAKS PREP

22. This problem will prepare you for the Multi-Step TAKS Prep on page 102.

When Alice meets the Pigeon in Wonderland, the Pigeon thinks she is a serpent. The Pigeon reasons that serpents eat eggs, and Alice confirms that she has eaten eggs.

a. Write "Serpents eat eggs" as a conditional statement.

b. Is the Pigeon's conclusion that Alice is a serpent valid? Explain your reasoning.

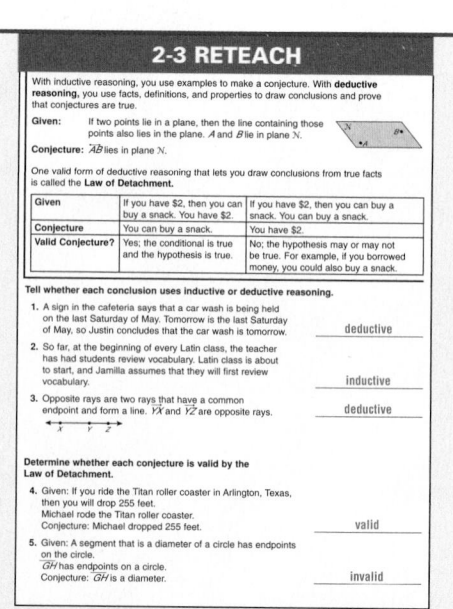

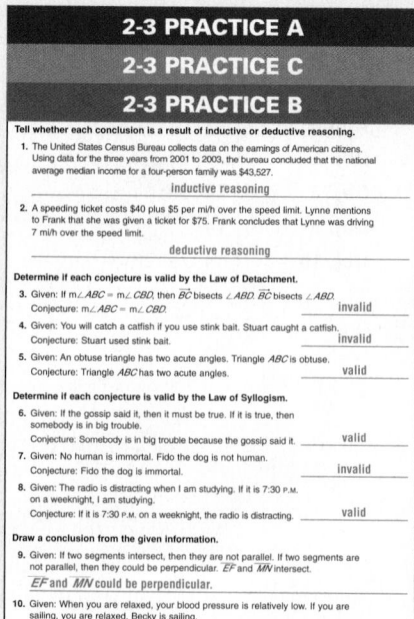
2-3 PRACTICE A
2-3 PRACTICE C
2-3 PRACTICE B

Tell whether each conclusion is a result of inductive or deductive reasoning.

1. The United States Census Bureau collects data on the earnings of American citizens. Using data for the three years from 2001 to 2003, the bureau concluded that the national average median income for a four-person family was $43,527.

inductive reasoning

2. A speeding ticket costs $40 plus $5 per mi/h over the speed limit. Lynne mentions to Frank that she was given a ticket for $75. Frank concludes that Lynne was driving 7 mi/h over the speed limit.

deductive reasoning

Determine if each conjecture is valid by the Law of Detachment.

3. Given: If m∠ABC = m∠CBD, then BC bisects ∠ABD. BC bisects ∠ABD. Conjecture: m∠ABC = m∠CBD. **invalid**

4. Given: You will catch a catfish if you use stink bait. Stuart caught a catfish. Conjecture: Stuart used stink bait. **invalid**

5. Given: An obtuse triangle has two acute angles. Triangle ABC is obtuse. Conjecture: Triangle ABC has two acute angles. **valid**

Determine if each conjecture is valid by the Law of Syllogism.

6. Given: If the gossip said it, then it must be true. If it is true, then somebody is in big trouble. Conjecture: Somebody is in big trouble because the gossip said it. **valid**

7. Given: No human is immortal. Fido the dog is not human. Conjecture: Fido the dog is immortal. **invalid**

8. Given: The radio is distracting when I am studying. If it's 7:30 P.M. on a weeknight, I am studying. Conjecture: If it is 7:30 P.M. on a weeknight, the radio is distracting. **valid**

Draw a conclusion from the given information.

9. Given: If two segments intersect, then they are not parallel. If two segments are not parallel, then they could be perpendicular. EF and MN intersect. **EF and MN could be perpendicular.**

10. Given: When you are relaxed, your blood pressure is relatively low. If you are sailing, you are relaxed. Becky is sailing. **Becky's blood pressure is relatively low.**

2-3 READING STRATEGIES

Conjectures can be verified by using deductive reasoning.

Types of Deductive Reasoning

Law of Detachment | Law of Syllogism

If p → q is a true statement and p is true, then q is true. | If p → q and q → r are true statements, then p → r is a true statement.

Given: If I get over 90%, I will receive an A. I got 96%. Conjecture: I have an A. | Given: If I oversleep, I will miss the bus. If I miss the bus, I will have to walk to school. Conjecture: If I oversleep, I will have to walk to school.

Apply the Laws of Deductive Reasoning.

1.
If two angles are congruent, then they have the same measure. ∠BAC ≅ ∠CAD.
Conjecture: m∠BAC = m∠CAD
Hypothesis: **Two angles are congruent.**
The conjecture is (valid/invalid) **valid** using the Law of **Detachment**

2.
You are given the following statements about ∠S.
If 90° < m∠S < 180°, then ∠S is obtuse. If ∠S is obtuse, then it is not a right angle.
Conjecture: If 90° < m∠S < 180°, then it is not a right angle.
If p → q and q → r, determine p, q, and r.
p **The measure of ∠S is greater than 90° and less than 180°.**
q **The angle is obtuse.**
r **The angle is not a right angle.**
The conjecture is (valid/invalid) **valid** based on the Law of **Syllogism**

2-3 RETEACH

With inductive reasoning, you use examples to make a conjecture. With **deductive reasoning**, you use facts, definitions, and properties to draw conclusions and prove that conjectures are true.

Given: If two points lie in a plane, then the line containing those points also lies in the plane. A and B lie in plane N.
Conjecture: AB lies in plane N.

One valid form of deductive reasoning that lets you draw conclusions from true facts is called the **Law of Detachment**.

Given	If you have $2, then you can buy a snack. You have $2.	If you have $2, then you can buy a snack.
Conjecture	You can buy a snack.	You have $2.
Valid Conjecture?	Yes; the conditional is true and the hypothesis is true.	No; the hypothesis may or may not be true. For example, if you borrowed money, you could also buy a snack.

Tell whether each conclusion uses inductive or deductive reasoning.

1. A sign in the cafeteria says that a car wash is being held on the last Saturday of May. Tomorrow is the last Saturday of May, so Justin concludes that the car wash is tomorrow. **deductive**

2. So far, at the beginning of every Latin class, the teacher has had students review vocabulary. Latin class is about to start, and Jamilla assumes that they will first review vocabulary. **inductive**

3. Opposite rays are two rays that have a common endpoint and form a line. YX and YZ are opposite rays. **deductive**

Determine whether each conjecture is valid by the Law of Detachment.

4. Given: If you ride the Titan roller coaster in Arlington, Texas, then you will drop 255 feet. Michael rode the Titan roller coaster. Conjecture: Michael dropped 255 feet. **valid**

5. Given: A segment that is a diameter of a circle has endpoints on the circle. GH has endpoints on a circle. Conjecture: GH is a diameter. **invalid**

23. The Supershots scored over 75 points in each of ten straight games. The newspaper predicts that they will score more than 75 points tonight. Which form of reasoning is this conclusion based on?

(A) Deductive reasoning, because the conclusion is based on logic

(B) Deductive reasoning, because the conclusion is based on a pattern

(C) Inductive reasoning, because the conclusion is based on logic

(D) Inductive reasoning, because the conclusion is based on a pattern

24. $\overrightarrow{HF}$ bisects $\angle EHG$. Which conclusion is NOT valid?

(F) E, F, and G are coplanar.

(G) $\angle EHF \cong \angle FHG$

(H) $\overline{EF} \cong \overline{FG}$

(J) $m\angle EHF = m\angle FHG$

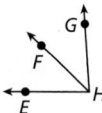

25. **Gridded Response** If Whitney plays a low G on her piano, the frequency of the note is 24.50 hertz. The frequency of a note doubles with each octave. What is the frequency in hertz of a G note that is 3 octaves above low G? **196**

CHALLENGE AND EXTEND

26. Either Andre is less than 35 years old, or he is not a natural-born citizen. Possible answer: Since there are 3 criteria to be eligible and he meets 1, he must not meet 1 of the remaining 2.

26. **Political Science** To be eligible to hold the office of the president of the United States, a person must be at least 35 years old, be a natural-born U.S. citizen, and have been a U.S. resident for at least 14 years. Given this information, what conclusion, if any, can be drawn from the statements below? Explain your reasoning.

Andre is not eligible to be the president of the United States.
Andre has lived in the United States for 16 years.

27. **Multi-Step** Consider the two conditional statements below.
If you live in San Diego, then you live in California.
If you live in California, then you live in the United States.

a. Draw a conclusion from the given conditional statements.

b. Write the contrapositive of each conditional statement.

c. Draw a conclusion from the two contrapositives.

d. How does the conclusion in part **a** relate to the conclusion in part **c**?

28. If Cassie goes to the skate park, Hanna and Amy will go. If Hanna or Amy goes to the skate park, then Marc will go. If Marc goes to the skate park, then Dallas will go. If only two of the five people went to the skate park, who were they? **Marc and Dallas**

SPIRAL REVIEW

Simplify each expression. *(Previous course)*

29. $2(x + 5)$
$2x + 10$

30. $(4y + 6) - (3y - 5)$
$y + 11$

31. $(3c + 4c) + 2(-7c + 7)$
$-7c + 14$

Find the coordinates of the midpoint of the segment connecting each pair of points. *(Lesson 1-6)*

32. $(1, 2)$ and $(4, 5)$
$(2.5, 3.5)$

33. $(-3, 6)$ and $(0, 1)$
$(-1.5, 3.5)$

34. $(-2.5, 9)$ and $(2.5, -3)$
$(0, 3)$

Identify the <u>hypothesis</u> and <u>conclusion</u> of each conditional statement. *(Lesson 2-2)*

35. If <u>the fire alarm rings</u>, then <u>everyone should exit the building</u>.

36. If <u>two different lines intersect</u>, then <u>they intersect at exactly one point</u>.

37. The statement <u>$\overline{AB} \cong \overline{CD}$</u> implies that <u>$AB = CD$</u>.

2-3 Using Deductive Reasoning to Verify Conjectures 93

 **TEST PREP DOCTOR +** For **Exercise 23**, remind students that they can use the definitions of *inductive reasoning* and *deductive reasoning* to eliminate choices **B** and **C**. Ask students whether the conclusion is based on a pattern or on logic, which should lead them to the correct choice, **D**.

Journal

Have students rewrite the Law of Detachment and the Law of Syllogism in words without using symbols.

ALTERNATIVE ASSESSMENT

Have students write a valid and an invalid application of the Law of Detachment and the Law of Syllogism. Have students exchange papers with a partner and then explain why each conclusion is or is not valid.

Power Presentations with PowerPoint®

2-3 Lesson Quiz

1. Is the conclusion a result of inductive or deductive reasoning?

At Reagan High School, students must pass Geometry before they take Algebra 2. Emily is in Algebra 2, so she must have passed Geometry.
deductive reasoning

Determine if each conjecture is valid.

2. Given: If n is a natural number, then n is an integer. If n is an integer, then n is a rational number. 0.875 is a rational number.

Conjecture: 0.875 is a natural number. not valid

3. Given: If an American citizen is at least 18 years old, then he or she is eligible to vote. Anna is a 20-year-old American citizen.

Conjecture: Anna is eligible to vote. valid

Also available on transparency

Lesson 2-3 **93**

Geometry LAB Organizer

Use with Lesson 2-3

Pacing:
Traditional 1 day
Block $\frac{1}{2}$ day

Objectives: Use tables to solve logic puzzles.

Use networks to solve logic puzzles.

 Online Edition

 Countdown to TAKS Week 3

Teach

Discuss

Emphasize that the key to solving logic puzzles is to systematically work through the given information one piece at a time. As you read each clue, draw any conclusions you can and mark the diagram carefully before moving on to the next clue. In **Activity 2,** suggest that students redraw the network on their own paper.

 Geometry TEKS

G.4 Geometric structure*
(A) select an appropriate representation (concrete, pictorial, graphical, verbal, or symbolic) in order to solve problems

* Knowledge and Skills See p. 72.

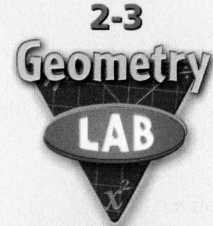

2-3 Geometry LAB

Use with Lesson 2-3

Solve Logic Puzzles

In Lesson 2-3, you used deductive reasoning to analyze the truth values of conditional statements. Now you will learn some methods for diagramming conditional statements to help you solve logic puzzles.

⭐ **TEKS G.4.A Geometric structure: select an appropriate representation ... in order to solve problems**

Activity 1

Bonnie, Cally, Daphne, and Fiona own a bird, cat, dog, and fish. No girl has a type of pet that begins with the same letter as her name. Bonnie is allergic to animal fur. Daphne feeds Fiona's bird when Fiona is away. Make a table to determine who owns which animal.

1 Since no girl has a type of pet that starts with the same letter as her name, place an X in each box along the diagonal of the table.

	Bird	Cat	Dog	Fish
Bonnie	✕			
Cally		✕		
Daphne			✕	
Fiona				✕

2 Bonnie cannot have a cat or dog because of her allergy. So she must own the fish, and no other girl can have the fish.

	Bird	Cat	Dog	Fish
Bonnie	✕	✕	✕	✓
Cally		✕		✕
Daphne			✕	✕
Fiona				✕

3 Fiona owns the bird, so place a check in Fiona's row, in the bird column. Place an X in the remaining boxes in the same column and row.

	Bird	Cat	Dog	Fish
Bonnie	✕	✕	✕	✓
Cally	✕	✕		✕
Daphne	✕		✕	✕
Fiona	✓	✕	✕	✕

4 Therefore, Daphne owns the cat, and Cally owns the dog.

	Bird	Cat	Dog	Fish
Bonnie	✕	✕	✕	✓
Cally	✕	✕	✓	✕
Daphne	✕	✓	✕	✕
Fiona	✓	✕	✕	✕

Try This

1. Because no one else can own the bird and Fiona owns only 1 pet.

1. After figuring out that Fiona owns the bird in Step 3, why can you place an X in every other box in that row and column?

2. Ally, Emily, Misha, and Tracy go to a dance with Danny, Frank, Jude, and Kian. Ally and Frank are siblings. Jude and Kian are roommates. Misha does not know Kian. Emily goes with Kian's roommate. Tracy goes with Ally's brother. Who went to the dance with whom?

	Danny	Frank	Jude	Kian
Ally	✕	✕	✕	✓
Emily	✕	✕	✓	✕
Misha	✓	✕	✕	✕
Tracy	✕	✓	✕	✕

Activity 2

A farmer has a goat, a wolf, and a cabbage. He wants to transport all three from one side of a river to the other. He has a boat, but it has only enough room for the farmer and one thing. The wolf will eat the goat if they are left alone together, and the goat will eat the cabbage if they are left alone. How can the farmer get everything to the other side of the river?

You can use a *network* to solve this kind of puzzle. A **network** is a diagram of *vertices* and *edges*, also known as a graph. An **edge** is a curve or a segment that joins two *vertices* of the graph. A **vertex** is a point on the graph.

❶ Let *F* represent the farmer, *W* represent the wolf, *G* represent the goat, and *C* represent the cabbage. Use an ordered pair to represent what is on each side of the river. The first ordered pair is (*FWGC*, —), and the desired result is (—, *FWGC*).

❷ Draw a vertex and label it with the first ordered pair. Then draw an edge and vertex for each possible trip the farmer could make across the river. If at any point a path results in an unworkable combination of things, no more edges can be drawn from that vertex.

❸ From each workable vertex, continue to draw edges and vertices that represent the next trip across the river. When you get to a vertex for (—, *FWGC*), the network is complete.

❹ Use the network to write out the solution in words.

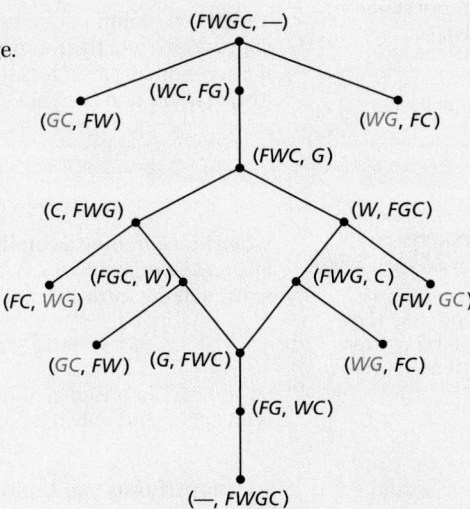

(FWGC, —)
(WC, FG)
(GC, FW)   (WG, FC)
(FWC, G)
(C, FWG)   (W, FGC)
(FC, WG) (FGC, W)   (FWG, C) (FW, GC)
(GC, FW) (G, FWC)   (WG, FC)
(FG, WC)
(—, FWGC)

Try This

3. What combinations are unworkable? Why? **WG and GC; because the wolf will eat the goat and the goat will eat the cabbage**

4. How many solutions are there to the farmer's transport problem? How many steps does each solution take? **2; 7**

5. What is the advantage of drawing a complete solution network rather than working out one solution with a diagram?

6. Madeline has two measuring cups—a 1-cup measuring cup and a $\frac{3}{4}$-cup measuring cup. Neither cup has any markings on it. How can Madeline get exactly $\frac{1}{2}$ cup of flour in the larger measuring cup? Complete the network below to solve the problem.

(0, 0)
(1, 0)   (0, $\frac{3}{4}$)

2-3 Geometry Lab **95**

Close

Key Concept

Many logic puzzles can be solved by the process of elimination if you work with the given clues in a careful and systematic way. Diagrams can be used to organize each piece of the puzzle and to help visualize the final outcome.

Assessment

Journal Have students explain how they reached their conclusions in one of the *Try This* puzzles.

Answers

5. Possible answer: You can see all solutions instead of just 1 possible solution.

6.
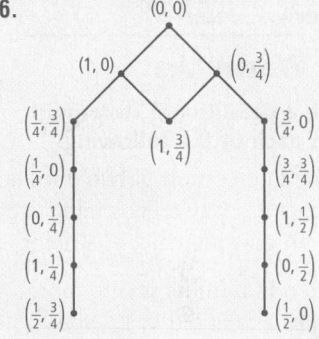

(0, 0)
(1, 0)   (0, $\frac{3}{4}$)
($\frac{1}{4}$, $\frac{3}{4}$)   ($\frac{3}{4}$, 0)
                 (1, $\frac{3}{4}$)
($\frac{1}{4}$, 0)   ($\frac{3}{4}$, $\frac{3}{4}$)
(0, $\frac{1}{4}$)   (1, $\frac{1}{2}$)
(1, $\frac{1}{4}$)   (0, $\frac{1}{2}$)
($\frac{1}{2}$, $\frac{3}{4}$)   ($\frac{1}{2}$, 0)

Possible answer: Fill the 1 c cup. Pour the contents into the $\frac{3}{4}$ c cup. Empty the $\frac{3}{4}$ c cup so you have $\frac{1}{4}$ c in the larger cup. Transfer this to the $\frac{3}{4}$ c cup, and fill the 1 c cup. Use the contents of the 1c cup to fill the $\frac{3}{4}$ c cup, leaving $\frac{1}{2}$ c in the 1 c cup.

Teacher to Teacher

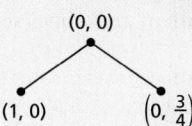

Some students really enjoy logic puzzles. I like to challenge these students with more complicated puzzles that don't have the grid already provided. Creating the grid makes students organize the information in the puzzle before trying to solve it.

Many grocery stores and bookstores sell magazines with logic puzzles. Internet sites are another good resource for logic puzzles.

Cynthia Hodges
Killeen, TX

2-3 Geometry Lab **95**

Objective: Write and analyze biconditional statements.

Geometry Lab
In *Texas Lab Manual*

Online Edition
Tutorial Videos

Countdown to TAKS Week 3

Power Presentations
with PowerPoint®

Warm Up

Write a conditional statement from each of the following.

1. The intersection of two lines is a point.   If two lines intersect, then they intersect in a point.

2. An odd number is one more than a multiple of 2.   If a number is odd, then it is one more than a multiple of 2.

3. Write the converse of the conditional "If Pedro lives in Chicago, then he lives in Illinois." Find its truth value.   If Pedro lives in Illinois, then he lives in Chicago; F.

Also available on transparency

Math Humor

Q: Why was the math book sad?
A: It had too many problems.

⭐ Geometry TEKS

G.3 Geometric structure*
(A) determine the validity of a conditional statement, its converse, inverse, and contrapositive
(B) construct and justify statements about geometric figures and their properties

* **Knowledge and Skills** See p. 72.

2-4 Biconditional Statements and Definitions

 TEKS G.3.A Geometric structure: determine the validity of a conditional statement, its converse, inverse, and contrapositive. Also G.3.B

Objective
Write and analyze biconditional statements.

Vocabulary
biconditional statement
definition
polygon
triangle
quadrilateral

Who uses this?
A gardener can plan the color of the hydrangeas she plants by checking the pH of the soil.

The pH of a solution is a measure of the concentration of hydronium ions in the solution. If a solution has a pH less than 7, it is an acid. Also, if a solution is an acid, it has a pH less than 7.

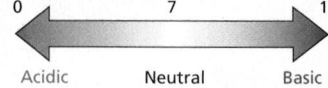

0   7   14
Acidic   Neutral   Basic

Writing Math
The biconditional "*p* if and only if *q*" can also be written as "*p* iff *q*" or $p \leftrightarrow q$.

When you combine a conditional statement and its converse, you create a *biconditional statement*. A **biconditional statement** is a statement that can be written in the form "*p* if and only if *q*." This means "if *p*, then *q*" and "if *q*, then *p*."

$$p \longleftrightarrow q \text{ means } p \longrightarrow q \text{ and } q \longrightarrow p$$

So you can define an acid with the following biconditional statement: A solution is an acid if and only if it has a pH less than 7.

EXAMPLE **1** **Identifying the Conditionals within a Biconditional Statement**

Write the conditional statement and converse within each biconditional.

A Two angles are congruent if and only if their measures are equal.
Let *p* and *q* represent the following.
  p: Two angles are congruent.
  q: Two angle measures are equal.
The two parts of the biconditional $p \leftrightarrow q$ are $p \rightarrow q$ and $q \rightarrow p$.
Conditional: If two angles are congruent, then their measures are equal.
Converse: If two angle measures are equal, then the angles are congruent.

B A solution is a base ↔ it has a pH greater than 7.
Let *x* and *y* represent the following.
  x: A solution is a base.
  y: A solution has a pH greater than 7.
The two parts of the biconditional $x \leftrightarrow y$ are $x \rightarrow y$ and $y \rightarrow x$.
Conditional: If a solution is a base, then it has a pH greater than 7.
Converse: If a solution has a pH greater than 7, then it is a base.

1a. Conditional: If an ∠ is acute, then its measure is greater than 0° and less than 90°. Converse: If an ∠'s measure is greater than 0° and less than 90°, then the ∠ is acute.

1b. Conditional: If Cho is a member, then he has paid the $5 dues. Converse: If Cho has paid the $5 dues, then he is a member.

 **CHECK IT OUT!** Write the conditional statement and converse within each biconditional.
1a. An angle is acute iff its measure is greater than 0° and less than 90°.
1b. Cho is a member if and only if he has paid the $5 dues.

---

1 Introduce

EXPLORATION
2-4 Biconditional Statements and Definitions

While studying geometric figures, a student invents the term *rectapentagon*. Here are examples of figures that are rectapentagons and figures that are not rectapentagons.

| Rectapentagons | Not Rectapentagons |

1. Which of the following figures do you think are rectapentagons?

2. Draw your own examples of figures that are rectapentagons and figures that are not rectapentagons.

3. What must be true about a figure for it to be a rectapentagon?

THINK AND DISCUSS
4. **Discuss** whether or not the following is a good definition: A rectapentagon is a geometric figure with two right angles.

Motivate

Ask students to give a definition for a common classroom object, such as a piece of chalk. Possible answer: something you write with Use the students' answers to demonstrate why a definition must be precise. For example, a pen is something you write with, but it is not chalk. Have the students refine their definition until it is sufficiently precise.

Explorations and answers are provided in the *Chapter 2 Resource Book*.

EXAMPLE 2 Writing a Biconditional Statement

For each conditional, write the converse and a biconditional statement.

A If $2x + 5 = 11$, then $x = 3$.
Converse: If $x = 3$, then $2x + 5 = 11$.
Biconditional: $2x + 5 = 11$ if and only if $x = 3$.

B If a point is a midpoint, then it divides the segment into two congruent segments.
Converse: If a point divides a segment into two congruent segments, then the point is a midpoint.
Biconditional: A point is a midpoint if and only if it divides the segment into two congruent segments.

2a. Converse: If it is Independence Day, then the date is July 4th. Biconditional: It is July 4th if and only if it is Independence Day.

2b. Converse: If pts. are collinear, then they lie on the same line. Biconditional: Pts. lie on the same line if and only if they are collinear.

 CHECK IT OUT! For each conditional, write the converse and a biconditional statement.

2a. If the date is July 4th, then it is Independence Day.
2b. If points lie on the same line, then they are collinear.

For a biconditional statement to be true, both the conditional statement and its converse must be true. If either the conditional or the converse is false, then the biconditional statement is false.

EXAMPLE 3 Analyzing the Truth Value of a Biconditional Statement

Determine if each biconditional is true. If false, give a counterexample.

A A square has a side length of 5 if and only if it has an area of 25.
Conditional: If a square has a side length of 5, then it has an area of 25. *The conditional is true.*
Converse: If a square has an area of 25, then it has a side length of 5. *The converse is true.*
Since the conditional and its converse are true, the biconditional is true.

B The number n is a positive integer $\leftrightarrow 2n$ is a natural number.
Conditional: If n is a positive integer, then $2n$ is a natural number. *The conditional is true.*
Converse: If $2n$ is a natural number, then n is a positive integer. *The converse is false.*
If $2n = 1$, then $n = \frac{1}{2}$, which is not an integer. Because the converse is false, the biconditional is false.

 **CHECK IT OUT!** Determine if each biconditional is true. If false, give a counterexample.

3a. An angle is a right angle iff its measure is 90°. T
3b. $y = -5 \leftrightarrow y^2 = 25$ F; $y = 5$

In geometry, biconditional statements are used to write *definitions*. A **definition** is a statement that describes a mathematical object and can be written as a true biconditional. Most definitions in the glossary are not written as biconditional statements, but they can be. The "if and only if" is implied.

2-4 Biconditional Statements and Definitions **97**

 Teach

Guided Instruction

Be sure that students understand the relationship between a conditional and its converse—that they are not necessarily logically equivalent—before introducing biconditional statements. Emphasize that biconditionals are used for definitions because they are conditionals in which the converse is also true. You may want to model something reversible for students, such as a reversible vest or jacket.

ENGLISH LANGUAGE LEARNERS

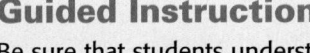 **Reaching All Learners**

Through Cooperative Learning

After you have discussed the concept of precise definitions on page 98, have each student write five definitions in biconditional form using the vocabulary terms from Chapters 1 and 2. Then have the students exchange papers and rewrite each definition in everyday language.

Power Presentations
with PowerPoint®

 Additional Examples

Example 1

Write the conditional statement and converse within each biconditional.

A. An angle is obtuse if and only if its measure is greater than 90° and less than 180°.
Cond.: If an ∠ is obtuse, then its measure is greater than 90° and less than 180°. Conv.: If the measure of an ∠ is greater than 90° and less than 180°, then the ∠ is obtuse.

B. A solution is neutral ↔ its pH is 7.
Cond.: If a solution is neutral, then its pH is 7. Conv.: If the pH of a solution is 7, then it is neutral.

Example 2

For each conditional, write the converse and a biconditional statement.

A. If $5x - 8 = 37$, then $x = 9$.
Conv.: If $x = 9$, then $5x - 8 = 37$. Bicond.: $5x - 8 = 37$ if and only if $x = 9$.

B. If two angles have the same measure, then they are congruent. Conv.: If 2 ∠s are ≅, then they have the same measure. Bicond.: 2 ∠s have the same measure if and only if they are ≅.

Also available on transparency

INTERVENTION ◄■►
Questioning Strategies

EXAMPLE 1
• What would be the effect if you reversed the order of the two statements that make up a biconditional? Explain.

EXAMPLE 2
• How do you form the converse of a conditional if the words *if* and *then* do not appear in the given statement?

Lesson 2-4 **97**

Power Presentations
with PowerPoint®

Additional Examples

Example 3

Determine if each biconditional is true. If false, give a counter-example.

A. A rectangle has side lengths of 12 cm and 25 cm if and only if its area is 300 cm².
F; possible answer: a rectangle with side lengths of 30 cm and 10 cm

B. A natural number *n* is odd ↔ n^2 is odd.   T

Example 4

Write each definition as a biconditional.

A. A pentagon is a five-sided polygon.   A figure is a pentagon if and only if it is a 5-sided polygon.

B. A right angle measures 90°.
An ∠ is a rt. ∠ if and only if it measures 90°.

Also available on transparency

INTERVENTION ◄═►
Questioning Strategies

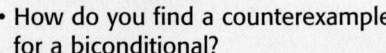

EXAMPLE 3

• How do you find a counterexample for a biconditional?

EXAMPLE 4

• Can any definition be written as a biconditional? Explain.

In the glossary, a **polygon** is defined as a closed plane figure formed by three or more line segments. Each segment intersects exactly two other segments only at their endpoints, and no two segments with a common endpoint are collinear.

Polygons	Not Polygons

A **triangle** is defined as a three-sided polygon, and a **quadrilateral** is a four-sided polygon.

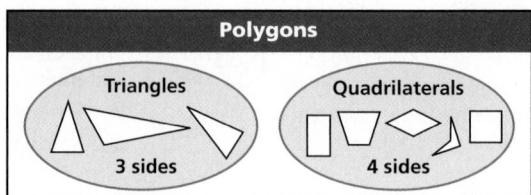

Polygons	
Triangles	Quadrilaterals
3 sides	4 sides

A good, precise definition can be used forward and backward. For example, if a figure is a quadrilateral, then it is a four-sided polygon. If a figure is a four-sided polygon, then it is a quadrilateral. To make sure a definition is precise, it helps to write it as a biconditional statement.

EXAMPLE 4 **Writing Definitions as Biconditional Statements**

Write each definition as a biconditional.

 A A triangle is a three-sided polygon.
A figure is a triangle if and only if it is a three-sided polygon.

B A segment bisector is a ray, segment, or line that divides a segment into two congruent segments.
A ray, segment, or line is a segment bisector if and only if it divides a segment into two congruent segments.

Helpful Hint
Think of definitions as being reversible. Postulates, however, are not necessarily true when reversed.

4a. A figure is a quad. if and only if it is a 4-sided polygon.

4b. An ∠ is a straight ∠ if and only if its measure is 180°.

 **CHECK IT OUT!** Write each definition as a biconditional.
4a. A quadrilateral is a four-sided polygon.
4b. The measure of a straight angle is 180°.

THINK AND DISCUSS

1. How do you determine if a biconditional statement is true or false?

2. Compare a triangle and a quadrilateral.

3. **GET ORGANIZED** Copy and complete the graphic organizer. Use the definition of a polygon to write a conditional, converse, and biconditional in the appropriate boxes.

 **Know it! Note**

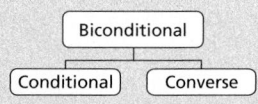

Biconditional
Conditional | Converse

3 Close

Summarize

Ask students the following questions.

• "Why is it necessary to be able to write a definition as a biconditional statement?"
Possible answer: so the definition is precise and reversible

• "When is a biconditional statement true?"
when the cond. statement and conv. it contains are both true

ONGOING ASSESSMENT
and INTERVENTION ◄═►

Diagnose *Before* the Lesson
2-4 Warm Up, TE p. 96

Monitor *During* the Lesson
Check It Out! Exercises, SE pp. 96–98
Questioning Strategies, TE pp. 97–98

Assess *After* the Lesson
2-4 Lesson Quiz, TE p. 101
Alternative Assessment, TE p. 101

Answers to *Think and Discuss*

1. Possible answer: Find the truth value of the conditional and the converse it contains. If both are true, then the biconditional is true.

2. A △ has 3 sides and 3 vertices. A quad. has 4 sides and 4 vertices.

3. See p. A3.

2-4 Exercises

go.hrw.com/Geo/TX
Homework Help Online
KEYWORD: MG7 2-4
Parent Resources Online
KEYWORD: MG7 Parent

GUIDED PRACTICE

1. **Vocabulary** How is a *biconditional statement* different from a conditional statement?

SEE EXAMPLE **1** p. 96

Write the conditional statement and converse within each biconditional.

2. Perry can paint the entire living room if and only if he has enough paint.

3. Your medicine will be ready by 5 P.M. if and only if you drop your prescription off by 8 A.M.

SEE EXAMPLE **2** p. 97

For each conditional, write the converse and a biconditional statement.

4. If a student is a sophomore, then the student is in the tenth grade.

5. If two segments have the same length, then they are congruent.

SEE EXAMPLE **3** p. 97

Multi-Step Determine if each biconditional is true. If false, give a counterexample.

6. $xy = 0 \leftrightarrow x = 0$ or $y = 0$. T

7. A figure is a quadrilateral if and only if it is a polygon.

   F; a △ is a polygon but not a quad.

SEE EXAMPLE **4** p. 98

Write each definition as a biconditional.

8. Parallel lines are two coplanar lines that never intersect.

9. A hummingbird is a tiny, brightly colored bird with narrow wings, a slender bill, and a long tongue.

PRACTICE AND PROBLEM SOLVING

Independent Practice

For Exercises	See Example
10–12	1
13–15	2
16–17	3
18–19	4

TEKS ⇌ TAKS

Skills Practice p. S6
Application Practice p. S29

Write the conditional statement and converse within each biconditional.

10. Three points are coplanar if and only if they lie in the same plane.

11. A parallelogram is a rectangle if and only if it has four right angles.

12. A lunar eclipse occurs if and only if Earth is between the Sun and the Moon.

For each conditional, write the converse and a biconditional statement.

13. If today is Saturday or Sunday, then it is the weekend.

14. If Greg has the fastest time, then he wins the race.

15. If a triangle contains a right angle, then it is a right triangle.

Multi-Step Determine if each biconditional is true. If false, give a counterexample.

16. Felipe is a swimmer if and only if he is an athlete.

16. F; possible answer: Felipe could be a runner.

17. The number $2n$ is even if and only if n is an integer. T

Write each definition as a biconditional.

18. A circle is the set of all points in a plane that are a fixed distance from a given point.

19. A catcher is a baseball player who is positioned behind home plate and who catches throws from the pitcher.

2-4 Biconditional Statements and Definitions **99**

2-4 Exercises

Assignment Guide

Assign *Guided Practice* exercises as necessary.

If you finished Examples **1–2**
   Basic 10–15
   Average 10–15
Advanced 10–15

If you finished Examples **1–4**
   Basic 10–21, 24, 28, 30–34, 37–41, 46–54
   Average 10–32, 35–41, 43–44, 46–54
   Advanced 10–29, 30–34 even, 35–54

Homework Quick Check
Quickly check key concepts.
Exercises: 10, 14, 16, 18, 24, 30

Answers

1. Possible answer: A biconditional contains the conditional and its converse. A conditional is not reversible, but a biconditional is.

2. Conditional: If Perry can paint the entire living room, then he has enough paint. Converse: If Perry has enough paint, then he can paint the entire living room.

3. Conditional: If your medicine will be ready by 5 P.M., then you dropped your prescription off by 8 A.M. Converse: If you drop your prescription off by 8 A.M., then your medicine will be ready by 5 P.M.

⬓TAKS Practice

Grades 9–11	Exercises
Obj. 2	20–23
Obj. 5	46–48
Obj. 6	34, 44, 49–51, 54
Obj. 7	33, 54
Obj. 10	30–32, 52–54

Answers

4. Converse: If a student is in the tenth grade, then the student is a sophomore. Biconditional: A student is a sophomore if and only if the student is in the tenth grade.

5. Converse: If 2 segs. are ≅, then they have the same length. Biconditional: 2 segs. have the same length if and only if they are ≅.

8. 2 lines are ‖ if and only if they are coplanar and never intersect.

9. An animal is a hummingbird if and only if it is a tiny, brightly colored bird with narrow wings, a slender bill, and a long tongue.

10. Conditional: If 3 pts. are coplanar, then they lie in the same plane. Converse: If 3 pts. lie in the same plane, then they are coplanar.

11. Conditional: If a ▱ is a rect., then it has 4 rt. ∡. Converse: If a ▱ has 4 rt. ∡, then it is a rect.

12. Conditional: If a lunar eclipse occurs, then Earth is between the Sun and the Moon. Converse: If Earth is between the Sun and the Moon, then a lunar eclipse occurs.

13. Converse: If it is the weekend, then today is Saturday or Sunday. Biconditional: Today is Saturday or Sunday if and only if it is the weekend.

14–15, 18–19. See p. A11.

Teaching Tip **Inclusion** If students have difficulty with **Exercises 21** and **22,** suggest that they solve the equation in the hypothesis and in the conclusion and see if the solutions are the same.

MULTI-STEP TAKS PREP **Exercise 37** involves writing statements as conditionals and then determining the truth value of the resulting biconditional. This exercise prepares students for the Multi-Step TAKS Prep on page 102.

Answers

24. An equil. △ is a △ with 3 ≅ sides.

25. A square is a quad. with 4 ≅ sides and 4 rt. ∠.

26. A cell is a white blood cell if and only if it defends the body against invading organisms by engulfing them or releasing antibodies.

27. Possible answer: A bicycle also moves along the ground but is not an automobile.

28. Possible answer: A computer is a machine that performs computations but is not a calculator.

29. Possible answer: The definition does not say that the rays have a common endpoint.

35–37. See p. A11.

---

20. no; possible answer: $a = 3$, $b = -3$

 Algebra Determine if a true biconditional can be written from each conditional statement. If not, give a counterexample.

20. If $a = b$, then $|a| = |b|$.

21. If $3x - 2 = 13$, then $\frac{4}{5}x + 8 = 12$. **yes**

22. If $y^2 = 64$, then $3y = 24$. **no; possible answer:** $y = -8$

23. If $x > 0$, then $x^2 > 0$. **no; possible answer:** $x = -2$

Use the diagrams to write a definition for each figure.

24.

Equilateral triangle   Not an equilateral triangle

25.

Square   Not squares

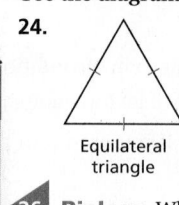

Biology

White blood cells live less than a few weeks. A drop of blood can contain anywhere from 7000 to 25,000 white blood cells.

26. **Biology** White blood cells are cells that defend the body against invading organisms by engulfing them or by releasing chemicals called *antibodies*. Write the definition of a white blood cell as a biconditional statement.

Explain why the given statement is not a definition.

27. An automobile is a vehicle that moves along the ground.

28. A calculator is a machine that performs computations with numbers.

29. An angle is a geometric object formed by two rays.

Chemistry Use the table for Exercises 30–32. Determine if a true biconditional statement can be written from each conditional.

30. If a solution has a pH of 4, then it is tomato juice. **no**

31. If a solution is bleach, then its pH is 13. **no**

32. If a solution has a pH greater than 7, then it is not battery acid. **no**

pH	Examples
0	Battery Acid
4	Acid rain, tomato juice
6	Saliva
8	Sea water
13	Bleach, oven cleaner
14	Drain cleaner

Complete each statement to form a true biconditional.

33. The circumference of a circle is 10π if and only if its radius is ___?___. **5**

34. Four points in a plane form a ___?___ if and only if no three of them are collinear. **quad.**

35. **Critical Thinking** Write the definition of a biconditional statement as a biconditional statement. Use the conditional and converse within the statement to explain why your biconditional is true.

36. **Write About It** Use the definition of an angle bisector to explain what is meant by the statement "A good definition is reversible."

MULTI-STEP TAKS PREP

37. This problem will prepare you for the Multi-Step TAKS Prep on page 102.
  a. Write "I say what I mean" and "I mean what I say" as conditionals.
  b. Explain why the biconditional statement implied by Alice is false.

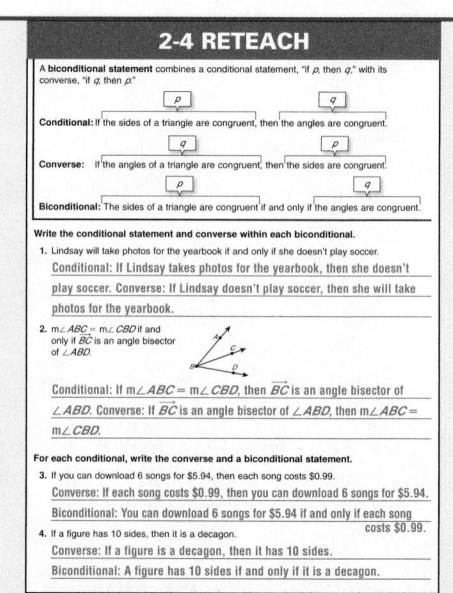

"Then you should say what you mean," the March Hare went on.

"I do," Alice hastily replied; "at least—at least I mean what I say—that's the same thing, you know."

38. Which is a counterexample for the biconditional "An angle measures 80° if and only if the angle is acute"?

   Ⓐ $m\angle S = 60°$ Ⓑ $m\angle S = 115°$ Ⓒ $m\angle S = 90°$ Ⓓ $m\angle S = 360°$

39. Which biconditional is equivalent to the spelling phrase "*I* before *E* except after *C*"?

   Ⓕ The letter *I* comes before *E* if and only if *I* follows *C*.
   Ⓖ The letter *E* comes before *I* if and only if *E* follows *C*.
   Ⓗ The letter *E* comes before *I* if and only if *E* comes before *C*.
   Ⓙ The letter *I* comes before *E* if and only if *I* comes before *C*.

40. Which conditional statement can be used to write a true biconditional?

   Ⓐ If a number is divisible by 4, then it is even.
   Ⓑ If a ratio compares two quantities measured in different units, the ratio is a rate.
   Ⓒ If two angles are supplementary, then they are adjacent.
   Ⓓ If an angle is right, then it is not acute.

41. Short Response Write the two conditional statements that make up the biconditional "You will get a traffic ticket if and only if you are speeding." Is the biconditional true or false? Explain your answer.

CHALLENGE AND EXTEND

43a. If an ∠ does not measure 105°, then the ∠ is not obtuse.

b. If an ∠ is not obtuse, then it does not measure 105°.

c. It is the contrapositive of the original.

d. F; the inverse is false, and its converse is true.

42. Critical Thinking Describe what the Venn diagram of a true biconditional statement looks like. How does this support the idea that a definition can be written as a true biconditional?

43. Consider the conditional "If an angle measures 105°, then the angle is obtuse."
   a. Write the inverse of the conditional statement.
   b. Write the converse of the inverse.
   c. How is the converse of the inverse related to the original conditional?
   d. What is the truth value of the biconditional statement formed by the inverse of the original conditional and the converse of the inverse? Explain.

44. Suppose *A*, *B*, *C*, and *D* are coplanar, and *A*, *B*, and *C* are not collinear. What is the truth value of the biconditional formed from the true conditional "If m∠*ABD* + m∠*DBC* = m∠*ABC*, then *D* is in the interior of ∠*ABC*"? Explain.

45. Find a counterexample for "*n* is divisible by 4 if and only if n^2 is even."
   Possible answer: $n = 2$

SPIRAL REVIEW

46. The graph is shifted 5 units up and is wider than the graph of the parent function.

52. F; possible answer: $n = 0$

53. F; possible answer: $x = 2$

Describe how the graph of each function differs from the graph of the parent function $y = x^2$. *(Previous course)*

   The graph is shifted 4 units down.

46. $y = \frac{1}{2}x^2 + 5$ **47.** $y = -2x^2 - 1$ **48.** $y = (x - 2)(x + 2)$

A transformation maps *S* onto *T* and *X* onto *Y*. Name each of the following. *(Lesson 1-7)*

49. the image of *S* *T*   **50.** the image of *X* *Y*   **51.** the preimage of *T* *S*

Determine if each conjecture is true. If not, give a counterexample. *(Lesson 2-1)*

52. If $n \geq 0$, then $\frac{n}{2} > 0$.   **53.** If *x* is prime, then *x* + 2 is also prime.

54. The vertices of the image of a figure under the translation $(x, y) \rightarrow (x + 0, y + 0)$ have the same coordinates as the preimage. **T**

Sidebar

TEST PREP DOCTOR If students answer **Exercise 38** incorrectly, ask them to write out the conditional and its converse as two separate statements and determine whether each is true or false. In this problem, the conditional is true, but its converse is false. The counterexample must be an acute angle, so the answer is **A.**

Answers

41–42, 44, 47. See p. A11.

✎ *Journal*

Ask students to use an example to explain a biconditional statement and to describe how it is related to the two conditionals it contains.

ALTERNATIVE ASSESSMENT

Have students look up two everyday words, such as shirt, book, tricycle, or house, in the dictionary. Have them use the dictionary definition to write a biconditional statement for each term. Then have them explain whether the dictionary definition qualifies as a "good" definition.

Power Presentations with PowerPoint®

 2-4 Lesson Quiz

1. For the conditional "If an angle is right, then its measure is 90°," write the converse and a biconditional statement. Conv.: If an ∠ measures 90°, then the ∠ is rt. Bicond.: An ∠ is rt. iff its measure is 90°.

2. Determine if the biconditional "Two angles are complementary if and only if they are both acute" is true. If false, give a counterexample. F; possible answer: 30° and 40°

3. Write the definition "An acute triangle is a triangle with three acute angles" as a biconditional. A △ is acute iff it has 3 acute ∡.

Also available on transparency

2-4 PROBLEM SOLVING

Use the table for Exercises 1–4. Determine if a true biconditional statement can be written from each conditional. If so, write a biconditional. If not, then explain why not.

Mountain Bike Races	Characteristics
Cross-country	A massed-start race. Riders must carry their own tools to make repairs.
Downhill	Riders start at intervals. The rider with the lowest time wins.
Freeride	Courses contain cliffs, drops, and ramps. Scoring depends on the style and the time.
Marathon	A massed-start race that covers more than 250 kilometers.

1. If a mountain bike race is mass-started, then it is a cross-country race.
No; marathon races are also mass-started, so the conditional is false.

2. If a mountain bike race is downhill, then time is a factor in who wins.
No; time is also a factor in freeride races, so the converse is false.

3. If a mountain bike race covers more than 250 kilometers, then it is a marathon race.
Yes; a mountain bike race covers 250 kilometers if and only if it is a marathon race.

4. If a race course contains cliffs, drops, and ramps, then it is a marathon race.
No; a downhill race does not contain cliffs, drops, and ramps, so the converse is false.

Choose the best answer.

5. The cat is the only species that can hold its tail vertically while it walks.
  A The converse of this statement is false.
  B The biconditional of this statement is false.
  Ⓒ The biconditional of this statement is true.
  D This statement cannot be written as a biconditional.

6. Which conditional statement can be used to write a true biconditional?
  F If you travel 2 miles in 4 minutes, then distance is a function of time.
  Ⓖ If the distance depends on the time, then distance is a function of time.
  H If *y* increases as *x* increases, then *y* is a function of *x*.
  J If *y* is not a function of *x*, then *y* does not increase as *x* increases.

2-4 CHALLENGE

A truth table is used to represent all of the possible outcomes of compound statements, where *p* is the hypothesis and *q* is the conclusion.

1. Complete the truth table below.

Hypothesis	Conclusion	Conditional	Converse	Biconditional
p	*q*	*p → q*	*q → p*	*p ↔ q*
T	T	T	T	T
T	F	F	T	F
F	T	T	F	F
F	F	T	T	T

2. Under what circumstances is a biconditional statement true?
when *p* and *q* are both true or when *p* and *q* are both false

3. Compare and contrast the truth values of conditional and biconditional statements.
The truth values are the same except when the hypothesis is false and the conclusion is true. In this case, the conditional is true and the biconditional is false.

4. Two statements are logically equivalent if they have the same truth table values. Suppose "Contrapositive" were added to the truth table. Which of the statements is logically equivalent to the contrapositive of *p → q*?
p → q; both are true except for the case when *p* is true and *q* is false.

5. Give an example in which a conditional statement is true, but its biconditional is false. Then explain why the biconditional is false.
Possible answer: If an angle measures 105°, then it is obtuse. Biconditional: An angle measures 105° if and only if it is obtuse. The biconditional is false because the converse is false.

Rewrite each definition in biconditional form.

6. The midpoint of $\overline{AB}$ is the point *M* such that *M* is on $\overline{AB}$ and $AM = MB$.
M is the midpoint of $\overline{AB}$ if and only if *M* is on $\overline{AB}$ and $AM = MB$.

7. A bisector of a segment is a line, ray, or segment that intersects the segment at its midpoint.
A figure is a bisector of a segment if and only if it is a line, ray, or segment that intersects the segment at its midpoint.

8. A chord of a circle is a segment that has its endpoints on the circle.
A segment is a chord of a circle if and only if the endpoints of the segment

MULTI-STEP TAKS PREP

Organizer

Objective: Assess students' ability to apply concepts and skills in Lessons 2-1 through 2-4 in a real-world format.

 Online Edition

Resources

 Geometry Assessments
www.mathtekstoolkit.org

Problem	Text Reference
1	Lesson 2-1
2	Lesson 2-2
3	Lesson 2-3
4	Lesson 2-4

Answers

3. No; no hypothesis is known to be true, so the Law of Detachment cannot be applied. No conclusion matches another hypothesis, so the Law of Syllogism cannot be applied.

4. I breathe if and only if I sleep. This biconditional is made of 2 conditionals: If I breathe, then I sleep, and if I sleep, then I breathe. The second is true, but the first is not. So the biconditional is false.

MULTI-STEP TAKS PREP

SECTION 2A

Inductive and Deductive Reasoning

Rhyme or Reason
Alice's Adventures in Wonderland originated as a story told by Charles Lutwidge Dodgson (Lewis Carroll) to three young traveling companions. The story is famous for its wordplay and logical absurdities.

1. When Alice first meets the Cheshire Cat, she asks what sort of people live in Wonderland. The Cat explains that everyone in Wonderland is mad. What conjecture might the Cat make since Alice, too, is in Wonderland? **Alice is mad.**

2. "I don't much care where—" said Alice.
   "Then it doesn't matter which way you go," said the Cat.
   "—so long as I get *somewhere*," Alice added as an explanation.
   "Oh, you're sure to do that," said the Cat, "if you only walk long enough."

Write the conditional statement implied by the Cat's response to Alice. **If you only walk long enough, then you're sure to get somewhere.**

3. "Well, then," the Cat went on, "you see a dog growls when it's angry, and wags its tail when it's pleased. Now I growl when I'm pleased, and wag my tail when I'm angry. Therefore I'm mad."

Is the Cat's conclusion valid by the Law of Detachment or the Law of Syllogism? Explain your reasoning.

4. "You might just as well say," added the Dormouse, who seemed to be talking in his sleep, "that 'I breathe when I sleep' is the same thing as 'I sleep when I breathe'!"

Write a biconditional statement from the Dormouse's example. Explain why the biconditional statement is false.

INTERVENTION

Scaffolding Questions

1. What pattern has the Cat noticed about the people in Wonderland? They are all mad.

2. What is the hypothesis of the Cat's statement? You walk long enough. What is the conclusion? You'll get somewhere.

3. What conditionals can be formed from the Cat's statements? If a dog is angry, then it growls. If a dog is pleased, then it wags its tail. If the Cat is pleased, then it growls. If the Cat is angry, then it wags its tail.

4. What conditional can you write based on the Dormouse's words? If I sleep, then I breathe. What is the converse? If I breathe, then I sleep.

Extension

The Footman tells Alice, "There might be some sense in your knocking, if we had the door between us." Assume that there is no sense in Alice's knocking. What can you conclude about a door between them? Explain. There is no door between them, by the Law of Contrapositive.

READY TO GO ON?

SECTION 2A

Quiz for Lessons 2-1 Through 2-4

2-1 Using Inductive Reasoning to Make Conjectures

Find the next item in each pattern.

1. 1, 10, 18, 25, … **31**
2. July, May, March, … **January**
3. $\frac{1}{8}, -\frac{1}{4}, \frac{1}{2}, …$ **−1**
4. |, ┼, ╫, … **╫**

5. A biologist recorded the following data about the weight of male lions in a wildlife park in Africa. Use the table to make a conjecture about the average weight of a male lion.

ID Number	Weight (lb)
A1902SM	387.2
A1904SM	420.5
A1920SM	440.6
A1956SM	398.7
A1974SM	415.0

6. Complete the conjecture "The sum of two negative numbers is   ? ." **negative**

7. Show that the conjecture "If an even number is divided by 2, then the result is an even number" is false by finding a counterexample. **Possible answer: 6**

2-2 Conditional Statements

8. Identify the hypothesis and conclusion of the conditional statement "An angle is obtuse if its measure is 107°."

Write a conditional statement from each of the following.

9. A whole number is an integer.
If a number is a whole number, then it is an integer.

10.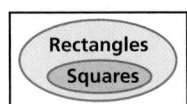
10. If a figure is a square, then it is a rect.

11. The diagonals of a square are congruent.
If a figure is a square, then its diags. are ≅.

Determine if each conditional is true. If false, give a counterexample.

12. If an angle is acute, then it has a measure of 30°. **F; possible answer: an ∠ that measures 60°**

13. If $9x - 11 = 2x + 3$, then $x = 2$. **T**

14. Write the converse, inverse, and contrapositive of the statement "If a number is even, then it is divisible by 4." Find the truth value of each.

2-3 Using Deductive Reasoning to Verify Conjectures

15. Determine if the following conjecture is valid by the Law of Detachment.
Given: If Sue finishes her science project, she can go to the movie. Sue goes to the movie. **not valid**
Conjecture: Sue finished her science project.

16. Use the Law of Syllogism to draw a conclusion from the given information.
Given: If one angle of a triangle is 90°, then the triangle is a right triangle. If a triangle is a right triangle, then its acute angle measures are complementary.
If 1 ∠ of a △ is 90°, then its acute ∠ measures are comp.

2-4 Biconditional Statements and Definitions

17. For the conditional "If two angles are supplementary, the sum of their measures is 180°," write the converse and a biconditional statement.

18. Determine if the biconditional "$\sqrt{x} = 4$ if and only if $x = 16$" is true. If false, give a counterexample. **T**

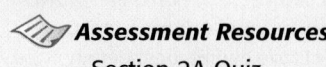

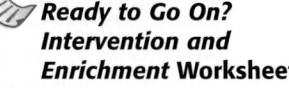

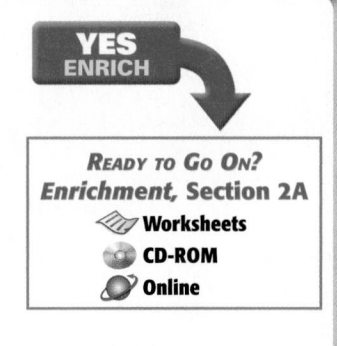

Mathematical Proof

 One-Minute Section Planner

Lesson	Lab Resources	Materials
Lesson 2-5 Algebraic Proof • Review properties of equality and use them to write algebraic proofs. • Identify properties of equality and congruence. ☑ Exit Level TAKS ☑ ACT ☐ SAT ☑ SAT Subject Tests		**Optional** mirror
Lesson 2-6 Geometric Proof • Write two-column proofs. • Prove geometric theorems by using deductive reasoning. ☐ Exit Level TAKS ☑ ACT ☐ SAT ☐ SAT Subject Tests		**Optional** geometry software, strips of paper
2-6 Geometry Lab Design Plans for Proofs • Learn strategies for planning the logical steps of a proof. ☐ Exit Level TAKS ☐ ACT ☐ SAT ☐ SAT Subject Tests		
Lesson 2-7 Flowchart and Paragraph Proofs • Write flowchart and paragraph proofs. • Prove geometric theorems by using deductive reasoning. ☐ Exit Level TAKS ☐ ACT ☐ SAT ☐ SAT Subject Tests	*Texas Lab Manual* 2-7 Technology Lab	**Optional** patty paper, colored pencils
Extension Introduction to Symbolic Logic • Analyze the truth value of conjunctions and disjunctions. • Construct truth tables to determine the truth value of logical statements. ☐ Exit Level TAKS ☐ ACT ☐ SAT ☐ SAT Subject Tests		**Optional** index cards

MK = *Manipulatives Kit*

Section Overview

Algebraic Proof

Why? Algebraic properties will be used as justifications in many of the geometric proofs throughout this course.

Properties of Equality

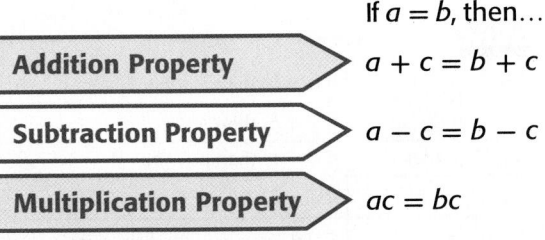

If $a = b$, then...

Addition Property ▷	$a + c = b + c$
Subtraction Property ▷	$a - c = b - c$
Multiplication Property ▷	$ac = bc$
Division Property ▷	$\frac{a}{c} = \frac{b}{c}, c \neq 0$

Reflexive Property ▷	$a = a$
Symmetric Property ▷	If $a = b$, then $b = a$.
Transitive Property ▷	If $a = b$ and $b = c$, then $a = c$.
Substitution Property ▷	If $a = b$, then b can be substituted for a in any expression.

Solving an equation is like writing a type of proof—an algebraic proof. The properties of equality are used to justify each step of the solution.

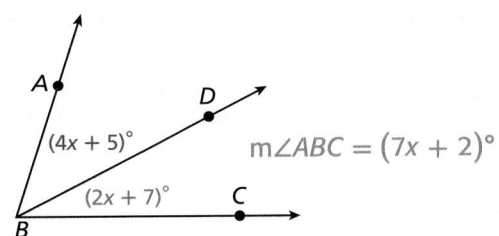

$(4x + 5)°$

$(2x + 7)°$

$m\angle ABC = (7x + 2)°$

$m\angle ABC = m\angle ABD + m\angle DBC$	Angle Addition Postulate
$7x + 2 = (4x + 5) + (2x + 7)$	Substitution Property of Equality
$7x + 2 = 6x + 12$	Simplify.
$x + 2 = 12$	Subtraction Property of Equality
$x = 10$	Subtraction Property of Equality

$$m\angle ABD = (4x + 5)° = [4(10) + 5]° = 45°$$

$$m\angle DBC = (2x + 7)° = [2(10) + 7]° = 27°$$

$$m\angle ABC = (7x + 2)° = [7(10) + 2]° = 72°$$

Geometric Proof

Why? Proofs are used to establish the validity of geometric relationships by using deductive reasoning in a format other people can follow.

When writing a geometric proof, you can use the following as justifications:

- definitions
- postulates
- theorems
- properties
- given information

This chapter covers three styles, or formats, for geometric proofs.

Two-Column Proof	**Flowchart Proof**	**Paragraph Proof**
The steps are listed in the left column, and the corresponding reasons are listed in the right column.	Boxes and arrows show the structure of the proof. Arrows connect the boxes and indicate the logical flow.	The steps and their reasons are written as sentences in a paragraph.

2-5 Organizer

Pacing: Traditional 1 day
Block $\frac{1}{2}$ day

Objectives: Review properties
of equality and use them to write
algebraic proofs.

Identify properties of equality and
congruence.

Online Edition
Tutorial Videos

**Countdown to
TAKS Week 4**

Power Presentations
with PowerPoint®

Warm Up

Solve each equation.

1. $3x + 5 = 17$ $x = 4$

2. $r - 3.5 = 8.7$ $r = 12.2$

3. $4t - 7 = 8t + 3$ $t = -\frac{5}{2}$

4. $\frac{n + 8}{5} = -6$ $n = -38$

5. $2(y - 5) - 20 = 0$ $y = 15$

Also available on transparency

Math Humor

Customer: How much are two eggs?

Waitress: $1.75.

Customer: How much is one egg?

Waitress: $1.50.

Customer: Then I'll have the other
one.

2-5 Algebraic Proof

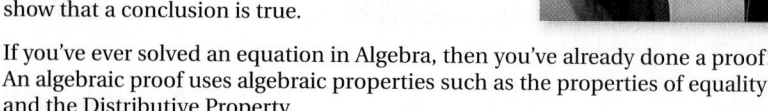

TEKS G.3.E Geometric structure: use deductive reasoning to prove a statement.
Also G.3.B, G.3.C

Objectives
Review properties of
equality and use them to
write algebraic proofs.

Identify properties of
equality and congruence.

Vocabulary
proof

Remember!

The Distributive
Property states that
$a(b + c) = ab + ac$.

Who uses this?

Game designers and animators solve equations
to simulate motion. (See Example 2.)

A **proof** is an argument that uses logic, definitions,
properties, and previously proven statements to
show that a conclusion is true.

If you've ever solved an equation in Algebra, then you've already done a proof!
An algebraic proof uses algebraic properties such as the properties of equality
and the Distributive Property.

Properties of Equality

Addition Property of Equality	If $a = b$, then $a + c = b + c$.
Subtraction Property of Equality	If $a = b$, then $a - c = b - c$.
Multiplication Property of Equality	If $a = b$, then $ac = bc$.
Division Property of Equality	If $a = b$ and $c \neq 0$, then $\frac{a}{c} = \frac{b}{c}$.
Reflexive Property of Equality	$a = a$
Symmetric Property of Equality	If $a = b$, then $b = a$.
Transitive Property of Equality	If $a = b$ and $b = c$, then $a = c$.
Substitution Property of Equality	If $a = b$, then b can be substituted for a in any expression.

As you learned in Lesson 2-3, if you start with a true statement and each logical
step is valid, then your conclusion is valid.

An important part of writing a proof is giving justifications to show that every
step is valid. For each justification, you can use a definition, postulate, property,
or a piece of information that is given.

EXAMPLE 1 **Solving an Equation in Algebra**

Solve the equation $-5 = 3n + 1$. Write a justification for each step.

$-5 = 3n + 1$	Given equation
$\underline{-1 \quad\quad -1}$	Subtraction Property of Equality
$-6 = 3n$	Simplify.
$\frac{-6}{3} = \frac{3n}{3}$	Division Property of Equality
$-2 = n$	Simplify.
$n = -2$	Symmetric Property of Equality

$\frac{1}{2}t = -7$ (Given);

$2\left(\frac{1}{2}t\right) = 2(-7)$

(Mult. Prop. of =);
$t = -14$ (Simplify.)

 **CHECK IT OUT!** **1.** Solve the equation $\frac{1}{2}t = -7$. Write a justification for each step.

Geometry TEKS

G.3 Geometric structure*
(B) construct and justify statements
about geometric figures and their
properties
(C) use logical reasoning to prove
statements are true and find
counterexamples to disprove
statements that are false
(E) use inductive reasoning to
formulate a conjecture

* **Knowledge and Skills** See p. 72.

1 Introduce

EXPLORATION

2-5 Algebraic Proof

The solution to an algebraic equation is a type of proof. The steps
must appear in the correct order, and you must be able to justify
each step.

1. Write a step-by-step solution of the linear equation by placing
the given equations in the correct order.

$3x - 12 + 5 = 17$	
$3x = 24$	
$3x - 7 = 17$	
$3(x - 4) + 5 = 17$	
$x = 8$	

2. What property do you use to go from step a to step b?

3. What do you do to the equation to go from step c to step d?

4. What do you do to the equation to go from step d to step e?

Motivate

Ask students to raise their hands if they have ever
written a proof. Then ask students to raise their
hands if they have ever solved an algebraic equation. Explain to students that if they have solved
an equation, then they have already written a type
of proof.

Explorations and answers are provided in the
Chapter 2 Resource Book.

EXAMPLE 2 | *Problem-Solving Application*

To simulate the motion of an object in a computer game, the designer uses the formula $sr = 3.6p$ to find the number of pixels the object must travel during each second of animation. In the formula, s is the desired speed of the object in kilometers per hour, r is the scale of pixels per meter, and p is the number of pixels traveled per second.

The graphics in a game are based on a scale of 6 pixels per meter. The designer wants to simulate a vehicle moving at 75 km/h. How many pixels must the vehicle travel each second? Solve the equation for p and justify each step.

1 **Understand the Problem**

The **answer** will be the number of pixels traveled per second.

List the important information:
- $sr = 3.6p$
- p: pixels traveled per second
- $s = 75$ km/h
- $r = 6$ pixels per meter

2 **Make a Plan**

Substitute the given information into the formula and solve.

3 **Solve**

$sr = 3.6p$	Given equation
$(75)(6) = 3.6p$	Substitution Property of Equality
$450 = 3.6p$	Simplify.
$\dfrac{450}{3.6} = \dfrac{3.6p}{3.6}$	Division Property of Equality
$125 = p$	Simplify.
$p = 125$ pixels	Symmetric Property of Equality

4 **Look Back**

Check your answer by substituting it back into the original formula.

$$sr = 3.6p$$
$$(75)(6) = 3.6(125)$$
$$450 = 450 \checkmark$$

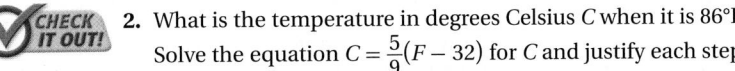

2. What is the temperature in degrees Celsius C when it is 86°F? Solve the equation $C = \dfrac{5}{9}(F - 32)$ for C and justify each step.

Like algebra, geometry also uses numbers, variables, and operations. For example, segment lengths and angle measures are numbers. So you can use these same properties of equality to write algebraic proofs in geometry.

---

2. $C = \dfrac{5}{9}(F - 32)$
(Given);
$C = \dfrac{5}{9}(86 - 32)$
(Subst.);
$C\dfrac{5}{9}(54)$(Simplify.);
$C = 30$(Simplify.)

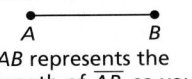

$\overset{\bullet}{A} \qquad \overset{\bullet}{B}$

AB represents the length of $\overline{AB}$, so you can think of AB as a variable representing a number.

Power Presentations
with PowerPoint®

Additional Examples

Example 1

Solve the equation $4m - 8 = -12$. Write a justification for each step.

$4m - 8 = -12$ (Given); $4m = -4$ (Add. Prop. of =); $m = -1$ (Div. Prop. of =)

Example 2

What is the temperature in degrees Fahrenheit F when it is 15°C? Solve the equation $F = \dfrac{9}{5}C + 32$ for F and justify each step.

$F = \dfrac{9}{5}C + 32$ (Given);
$F = \dfrac{9}{5}(15) + 32$ (Subst.);
$F = 27 + 32$ (Simplify.); $F = 59$ (Simplify.)

Also available on transparency

INTERVENTION
Questioning Strategies

EXAMPLE 1

- When an equation contains multiple operations, how do you know which step to do first?

EXAMPLE 2

- When you are working with a formula that contains several variables, how can you make sure you are substituting the correct numbers for the variables?

---

2 Teach

Guided Instruction

Review how to solve linear equations by using inverse operations to isolate the variable. Explain that each step is valid because it uses a property of equality. Then show students how to identify the properties of congruence, and explain that any of these properties can be used as a justification in a geometric proof.

Visual Go through the examples on the board to show how the justifications validate each step.

Reaching All Learners
Through Kinesthetic Experience

Have students act out the properties of congruence. For the Reflexive Property, have students look in a mirror. For the Symmetric Property, have two students stand next to each other and then change places. For the Transitive Property, have one student give a second student a sheet of paper, and have the second student give the paper to a third. The result is the same as if the first student had given the paper directly to the third.

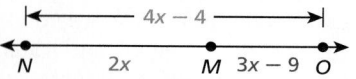

Additional Examples

Example 3

Write a justification for each step.

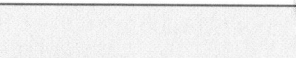

$$NO = NM + MO$$
Seg. Add. Post.
$$4x - 4 = 2x + (3x - 9)$$
Subst. Prop. of =
$$4x - 4 = 5x - 9$$
Simplify.
$$-4 = x - 9$$
Subtr. Prop. of =
$$5 = x$$
Add. Prop. of =

Example 4

Identify the property that justifies each statement.

A. $\angle QRS \cong \angle QRS$ Reflex. Prop. of $\cong$

B. $m\angle 1 = m\angle 2$, so $m\angle 2 = m\angle 1$. Sym. Prop. of =

C. $\overline{AB} \cong \overline{CD}$ and $\overline{CD} \cong \overline{EF}$, so $\overline{AB} \cong \overline{EF}$.   Trans. Prop. of $\cong$

D. $32° = 32°$ Reflex. Prop. of =

Also available on transparency

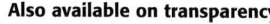

INTERVENTION
Questioning Strategies

EXAMPLE 3

• What properties are you using when you simplify in this equation?

EXAMPLE 4

• How can you remember the difference between the Reflexive, Symmetric, and Transitive Properties?

Teaching Tip **Auditory** Say the words *reflexive, symmetric,* and *transitive* aloud, and ask students what the words bring to mind. For example, *reflexive* might remind students of a reflection in a mirror. You see the same thing on both sides of a mirror, so $a = a$.

EXAMPLE 3

Solving an Equation in Geometry

Write a justification for each step.

$$KM = KL + LM$$
Segment Addition Postulate
$$5x - 4 = (x + 3) + (2x - 1)$$
Substitution Property of Equality
$$5x - 4 = 3x + 2$$
Simplify.
$$2x - 4 = 2$$
Subtraction Property of Equality
$$2x = 6$$
Addition Property of Equality
$$x = 3$$
Division Property of Equality

CHECK IT OUT! **3.** Write a justification for each step.

$$m\angle ABC = m\angle ABD + m\angle DBC$$
$$8x° = (3x + 5)° + (6x - 16)°$$
$$8x = 9x - 11$$
$$-x = -11$$
$$x = 11$$

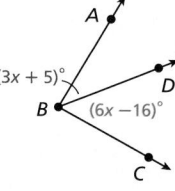

$m\angle ABC = 8x°$

3. $\angle$ Add. Post.
Subst.
Simplify.
Subtr. Prop. of =
Mult. Prop. of =

You learned in Chapter 1 that segments with equal lengths are congruent and that angles with equal measures are congruent. So the Reflexive, Symmetric, and Transitive Properties of Equality have corresponding properties of congruence.

Know it! Note

Properties of Congruence

SYMBOLS	EXAMPLE
Reflexive Property of Congruence figure A $\cong$ figure A (Reflex. Prop. of $\cong$)	$\overline{EF} \cong \overline{EF}$
Symmetric Property of Congruence If figure A $\cong$ figure B, then figure B $\cong$ figure A. (Sym. Prop. of $\cong$)	If $\angle 1 \cong \angle 2$, then $\angle 2 \cong \angle 1$.
Transitive Property of Congruence If figure A $\cong$ figure B and figure B $\cong$ figure C, then figure A $\cong$ figure C. (Trans. Prop. of $\cong$)	If $\overline{PQ} \cong \overline{RS}$ and $\overline{RS} \cong \overline{TU}$, then $\overline{PQ} \cong \overline{TU}$.

EXAMPLE 4

Identifying Properties of Equality and Congruence

Identify the property that justifies each statement.

A $m\angle 1 = m\angle 1$ Reflex. Prop. of =

B $\overline{XY} \cong \overline{VW}$, so $\overline{VW} \cong \overline{XY}$.   Sym. Prop. of $\cong$

C $\angle ABC \cong \angle ABC$ Reflex. Prop. of $\cong$

D $\angle 1 \cong \angle 2$, and $\angle 2 \cong \angle 3$. So $\angle 1 \cong \angle 3$.   Trans. Prop. of $\cong$

Remember!

Numbers are equal (=) and figures are congruent ($\cong$).

4a. Sym. Prop. of =
4b. Reflex. Prop. of =
4c. Trans. Prop. of =
4d. Sym. Prop. of $\cong$

CHECK IT OUT! Identify the property that justifies each statement.

4a. $DE = GH$, so $GH = DE$.   **4b.** $94° = 94°$
4c. $0 = a$, and $a = x$. So $0 = x$.   **4d.** $\angle A \cong \angle Y$, so $\angle Y \cong \angle A$.

---

3 Close

Summarize

Review the eight properties of equality on page 104. Ask students which properties of equality have corresponding properties of congruence. reflexive, symmetric, and transitive Also remind students when to use an equal sign and when to use a congruence symbol.

ONGOING ASSESSMENT

and INTERVENTION

Diagnose Before the Lesson
2-5 Warm Up, TE p. 104

Monitor During the Lesson
Check It Out! Exercises, SE pp. 104–106
Questioning Strategies, TE pp. 105–106

Assess After the Lesson
2-5 Lesson Quiz, TE p. 109
Alternative Assessment, TE p. 109

THINK AND DISCUSS

1. Tell what property you would use to solve the equation $\frac{k}{6} = 3.5$.

2. Explain when to use a congruence symbol instead of an equal sign.

3. GET ORGANIZED Copy and complete the graphic organizer. In each box, write an example of the property, using the correct symbol.

Property	Equality	Congruence
Reflexive		
Symmetric		
Transitive		

Answers to *Think and Discuss*

1. Mult. Prop. of =

2. Use a ≅ symbol for geometric figures. Use an = sign for numbers.

3. See p. A3.

2-5 Exercises

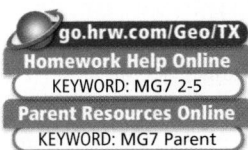
go.hrw.com/Geo/TX
Homework Help Online
KEYWORD: MG7 2-5
Parent Resources Online
KEYWORD: MG7 Parent

2-5 Exercises

GUIDED PRACTICE

1. Vocabulary Write the definition of *proof* in your own words.

SEE EXAMPLE 1 p. 104

Multi-Step Solve each equation. Write a justification for each step.

2. $y + 1 = 5$

3. $t - 3.2 = -8.3$

4. $2p - 30 = -4p + 6$

5. $\frac{x + 3}{-2} = 8$

6. $\frac{1}{2}n = \frac{3}{4}$

7. $0 = 2(r - 3) + 4$

SEE EXAMPLE 2 p. 105

8. Nutrition Amy's favorite breakfast cereal has 102 Calories per serving. The equation $C = 9f + 90$ relates the grams of fat f in one serving to the Calories C in one serving. How many grams of fat are in one serving of the cereal? Solve the equation for f and justify each step.

9. Movie Rentals The equation $C = \$5.75 + \$0.89m$ relates the number of movie rentals m to the monthly cost C of a movie club membership. How many movies did Elias rent this month if his membership cost \$11.98? Solve the equation for m and justify each step.

SEE EXAMPLE 3 p. 106

Write a justification for each step.

10.

5y + 6   2y + 21

A   B   C

$AB = BC$	Def. of ≅ segs.
$5y + 6 = 2y + 21$	Subst.
$3y + 6 = 21$	Subtr. Prop. of =
$3y = 15$	Subtr. Prop. of =
$y = 5$	Div. Prop. of =

11.

9n − 5

P   3n   Q   25   R

$PQ + QR = PR$	Seg. Add. Post.
$3n + 25 = 9n - 5$	Subst.
$25 = 6n - 5$	Subtr. Prop. of =
$30 = 6n$	Add. Prop. of =
$5 = n$	Div. Prop. of =

SEE EXAMPLE 4 p. 106

Identify the property that justifies each statement.

12. $\overline{AB} \cong \overline{AB}$

13. $m\angle 1 = m\angle 2$, and $m\angle 2 = m\angle 4$. So $m\angle 1 = m\angle 4$.

14. $x = y$, so $y = x$.

15. $\overline{ST} \cong \overline{YZ}$, and $\overline{YZ} \cong \overline{PR}$. So $\overline{ST} \cong \overline{PR}$.

2-5 Algebraic Proof **107**

Answers

2. $y + 1 = 5$ (Given); $y = 4$ (Subtr. Prop. of =)

3. $t - 3.2 = -8.3$ (Given); $t = -5.1$ (Add. Prop. of =)

4. $2p - 30 = -4p + 6$ (Given); $6p - 30 = 6$ (Add. Prop. of =); $6p = 36$ (Add. Prop. of =); $p = 6$ (Div. Prop. of =)

5. $\frac{x + 3}{2} = 8$ (Given); $x + 3 = -16$ (Mult. Prop. of =); $x = -19$ (Subtr. Prop. of =)

6. $\frac{1}{2}n = \frac{3}{4}$ (Given); $n = \frac{3}{2}$ (Mult. Prop. of =)

7. $0 = 2(r - 3) + 4$ (Given); $0 = 2r - 6 + 4$ (Distrib. Prop.); $0 = 2r - 2$ (Simplify.); $2 = 2r$ (Add. Prop. of =); $1 = r$ (Div. Prop. of =)

8. $C = 9f + 90$ (Given); $102 = 9f + 90$ (Subst.); $12 = 9f$ (Subtr. Prop. of =); $\frac{4}{3} = f$ (Div. Prop. of =)

9. $C = \$5.75 + \$0.89m$ (Given); $\$11.98 = \$5.75 + \$0.89m$ (Subst.); $\$6.23 = \$0.89m$ (Subtr. Prop. of =); $m = 7$ (Div. Prop. of =)

12. Reflex. Prop. of ≅

13. Trans. Prop. of =

14. Sym. Prop. of =

15. Trans. Prop. of ≅

Assignment Guide

Assign *Guided Practice* exercises as necessary.

If you finished Examples **1–2**
Basic 16–22, 33
Average 16–22, 33–35
Advanced 16–22, 29, 34, 35

If you finished Examples **1–4**
Basic 16–28, 30–33, 37–42, 46–50
Average 16–28, 30–34, 36–43, 45–50
Advanced 16–29, 33–50

Homework Quick Check
Quickly check key concepts.
Exercises: 20, 22, 24, 28, 34

Answers

1. Possible answer: A proof is an argument that uses logic, definitions, and previously proven statements to show that another statement is always true.

TAKS Practice

Grades 9–11	Exercises
Obj. 1	34, 35, 40, 46
Obj. 2	34, 35
Obj. 4	37, 45
Obj. 7	33
Obj. 10	34, 35, 46

Answers

16. $5x - 3 = 4(x + 2)$ (Given);
$5x - 3 = 4x + 8$ (Distrib. Prop.);
$x - 3 = 8$ (Subtr. Prop. of =);
$x = 11$ (Add. Prop. of =)

17. $1.6 = 3.2n$ (Given); $0.5 = n$ (Div. Prop. of =)

18. $\frac{z}{3} - 2 = -10$ (Given); $\frac{z}{3} = -8$ (Add. Prop. of =); $z = -24$ (Mult. Prop. of =)

19. $-(h + 3) = 72$ (Given); $-h - 3 = 72$ (Distrib. Prop.); $-h = 75$ (Add. Prop. of =); $h = -75$ (Mult. Prop. of =)

20. $9y + 17 = -19$ (Given); $9y = -36$ (Subtr. Prop. of =); $y = -4$ (Div. Prop. of =)

21. $\frac{1}{2}(p - 16) = 13$ (Given);

$\frac{1}{2}p - 8 = 13$ (Distrib. Prop.);

$\frac{1}{2}p = 21$ (Add. Prop. of =);

$p = 42$ (Mult. Prop. of =)

22. $T = 0.03c + 0.05b$ (Given); $147 = 0.03c + 0.05(150)$ (Subst.); $147 = 0.03c + 7.5$ (Simplify.); $139.5 = 0.03c$ (Subtr. Prop. of =); $4650 = c$ (Div. Prop. of =)

29, 33–35a, 36. See p. A12.

108 *Chapter 2*

PRACTICE AND PROBLEM SOLVING

Multi-Step Solve each equation. Write a justification for each step.

16. $5x - 3 = 4(x + 2)$

17. $1.6 = 3.2n$

18. $\frac{z}{3} - 2 = -10$

19. $-(h + 3) = 72$

20. $9y + 17 = -19$

21. $\frac{1}{2}(p - 16) = 13$

22. **Ecology** The equation $T = 0.03c + 0.05b$ relates the numbers of cans c and bottles b collected in a recycling rally to the total dollars T raised. How many cans were collected if \$147 was raised and 150 bottles were collected? Solve the equation for c and justify each step.

Write a justification for each step.

23. $\angle$ Add. Post.
Subst.
Simplify.
Subtr. Prop. of =
Add. Prop. of =
Div. Prop. of =

23. $m\angle XYZ = m\angle 2 + m\angle 3$
$4n - 6 = 58 + (2n - 12)$
$4n - 6 = 2n + 46$
$2n - 6 = 46$
$2n = 52$
$n = 26$

24. $\angle$ Add. Post.
Subst.
Distrib. Prop.
Simplify.
Subtr. Prop. of =
Div. Prop. of =

24. $m\angle WYV = m\angle 1 + m\angle 2$
$5n = 3(n - 2) + 58$
$5n = 3n - 6 + 58$
$5n = 3n + 52$
$2n = 52$
$n = 26$

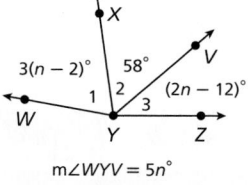

$m\angle WYV = 5n°$
$m\angle XYZ = (4n - 6)°$

Identify the property that justifies each statement.

25. $\overline{KL} \cong \overline{PR}$, so $\overline{PR} \cong \overline{KL}$. **Sym. Prop. of $\cong$**

26. $412 = 412$ **Reflex. Prop. of =**

27. If $a = b$ and $b = 0$, then $a = 0$. **Trans. Prop. of =**

28. figure $A \cong$ figure A **Reflex. Prop. of $\cong$**

29. **Estimation** Round the numbers in the equation $2(3.1x - 0.87) = 94.36$ to the nearest whole number and estimate the solution. Then solve the equation, justifying each step. Compare your estimate to the exact solution.

Use the indicated property to complete each statement.

$3x - 1$ 30. Reflexive Property of Equality: $3x - 1 = \underline{?}$

$\angle A \cong \angle T$ 31. Transitive Property of Congruence: If $\angle A \cong \angle X$ and $\angle X \cong \angle T$, then $\underline{?}$.

$\overline{NP} \cong \overline{BC}$ 32. Symmetric Property of Congruence: If $\overline{BC} \cong \overline{NP}$, then $\underline{?}$.

33. **Recreation** The north campground is midway between the Northpoint Overlook and the waterfall. Use the midpoint formula to find the values of x and y, and justify each step.

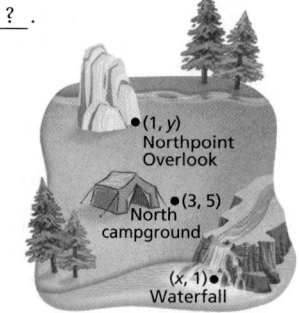

• $(1, y)$ Northpoint Overlook
• $(3, 5)$ North campground
$(x, 1)$ • Waterfall

34. **Business** A computer repair technician charges \$35 for each job plus \$21 per hour of labor and 110% of the cost of parts. The total charge for a 3-hour job was \$169.50. What was the cost of parts for this job? Write and solve an equation and justify each step in the solution.

35. **Finance** Morgan spent a total of \$1,733.65 on her car last year. She spent \$92.50 on registration, \$79.96 on maintenance, and \$983 on insurance. She spent the remaining money on gas. She drove a total of 10,820 miles.

   a. How much on average did the gas cost per mile? Write and solve an equation and justify each step in the solution.

   b. **What if...?** Suppose Morgan's car averages 32 miles per gallon of gas. How much on average did Morgan pay for a gallon of gas? **\$1.71**

36. **Critical Thinking** Use the definition of segment congruence and the properties of equality to show that all three properties of congruence are true for segments.

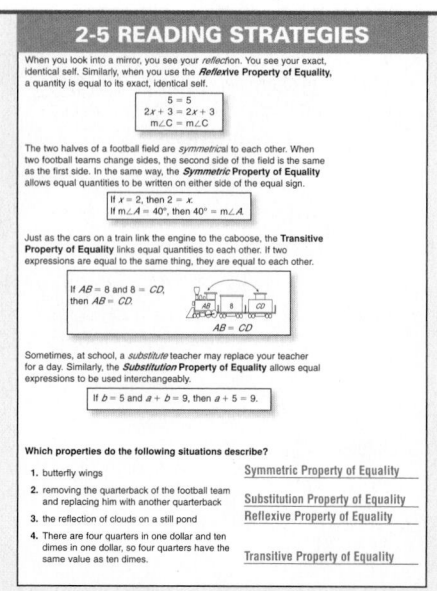

37. This problem will prepare you for the Multi-Step TAKS Prep on page 126.

Recall from Algebra 1 that the Multiplication and Division Properties of Inequality tell you to reverse the inequality sign when multiplying or dividing by a negative number.

 a. Solve the inequality $x + 15 \leq 63$ and write a justification for each step.

 b. Solve the inequality $-2x > 36$ and write a justification for each step.

38. Write About It Compare the conclusion of a deductive proof and a conjecture based on inductive reasoning.

 **TEST PREP**

39. Which could NOT be used to justify the statement $\overline{AB} \cong \overline{CD}$?
 (A) Definition of congruence
 (C) Symmetric Property of Congruence
 (B) Reflexive Property of Congruence
 (D) Transitive Property of Congruence

40. A club membership costs $35 plus $3 each time t the member uses the pool. Which equation represents the total cost C of the membership?
 (F) $35 = C + 3t$ (G) $C + 35 = 3t$ (H) $C = 35 + 3t$ (J) $C = 35t + 3$

41. Which statement is true by the Reflexive Property of Equality?
 (A) $x = 35$ (B) $\overline{CD} = \overline{CD}$ (C) $\overline{RT} \cong \overline{TR}$ (D) $CD = CD$

42. Gridded Response In the triangle, $m\angle 1 + m\angle 2 + m\angle 3 = 180°$. If $m\angle 3 = 2m\angle 1$ and $m\angle 1 = m\angle 2$, find $m\angle 3$ in degrees. **90**

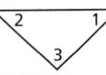

CHALLENGE AND EXTEND

44. Possible answer: You cannot add geometric figures.

43. In the gate, $PA = QB$, $QB = RA$, and $PA = 18$ in. Find PR, and justify each step.

44. Critical Thinking Explain why there is no Addition Property of Congruence.

45. Algebra Justify each step in the solution of the inequality $7 - 3x > 19$.

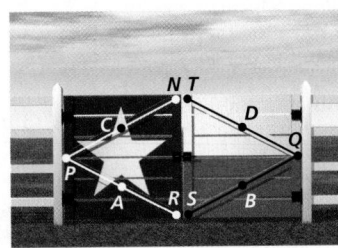

SPIRAL REVIEW

46. The members of a high school band have saved $600 for a trip. They deposit the money in a savings account. What additional information is needed to find the amount of interest the account earns during a 3-month period? *(Previous course)* **the interest rate the account earns**

Use a compass and straightedge to construct each of the following. *(Lesson 1-2)*

47. $\overline{JK}$ congruent to $\overline{MN}$

M •———————————————• N

48. a segment bisector of $\overline{JK}$
 47–48. Check students' constructions.

Identify whether each conclusion uses inductive or deductive reasoning. *(Lesson 2-3)*

49. deductive reasoning

49. A triangle is obtuse if one of its angles is obtuse. Jacob draws a triangle with two acute angles and one obtuse angle. He concludes that the triangle is obtuse.

50. inductive reasoning

50. Tonya studied 3 hours for each of her last two geometry tests. She got an A on both tests. She concludes that she will get an A on the next test if she studies for 3 hours.

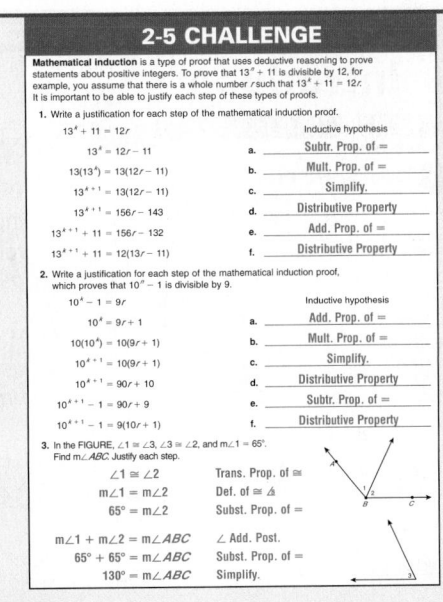

2-5 Algebraic Proof **109**

Objectives: Write two-column proofs.

Prove geometric theorems by using deductive reasoning.

 Online Edition
Tutorial Videos

 Countdown to TAKS Week 4

Power Presentations
with PowerPoint®

Warm Up

Determine whether each statement is true or false. If false, give a counterexample.

1. If two angles are complementary, then they are not congruent.   F; 45° and 45°

2. If two angles are congruent to the same angle, then they are congruent to each other.   T

3. Supplementary angles are congruent.   F; 60° and 120°

Also available on transparency

Math Humor

Q: What do you have to know to get top grades in geometry?

A: All the angles!

Geometry TEKS

G.1 Geometric structure*
(A) develop an awareness of the structure of a mathematical system, connecting definitions, postulates, …

G.3 Geometric structure*
(B) … justify statements about geometric figures …
(C) use logical reasoning to prove statements are true and find counterexamples to disprove statements that are false
(E) use inductive reasoning to formulate a conjecture

* Knowledge and Skills See p. 72.

2-6 Geometric Proof

★ **TEKS G.1.A Geometric structure: develop an awareness of the structure of a mathematical system, connecting definitions, postulates, logical reasoning, and theorems.**

Objectives
Write two-column proofs.

Prove geometric theorems by using deductive reasoning.

Vocabulary
theorem
two-column proof

★ **Also G.3.B, G.3.C, G.3.E**

Who uses this?
To persuade your parents to increase your allowance, your argument must be presented logically and precisely.

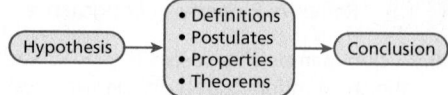

When writing a geometric proof, you use deductive reasoning to create a chain of logical steps that move from the hypothesis to the conclusion of the conjecture you are proving. By proving that the conclusion is true, you have proven that the original conjecture is true.

$$\text{Hypothesis} \rightarrow \begin{array}{l}\bullet \text{ Definitions} \\ \bullet \text{ Postulates} \\ \bullet \text{ Properties} \\ \bullet \text{ Theorems}\end{array} \rightarrow \text{Conclusion}$$

When writing a proof, it is important to justify each logical step with a reason. You can use symbols and abbreviations, but they must be clear enough so that anyone who reads your proof will understand them.

EXAMPLE 1 **Writing Justifications**

Helpful Hint
When a justification is based on more than the previous step, you can note this after the reason, as in Example 1 Step 5.

Write a justification for each step, given that ∠A and ∠B are complementary and ∠A ≅ ∠C.

1. ∠A and ∠B are complementary.   Given information
2. m∠A + m∠B = 90°   Def. of comp. ∠
3. ∠A ≅ ∠C   Given information
4. m∠A = m∠C   Def. of ≅ ∠
5. m∠C + m∠B = 90°   Subst. Prop. of =   *Steps 2, 4*
6. ∠C and ∠B are complementary.   Def. of comp. ∠

 **1.** Write a justification for each step, given that B is the midpoint of $\overline{AC}$ and $\overline{AB} \cong \overline{EF}$.

1. Given
2. Def. of mdpt.
3. Given
4. Trans. Prop. of ≅

1. B is the midpoint of $\overline{AC}$.
2. $\overline{AB} \cong \overline{BC}$
3. $\overline{AB} \cong \overline{EF}$
4. $\overline{BC} \cong \overline{EF}$

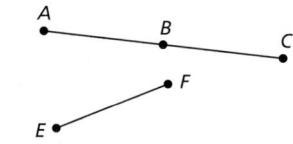

A **theorem** is any statement that you can prove. Once you have proven a theorem, you can use it as a reason in later proofs.

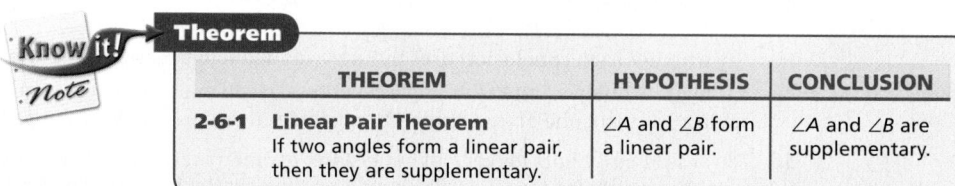

Theorem

	THEOREM	HYPOTHESIS	CONCLUSION
2-6-1	**Linear Pair Theorem** If two angles form a linear pair, then they are supplementary.	∠A and ∠B form a linear pair.	∠A and ∠B are supplementary.

---

1 Introduce

EXPLORATION

2-6 Geometric Proof

Use geometry software to construct angles that form a linear pair.

1. Draw a segment $\overline{AB}$.

2. Construct a point C between A and B.

3. Draw a segment $\overline{CD}$ such that point D is not on $\overline{AB}$.

4. Measure ∠ACD and ∠BCD. Calculate the sum of m∠ACD and m∠BCD.

5. Drag point C. What do you notice?

6. Drag point D. What do you notice?

THINK AND DISCUSS

Motivate

Discuss with students the scenario in the opening cartoon. Ask "If the student's argument for a raise in allowance is not precise, what might the parent's reaction be?" Possible answer: The parent might not agree to raise the student's allowance. Have students describe the argument they would use. Explain that this lesson focuses on how to write precise, logical arguments in geometry.

Explorations and answers are provided in the *Chapter 2 Resource Book.*

Theorem

THEOREM	HYPOTHESIS	CONCLUSION
2-6-2 **Congruent Supplements Theorem** If two angles are supplementary to the same angle (or to two congruent angles), then the two angles are congruent.	∠1 and ∠2 are supplementary. ∠2 and ∠3 are supplementary.	∠1 ≅ ∠3

A geometric proof begins with *Given* and *Prove* statements, which restate the hypothesis and conclusion of the conjecture. In a **two-column proof**, you list the steps of the proof in the left column. You write the matching reason for each step in the right column.

EXAMPLE 2 **Completing a Two-Column Proof**

Fill in the blanks to complete a two-column proof of the Linear Pair Theorem.
Given: ∠1 and ∠2 form a linear pair.
Prove: ∠1 and ∠2 are supplementary.
Proof:

Writing Math

Since there is no other substitution property, the Substitution Property of Equality is often written as "Substitution" or "Subst."

Statements	Reasons
1. ∠1 and ∠2 form a linear pair.	**1.** Given
2. $\overrightarrow{BA}$ and $\overrightarrow{BC}$ form a line.	**2.** Def. of lin. pair
3. m∠ABC = 180°	**3.** Def. of straight ∠
4. a. ?	**4.** ∠ Add. Post.
5. b. ?	**5.** Subst. *Steps 3, 4*
6. ∠1 and ∠2 are supplementary.	**6. c.** ?

Use the existing statements and reasons in the proof to fill in the blanks.
    a. m∠1 + m∠2 = m∠ABC   *The ∠ Add. Post. is given as the reason.*
    b. m∠1 + m∠2 = 180°   *Substitute 180° for m∠ABC.*
    c. Def. of supp. ∠   *The measures of supp. ∠ add to 180° by def.*

CHECK IT OUT! **2.** Fill in the blanks to complete a two-column proof of one case of the Congruent Supplements Theorem.

Given: ∠1 and ∠2 are supplementary, and ∠2 and ∠3 are supplementary.
Prove: ∠1 ≅ ∠3
Proof:

Statements	Reasons
1. a. ?	**1.** Given
2. m∠1 + m∠2 = 180° m∠2 + m∠3 = 180°	**2.** Def. of supp. ∠
3. b. ?	**3.** Subst.
4. m∠2 = m∠2	**4.** Reflex. Prop. of =
5. m∠1 = m∠3	**5. c.** ?
6. d. ?	**6.** Def. of ≅ ∠

2a. ∠1 and ∠2 are supp., and ∠2 and ∠3 are supp.
2b. m∠1 + m∠2 = m∠2 + m∠3
2c. Subtr. Prop. of =
2d. ∠1 ≅ ∠3

When writing a proof, some students may incorrectly assume things from the figure. If students make this mistake, refer them back to page 73.

Power Presentations with PowerPoint®

Additional Examples

Example 1

Write a justification for each step, given that ∠A and ∠B are supplementary and m∠A = 45°.

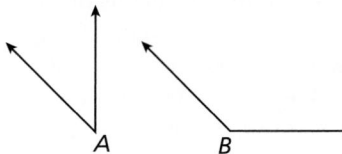

1. ∠A and ∠B are supplementary. m∠A = 45° Given
2. m∠A + ∠B = 180° Def. of supp. ∠
3. 45° + m∠B = 180° Subst.
4. m∠B = 135° Subtr. Prop. of =

Example 2

Fill in the blanks to complete the two-column proof.

Given: $\overline{XY}$
Prove: $\overline{XY} \cong \overline{XY}$

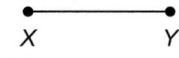

1. ? (Given) $\overline{XY}$
2. XY = XY (?) Reflex. Prop. of =
3. ? (Def. of ≅ segs.) $\overline{XY} \cong \overline{XY}$

Also available on transparency

INTERVENTION
Questioning Strategies

EXAMPLE 1
• Is it possible that two different reasons could be used to justify a step in a proof? Why or why not?

EXAMPLE 2
• When filling in missing information in a proof, should you work down the columns or across the rows?

---

2 Teach

Guided Instruction

Explain to students that in a proof, every statement must be justified by a reason. Use the graphic on page 110 to emphasize that the reasons will be definitions, postulates, properties, and theorems, as well as information in the Given statement.

Teaching Tip **Auditory** When reviewing the examples, say each step of the proof aloud and have students speak each justification.

Reaching All Learners
Through Critical Thinking

Have students write the statements and reasons for the proofs presented in the examples on individual strips of paper. Have students exchange complete sets and rearrange them into a two-column proof.

Example 3

Use the given plan to write a two-column proof.

Given: ∠1 and ∠2 are supp.
∠1 ≅ ∠3

Prove: ∠3 and ∠2 are supp.

Plan: Use the definitions of supplementary and congruent angles and substitution to show that m∠3 + m∠2 = 180°. By the definition of supplementary angles, ∠3 and ∠2 are supplementary.

Answer Note: Two-column proofs in the answers are given in the format *Statement* (*Reason*).

1. ∠1 and ∠2 are supp. ∠1 ≅ ∠3 (Given)

2. m∠1 + m∠2 = 180° (Def. of supp. ∡)

3. m∠1 = m∠3 (Def. of ≅ ∡)

4. m∠3 + m∠2 = 180° (Subst.)

5. ∠3 and ∠2 are supp. (Def. of supp. ∡)

Also available on transparency

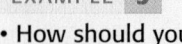

INTERVENTION ◄—►
Questioning Strategies

EXAMPLE 3

- How should you mark a figure when starting a proof?

- How does a plan help in writing a two-column proof?

Kinesthetic Some students may have difficulty deciding which statement a reason goes with. Have students point at the conclusion of the reason. The conclusion must match the statement that it is aligned with.

Inclusion When students are using a definition as a justification, suggest that they write the definition as a conditional statement in the order needed to apply it.

Before you start writing a proof, you should plan out your logic. Sometimes you will be given a plan for a more challenging proof. This plan will detail the major steps of the proof for you.

 **Theorems**

	THEOREM	HYPOTHESIS	CONCLUSION
2-6-3	**Right Angle Congruence Theorem** All right angles are congruent.	∠A and ∠B are right angles.	∠A ≅ ∠B
2-6-4	**Congruent Complements Theorem** If two angles are complementary to the same angle (or to two congruent angles), then the two angles are congruent.	∠1 and ∠2 are complementary. ∠2 and ∠3 are complementary.	∠1 ≅ ∠3

EXAMPLE 3 **Writing a Two-Column Proof from a Plan**

Use the given plan to write a two-column proof of the Right Angle Congruence Theorem.
Given: ∠1 and ∠2 are right angles.
Prove: ∠1 ≅ ∠2

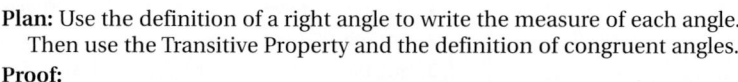

Helpful Hint

If a diagram for a proof is not provided, draw your own and mark the given information on it. But do not mark the information in the Prove statement on it.

Plan: Use the definition of a right angle to write the measure of each angle. Then use the Transitive Property and the definition of congruent angles.

Proof:

Statements	Reasons
1. ∠1 and ∠2 are right angles.	1. Given
2. m∠1 = 90°, m∠2 = 90°	2. Def. of rt. ∠
3. m∠1 = m∠2	3. Trans. Prop. of =
4. ∠1 ≅ ∠2	4. Def. of ≅ ∡

 **3.** Use the given plan to write a two-column proof of one case of the Congruent Complements Theorem.

1. ∠1 and ∠2 are comp. ∠2 and ∠3 are comp. (Given)
2. m∠1 + m∠2 = 90°, m∠2 + m∠3 = 90° (Def. of comp. ∡)
3. m∠1 + m∠2 = m∠2 + m∠3 (Subst.)
4. m∠2 = m∠2 (Reflex. Prop. of =)
5. m∠1 = m∠3 (Subtr. Prop. of =)
6. ∠1 ≅ ∠3 (Def. of ≅ ∡)

Given: ∠1 and ∠2 are complementary, and ∠2 and ∠3 are complementary.

Prove: ∠1 ≅ ∠3

Plan: The measures of complementary angles add to 90° by definition. Use substitution to show that the sums of both pairs are equal. Use the Subtraction Property and the definition of congruent angles to conclude that ∠1 ≅ ∠3.

The Proof Process
1. Write the conjecture to be proven.
2. Draw a diagram to represent the hypothesis of the conjecture.
3. State the given information and mark it on the diagram.
4. State the conclusion of the conjecture in terms of the diagram.
5. Plan your argument and prove the conjecture.

---

3 Close

Summarize

Review with students the steps of the proof process in the summary box on page 112. Ask students to list the four parts of a two-column proof. Given statement, Prove statement, statements, and reasons

Also review the four theorems presented in the lesson:

- Linear Pair Theorem
- Congruent Supplements Theorem
- Right Angle Congruence Theorem
- Congruent Complements Theorem

ONGOING ASSESSMENT
and INTERVENTION ◄—►

Diagnose Before the Lesson
2-6 Warm Up, TE p. 110

Monitor During the Lesson
Check It Out! Exercises, SE pp. 110–112
Questioning Strategies, TE pp. 111–112

Assess After the Lesson
2-6 Lesson Quiz, TE p. 116
Alternative Assessment, TE p. 116

THINK AND DISCUSS
1. Which step in a proof should match the Prove statement?
2. Why is it important to include every logical step in a proof?
3. List four things you can use to justify a step in a proof.

 Know it! Note

4. **GET ORGANIZED** Copy and complete the graphic organizer. In each box, describe the steps of the proof process.

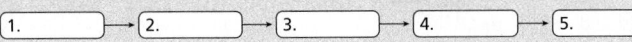

1. ⟶ 2. ⟶ 3. ⟶ 4. ⟶ 5.

2-6 Exercises

go.hrw.com/Geo/TX
Homework Help Online
KEYWORD: MG7 2-6
Parent Resources Online
KEYWORD: MG7 Parent

GUIDED PRACTICE

Vocabulary Apply the vocabulary from this lesson to answer each question.

1. In a *two-column proof*, you list the ___?___ in the left column and the ___?___ in the right column. (*statements* or *reasons*) **statements; reasons**

2. A ___?___ is a statement you can prove. (*postulate* or *theorem*) **theorem**

SEE EXAMPLE **1**
p. 110

3. Write a justification for each step, given that $m\angle A = 60°$ and $m\angle B = 2m\angle A$.

1. $m\angle A = 60°$, $m\angle B = 2m\angle A$ **Given**
2. $m\angle B = 2(60°)$ **Subst.**
3. $m\angle B = 120°$ **Simplify.**
4. $m\angle A + m\angle B = 60° + 120°$ **Add. Prop. of =**
5. $m\angle A + m\angle B = 180°$ **Simplify.**
6. $\angle A$ and $\angle B$ are supplementary. **Def. of supp. ∡**

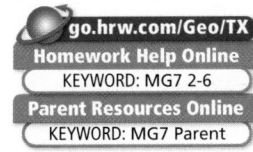

SEE EXAMPLE **2**
p. 111

4. Fill in the blanks to complete the two-column proof.

Given: $\angle 2 \cong \angle 3$
Prove: $\angle 1$ and $\angle 3$ are supplementary.
Proof:

Statements	Reasons
1. $\angle 2 \cong \angle 3$	1. Given
2. $m\angle 2 = m\angle 3$	2. a. ___?___
3. b. ___?___	3. Lin. Pair Thm.
4. $m\angle 1 + m\angle 2 = 180°$	4. Def. of supp. ∡
5. $m\angle 1 + m\angle 3 = 180°$	5. c. ___?___ Steps 2, 4
6. d. ___?___	6. Def. of supp. ∡

a. Def. of ≅ ∡

b. $\angle 1$ and $\angle 2$ are supp.

c. Subst.

d. $\angle 1$ and $\angle 3$ are supp.

SEE EXAMPLE **3**
p. 112

5. Use the given plan to write a two-column proof.

Given: X is the midpoint of $\overline{AY}$, and Y is the midpoint of $\overline{XB}$.
Prove: $\overline{AX} \cong \overline{YB}$

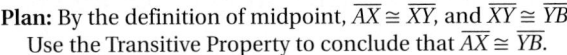

Plan: By the definition of midpoint, $\overline{AX} \cong \overline{XY}$, and $\overline{XY} \cong \overline{YB}$. Use the Transitive Property to conclude that $\overline{AX} \cong \overline{YB}$.

2-6 Geometric Proof **113**

Answers

5. 1. X is the mdpt. of $\overline{AY}$. Y is the mdpt. of $\overline{XB}$. (Given)
   2. $\overline{AX} \cong \overline{XY}$, $\overline{XY} \cong \overline{YB}$ (Def. of mdpt.)
   3. $\overline{AX} \cong \overline{YB}$ (Trans. Prop. of ≅)

2-6 Exercises

Assignment Guide

Assign *Guided Practice* exercises as necessary.

If you finished Examples **1–2**
  Basic 6–8, 12
  Average 6–8, 11, 12, 14
  Advanced 6–8, 11, 12–22 even

If you finished Examples **1–3**
  Basic 6–12, 16–20, 22–27, 31–36
  Average 6–16, 18–22 even, 23–27, 31–36
  Advanced 6–16, 18, 21–36

Homework Quick Check
Quickly check key concepts.
Exercises: 6, 8, 10, 16, 20

⬇TAKS Practice

Grades 9–11	Exercises
Obj. 4	20–22, 29, 30
Obj. 10	31, 32

PRACTICE AND PROBLEM SOLVING

Independent Practice

For Exercises	See Example
6	1
7–8	2
9–10	3

TEKS → **TAKS**

Skills Practice p. S7
Application Practice p. S29

6. Write a justification for each step, given that $\overrightarrow{BX}$ bisects $\angle ABC$ and $m\angle XBC = 45°$.

1. $\overrightarrow{BX}$ bisects $\angle ABC$.   1. Given
2. $\angle ABX \cong \angle XBC$ 2. Def. of $\angle$ bisector
3. $m\angle ABX = m\angle XBC$ 3. Def. of $\cong$ $\angle$
4. $m\angle XBC = 45°$ 4. Given
5. $m\angle ABX = 45°$ 5. Subst.
6. $m\angle ABX + m\angle XBC = m\angle ABC$ 6. $\angle$ Add. Post.
7. $45° + 45° = m\angle ABC$ 7. Subst.
8. $90° = m\angle ABC$ 8. Simplify.
9. $\angle ABC$ is a right angle.   9. Def. of rt. $\angle$

Fill in the blanks to complete each two-column proof.

7. **Given:** $\angle 1$ and $\angle 2$ are supplementary, and $\angle 3$ and $\angle 4$ are supplementary. $\angle 2 \cong \angle 3$

Prove: $\angle 1 \cong \angle 4$

Proof:

7a. $m\angle 1 + m\angle 2 = 180°$, $m\angle 3 + m\angle 4 = 180°$

Statements	Reasons
1. $\angle 1$ and $\angle 2$ are supplementary. $\angle 3$ and $\angle 4$ are supplementary.	1. Given
2. a. ___?___	2. Def. of supp. $\angle$s
3. $m\angle 1 + m\angle 2 = m\angle 3 + m\angle 4$	3. b. ___?___ Subst.
4. $\angle 2 \cong \angle 3$	4. Given
5. $m\angle 2 = m\angle 3$	5. Def. of $\cong$ $\angle$s
6. c. ___?___ $m\angle 1 = m\angle 4$	6. Subtr. Prop. of = *Steps 3, 5*
7. $\angle 1 \cong \angle 4$	7. d. ___?___ Def. of $\cong$ $\angle$s

8. **Given:** $\angle BAC$ is a right angle. $\angle 2 \cong \angle 3$

Prove: $\angle 1$ and $\angle 3$ are complementary.

Proof:

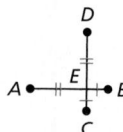

Statements	Reasons
1. $\angle BAC$ is a right angle.	1. Given
2. $m\angle BAC = 90°$	2. a. ___?___
3. b. ___?___	3. $\angle$ Add. Post.
4. $m\angle 1 + m\angle 2 = 90°$	4. Subst. *Steps 2, 3*
5. $\angle 2 \cong \angle 3$	5. Given
6. c. ___?___	6. Def. of $\cong$ $\angle$s
7. $m\angle 1 + m\angle 3 = 90°$	7. d. ___?___ *Steps 4, 6*
8. e. ___?___	8. Def. of comp. $\angle$s

a. Def. of rt. $\angle$
b. $m\angle 1 + m\angle 2 = m\angle BAC$
c. $m\angle 2 = m\angle 3$
d. Subst.
e. $\angle 1$ and $\angle 3$ are comp.

Use the given plan to write a two-column proof.

9. **Given:** $\overline{BE} \cong \overline{CE}$, $\overline{DE} \cong \overline{AE}$

Prove: $\overline{AB} \cong \overline{CD}$

Plan: Use the definition of congruent segments to write the given information in terms of lengths. Then use the Segment Addition Postulate to show that $AB = CD$ and thus $\overline{AB} \cong \overline{CD}$.

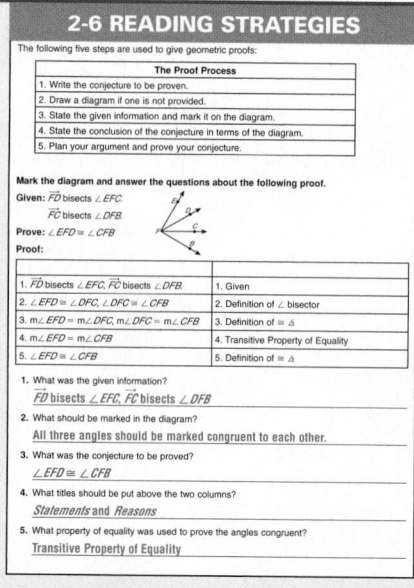

Use the given plan to write a two-column proof.

10. **Given:** ∠1 and ∠3 are complementary, and ∠2 and ∠4 are complementary. ∠3 ≅ ∠4

    Prove: ∠1 ≅ ∠2

    Plan: Since ∠1 and ∠3 are complementary and ∠2 and ∠4 are complementary, both pairs of angle measures add to 90°. Use substitution to show that the sums of both pairs are equal. Since ∠3 ≅ ∠4, their measures are equal. Use the Subtraction Property of Equality and the definition of congruent angles to conclude that ∠1 ≅ ∠2.

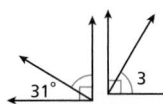

Find each angle measure.

11. m∠1
    132°
    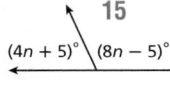

12. m∠2
    27°
    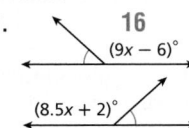

13. m∠3
    59°
    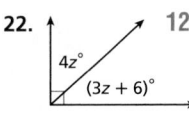

14. **Engineering** The Bluff Dale Bridge is 140 feet long and spans the Paluxy River in Bluff Dale, Texas. If ∠1 ≅ ∠2, which theorem can you use to conclude that ∠3 ≅ ∠4? ≅ **Supps. Thm.**

15. **Critical Thinking** Explain why there are two cases to consider when proving the Congruent Supplements Theorem and the Congruent Complements Theorem.

Tell whether each statement is sometimes, always, or never true.

16. An angle and its complement are congruent. **S**

17. A pair of right angles forms a linear pair. **S**

18. An angle and its complement form a right angle. **S**

19. A linear pair of angles is complementary. **N**

Algebra Find the value of each variable.

20.
    15
    (4n + 5)° (8n − 5)°

21. 16
    (9x − 6)°
    (8.5x + 2)°

22. 12
    4z°
    (3z + 6)°
    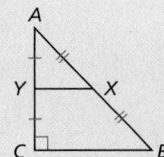

23. **Write About It** How are a theorem and a postulate alike? How are they different?

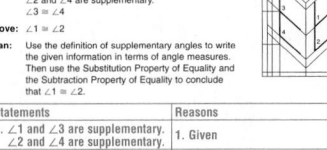
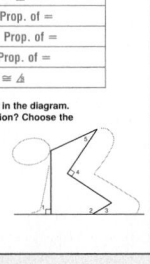
MULTI-STEP TAKS PREP

24. This problem will prepare you for the Multi-Step TAKS Prep on page 126.

    Sometimes you may be asked to write a proof without a specific statement of the Given and Prove information being provided for you. For each of the following situations, use the triangle to write a Given and Prove statement.

    a. The segment connecting the midpoints of two sides of a triangle is half as long as the third side.

    b. The acute angles of a right triangle are complementary.

    c. In a right triangle, the sum of the squares of the legs is equal to the square of the hypotenuse.

2-6 Geometric Proof **115**

Communicating Math

Teaching Tip Remind students that arc marks are used to indicate congruent angles in **Exercises 13** and **21**.

 **MULTI-STEP TAKS PREP** **Exercise 24** involves writing the Given and Prove statements for a proof when they are not explicitly stated. This exercise prepares students for the Multi-Step TAKS Prep on page 126.

Answers

10. 1. ∠1 and ∠3 are comp. ∠2 and ∠4 are comp. (Given)
    2. m∠1 + m∠3 = 90°, m∠2 + m∠4 = 90° (Def. of comp. ∠)
    3. m∠1 + m∠3 = m∠2 + m∠4 (Subst.)
    4. ∠3 ≅ ∠4 (Given)
    5. m∠3 = m∠4 (Def. of ≅ ∠)
    6. m∠1 = m∠2 (Subtr. Prop. of =)
    7. ∠1 ≅ ∠2 (Def. of ≅ ∠)

15. Possible answer: because the ∠ can be supp. or comp. to the same ∠ or to 2 ≅ ∠

23. Possible answer: A thm. and a post. are both true statements of geometric facts. They are different because a post. is assumed to be true, while a thm. must be proven to be true.

24a. **Given:** Y is the mdpt. of $\overline{AC}$. X is the mdpt. of $\overline{AB}$.
    Prove: $XY = \frac{1}{2}BC$

b. **Given:** ∠C is a rt. ∠.
    Prove: ∠A and ∠B are comp.

c. **Given:** ∠C is a rt. ∠.
    Prove: $(AB)^2 = (AC)^2 + (BC)^2$

Lesson 2-6 **115**

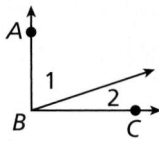

2-6 Lesson Quiz

1. Write a justification for each step, given that m∠ABC = 90° and m∠1 = 4m∠2.

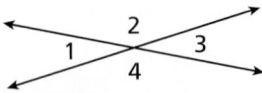

1. m∠ABC = 90°, m∠1 = 4m∠2   Given

2. m∠1 + m∠2 = m∠ABC   ∠ Add. Post.

3. 4m∠2 + m∠2 = 90°   Subst.

4. 5m∠2 = 90°   Simplify.

5. m∠2 = 18°   Div. Prop. of =

2. Use the given plan to write a two-column proof.

Given: ∠1, ∠2, ∠3, and ∠4
Prove: m∠1 + m∠2 = m∠1 + m∠4

Plan: Use the Linear Pair Theorem to show that the angle pairs are supplementary. Then use the definition of supplementary and substitution.

1. ∠1 and ∠2 are supp. ∠1 and ∠4 are supp. (Lin. Pair Thm.)

2. m∠1 + m∠2 = 180°, m∠1 + m∠4 = 180° (Def. of supp. ∠)

3. m∠1 + m∠2 = m∠1 + m∠4 (Subst.)

Also available on transparency

TEST PREP

25. Which theorem justifies the conclusion that ∠1 ≅ ∠4?

Ⓐ Linear Pair Theorem
Ⓑ Congruent Supplements Theorem
Ⓒ Congruent Complements Theorem
Ⓓ Right Angle Congruence Theorem

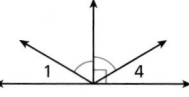

26. What can be concluded from the statement m∠1 + m∠2 = 180°?

Ⓕ ∠1 and ∠2 are congruent.
Ⓖ ∠1 and ∠2 are supplementary.
Ⓗ ∠1 and ∠2 are complementary.
Ⓙ ∠1 and ∠2 form a linear pair.

27. Given: Two angles are complementary. The measure of one angle is 10° less than the measure of the other angle. Conclusion: The measures of the angles are 85° and 95°. Which statement is true?

Ⓐ The conclusion is correct because 85° is 10° less than 95°.
Ⓑ The conclusion is verified by the first statement given.
Ⓒ The conclusion is invalid because the angles are not congruent.
Ⓓ The conclusion is contradicted by the first statement given.

CHALLENGE AND EXTEND

28. Write a two-column proof.
   Given: m∠LAN = 30°, m∠1 = 15°
   Prove: $\overrightarrow{AM}$ bisects ∠LAN.

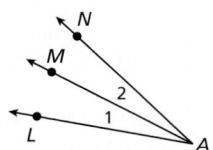

Multi-Step Find the value of the variable and the measure of each angle.

29.

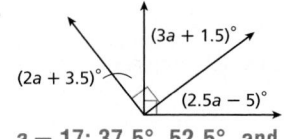

$a = 17$; 37.5°, 52.5°, and 37.5°

30.

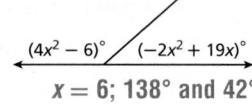

$x = 6$; 138° and 42°

SPIRAL REVIEW

The table shows the number of tires replaced by a repair company during one week, classified by the mileage on the tires when they were replaced. Use the table for Exercises 31 and 32. *(Previous course)*

Mileage on Replaced Tires	
Mileage	Tires
40,000–49,999	60
50,000–59,999	82
60,000–69,999	54
70,000–79,999	40
80,000–89,999	14

31. What percent of the tires had mileage between 40,000 and 49,999 when replaced? **24%**

32. If the company replaces twice as many tires next week, about how many tires would you expect to have lasted between 80,000 and 89,999 miles?
28 tires

Sketch a figure that shows each of the following. *(Lesson 1-1)* **33–34. Possible answers:**

33. Through any two collinear points, there is more than one plane containing them.

34. A pair of opposite rays forms a line. ←——•——•——→

Identify the property that justifies each statement. *(Lesson 2-5)*   Trans. Prop. of =
35. $\overline{JK} \cong \overline{KL}$, so $\overline{KL} \cong \overline{JK}$. Sym. Prop. of ≅   **36.** If $m = n$ and $n = p$, then $m = p$.

33.

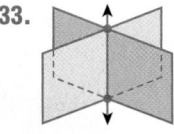

Answers

28. 1. m∠LAN = 30° (Given)
2. m∠1 + m∠2 = m∠LAN (∠ Add. Post.)
3. m∠1 + m∠2 = 30° (Subst.)
4. m∠1 = 15° (Given)
5. 15° + m∠2 = 30° (Subst.)
6. m∠2 = 15° (Subtr. Prop. of =)
7. m∠1 = m∠2 (Trans. Prop. of =)
8. ∠1 ≅ ∠2 (Def. of ≅ ∠)
9. $\overrightarrow{AM}$ bisects ∠LAN. (Def. of ∠ bisector)

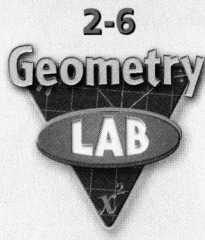

2-6 Geometry LAB

Use with Lesson 2-6

Design Plans for Proofs

Sometimes the most challenging part of writing a proof is planning the logical steps that will take you from the Given statement to the Prove statement. Like working a jigsaw puzzle, you can start with any piece. Write down everything you know from the Given statement. If you don't see the connection right away, start with the Prove statement and work backward. Then connect the pieces into a logical order.

⭐ TEKS G.1.A Geometric structure: develop an awareness of the structure of a mathematical system... Also G.3.B, G.3.C, G.3.E

Activity

Prove the Common Angles Theorem.
Given: ∠AXB ≅ ∠CXD
Prove: ∠AXC ≅ ∠BXD

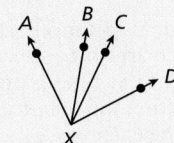

1 Start by considering the difference in the Given and Prove statements. How does ∠AXB compare to ∠AXC? How does ∠CXD compare to ∠BXD?

In both cases, ∠BXC is combined with the first angle to get the second angle.

2 The situation involves combining adjacent angle measures, so list any definitions, properties, postulates, and theorems that might be helpful.

Definition of congruent angles, Angle Addition Postulate, properties of equality, and Reflexive, Symmetric, and Transitive Properties of Congruence

3 Start with what you are given and what you are trying to prove and then work toward the middle.

∠AXB ≅ ∠CXD	*The first reason will be "Given."*
m∠AXB = m∠CXD	*Def. of ≅ ⦟*
???	*???*
m∠AXC = m∠BXD	*Def. of ≅ ⦟*
∠AXC ≅ ∠BXD	*The last statement will be the Prove statement.*

4 Based on Step 1, ∠BXC is the missing piece in the middle of the logical flow. So write down what you know about ∠BXC.

∠BXC ≅ ∠BXC	*Reflex. Prop. of ≅*
m∠BXC = m∠BXC	*Reflex. Prop. of =*

5 Now you can see that the Angle Addition Postulate needs to be used to complete the proof.

m∠AXB + m∠BXC = m∠AXC	*∠ Add. Post.*
m∠BXC + m∠CXD = m∠BXD	*∠ Add. Post.*

6 Reorder the pieces above to write a two-column proof of the Common Angles Theorem.

Try This

1. Describe how a plan for a proof differs from the actual proof.

2. Write a plan and a two-column proof.
   Given: $\overrightarrow{BD}$ bisects ∠ABC.
   Prove: 2m∠1 = m∠ABC

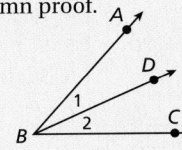

3. Write a plan and a two-column proof.
   Given: ∠LXN is a right angle.
   Prove: ∠1 and ∠2 are complementary.

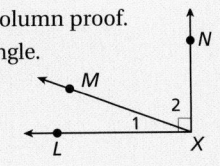

Answers to *Activity*

6. 1. ∠AXB ≅ ∠CXD (Given)
   2. m∠AXB = m∠CXD (Def. of ≅ ⦟)
   3. m∠BXC = m∠BXC (Reflex. Prop. of =)
   4. m∠AXB + m∠BXC = m∠CXD + m∠BXC (Add. Prop. of =)
   5. m∠AXB + m∠BXC = m∠AXC, m∠BXC + m∠CXD = m∠BXD (∠ Add. Post.)
   6. m∠AXC = m∠BXD (Subst.)
   7. ∠AXC ≅ ∠BXD (Def. of ≅ ⦟)

Answers to *Try This*

1. Possible answer: A plan for a proof is less formal than a proof. A formal proof presents every logical step in detail, but a plan describes only the key logical steps.

2–3. See p. A12.

Geometry Organizer
LAB

Use with Lesson 2-6

Pacing:
Traditional 1 day
Block $\frac{1}{2}$ day

Objective: Learn strategies for planning the logical steps of a proof.

🪐 **Online Edition**

Countdown to TAKS Week 4

Teach

Discuss

Emphasize that writing a proof requires an organized approach similar to solving logic puzzles. Instruct students to think about what they are trying to prove before they begin writing. Does it make sense? Why? Brainstorming like this can give students an idea of how to start the proof.

Close

Key Concept

As with problem solving, there are many strategies for writing a proof. Writing a plan first helps you organize your thoughts.

Assessment

Journal Have students describe in their own words what they have learned about planning a geometric proof.

⭐ *Geometry TEKS*

G.1 Geometric structure*
(A) develop an awareness of the structure of a mathematical system, connecting definitions, postulates, …

G.3 Geometric structure*
(B) construct and justify statements about geometric figures and their properties
(C) use logical reasoning to prove statements are true and find counterexamples to disprove statements that are false
(E) use inductive reasoning to formulate a conjecture

* **Knowledge and Skills** See p. 72.

Objectives: Write flowchart and paragraph proofs.

Prove geometric theorems by using deductive reasoning.

Technology Lab
In *Texas Lab Manual*

Online Edition
Tutorial Videos, Interactivity

Countdown to TAKS Week 4

Power Presentations
with PowerPoint®

Warm Up

Complete each sentence.

1. If the measures of two angles are ___?___, then the angles are congruent.   equal

2. If two angles form a ___?___, then they are supplementary.
linear pair

3. If two angles are complementary to the same angle, then the two angles are ___?___.
congruent

Also available on transparency

Math Humor

Q: What do you call two fishermen standing up?

A: Vertical anglers.

★ Geometry TEKS

G.1 Geometric structure*
(A) develop an awareness of the structure of a mathematical system, connecting definitions, postulates, ...

G.2 Geometric structure*
(B) make conjectures ... and determine the validity of the conjectures, choosing from a variety of approaches such as ... axiomatic

G.3 Geometric structure*
(C) use logical reasoning to prove statements are true ...
(E) use inductive reasoning to formulate a conjecture

* Knowledge and Skills See p. 72.

2-7 # Flowchart and Paragraph Proofs

★ TEKS G.1.A Geometric structure: develop an awareness of the structure of a mathematical system, connecting definitions, postulates, logical reasoning, and theorems. Also G.2.B, G.3.C, G.3.E

Objectives
Write flowchart and paragraph proofs.

Prove geometric theorems by using deductive reasoning.

Vocabulary
flowchart proof
paragraph proof

Why learn this?

Flowcharts make it easy to see how the steps of a process are linked together.

A second style of proof is a **flowchart proof**, which uses boxes and arrows to show the structure of the proof. The steps in a flowchart proof move from left to right or from top to bottom, shown by the arrows connecting each box. The justification for each step is written below the box.

Know it!
.Note

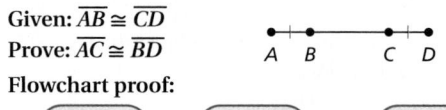
Theorem 2-7-1 Common Segments Theorem

THEOREM	HYPOTHESIS	CONCLUSION
Given collinear points A, B, C, and D arranged as shown, if $\overline{AB} \cong \overline{CD}$, then $\overline{AC} \cong \overline{BD}$. A B C D	$\overline{AB} \cong \overline{CD}$	$\overline{AC} \cong \overline{BD}$

E X A M P L E 1 **Reading a Flowchart Proof**

Use the given flowchart proof to write a two-column proof of the Common Segments Theorem.

Given: $\overline{AB} \cong \overline{CD}$
Prove: $\overline{AC} \cong \overline{BD}$ A   B   C   D

Flowchart proof:

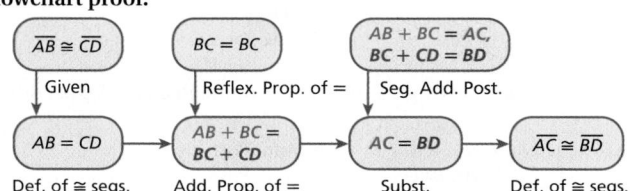

Two-column proof:

Statements	Reasons
1. $\overline{AB} \cong \overline{CD}$	1. Given
2. $AB = CD$	2. Def. of ≅ segs.
3. $BC = BC$	3. Reflex. Prop. of =
4. $AB + BC = BC + CD$	4. Add. Prop. of =
5. $AB + BC = AC, BC + CD = BD$	5. Seg. Add. Post.
6. $AC = BD$	6. Subst.
7. $\overline{AC} \cong \overline{BD}$	7. Def. of ≅ segs.

---

1 # Introduce

EXPLORATION

2-7 **Flowchart and Paragraph Proofs**

You can use paper folding to explore an important theorem about angles.

1. Fold a sheet of paper to make a crease. Then unfold the paper.

2. Fold the sheet again to make a new crease that intersects the first one. Unfold the paper.

3. Label the angles.

4. Use a protractor to measure ∠1, ∠2, ∠3, and ∠4. Record the results.

5. Repeat the process by making different creases on a new sheet of paper.

6. Which pairs of angles are vertical angles?

Motivate

Ask students to name different styles of poetry they may have seen in their language arts classes. Possible answers: sonnet, limerick, ballad, haiku, free verse Discuss the idea that just as thoughts and feelings can be expressed in different forms of poetry, a logical argument can be presented in different styles of proof. Writers may have a favorite poetry style, and students may have a favorite proof style.

Explorations and answers are provided in the *Chapter 2 Resource Book.*

1. Use the given flowchart proof to write a two-column proof.

Given: $RS = UV$, $ST = TU$
Prove: $\overline{RT} \cong \overline{TV}$

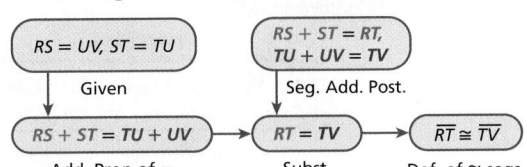

Flowchart proof:

1. $RS = UV$, $ST = TU$ (Given)
2. $RS + ST = TU + UV$
   (Add. Prop. of $=$)
3. $RS + ST = RT$, $TU + UV = TV$
   (Seg. Add. Post.)
4. $RT = TV$ (Subst.)
5. $\overline{RT} \cong \overline{TV}$ (Def. of $\cong$ segs.)

$RS = UV$, $ST = TU$	$RS + ST = RT$, $TU + UV = TV$
Given	Seg. Add. Post.

$RS + ST = TU + UV$ → $RT = TV$ → $\overline{RT} \cong \overline{TV}$

Add. Prop of $=$ Subst.   Def. of $\cong$ segs.

EXAMPLE 2 **Writing a Flowchart Proof**

Use the given two-column proof to write a flowchart proof of the Converse of the Common Segments Theorem.

Given: $\overline{AC} \cong \overline{BD}$
Prove: $\overline{AB} \cong \overline{CD}$

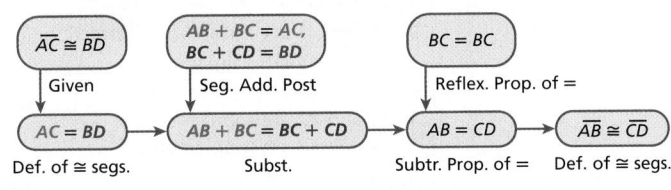

Two-column proof:

Statements	Reasons
1. $\overline{AC} \cong \overline{BD}$	1. Given
2. $AC = BD$	2. Def. of $\cong$ segs.
3. $AB + BC = AC$, $BC + CD = BD$	3. Seg. Add. Post.
4. $AB + BC = BC + CD$	4. Subst. *Steps 2, 3*
5. $BC = BC$	5. Reflex. Prop. of $=$
6. $AB = CD$	6. Subtr. Prop. of $=$
7. $\overline{AB} \cong \overline{CD}$	7. Def. of $\cong$ segs.

Helpful Hint

Like the converse of a conditional statement, the converse of a theorem is found by switching the hypothesis and conclusion.

Flowchart proof:

$\overline{AC} \cong \overline{BD}$	$AB + BC = AC$, $BC + CD = BD$	$BC = BC$
Given	Seg. Add. Post	Reflex. Prop. of $=$

$AC = BD$ → $AB + BC = BC + CD$ → $AB = CD$ → $\overline{AB} \cong \overline{CD}$

Def. of $\cong$ segs.   Subst.   Subtr. Prop. of $=$ Def. of $\cong$ segs.

2. Use the given two-column proof to write a flowchart proof.

Given: $\angle 2 \cong \angle 4$
Prove: $m\angle 1 = m\angle 3$

Two-column proof:

Statements	Reasons
1. $\angle 2 \cong \angle 4$	1. Given
2. $\angle 1$ and $\angle 2$ are supplementary. $\angle 3$ and $\angle 4$ are supplementary.	2. Lin. Pair Thm.
3. $\angle 1 \cong \angle 3$	3. $\cong$ Supps. Thm.
4. $m\angle 1 = m\angle 3$	4. Def. of $\cong$ $\angle$

$\angle 1$, $\angle 2$ are supp. $\angle 3$, $\angle 4$ are supp.	
Lin. Pair Thm.	

$\angle 2 \cong \angle 4$ → $\angle 1 \cong \angle 3$

Given $\cong$ Supps. Thm.

$m\angle 1 = m\angle 3$

Def. of $\cong$ $\angle$

2-7 Flowchart and Paragraph Proofs **119**

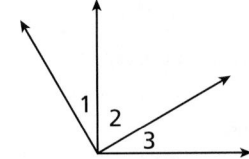

Additional Examples

Example 1

Use the given flowchart proof to write a two-column proof.

Given: $\angle 2$ and $\angle 3$ are comp.
$\angle 1 \cong \angle 3$
Prove: $\angle 2$ and $\angle 1$ are comp.

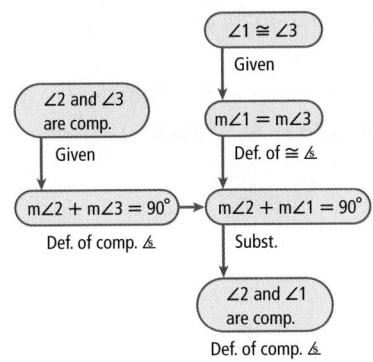

Flowchart proof:

$\angle 2$ and $\angle 3$ are comp.	$\angle 1 \cong \angle 3$
Given	Given

| $m\angle 2 + m\angle 3 = 90°$ | $m\angle 1 = m\angle 3$ |
| Def. of comp. $\angle$ | Def. of $\cong$ $\angle$ |

$m\angle 2 + m\angle 1 = 90°$

Subst.

$\angle 2$ and $\angle 1$ are comp.

Def. of comp. $\angle$

1. $\angle 2$ and $\angle 3$ are comp. $\angle 1 \cong \angle 3$ (Given)
2. $m\angle 2 + m\angle 3 = 90°$ (Def. of comp. $\angle$)
3. $m\angle 1 = m\angle 3$ (Def. of $\cong$ $\angle$)
4. $m\angle 2 + m\angle 1 = 90°$ (Subst.)
5. $\angle 2$ and $\angle 1$ are comp. (Def. of comp. $\angle$)

Example 2

See TE margin on p. 120.

Also available on transparency

INTERVENTION
Questioning Strategies

EXAMPLE 1

• When you change a proof from flowchart style to two-column style, how do you decide what order to list the steps in?

---

2 Teach

Guided Instruction

Remind students of the structure of a two-column proof. Explain that flowchart and paragraph proofs are two more styles of proofs. Point out that some boxes in a flowchart proof may have more than one arrow pointing to or away from them.

Teaching Tip **Multiple Representations**
Writing proofs in different styles lets students see different representations of the same logical argument. Some students may find it easier to follow the logic in a flowchart proof.

Reaching All Learners

Through Visual Cues

Emphasize the importance of focusing on the diagram and the Given statement before beginning to write a proof. For every proof, students should first copy the diagram from the textbook onto their paper. They should ask themselves what the diagram tells them. Then they should mark the diagram with any additional information from the Given statement, such as congruent segments, congruent angles, or right angles.

Lesson 2-7 **119**

Example 2

Use the given two-column proof to write a flowchart proof.

Given: B is the midpoint of $\overline{AC}$.
Prove: $2AB = AC$

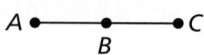

Two-Column proof:

1. B is the midpoint of $\overline{AC}$. (Given)
2. $\overline{AB} \cong \overline{BC}$ (Def. of mdpt.)
3. $AB = BC$ (Def. of $\cong$ segs.)
4. $AB + BC = AC$ (Seg. Add. Post.)
5. $AB + AB = AC$ (Subst.)
6. $2AB = AC$ (Simplify.)

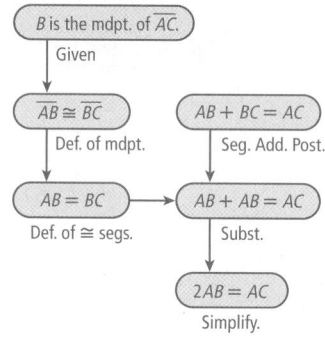

Example 3

Use the given paragraph proof to write a two-column proof.

Given: $m\angle 1 + m\angle 2 = m\angle 4$
Prove: $m\angle 3 + m\angle 1 + m\angle 2 = 180°$

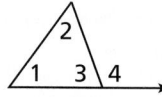

Paragraph proof: It is given that $m\angle 1 + m\angle 2 = m\angle 4$. $\angle 3$ and $\angle 4$ are supplementary by the Lin. Pair Thm. So $m\angle 3 + m\angle 4 = 180°$ by def. By Subst., $m\angle 3 + m\angle 1 + m\angle 2 = 180°$.

1. $m\angle 1 + m\angle 2 = m\angle 4$ (Given)
2. $\angle 3$ and $\angle 4$ are supp. (Lin. Pair Thm.)
3. $m\angle 3 + m\angle 4 = 180°$ (Def. of supp. $\angle$)
4. $m\angle 3 + m\angle 1 + m\angle 2 = 180°$ (Subst.)

Also available on transparency

A **paragraph proof** is a style of proof that presents the steps of the proof and their matching reasons as sentences in a paragraph. Although this style of proof is less formal than a two-column proof, you still must include every step.

Know it! Note • **Theorems**

THEOREM	HYPOTHESIS	CONCLUSION
2-7-2 **Vertical Angles Theorem** Vertical angles are congruent.	$\angle A$ and $\angle B$ are vertical angles.	$\angle A \cong \angle B$
2-7-3 If two congruent angles are supplementary, then each angle is a right angle. ($\cong \angle$ supp. $\rightarrow$ rt. $\angle$)	$\angle 1 \cong \angle 2$ $\angle 1$ and $\angle 2$ are supplementary.	$\angle 1$ and $\angle 2$ are right angles.

EXAMPLE 3 **Reading a Paragraph Proof**

Use the given paragraph proof to write a two-column proof of the Vertical Angles Theorem.

Given: $\angle 1$ and $\angle 3$ are vertical angles.
Prove: $\angle 1 \cong \angle 3$

Paragraph proof: $\angle 1$ and $\angle 3$ are vertical angles, so they are formed by intersecting lines. Therefore $\angle 1$ and $\angle 2$ are a linear pair, and $\angle 2$ and $\angle 3$ are a linear pair. By the Linear Pair Theorem, $\angle 1$ and $\angle 2$ are supplementary, and $\angle 2$ and $\angle 3$ are supplementary. So by the Congruent Supplements Theorem, $\angle 1 \cong \angle 3$.

Two-column proof:

Statements	Reasons
1. $\angle 1$ and $\angle 3$ are vertical angles.	1. Given
2. $\angle 1$ and $\angle 3$ are formed by intersecting lines.	2. Def. of vert. $\angle$
3. $\angle 1$ and $\angle 2$ are a linear pair. $\angle 2$ and $\angle 3$ are a linear pair.	3. Def. of lin. pair
4. $\angle 1$ and $\angle 2$ are supplementary. $\angle 2$ and $\angle 3$ are supplementary.	4. Lin. Pair Thm.
5. $\angle 1 \cong \angle 3$	5. $\cong$ Supps. Thm.

 **CHECK IT OUT!**

1. $\angle WXY$ is a rt. $\angle$. (Given)
2. $m\angle WXY = 90°$ (Def. of rt. $\angle$)
3. $m\angle 2 + m\angle 3 = m\angle WXY$ ($\angle$ Add. Post.)
4. $m\angle 2 + m\angle 3 = 90°$ (Subst.)
5. $\angle 1 \cong \angle 3$ (Given)
6. $m\angle 1 = m\angle 3$ (Def. of $\cong \angle$)
7. $m\angle 2 + m\angle 1 = 90°$ (Subst.)
8. $\angle 1$ and $\angle 2$ are comp. (Def. of comp. $\angle$)

3. Use the given paragraph proof to write a two-column proof.

Given: $\angle WXY$ is a right angle. $\angle 1 \cong \angle 3$
Prove: $\angle 1$ and $\angle 2$ are complementary.

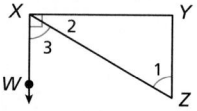

Paragraph proof: Since $\angle WXY$ is a right angle, $m\angle WXY = 90°$ by the definition of a right angle. By the Angle Addition Postulate, $m\angle WXY = m\angle 2 + m\angle 3$. By substitution, $m\angle 2 + m\angle 3 = 90°$. Since $\angle 1 \cong \angle 3$, $m\angle 1 = m\angle 3$ by the definition of congruent angles. Using substitution, $m\angle 2 + m\angle 1 = 90°$. Thus by the definition of complementary angles, $\angle 1$ and $\angle 2$ are complementary.

INTERVENTION ◄═►
Questioning Strategies

EXAMPLE 2

• Why might a flowchart proof you write look different from another person's flowchart proof of the same thing?

EXAMPLE 3

• In a paragraph proof, what distinguishes between the statements and the reasons?

EXAMPLE **4** **Writing a Paragraph Proof**

Use the given two-column proof to write a paragraph proof of Theorem 2-7-3.

Given: ∠1 and ∠2 are supplementary. ∠1 ≅ ∠2
Prove: ∠1 and ∠2 are right angles.

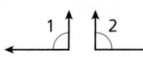

Two-column proof:

Statements	Reasons
1. ∠1 and ∠2 are supplementary. ∠1 ≅ ∠2	1. Given
2. m∠1 + m∠2 = 180°	2. Def. of supp. ∡
3. m∠1 = m∠2	3. Def. of ≅ ∡ *Step 1*
4. m∠1 + m∠1 = 180°	4. Subst. *Steps 2, 3*
5. 2m∠1 = 180°	5. Simplification
6. m∠1 = 90°	6. Div. Prop. of =
7. m∠2 = 90°	7. Trans. Prop. of = *Steps 3, 6*
8. ∠1 and ∠2 are right angles.	8. Def. of rt. ∠

Paragraph proof: ∠1 and ∠2 are supplementary, so m∠1 + m∠2 = 180° by the definition of supplementary angles. They are also congruent, so their measures are equal by the definition of congruent angles. By substitution, m∠1 + m∠1 = 180°, so m∠1 = 90° by the Division Property of Equality. Because m∠1 = m∠2, m∠2 = 90° by the Transitive Property of Equality. So both are right angles by the definition of a right angle.

 **4.** Use the given two-column proof to write a paragraph proof.

Given: ∠1 ≅ ∠4
Prove: ∠2 ≅ ∠3

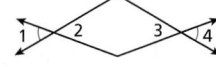

Two-column proof:

It is given that ∠1 ≅ ∠4.
By the Vert. ∡ Thm.,
∠1 ≅ ∠2 and ∠3 ≅ ∠4.
By the Trans. Prop. of ≅,
∠2 ≅ ∠4. Similarly, ∠2 ≅ ∠3.

Statements	Reasons
1. ∠1 ≅ ∠4	1. Given
2. ∠1 ≅ ∠2, ∠3 ≅ ∠4	2. Vert. ∡ Thm.
3. ∠2 ≅ ∠4	3. Trans. Prop. of ≅ *Steps 1, 2*
4. ∠2 ≅ ∠3	4. Trans. Prop. of ≅ *Steps 2, 3*

2-7 Flowchart and Paragraph Proofs **121**

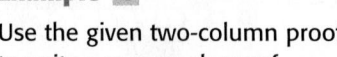

Power Presentations
with PowerPoint®

Additional Examples

Example **4**

Use the given two-column proof to write a paragraph proof.

Given: ∠1 and ∠2 are comp.
Prove: ∠3 and ∠4 are comp.

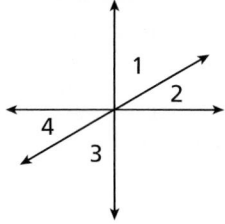

Two-Column proof:
1. ∠1 and ∠2 are comp. (Given)
2. m∠1 + m∠2 = 90° (Def. of comp. ∡)
3. ∠1 ≅ ∠3, ∠2 ≅ ∠4 (Vert. ∡ Thm.)
4. m∠1 = m∠3, m∠2 = m∠4 (Def. of ≅ ∡)
5. m∠3 + m∠4 = 90° (Subst.)
6. m∠3 and m∠4 are comp. (Def. of comp. ∡)

∠1 and ∠2 are comp., so m∠1 + m∠2 = 90° by the def. of comp. ∡. ∠1 ≅ ∠3 and ∠2 ≅ ∠4 by the Vert. ∡ Thm. So m∠1 = m∠3 and m∠2 = m∠4 by the def. of ≅ ∡. By Subst., m∠3 + m∠4 = 90°, so ∠3 and ∠4 are comp. by the def. of comp. ∡.

Also available on transparency

---

3 **Close**

Summarize

Review the three proof styles that have been introduced. Lead a brief discussion on how to write a proof in one format and how to rewrite it in a different format.

Also review the three theorems presented in the lesson:

• Common Segments Theorem
• Vertical Angles Theorem
• If two congruent angles are supplementary, then each is a right angle.

Answers to *Think and Discuss*

1. Possible answer: There may be more than one thm. that you can apply to a proof, and the steps in a proof may sometimes be written in a different order.

2. Answers will vary.

3. See p. A3.

THINK AND DISCUSS

1. Explain why there might be more than one correct way to write a proof.

2. Describe the steps you take when writing a proof.

3. **GET ORGANIZED**
Copy and complete the graphic organizer. In each box, describe the proof style in your own words.

```
                    Proof Styles
        ┌───────────────┼───────────────┐
   Two-column      Flowchart        Paragraph
```

2-7 **Exercises**

2-7 Exercises

go.hrw.com/Geo/TX
Homework Help Online
KEYWORD: MG7 2-7
Parent Resources Online
KEYWORD: MG7 Parent

Assignment Guide

Assign *Guided Practice* exercises as necessary.

If you finished Examples **1–2**
  Basic 7, 8, 12–16
  Average 7, 8, 11, 12–16 even
Advanced 7, 8, 11–16

If you finished Examples **1–4**
  Basic 7–18, 20–23, 28–36
  Average 7–10, 12–16 even, 17–23, 26–36
Advanced 7–10, 12–16 even, 18–36

Homework Quick Check
Quickly check key concepts.
Exercises: 7–10, 12, 16

TAKS Practice

Grades 9–11	Exercises
Obj. 4	14–16, 27–30
Obj. 10	11–13

GUIDED PRACTICE

Vocabulary Apply the vocabulary from this lesson to answer each question.

1. In a ___?___ proof, the logical order is represented by arrows that connect each step. (*flowchart* or *paragraph*) **flowchart**

2. The steps and reasons of a ___?___ proof are written out in sentences. (*flowchart* or *paragraph*) **paragraph**

SEE EXAMPLE 1
p. 118

3. Use the given flowchart proof to write a two-column proof.

Given: ∠1 ≅ ∠2
Prove: ∠1 and ∠2 are right angles.

Flowchart proof:

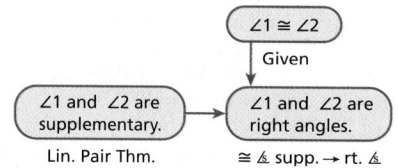

1. ∠1 ≅ ∠2 (Given)
2. ∠1 and ∠2 are supp. (Lin. Pair Thm.)
3. ∠1 and ∠2 are rt. ∡. (≅ ∡ supp. → rt. ∡)

SEE EXAMPLE 2
p. 119

4. Use the given two-column proof to write a flowchart proof.

Given: ∠2 and ∠4 are supplementary.
Prove: m∠2 = m∠3

Two-column proof:

Statements	Reasons
1. ∠2 and ∠4 are supplementary.	1. Given
2. ∠3 and ∠4 are supplementary.	2. Lin. Pair Thm.
3. ∠2 ≅ ∠3	3. ≅ Supps. Thm. *Steps 1, 2*
4. m∠2 = m∠3	4. Def. of ≅ ∡

122 *Chapter 2 Geometric Reasoning*

Answers

4.

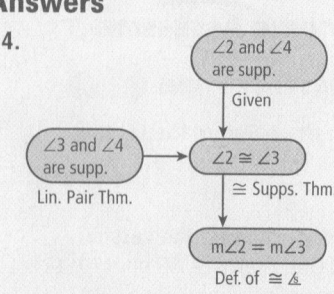

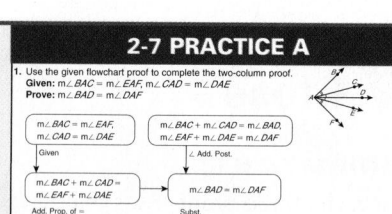

5. Use the given paragraph proof to write a two-column proof.

Given: $\angle 2 \cong \angle 4$
Prove: $\angle 1 \cong \angle 3$

1. $\angle 2 \cong \angle 4$ (Given)
2. $\angle 1 \cong \angle 2$, $\angle 3 \cong \angle 4$ (Vert. $\angle$s Thm.)
3. $\angle 1 \cong \angle 4$ (Trans. Prop. of $\cong$)
4. $\angle 1 \cong \angle 3$ (Trans. Prop. of $\cong$)

Paragraph proof:
By the Vertical Angles Theorem, $\angle 1 \cong \angle 2$, and $\angle 3 \cong \angle 4$. It is given that $\angle 2 \cong \angle 4$. By the Transitive Property of Congruence, $\angle 1 \cong \angle 4$, and thus $\angle 1 \cong \angle 3$.

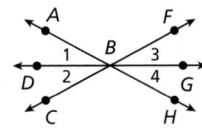

6. Use the given two-column proof to write a paragraph proof.

Given: $\overrightarrow{BD}$ bisects $\angle ABC$.
Prove: $\overrightarrow{BG}$ bisects $\angle FBH$.

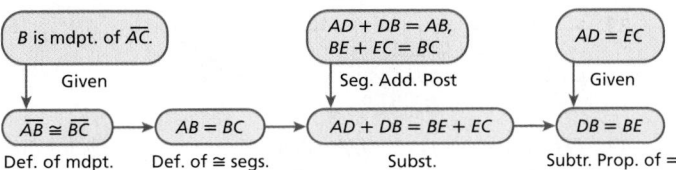

Two-column proof:

Statements	Reasons
1. $\overrightarrow{BD}$ bisects $\angle ABC$.	1. Given
2. $\angle 1 \cong \angle 2$	2. Def. of $\angle$ bisector
3. $\angle 1 \cong \angle 4$, $\angle 2 \cong \angle 3$	3. Vert. $\angle$s Thm.
4. $\angle 4 \cong \angle 2$	4. Trans. Prop. of $\cong$ *Steps 2, 3*
5. $\angle 4 \cong \angle 3$	5. Trans. Prop. of $\cong$ *Steps 3, 4*
6. $\overrightarrow{BG}$ bisects $\angle FBH$.	6. Def. of $\angle$ bisector

PRACTICE AND PROBLEM SOLVING

Independent Practice

For Exercises	See Example
7	1
8	2
9	3
10	4

TEKS • **TAKS**

Skills Practice p. S7
Application Practice p. S29

7. Use the given flowchart proof to write a two-column proof.

Given: B is the midpoint of $\overline{AC}$.
$AD = EC$
Prove: $DB = BE$

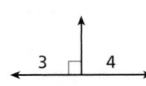

Flowchart proof:

```
B is mdpt. of AC.        AD + DB = AB,        AD = EC
                         BE + EC = BC
     Given                 Seg. Add. Post        Given

AB ≅ BC  →  AB = BC  →  AD + DB = BE + EC  →  DB = BE
Def. of mdpt.  Def. of ≅ segs.    Subst.      Subtr. Prop. of =
```

8. Use the given two-column proof to write a flowchart proof.

Given: $\angle 3$ is a right angle.
Prove: $\angle 4$ is a right angle.

Two-column proof:

Statements	Reasons
1. $\angle 3$ is a right angle.	1. Given
2. $m\angle 3 = 90°$	2. Def. of rt. $\angle$
3. $\angle 3$ and $\angle 4$ are supplementary.	3. Lin. Pair Thm.
4. $m\angle 3 + m\angle 4 = 180°$	4. Def. of supp. $\angle$s
5. $90° + m\angle 4 = 180°$	5. Subst. *Steps 2, 4*
6. $m\angle 4 = 90°$	6. Subtr. Prop. of =
7. $\angle 4$ is a right angle.	7. Def. of rt. $\angle$

Reading Math Some students may have difficulty following the logic in a paragraph proof since the steps are not always clearly separated. In **Exercise 5,** have students rewrite the paragraph proof on their own paper and then underline each statement in a different color of pencil. Have them circle the corresponding reason in the same color. This is very helpful with long paragraph proofs, such as in **Exercise 9.**

Answers

6. It is given that $\overrightarrow{BD}$ bisects $\angle ABC$, so $\angle 1 \cong \angle 2$ by the def. of $\angle$ bisector. By the Vert. $\angle$s Thm., $\angle 1 \cong \angle 4$ and $\angle 2 \cong \angle 3$. By the Trans. Prop. of $\cong$, $\angle 4 \cong \angle 2$, and thus $\angle 4 \cong \angle 3$. Therefore $\overrightarrow{BG}$ bisects $\angle FBH$ by the def. of $\angle$ bisector.

7. 1. B is the mdpt. of $\overline{AC}$. (Given)
   2. $\overline{AB} \cong \overline{BC}$ (Def. of mdpt.)
   3. $AB = BC$ (Def. of $\cong$ segs.)
   4. $AD + DB = AB$, $BE + EC = BC$ (Seg. Add. Post.)
   5. $AD + DB = BE + EC$ (Subst.)
   6. $AD = EC$ (Given)
   7. $DB = BE$ (Subtr. Prop. of =)

8.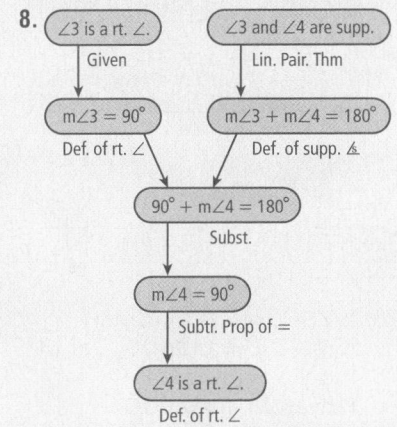

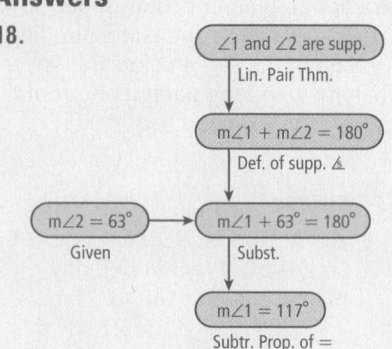

MULTI-STEP TAKS PREP **Exercise 18** involves arranging the pieces of a logical argument into a flowchart proof. This exercise prepares students for the Multi-Step TAKS Prep on page 126.

Answers

18.

```
      ∠1 and ∠2 are supp.
            |
        Lin. Pair Thm.
            |
      m∠1 + m∠2 = 180°
            |
        Def. of supp. ∡
            |
  m∠2 = 63°   m∠1 + 63° = 180°
   Given          Subst.
            |
        m∠1 = 117°
      Subtr. Prop. of =
```

19. Possible answer: Both ∡ adj. to the given rt. ∠ must be rt. ∡ because they form lin. pairs with the given ∠. The fourth ∠ is a vert. ∠ of the given ∠, so it, too, is a rt. ∠. Since all 4 ∠s are rt. ∡, they are all ≅ by the Rt. ∠ ≅ Thm.

24.

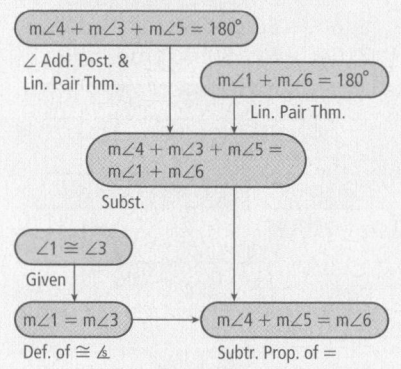

```
  m∠4 + m∠3 + m∠5 = 180°
            |
  ∠ Add. Post. &      m∠1 + m∠6 = 180°
  Lin. Pair Thm.            |
                       Lin. Pair Thm.
            |
      m∠4 + m∠3 + m∠5 =
          m∠1 + m∠6
            |
          Subst.
            |
      ∠1 ≅ ∠3
      Given
            |
  m∠1 = m∠3      m∠4 + m∠5 = m∠6
  Def. of ≅ ∡       Subtr. Prop. of =
```

25. 1. ∠AOC ≅ ∠BOD (Given)
2. m∠AOC = m∠BOD (Def. of ≅ ∡)
3. m∠AOB + m∠BOC = m∠AOC, m∠BOC + m∠COD = m∠BOD (∠ Add. Post.)
4. m∠AOB + m∠BOC = m∠BOC + m∠COD (Subst.)
5. m∠BOC = m∠BOC (Reflex. Prop. of =)
6. m∠AOB = m∠COD (Subtr. Prop. of =)
7. ∠AOB ≅ ∠COD (Def. of ≅ ∡)

26. It is given that ∠2 and ∠5 are rt. ∡. So by the Rt. ∠ ≅ Thm., ∠2 ≅ ∠5. By the def. of ≅ ∡, m∠2 = m∠5. It is also given that m∠1 + m∠2 + m∠3 = m∠4 + m∠5 + m∠6. By the Subtr. Prop. of =, m∠1 + m∠3 = m∠4 + m∠6. ∠3 ≅ ∠6 by the Vert. ∡ Thm., so m∠3 = m∠6 by the def. of ≅ ∡. By the Subtr. Prop. of =, m∠1 = m∠4. So by the def. of ≅ ∡, ∠1 ≅ ∠4.

---

1. ∠1 ≅ ∠4 (Given)
2. ∠1 ≅ ∠2 (Vert. ∡ Thm.)
3. ∠4 ≅ ∠2 (Trans. Prop. of ≅)
4. m∠4 = m∠2 (Def. of ≅ ∡)
5. ∠3 and ∠4 are supp. (Lin. Pair Thm.)
6. m∠3 + m∠4 = 180° (Def. of supp. ∡)
7. m∠3 + m∠2 = 180° (Subst.)
8. ∠2 and ∠3 are supp. (Def. of supp. ∡)

17. A; the diagram is marked with the Prove information instead of the Given information.

---

9. Use the given paragraph proof to write a two-column proof.

Given: ∠1 ≅ ∠4
Prove: ∠2 and ∠3 are supplementary.

Paragraph proof:

∠4 and ∠3 form a linear pair, so they are supplementary by the Linear Pair Theorem. Therefore, m∠4 + m∠3 = 180°. Also, ∠1 and ∠2 are vertical angles, so ∠1 ≅ ∠2 by the Vertical Angles Theorem. It is given that ∠1 ≅ ∠4. So by the Transitive Property of Congruence, ∠4 ≅ ∠2, and by the definition of congruent angles, m∠4 = m∠2. By substitution, m∠2 + m∠3 = 180°, so ∠2 and ∠3 are supplementary by the definition of supplementary angles.

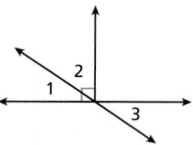

10. Use the given two-column proof to write a paragraph proof.

Given: ∠1 and ∠2 are complementary.
Prove: ∠2 and ∠3 are complementary.

Two-column proof:

Statements	Reasons
1. ∠1 and ∠2 are complementary.	1. Given
2. m∠1 + m∠2 = 90°	2. Def. of comp. ∡
3. ∠1 ≅ ∠3	3. Vert. ∡ Thm.
4. m∠1 = m∠3	4. Def. of ≅ ∡
5. m∠3 + m∠2 = 90°	5. Subst. *Steps 2, 4*
6. ∠2 and ∠3 are complementary.	6. Def. of comp. ∡

Since ∠1 and ∠2 are comp., m∠1 + m∠2 = 90°. ∠1 ≅ ∠3 by the Vert. ∡ Thm. Thus m∠1 = m∠3. By subst., m∠2 + m∠3 = 90°, so ∠2 and ∠3 are comp.

Find each measure and name the theorem that justifies your answer.

11. *AB*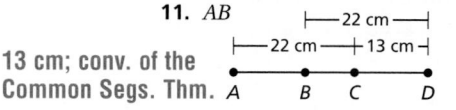

13 cm; conv. of the Common Segs. Thm.

12. m∠2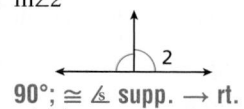

90°; ≅ ∡ supp. → rt. ∡

13. m∠3

37°, Vert. ∡ Thm.

Algebra Find the value of each variable.

14.  2

15. 11

16. 8

17. ///ERROR ANALYSIS/// Below are two drawings for the given proof. Which is incorrect? Explain the error.

Given: $\overline{AB} \cong \overline{BC}$
Prove: ∠A ≅ ∠C

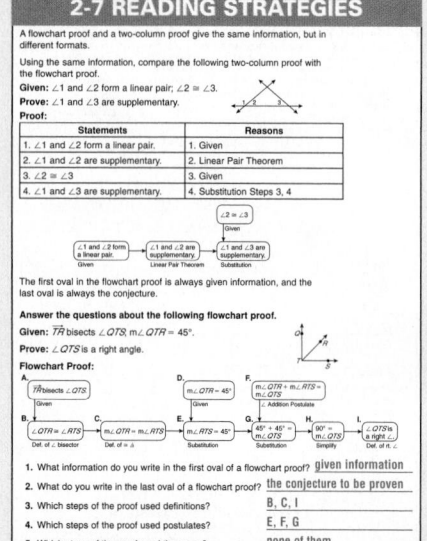
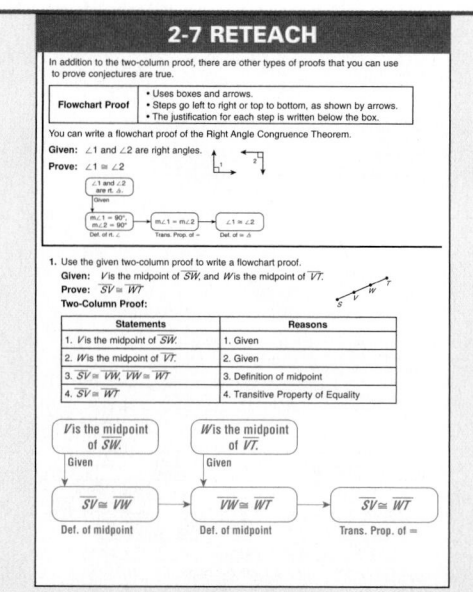

MULTI-STEP TAKS PREP

18. This problem will prepare you for the Multi-Step TAKS Prep on page 126.

Rearrange the pieces to create a flowchart proof.

m∠1 + m∠2 = 180°	m∠1 = 117°	∠1 and ∠2 are supplementary.	m∠2 = 63°	m∠1 + 63° = 180°
Def. of supp. ∡	Subtr. Prop. of =	Lin. Pair Thm.	Given	Subst.

124 Chapter 2 Geometric Reasoning

2-7 READING STRATEGIES

A flowchart proof and a two-column proof give the same information, but in different formats.

Using the same information, compare the following two-column proof with the flowchart proof.

Given: ∠1 and ∠2 form a linear pair; ∠2 ≅ ∠3.
Prove: ∠1 and ∠3 are supplementary.
Proof:

Statements	Reasons
1. ∠1 and ∠2 form a linear pair.	1. Given
2. ∠1 and ∠2 are supplementary.	2. Linear Pair Theorem
3. ∠2 ≅ ∠3	3. Given
4. ∠1 and ∠3 are supplementary.	4. Substitution Steps 3, 4

The first oval in the flowchart proof is always given information, and the last oval is always the conjecture.

Answer the questions about the following flowchart proof.

Given: $\overrightarrow{TR}$ bisects ∠QTS; m∠QTR = 45°.
Prove: ∠QTS is a right angle.
Flowchart Proof:

1. What information do you write in the first oval of a flowchart proof? given information
2. What do you write in the last oval of a flowchart proof? the conjecture to be proven
3. Which steps of the proof used definitions? B, C, I
4. Which steps of the proof used postulates? E, F, G
5. Which steps of the proof used theorems? none of them

2-7 RETEACH

In addition to the two-column proof, there are other types of proofs that you can use to prove conjectures are true.

Flowchart Proof	• Uses boxes and arrows. • Steps go left to right or top to bottom, as shown by arrows. • The justification for each step is written below the box.

You can write a flowchart proof of the Right Angle Congruence Theorem.

Given: ∠1 and ∠2 are right angles.
Prove: ∠1 ≅ ∠2

1. Use the given two-column proof to write a flowchart proof.
Given: *V* is the midpoint of $\overline{SW}$, and *W* is the midpoint of $\overline{VT}$.
Prove: $\overline{SV} \cong \overline{WT}$
Two-Column Proof:

Statements	Reasons
1. *V* is the midpoint of $\overline{SW}$.	1. Given
2. *W* is the midpoint of $\overline{VT}$.	2. Given
3. $\overline{SV} \cong \overline{VW}$, $\overline{VW} \cong \overline{WT}$	3. Definition of midpoint
4. $\overline{SV} \cong \overline{WT}$	4. Transitive Property of Equality

---

124 Chapter 2

19. Critical Thinking Two lines intersect, and one of the angles formed is a right angle. Explain why all four angles are congruent.

20. Write About It Which style of proof do you find easiest to write? to read?
Answers will vary.

TEST PREP

21. Which pair of angles in the diagram must be congruent?

Ⓐ ∠1 and ∠5   Ⓒ ∠5 and ∠8
Ⓑ ∠3 and ∠4   Ⓓ None of the above

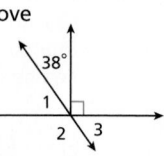

22. What is the measure of ∠2?

Ⓕ 38°   Ⓗ 128°
Ⓖ 52°   Ⓙ 142°

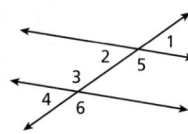

23. Which statement is NOT true if ∠2 and ∠6 are supplementary?

Ⓐ m∠2 + m∠6 = 180°
Ⓑ ∠2 and ∠3 are supplementary.
Ⓒ ∠1 and ∠6 are supplementary.
Ⓓ m∠1 + m∠4 = 180°

CHALLENGE AND EXTEND

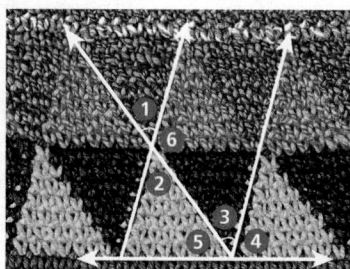

24. Textiles Use the woven pattern to write a flowchart proof.

Given: ∠1 ≅ ∠3
Prove: m∠4 + m∠5 = m∠6

35. Converse: If a positive integer is a composite number, then it has more than 2 factors.
Biconditional: A positive integer has more than 2 factors if and only if it is a composite number.

25. Write a two-column proof.
Given: ∠AOC ≅ ∠BOD
Prove: ∠AOB ≅ ∠COD

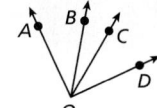

26. Write a paragraph proof.
Given: ∠2 and ∠5 are right angles.
m∠1 + m∠2 + m∠3 = m∠4 + m∠5 + m∠6
Prove: ∠1 ≅ ∠4

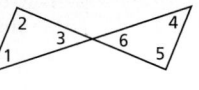

27. Multi-Step Find the value of each variable and the measures of all four angles.
$x = 31$ and $y = 11.5$; 86°, 94°, 86°, and 94°

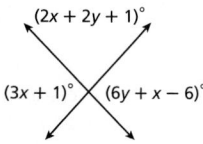

SPIRAL REVIEW

36. Converse: If a quad. has exactly 1 pair of ∥ sides, then it is a trap.
Biconditional: A quad. is a trap. if and only if it has exactly 1 pair of ∥ sides.

Solve each system of equations. Check your solution. *(Previous course)*

28. $\begin{cases} y = 2x + 14 \\ y = -6x + 18 \end{cases}$ $\left(\dfrac{1}{2}, 15\right)$

29. $\begin{cases} 7x - y = -33 \\ 3x + y = -7 \end{cases}$ $(-4, 5)$

30. $\begin{cases} 2x + y = 8 \\ -x + 3y = 10 \end{cases}$ $(2, 4)$

Use a protractor to draw an angle with each of the following measures. *(Lesson 1-3)*

31. 125°   **32.** 38°   **33.** 94°   **34.** 175°
31–34. Check students' drawings.

For each conditional, write the converse and a biconditional statement. *(Lesson 2-4)*

35. If a positive integer has more than two factors, then it is a composite number.

36. If a quadrilateral is a trapezoid, then it has exactly one pair of parallel sides.

2-7 Flowchart and Paragraph Proofs **125**

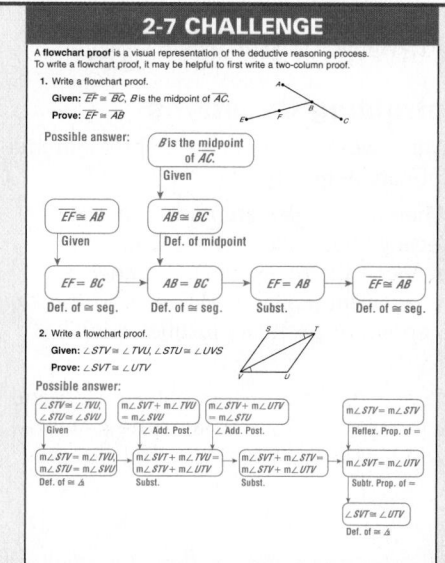

2-7 PROBLEM SOLVING

The diagram shows the second-floor glass railing at a mall.

1. Use the given two-column proof to write a flowchart proof.
   Given: ∠2 and ∠3 are supplementary.
   Prove: ∠1 and ∠3 are supplementary.
   Two-Column Proof:

Statements	Reasons
1. ∠2 and ∠3 are supplementary.	1. Given
2. m∠2 + m∠3 = 180°	2. Def. of supp. ∡
3. ∠2 ≅ ∠1	3. Vert. ∡ Thm.
4. m∠2 = m∠1	4. Def. of ≅ ∡
5. m∠1 + m∠3 = 180°	5. Subst.
6. ∠1 and ∠3 are supplementary.	6. Def. of supp. ∡

Choose the best answer.

2. Which would NOT be included in a paragraph proof of the two-column proof above?
   Ⓐ Since ∠2 and ∠3 are supplementary, m∠2 = m∠3.
   B ∠2 ≅ ∠1 by the Vertical Angles Theorem.
   C Using substitution, m∠1 + m∠3 = 180°.
   D m∠2 = m∠1 by the definition of congruent angles.

2-7 CHALLENGE

A flowchart proof is a visual representation of the deductive reasoning process. To write a flowchart proof, it may be helpful to first write a two-column proof.

1. Write a flowchart proof.
   Given: $\overline{EF} \cong \overline{BC}$, B is the midpoint of $\overline{AC}$.
   Prove: $\overline{EF} \cong \overline{AB}$

Possible answer:

2. Write a flowchart proof.
   Given: ∠STV ≅ ∠TVU, ∠STU ≅ ∠UVS
   Prove: ∠SVT ≅ ∠UTV

Possible answer:

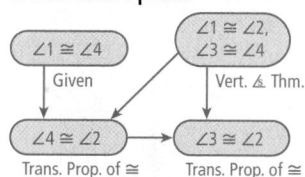

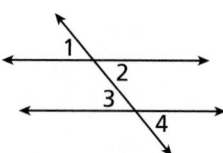

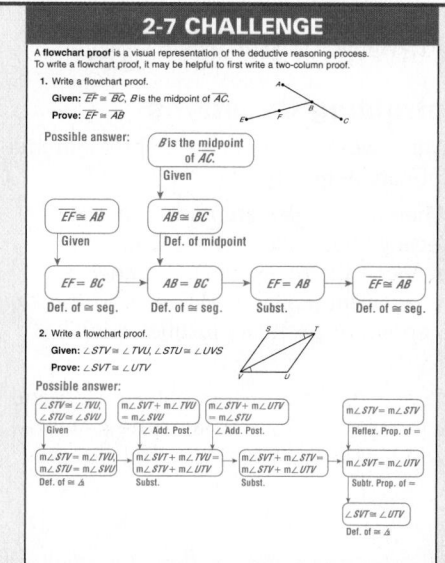

Lesson 2-7 **125**

MULTI-STEP TAKS PREP

MULTI-STEP TAKS PREP

Organizer

Objective: Assess students' ability to apply concepts and skills in Lessons 2-5 through 2-7 in a real-world format.

 Online Edition

Resources

 **Geometry Assessments**
www.mathtekstoolkit.org

Problem	Text Reference
1	Skills Bank page S59
2	Skills Bank page S60, Lesson 2-5
3	Lesson 2-6
4	Lesson 2-7

Answers

3–4. See p. A12.

Mathematical Proof

Intersection Inspection According to the U.S. Department of Transportation, it is ideal for two intersecting streets to form four 90° angles. If this is not possible, roadways should meet at an angle of 75° or greater for maximum safety and visibility.

1. Write a compound inequality to represent the range of measures an angle in an intersection should have. $75° \le x \le 90°$

2. Suppose that an angle in an intersection meets the guidelines specified by the U.S. Department of Transportation. Find the range of measures for the adjacent angle in the intersection. $90° \le y \le 105°$

The intersection of West Elm Street and Lamar Boulevard has a history of car accidents. The Southland neighborhood association is circulating a petition to have the city reconstruct the intersection. A surveyor measured the intersection, and one of the angles measures 145°.

3. Given that m∠2 = 145°, write a two-column proof to show that m∠1 and m∠3 are less than 75°.

4. Write a paragraph proof to justify the argument that the intersection of West Elm Street and Lamar Boulevard should be reconstructed.

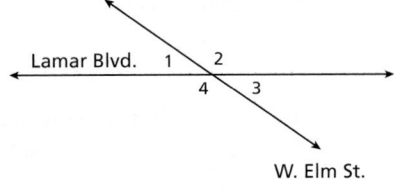

INTERVENTION

Scaffolding Questions

1. Which word or words in the problem indicate an inequality? greater

2. When four angles are formed by intersecting lines, what is the relationship between the measures of an angle and an adjacent angle? They are supp. Which theorem or postulate justifies this? Lin. Pair Thm.

3. What is the relationship between ∠2 and ∠1? They are supp. What is the relationship between ∠1 and ∠3? They are ≅.

4. If m∠1 and m∠3 are each less than 75°, why can you conclude that the intersection should be reconstructed? because the DOT guidelines specify that these angles should each measure at least 75°

Extension

At another intersection, two roads form a 106° angle. Should this intersection be reconstructed? Explain. Yes, because the adjacent angle measures 73°, which does not meet the DOT guidelines.

Quiz for Lessons 2-5 Through 2-7

2-5 **Algebraic Proof**

Solve each equation. Write a justification for each step.

1. $m - 8 = 13$ **2.** $4y - 1 = 27$ **3.** $-\dfrac{x}{3} = 2$

$m - 8 = 13$ (Given); $m = 21$ (Add. Prop. of =)

2. $4y - 1 = 27$ (Given); $4y = 28$ (Add. Prop. of =); $y = 7$ (Div. Prop. of =)

3. $-\dfrac{x}{3} = 2$ (Given); $-x = 6$ (Mult. Prop. of =); $x = -6$ (Div. Prop. of =)

Identify the property that justifies each statement. **4.** Sym. Prop. of =

4. $m\angle XYZ = m\angle PQR$, so $m\angle PQR = m\angle XYZ$.

5. $\overline{AB} \cong \overline{AB}$ Reflex. Prop. of $\cong$

6. $\angle 4 \cong \angle A$, and $\angle A \cong \angle 1$. So $\angle 4 \cong \angle 1$. Trans. Prop. of $\cong$

7. $k = 7$, and $m = 7$. So $k = m$. Trans. Prop. of =

2-6 **Geometric Proof**

8. Fill in the blanks to complete the two-column proof.

Given: $m\angle 1 + m\angle 3 = 180°$
Prove: $\angle 1 \cong \angle 4$
Proof:

Statements	Reasons
1. $m\angle 1 + m\angle 3 = 180°$	1. a. ___?___
2. b. ___?___	2. Def. of supp. $\angle$
3. $\angle 3$ and $\angle 4$ are supplementary.	3. Lin. Pair Thm.
4. $\angle 3 \cong \angle 3$	4. c. ___?___
5. d. ___?___	5. $\cong$ Supps. Thm.

a. Given
b. $\angle 1$ and $\angle 3$ are supp.
c. Reflex. Prop. of $\cong$
d. $\angle 1 \cong \angle 4$

9. Use the given plan to write a two-column proof of the Symmetric Property of Congruence.

Given: $\overline{AB} \cong \overline{EF}$
Prove: $\overline{EF} \cong \overline{AB}$

Plan: Use the definition of congruent segments to write $\overline{AB} \cong \overline{EF}$ as a statement of equality. Then use the Symmetric Property of Equality to show that $EF = AB$. So $\overline{EF} \cong \overline{AB}$ by the definition of congruent segments.

2-7 **Flowchart and Paragraph Proofs**

Use the given two-column proof to write the following.

Given: $\angle 1 \cong \angle 3$
Prove: $\angle 2 \cong \angle 4$
Proof:

Statements	Reasons
1. $\angle 1 \cong \angle 3$	1. Given
2. $\angle 1 \cong \angle 2$, $\angle 3 \cong \angle 4$	2. Vert. $\angle$ Thm.
3. $\angle 2 \cong \angle 3$	3. Trans. Prop. of $\cong$
4. $\angle 2 \cong \angle 4$	4. Trans. Prop. of $\cong$

11. It is given that $\angle 1 \cong \angle 3$. By the Vert. $\angle$ Thm., $\angle 1 \cong \angle 2$ and $\angle 3 \cong \angle 4$. By the Trans. Prop. of $\cong$, $\angle 2 \cong \angle 3$. Thus, $\angle 2 \cong \angle 4$.

10. a flowchart proof

11. a paragraph proof

Organizer

Objective: Assess students' mastery of concepts and skills in Lessons 2-5 through 2-7.

Resources

Assessment Resources
    Section 2B Quiz

Test & Practice Generator
One-Stop Planner®

INTERVENTION ⬅▶

Resources

Ready to Go On? Intervention and Enrichment Worksheets

Ready to Go On? CD-ROM

Ready to Go On? Online

my.hrw.com

Answers

9–10. See p. A12.

READY TO GO ON?

Diagnose and Prescribe

NO INTERVENE

YES ENRICH

READY TO GO ON? Intervention, Section 2B			
Ready to Go On? Intervention	*Worksheets*	*CD-ROM*	*Online*
✓ Lesson 2-5	2-5 Intervention	Activity 2-5	Diagnose and Prescribe Online
✓ Lesson 2-6	2-6 Intervention	Activity 2-6	
✓ Lesson 2-7	2-7 Intervention	Activity 2-7	

READY TO GO ON? Enrichment, Section 2B
    Worksheets
    CD-ROM
    Online

Objectives: Analyze the truth value of conjunctions and disjunctions.

Construct truth tables to determine the truth value of logical statements.

Online Edition

Using the Extension

In Lessons 2-3 and 2-4, students used deductive reasoning to determine the truth value of written statements. In this extension, students learn to write truth tables to evaluate symbolic statements in an organized way. This is a brief introduction to symbolic logic, which is studied in depth in higher-level mathematics and philosophy courses.

EXTENSION
Introduction to Symbolic Logic

TEKS G.4.A Select an appropriate representation ... in order to solve problems.
Also G.3.C

Symbolic logic is used by computer programmers, mathematicians, and philosophers to analyze the truth value of statements, independent of their actual meaning.

A **compound statement** is created by combining two or more statements. Suppose p and q each represent a statement. Two compound statements can be formed by combining p and q: a *conjunction* and a *disjunction*.

Objectives
Analyze the truth value of conjunctions and disjunctions.

Construct truth tables to determine the truth value of logical statements.

Vocabulary
compound statement
conjunction
disjunction
truth table

Know it!
.Note

Compound Statements

TERM	WORDS	SYMBOLS	EXAMPLE
Conjunction	A compound statement that uses the word *and*	p AND q $p \land q$	Pat is a band member AND Pat plays tennis.
Disjunction	A compound statement that uses the word *or*	p OR q $p \lor q$	Pat is a band member OR Pat plays tennis.

A conjunction is true only when all of its parts are true. A disjunction is true if any one of its parts is true.

EXAMPLE 1 **Analyzing Truth Values of Conjunctions and Disjunctions**

Use p, q, and r to find the truth value of each compound statement.
p: Washington, D.C., is the capital of the United States.
q: The day after Monday is Tuesday.
r: California is the largest state in the United States.

A $q \lor r$
Since q is true,
the disjunction is true.

B $r \land p$
Since r is false,
the conjunction is false.

CHECK IT OUT! Use the information given above to find the truth value of each compound statement.
1a. $r \lor p$ T
1b. $p \land q$ T

A table that lists all possible combinations of truth values for a statement is called a **truth table**. A truth table shows you the truth value of a compound statement, based on the possible truth values of its parts.

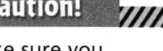
Caution!
Make sure you include all possible combinations of truth values for each piece of the compound statement.

p	q	$p \rightarrow q$	$p \land q$	$p \lor q$
T	T	T	T	T
T	F	F	F	T
F	T	T	F	T
F	F	T	F	F

Geometry TEKS

G.3 Geometric structure*
(C) using logical reasoning to prove statements are true ...

G.4 Geometric structure*
(A) select an appropriate representation (concrete, pictorial, graphical, verbal, or symbolic) in order to solve problems
***Knowledge and Skills** See p. 72.

---

1 Introduce

Motivate

In Lesson 2-3, students learned how to determine whether a logical argument is valid based on the Law of Detachment or the Law of Syllogism. By representing statements with symbols, you can evaluate the validity of an argument without being distracted by the words themselves. A truth table provides a systematic way to consider the different combinations of true and false statements that make up a logical argument.

---

2 Teach

Guided Instruction

Review how symbols were used to represent statements in Lessons 2-2, 2-3, and 2-4. Remind students that a conditional statement is false *only* when the hypothesis is true and the conclusion is false.

Teaching Tip **Visual** Have students write basic truth tables for $p \rightarrow q$, $p \lor q$, $p \land q$, and ~ p on index cards as a reference for more complicated truth tables.

EXAMPLE 2 **Constructing Truth Tables for Compound Statements**

Construct a truth table for the compound statement $\sim u \wedge (v \vee w)$.

Since u, v, and w can each be either true or false, the truth table will have $(2)(2)(2) = 8$ rows.

u	v	w	$\sim u$	$v \vee w$	$\sim u \wedge (v \vee w)$
T	T	T	F	T	F
T	T	F	F	T	F
T	F	T	F	T	F
T	F	F	F	F	F
F	T	T	T	T	T
F	T	F	T	T	T
F	F	T	T	T	T
F	F	F	T	F	F

Remember!

The negation ($\sim$) of a statement has the opposite truth value.

 **CHECK IT OUT!**

2. Construct a truth table for the compound statement $\sim u \wedge \sim v$.

u	v	$\sim u$	$\sim v$	$\sim u \wedge \sim v$
T	T	F	F	F
T	F	F	T	F
F	T	T	F	F
F	F	T	T	T

EXTENSION

 **Exercises**

Use p, q, and r to find the truth value of each compound statement.
p: The day after Friday is Sunday.
q: $\frac{1}{2} = 0.5$
r: If $-4x - 2 = 10$, then $x = 3$.

1. $r \wedge q$ F
2. $r \vee p$ F
3. $p \vee r$ F
4. $q \wedge \sim q$ F
5. $\sim q \vee q$ T
6. $q \vee r$ T

Construct a truth table for each compound statement.

7. $s \wedge \sim t$
8. $\sim u \vee t$
9. $\sim u \vee (s \wedge t)$

Use a truth table to show that the two statements are logically equivalent.

10. $p \to q$; $\sim q \to \sim p$
11. $q \to p$; $\sim p \to \sim q$

12. A biconditional statement can be written as $(p \to q) \wedge (q \to p)$. Construct a truth table for this compound statement.

13. DeMorgan's Laws state that $\sim(p \wedge q) = \sim p \vee \sim q$ and that $\sim(p \vee q) = \sim p \wedge \sim q$.
    a. Use truth tables to show that both statements are true.
    b. If you think of disjunction and conjunction as inverse operations, DeMorgan's Laws are similar to which algebraic property? **Distrib. Prop.**

14. The Law of Disjunctive Inference states that if $p \vee q$ is true and p is false, then q must be true.
    a. Construct a truth table for $p \vee q$.
    b. Use the truth table to explain why the Law of Disjunctive Inference is true.

Chapter 2 Extension **129**

3 Close

Summarize

Remind students that the variables in a truth table represent a statement that can be either true or false. Have students complete the truth table below.

p	q	$\sim p$	$\sim p \wedge q$
T	T	F	F
T	F	F	F
F	T	T	T
F	F	T	F

Answers

7–13a. See p. A12.

14a.

p	q	$p \vee q$
T	T	T
T	F	T
F	T	T
F	F	F

b. $p \vee q$ is true in the first, second, and third lines. p is false in the third and fourth lines. So the third line contains the premises of the Law of Disjunctive Inference, and in this case, q is true.

COMMON ERROR ALERT

Some students assume that a conjunction is true only if one, but not both, statements are true. Explain the difference between the *inclusive* OR used in mathematics, which means "one or the other or both," and the *exclusive* OR used in English, which means "one or the other, but *not* both."

ENGLISH LANGUAGE LEARNERS

Power Presentations with PowerPoint®

 **Additional Examples**

Example 1

Use p, q, and r to find the truth value of each compound statement.
p: The month after April is May.
q: The next prime number after 13 is 17.
r: Half of 19 is 9.

A. $p \vee q$ T
B. $q \wedge r$ F

Example 2

Construct a truth table for the compound statement $\sim p \vee \sim q$.

p	q	$\sim p$	$\sim q$	$\sim p \vee \sim q$
T	T	F	F	F
T	F	F	T	T
F	T	T	F	T
F	F	T	T	T

Also available on transparency

INTERVENTION
Questioning Strategies

EXAMPLE 1

• How can you remember which symbol means "and" and which symbol means "or"?

EXAMPLE 2

• When you construct a truth table, how do you decide what to put at the top of each column?
• If you constructed a truth table for a valid form of argument, such as the Law of Detachment or the Law of Syllogism, what would you expect to find in the last column?

Answers

27. yes

28. no; possible answer: $x = 2$

29. no; possible answer: a seg. with endpoints $(3, 7)$ and $(-5, 1)$

30. yes

31. comp.

32. positive

33. greater than 50 mi/h

34. $4s$

35. $\frac{m}{-5} + 3 = -4.5$ (Given);

$\frac{m}{-5} = -7.5$ (Subtr. Prop. of =);

$m = 37.5$ (Mult. Prop. of =)

36. $-47 = 3x - 59$ (Given);

$12 = 3x$ (Add. Prop. of =);

$4 = x$ (Div. Prop. of =)

37. Reflex. Prop. of =

38. Sym. Prop. of ≅

39. Trans. Prop. of =

40. figure $ABCD$

41. $m\angle 5 = m\angle 2$

42. $\overline{CD} \cong \overline{EF}$

43. $I = Prt$ (Given);

$4200 = P(0.06)(4)$ (Subst.);

$4200 = P(0.24)$ (Simplify.);

$17{,}500 = P$ (Div. Prop. of =)

2-4 Biconditional Statements and Definitions (pp. 96–101)

 TEKS G.3.A, G.3.B

EXAMPLES

■ For the conditional "If a number is divisible by 10, then it ends in 0", write the converse and a biconditional statement.

Converse: If a number ends in 0, then it is divisible by 10.

Biconditional: A number is divisible by 10 if and only if it ends in 0.

■ Determine if the biconditional "The sides of a triangle measure 3, 7, and 15 if and only if the perimeter is 25" is true. If false, give a counterexample.

Conditional: If the sides of a triangle measure 3, 7, and 15, then the perimeter is 25. True.

Converse: If the perimeter of a triangle is 25, then its sides measure 3, 7, and 15. False; a triangle with side lengths of 6, 10, and 9 also has a perimeter of 25.

Therefore the biconditional is false.

EXERCISES

Determine if a true biconditional can be written from each conditional statement. If not, give a counterexample.

27. If $3 - \frac{2x}{5} = 2$, then $x = \frac{5}{2}$.

28. If $x < 0$, then the value of x^4 is positive.

29. If a segment has endpoints at $(1, 5)$ and $(-3, 1)$, then its midpoint is $(-1, 3)$.

30. If the measure of one angle of a triangle is 90°, then the triangle is a right triangle.

Complete each statement to form a true biconditional.

31. Two angles are ___?___ if and only if the sum of their measures is 90°.

32. $x^3 > 0$ if and only if x is ___?___.

33. Trey can travel 100 miles in less than 2 hours if and only if his average speed is ___?___.

34. The area of a square is equal to s^2 if and only if the perimeter of the square is ___?___.

2-5 Algebraic Proof (pp. 104–109)

 TEKS G.3.B, G.3.C, G.3.E

EXAMPLES

■ Solve the equation $5x - 3 = -18$. Write a justification for each step.

$5x - 3 = -18$	Given
$\underline{+3 \qquad +3}$	Add. Prop. of =
$5x = -15$	Simplify.
$\frac{5x}{5} = \frac{-15}{5}$	Div. Prop. of =
$x = -3$	Simplify.

■ Write a justification for each step.

$RS = ST$	Given
$5x - 18 = 4x$	Subst. Prop. of =
$x - 18 = 0$	Subtr. Prop. of =
$x = 18$	Add. Prop. of =

Identify the property that justifies each statement.

■ $\angle X \cong \angle 2$, so $\angle 2 \cong \angle X$.

Symmetric Property of Congruence

■ If $m\angle 2 = 180°$ and $m\angle 3 = 180°$, then $m\angle 2 = m\angle 3$.

Transitive Property of Equality

EXERCISES

Solve each equation. Write a justification for each step.

35. $\frac{m}{-5} + 3 = -4.5$ 36. $-47 = 3x - 59$

Identify the property that justifies each statement.

37. $a + b = a + b$

38. If $\angle RST \cong \angle ABC$, then $\angle ABC \cong \angle RST$.

39. $2x = 9$, and $y = 9$. So $2x = y$.

Use the indicated property to complete each statement.

40. Reflex. Prop. of ≅: figure $ABCD \cong$ ___?___

41. Sym. Prop. of =: If $m\angle 2 = m\angle 5$, then ___?___.

42. Trans. Prop. of ≅: If $\overline{AB} \cong \overline{CD}$ and $\overline{AB} \cong \overline{EF}$, then ___?___.

43. Kim borrowed money at an annual simple interest rate of 6% to buy a car. How much did she borrow if she paid $4200 in interest over the life of the 4-year loan? Solve the equation $I = Prt$ for P and justify each step.

2-6 Geometric Proof (pp. 110–116)

TEKS G.1.A, G.3.B, G.3.C, G.3.E

EXAMPLES

■ Write a justification for each step, given that $m\angle 2 = 2m\angle 1$.

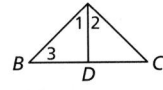

1. $\angle 1$ and $\angle 2$ supp.	Lin. Pair Thm.
2. $m\angle 1 + m\angle 2 = 180°$	Def. of supp. $\angle$s
3. $m\angle 2 = 2m\angle 1$	Given
4. $m\angle 1 + 2m\angle 1 = 180°$	Subst. *Steps 2, 3*
5. $3m\angle 1 = 180°$	Simplify
6. $m\angle 1 = 60°$	Div. Prop. of =

■ Use the given plan to write a two-column proof.

Given: $\overline{AD}$ bisects $\angle BAC$.
$\angle 1 \cong \angle 3$
Prove: $\angle 2 \cong \angle 3$

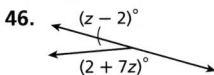

Plan: Use the definition of angle bisector to show that $\angle 1 \cong \angle 2$. Use the Transitive Property to conclude that $\angle 2 \cong \angle 3$.

Two-column proof:

Statements	Reasons
1. $\overline{AD}$ bisects $\angle BAC$.	1. Given
2. $\angle 1 \cong \angle 2$	2. Def. of $\angle$ bisector
3. $\angle 1 \cong \angle 3$	3. Given
4. $\angle 2 \cong \angle 3$	4. Trans. Prop. of $\cong$

EXERCISES

44. Write a justification for each step, given that $\angle 1$ and $\angle 2$ are complementary, and $\angle 1 \cong \angle 3$.

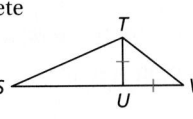

1. $\angle 1$ and $\angle 2$ comp.
2. $m\angle 1 + m\angle 2 = 90°$
3. $\angle 1 \cong \angle 3$
4. $m\angle 1 = m\angle 3$
5. $m\angle 3 + m\angle 2 = 90°$
6. $\angle 3$ and $\angle 2$ comp.

45. Fill in the blanks to complete the two-column proof.
Given: $\overline{TU} \cong \overline{UV}$
Prove: $SU + TU = SV$
Two-column proof:

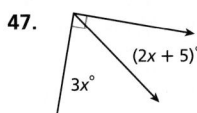

Statements	Reasons
1. $\overline{TU} \cong \overline{UV}$	1. a. ___?___
2. b. ___?___	2. Def. of $\cong$ segs.
3. c. ___?___	3. Seg. Add. Post.
4. $SU + TU = SV$	4. d. ___?___

Find the value of each variable.

46.

47.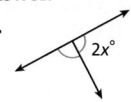

2-7 Flowchart and Paragraph Proofs (pp. 118–125)

TEKS G.1.A, G.2.B, G.3.C, G.3.E

EXAMPLES

Use the two-column proof in the example for Lesson 2-6 above to write each of the following.

■ a flowchart proof

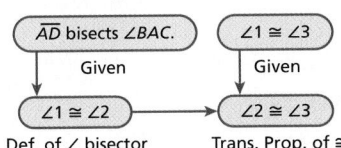

■ a paragraph proof

Since $\overline{AD}$ bisects $\angle BAC$, $\angle 1 \cong \angle 2$ by the definition of angle bisector. It is given that $\angle 1 \cong \angle 3$. Therefore, $\angle 2 \cong \angle 3$ by the Transitive Property of Congruence.

EXERCISES

Use the given plan to write each of the following.
Given: $\angle ADE$ and $\angle DAE$ are complementary.
$\angle ADE$ and $\angle BAC$ are complementary.
Prove: $\angle DAC \cong \angle BAE$

Plan: Use the Congruent Complements Theorem to show that $\angle DAE \cong \angle BAC$. Since $\angle CAE \cong \angle CAE$, $\angle DAC \cong \angle BAE$ by the Common Angles Theorem.

48. a flowchart proof   **49.** a paragraph proof

Find the value of each variable and name the theorem that justifies your answer.

50.
 $135°$
 $3w°$

51. $2x°$

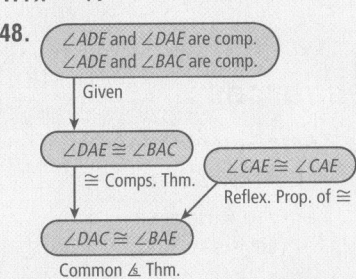

Answers

44. 1. Given
2. Def. of comp. $\angle$s
3. Given
4. Def. of $\cong$ $\angle$s
5. Subst.
6. Def. of comp. $\angle$s

45a. Given
b. $TU = UV$
c. $SU + UV = SV$
d. Subst.

46. $z = 22.5$

47. $x = 17$

48.

```
┌──────────────────────────┐
│ ∠ADE and ∠DAE are comp.  │
│ ∠ADE and ∠BAC are comp.  │
└──────────────────────────┘
         Given
            │
     ┌─────────────┐      ┌─────────────┐
     │ ∠DAE ≅ ∠BAC │      │ ∠CAE ≅ ∠CAE │
     └─────────────┘      └─────────────┘
     ≅ Comps. Thm.      Reflex. Prop. of ≅
            │                    │
     ┌─────────────┐
     │ ∠DAC ≅ ∠BAE │
     └─────────────┘
      Common ∠s Thm.
```

49. It is given that $\angle ADE$ and $\angle DAE$ are comp. and $\angle ADE$ and $\angle BAC$ are comp. By the $\cong$ Comps. Thm., $\angle DAE \cong \angle BAC$. By the Reflex. Prop. of $\cong$, $\angle CAE \cong \angle CAE$. By the Common $\angle$s Thm., $\angle DAC \cong \angle BAE$.

50. $w = 45$; Vert. $\angle$s Thm.

51. $x = 45$; $\cong$ $\angle$s supp. $\rightarrow$ rt. $\angle$s

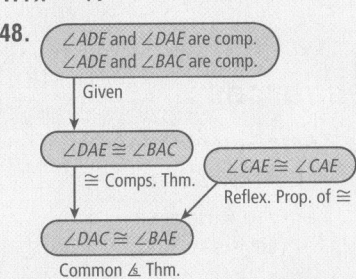

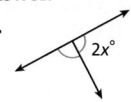

Organizer

Objective: Assess students' mastery of concepts and skills in Chapter 2.

Online Edition

Resources

Assessment Resources

Chapter 2 Tests
- Free Response (Levels A, B, C)
- Multiple Choice (Levels A, B, C)
- Performance Assessment

IDEA Works! CD-ROM

Modified Chapter 2 Test

**Test & Practice Generator**
One-Stop Planner®

**TAKS Practice**

Grades 9–11	Items
Obj. 2	16–18
Obj. 10	1–4

Find the next item in each pattern.

1.

2. 405, 135, 45, 15, … **5**

3. Complete the conjecture "The sum of two even numbers is __?__ ." **even**

4. Show that the conjecture "All complementary angles are adjacent" is false by finding a counterexample.

5. Identify the hypothesis and conclusion of the conditional statement "The show is cancelled if it rains."

6. Write a conditional statement from the sentence "Parallel lines do not intersect." **If 2 lines are ∥, then they do not intersect.**

Determine if each conditional is true. If false, give a counterexample.

7. If two lines intersect, then they form four right angles. **F**

8. If a number is divisible by 10, then it is divisible by 5. **T**

Use the conditional "If you live in the United States, then you live in Kentucky" for Items 9–11. Write the indicated type of statement and determine its truth value.

9. converse   10. inverse   11. contrapositive

12. Determine if the following conjecture is valid by the Law of Detachment.
Given: If it is colder than 50°F, Tom wears a sweater. It is 46°F today.
Conjecture: Tom is wearing a sweater. **valid**

13. Use the Law of Syllogism to draw a conclusion from the given information.
Given: If a figure is a square, then it is a quadrilateral. If a figure is a quadrilateral, then it is a polygon. Figure *ABCD* is a square. **Figure *ABCD* is a polygon.**

14. Write the conditional statement and converse within the biconditional "Chad will work on Saturday if and only if he gets paid overtime."

15. Determine if the biconditional "*B* is the midpoint of $\overline{AC}$ iff $AB = BC$" is true. If false, give a counterexample. **F; *B* is not between *A* and *C*.**

Solve each equation. Write a justification for each step.

16. $8 - 5s = 1$ 17. $0.4t + 3 = 1.6$ 18. $38 = -3w + 2$

Identify the property that justifies each statement.

19. If $2x = y$ and $y = 7$, then $2x = 7$. **Trans. Prop. of =**

20. $m\angle DEF = m\angle DEF$ **Reflex. Prop. of =**

21. $\angle X \cong \angle P$, and $\angle P \cong \angle D$. So $\angle X \cong \angle D$. **Trans. Prop. of ≅**

22. If $\overline{ST} \cong \overline{XY}$, then $\overline{XY} \cong \overline{ST}$. **Sym. Prop. of ≅**

Use the given plan to write a proof in each format.

Given: $\angle AFB \cong \angle EFD$
Prove: $\overrightarrow{FB}$ bisects $\angle AFC$.
Plan: Since vertical angles are congruent, $\angle EFD \cong \angle BFC$. Use the Transitive Property to conclude that $\angle AFB \cong \angle BFC$. Thus $\overrightarrow{FB}$ bisects $\angle AFC$ by the definition of angle bisector.

23. two-column proof   24. paragraph proof   25. flowchart proof

---

Answers

4. Possible answer: $\angle 1$ and $\angle 2$ are comp., but not adj.

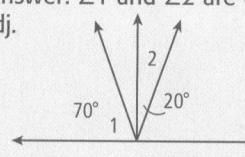

7. Possible answer:

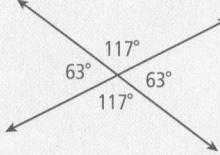

9. If you live in Kentucky, then you live in the United States; T.

10. If you do not live in the United States, then you do not live in Kentucky; T.

11. If you do not live in Kentucky, then you do not live in the United States; F.

14. Conditional: If Chad works on Saturday, then he gets paid overtime. Converse: If Chad gets paid overtime, then he will work on Saturday.

16. $8 - 5s = 1$ (Given); $-5s = -7$ (Subtr. Prop. of =); $s = 1.4$ (Div. Prop. of =)

17. $0.4t + 3 = 1.6$ (Given); $0.4t = -1.4$ (Subtr. Prop. of =); $t = -3.5$ (Div. Prop. of =)

18. $38 = -3w + 2$ (Given); $36 = -3w$ (Subtr. Prop. of =); $-12 = w$ (Div. Prop. of =)

23–25. See p. A13.

COLLEGE ENTRANCE EXAM PRACTICE

FOCUS ON SAT MATHEMATICS SUBJECT TESTS

Some colleges require that you take the SAT Subject Tests. There are two math subject tests—Level 1 and Level 2. Take the Mathematics Subject Test Level 1 when you have completed three years of college-prep mathematics courses.

You may want to time yourself as you take this practice test. It should take you about 6 minutes to complete.

On SAT Mathematics Subject Test questions, you receive one point for each correct answer, but you lose a fraction of a point for each incorrect response. Guess only when you can eliminate at least one of the answer choices.

---

1. In the figure below, m∠1 = m∠2. What is the value of *y*?

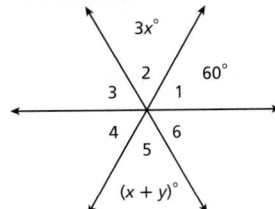

Note: Figure not drawn to scale.

(A) 10   (B) 30

(C) 40   (D) 50

(E) 60

---

2. The statement "I will cancel my appointment if and only if I have a conflict" is true. Which of the following can be concluded?

    I. If I have a conflict, then I will cancel my appointment.

    II. If I do not cancel my appointment, then I do not have a conflict.

    III. If I cancel my appointment, then I have a conflict.

(A) I only   (B) II only

(C) III only   (D) I and III

(E) I, II, and III

---

3. What is the contrapositive of the statement "If it is raining, then the football team will win"?

(A) If it is not raining, then the football team will not win.

(B) If it is raining, then the football team will not win.

(C) If the football team wins, then it is raining.

(D) If the football team does not win, then it is not raining.

(E) If it is not raining, then the football team will win.

---

4. Given the points $D(1, 5)$ and $E(-2, 3)$, which conclusion is NOT valid?

(A) The midpoint of $\overline{DE}$ is $\left(-\frac{1}{2}, 4\right)$.

(B) D and E are collinear.

(C) The distance between D and E is $\sqrt{5}$.

(D) $\overline{DE} \cong \overline{ED}$

(E) D and E are distinct points.

---

5. For all integers x, what conclusion can be drawn about the value of the expression $\frac{x^2}{2}$?

(A) The value is negative.

(B) The value is not negative.

(C) The value is even.

(D) The value is odd.

(E) The value is not a whole number.

Organizer

Objective: Provide practice for college entrance exams such as the SAT Mathematics Subject Test Level 1.

 **Online Edition**

Resources

✎ *College Entrance Exam Practice*

Questions on the SAT Mathematics Subject Test Level 1 represent the following math content areas:

Algebra, 30%

Plane Euclidean Geometry, 20%

Coordinate Geometry, 12%

Three-dimensional Geometry, 6%

Trigonometry, 8%

Functions, 12%

Statistics/Probability, 6%

Miscellaneous, 6%

Items on this page focus on:

• Algebra

• Plane Euclidean Geometry

• Coordinate Geometry

• Miscellaneous

Text References:

Item	1	2	3	4	5
Lesson	2-7	2-4	2-2	2-5	2-1

TEST PREP DOCTOR ✚

1. Students may not know how to approach this problem. Suggest that they use the fact that m∠1 = m∠2 to solve for *x*, and then use the Vertical Angles Theorem to solve for *y*.

2. Students may choose **D** if they do not recognize that II is the contrapositive of the conditional within the given biconditional. Remind students that a conditional and its contrapositive are logically equivalent, and that a biconditional is true only when the conditional and its converse are true.

3. Students who chose **A** chose the inverse of the statement, and students who chose **C** chose the converse of the statement. Remind students that the contrapositive of a statement is found by exchanging and negating the hypothesis and conclusion.

4. Students who chose **B** may not remember that any two points are collinear. Students who chose **E** may not know what the term *distinct* means. Encourage students to check each answer choice before choosing their final answer.

5. Remind students to substitute multiple values for the variable before making a conjecture. Students who chose **C, D,** or **E** may have selected only one value for *x*. Remind students that the square of any number is not negative, so the correct answer is **B**.

Organizer

Objective: Provide opportunities to learn and practice common test-taking strategies.

Online Edition

Resources

 TAKS Prep Workbook

 TAKS Prep **CD-ROM**

 TAKS Practice **Online**

go.hrw.com/Geo/TX
KEYWORD: MG7 TestPrep

 This TAKS Tackler **TAKS PREP DOCTOR** focuses on how to correctly fill in a grid when answering gridded-response items. Often students solve the test item correctly, but get the problem wrong because they fill in the answer improperly. This strategy reviews the rules for filling in an answer and helps students identify common mistakes in gridded answers.

Remind students that it is okay for the first answer box at the top of the grid to be blank, as long as there are no blanks between numbers or between the decimal point and number. Compare the gridded answers in the examples to demonstrate.

Gridded Response: Record Your Answer

When responding to a gridded-response test item, you must fill out the grid on your answer sheet correctly, or the item will be marked as incorrect.

EXAMPLE 1

Gridded Response: Solve the equation $1258 - 2(3x - 72) = -80$.

The value of x is 247.

- Using a pencil, write your answer in the answer boxes at the top of the grid.
- Put only one digit in each box. The decimal point has a designated column.
- Do not leave a blank box in the middle of an answer.
- For each digit, shade the bubble that is in the same column as the digit in the answer box.

EXAMPLE 2

Gridded Response: The perimeter of a rectangle is 90 in. The width of the rectangle is 18 in. Find the length of the rectangle in feet.

The length of the rectangle is 27 inches, but the problem asks for the measurement in feet.

27 inches $= \dfrac{9}{4}$, or 2.25, feet

- Fractions and mixed numbers cannot be gridded, so you must grid the answer as 2.25.
- Using a pencil, write your answer in the answer boxes at the top of the grid.
- Put only one digit in each box. The decimal point has a designated column.
- Do not leave a blank box in the middle of an answer.
- For each digit, shade the bubble that is in the same column as the digit in the answer box.

You cannot grid a negative number in a gridded-response item because the grid does not include the negative sign (−). So if you get a negative answer to a test item, rework the problem. You probably made a math error.

Read each statement and answer the questions that follow.

Sample A
The correct answer to a test item is 1.6. A student gridded this answer as shown.

1. What error did the student make when filling out the grid?

2. Another student got an answer of −1.6. Explain why the student knew this answer was wrong.

Sample B
The perimeter of a triangle is $2\frac{3}{4}$ feet. A student gridded this answer as shown.

3. What error did the student make when filling out the grid?

4. Explain how to correctly grid the answer.

Sample C
The length of a segment is $897\frac{2}{5}$ units. A student gridded this answer as shown.

5. What answer does the grid show?

6. Explain why you cannot grid a fraction or a mixed number.

7. Write the answer $897\frac{2}{5}$ in a form that could be entered in the grid correctly.

8. Another student got an answer of 10,216.5 units. Explain why the student knew this answer was wrong.

Sample D
The measure of an angle is 48.9°. A student gridded this answer as shown.

9. What answer does the grid show?

10. What error did the student make when filling out the grid?

11. Explain how to correctly grid the answer.

Answers

Possible answers:

1. The student left a space between the decimal point and 6.

2. You cannot grid a negative number, so the correct answer cannot possibly be negative.

3. You cannot grid units of measurement, so you must grid the answer in the units asked for in the problem.

4. Grid the answer as a decimal, 2.75.

5. The grid shows 8972.5, which is not equal to $897\frac{2}{5}$.

6. The grid does not include a fraction bar.

7. Grid the answer as a decimal, 897.4.

8. The grid does not include a column for the ten thousand's digit.

9. The grid shows 0.489.

10. The student gridded all three digits to the right of the decimal point.

11. Grid the 4 and 8 to the left of the decimal point and grid the 9 to the right of the decimal point.

Organizer

Objective: Provide review and practice for Chapters 1–2 and standardized tests.

 Online Edition

Resources

 Assessment Resources
Chapter 2 Cumulative Test

 TAKS Prep Workbook

 TAKS Prep CD-ROM

TAKS Practice Online
go.hrw.com/Geo/TX
KEYWORD: MG7 TestPrep

CUMULATIVE ASSESSMENT, CHAPTERS 1–2

Multiple Choice

Use the figure below for Items 1 and 2. In the figure, $\overrightarrow{DB}$ bisects $\angle ADC$.

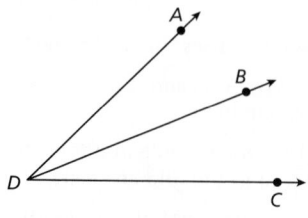

1. Which best describes the intersection of $\angle ADB$ and $\angle BDC$?

- Ⓐ Exactly one ray
- Ⓑ Exactly one point
- Ⓒ Exactly one angle
- Ⓓ Exactly one segment

2. Which expression is equal to the measure of $\angle ADC$?

- Ⓕ $2(m\angle ADB)$
- Ⓖ $90° - m\angle BDC$
- Ⓗ $180° - 2(m\angle ADC)$
- Ⓙ $m\angle BDC - m\angle ADB$

3. What is the inverse of the statement, "If a polygon has 8 sides, then it is an octagon"?

- Ⓐ If a polygon is an octagon, then it has 8 sides.
- Ⓑ If a polygon is not an octagon, then it does not have 8 sides.
- Ⓒ If an octagon has 8 sides, then it is a polygon.
- Ⓓ If a polygon does not have 8 sides, then it is not an octagon.

4. Lily conjectures that if a number is divisible by 15, then it is also divisible by 9. Which of the following is a counterexample?

- Ⓕ 45
- Ⓖ 50
- Ⓗ 60
- Ⓙ 72

5. A diagonal of a polygon connects nonconsecutive vertices. The table shows the number of diagonals in a polygon with n sides.

Number of Sides	Number of Diagonals
4	2
5	5
6	9
7	14

If the pattern continues, how many diagonals does a polygon with 8 sides have?

- Ⓐ 17
- Ⓑ 19
- Ⓒ 20
- Ⓓ 21

6. Which type of transformation maps figure $LMNP$ onto figure $L'M'N'P'$?

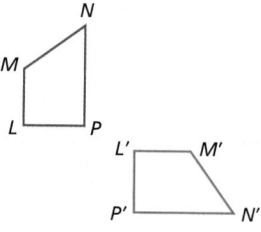

- Ⓕ Reflection
- Ⓖ Rotation
- Ⓗ Translation
- Ⓙ None of these

7. Miyoko went jogging on July 25, July 28, July 31, and August 3. If this pattern continues, when will Miyoko go jogging next?

- Ⓐ August 5
- Ⓑ August 6
- Ⓒ August 7
- Ⓓ August 8

8. Congruent segments have equal measures. A segment bisector divides a segment into two congruent segments. $\overleftrightarrow{XY}$ intersects $\overline{DE}$ at X and bisects $\overline{DE}$. Which conjecture is valid?

- Ⓕ $m\angle YXD = m\angle YXE$
- Ⓖ Y is between D and E.
- Ⓗ $DX = XE$
- Ⓙ $DE = YE$

TAKS Practice

Grades 9–11	Items
Obj. 2	5
Obj. 6	6
Obj. 7	11–13
Obj. 8	15
Obj. 10	4, 7

TAKS PREP DOCTOR ✛

For **Item 15,** students who answered 2.56 did not divide the perimeter by 4 before squaring the number. Students who answered 0.4 found the side length of the field rather than the area.

For **Item 18,** encourage students to draw a picture. Sometimes it is easier to find a counterexample to a geometric statement by drawing a picture.

9. Which statement is true by the Symmetric Property of Congruence?

- (A) $\overline{ST} \cong \overline{ST}$
- (B) $15 + MN = MN + 15$
- (C) If $\angle P \cong \angle Q$, then $\angle Q \cong \angle P$.
- (D) If $\angle D \cong \angle E$ and $\angle E \cong \angle F$, then $\angle D \cong \angle F$.

 To find a counterexample for a biconditional statement, write the conditional statement and converse it contains. Then try to find a counterexample for one of these statements.

10. Which is a counterexample for the following biconditional statement?

A pair of angles is supplementary if and only if the angles form a linear pair.

- (F) The measures of supplementary angles add to 180°.
- (G) A linear pair of angles is supplementary.
- (H) Complementary angles do not form a linear pair.
- (J) Two supplementary angles are not adjacent.

11. K is between J and L. The distance between J and K is 3.5 times the distance between K and L. If $JK = 14$, what is JL?

- (A) 10.5
- (C) 24.5
- (B) 18
- (D) 49

12. What is the length of the segment connecting the points $(-7, -5)$ and $(5, -2)$?

- (F) $\sqrt{13}$
- (H) $3\sqrt{17}$
- (G) $\sqrt{53}$
- (J) $\sqrt{193}$

Gridded Response

13. A segment has an endpoint at $(5, -2)$. The midpoint of the segment is $(2, 2)$. What is the length of the segment? **10**

14. $\angle P$ measures 30° more than the measure of its supplement. What is the measure of $\angle P$ in degrees? **105°**

15. The perimeter of a square field is 1.6 kilometers. What is the area of the field in square kilometers?

0.16

18c. F; possible answer: if m∠1 = 60° and m∠2 = 80°, then the ∡ are acute, but they are not comp.

Short Response

16. Solve the equation $2(AB) + 16 = 24$ to find the length of segment AB. Write a justification for each step.

17. Use the given two-column proof to write a flowchart proof.

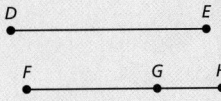

Given: $\overline{DE} \cong \overline{FH}$
Prove: $DE = FG + GH$

Two-column proof:

Statements	Reasons
1. $\overline{DE} \cong \overline{FH}$	1. Given
2. $DE = FH$	2. Def. of ≅ segs.
3. $FG + GH = FH$	3. Seg. Add. Post.
4. $DE = FG + GH$	4. Subst.

18. Consider the following conditional statement.

If two angles are complementary, then the angles are acute.

a. Determine if the conditional is true or false. If false, give a counterexample. **T**

b. Write the converse of the conditional statement.

c. Determine whether the converse is true or false. If false, give a counterexample.

18b. If 2 ∡ are acute, then they are comp.

Extended Response

19. The figure below shows the intersection of two lines.

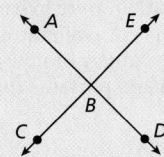

a. Name the linear pairs of angles in the figure. What conclusion can you make about each pair? Explain your reasoning.

b. Name the pairs of vertical angles in the figure. What conclusion can you make about each pair? Explain your reasoning.

c. Suppose m∠EBD = 90°. What are the measures of the other angles in the figure? Write a two-column proof to support your answer.

Short-Response Rubric

Items 16–18

2 Points = The student's answer is an accurate and complete execution of the task or tasks.

1 Point = The student's answer contains attributes of an appropriate response but is flawed.

0 Points = The student's answer contains no attributes of an appropriate response.

Extended-Response Rubric

Item 19

4 Points = The student correctly identifies the linear pairs of angles and the pairs of vertical angles, describing the correct relationship between each type of pair. All steps of the proof in part **c** are shown.

3 Points = The student correctly identifies some of the angle pairs in parts **a** and **b** but does not justify their relationships. The proof in part **c** is correct but contains minor flaws.

2 Points = The student answers parts **a** and **b** correctly but without justification. The student answers part **c** but does not write a proof to justify the conclusion.

1 Point = The student attempts to answer all parts of the problem, but does not do so correctly. The student attempts to justify the answers.

0 Points = The student does not answer correctly and does not attempt all parts of the problem.

Answers

16. $2(AB) + 16 = 24$ (Given); $2(AB) = 8$ (Subtr. Prop. of =); $AB = 4$ (Div. Prop. of =)

17.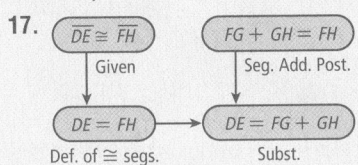

19a. ∠ABC and ∠CBD, ∠CBD and ∠DBE, ∠DBE and ∠EBA, and ∠EBA and ∠ABC; each pair of ∡ is supp. by the Lin. Pair Thm.

b. ∠ABC and ∠DBE, ∠EBA and ∠CBD; each pair of vert. ∡ is ≅ by the Vert. ∡ Thm.

19c. If m∠EBD = 90°, then m∠EBA = m∠ABC = m∠CBD = 90°.
Two-column proof:
1. m∠EBD = 90° (Given)
2. m∠EBD and ∠CBD are supp. (Lin. Pair Thm.)
3. m∠EBD + m∠CBD = 180° (Def. of supp. ∡)
4. 90° + m∠CBD = 180° (Subst.)
5. m∠CBD = 90° (Subtr. Prop. of =)
6. ∠CBD ≅ ∠EBA, ∠EBD ≅ ∠ABC (Vert. ∡ Thm.)
7. m∠CBD = m∠EBA, m∠EBD = m∠ABC (Def. of ≅ ∡)
8. m∠EBA = 90°, m∠ABC = 90° (Trans. Prop. of =)

Problem Solving on Location

TEXAS

TAKS Grades 9–11 Obj. 10

Austin

The Freescale Marathon

Every February, runners take to the streets of Austin to participate in a 26-mile marathon. The course travels mostly downhill, with a net drop in elevation of more than 400 feet from beginning to end. But don't be fooled; many former participants strongly recommend hill training for this course!

Choose one or more strategies to solve each problem.

1. During the marathon, a runner maintains a steady pace and completes the first 2.6 miles in 20 minutes. After 1 hour 20 minutes, she has completed 10.4 miles. Make a conjecture about the runner's average speed in miles per hour. How long do you expect her to take to complete the marathon? 7.8 mi/h; $3\frac{1}{3}$ h

2. The course features fully equipped aid stations with medical support for the complete eight-hour duration of the race. From mile 2 to mile 6, these stations are located every other mile. After that, they are located every mile to the finish. Portable toilets are available at each mile marker and at the end of the course. At how many points are there both an aid station and portable toilets? **23**

For 3, use the map.

3. The course includes a straight section along Forty-fifth Street from Shoal Creek Boulevard to Duval Street. The distance from Guadalupe Street to Duval is twice the distance from Burnet Road to Lamar Boulevard. The distance from Lamar to Guadalupe is 210 feet greater than the distance from Shoal Creek to Burnet. What is the distance from Guadalupe to Duval? **3150 ft**

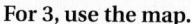

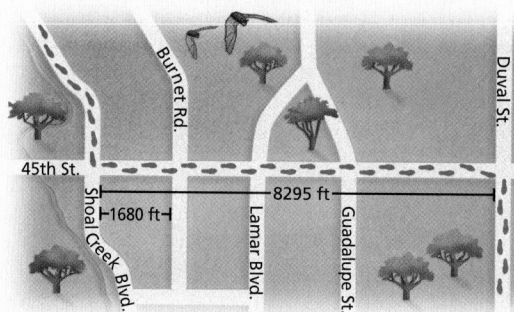

140 Chapter 2 Geometric Reasoning

Problem-Solving Focus

For **Problem 2**, focus on the second step of the problem-solving process:
(2) Make a Plan. Ask students what strategy or strategies they can use to solve the problem. Possible answer: Use the strategies Make an Organized List and Solve a Simpler Problem. Since there are portable toilets at each mile marker, you need to consider only the locations of the aid stations. There are 3 aid stations from mile 1 to mile 6 and 20 aid stations from mile 7 to mile 26, for a total of 23 stations.

Show Caves

2a. F; Cascade Caverns is more than 100 ft deep but only 1700 ft long.

The region between San Antonio and Austin, known as the Texas Hill Country, is home to six of the seven show caves in the state. A show cave is a cave developed for public use, typically with amenities such as lighting and groomed trails. The seventh show cave in Texas, the Caverns of Sonora, is internationally recognized as one of the most beautiful in the world.

1. Longhorn Cavern or Natural Bridge Caverns

Problem Solving Strategies

Draw a Diagram
Make a Model
Guess and Test
Work Backward
Find a Pattern
Make a Table
Solve a Simpler Problem
Use Logical Reasoning
Use a Venn Diagram
Make an Organized List

Choose one or more strategies to solve each problem.

1. Jared took a tour at least $\frac{5}{8}$ mi long and saw a cave that is less than 10,000 ft in length. Which caves might Jared have visited?

2. A travel brochure includes the following statements about Texas show caves. Determine whether each statement is true or false. If false, explain why.

a. If you tour a cave that is more than 100 ft deep, then you'll see a cave that is more than 8000 ft in length.

b. If you haven't been to the Caverns of Sonora, then you haven't seen a cave that is at least 15,000 ft long.

c. If you don't want to walk more than a mile, but you want to see a cave with a depth of at least 150 ft, then you should visit Natural Bridge Caverns. **T**

3. Inner Space Cavern has a second tour, which Ingrid completes in 18 min and 45 s. If Ingrid walks 12,672 ft in 1 h, what is the length of the second tour? **0.75 mi**

2b. F; Inner Space Cavern is 15,000 ft long.

Texas Show Caves

Cave	Length (ft)	Approximate Depth (ft)	Tour Length (mi)
Cascade Caverns	1,700	132	0.25
Cave Without a Name	14,211	89	0.25
Caverns of Sonora	20,000	150	1.5
Inner Space Cavern	15,000	80	1.2
Longhorn Cavern	9,850	23	0.625
Natural Bridge Caverns	8,600	250	0.75
Wonder Cave	1,296	91	0.08

Show Caves

Reading Strategies
ENGLISH LANGUAGE LEARNERS

Make sure that students understand the difference between the *length* of a cave and the *depth* of a cave. A cave's length is the length of the complete passageway through the cave, and its depth is the vertical distance between the top and bottom of the cave. Draw and label a simple sketch to illustrate these terms.

Using Data Have students review the data in the table before they begin solving the problems. Ask whether there is any correlation between the length of a cave and the depth of a cave. no Also ask whether there is a strong correlation between a cave's length and the length of the tour through the cave. Discuss why. No; possible answer: some parts of a cave may not be passable.

Problem-Solving Focus

Ask students to explain what strategy they would use to solve **Problem 1.** Possible answer: Use a Venn diagram. One region contains names of caves with tour lengths of at least $\frac{5}{8}$ mi, and the other region contains names of caves less than 10,000 ft in length. The intersection of the regions is the solution.

Discuss additional reasoning questions similar to the ones posed in **Problems 1** and **2.** For example, encourage students to use the data in the table to develop their own true or false conditional statements. Then have students share the statements with classmates, challenging them to determine the truth value of each.

CHAPTER

3 Parallel and Perpendicular Lines

Section 3A	Section 3B
Lines with Transversals	**Coordinate Geometry**

Section 3A
Lines with Transversals

3-1 **Lines and Angles**
On Track for TAKS Systems of Equations
3-2 **Technology Lab** Explore Parallel Lines and Transversals
3-2 **Angles Formed by Parallel Lines and Transversals**
3-3 **Proving Lines Parallel**
3-3 **Geometry Lab** Construct Parallel Lines
3-4 **Perpendicular Lines**
3-4 **Geometry Lab** Construct Perpendicular Lines

Section 3B
Coordinate Geometry

3-5 **Slopes of Lines**
3-6 **Technology Lab** Explore Parallel and Perpendicular Lines
3-6 **Lines in the Coordinate Plane**
On Track for TAKS Scatter Plots and Lines of Best Fit

Pacing Guide for 45-Minute Classes

Calendar Planner
One-Stop Planner®

Chapter 3

Countdown to TAKS Weeks ⑤, ⑥

DAY 1	DAY 2	DAY 3	DAY 4	DAY 5
3-1 Lesson	On Track for TAKS 3-2 Technology Lab	3-2 Lesson	3-3 Lesson	3-3 Geometry Lab 3-4 Lesson
DAY 6	**DAY 7**	**DAY 8**	**DAY 9**	**DAY 10**
3-4 Lesson 3-4 Geometry Lab	Multi-Step TAKS Prep Ready to Go On?	3-5 Lesson	3-6 Technology Lab 3-6 Lesson	3-6 Lesson On Track for TAKS
DAY 11	**DAY 12**	**DAY 13**		
Multi-Step TAKS Prep Ready to Go On?	Chapter 3 Review	Chapter 3 Test		

Pacing Guide for 90-Minute Classes

Calendar Planner
One-Stop Planner®

Chapter 3

DAY 1	DAY 2	DAY 3	DAY 4	DAY 5
Chapter 2 Test 3-1 Lesson	On Track for TAKS 3-2 Technology Lab 3-2 Lesson	3-3 Lesson 3-3 Geometry Lab 3-4 Lesson	3-4 Lesson 3-4 Geometry Lab Multi-Step TAKS Prep Ready to Go On?	3-5 Lesson 3-6 Technology Lab 3-6 Lesson
DAY 6	**DAY 7**			
3-6 Lesson On Track for TAKS Multi-Step TAKS Prep Ready to Go On?	Chapter 3 Review Chapter 3 Test			

ONGOING ASSESSMENT and INTERVENTION

DIAGNOSE	PRESCRIBE

Assess Prior Knowledge

Before Chapter 3

Diagnose readiness for the chapter.

Are You Ready? SE p. 143

Prescribe intervention.

Are You Ready? Intervention Skills 23, 25, 60, 69, 88

Formative Assessment

Before Every Lesson

Diagnose readiness for the lesson.

Warm Up TE, every lesson

Prescribe intervention.

Skills Bank SE pp. S50–S81

Reteach CRB, Ch. 1–3

During Every Lesson

Diagnose understanding of lesson concepts.

Check It Out! SE, every example

Think and Discuss SE, every lesson

Write About It SE, every lesson

Journal TE, every lesson

Prescribe intervention.

Questioning Strategies TE, every example

Reading Strategies CRB, every lesson

Success for ELL pp. 29–40

After Every Lesson

Diagnose mastery of lesson concepts.

Lesson Quiz TE, every lesson

Alternative Assessment TE, every lesson

Test Prep SE, every lesson

Test and Practice Generator

Prescribe intervention.

Reteach CRB, every lesson

Problem Solving CRB, every lesson

Test Prep Doctor TE, every lesson

Homework Help Online

Before Chapter 3 Testing

Diagnose mastery of concepts in the chapter.

Ready to Go On? SE pp. 181, 201

Multi-Step TAKS Prep SE pp. 180, 200

Section Quizzes AR pp. 45–46

Test and Practice Generator

Prescribe intervention.

Ready to Go On? Intervention pp. 29–40

Scaffolding Questions TE pp. 180, 200

Before High Stakes Testing

Diagnose mastery of benchmark concepts.

Ready for TAKS? Benchmark Tests

College Entrance Exam Practice SE p. 207

TAKS Prep SE pp. 210–211

TAKS Prep CD-ROM

Prescribe intervention.

Ready for TAKS? Intervention

College Entrance Exam Practice

TAKS Prep Workbook

Summative Assessment

After Chapter 3

Check mastery of chapter concepts.

Multiple-Choice Tests (Forms A, B, C)

Free-Response Tests (Forms A, B, C)

Performance Assessment AR pp. 47–60

Test and Practice Generator

Prescribe intervention.

Reteach CRB, every lesson

Lesson Tutorial Videos Chapter 3

Check mastery of benchmark concepts.

TAKS Tests

College Entrance Exams

Prescribe intervention.

TAKS Prep Workbook

College Entrance Exam Practice

KEY: **SE** = *Student Edition* **TE** = *Teacher's Edition* **CRB** = *Chapter Resource Book* **AR** = *Assessment Resources* 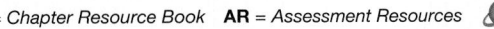 Available online 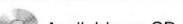 Available on CD-ROM

142B

CHAPTER 3

Supporting the Teacher

Chapter 3 Resource Book

Practice A, B, C
pp. 3–5, 11–13, 19–21, 27–29, 35–37, 43–45

Reading Strategies ELL
pp. 10, 18, 26, 34, 42, 50

Reteach
pp. 6–7, 14–15, 22–23, 30–31, 38–39, 46–47

Problem Solving
pp. 9, 17, 25, 33, 41, 49

Challenge
pp. 8, 16, 24, 32, 40, 48

Parent Letter   pp. 1–2

Transparencies

Lesson Transparencies, Volume 1 .... Chapter 3
• Teaching Tools
• Warm Ups
• Teaching Transparencies
• Additional Examples
• Lesson Quizzes

Alternate Openers: Explorations .... pp. 15–20

Countdown to TAKS .... pp. 9–12

Know-It Notebook .... Chapter 3
• Graphic Organizers
• Key Concepts
• Vocabulary
• Chapter Review
• Big Ideas
• Postulates
• Theorems

Teacher Tools

Power Presentations®
Complete PowerPoint® presentations for Chapter 3 lessons

Lesson Tutorial Videos®
Holt authors Ed Burger and Freddie Renfro present tutorials to support the Chapter 3 lessons.

One-Stop Planner®
Easy access to all Chapter 3 resources and assessments, as well as software for lesson planning, test generation, and puzzle creation

IDEA Works!®
Key Chapter 3 resources and assessments modified to address special learning needs

Lesson Plans .... pp. 15–20

Solutions Key .... p. 165

Geometry Posters .... Chapter 3

TechKeys   **Lab Resources**

Project Teacher Support   **Parent Resources**

Workbooks

Homework and Practice Workbook
Teacher's Guide .... pp. 15–20

Know-It Notebook
Teacher's Guide .... pp. 35–48

Problem Solving Workbook
Teacher's Guide .... pp. 15–20

TAKS Prep Workbook
Teacher's Guide

Technology Highlights for the Teacher

Power Presentations
Dynamic presentations to engage students. Complete PowerPoint® presentations for every lesson in Chapter 3.

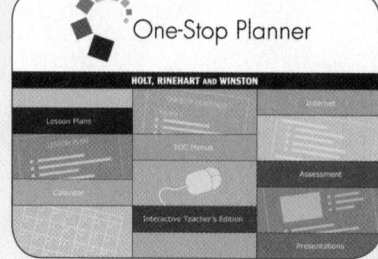

One-Stop Planner
Easy access to Chapter 3 resources and assessments. Includes lesson-planning, test-generation, and puzzle-creation software.

Premier Online Edition
Chapter 3 includes Tutorial Videos, Lesson Activities, Lesson Quizzes, Homework Help, and Chapter Project.

CHAPTER 3

 # Reaching All Learners

Resources for All Learners

Texas Lab Manual	Chapter 3
Homework and Practice Workbook	pp. 15–20
Know-It Notebook	pp. 35–48
Problem Solving Workbook	pp. 15–20

DEVELOPING LEARNERS

Practice A	CRB, every lesson
Reteach	CRB, every lesson
Inclusion	TE pp. 148, 152, 176, 184, 186, 195
Questioning Strategies	TE, every example
Modified Chapter 3 Resources	*IDEA Works!*
Homework Help Online	

ON-LEVEL LEARNERS

Practice B	CRB, every lesson
Multiple Representations	TE p. 156
Modeling	TE p. 173

ADVANCED LEARNERS

Practice C	CRB, every lesson
Challenge	CRB, every lesson
Reading and Writing Math EXTENSION	TE p. 145
Multi-Step TAKS Prep EXTENSION	TE pp. 180, 200
Critical Thinking	TE p. 175

English Language Learners

 **ENGLISH LANGUAGE LEARNERS**

Are You Ready? Vocabulary	SE p. 143
Vocabulary Connections	SE p. 144
Lesson Vocabulary	SE, every lesson
Vocabulary Exercises	SE, every exercise set
Vocabulary Review	SE p. 202
English Language Learners	TE pp. 145, 147, 165
Reading Strategies	CRB, every lesson
Success for English Language Learners	pp. 29–40
Multilingual Glossary	

Reaching All Learners Through...

Inclusion	TE pp. 148, 152, 176, 184, 186, 195
Kinesthetic Experience	TE pp. 149, 156, 183, 194
Multiple Representations	TE p. 156
Visual Cues	TE pp. 156, 160, 175
Auditory Cues	TE pp. 157, 173, 195
Diversity	TE p. 159
Concrete Manipulatives	TE p. 163
Modeling	TE p. 173
Critical Thinking	TE p. 175
Curriculum Integration	TE p. 191
Test Prep Doctor	TE pp. 150, 160, 168, 177, 187, 196, 207, 208, 210
Common Error Alerts	TE pp. 149, 151, 157, 159, 161, 163, 167, 169, 173, 191, 193, 197
Scaffolding Questions	TE pp. 180, 200

Technology Highlights for Reaching All Learners

Lesson Tutorial Videos

Starring Holt authors Ed Burger and Freddie Renfro! Live tutorials to support every lesson in Chapter 4.

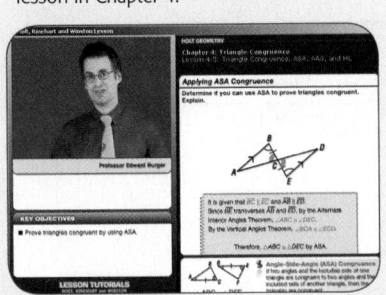

Multilingual Glossary

Searchable glossary includes definitions in English, Spanish, Vietnamese, Chinese, Hmong, Korean, and 4 other languages.

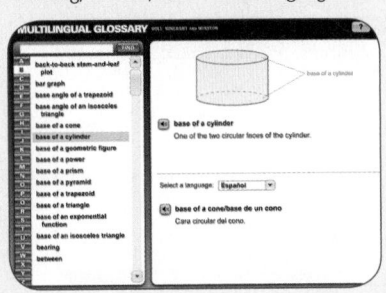

Online Interactivities

Interactive tutorials provide visually engaging alternative opportunities to learn concepts and master skills.

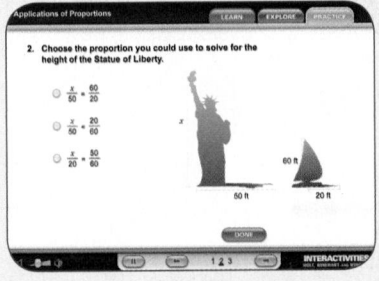

KEY: SE = *Student Edition* **TE** = *Teacher's Edition* **CRB** = *Chapter Resource Book*  Spanish version available Available online Available on CD-ROM

Ongoing Assessment

Assessing Prior Knowledge

Determine whether students have the prerequisite concepts and skills for success in Chapter 3.

Are You Ready? .... SE p. 143
Warm Up .... TE, every lesson

Test Preparation

Provide review and practice for Chapter 3 and standardized tests.

Multi-Step TAKS Prep .... SE pp. 180, 200
Study Guide: Review .... SE pp. 202–205
TAKS Tackler .... SE pp. 208–209
TAKS Prep .... SE pp. 210–211
College Entrance Exam Practice .... SE p. 207
Countdown to TAKS **Transparencies** .... pp. 9–12
Ready for TAKS?
TAKS Prep **Workbook**
TAKS Prep **CD-ROM**
IDEA Works!

Alternative Assessment

Assess students' understanding of Chapter 3 concepts and combined problem-solving skills.

Chapter 3 Project .... SE p. 142
Alternative Assessment .... TE, every lesson
Performance Assessment .... AR pp. 59–60
Portfolio Assessment .... AR p. xxxiv

Daily Assessment

Provide formative assessment for each day of Chapter 3.

Questioning Strategies .... TE, every example
Think and Discuss .... SE, every lesson
Check It Out! Exercises .... SE, every example
Write About It .... SE, every lesson
Journal .... TE, every lesson
Lesson Quiz .... TE, every lesson
Alternative Assessment .... TE, every lesson
Modified Lesson Quizzes .... *IDEA Works!*

Weekly Assessment

Provide formative assessment for each week of Chapter 3.

Multi-Step TAKS Prep .... SE pp. 180, 200
Ready to Go On? .... SE pp. 181, 201
Cumulative Assessment .... SE pp. 210–211
Test and Practice Generator SPANISH ..*One-Stop Planner*

Formal Assessment

Provide summative assessment of Chapter 3 mastery.

Section Quizzes .... AR pp. 45–46
Chapter 3 Test .... SE p. 206
Chapter Test (Levels A, B, C) .... AR pp. 47–58
  • Multiple Choice • Free Response
Cumulative Test .... AR pp. 61–64
Test and Practice Generator SPANISH ..*One-Stop Planner*
Modified Chapter 3 Test .... *IDEA Works!*

Technology Highlights for Ongoing Assessment

Are You Ready?

Automatically assess readiness and prescribe intervention for Chapter 3 prerequisite skills.

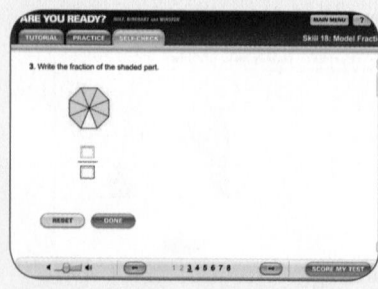

Ready to Go On? SPANISH

Automatically assess understanding of and prescribe intervention for Sections 3A and 3B.

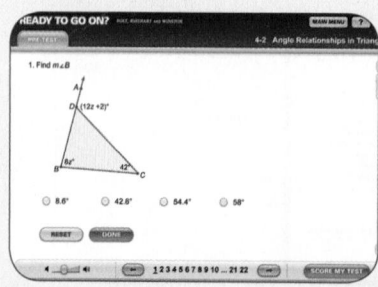

Ready for TAKS? SPANISH

Automatically assess proficiency with and provide intervention for TAKS objectives. Grade 6 through Exit Level.

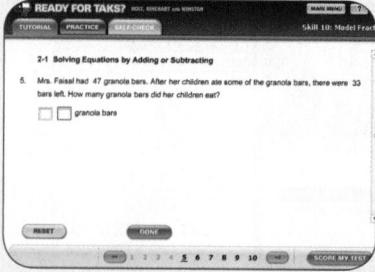

KEY: **SE** = *Student Edition* **TE** = *Teacher's Edition* **AR** = Assessment Resources SPANISH Spanish version available Available online Available on CD-ROM

CHAPTER 3

Formal Assessment

Three levels (A, B, C) of multiple-choice and free-response chapter tests are available in the *Assessment Resources.*

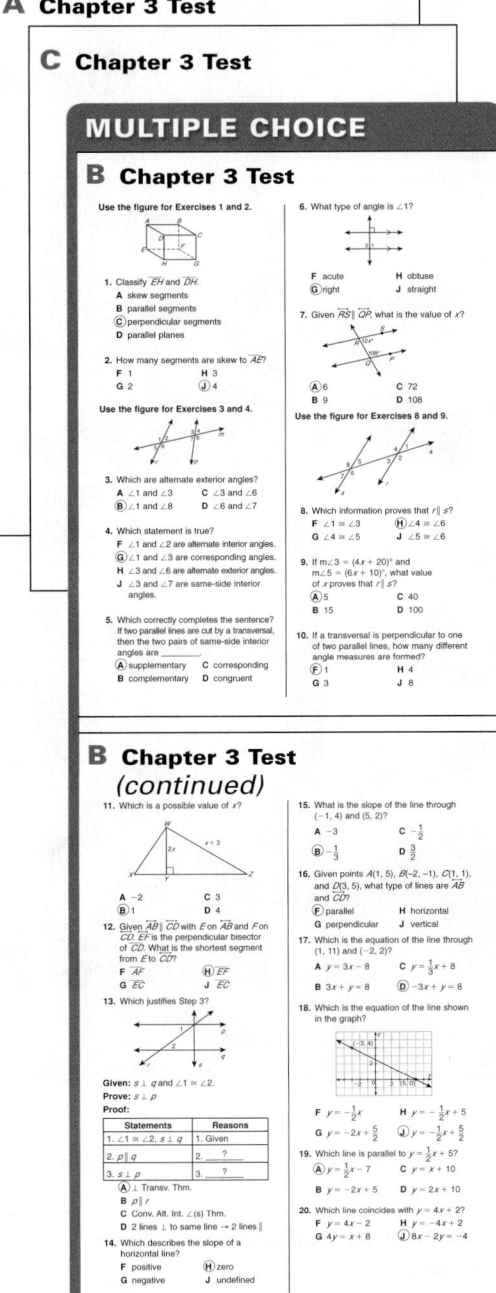

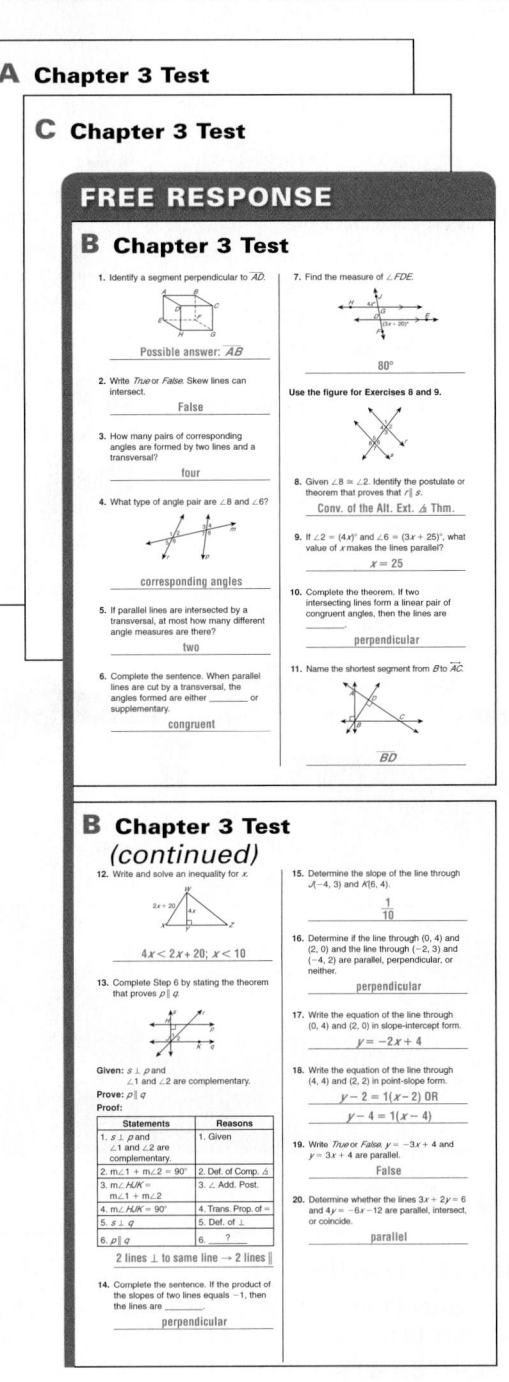

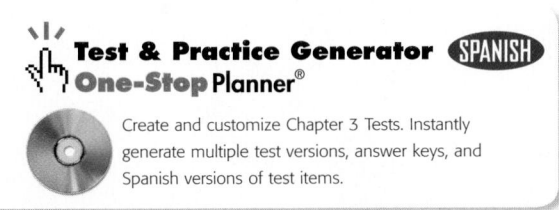

Test & Practice Generator SPANISH
One-Stop Planner®

Create and customize Chapter 3 Tests. Instantly generate multiple test versions, answer keys, and Spanish versions of test items.

Parallel and Perpendicular Lines

SECTION **3A**
Lines with Transversals

On page 180, students use properties of parallel and perpendicular lines to model a real-world attraction known as a mystery spot.

Exercises designed to prepare students for success on the Multi-Step TAKS Prep can be found on pages 150, 160, 168, and 176.

SECTION **3B**
Coordinate Geometry

On page 200, students write equations and graph lines to model a real-world traffic situation.

Exercises designed to prepare students for success on the Multi-Step TAKS Prep can be found on pages 186 and 196.

go.hrw.com/Geo/TX
Chapter Project Online
KEYWORD: MG7 ChProj

Sailboats at the
Corpus Christi
Municipal Marina

About the Project

Seeing is Disbelieving

In this Chapter Project, students study the mathematics behind optical illusions. They begin by using parallel lines and transversals to draw an "impossible figure." Then they use theorems from the chapter to analyze an optical illusion and create one of their own.

Project Resources

All project resources for teachers and students are provided online.

go.hrw.com/Geo/TX
Project Teacher Support
KEYWORD: MG7 ProjectTS

Geometry in Texas

The masts of these boats in Corpus Christi harbor are all perpendicular to the surface of the water. In this chapter, students will learn that if two lines are perpendicular to a given line, then the two lines are parallel.

ARE YOU READY?

☑ Vocabulary

Match each term on the left with a definition on the right.

1. acute angle **F**   **A.** segments that have the same length
2. congruent angles **D**   **B.** an angle that measures greater than 90° and less than 180°
3. obtuse angle **B**   **C.** points that lie in the same plane
4. collinear **E**   **D.** angles that have the same measure
5. congruent segments **A**   **E.** points that lie on the same line
                              F. an angle that measures greater than 0° and less than 90°

☑ Conditional Statements

Identify the <u>hypothesis</u> and <u>conclusion</u> of each conditional.

6. If E is on $\overleftrightarrow{AC}$, then E lies in plane $\mathcal{P}$.
7. If A is not in plane $\mathcal{Q}$, then A is not on $\overleftrightarrow{BD}$.
8. If plane $\mathcal{P}$ and plane $\mathcal{Q}$ intersect, then they intersect in a line.

☑ Name and Classify Angles

Name and classify each angle. **Possible answers:**

9.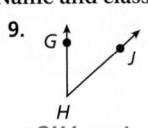
$\angle GHJ$; acute

10.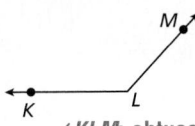
$\angle KLM$; obtuse

11.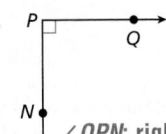
$\angle QPN$; right

12.
$\angle RST$; straight

☑ Angle Relationships

Give an example of each angle pair. **Possible answers:**

13. vertical angles $\angle AGB$ and $\angle EGD$
14. adjacent angles $\angle AGB$ and $\angle BGC$
15. complementary angles $\angle BGC$ and $\angle CGD$
16. supplementary angles $\angle AGC$ and $\angle CGD$

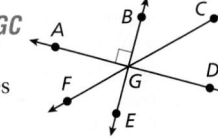

☑ Evaluate Expressions

Evaluate each expression for the given value of the variable.

17. $4x + 9$ for $x = 31$ **133**
18. $6x - 16$ for $x = 43$ **242**
19. $97 - 3x$ for $x = 20$ **37**
20. $5x + 3x + 12$ for $x = 17$ **148**

☑ Solve Multi-Step Equations

Solve each equation for x.

21. $4x + 8 = 24$ $x = 4$
22. $2 = 2x - 8$ $x = 5$
23. $4x + 3x + 6 = 90$ $x = 12$
24. $21x + 13 + 14x - 8 = 180$ $x = 5$

Parallel and Perpendicular Lines **143**

ARE YOU READY?

Organizer

Objective: Assess students' understanding of prerequisite skills.

Prerequisite Skills

Conditional Statements
Name and Classify Angles
Angle Relationships
Evaluate Expressions
Solve Multi-Step Equations

Assessing Prior Knowledge

INTERVENTION ◀◆▶

Diagnose and Prescribe
Use this page to determine whether intervention is necessary or whether enrichment is appropriate.

Resources

 *Are You Ready? Intervention and Enrichment* Worksheets

💿 *Are You Ready?* CD-ROM

🪐 *Are You Ready?* Online

my.hrw.com

ARE YOU READY?

Diagnose and Prescribe

 **NO INTERVENE**

 YES ENRICH

☑ Prerequisite Skill	🖋 Worksheets	💿 CD-ROM	🪐 Online
☑ Conditional Statements	Skill 88	Activity 88	
☑ Name and Classify Angles	Skill 23	Activity 23	
☑ Angle Relationships	Skill 25	Activity 25	Diagnose and Prescribe Online
☑ Evaluate Expressions	Skill 60	Activity 60	
☑ Solve Multi-Step Equations	Skill 69	Activity 69	

ARE YOU READY? Intervention, Chapter 3

ARE YOU READY? Enrichment, Chapter 3
🖋 Worksheets
💿 CD-ROM
🪐 Online

Are You Ready? **143**

Organizer

Objective: Help students organize the new concepts they will learn in Chapter 3.

Online Edition
Multilingual Glossary

Resources

PuzzlePro
One-Stop Planner®

***Multilingual Glossary* Online**
go.hrw.com/Geo/TX
KEYWORD: MG7 Glossary

Answers to Vocabulary Connections

1. crosses the two lines
2. the steepness of the line in a plane
3. matching; ∠ that are in matching positions
4. inside; the area between the lines; between the two lines, on opposite sides of the third line

---

Key Vocabulary/Vocabulario

alternate exterior angles	ángulos alternos externos
alternate interior angles	ángulos alternos internos
corresponding angles	ángulos correspondientes
parallel lines	líneas paralelas
perpendicular bisector	mediatriz
perpendicular lines	líneas perpendiculares
same-side interior angles	ángulos internos del mismo lado
slope	pendiente
transversal	transversal

Vocabulary Connections

To become familiar with some of the vocabulary terms in the chapter, answer the following questions. You may refer to the chapter, the glossary, or a dictionary if you like.

1. The root *trans-* means "across." What do you think a **transversal** of two lines does?

2. The *slope* of a mountain trail describes the steepness of the climb. What might the **slope** of a line describe?

3. What does the word *corresponding* mean? What do you think the term **corresponding angles** means?

4. What does the word *interior* mean? What might the phrase "interior of a pair of lines" describe? The word *alternate* means "to change from one to another." If two lines are crossed by a third line, where do you think a pair of **alternate interior angles** might be?

★ Geometry TEKS

Geometry TEKS	Les. 3-1	3-2 Tech. Lab	Les. 3-2	Les. 3-3	3-3 Geo. Lab	Les. 3-4	3-4 Geo. Lab	Les. 3-5	3-6 Tech. Lab	Les. 3-6
G.1.A Geometric Structure* develop an awareness of the structure of a mathematical system, connecting definitions, postulates, logical reasoning, and theorems					★		★			
G.2.A Geometric Structure* use construction to explore attributes of geometric figures and to make conjectures about geometric relationships						★	★	★		
G.3.C Geometric Structure* use logical reasoning to prove statements are true ...			★	★		★				★
G.7.B Dimensionality and the geometry of location* use slopes and equations of lines to investigate geometric relationships, including parallel lines, perpendicular lines ...								★	★	★
G.7.C Dimensionality and the geometry of location* develop and use formulas involving ... slope ...								★		
G.9.A Congruence and the geometry of size* formulate and test conjectures about the properties of parallel and perpendicular lines based on explorations	★	★	★	★	★	★				

* Knowledge and skills are written out completely on pages TX28–TX35.

★ *Geometry TEKS—Knowledge and Skills*

G.1 Geometric structure The student understands the structure of, and relationships within, an axiomatic system.

G.2 Geometric structure The student analyzes geometric relationships in order to make and verify conjectures.

G.3 Geometric structure The student applies logical reasoning to justify and prove mathematical statements.

G.7 Dimensionality and the geometry of location The student understands that coordinate systems provide convenient and efficient ways of representing geometric figures and uses them accordingly.

G.9 Congruence and the geometry of size The student analyzes properties and describes relationships in geometric figures.

Study Strategy: Take Effective Notes

Taking effective notes is an important study strategy. The Cornell system of note taking is a good way to organize and review main ideas. In the Cornell system, the paper is divided into three main sections. The note-taking column is where you take notes during lecture. The cue column is where you write questions and key phrases as you review your notes. The summary area is where you write a brief summary of the lecture.

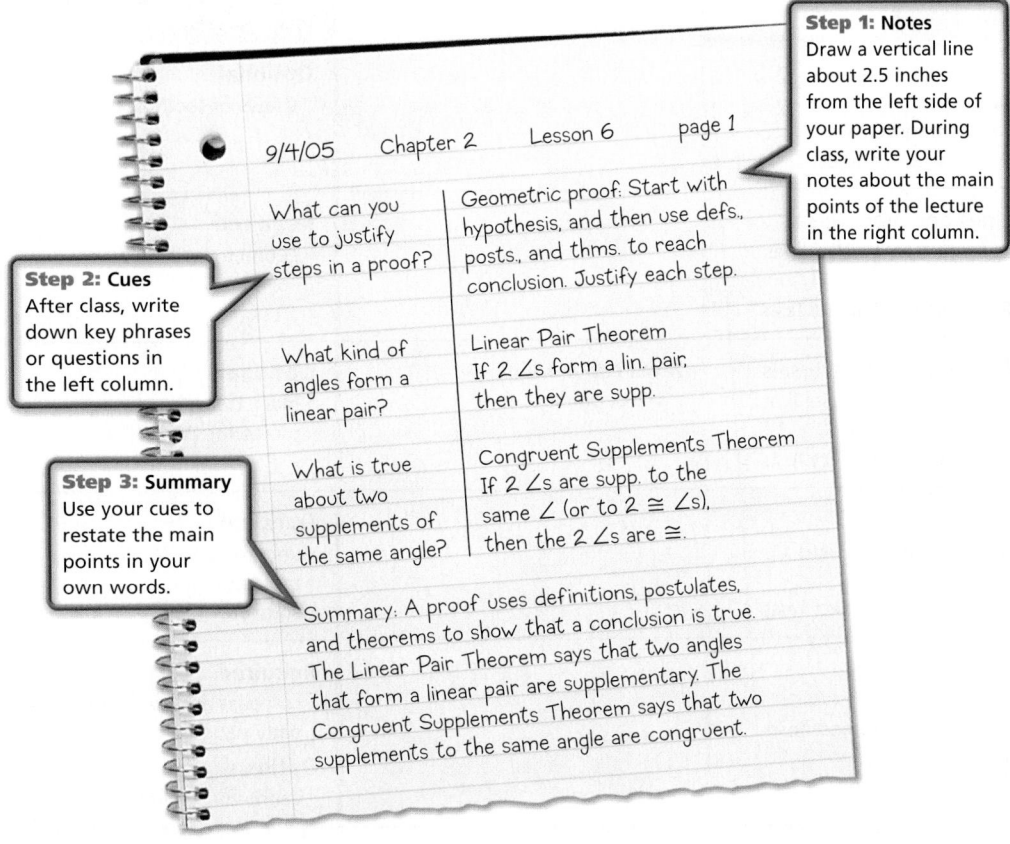

Step 1: Notes
Draw a vertical line about 2.5 inches from the left side of your paper. During class, write your notes about the main points of the lecture in the right column.

Step 2: Cues
After class, write down key phrases or questions in the left column.

Step 3: Summary
Use your cues to restate the main points in your own words.

9/4/05   Chapter 2   Lesson 6   page 1

What can you use to justify steps in a proof?

Geometric proof: Start with hypothesis, and then use defs., posts., and thms. to reach conclusion. Justify each step.

What kind of angles form a linear pair?

Linear Pair Theorem
If 2 ∠s form a lin. pair, then they are supp.

What is true about two supplements of the same angle?

Congruent Supplements Theorem
If 2 ∠s are supp. to the same ∠ (or to 2 ≅ ∠s), then the 2 ∠s are ≅.

Summary: A proof uses definitions, postulates, and theorems to show that a conclusion is true. The Linear Pair Theorem says that two angles that form a linear pair are supplementary. The Congruent Supplements Theorem says that two supplements to the same angle are congruent.

Try This

1. Research and write a paragraph describing the Cornell system of note taking. Describe how you can benefit from using this type of system.

2. In your next class, use the Cornell system of note taking. Compare these notes to your notes from a previous lecture.

Reading and Writing Math

Organizer

Objective: Apply study strategies to understand and retain key concepts.

PREMIER **Online Edition**

Resources

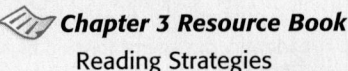 ***Chapter 3 Resource Book***
Reading Strategies

Study Strategy: Take Effective Notes

ENGLISH LANGUAGE LEARNERS

Discuss The physical act of writing helps students reinforce the concepts that they hear and see as each lesson is presented.

Organizing their notes in a systematic way helps students organize concepts in their minds.

Extend Too often students do not refer to their notes because the notes are disorganized and difficult to follow. Encourage students to use a notetaking system and to review their notes before beginning their homework.

As students review their notes, they may find it helpful to use colored pens or highlighters to emphasize important concepts.

As the class explores the topics in Chapter 3, ask students to share their questions and summaries with the class. Any student who is having difficulty understanding a topic may benefit from hearing other points of view and explanations.

Answers to *Try This*

1–2. Check students' work.

🗹 TAKS Objectives

Grades 9–11

Obj. 1 Functional Relationships: A.1.A, A.2.B, A.1.E

Obj. 2 Properties and Attributes of Functions: A.2.B

Obj. 3 Linear Functions: A.5.C, A.3.A, A.3.B, A.4.B, A.4.C

Obj. 5 Quadratic and Other Nonlinear Functions: A.11.A

Obj. 6 Geometric Relationships and Spatial Reasoning: 8.6.B, 8.7.D, G.7.A

Obj. 7 Two- and Three-Dimensional Representations: G.7.A

Obj. 10 Mathematical Processes and Tools: 8.14.A, 8.14.C, 8.15.A

Lines with Transversals

One-Minute Section Planner

Lesson	Lab Resources	Materials
Lesson 3-1 Lines and Angles • Identify parallel, perpendicular, and skew lines. • Identify the angles formed by two lines and a transversal. ☑ Exit Level TAKS ☑ ACT ☑ SAT ☑ SAT Subject Tests		**Optional** straws or toothpicks, paper
3-2 Technology Lab Explore Parallel Lines and Transversals • Use geometry software to explore angles formed by parallel lines and transversals. ☐ Exit Level TAKS ☑ ACT ☑ SAT ☑ SAT Subject Tests		**Required** geometry software
Lesson 3-2 Angles Formed by Parallel Lines and Transversals • Prove and use theorems about the angles formed by parallel lines and transversals. ☑ Exit Level TAKS ☑ ACT ☑ SAT ☑ SAT Subject Tests	*Texas Lab Manual* 3-2 Geometry Lab	**Optional** blank transparency, patty paper, protractor (MK)
Lesson 3-3 Proving Lines Parallel • Use the angles formed by a transversal to prove two lines are parallel. ☐ Exit Level TAKS ☑ ACT ☑ SAT ☑ SAT Subject Tests		**Optional** uncooked spaghetti, tape, protractor, ruler (MK), geometry software
3-3 Geometry Lab Construct Parallel Lines • Use various methods to construct parallel lines. ☐ Exit Level TAKS ☑ ACT ☑ SAT ☑ SAT Subject Tests		**Required** compass and straightedge (MK), patty paper **Optional** geometry software
Lesson 3-4 Perpendicular Lines • Prove and apply theorems about perpendicular lines. ☐ Exit Level TAKS ☑ ACT ☑ SAT ☐ SAT Subject Tests	*Texas Lab Manual* 3-4 Geometry Lab	**Required** compass and straightedge (MK) **Optional** patty paper
3-4 Geometry Lab Construct Perpendicular Lines • Construct a line perpendicular to a given line through a given point. ☐ Exit Level TAKS ☑ ACT ☑ SAT ☑ SAT Subject Tests		**Required** compass and straightedge (MK)

MK = *Manipulatives Kit*

Section Overview

Exploring Lines and Angles

Lesson 3-1

 Why? Basic postulates about lines and planes will provide essential concepts for the deductive development of geometry.

Definition	Examples
Parallel lines lie in the same plane and do not intersect.	$\overleftrightarrow{CG} \parallel \overleftrightarrow{BF}$
Perpendicular lines intersect at right angles.	$\overleftrightarrow{BC} \perp \overleftrightarrow{BF}$
Skew lines are not coplanar, are not parallel, and do not intersect.	$\overleftrightarrow{FG}$ and $\overleftrightarrow{AE}$ are skew.
Parallel planes do not intersect.	plane *BCG* ∥ plane *ADH*

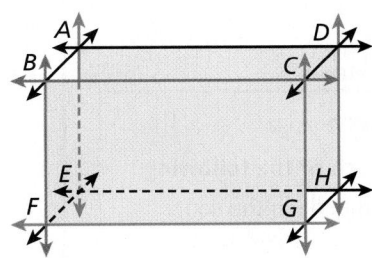

Exploring Parallel Lines and Transversals

Lessons 3-2, 3-3

 Why? Students will use properties of parallel lines and related angles to justify theorems about triangle congruence and similarity.

Given: two lines *m* and *n* cut by a transversal *t*

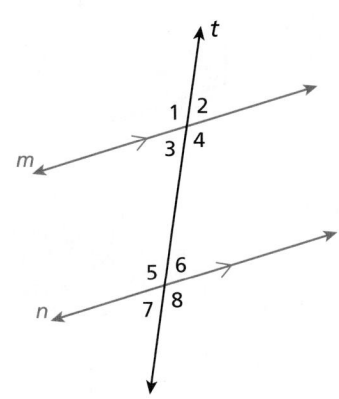

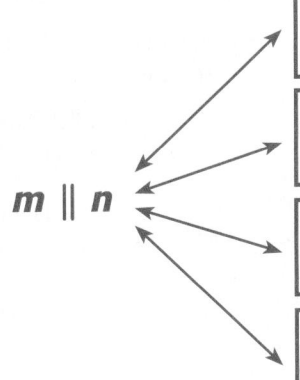

$m \parallel n$

Corresponding ∠s

$\angle 1 \cong \angle 5 \quad \angle 3 \cong \angle 7 \quad \angle 2 \cong \angle 6 \quad \angle 4 \cong \angle 8$

Alternate interior ∠s

$\angle 3 \cong \angle 6 \quad \angle 4 \cong \angle 5$

Alternate exterior ∠s

$\angle 1 \cong \angle 8 \quad \angle 2 \cong \angle 7$

Same-side interior ∠s are supplementary.

$m\angle 3 + m\angle 5 = \angle 180° \quad m\angle 4 + m\angle 6 = \angle 180°$

Exploring Perpendicular Lines

Lesson 3-4

 Why? Students will apply their knowledge of perpendicular lines when they study properties of polygons, quadrilaterals, solids, and circles.

If $\angle 1 \cong \angle 2$, then $\ell \perp m$.

If $\ell \perp p$ and $p \parallel m$, then $\ell \perp m$.

If $p \perp \ell$ and $\ell \perp m$, then $p \parallel m$.

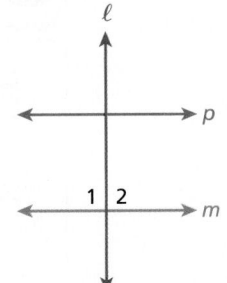

Pacing: Traditional 1 day
Block $\frac{1}{2}$ day

Objectives: Identify parallel, perpendicular, and skew lines.

Identify the angles formed by two lines and a transversal.

 Online Edition
Tutorial Videos

 Countdown to TAKS Week 5

Power Presentations
with PowerPoint®

Warm Up

Identify each of the following.

1. points that lie in the same plane   coplanar points

2. two angles whose sum is 180°   supplementary angles

3. the intersection of two distinct intersecting lines   point

4. a pair of adjacent angles whose noncommon sides are opposite rays   linear pair

Also available on transparency

 **Math Humor**

Line ℓ: Look out! You almost intersected me!

Line m: Well, *skew's* me!

3-1 Lines and Angles

Objectives
Identify parallel, perpendicular, and skew lines.

Identify the angles formed by two lines and a transversal.

Vocabulary
parallel lines
perpendicular lines
skew lines
parallel planes
transversal
corresponding angles
alternate interior angles
alternate exterior angles
same-side interior angles

Who uses this?
Card architects use playing cards to build structures that contain parallel and perpendicular planes.

Bryan Berg uses cards to build structures like the one at right. In 1992, he broke the Guinness World Record for card structures by building a tower 14 feet 6 inches tall. Since then, he has built structures more than 25 feet tall.

Parallel, Perpendicular, and Skew Lines

Parallel lines (∥) are coplanar and do not intersect. In the figure, $\overleftrightarrow{AB} \parallel \overleftrightarrow{EF}$, and $\overleftrightarrow{EG} \parallel \overleftrightarrow{FH}$.

Perpendicular lines (⊥) intersect at 90° angles. In the figure, $\overleftrightarrow{AB} \perp \overleftrightarrow{AE}$, and $\overleftrightarrow{EG} \perp \overleftrightarrow{GH}$.

Skew lines are not coplanar. Skew lines are not parallel and do not intersect. In the figure, $\overleftrightarrow{AB}$ and $\overleftrightarrow{EG}$ are skew.

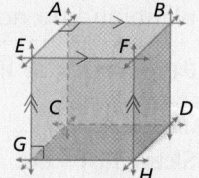 *Know it! Note*

Parallel planes are planes that do not intersect. In the figure, plane *ABE* ∥ plane *CDG*.

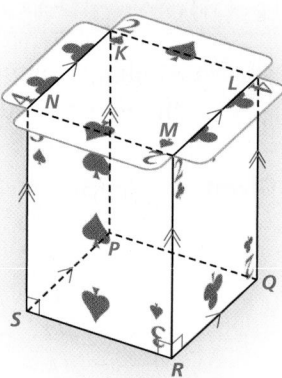

Arrows are used to show that $\overleftrightarrow{AB} \parallel \overleftrightarrow{EF}$ and $\overleftrightarrow{EG} \parallel \overleftrightarrow{FH}$.

EXAMPLE 1 Identifying Types of Lines and Planes

Identify each of the following.

A a pair of parallel segments
$\overline{KN} \parallel \overline{PS}$

Helpful Hint
Segments or rays are parallel, perpendicular, or skew if the lines that contain them are parallel, perpendicular, or skew.

B a pair of skew segments
$\overline{LM}$ and $\overline{RS}$ are skew.

C a pair of perpendicular segments
$\overline{MR} \perp \overline{RS}$

D a pair of parallel planes
plane *KPS* ∥ plane *LQR*

Possible answers:
1a. $\overline{BF} \parallel \overline{EJ}$
1b. $\overline{BF}$ and $\overline{DE}$ are skew.
1c. $\overline{BF} \perp \overline{FJ}$
1d. plane *FJH* ∥ plane *BCD*

 **CHECK IT OUT!**

Identify each of the following.

1a. a pair of parallel segments
1b. a pair of skew segments
1c. a pair of perpendicular segments
1d. a pair of parallel planes

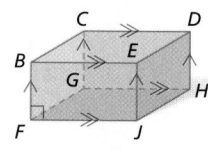

146   Chapter 3 Parallel and Perpendicular Lines

 **Introduce**

EXPLORATION

3-1 Lines and Angles

Use paper folding to explore relationships between pairs of lines.

1. Fold a rectangular piece of paper in half. Then fold it in half again in the same direction.

2. Now fold the paper in half in the opposite direction.

3. Unfold the paper. Label the lines formed by the folds as shown.

4. Name pairs of lines on your paper that do not intersect.

5. Name pairs of lines on your paper that appear to intersect at a 90° angle. Check with a protractor.

THINK AND DISCUSS

6. **Describe** how you could fold a sheet of paper to create two lines that intersect at an angle other than 90°.

Motivate

Have students describe in their own words the relationship between the lines represented by the two vertical sides of a door. Be sure students recognize that the lines are always the same distance apart. Then ask students to describe the relationship between the lines represented by the top and one of the vertical sides of the door. Lead them to conclude that these lines form a right angle.

Explorations and answers are provided in the *Explorations* binder.

Angle Pairs Formed by a Transversal

TERM	EXAMPLE
A **transversal** is a line that intersects two coplanar lines at two different points. The transversal *t* and the other two lines *r* and *s* form eight angles.	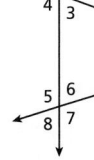
Corresponding angles lie on the same side of the transversal *t*, on the same sides of lines *r* and *s*.	∠1 and ∠5
Alternate interior angles are nonadjacent angles that lie on opposite sides of the transversal *t*, between lines *r* and *s*.	∠3 and ∠6
Alternate exterior angles lie on opposite sides of the transversal *t*, outside lines *r* and *s*.	∠1 and ∠8
Same-side interior angles or *consecutive interior angles* lie on the same side of the transversal *t*, between lines *r* and *s*.	∠3 and ∠5

EXAMPLE 2 Classifying Pairs of Angles

Give an example of each angle pair.

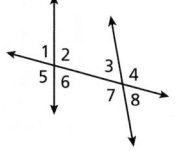

A corresponding angles
∠4 and ∠8

B alternate interior angles
∠4 and ∠6

C alternate exterior angles
∠2 and ∠8

D same-side interior angles
∠4 and ∠5

Possible answers:
2a. ∠1 and ∠3
2b. ∠2 and ∠7
2c. ∠1 and ∠8
2d. ∠2 and ∠3

 **CHECK IT OUT!** Give an example of each angle pair.
2a. corresponding angles
2b. alternate interior angles
2c. alternate exterior angles
2d. same-side interior angles

EXAMPLE 3 Identifying Angle Pairs and Transversals

Identify the transversal and classify each angle pair.

A ∠1 and ∠5
transversal: *n*; alternate interior angles

B ∠3 and ∠6
transversal: *m*; corresponding angles

C ∠1 and ∠4
transversal: *ℓ*; alternate exterior angles

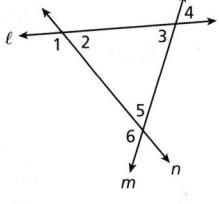

> **Helpful Hint**
> To determine which line is the transversal for a given angle pair, locate the line that connects the vertices.

CHECK IT OUT! 3. Identify the transversal and classify the angle pair ∠2 and ∠5 in the diagram above. transv.: *n*; same-side int. ∠

Additional Examples

Example 1

Use the diagram in Example 1. Identify each of the following.

A. a pair of parallel segments
$\overline{LM} \parallel \overline{QR}$

B. a pair of skew segments
$\overline{KN}$ and $\overline{PQ}$

C. a pair of perpendicular segments $\overline{NS} \perp \overline{SP}$

D. a pair of parallel planes
plane NMR ∥ plane KLQ

Example 2

Use the diagram in Example 2. Give an example of each angle pair.

A. corresponding angles
∠1 and ∠5

B. alternate interior angles
∠3 and ∠5

C. alternate exterior angles
∠1 and ∠7

D. same-side interior angles
∠3 and ∠6

Example 3

Use the diagram in Example 3. Identify the transversal and classify each angle pair.

A. ∠1 and ∠3   line *ℓ*; corr. ∠

B. ∠2 and ∠6   line *n*; alt. int. ∠

C. ∠4 and ∠6   line *m*; alt. ext. ∠

Also available on transparency

INTERVENTION ◄━►
Questioning Strategies

EXAMPLES **1–3**

• Can you identify more possible answers?

---

2 Teach

Guided Instruction

Review the definition of a linear pair of angles. Also discuss the meanings of the words *alternate, interior,* and *exterior.* Be sure that students can identify a transversal before introducing the pairs of angles in the lesson.

 **Reading Math** Corresponding angles are in corresponding, or matching, positions on the same side of the transversal.

ENGLISH LANGUAGE LEARNERS

3 Close

Summarize

Have students name the different pairs of angles formed when two lines are cut by a transversal. Alt. int. angles, alt. ext. angles, corr. angles, and same-side int. angles

Have students explain the difference between parallel lines and skew lines. Parallel lines are coplanar; skew lines are not.

ONGOING ASSESSMENT
and INTERVENTION ◄━►

Diagnose *Before* the Lesson
3-1 Warm Up, TE p. 146

Monitor *During* the Lesson
Check It Out! Exercises, SE pp. 146–147
Questioning Strategies, TE p. 147

Assess *After* the Lesson
3-1 Lesson Quiz, TE p. 151
Alternative Assessment, TE p. 151

Answers to *Think and Discuss*

1. Intersecting lines can intersect at any ∠. ⊥ lines intersect at 90° ∡.
2. The ∡ are outside lines *m* and *n*, on opposite sides of line *p*.
3. See p. A3.

THINK AND DISCUSS

1. Compare perpendicular and intersecting lines.
2. Describe the positions of two alternate exterior angles formed by lines *m* and *n* with transversal *p*.
3. **GET ORGANIZED** Copy the diagram and graphic organizer. In each box, list all the angle pairs of each type in the diagram.

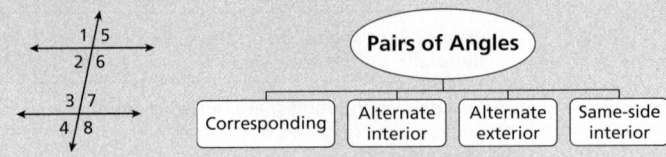

3-1 Exercises

3-1 Exercises

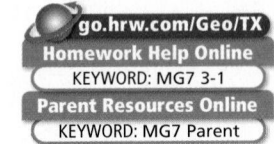

go.hrw.com/Geo/TX
Homework Help Online
KEYWORD: MG7 3-1
Parent Resources Online
KEYWORD: MG7 Parent

Assignment Guide

Assign *Guided Practice* exercises as necessary.

If you finished Examples **1–3**
  Basic 14–29, 33, 35–37, 43–48, 55–62
  Average 14–24 even, 26–52, 55–62
  Advanced 14–24 even, 26–34, 41–62

Homework Quick Check
Quickly check key concepts.
Exercises: 14, 18, 22, 28, 40

 Inclusion To determine which line is the transversal in **Exercises 10–13**, locate the line that connects the vertices of the angles.

⬥ TAKS Practice

Grades 9–11	Exercises
Obj. 2	55–57
Obj. 6	60–62
Obj. 8	58, 59

GUIDED PRACTICE

1. **Vocabulary** __?__ are located on opposite sides of a transversal, between the two lines that intersect the transversal. (*corresponding angles, alternate interior angles, alternate exterior angles*, or *same-side interior angles*) **alternate interior angles**

SEE EXAMPLE **1**
p. 146

Identify each of the following. **Possible answers:**
2. one pair of perpendicular segments *EH* ⊥ *DH*
3. one pair of skew segments *AB* and *DH* are skew.
4. one pair of parallel segments *AB* ∥ *CD*
5. one pair of parallel planes plane *ABC* ∥ plane *EFG*

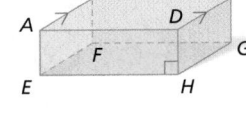

SEE EXAMPLE **2**
p. 147

Give an example of each angle pair. **Possible answers:**
6. alternate interior angles ∠2 and ∠4
7. alternate exterior angles ∠6 and ∠8
8. corresponding angles ∠6 and ∠3
9. same-side interior angles ∠2 and ∠3

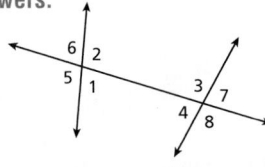

SEE EXAMPLE **3**
p. 147

Identify the transversal and classify each angle pair.
10. ∠1 and ∠2 transv.: *n*; corr. ∡
11. ∠2 and ∠3 transv.: *m*; alt. ext. ∡
12. ∠2 and ∠4 transv.: *n*; alt. int. ∡
13. ∠4 and ∠5 transv.: *p*; same-side int. ∡

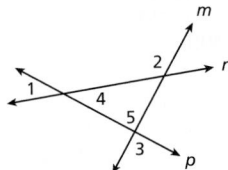

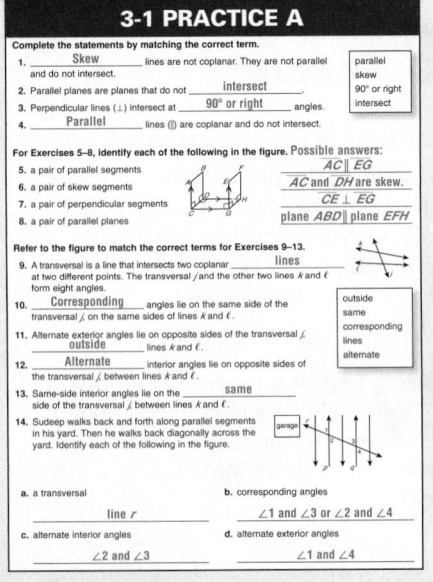

PRACTICE AND PROBLEM SOLVING

Independent Practice

For Exercises	See Example
14–17	1
18–21	2
22–25	3

TEKS ❖ TAKS

Skills Practice p. S8
Application Practice p. S30

Identify each of the following. Possible answers:

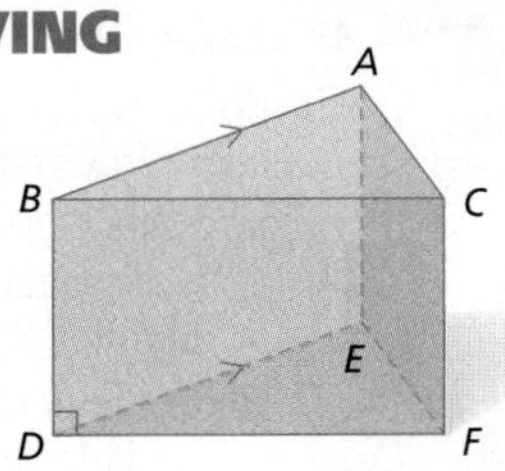

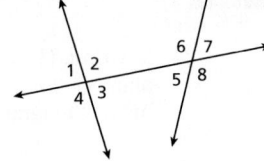

14. one pair of parallel segments
 $\overline{AB} \parallel \overline{DE}$

15. one pair of skew segments
 $\overline{AB}$ and $\overline{CF}$ are skew.

16. one pair of perpendicular segments
 $\overline{BD} \perp \overline{DF}$

17. one pair of parallel planes
 plane $ABC \parallel$ plane DEF

Give an example of each angle pair. Possible answers:

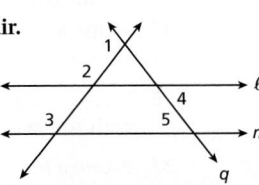

18. same-side interior angles $\angle 2$ and $\angle 6$

19. alternate exterior angles $\angle 1$ and $\angle 8$

20. corresponding angles $\angle 1$ and $\angle 6$

21. alternate interior angles $\angle 2$ and $\angle 5$

Identify the transversal and classify each angle pair.

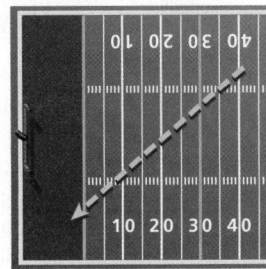

22. $\angle 2$ and $\angle 3$ transv.: p; corr. $\angle\!\!\angle$

23. $\angle 4$ and $\angle 5$ transv.: q; alt. int. $\angle\!\!\angle$

24. $\angle 2$ and $\angle 4$ transv.: ℓ; alt. ext. $\angle\!\!\angle$

25. $\angle 1$ and $\angle 2$ transv.: p; same-side int. $\angle\!\!\angle$

26. **Sports** A football player runs across the 30-yard line at an angle. He continues in a straight line and crosses the goal line at the same angle. Describe two parallel lines and a transversal in the diagram.
The 30-yard line and goal line are ∥, and the path of the runner is the transv.

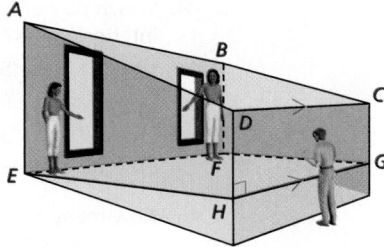

Name the type of angle pair shown in each letter. Possible answers:

 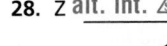 

27. F corr. $\angle\!\!\angle$ 28. Z alt. int. 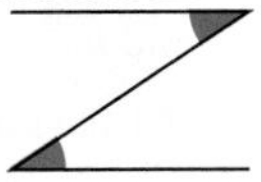 $\angle\!\!\angle$ 29. C same-side int. $\angle\!\!\angle$

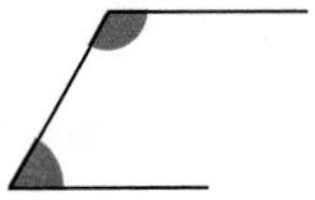

Entertainment

In an Ames room, two people of the same height that are standing in different parts of the room appear to be different sizes.

Entertainment Use the following information for Exercises 30–32.

In an Ames room, the floor is tilted and the back wall is closer to the front wall on one side.

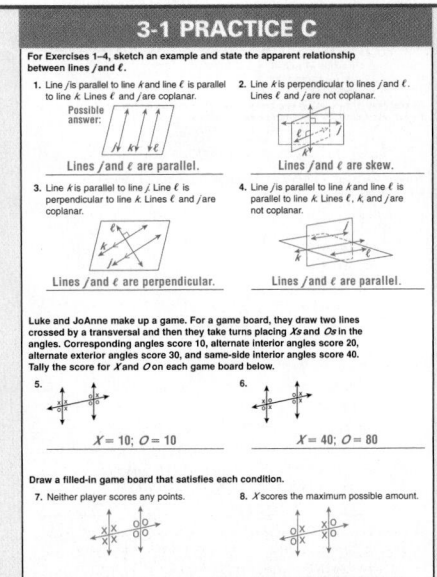

30. Name a pair of parallel segments in the diagram. $\overline{CD} \parallel \overline{GH}$

31. Name a pair of skew segments in the diagram. Possible answer: $\overline{CD}$ and $\overline{FG}$

32. Name a pair of perpendicular segments in the diagram. $\overline{DH} \perp \overline{GH}$

COMMON ERROR ALERT

In **Exercises 38–40,** some students may have difficulty choosing the correct transversal because three intersecting lines can be visually distracting. Suggest that these students redraw or trace the diagram for each exercise, labeling only the necessary angles.

Teaching Tip

Kinesthetic Students who have trouble visualizing skew lines in **Exercise 15** may benefit from building models of skew lines and parallel lines out of straws or toothpicks.

3-1 PRACTICE B

For Exercises 1–4, identify each of the following in the figure. Possible answers:

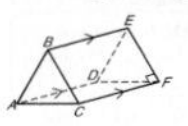

1. a pair of parallel segments — $\overline{BE} \parallel \overline{AD}$
2. a pair of skew segments — $\overline{AB}$ and $\overline{CF}$ are skew.
3. a pair of perpendicular segments — $\overline{CF} \perp \overline{EF}$
4. a pair of parallel planes — plane $ABC \parallel$ plane DEF

In Exercises 5–10, give one example of each from the figure.

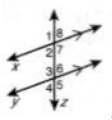

5. a transversal — line z
6. parallel lines — lines x and y
7. corresponding angles — Possible answer: $\angle 1$ and $\angle 3$
8. alternate interior angles — Possible answer: $\angle 2$ and $\angle 6$
9. alternate exterior angles — Possible answer: $\angle 1$ and $\angle 5$
10. same-side interior angles — Possible answer: $\angle 2$ and $\angle 3$

Use the figure for Exercises 11–14. The figure shows a utility pole with an electrical wire and a telephone line. For each angle pair given, identify the transversal and classify the angle pair. (*Hint:* Think of the utility pole as a line for these problems.)

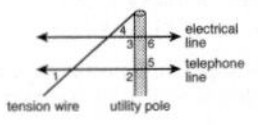

11. $\angle 5$ and $\angle 6$ — transv.: utility pole; same-side interior angles
12. $\angle 1$ and $\angle 4$ — transv.: tension wire; alternate exterior angles
13. $\angle 1$ and $\angle 2$ — transv.: telephone line; corresponding angles
14. $\angle 5$ and $\angle 3$ — transv.: utility pole; alternate interior angles

---

3-1 PRACTICE C

For Exercises 1–4, sketch an example and state the apparent relationship between lines j and ℓ.

1. Line k is parallel to line j and line ℓ is parallel to line k. Lines ℓ and j are coplanar.
 Possible answer: Lines j and ℓ are parallel.

2. Line k is perpendicular to lines j and ℓ. Lines ℓ and j are not coplanar.
 Lines j and ℓ are skew.

3. Line k is parallel to line j. Line ℓ is perpendicular to line k. Lines ℓ and j are coplanar.
 Lines j and ℓ are perpendicular.

4. Line j is parallel to line k and line ℓ is parallel to line k. Lines ℓ, k, and j are not coplanar.
 Lines j and ℓ are parallel.

Luke and JoAnne make up a game. For a game board, they draw two lines crossed by a transversal and then they take turns placing Xs and Os in the angles. Corresponding angles score 10, alternate interior angles score 20, alternate exterior angles score 30, and same-side interior angles score 40. Tally the score for X and O on each game board below.

5. $X = 10$; $O = 10$
6. $X = 40$; $O = 80$

Draw a filled-in game board that satisfies each condition.

7. Neither player scores any points.
8. X scores the maximum possible amount.

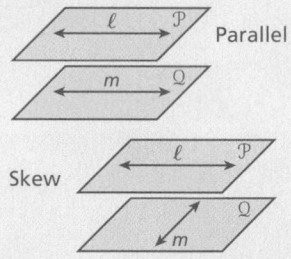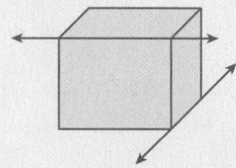

33. This problem will prepare you for the Multi-Step TAKS Prep on p 180.
Buildings that are tilted like the one shown are sometimes called mystery spots.
  a. Name a plane parallel to plane *KLP*, a plane parallel to plane *KNP*, and a plane parallel to *KLM*.
  b. In the diagram, $\overline{QR}$ is a transversal to $\overline{PQ}$ and $\overline{RS}$. What type of angle pair is ∠*PQR* and ∠*QRS*?

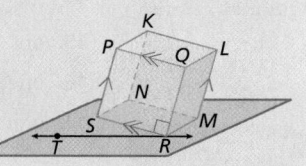

34. **Critical Thinking** Line ℓ is contained in plane *P* and line *m* is contained in plane *Q*. If *P* and *Q* are parallel, what are the possible classifications of ℓ and *m*? Include diagrams to support your answer.

Use the diagram for Exercises 35–40. Possible answers:

35. Name a pair of alternate interior angles with transversal *n*. ∠5 and ∠8

36. Name a pair of same-side interior angles with transversal ℓ. ∠2 and ∠7

37. Name a pair of corresponding angles with transversal *m*. ∠1 and ∠5

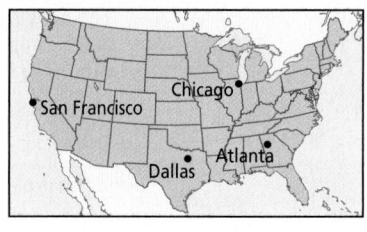

38. Identify the transversal and classify the angle pair for ∠3 and ∠7. transv.: ℓ; corr. ∠

39. Identify the transversal and classify the angle pair for ∠5 and ∠8. transv.: *n*; alt. int. ∠
transv.: *m*; alt. ext. ∠
40. Identify the transversal and classify the angle pair for ∠1 and ∠6.

41. **Aviation** Describe the type of lines formed by two planes when flight 1449 is flying from San Francisco to Atlanta at 32,000 feet and flight 2390 is flying from Dallas to Chicago at 28,000 feet. The lines are skew.

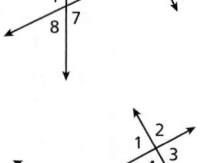

42. **Multi-Step** Draw line *p*, then draw two lines *m* and *n* that are both perpendicular to *p*. Make a conjecture about the relationship between lines *m* and *n*. *m* ∥ *n*

 43. **Write About It** Discuss a real-world example of skew lines. Include a sketch.

 **TEST PREP**

44. Which pair of angles in the diagram are alternate interior angles?
  Ⓐ ∠1 and ∠5
  Ⓑ ∠2 and ∠6
  Ⓒ ∠7 and ∠5
  Ⓓ ∠2 and ∠3

45. How many pairs of corresponding angles are in the diagram?
  Ⓕ 2   Ⓗ 8
  Ⓖ 4   Ⓙ 16

3-1 READING STRATEGIES

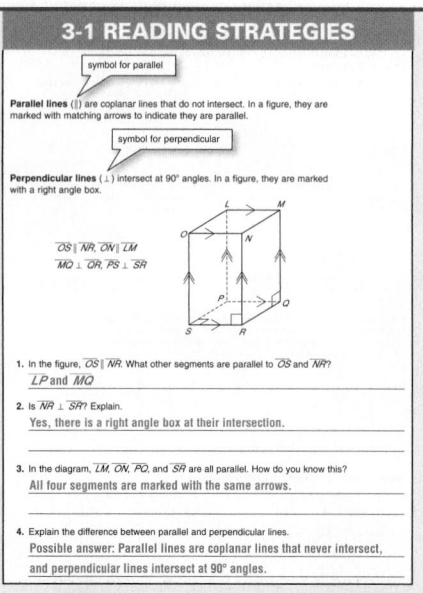

3-1 RETEACH

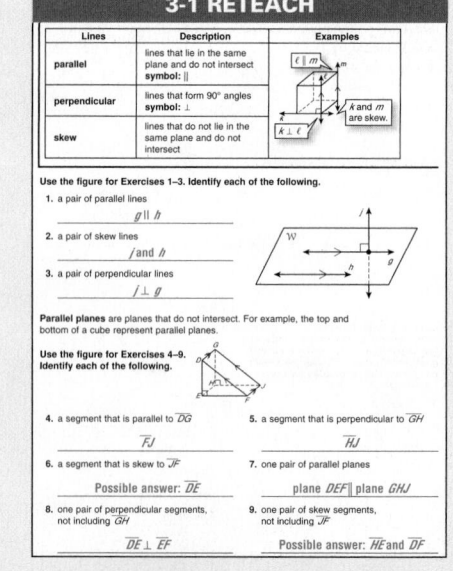

46. Which type of lines are NOT represented in the diagram?

(A) Parallel lines (C) Skew lines

(B) Intersecting lines (D) Perpendicular lines

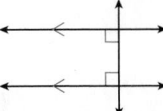

47. For two lines and a transversal, ∠1 and ∠8 are alternate exterior angles, and ∠1 and ∠5 are corresponding angles. Classify the angle pair ∠5 and ∠8.

(F) Vertical angles

(G) Alternate interior angles

(H) Adjacent angles

(J) Same-side interior angles

48. Which angles in the diagram are NOT corresponding angles?

(A) ∠1 and ∠5 (C) ∠4 and ∠8

(B) ∠2 and ∠6 (D) ∠2 and ∠7

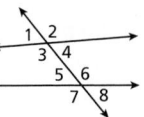

CHALLENGE AND EXTEND

Name all the angle pairs of each type in the diagram. Identify the transversal for each pair.

49. corresponding **50.** alternate interior

51. alternate exterior **52.** same-side interior

53. Multi-Step Draw two lines and a transversal such that ∠1 and ∠3 are corresponding angles, ∠1 and ∠2 are alternate interior angles, and ∠3 and ∠4 are alternate exterior angles. What type of angle pair is ∠2 and ∠4? **corr. ∠**

54. If the figure shown is folded to form a cube, which faces of the cube will be parallel?
the red and orange faces, the blue and purple faces, and the yellow and green faces

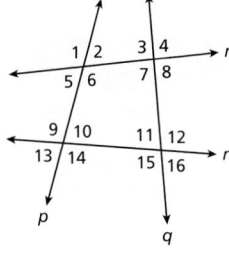

SPIRAL REVIEW

Evaluate each function for $x = -1, 0, 1, 2,$ and 3. *(Previous course)*

55. $y = 4x^2 - 7$
$-3; -7; -3; 9; 29$

56. $y = -2x^2 + 5$
$3; 5; 3; -3; -13$

57. $y = (x + 3)(x - 3)$
$-8; -9; -8; -5; 0$

Find the circumference and area of each circle. Use the π key on your calculator and round to the nearest tenth. *(Lesson 1-5)*

58.
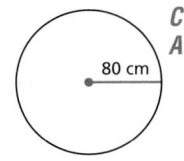
80 cm
$C = 502.7$ cm;
$A = 20{,}106.2$ cm^2

59.
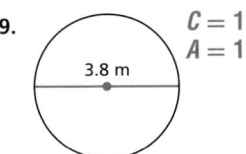
3.8 m
$C = 11.9$ m;
$A = 11.3$ m^2

Write a justification for each statement, given that ∠1 and ∠3 are right angles. *(Lesson 2-6)*

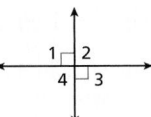

60. ∠1 ≅ ∠3 **Rt. ∠ ≅ Thm. or Vert. ∠ Thm.**

61. m∠1 + m∠2 = 180° **Lin. Pair Thm.**

62. ∠2 ≅ ∠4 **Vert. ∠ Thm.**

3-1 PROBLEM SOLVING

Use the diagram of the rectangular box for Exercises 1 and 2. Refer to the diagram to help justify your answer.

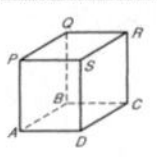

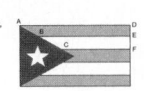

1. Is the relationship "is skew to" transitive?
   Possible answer: No; $\overline{AP}$ is skew to $\overline{RS}$ and $\overline{RS}$ is skew to $\overline{AD}$, but $\overline{AP}$ is not skew to $\overline{AD}$.

2. If a segment is skew to one of two parallel segments, must it be skew to the other?
   Possible answer: No; $\overline{PQ}$ is skew to $\overline{AD}$ but not to $\overline{PS}$.

Use the flag of Puerto Rico for Exercises 3 and 4.

3. If ∠DFC and ∠ACF are same-side interior angles, identify the transversal.
   $\overline{CF}$

4. Name a pair of alternate interior angles if the transversal is $\overline{BE}$.
   Possible answer: ∠DEB and ∠CBE

Choose the best answer.

5. Describe the type of lines suggested by the two skis of a person water skiing.
   A intersecting lines
   (B) parallel lines
   C perpendicular lines
   D skew lines

6. Describe the type of lines suggested by the paths of two people at a fair when one person is riding the aerial ride from one end of the fair to the other, and the other person is walking in a different direction on the ground.
   F intersecting H perpendicular
   G parallel (J) skew

7. In the quilt pattern, which is a true statement about the angles formed by the transversal $\overline{HK}$ and $\overline{HM}$ and $\overline{JL}$?
   (A) ∠LSK and ∠PHQ are corresponding angles.
   B ∠JSQ and ∠JQH are corresponding angles.
   C ∠LSK and ∠QSJ are same-side interior angles.
   D ∠PHQ and ∠RLS are same-side interior angles.

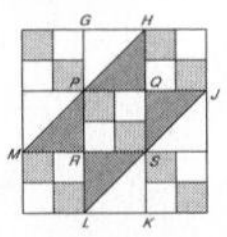

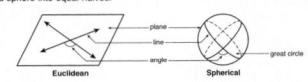

3-1 CHALLENGE

In Euclidean geometry, a line is a straight path that extends forever in two directions in a plane. In *spherical geometry*, a line is a **great circle**. This is a circle that divides a sphere into equal halves.

Euclidean Spherical

Answer *yes* or *no* for Exercises 1 and 2.

1. Does a line have endpoints in Euclidean geometry? in spherical geometry?
   no; no

2. Does a line have a measurable length in Euclidean geometry? in spherical geometry?
   no; yes

Use the figures at right for Exercises 3 and 4.

In each figure, P, Q, and R are collinear points and R is between points P and Q.

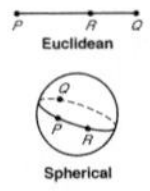

3. In the Euclidean figure, what conclusion is drawn from the Segment Addition Postulate?
   $PR + RQ = PQ$

4. Can you draw the same conclusion about the spherical figure? Explain.
   The distance $PR + RQ$, the length of the path from P to Q traveling in a *counterclockwise* direction, is much longer than the length of the path traveling from P to Q in a *clockwise* direction. So, $PR + RQ \neq PQ$.

Each statement below is true in Euclidean geometry. Explain why it is false in spherical geometry.

5. If two lines intersect, then their intersection is exactly one point.
   Any two lines will intersect at exactly two points.

6. One and only one line contains two given points.
   If the two points are at opposite "poles," then infinitely many lines will pass through them.

Answers

49–53. See p. A13.

✎ *Journal*

Have students draw a cube with each vertex labeled. Ask them to list a pair of perpendicular segments, a pair of parallel segments, and a pair of skew segments.

ALTERNATIVE ASSESSMENT

Have students sketch two parallel planes. Include an example of parallel lines, perpendicular lines, and skew lines in the sketch. Then have them sketch two lines cut by a transversal. Ask them to identify all pairs of alternate interior angles, alternate exterior angles, same-side interior angles, and corresponding angles.

Power Presentations with PowerPoint®

3-1 Lesson Quiz

Identify each of the following.

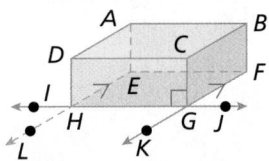

1. one pair of parallel segments
   $\overline{EH} \parallel \overline{FG}$

2. one pair of skew segments
   $\overline{BF}$ and $\overline{EH}$

3. one pair of perpendicular segments $\overline{CG} \perp \overline{GH}$

4. one pair of parallel planes
   ABC and *EFG*

5. one pair of alternate interior angles ∠EHG and ∠HGK

6. one pair of corresponding angles ∠EHG and ∠FGJ

7. one pair of alternate exterior angles ∠IHE and ∠JGK

8. one pair of same-side interior angles ∠EHG and ∠HGF

Also available on transparency

Organizer

See Skills Bank
page S67

Pacing:
Traditional $\frac{1}{2}$ day
Block $\frac{1}{4}$ day

Objective: Find angle measures
by solving systems of equations.

 Online Edition

Teach

Remember

Review with students the properties
of vertical angles and linear pairs
and how to solve systems of
equations.

INTERVENTION ◄═► For additional review and practice on solving
systems of equations, see Skills Bank
page S67.

Teaching Tip | **Inclusion** Some students
may prefer solving systems
of equations by other
methods, such as graphing or
substitution.

Close

Assess

Have students draw two intersecting lines and measure the angles
formed. Have them choose values
of x and y, and then write linear
expressions in terms of x and y for
two of the angle measures to form
a system of equations. Have them
show how to solve the system to
find x and y.

◆ TAKS *On Track for TAKS*
connects TAKS objectives across the
grade levels.

Grades 9–11
**Obj. 2 Properties and Attributes
of Functions** A.4.A find specific
function values, simplify polynomial
expressions, … solve equations … as
necessary in problem situations
**Obj. 4 Linear Equations and
Inequalities** A.8.B solve systems
of linear equations using concrete
models, graphs, tables, and algebraic
methods
**Obj. 6 Geometric Relationships
and Spatial Reasoning** G.5.B use
numeric and geometric patterns to
make generalizations about geometric
properties …

152 *Chapter 3*

Systems of Equations

Algebra

Sometimes angle measures are given as algebraic expressions. When you
know the relationship between two angles, you can write and solve a system
of equations to find angle measures.

*See Skills Bank
page S67*

Solving Systems of Equations by Using Elimination
Step 1 Write the system so that like terms are under one another.
Step 2 Eliminate one of the variables.
Step 3 Substitute that value into one of the original equations and solve.
Step 4 Write the answers as an ordered pair, (x, y).
Step 5 Check your solution.

Example 1

Solve for x and y.

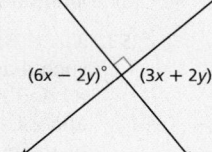

Since the lines are perpendicular, all of the angles are right angles.
To write two equations, you can set each expression equal to 90°.

$$(3x + 2y)° = 90°, (6x - 2y)° = 90°$$

Step 1 $3x + 2y = 90$
$\underline{6x - 2y = 90}$ *Write the system so that like terms are under one another.*

Step 2 $9x + 0 = 180$ *Add like terms on each side of the equations.
The y-term has been eliminated.*

$x = 20$ *Divide both sides by 9 to solve for x.*

Step 3 $3x + 2y = 90$ *Write one of the original equations.*

$3(20) + 2y = 90$ *Substitute 20 for x.*

$60 + 2y = 90$ *Simplify.*

$2y = 30$ *Subtract 60 from both sides.*

$y = 15$ *Divide by 2 on both sides.*

Step 4 $(20, 15)$ *Write the solution as an ordered pair.*

Step 5 Check the solution by substituting 20 for x and 15 for y in the original equations.

$3x$	$+$	$2y$	$= 90$			$6x$	$-$	$2y$	$= 90$	
$3(20)$	$+$	$2(15)$		90		$6(20)$	$-$	$2(15)$		90
60	$+$	30		90		120	$-$	30		90
		90		90 ✓				90		90 ✓

In some cases, before you can do Step 1 you will need to multiply one or
both of the equations by a number so that you can eliminate a variable.

Example 2

Solve for x and y.

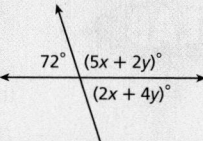

$(2x + 4y)° = 72°$ *Vertical Angles Theorem*

$(5x + 2y)° = 108°$ *Linear Pair Theorem*

The equations cannot be added or subtracted to eliminate a variable.
Multiply the second equation by -2 to get opposite y-coefficients.

$$5x + 2y = 108 \rightarrow -2(5x + 2y) = -2(108) \rightarrow -10x - 4y = -216$$

Step 1
$$\begin{aligned} 2x + 4y &= 72 \\ -10x - 4y &= -216 \end{aligned}$$
Write the system so that like terms are under one another.

Step 2
$$-8x = -144$$
Add like terms on both sides of the equations. The y-term has been eliminated.

$$x = 18$$
Divide both sides by -8 to solve for x.

Step 3
$$2x + 4y = 72$$
Write one of the original equations.

$$2(18) + 4y = 72$$
Substitute 18 for x.

$$36 + 4y = 72$$
Simplify.

$$4y = 36$$
Subtract 36 from both sides.

$$y = 9$$
Divide by 4 on both sides.

Step 4
$$(18, 9)$$
Write the solution as an ordered pair.

Step 5   Check the solution by substituting 18 for x and 9 for y in the original equations.

$2x$	$+$	$4y$	$= 72$	
$3(18)$	$+$	$4(9)$		72
36	$+$	36		72
		72		72 ✓

$5x$	$+$	$2y$	$= 108$	
$5(18)$	$+$	$2(9)$		108
90	$+$	18		108
		108		108 ✓

Try This

TAKS Grades 9–11 Obj. 2, 4, 6

Solve for x and y.

1.

$(10x + 4y)°$ $(26x - 4y)°$

$x = 5; y = 10$

2.

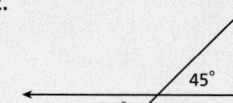

$45°$

$(3x + 3y)°$ $(-3x + 17y)°$

$x = 6; y = 9$

3.

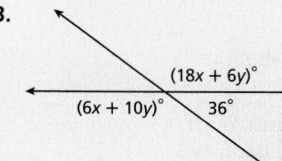

$(18x + 6y)°$

$(6x + 10y)°$ $36°$

$x = 4; y = 12$

4.

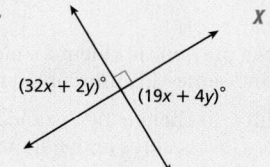

$(32x + 2y)°$ $(19x + 4y)°$

$x = 2; y = 13$

Technology Organizer
LAB

Use with Lesson 3-2

Pacing:
Traditional $\frac{1}{2}$ day
Block $\frac{1}{4}$ day

Objective: Use geometry software to explore angles formed by parallel lines and transversals.

Materials: geometry software

Online Edition
TechKeys

Countdown to TAKS Week 5

Teach

Discuss

Ask students what they think is true of any pair of angles they created. They are either supp. or ≅.

Close

Key Concept

For two parallel lines cut by a transversal, the corr., alt. int., and alt. ext. ∡ are ≅, and the same-side int. ∡ are supp.

Assessment

Journal Have students draw two nonparallel lines and a transversal, measure the angles formed, and make a conjecture.

Geometry TEKS

G.9 Congruence and the geometry of size*
(A) formulate and test conjectures about the properties of parallel and perpendicular lines based on explorations ...

* **Knowledge and Skills** See p. 144.

3-2
Technology LAB

Explore Parallel Lines and Transversals

Geometry software can help you explore angles that are formed when a transversal intersects a pair of parallel lines.

Use with Lesson 3-2

 TEKS G.9.A Congruence and the geometry of size: formulate and test conjectures about the properties of parallel and perpendicular lines based on explorations ....

go.hrw.com/Geo/TX
Lab Resources Online
KEYWORD: MG7 Lab3

Activity

1. Construct a line and label two points on the line A and B.

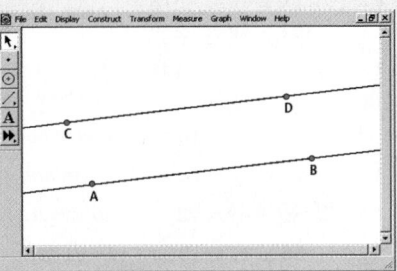

2. Create point C not on $\overleftrightarrow{AB}$. Construct a line parallel to $\overleftrightarrow{AB}$ through point C. Create another point on this line and label it D.

3. Create two points outside the two parallel lines and label them E and F. Construct transversal $\overleftrightarrow{EF}$. Label the points of intersection G and H.

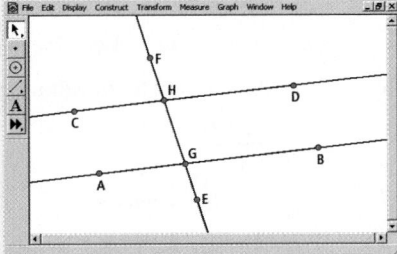

4. Measure the angles formed by the parallel lines and the transversal. Write the angle measures in a chart like the one below. Drag point E or F and chart with the new angle measures. What relationships do you notice about the angle measures? What conjectures can you make?

Angle	∠AGE	∠BGE	∠AGH	∠BGH	∠CHG	∠DHG	∠CHF	∠DHF
Measure	100°	80°	80°	100°	100°	80°	80°	100°
Measure	72°	108°	108°	72°	72°	108°	108°	72°

4. Possible measures are given in the table. Possible answer: All acute ∡ are ≅. All obtuse ∡ are ≅. Any acute ∠ is supp. to any obtuse ∠.

 **Try This**
1. The corr. ∡ are the pairs ∠AGE and ∠CHG, ∠BGE and ∠DHG, ∠AGH and ∠CHF, and ∠BGH and ∠DHF. The ∡ in each pair have = measures.

1. Identify the pairs of corresponding angles in the diagram. What conjecture can you make about their angle measures? Drag a point in the figure to confirm your conjecture.

2. Repeat steps in the previous problem for alternate interior angles, alternate exterior angles, and same-side interior angles.

3. Try dragging point C to change the distance between the parallel lines. What happens to the angle measures in the figure? Why do you think this happens?

Answers to *Try This*

2. The alt. int. ∡ are the pairs ∠CHG and ∠BGH, and ∠AGH and ∠DHG.
The ∡ in each pair have = measures.

The alt. ext. ∡ are the pairs ∠AGE and ∠DHF, and ∠BGE and ∠CHF.
The ∡ in each pair have = measures.

The same-side int. ∡ are the pairs ∠CHG and ∠AGH, and ∠BGH and ∠DHG.
The angles in each pair have measures that add up to 180°.

3. Possible answer: If the ∥ lines are dragged farther apart or closer together, there is no change in the ∠ measures. Since the lines remain ∥, the amount of "tilt" of the line remains the same, so the ∠ measures remain the same.

3-2 Angles Formed by Parallel Lines and Transversals

⭐ TEKS G.3.C Geometric structure: use logical reasoning to prove statements are true .... Also G.3.E, G.9.A

Objective
Prove and use theorems about the angles formed by parallel lines and a transversal.

Who uses this?
Piano makers use parallel strings for the higher notes. The longer strings used to produce the lower notes can be viewed as transversals. (See Example 3.)

When parallel lines are cut by a transversal, the angle pairs formed are either congruent or supplementary.

 Know it! Note

Postulate 3-2-1 — Corresponding Angles Postulate

THEOREM	HYPOTHESIS	CONCLUSION
If two parallel lines are cut by a transversal, then the pairs of corresponding angles are congruent.		$\angle 1 \cong \angle 3$ $\angle 2 \cong \angle 4$ $\angle 5 \cong \angle 7$ $\angle 6 \cong \angle 8$

EXAMPLE 1 — Using the Corresponding Angles Postulate

Find each angle measure.

A $m\angle ABC$

$$x = 80 \qquad \text{Corr. } \angle \text{s Post.}$$
$$m\angle ABC = 80°$$

Algebra

B $m\angle DEF$

$$(2x - 45)° = (x + 30)° \qquad \text{Corr. } \angle \text{s Post.}$$
$$x - 45 = 30 \qquad \text{Subtract x from both sides.}$$
$$x = 75 \qquad \text{Add 45 to both sides.}$$
$$m\angle DEF = x + 30$$
$$= 75 + 30 \qquad \text{Substitute 75 for x.}$$
$$= 105°$$

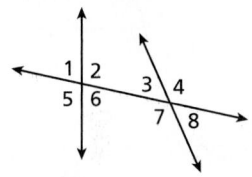

CHECK IT OUT!

1. Find $m\angle QRS$.
   $m\angle QRS = 62°$

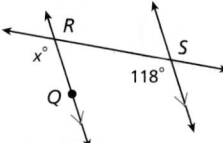

Remember that postulates are statements that are accepted without proof. Since the Corresponding Angles Postulate is given as a postulate, it can be used to prove the next three theorems.

Pacing: Traditional 1 day
Block $\frac{1}{2}$ day

Objective: Prove and use theorems about the angles formed by parallel lines and a transversal.

▽ **Geometry Lab**
In *Texas Lab Manual*

🪐 **Online Edition**
Tutorial Videos, Interactivity

🧊 **Countdown to TAKS Week 5**

Power Presentations with PowerPoint®

Warm Up

Identify each angle pair.

1. $\angle 1$ and $\angle 3$ — corr. ∠s
2. $\angle 3$ and $\angle 6$ — alt. int. ∠s
3. $\angle 4$ and $\angle 5$ — alt. ext. ∠s
4. $\angle 6$ and $\angle 7$ — same-side int. ∠s

Also available on transparency

Math Humor

Home owner: How do I know these two doors are the same size?

Carpenter: They're alternate exterior doors.

---

1 Introduce

3-2 Angles Formed by Parallel Lines and Transversals

Use two pieces of patty paper to explore the angles formed by two parallel lines and a transversal.

1. Use the opposite edges of a straightedge to draw two parallel lines on a piece of patty paper. 	2. Draw a transversal. Then label the angles as shown. 
3. Place a second piece of patty paper on top of the first and carefully trace the figure. 	4. Slide the top piece of paper down so that $\angle 1$ is on top of $\angle 5$.

5. How are the following pairs of angles related?
   $\angle 1$ and $\angle 5$ $\angle 1$ and $\angle 8$ $\angle 3$ and $\angle 6$ $\angle 3$ and $\angle 5$

THINK AND DISCUSS

6. Describe the pairs of congruent angles that are formed when parallel lines are cut by a transversal.

Motivate

Have students look through magazines to find pictures with parallel lines and transversals, such as bridges, fences, furniture, etc. Use markers or colored tape to mark the lines, and then identify angles that appear to be congruent and angles that appear to be supplementary.

Explorations and answers are provided in the *Explorations* binder.

⭐ Geometry TEKS

G.3 Geometric structure*
(C) use logical reasoning to prove statements are true ...
(E) use deductive reasoning to prove a statement

G.9 Congruence and the geometry of size*
(A) formulate and test conjectures about the properties of parallel and perpendicular lines based on explorations and concrete models

* Knowledge and Skills See p. 144.
Blue text indicates coverage in TE.

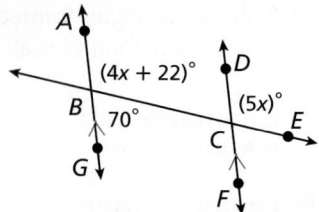

Additional Examples

Example 1

Find each angle measure.

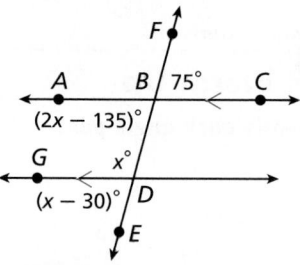

A. m∠ECF   70°

B. m∠DCE   110°

Example 2

Find each angle measure.

A. m∠EDG   75°

B. m∠BDG   105°

Also available on transparency

INTERVENTION ◀━▶
Questioning Strategies

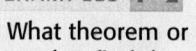
EXAMPLES 1–2

• What theorem or postulate was used to find the answer in each part of the example? How was it used?

• What equation was used to find the answer?

• Is the answer always x? Why or why not?

Visual Have students use lined paper to draw two parallel lines and a transversal that is not perpendicular to the lines. Instruct students to shade the acute angles one color and the obtuse angles another color. Let students use a protractor (MK) to see that all the angles shaded the same color are congruent and that pairs of angles shaded different colors are supplementary. Protractors can be found in the Manipulatives Kit (MK).

 **Theorems** (**Parallel Lines and Angle Pairs**)

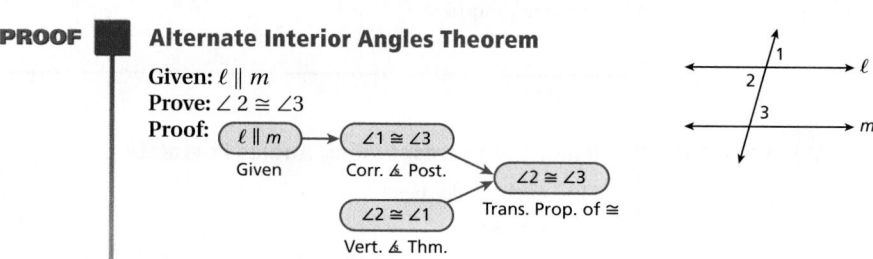

	THEOREM	HYPOTHESIS	CONCLUSION
3-2-2	**Alternate Interior Angles Theorem** If two parallel lines are cut by a transversal, then the pairs of alternate interior angles are congruent.		∠1 ≅ ∠3 ∠2 ≅ ∠4
3-2-3	**Alternate Exterior Angles Theorem** If two parallel lines are cut by a transversal, then the two pairs of alternate exterior angles are congruent.		∠5 ≅ ∠7 ∠6 ≅ ∠8
3-2-4	**Same-Side Interior Angles Theorem** If two parallel lines are cut by a transversal, then the two pairs of same-side interior angles are supplementary.		m∠1 + m∠4 = 180° m∠2 + m∠3 = 180°

Helpful Hint

If a transversal is perpendicular to two parallel lines, all eight angles are congruent.

You will prove Theorems 3-2-3 and 3-2-4 in Exercises 25 and 26.

PROOF ■ **Alternate Interior Angles Theorem**

Given: ℓ ∥ m
Prove: ∠2 ≅ ∠3
Proof:

ℓ ∥ m → ∠1 ≅ ∠3
Given   Corr. ∠ Post.

∠2 ≅ ∠1   → ∠2 ≅ ∠3
Vert. ∠ Thm.   Trans. Prop. of ≅

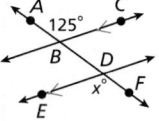

EXAMPLE 2 **Finding Angle Measures**

Find each angle measure.

A m∠EDF
       x = 125
       m∠EDF = 125°   *Alt. Ext. ∠ Thm.*

x² Algebra

B m∠TUS
       13x° + 23x° = 180°   *Same-Side Int. ∠ Thm.*
       36x = 180   *Combine like terms.*
       x = 5   *Divide both sides by 36.*
       m∠TUS = 23(5) = 115°   *Substitute 5 for x.*

 2. Find m∠ABD.
       m∠ABD = 60°

156   *Chapter 3 Parallel and Perpendicular Lines*

2 Teach

Guided Instruction

Review pairs of angles that are formed when two lines are cut by a transversal. Discuss the angle measures when the two lines are parallel. Remind students that arrows on a figure indicate parallel lines.

Multiple Representations Draw parallel lines and a transversal on a transparency. Trace an acute angle and an obtuse angle onto another transparency, and move them over each angle to show congruence.

Reaching All Learners
Through Kinesthetic Experience

Have students draw a pair of parallel lines and a transversal on patty paper. Tear the paper between the parallel lines, and overlay the two parts to show that the angles are congruent.

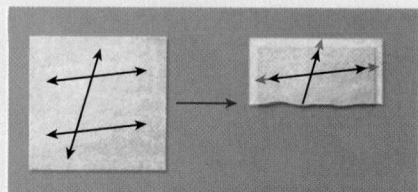

Student to Student

Nancy Martin
East Branch
High School

Parallel Lines and Transversals

When I solve problems with parallel lines and transversals, I remind myself that every pair of angles is either congruent or supplementary.

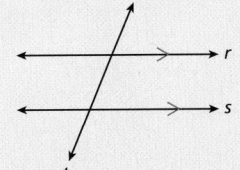

If r ‖ s, all the acute angles are congruent and all the obtuse angles are congruent. The acute angles are supplementary to the obtuse angles.

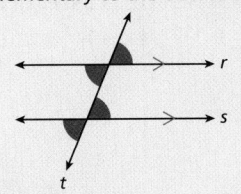

EXAMPLE 3 **Music Application**

xy Algebra

The treble strings of a grand piano are parallel. Viewed from above, the bass strings form transversals to the treble strings. Find *x* and *y* in the diagram.

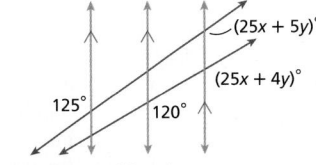

Bass strings   Treble strings

By the Alternate Exterior Angles Theorem, $(25x + 5y)° = 125°$.

By the Corresponding Angles Postulate, $(25x + 4y)° = 120°$.

$$25x + 5y = 125$$
$$-(25x + 4y = 120)$$
$$y = 5$$

Subtract the second equation from the first equation.

$$25x + 5(5) = 125$$

Substitute 5 for y in 25x + 5y = 125. Simplify and solve for x.

$$x = 4, y = 5$$

CHECK IT OUT! **3.** Find the measures of the acute angles in the diagram.
55° and 60°

THINK AND DISCUSS

1. Explain why a transversal that is perpendicular to two parallel lines forms eight congruent angles.

Know it! Note

2. GET ORGANIZED Copy the diagram and graphic organizer. Complete the graphic organizer by explaining why each of the three theorems is true.

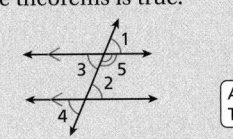

Corr. ∡ Post.

| Alt. Int. ∡ Thm. | Alt. Ext. ∡ Thm. | Same-Side Int. ∡ Thm. |

3-2 Angles Formed by Parallel Lines and Transversals **157**

Students may incorrectly apply the postulates and theorems presented in this lesson when lines cut by a transversal are not parallel. Remind them that the postulates and theorems are only true for parallel lines.

Teaching Tip **Auditory** As you work through the examples, call on students to read aloud the statement of each postulate or theorem when it is used as a justification in a solution.

Power Presentations with PowerPoint®

Additional Examples

Example 3

Find *x* and *y* in the diagram.

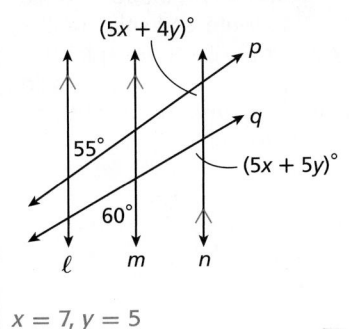

$x = 7, y = 5$

Also available on transparency

INTERVENTION ◄►
Questioning Strategies

EXAMPLE 3

• Which transversals intersect parallel lines?

• Which transversals intersect non-parallel lines?

---

3 Close

Summarize

Have students look at the diagram for the Corresponding Angles Postulate on p. 155. Have them identify the following:

Parallel lines *p* and *q*
Transversal *t*
Congruent angles:
  Corresponding ∠1 ≅ ∠3; ∠2 ≅ ∠4;
  ∠5 ≅ ∠7; ∠6 ≅ ∠8
  Alternate interior ∠2 ≅ ∠7; ∠3 ≅ ∠6
  Alternate exterior ∠1 ≅ ∠8; ∠4 ≅ ∠5
Supplementary angles:
  Same-side interior ∠2 and ∠3; ∠6
  and ∠7

ONGOING ASSESSMENT
and INTERVENTION ◄►

Diagnose Before the Lesson
3-2 Warm Up, TE p. 155

Monitor During the Lesson
Check It Out! Exercises, SE pp. 155–157
Questioning Strategies, TE pp. 156–157

Assess After the Lesson
3-2 Lesson Quiz, TE p. 161
Alternative Assessment, TE p. 161

Answers to Think and Discuss

1. If the transv. is ⊥, all the ∡ formed are rt. ∡, and all rt. ∡ are ≅.

2. See p. A3.

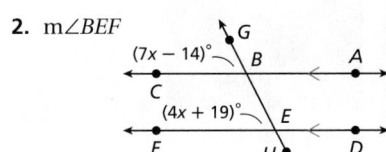

go.hrw.com/Geo/TX
Homework Help Online
KEYWORD: MG7 3-2
Parent Resources Online
KEYWORD: MG7 Parent

Assignment Guide

Assign *Guided Practice* exercises as necessary.

If you finished Examples **1–3**
  Basic 6–25, 29, 31, 33–36, 41–47
  Average 6–12, 14–18 even, 20–38, 41–47
  Advanced 6–12, 14–18 even, 20–30, 32–47

Homework Quick Check
Quickly check key concepts.
Exercises: 6, 8, 12, 20, 25

 Teaching Tip **Algebra** For **Exercises 7** and **9–11**, students need to write and solve multi-step equations. Be sure students know whether to set the expressions equal to each other or to set their sum equal to 180°.

GUIDED PRACTICE

SEE EXAMPLE 1 p. 155

Find each angle measure.

1. m∠JKL

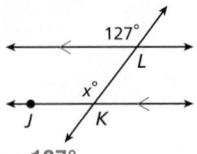

m∠JKL = 127°

2. m∠BEF

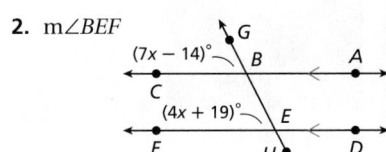

m∠BEF = 63°

SEE EXAMPLE 2 p. 156

3. m∠1

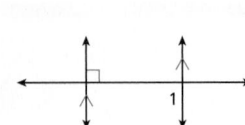

m∠1 = 90°

4. m∠CBY

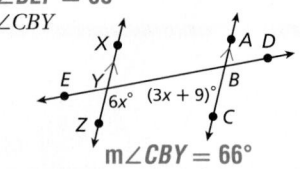

m∠CBY = 66°

SEE EXAMPLE 3 p. 157

5. Safety The railing of a wheelchair ramp is parallel to the ramp. Find *x* and *y* in the diagram.

x = 8; *y* = 9

PRACTICE AND PROBLEM SOLVING

Independent Practice

For Exercises	See Example
6–7	1
8–11	2
12	3

TEKS ⬤ TAKS
Skills Practice p. S8
Application Practice p. S30

Find each angle measure.

6. m∠KLM

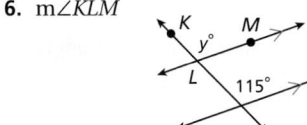

m∠KLM = 115°

7. m∠VYX

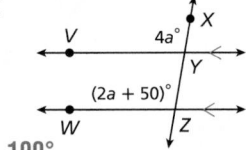

m∠VYX = 100°

8. m∠ABC

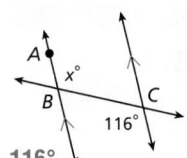

m∠ABC = 116°

9. m∠EFG

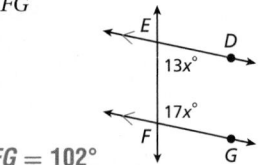

m∠EFG = 102°

10. m∠PQR

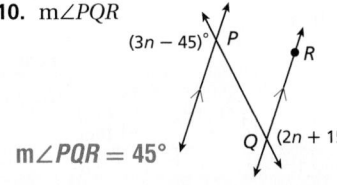

m∠PQR = 45°

11. m∠STU

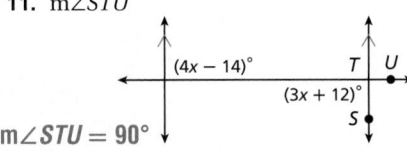

m∠STU = 90°

🔷 TAKS Practice

Grades 9–11	Exercises
Obj. 2	20–23, 30, 34
Obj. 3	41, 42
Obj. 4	20–23, 30

3-2 PRACTICE A

1. The Corresponding Angles Postulate states that if two parallel lines are cut by a transversal, then the pairs of corresponding angles are _____ **congruent** .

2. Congruent angles have _____ **equal** _____ measures.

Find each angle measure.

3. m∠1 _____ **140°**

4. m∠2 _____ **70°**

Find x.

5. _____ **75**

6. _____ **150**

Fill in the blanks to complete these theorems about angle pairs.

7. If two _____ **parallel** _____ lines are cut by a _____ **transversal** _____ then the two pairs of alternate interior angles are congruent.

8. If two parallel lines are cut by a transversal, then the two pairs of same-side interior angles are _____ **supplementary** _____ .

9. If two parallel lines are cut by a transversal, then the two pairs of alternate exterior angles are _____ **congruent** _____ .

Give two examples of each kind of angle pair in the figure.

10. alternate interior angles _____ ∠3 and ∠5; ∠4 and ∠6

11. alternate exterior angles _____ ∠1 and ∠7; ∠2 and ∠8

12. same-side interior angles _____ ∠3 and ∠6; ∠4 and ∠5

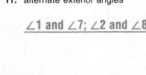

13. 120°; Corr. ∠ Post.

14. 60°; Lin. Pair Thm.

15. 60°; Same-Side Int. ∠ Thm.

16. 120°; Alt. Int. ∠ Thm.

17. 60°; Lin. Pair Thm.

18. 60°; Lin. Pair Thm.

12. Parking In the parking lot shown, the lines that mark the width of each space are parallel.

$m\angle 1 = (2x - 3y)°$

$m\angle 2 = (x + 3y)°$

Find x and y.

$x = 60, y = 20$

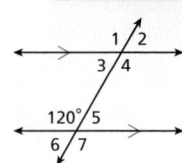

Find each angle measure. Justify each answer with a postulate or theorem.

13. m∠1 **14.** m∠2 **15.** m∠3

16. m∠4 **17.** m∠5 **18.** m∠6

19. m∠7 120°; Vert. ∠ Thm.

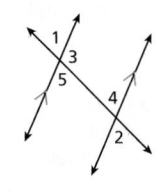

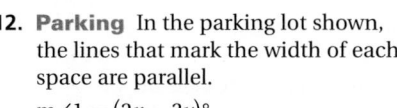
Architecture

The Luxor hotel is 600 feet wide, 600 feet long, and 350 feet high. The atrium in the hotel measures 29 million cubic feet.

x² Algebra State the theorem or postulate that is related to the measures of the angles in each pair. Then find the angle measures.

20. $m\angle 1 = (7x + 15)°$, $m\angle 2 = (10x - 9)°$

21. $m\angle 3 = (23x + 11)°$, $m\angle 4 = (14x + 21)°$

22. $m\angle 4 = (37x - 15)°$, $m\angle 5 = (44x - 29)°$

23. $m\angle 1 = (6x + 24)°$, $m\angle 4 = (17x - 9)°$

20. $x = 8$; Alt. Ext. ∠ Thm.; m∠1 = m∠2 = 71°

21. $x = 4$; Same-Side Int. ∠ Thm.; m∠3 =103°; m∠4= 77°

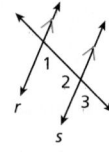

24. Architecture The Luxor Hotel in Las Vegas, Nevada, is a 30-story pyramid. The hotel uses an elevator called an inclinator to take people up the side of the pyramid. The inclinator travels at a 39° angle. Which theorem or postulate best illustrates the angles formed by the path of the inclinator and each parallel floor? (*Hint:* Draw a picture.) Corr. ∠ Post.

25. Complete the two-column proof of the Alternate Exterior Angles Theorem.

Given: ℓ ∥ m

Prove: ∠1 ≅ ∠2

Proof:

Statements	Reasons
1. ℓ ∥ m	1. Given
2. a. ___?___	2. Vert. ∠ Thm.
3. ∠3 ≅ ∠2	3. b. ___?___
4. c. ___?___	4. d. ___?___

a. ∠1 ≅ ∠3
b. Corr. ∠ Post.
c. ∠1 ≅ ∠2
d. Trans. Prop. of ≅

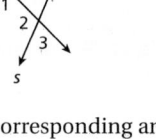

26. Write a paragraph proof of the Same-Side Interior Angles Theorem.

Given: r ∥ s

Prove: m∠1 + m∠2 = 180°

28. The situation is impossible because when ∥ lines are intersected by a transv., same-side int. ∠ are supp.

Draw the given situation or tell why it is impossible.

27. Two parallel lines are intersected by a transversal so that the corresponding angles are supplementary.

28. Two parallel lines are intersected by a transversal so that the same-side interior angles are complementary.

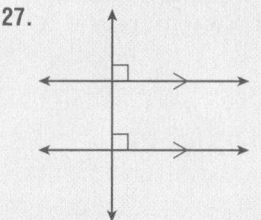

Answers

22. $x = 2$; Alt. Int. ∠ Thm.; m∠4 = m∠5 = 59°

23. $x = 3$; Corr. ∠ Post.; m∠1 = m∠4 = 42°

26. It is given that $r ∥ s$. By the Corr. ∠ Post., ∠1 ≅ ∠3; so m∠1 = m∠3 by def. of ≅ ∠. By the Lin. Pair Thm., m∠3 + m∠2 = 180°. By subst. m∠1 + m∠2 = 180°.

27.

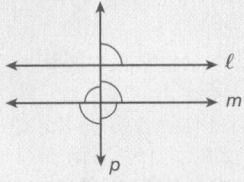
30. The ∠ are same-side int. ∠; m∠1 = 72°; and m∠2 = 108°.

31. A is incorrect because the ∠ are supp, not ≅.

32. By the Alt. Int. ∠ Thm., $x° = y°$, so $\dfrac{x}{y} = 1$.

29. This problem will prepare you for the Multi-Step TAKS Prep on page 180.

In the diagram, which represents the side view of a mystery spot, m∠SRT = 25°. $\overleftrightarrow{RT}$ is a transversal to $\overleftrightarrow{PS}$ and $\overleftrightarrow{QR}$.

a. What type of angle pair is ∠QRT and ∠STR? ⟵ same-side int. ∠

b. Find m∠STR. Use a theorem or postulate to justify your answer.

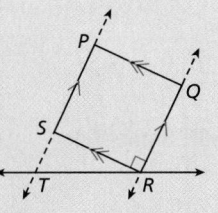

29b. By the Same-Side Int. ∠ Thm., m∠QRT + m∠STR = 180°. m∠QRT = 25° + 90° = 115°, so m∠STR = 65°.

30. Land Development A piece of property lies between two parallel streets as shown. m∠1 = $(2x + 6)°$, and m∠2 = $(3x + 9)°$. What is the relationship between the angles? What are their measures?

31. ///ERROR ANALYSIS/// In the figure, m∠ABC = $(15x + 5)°$, and m∠BCD = $(10x + 25)°$. Which value of m∠BCD is incorrect? Explain.

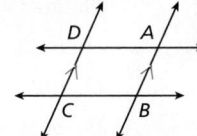

A

$$15x + 5 = 10x + 25$$
$$-10x \qquad -10x$$
$$5x + 5 = 25$$
$$-5 \qquad -5$$
$$5x = 20$$
$$x = 4$$

m∠BCD = 10(4) + 25 = 65°

B

$$(15x + 5) + (10x + 25) = 180$$
$$25x + 30 = 180$$
$$-30 \quad -30$$
$$25x = 150$$
$$x = 6$$

m∠BCD = 10(6) + 25 = 85°

32. Critical Thinking In the diagram, $\ell \parallel m$. Explain why $\dfrac{x}{y} = 1$.

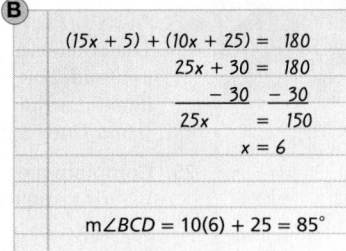

33. Write About It Suppose that lines ℓ and m are intersected by transversal p. One of the angles formed by ℓ and p is congruent to every angle formed by m and p. Draw a diagram showing lines ℓ, m, and p, mark any congruent angles that are formed, and explain what you know is true.

 **TEST PREP**

34. m∠RST = $(x + 50)°$, and m∠STU = $(3x + 20)°$. Find m∠RVT.

(A) 15° (C) 65°

(B) 27.5° (D) 77.5°

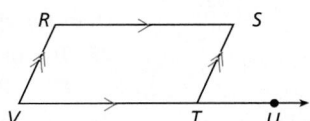

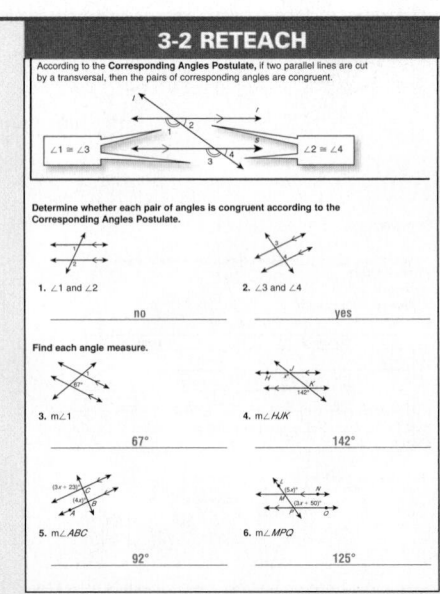

35. For two parallel lines and a transversal, m∠1 = 83°. For which pair of angle measures is the sum the least?

36. By the Lin. Pair Thm., m∠1 + m∠2 = 180°. By the Alt. Int. ∠Thm., ∠2 ≅ ∠3, so m∠2 = m∠3. By subst., m∠1 + m∠3 = 180°, so ∠1 and ∠3 are supp.

   Ⓕ ∠1 and a corresponding angle

   Ⓖ ∠1 and a same-side interior angle

   Ⓗ ∠1 and its supplement

   Ⓙ ∠1 and its complement

36. Short Response Given a ∥ b with transversal t, explain why ∠1 and ∠3 are supplementary.

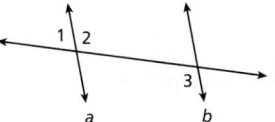

CHALLENGE AND EXTEND

Multi-Step Find m∠1 in each diagram. (*Hint:* Draw a line parallel to the given parallel lines.)

37. m∠1 = 75°

145°

1

40°

38. m∠1 = 155°

1

105°

80°

39. By the Same-Side Int. ∠ Thm., 10x + 5y + 80 = 180 and 15x + 4y + 72 = 180. So x = 4 and y = 12.

39. Find x and y in the diagram. Justify your answer.

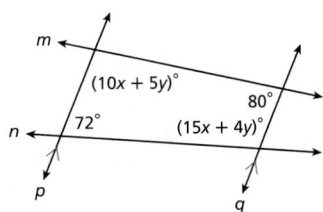

40. Two lines are parallel. The measures of two corresponding angles are a° and 2b°, and the measures of two same-side interior angles are a° and b°. Find the value of a.
a = 120

SPIRAL REVIEW

If the first quantity increases, tell whether the second quantity is likely to increase, decrease, or stay the same. (*Previous course*)

41. time in years and average cost of a new car **increase**

42. age of a student and length of time needed to read 500 words **decrease**

Use the Law of Syllogism to draw a conclusion from the given information. (*Lesson 2-3*)

43. If two angles form a linear pair, then they are supplementary. If two angles are supplementary, then their measures add to 180°. ∠1 and ∠2 form a linear pair.
        m∠1 + m∠2 = 180°

44. If a figure is a square, then it is a rectangle. If a figure is a rectangle, then its sides are perpendicular. Figure *ABCD* is a square. **The sides of *ABCD* are ⊥.**

Give an example of each angle pair. (*Lesson 3-1*) **Possible answers:**

45. alternate interior angles **∠3 and ∠6**

46. alternate exterior angles **∠1 and ∠8**

47. same-side interior angles **∠3 and ∠5**

3-2 PROBLEM SOLVING

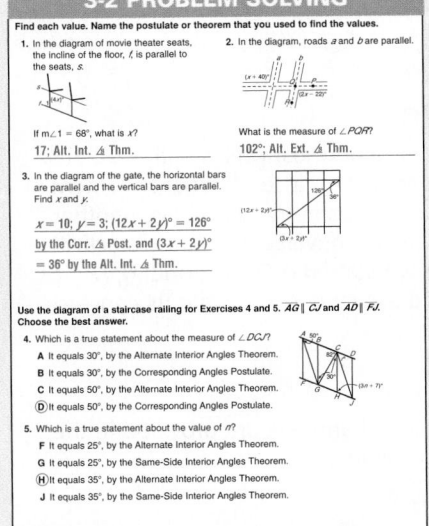

3-2 CHALLENGE

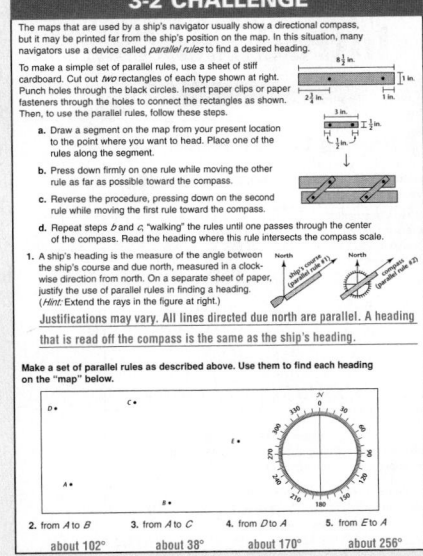

✎ *Journal*

Have students list examples in the real world where they have seen parallel lines cut by a transversal.

ALTERNATIVE ASSESSMENT

Have students sketch and label two parallel lines cut by a transversal. Have them use a protractor to measure the angles. Then they should use the sketch to explain the relationships among all the angles.

Power Presentations with PowerPoint®

3-2 Lesson Quiz ✓

State the theorem or postulate that is related to the measures of the angles in each pair. Then find the unknown angle measures.

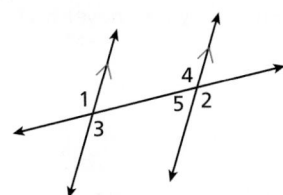

1. m∠1 = 120°, m∠2 = (60x)°
Alt. Ext. ∠ Thm.; m∠2 = 120°

2. m∠2 = (75x − 30)°, m∠3 = (30x + 60)°   Corr. ∠ Post.; m∠2 = 120°, m∠3 = 120°

3. m∠3 = (50x + 20)°, m∠4 = (100x − 80)°   Alt. Int. ∠ Thm.; m∠3 = 120°, m∠4 = 120°

4. m∠3 = (45x + 30)°, m∠5 = (25x + 10)°   Same-Side Int. ∠ Thm.; m∠3 = 120°, m∠5 = 60°

Also available on transparency

3-3 Proving Lines Parallel

⭐ TEKS G.3.C Geometric structure: use logical reasoning to prove statements are true …. Also G.1.A, G.3.E, G.9.A

Objective
Use the angles formed by a transversal to prove two lines are parallel.

Who uses this?
Rowers have to keep the oars on each side parallel in order to travel in a straight line. (See Example 4.)

Recall that the converse of a theorem is found by exchanging the hypothesis and conclusion. The converse of a theorem is not automatically true. If it is true, it must be stated as a postulate or proved as a separate theorem.

Know it! *Note*

Postulate 3-3-1	Converse of the Corresponding Angles Postulate	
THEOREM	**HYPOTHESIS**	**CONCLUSION**
If two coplanar lines are cut by a transversal so that a pair of corresponding angles are congruent, then the two lines are parallel.	$\angle 1 \cong \angle 2$	$m \parallel n$

EXAMPLE 1 Using the Converse of the Corresponding Angles Postulate

Use the Converse of the Corresponding Angles Postulate and the given information to show that $\ell \parallel m$.

A $\angle 1 \cong \angle 5$
$\angle 1 \cong \angle 5$ $\angle 1$ and $\angle 5$ are corresponding angles.
$\ell \parallel m$ Conv. of Corr. $\angle$s Post.

 Algebra

B $m\angle 4 = (2x + 10)°, m\angle 8 = (3x - 55)°, x = 65$
$m\angle 4 = 2(65) + 10 = 140$ Substitute 65 for x.
$m\angle 8 = 3(65) - 55 = 140$ Substitute 65 for x.
$m\angle 4 = m\angle 8$ Trans. Prop. of Equality
$\angle 4 \cong \angle 8$ Def. of $\cong \angle$
$\ell \parallel m$ Conv. of Corr. $\angle$ Post.

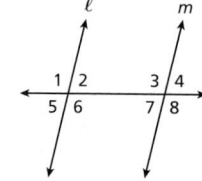
CHECK IT OUT! Use the Converse of the Corresponding Angles Postulate and the given information to show that $\ell \parallel m$.

1a. $m\angle 1 = m\angle 3$
1b. $m\angle 7 = (4x + 25)°$,
     $m\angle 5 = (5x + 12)°, x = 13$

1a. $\angle 1 \cong \angle 3$, so $\ell \parallel m$ by the Conv. of the Corr. $\angle$ Post.

1b. $m\angle 7 = 77°$ and $m\angle 5 = 77°$, so $\angle 7 \cong \angle 5$. $\ell \parallel m$ by the Conv. of the Corr. $\angle$ Post.

1 Introduce

EXPLORATION
3-3 Proving Lines Parallel

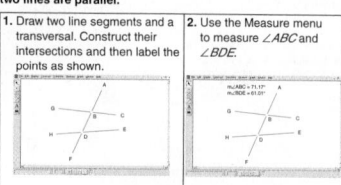

Use geometry software to explore conditions under which two lines are parallel.

1. Draw two line segments and a transversal. Construct their intersections and then label the points as shown.

2. Use the Measure menu to measure $\angle ABC$ and $\angle BDE$.

3. Drag one or more points so that $m\angle ABC = m\angle BDE$. What appears to be true about $\overrightarrow{GC}$ and $\overrightarrow{HE}$?

4. Drag the segments into new positions and then measure $\angle ABC$ and $\angle HDF$. Drag points so that $m\angle ABC = m\angle HDF$. What appears to be true about $\overrightarrow{GC}$ and $\overrightarrow{HE}$?

5. Drag the segments into new positions and then measure $\angle GBD$ and $\angle BDE$. Drag points so that $m\angle GBD = m\angle BDE$. What appears to be true about $\overrightarrow{GC}$ and $\overrightarrow{HE}$?

Motivate

Review the concept of converses with students. Have a volunteer state a conditional statement that is not about geometry. Then have another volunteer state its converse. Repeat this activity a few times. Then state the Corresponding Angles Postulate and ask students to state its converse.

Explorations and answers are provided in the *Explorations* binder.

 **Postulate 3-3-2** (**Parallel Postulate**)

Through a point P not on line ℓ, there is exactly one line parallel to ℓ.

The Converse of the Corresponding Angles Postulate is used to construct parallel lines. The Parallel Postulate guarantees that for any line ℓ, you can always construct a parallel line through a point that is not on ℓ.

 **Construction** Parallel Lines

1 Draw a line ℓ and a point P that is not on ℓ.

2 Draw a line m through P that intersects ℓ. Label the angle 1.

3 Construct an angle congruent to $\angle 1$ at P. By the converse of the Corresponding Angles Postulate, $\ell \parallel n$.

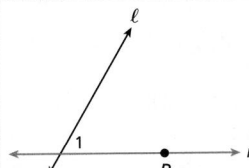 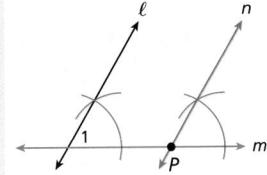

 **Theorems** (**Proving Lines Parallel**)

THEOREM		HYPOTHESIS	CONCLUSION
3-3-3	**Converse of the Alternate Interior Angles Theorem** If two coplanar lines are cut by a transversal so that a pair of alternate interior angles are congruent, then the two lines are parallel.	$\angle 1 \cong \angle 2$	$m \parallel n$
3-3-4	**Converse of the Alternate Exterior Angles Theorem** If two coplanar lines are cut by a transversal so that a pair of alternate exterior angles are congruent, then the two lines are parallel.	$\angle 3 \cong \angle 4$	$m \parallel n$
3-3-5	**Converse of the Same-Side Interior Angles Theorem** If two coplanar lines are cut by a transversal so that a pair of same-side interior angles are supplementary, then the two lines are parallel.	$m\angle 5 + m\angle 6 = 180°$	$m \parallel n$

You will prove Theorems 3-3-3 and 3-3-5 in Exercises 38–39.

As you work through the examples, watch for students who use a postulate or theorem for justification when its converse should be used. To help them choose the correct conditional, point out that any given information corresponds to the hypothesis in a conditional statement.

Power Presentations with PowerPoint®

Additional Examples

Example 1

Use the Converse of the Corresponding Angles Postulate and the given information to show that $\ell \parallel m$.

A. $\angle 4 \cong \angle 8$

$\angle 4$ and $\angle 8$ are corr. $\angle$., so $\ell \parallel m$ by the Conv. of Corr. $\angle$ Post.

B. $m\angle 3 = (4x - 80)°$, $m\angle 7 = (3x - 50)°$, $x = 30$

$m\angle 3 = 4(30) - 80 = 40$
$m\angle 7 = 3(30) - 50 = 40$
$m\angle 3 = m\angle 7$, so $\angle 3 \cong \angle 7$.
$\ell \parallel m$ by the Conv. of Corr. $\angle$ Post.

Also available on transparency

INTERVENTION ◄►
Questioning Strategies

EXAMPLE 1

• What other pairs of angles can you use with the Converse of the Corresponding Angles Postulate to prove the lines parallel?

 Construction

Ask students why the lines constructed must be parallel.
We constructed congruent corresponding angles.

 Teaching Tip **Math Background** The Parallel Postulate is needed to prove many important theorems in Euclidean geometry. It is not true in spherical geometry, which will be studied in Chapter 10.

2 Teach

Guided Instruction

As you present the postulates and theorems in this lesson, have students compare them with their related postulates and theorems in the previous lesson.

In Lesson 3-2, parallel lines and a transversal were used to prove that angles were congruent. In this lesson, congruent angles will be used to prove that lines are parallel.

Reaching All Learners
Through Concrete Manipulatives

Have students tape two pieces of uncooked spaghetti together to form four angles, and measure one angle. Have them place another piece of spaghetti so that the corresponding angle is congruent to the measured angle. Repeat with different angle pairs.

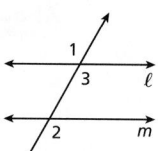

Additional Examples

Example 2

Use the diagram in Example 2, the given information, and the theorems you have learned to show that $r \parallel s$.

A. $\angle 4 \cong \angle 8$

$\angle 4$ and $\angle 8$ are alt. ext. $\angle$., so $r \parallel s$ by the Conv. of Alt. Ext. $\angle$ Thm.

B. $m\angle 2 = (10x + 8)°$, $m\angle 3 = (25x - 3)°$, $x = 5$

$m\angle 2 = 58°$; $m\angle 3 = 122°$; $m\angle 2 + m\angle 3 = 58° + 122° = 180°$; $\angle 2$ and $\angle 3$ are supp. same-side int. $\angle$., so $r \parallel s$ by the Conv. of Same-Side Int. $\angle$ Thm.

Example 3

Use the diagram in Example 3.

Given: $p \parallel r$, $\angle 1 \cong \angle 3$
Prove: $\ell \parallel m$

1. $p \parallel r$ (Given)
2. $\angle 3 \cong \angle 2$ (Alt. Ext. $\angle$ Thm.)
3. $\angle 1 \cong \angle 3$ (Given)
4. $\angle 1 \cong \angle 2$ (Trans. Prop. of $\cong$)
5. $\ell \parallel m$ (Conv. of Corr. $\angle$ Post.)

Also available on transparency

INTERVENTION ⬅️➡️
Questioning Strategies

EXAMPLE **2**

- What are some angle pairs that must be congruent for the lines to be parallel?
- What are some angle pairs that must be supplementary for the lines to be parallel?

EXAMPLE **3**

- Classify the special angle pairs in the diagram. What is the transversal for each pair?

PROOF ▪ **Converse of the Alternate Exterior Angles Theorem**

Given: $\angle 1 \cong \angle 2$
Prove: $\ell \parallel m$
Proof: It is given that $\angle 1 \cong \angle 2$. Vertical angles are congruent, so $\angle 1 \cong \angle 3$. By the Transitive Property of Congruence, $\angle 2 \cong \angle 3$. So $\ell \parallel m$ by the Converse of the Corresponding Angles Postulate.

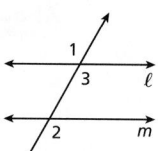

EXAMPLE 2 **Determining Whether Lines are Parallel**

Use the given information and the theorems you have learned to show that $r \parallel s$.

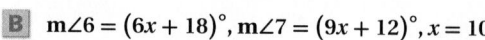

A $\angle 2 \cong \angle 6$

$\angle 2 \cong \angle 6$ $\angle 2$ and $\angle 6$ are alternate interior angles.
$r \parallel s$ Conv. of Alt. Int. $\angle$ Thm.

 **Algebra**

B $m\angle 6 = (6x + 18)°$, $m\angle 7 = (9x + 12)°$, $x = 10$

$m\angle 6 = 6x + 18$
$\quad = 6(10) + 18 = 78°$ *Substitute 10 for x.*
$m\angle 7 = 9x + 12$
$\quad = 9(10) + 12 = 102°$ *Substitute 10 for x.*
$m\angle 6 + m\angle 7 = 78° + 102°$
$\quad = 180°$ *$\angle 6$ and $\angle 7$ are same-side interior angles.*
$r \parallel s$ *Conv. of Same-Side Int. $\angle$ Thm.*

CHECK IT OUT! Refer to the diagram above. Use the given information and the theorems you have learned to show that $r \parallel s$.

2a. $m\angle 4 = m\angle 8$ **2b.** $m\angle 3 = 2x°$, $m\angle 7 = (x + 50)°$, $x = 50$

2a. $\angle 4 \cong \angle 8$, so $r \parallel s$ by the Conv. of the Alt. Ext. $\angle$ Thm.

2b. $m\angle 3 = 100°$ and $m\angle 7 = 100°$, so $\angle 3 \cong \angle 7$. $r \parallel s$ by the Conv. of the Alt. Int. $\angle$ Thm.

EXAMPLE 3 **Proving Lines Parallel**

Given: $\ell \parallel m$, $\angle 1 \cong \angle 3$
Prove: $r \parallel p$

Proof:

Statements	Reasons
1. $\ell \parallel m$	1. Given
2. $\angle 1 \cong \angle 2$	2. Corr. $\angle$ Post.
3. $\angle 1 \cong \angle 3$	3. Given
4. $\angle 2 \cong \angle 3$	4. Trans. Prop. of $\cong$
5. $r \parallel p$	5. Conv. of Alt. Ext. $\angle$ Thm.

1. $\angle 1 \cong \angle 4$ (Given)
2. $m\angle 1 = m\angle 4$ (Def. $\cong$ $\angle$)
3. $\angle 3$ and $\angle 4$ are supp. (Given)
4. $m\angle 3 + m\angle 4 = 180°$ (Def. supp. $\angle$)
5. $m\angle 3 + m\angle 1 = 180°$ (Subst.)
6. $m\angle 2 = m\angle 3$ (Vert. $\angle$ Thm.)
7. $m\angle 2 + m\angle 1 = 180°$ (Subst.)
8. $\ell \parallel m$ (Conv. of Same-Side Int. $\angle$ Thm.)

CHECK IT OUT! **3.** **Given:** $\angle 1 \cong \angle 4$, $\angle 3$ and $\angle 4$ are supplementary.
Prove: $\ell \parallel m$

EXAMPLE **4** *Sports Application*

During a race, all members of a rowing team should keep the oars parallel on each side. If $m\angle 1 = (3x + 13)°$, $m\angle 2 = (5x - 5)°$, and $x = 9$, show that the oars are parallel.

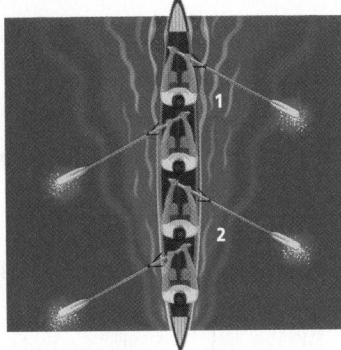

A line through the center of the boat forms a transversal to the two oars on each side of the boat.

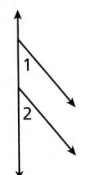

$\angle 1$ and $\angle 2$ are corresponding angles. If $\angle 1 \cong \angle 2$, then the oars are parallel.

Substitute 9 for x in each expression:

$m\angle 1 = 3x + 13$

$\quad = 3(9) + 13 = 40°$ *Substitute 9 for x in each expression.*

$m\angle 2 = 5x - 5$

$\quad = 5(9) - 5 = 40°$ $m\angle 1 = m\angle 2$, so $\angle 1 \cong \angle 2$.

The corresponding angles are congruent, so the oars are parallel by the Converse of the Corresponding Angles Postulate.

 **4.** **What if...?** Suppose the corresponding angles on the opposite side of the boat measure $(4y - 2)°$ and $(3y + 6)°$, where $y = 8$. Show that the oars are parallel.

$4y - 2 = 4(8) - 2 = 30°$ $3y + 6 = 3(8) + 6 = 30°$

The $\angle$ are $\cong$, so the oars are $\parallel$ by the Conv. of the Corr. $\angle$ Post.

THINK AND DISCUSS

1. Explain three ways of proving that two lines are parallel.

2. If you know $m\angle 1$, how could you use the measures of $\angle 5$, $\angle 6$, $\angle 7$, or $\angle 8$ to prove $m \parallel n$?

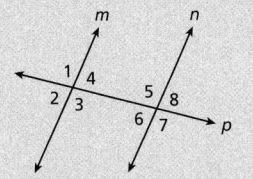

 **3.** **GET ORGANIZED** Copy and complete the graphic organizer. Use it to compare the Corresponding Angles Postulate with the Converse of the Corresponding Angles Postulate.

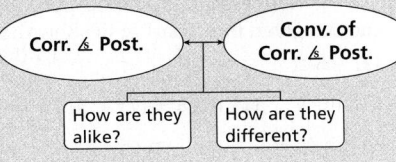

Example 4

A carpenter is creating a woodwork pattern and wants two long pieces to be parallel. $m\angle 1 = (8x + 20)°$ and $m\angle 2 = (2x + 10)°$. If $x = 15$, show that pieces A and B are parallel.

Piece A   Piece B

The horizontal piece forms a transversal to pieces A and B. Substituting 15 for x, $m\angle 1 = 140°$ and $m\angle 2 = 40°$. Since $\angle 1$ and $\angle 2$ are same-side interior angles, pieces A and B are parallel by the Conv. of Same-Side Int. $\angle$ Thm.

Also available on transparency

INTERVENTION ◄══►
Questioning Strategies

EXAMPLE **4**

• What other pair of angles could you use to determine if the oars or wood pieces are parallel?

Teaching Tip   **Reading Math** Point out to students that the word *converse* comes from the Latin *conversus*, which means "to turn around".

ENGLISH LANGUAGE LEARNERS

---

3 **Close**

Summarize

Review the four angle relationships that would prove that two lines are parallel.

• a pair of corresponding angles that are congruent

• a pair of alternate interior angles that are congruent

• a pair of alternate exterior angles that are congruent

• a pair of same-side interior angles that are supplementary

ONGOING ASSESSMENT
and INTERVENTION ◄══►

Diagnose Before the Lesson
3-3 Warm Up, TE p. 162

Monitor During the Lesson
Check It Out! Exercises, SE pp. 162–165
Questioning Strategies, TE pp. 163–165

Assess After the Lesson
3-3 Lesson Quiz, TE p. 169
Alternative Assessment, TE p. 169

Answers to *Think and Discuss*

1. Prove 2 corr. $\angle$ are $\cong$, prove 2 same-side int. $\angle$ are supp., or prove 2 alt. int. $\angle$ are $\cong$.

2. If $m\angle 5 = m\angle 1$, then $m \parallel n$ by the Conv. of the Corr. $\angle$ Post. If $m\angle 7 = m\angle 1$, then $m \parallel n$ by the Conv. of the Alt. Ext. $\angle$ Thm. $\angle 6$ and $\angle 8$ each form a lin. pair with $\angle 5$, so you could use the Lin. Pair Thm. and the Conv. of the Corr. $\angle$ Post.

3. See p. A3.

go.hrw.com/Geo/TX
Homework Help Online
KEYWORD: MG7 3-3
Parent Resources Online
KEYWORD: MG7 Parent

Assignment Guide

Assign *Guided Practice* exercises as necessary.

If you finished Examples **1–2**
  Basic 12–20, 24–34 even
  Average 12–20, 24–34
Advanced 12–20, 24–35

If you finished Examples **1–4**
  Basic 12–21, 24–36 even,
    37, 40, 42–45, 57–65
  Average 12–22 even, 25–53,
    57–65
Advanced 12–36 even, 37–65

Homework Quick Check
Quickly check key concepts.
Exercises: 12, 16, 21, 22, 28, 34

Answers

2. $m\angle 1 = 128°$, and $m\angle 8 = 128°$, so $\angle 1 \cong \angle 8$. $p \parallel q$ by the Conv. of the Corr. ∠ Post.

3. $m\angle 4 = 47°$, and $m\angle 5 = 47°$, so $\angle 4 \cong \angle 5$. $p \parallel q$ by the Conv. of the Corr. ∠ Post.

7. $m\angle 4 = 61°$, and $m\angle 8 = 61°$, so $\angle 4 \cong \angle 8$. $r \parallel s$ by the Conv. of the Alt. Int. ∠ Thm.

8. $m\angle 8 = 139°$, and $m\angle 7 = 41°$. $139° + 41° = 180°$, so $\angle 8$ and $\angle 7$ are supp. $r \parallel s$ by the Conv. of the Same-Side Int. ∠ Thm.

13. $m\angle 4 = 54°$, and $m\angle 8 = 54°$, so $\angle 4 \cong \angle 8$. $\ell \parallel m$ by the Conv. of the Corr. ∠ Post.

14. $m\angle 2 = 124°$, and $m\angle 6 = 124°$, so $\angle 2 \cong \angle 6$. $\ell \parallel m$ by the Conv. of the Corr. ∠ Post.

⬥TAKS Practice

Grades 9–11	Exercises
Obj. 2	57–59

GUIDED PRACTICE

SEE EXAMPLE 1
p. 162

Use the Converse of the Corresponding Angles Postulate and the given information to show that $p \parallel q$.
1. $\angle 4 \cong \angle 5$ $\angle 4 \cong \angle 5$, so $p \parallel q$ by the Conv. of the Corr. ∠ Post.
2. $m\angle 1 = (4x + 16)°$, $m\angle 8 = (5x - 12)°$, $x = 28$
3. $m\angle 4 = (6x - 19)°$, $m\angle 5 = (3x + 14)°$, $x = 11$

SEE EXAMPLE 2
p. 164

5. $\angle 3$ and $\angle 4$ are supp., so $r \parallel s$ by the Conv. of the Same-Side Int. ∠ Thm.

Use the theorems and given information to show that $r \parallel s$.
4. $\angle 1 \cong \angle 5$
5. $m\angle 3 + m\angle 4 = 180°$
6. $\angle 3 \cong \angle 7$
7. $m\angle 4 = (13x - 4)°$, $m\angle 8 = (9x + 16)°$, $x = 5$
8. $m\angle 8 = (17x + 37)°$, $m\angle 7 = (9x - 13)°$, $x = 6$
9. $m\angle 2 = (25x + 7)°$, $m\angle 6 = (24x + 12)°$, $x = 5$

4. $\angle 1 \cong \angle 5$, so $r \parallel s$ by the Conv. of the Alt. Ext. ∠ Thm.
6. $\angle 3 \cong \angle 7$, so $r \parallel s$ by the Conv. of the Alt. Int. ∠ Thm.
9. $m\angle 2 = 132°$, and $m\angle 6 = 132°$, so $\angle 2 \cong \angle 6$. $r \parallel s$ by the Conv. of the Alt. Ext. ∠ Thm.

SEE EXAMPLE 3
p. 164

10. Complete the following two-column proof.
Given: $\angle 1 \cong \angle 2$, $\angle 3 \cong \angle 1$
Prove: $XY \parallel WV$
Proof:

Statements	Reasons
1. $\angle 1 \cong \angle 2$, $\angle 3 \cong \angle 1$	1. Given
2. $\angle 2 \cong \angle 3$	2. a. ___?___ Trans. Prop. of $\cong$
3. b. ___?___ $\overline{XY} \parallel \overline{WV}$	3. c. ___?___ Conv. of the Alt. Int. ∠ Thm.

SEE EXAMPLE 4
p. 165

11. **Architecture** In the fire escape, $m\angle 1 = (17x + 9)°$, $m\angle 2 = (14x + 18)°$, and $x = 3$. Show that the two landings are parallel.
$m\angle 1 = 60°$, and $m\angle 2 = 60°$, so $\angle 1 \cong \angle 2$. By the Conv. of the Alt. Int. ∠ Thm., the landings are $\parallel$.

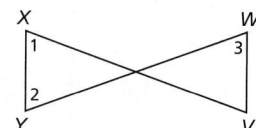

PRACTICE AND PROBLEM SOLVING

Use the Converse of the Corresponding Angles Postulate and the given information to show that $\ell \parallel m$.

15. $m\angle 1 = 55°$, and $m\angle 5 = 55°$, so $\angle 1 \cong \angle 5$. $\ell \parallel m$ by the Conv. of the Corr. ∠ Post.

12. $\angle 3 \cong \angle 7$ $\angle 3 \cong \angle 7$, so $\ell \parallel m$ by the Conv. of the Corr. ∠ Post.
13. $m\angle 4 = 54°$, $m\angle 8 = (7x + 5)°$, $x = 7$
14. $m\angle 2 = (8x + 4)°$, $m\angle 6 = (11x - 41)°$, $x = 15$
15. $m\angle 1 = (3x + 19)°$, $m\angle 5 = (4x + 7)°$, $x = 12$

3-3 PRACTICE A

1. The Converse of the Corresponding Angles Postulate states that if two coplanar lines are cut by a transversal so that a pair of corresponding angles is congruent, then the two lines are ____parallel____.

Use the figure for Exercises 2 and 3. Given the information in each exercise, state the reason why lines *b* and *c* are parallel.

2. $\angle 4 \cong \angle 8$
   ____Conv. of Corr. ∠ Post.____

3. $m\angle 3 = 68°$, $m\angle 7 = (5x + 3)°$, $x = 13$
   $m\angle 7 = 68°$, $\angle 3 \cong \angle 7$, Conv. of ____Corr. ∠ Post.____

Fill in the blanks to complete these theorems about parallel lines.

4. If two coplanar lines are cut by a ____transversal____ so that a pair of alternate interior angles are ____congruent____, then the two lines are parallel.

5. If two coplanar lines are cut by a transversal so that a pair of same-side interior angles are ____supplementary____, then the two lines are parallel.

6. If two coplanar lines are cut by a transversal so that a pair of alternate exterior angles are congruent, then the two lines are ____parallel____.

7. Shu believes that a theorem is missing from the lesson. His conjecture is that if two coplanar lines are cut by a transversal so that a pair of same-side exterior angles are supplementary, then the two lines are parallel. Complete the two-column proof with the statements and reasons provided.

Given: $\angle 1$ and $\angle 3$ are supplementary.
Prove: $m \parallel n$
Proof:

Statements	Reasons
1. $\angle 1$ and $\angle 3$ are supplementary.	1. a. ____Given____
2. b. $\angle 2$ and $\angle 3$ are supplementary.	2. Linear Pair Thm.
3. $\angle 1 \cong \angle 2$	3. c. ____$\cong$ Supps. Thm.____
4. d. ____$m \parallel n$____	4. Conv. of Corr. ∠ Post.

$m \parallel n$,
$\angle 2$ and $\angle 3$ are supplementary.
Given
$\cong$ Supps. Thm.

3-3 PRACTICE B

Use the figure for Exercises 1–8. Tell whether lines *m* and *n* must be parallel from the given information. If they are, state your reasoning. (*Hint:* The angle measures may change for each exercise, and the figure is for reference only.)

1. $\angle 7 \cong \angle 3$
   m $\parallel$ *n*, Conv. of Alt. Int. ∠ Thm.

2. $m\angle 3 = (15x + 22)°$, $m\angle 1 = (19x - 10)°$, $x = 8$
   m $\parallel$ *n*, Conv. of Corr. ∠ Post.

3. $\angle 7 \cong \angle 6$
   m and *n* do not have to be parallel.

4. $m\angle 2 = (5x + 3)°$, $m\angle 3 = (8x - 5)°$, $x = 14$
   m $\parallel$ *n*, Conv. of Same-Side Int. ∠ Thm.

5. $m\angle 8 = (6x - 1)°$, $m\angle 4 = (5x + 3)°$, $x = 9$
   m and *n* are not parallel.

6. $\angle 5 \cong \angle 7$
   m $\parallel$ *n*, Conv. of Corr. ∠ Post.

7. $\angle 1 \cong \angle 5$
   m $\parallel$ *n*, Conv. of Alt. Ext. ∠ Thm.

8. $m\angle 6 = (x + 10)°$, $m\angle 2 = (x + 15)°$
   m and *n* are not parallel.

9. Look at some of the printed letters in a textbook. The small horizontal and vertical segments attached to the ends of the letters are called *serifs*. Most of the letters in a textbook are in a serif typeface. The letters on this page do not have serifs, so these letters are in a sans-serif typeface. (*Sans* means "without" in French.) The figure shows a capital letter *A* with serifs. Use the given information to write a paragraph proof that the serif, segment $\overline{HI}$, is parallel to segment $\overline{JK}$.

Given: $\angle 1$ and $\angle 3$ are supplementary.
Prove: $\overline{HI} \parallel \overline{JK}$

Possible answer: The given information states that $\angle 1$ and $\angle 3$ are supplementary. $\angle 1$ and $\angle 2$ are also supplementary by the Linear Pair Theorem. Therefore $\angle 3$ and $\angle 2$ must be congruent by the Congruent Supplements Theorem. Since $\angle 3$ and $\angle 2$ are congruent, $\overline{HI}$ and $\overline{JK}$ are parallel by the Converse of the Corresponding Angles Postulate.

Use the theorems and given information to show that $n \parallel p$.

16. $\angle 3 \cong \angle 6$

17. $\angle 2 \cong \angle 7$

18. $m\angle 4 + m\angle 6 = 180°$

19. $m\angle 1 = (8x - 7)°$, $m\angle 8 = (6x + 21)°$, $x = 14$

20. $m\angle 4 = (4x + 3)°$, $m\angle 5 = (5x - 22)°$, $x = 25$

21. $m\angle 3 = (2x + 15)°$, $m\angle 5 = (3x + 15)°$, $x = 30$

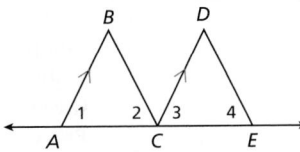

22. Complete the following two-column proof.

Given: $\overline{AB} \parallel \overline{CD}$, $\angle 1 \cong \angle 2$, $\angle 3 \cong \angle 4$
Prove: $\overline{BC} \parallel \overline{DE}$

Proof:

Statements	Reasons
1. $\overline{AB} \parallel \overline{CD}$	1. Given
2. $\angle 1 \cong \angle 3$	2. a. ___?___ Corr. ∡ Post.
3. $\angle 1 \cong \angle 2$, $\angle 3 \cong \angle 4$	3. b. ___?___ Given
4. $\angle 2 \cong \angle 4$	4. c. ___?___ Trans. Prop. of $\cong$
5. d. ___?___ $\overline{BC} \parallel \overline{DE}$	5. e. ___?___ Conv. of Corr. ∡ Post.

23. If $x = 6$, then $m\angle 1 = 20°$ and $m\angle 2 = 20°$. So $\overline{DJ} \parallel \overline{EK}$ by the Conv. of the Corr. ∡ Post.

23. **Art** Edmund Dulac used perspective when drawing the floor titles in this illustration for *The Wind's Tale* by Hans Christian Andersen. Show that $DJ \parallel EK$ if $m\angle 1 = (3x + 2)°$, $m\angle 2 = (5x - 10)°$, and $x = 6$.

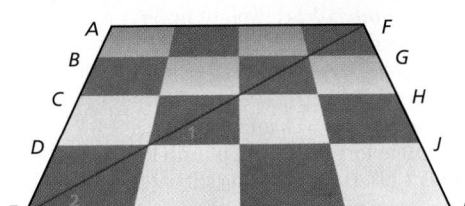

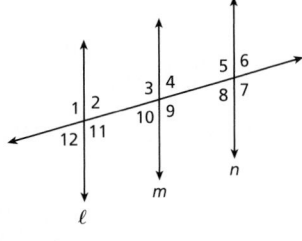

Name the postulate or theorem that proves that $\ell \parallel m$.

24. Conv. of the Corr. ∡ Post.

24. $\angle 8 \cong \angle 6$ 25. $\angle 8 \cong \angle 4$

25. Conv. of the Alt. Ext. ∡ Thm.

26. $\angle 2 \cong \angle 6$ 27. $\angle 7 \cong \angle 5$

26. Conv. of the Alt. Int. ∡ Thm.

28. $\angle 3 \cong \angle 7$ 29. $m\angle 2 + m\angle 3 = 180°$

27. Conv. of the Corr. ∡ Post.

For the given information, tell which pair of lines must be parallel. Name the postulate or theorem that supports your answer.

30. $m\angle 2 = m\angle 10$ 31. $m\angle 8 + m\angle 9 = 180°$

28. Conv. of the Alt. Int. ∡ Thm.

32. $\angle 1 \cong \angle 7$ 33. $m\angle 10 = m\angle 6$

34. $\angle 11 \cong \angle 5$ 35. $m\angle 2 + m\angle 5 = 180°$

29. Conv. of the Same-Side Int. ∡ Thm.

36. **Multi-Step** Two lines are intersected by a transversal so that $\angle 1$ and $\angle 2$ are corresponding angles, $\angle 1$ and $\angle 3$ are alternate exterior angles, and $\angle 3$ and $\angle 4$ are corresponding angles. If $\angle 2 \cong \angle 4$, what theorem or postulate can be used to prove the lines parallel?
Conv. of Alt. Int. ∡ Thm.

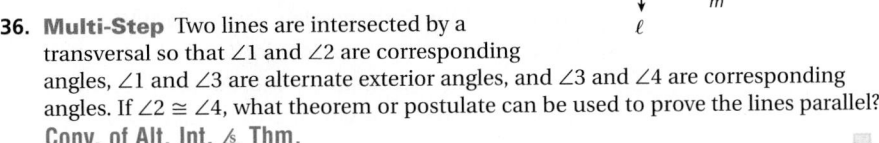

COMMON ERROR ALERT

Students who justified **Step 2** in **Exercise 22**, with the incorrect theorem may benefit from drawing just $\overleftrightarrow{AB}$, $\overleftrightarrow{CD}$, $\overleftrightarrow{AE}$, $\angle 1$, and $\angle 3$. This may make it easier to see the relationship between the angles and the lines.

Teaching Tip   **Algebra** In **Step 4** of **Exercise 22**, help students understand the double application of the Transitive Property of Congruence. Ask them what conclusion they can draw if $a = b$, $b = c$, and $c = d$, using the Transitive Property of Equality. $a = d$

Answers

16. $\angle 3 \cong \angle 6$, so $n \parallel p$ by the Conv. of the Alt. Int. ∡ Thm.

17. $\angle 2 \cong \angle 7$, so $n \parallel p$ by the Conv. of the Alt. Ext. ∡ Thm.

18. $\angle 4$ and $\angle 6$ are supp., so $n \parallel p$ by the Conv. of the Same-Side Int. ∡ Thm.

19. $m\angle 1 = 105°$, and $m\angle 8 = 105°$, so $\angle 1 \cong \angle 8$. $n \parallel p$ by the Conv. of the Alt. Ext. ∡ Thm.

20. $m\angle 4 = 103°$, and $m\angle 5 = 103°$, so $\angle 4 \cong \angle 5$. $n \parallel p$ by the Conv. of the Alt. Int. ∡ Thm.

21. $m\angle 3 = 75°$, and $m\angle 5 = 105°$. $75° + 105° = 180°$, so $\angle 3$ and $\angle 5$ are supp. $\ell \parallel m$ by the Conv. of the Same-Side Int. ∡ Thm.

30. $\ell \parallel m$; Conv. of the Alt. Int. ∡ Thm.

31. $m \parallel n$; Conv. of the Same-Side Int. ∡ Thm.

32. $\ell \parallel n$; Conv. of the Alt. Ext. ∡ Thm.

33. $m \parallel n$; Conv. of the Alt. Ext. ∡ Thm.

34. $\ell \parallel n$; Conv. of the Alt. Int. ∡ Thm.

35. $\ell \parallel n$; Conv. of the Same-Side Int. ∡ Thm.

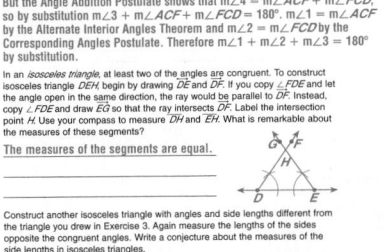

37. This problem will prepare you for the Multi-Step TAKS Prep on page 180.

In the diagram, which represents the side view of a mystery spot, $m\angle SRT = 25°$, and $m\angle SUR = 65°$.

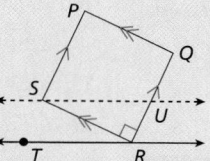

  a. Name a same-side interior angle of $\angle SUR$ for lines $\overleftrightarrow{SU}$ and $\overleftrightarrow{RT}$ with transversal $\overleftrightarrow{RU}$. What is its measure? Explain your reasoning.

  b. Prove that $\overleftrightarrow{SU}$ and $\overleftrightarrow{RT}$ are parallel.

38. Complete the flowchart proof of the Converse of the Alternate Interior Angles Theorem.

  Given: $\angle 2 \cong \angle 3$
  Prove: $\ell \parallel m$
  Proof:

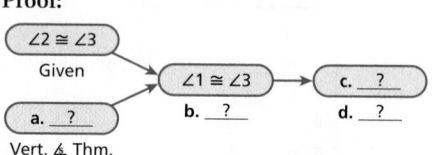

  a. $\angle 1 \cong \angle 2$
  b. Trans. Prop. of $\cong$
  c. $\ell \parallel m$
  d. Conv. of Corr. $\angle$ Post.

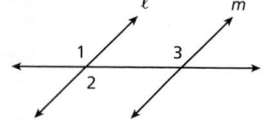

39. Use the diagram to write a paragraph proof of the Converse of the Same-Side Interior Angles Theorem.

  Given: $\angle 1$ and $\angle 2$ are supplementary.
  Prove: $\ell \parallel m$

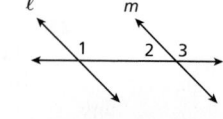

40. Carpentry A *plumb bob* is a weight hung at the end of a string, called a *plumb line*. The weight pulls the string down so that the plumb line is perfectly vertical. Suppose that the angle formed by the wall and the roof is 123° and the angle formed by the plumb line and the roof is 123°. How does this show that the wall is perfectly vertical?

41. Critical Thinking Are the Reflexive, Symmetric, and Transitive Properties true for parallel lines? Explain why or why not.

  Reflexive: $\ell \parallel \ell$
  Symmetric: If $\ell \parallel m$, then $m \parallel \ell$.
  Transitive: If $\ell \parallel m$ and $m \parallel n$, then $\ell \parallel n$.

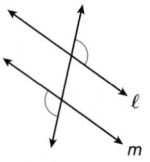

42. Write About It Does the information given in the diagram allow you to conclude that $a \parallel b$? Explain.

TEST PREP

43. Which postulate or theorem can be used to prove $\ell \parallel m$?

  Ⓐ Converse of the Corresponding Angles Postulate
  Ⓑ Converse of the Alternate Interior Angles Theorem
  Ⓒ Converse of the Alternate Exterior Angles Theorem
  Ⓓ Converse of the Same-Side Interior Angles Theorem

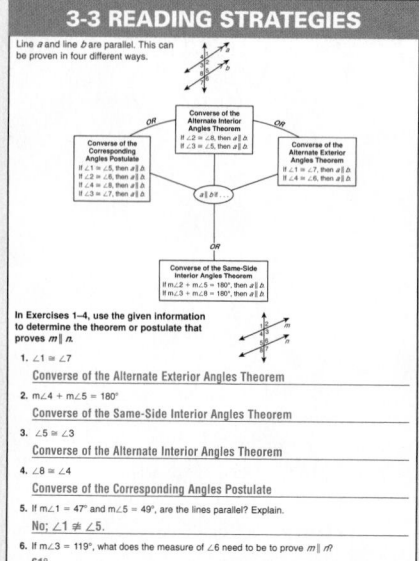
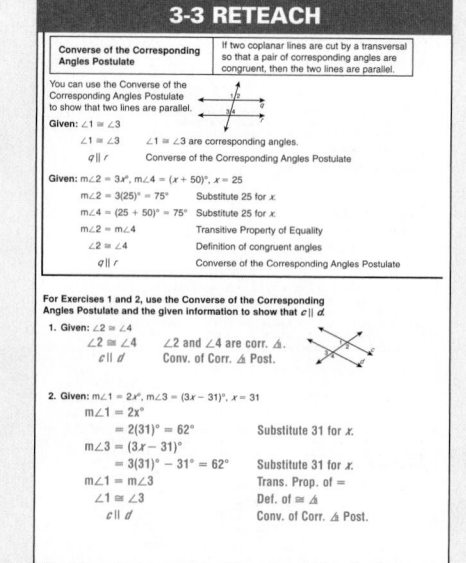

44. Two coplanar lines are cut by a transversal. Which condition does NOT guarantee that the two lines are parallel?

　(A) A pair of alternate interior angles are congruent.

　(B) A pair of same-side interior angles are supplementary.

　(C) A pair of corresponding angles are congruent.

　(D) A pair of alternate exterior angles are complementary.

45. Gridded Response Find the value of *x* so that
$\ell \parallel m$. **15**

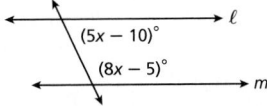

CHALLENGE AND EXTEND

46. $q \parallel r$ by the Conv. of the Alt. Ext. ∡ Thm.

47. No lines can be proven ∥.

48. $s \parallel t$ by the Conv. of the Corr. ∡ Post.

49. $q \parallel r$ by the Conv. of the Alt. Int. ∡ Thm.

50. No lines can be proven ∥.

51. $s \parallel t$ by the Conv. of the Alt. Ext. ∡ Thm.

52. $s \parallel t$ by the Conv. of the Same-Side Int. ∡ Thm.

Determine which lines, if any, can be proven parallel using the given information. Justify your answers.

46. $\angle 1 \cong \angle 15$　　**47.** $\angle 8 \cong \angle 14$

48. $\angle 3 \cong \angle 7$　　**49.** $\angle 8 \cong \angle 10$

50. $\angle 6 \cong \angle 8$　　**51.** $\angle 13 \cong \angle 11$

52. $m\angle 12 + m\angle 15 = 180°$　**53.** $m\angle 5 + m\angle 8 = 180°$

54. Write a paragraph proof that $\overline{AE} \parallel \overline{BD}$.

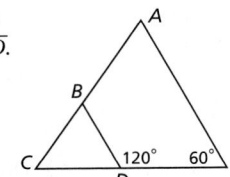

53. No lines can be proven ∥.

54. It is given that $m\angle E = 60°$ and $m\angle BDE = 120°$, so $m\angle E + m\angle BDE = 180°$. $\angle E$ and $\angle BDE$ are supp., so $\overline{AE} \parallel \overline{BD}$ by the Conv. of the Same-Side Int. ∡ Thm.

Use the diagram for Exercises 55 and 56.

55. Given: $m\angle 2 + m\angle 3 = 180°$
Prove: $\ell \parallel m$

56. Given: $m\angle 2 + m\angle 5 = 180°$
Prove: $\ell \parallel n$

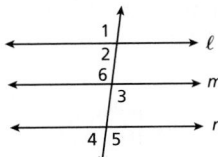

SPIRAL REVIEW

Solve each equation for the indicated variable. *(Previous course)*

57. $a - b = -c$, for a
$a = b - c$

58. $y = \frac{1}{2}x - 10$, for x
$x = 2y + 20$

59. $4y + 6x = 12$, for y
$y = -\frac{3}{2}x + 3$

Write the converse, inverse, and contrapositive of each conditional statement. Find the truth value of each. *(Lesson 2-2)*

60. If an animal is a bat, then it has wings.

61. If a polygon is a triangle, then it has exactly three sides.

62. If the digit in the ones place of a whole number is 2, then the number is even.

Identify each of the following. *(Lesson 3-1)*

63. one pair of parallel segments $\overline{AD} \parallel \overline{BC}$

64. one pair of skew segments

64. Possible answer: $\overline{AB}$ and $\overline{DE}$ are skew.

65. one pair of perpendicular segments $\overline{AB} \perp \overline{AD}$

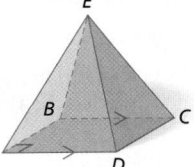

**COMMON ERROR
//// ALERT **

In **Exercises 46–53**, remind students that they should not assume that lines in the diagram are parallel only because they appear to be parallel. They should justify each answer with a postulate or theorem learned in this lesson.

Answers
55–56, 60–62. See p. A13.

Journal
Have students explain how to construct parallel lines using one of the postulates or theorems in the lesson.

ALTERNATIVE ASSESSMENT

Have students draw two lines by holding a ruler (MK) in place and drawing a line on each side. Then have students draw a transversal and use angle measures to confirm that the lines are parallel.

**Power Presentations
with PowerPoint®**

✓ 3-3 Lesson Quiz

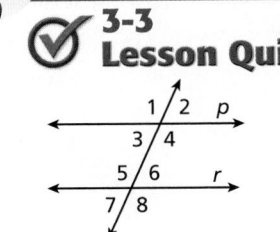

Name the postulate or theorem that proves $p \parallel r$.

1. $\angle 4 \cong \angle 5$
Conv. of Alt. Int. ∡ Thm.

2. $\angle 2 \cong \angle 7$
Conv. of Alt. Ext. ∡ Thm.

3. $\angle 3 \cong \angle 7$
Conv. of Corr. ∡ Post.

4. $\angle 3$ and $\angle 5$ are supplementary. Conv. of Same-Side Int. ∡ Thm.

Use the theorems and given information to prove $p \parallel r$.

5. $m\angle 2 = (5x + 20)°$, $m\angle 7 = (7x + 8)°$, and $x = 6$
$m\angle 2 = 5(6) + 20 = 50°$
$m\angle 7 = 7(6) + 8 = 50°$
$m\angle 2 = m\angle 7$, so $\angle 2 \cong \angle 7$.
$p \parallel r$ by the Conv. of Alt. Ext. ∡ Thm.

Also available on transparency

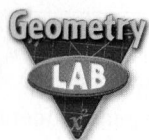

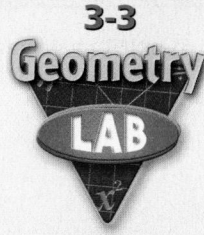

Construct Parallel Lines

In Lesson 3-3, you learned one method of constructing parallel lines using a compass and straightedge. Another method, called the rhombus method, uses a property of a figure called a *rhombus,* which you will study in Chapter 6. The rhombus method is shown below.

Use with Lesson 3-3

⭐ **TEKS G.2.A Geometric structure:** use constructions to explore attributes of geometric figures and to make conjectures about geometric relationships. Also G.9.A

Activity 1

① Draw a line ℓ and a point P not on the line.

② Choose a point Q on the line. Place your compass point at Q and draw an arc through P that intersects ℓ. Label the intersection R.

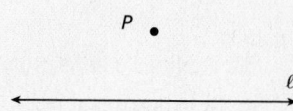

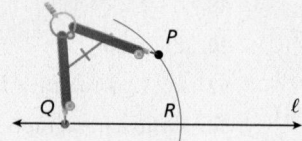

③ Using the same compass setting as the first arc, draw two more arcs: one from P, the other from R. Label the intersection of the two arcs S.

④ Draw $\overleftrightarrow{PS} \parallel \ell$.

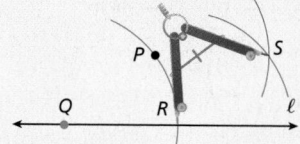

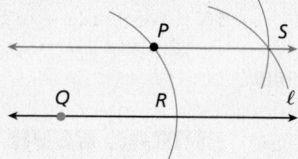

Try This

1. Repeat Activity 1 using a different point not on the line. Are your results the same? **Yes; the lines are still** $\parallel$.

2. Using the lines you constructed in Problem 1, draw transversal $\overleftrightarrow{PQ}$. Verify that the lines are parallel by using a protractor to measure alternate interior angles. **Check students' work.**

3. What postulate ensures that this construction is always possible? $\parallel$ **Post.**

4. A *rhombus* is a quadrilateral with four congruent sides. Explain why this method is called the rhombus method. **If you draw quadrilateral *PQRS* in the diagram, then it is a rhombus, because the same compass setting was used to construct all 4 side lengths.**

Activity 2

1 Draw a line ℓ and point P on a piece of patty paper.

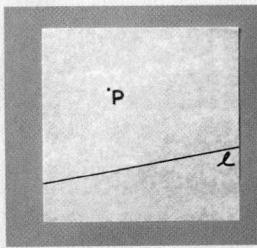

2 Fold the paper through P so that both sides of line ℓ match up

3 Crease the paper to form line m. P should be on line m.

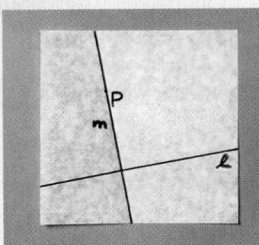

4 Fold the paper again through P so that both sides of line m match up.

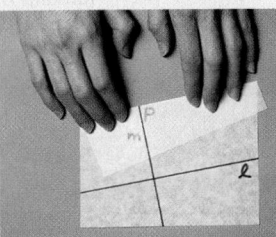

5 Crease the paper to form line n. Line n is parallel to line ℓ through P.

Try This

5. Repeat Activity 2 using a point in a different place not on the line. Are your results the same? **Yes; the lines are still ∥.**

6. Use a protractor to measure corresponding angles. How can you tell that the lines are parallel? **The corr. ∡ measure 90°. By the Conv. of the Corr. ∡ Post., the lines must be ∥.**

7. Draw a triangle and construct a line parallel to one side through the vertex that is not on that side. **Check students' work.**

8. Line m is perpendicular to both ℓ and n. Use this statement to complete the following conjecture: If two lines in a plane are perpendicular to the same line, then _____?_____. **the lines are ∥**

Teacher to Teacher

I like to give students the opportunity to try these constructions using geometry software. Although constructing parallel lines is much easier with geometry software, the following instructions allow students to duplicate the rhombus method.

Draw a line $\overleftrightarrow{AB}$ and a point P. Draw a circle centered at A that passes through P. This circle intersects line $\overleftrightarrow{AB}$ in two places. Label point C, the intersection closer to point P. Draw a circle centered at P that passes through A. Then draw another circle centered at C that passes through A. These circles intersect at point A and another point. Label the other point Q. Draw line $\overleftrightarrow{PQ}$. Then $\overleftrightarrow{AB} \parallel \overleftrightarrow{PQ}$.

Anthony Gugliotta
Rumson, NJ

Key Concepts

You can use properties of a figure called a *rhombus* to construct parallel lines.

You can also use this fact, which is stated as a theorem in Lesson 3-4: If two coplanar lines are perpendicular to a third line, then those two lines are parallel to each other.

Assessment

Journal Have students use the postulate and theorems from Lesson 3-3 to explain why the lines in each construction are parallel.

Pacing: Traditional 1 day
Block $\frac{1}{2}$ day

Objective: Prove and apply theorems about perpendicular lines.

Geometry Lab
In *Texas Lab Manual*

Online Edition
Tutorial Videos

Countdown to TAKS Week 6

Power Presentations
with PowerPoint®

Warm Up

Solve each inequality.

1. $x - 5 < 8$ $x < 13$

2. $3x + 1 > x$ $x > -\frac{1}{2}$

Solve each equation.

3. $5y = 90$ $y = 18$

4. $5x + 15 = 90$ $x = 15$

Solve the system of equations.

5. $\begin{cases} 6y = 90 \\ 8y - 3x = 90 \end{cases}$
   $x = 10, y = 15$

Also available on transparency

Math Humor

Q: Why is the angle formed by two perpendicular lines never wrong?

A: Because it's always *right*!

⭐ Geometry TEKS

G.1 Geometric structure*
(A) develop an awareness of the structure of a mathematical system ...

G.2 Geometric structure*
(A) use constructions to explore attributes of geometric figures ...

G.3 Geometric structure*
(C) use logical reasoning to prove statements are true ...
(E) use deductive reasoning ...

G.9 Congruence and the geometry of size*

(A) ... test conjectures about the properties of ... perpendicular lines ...

* **Knowledge and Skills** See p. 144.

TEKS G.1.A Geometric structure: ... connecting definitions ... logical reasoning, and theorems. Also G.2.A, G.3.C, G.3.E, G.9.A

Objective
Prove and apply theorems about perpendicular lines.

Vocabulary
perpendicular bisector
distance from a point to a line

Why learn this?
Rip currents are strong currents that flow away from the shoreline and are perpendicular to it. A swimmer who gets caught in a rip current can get swept far out to sea. (See Example 3.)

The **perpendicular bisector** of a segment is a line perpendicular to a segment at the segment's midpoint. A construction of a perpendicular bisector is shown below.

Construction   Perpendicular Bisector of a Segment

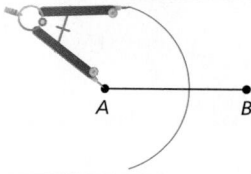   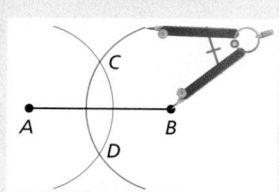   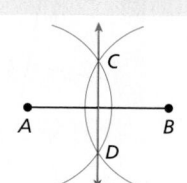

1 Draw $\overline{AB}$. Open the compass wider than half of AB and draw an arc centered at A.

2 Using the same compass setting, draw an arc centered at B that intersects the first arc at C and D.

3 Draw $\overleftrightarrow{CD}$. $\overleftrightarrow{CD}$ is the perpendicular bisector of $\overline{AB}$.

The shortest segment from a point to a line is perpendicular to the line. This fact is used to define the **distance from a point to a line** as the length of the perpendicular segment from the point to the line.

EXAMPLE 1   **Distance From a Point to a Line**

A Name the shortest segment from P to $\overleftrightarrow{AC}$.

The shortest distance from a point to a line is the length of the perpendicular segment, so $\overline{PB}$ is the shortest segment from P to $\overleftrightarrow{AC}$.

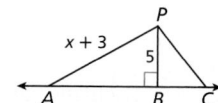

x²ʸ Algebra

B Write and solve an inequality for x.

$PA > PB$ $\overline{PB}$ is the shortest segment.

$x + 3 > 5$ *Substitute $x + 3$ for PA and 5 for PB.*

$\underline{-3 -3}$ *Subtract 3 from both sides of the inequality.*

$ x > 2$

1a. $\overline{AB}$

1b. $x - 5 < 12$; $x < 17$

CHECK IT OUT!

1a. Name the shortest segment from A to $\overleftrightarrow{BC}$.

1b. Write and solve an inequality for x.

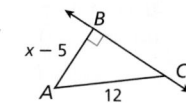

1 Introduce

EXPLORATION

3-4   **Perpendicular Lines**

Use a sheet of patty paper, a ruler, and a protractor for this Exploration.

1. Draw a line ℓ and a point P not on the line.

2. Fold the paper through P so that both sides of line ℓ match up.

3. Unfold the paper. Label the intersection of the fold and line ℓ as point X.

4. Make three more folds that pass through P and that intersect line ℓ. Label them as shown.

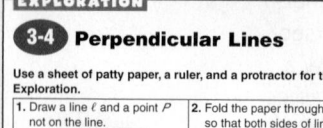

5. Use a protractor to measure $\angle PXC$. What is special about the line through point X?

6. Use a ruler to measure $\overline{PX}$, $\overline{PA}$, $\overline{PB}$, and $\overline{PC}$. Which segment is shortest?

THINK AND DISCUSS

7. Describe the shortest segment from a point to a line.

Motivate

Show students a sketch or picture of a rectangular picture frame. Explain that in order to make the glass fit correctly in the frame, the framer must make sure that both sides are perpendicular to the top and the bottom of the frame. Ask students to name other objects in which sides must be perpendicular.

Explorations and answers are provided in the *Explorations* binder.

Theorems

	THEOREM	DIAGRAM	EXAMPLE
3-4-1	If two intersecting lines form a linear pair of congruent angles, then the lines are perpendicular. (2 intersecting lines form lin. pair of ≅ ⦤ → lines ⊥.)	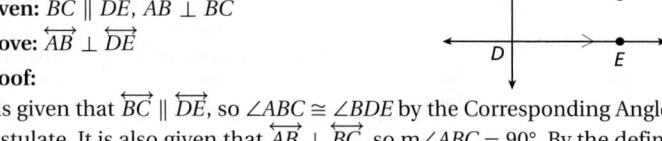	$\ell \perp m$
3-4-2	**Perpendicular Transversal Theorem** In a plane, if a transversal is perpendicular to one of two parallel lines, then it is perpendicular to the other line.		$q \perp p$
3-4-3	If two coplanar lines are perpendicular to the same line, then the two lines are parallel to each other. (2 lines ⊥ to same line → 2 lines ∥.)		$r \parallel s$

You will prove Theorems 3-4-1 and 3-4-3 in Exercises 37 and 38.

PROOF █ **Perpendicular Transversal Theorem**

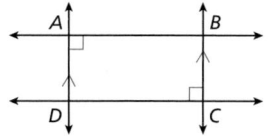

Given: $\overleftrightarrow{BC} \parallel \overleftrightarrow{DE}$, $\overleftrightarrow{AB} \perp \overleftrightarrow{BC}$

Prove: $\overleftrightarrow{AB} \perp \overleftrightarrow{DE}$

Proof:

It is given that $\overleftrightarrow{BC} \parallel \overleftrightarrow{DE}$, so $\angle ABC \cong \angle BDE$ by the Corresponding Angles Postulate. It is also given that $\overleftrightarrow{AB} \perp \overleftrightarrow{BC}$, so $m\angle ABC = 90°$. By the definition of congruent angles, $m\angle ABC = m\angle BDE$, so $m\angle BDE = 90°$ by the Transitive Property of Equality. By the definition of perpendicular lines, $\overleftrightarrow{AB} \perp \overleftrightarrow{DE}$.

E X A M P L E **2**   **Proving Properties of Lines**

Write a two-column proof.

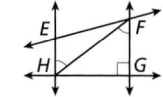

Given: $\overleftrightarrow{AD} \parallel \overleftrightarrow{BC}$, $\overleftrightarrow{AD} \perp \overleftrightarrow{AB}$, $\overleftrightarrow{BC} \perp \overleftrightarrow{DC}$

Prove: $\overleftrightarrow{AB} \parallel \overleftrightarrow{DC}$

Proof:

Statements	Reasons
1. $\overleftrightarrow{AD} \parallel \overleftrightarrow{BC}$, $\overleftrightarrow{BC} \perp \overleftrightarrow{DC}$	1. Given
2. $\overleftrightarrow{AD} \perp \overleftrightarrow{DC}$	2. ⊥ Transv. Thm.
3. $\overleftrightarrow{AD} \perp \overleftrightarrow{AB}$	3. Given
4. $\overleftrightarrow{AB} \parallel \overleftrightarrow{DC}$	4. 2 lines ⊥ to same line → 2 lines ∥.

1. $\angle EHF \cong \angle HFG$ (Given)

2. $\overleftrightarrow{EH} \parallel \overleftrightarrow{FG}$ (Conv. of Alt. Int. ⦤ Thm.)

3. $\overleftrightarrow{FG} \perp \overleftrightarrow{GH}$ (Given)

4. $\overleftrightarrow{EH} \perp \overleftrightarrow{GH}$ (⊥ Transv. Thm.)

✓ CHECK IT OUT!   2. Write a two-column proof.

Given: $\angle EHF \cong \angle HFG$, $\overleftrightarrow{FG} \perp \overleftrightarrow{GH}$

Prove: $\overleftrightarrow{EH} \perp \overleftrightarrow{GH}$

3-4 Perpendicular Lines **173**

Power Presentations with PowerPoint®

Additional Examples

Example **1**

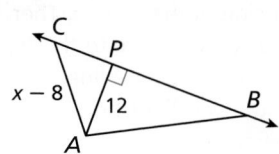

A. Name the shortest segment from point A to $\overleftrightarrow{BC}$. $\overline{AP}$

B. Write and solve an inequality for x. $AC > AP; x - 8 > 12;$ $x > 20$

Example **2**

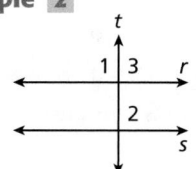

Write a two-column proof.

Given: $r \parallel s$, $\angle 1 \cong \angle 2$

Prove: $r \perp t$

1. $r \parallel s$, $\angle 1 \cong \angle 2$ (Given)

2. $\angle 2 \cong \angle 3$ (Corr. ⦤ Post.)

3. $\angle 1 \cong \angle 3$ (Trans. Prop. of ≅)

4. $r \perp t$ (2 intersecting lines form lin. pair of ≅ ⦤ → lines ⊥)

Also available on transparency

INTERVENTION ◄►
Questioning Strategies

EXAMPLE **1**

• How does the solution in **Example 1B** confirm your choice for the shortest segment?

EXAMPLE **2**

• Explain your reasoning from the given information to the conclusion.

▶2 Teach

Guided Instruction

Make sure students understand that a perpendicular bisector of a segment must be perpendicular to the segment *and* that it must bisect the segment. Compare and contrast the theorems in the lesson.

Teaching Tip **Reading Math** Discuss how the definition of the distance from a point to a line may differ from students' idea of the distance from their school to the street where they live.

🙌 Reaching All Learners
Through Modeling

Students who have difficulty with compass and straightedge constructions may want to use patty paper or a Mira to construct the perpendicular bisector of a segment.

Teaching Tip **Auditory** Ask for several volunteers to demonstrate the construction of a perpendicular bisector of a segment. As they construct the bisector, ask them to explain what they are doing in each step.

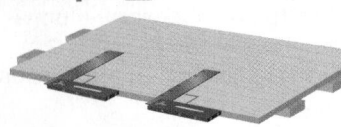
Example 3

A *carpenter's square* forms a right angle. A carpenter places the square so that one side is parallel to an edge of a board, and then draws a line along the other side of the square. Then he slides the square to the right and draws a second line. Why must the two lines be parallel?

Both lines are perpendicular to the edge of the board. If two coplanar lines are perpendicular to the same line, then the two lines are parallel to each other, so the lines must be parallel to each other.

Also available on transparency

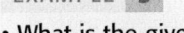

INTERVENTION ◀▶
Questioning Strategies

EXAMPLE **3**

• What is the given information?
• What do you need to show?
• Which theorem will you use?

EXAMPLE **3** *Oceanography Application*

Rip currents may be caused by a sandbar parallel to the shoreline. Waves cause a buildup of water between the sandbar and the shoreline. When this water breaks through the sandbar, it flows out in a direction perpendicular to the sandbar. Why must the rip current be perpendicular to the shoreline?

The rip current forms a transversal to the shoreline and the sandbar.

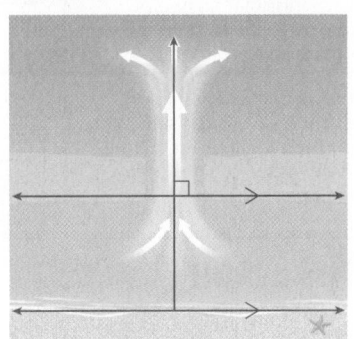

The shoreline and the sandbar are parallel, and the rip current is perpendicular to the sandbar. So by the Perpendicular Transversal Theorem, the rip current is perpendicular to the shoreline.

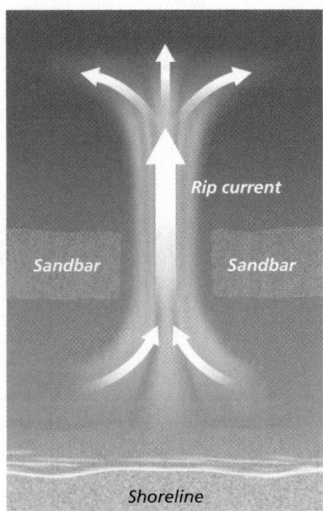
Rip current
Sandbar
Sandbar
Shoreline

TEXAS LINK
Oceanography

The National Weather Service in Brownsville provides a rip current forecast for South Padre Island and other Texas beaches. Park officials also post flags on the beach to warn of rip current danger.
Source: www.ripcurrents.noaa.gov

✓ **CHECK IT OUT!**

3. A swimmer who gets caught in a rip current should swim in a direction perpendicular to the current. Why should the path of the swimmer be parallel to the shoreline?
The shoreline and the path of the swimmer should both be ⊥ to the current, so they should be ∥ to each other.

THINK AND DISCUSS

1. Describe what happens if two intersecting lines form a linear pair of congruent angles.

2. Explain why a transversal that is perpendicular to two parallel lines forms eight congruent angles.

Know it!
.Note

3. **GET ORGANIZED** Copy and complete the graphic organizer. Use the diagram and the theorems from this lesson to complete the table.

Diagram	If you are given . . .	Then you can conclude . . .
	$m\angle 1 = m\angle 2$	$m \perp p$
	$m\angle 2 = 90°$ $m\angle 3 = 90°$	$m \parallel n$
	$m\angle 2 = 90°$ $m \parallel n$	$n \perp p$

---

3 Close

Summarize
Review the main points of the lesson:
• A perpendicular bisector of a segment is both perpendicular and bisects the segment.
• The distance from a point not on a line to the line is the perpendicular distance.
Review the three theorems with the given diagrams on page 173.

ONGOING ASSESSMENT
and INTERVENTION ◀▶

Diagnose Before the Lesson
3-4 Warm Up, TE p. 172

Monitor During the Lesson
Check It Out! Exercises, SE pp. 172–174
Questioning Strategies, TE pp. 173–174

Assess After the Lesson
3-4 Lesson Quiz, TE p. 178
Alternative Assessment, TE p. 178

Answers to *Think and Discuss*

1. If two intersecting lines form a lin. pair of ≅ ∡, then the ∡ in the lin. pair have the same measure. By the Lin. Pair Thm., they are also supp., so their measures add to 180°. This means the measure of each ∠ must be 90°, so the lines must be ⊥.

2. If a transv. is ⊥ to the ∥ lines, all pairs of corr. ∡ must be rt. ∡. Since all rt. ∡ are ≅, the transv. and the ∥ lines form 8 ≅ ∡.

3-4 **Exercises**

GUIDED PRACTICE

1. **Vocabulary** $\overleftrightarrow{CD}$ is the *perpendicular bisector* of $\overline{AB}$. $\overleftrightarrow{CD}$ intersects $\overline{AB}$ at C. What can you say about $\overline{AB}$ and $\overleftrightarrow{CD}$? What can you say about $\overline{AC}$ and $\overline{BC}$?
   $\overline{AB}$ **and** $\overleftrightarrow{CD}$ **are** $\perp$. $\overline{AC}$ **and** $\overline{BC}$ **are** $\cong$.

SEE EXAMPLE **1**
p. 172

2. Name the shortest segment from point E to $\overleftrightarrow{AD}$. **$\overline{EB}$**

3. Write and solve an inequality for x.
   $x + 12 > 7;\ x > -5$

SEE EXAMPLE **2**
p. 173

4. Complete the two-column proof.
   Given: $\angle ABC \cong \angle CBE$, $\overrightarrow{DE} \perp \overleftrightarrow{AF}$
   Prove: $\overrightarrow{CB} \parallel \overrightarrow{DE}$
   Proof:

Statements	Reasons
1. $\angle ABC \cong \angle CBE$	1. Given
2. $\overrightarrow{CB} \perp \overleftrightarrow{AF}$	2. a. ___?___
3. b. ___?___ $\overrightarrow{DE} \perp \overleftrightarrow{AF}$	3. Given
4. $\overrightarrow{CB} \parallel \overrightarrow{DE}$	4. c. ___?___

a. 2 intersecting lines form lin. pair of $\cong \angle \!\!\!\angle \to$ lines $\perp$.

c. 2 lines $\perp$ to same line $\to$ 2 lines $\parallel$.

SEE EXAMPLE **3**
p. 174

5. **Sports** The center line in a tennis court is perpendicular to both service lines. Explain why the service lines must be parallel to each other.
   The service lines are coplanar lines that are $\perp$ to the same line (the center line), so they must be $\parallel$ to each other.

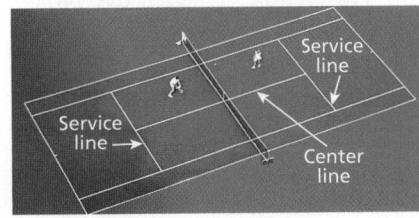
Service line
Service line
Center line

PRACTICE AND PROBLEM SOLVING

6. Name the shortest segment from point W to $\overline{XZ}$. **$\overline{WY}$**

7. Write and solve an inequality for x. $x + 8 < 19;\ x < 11$

8. Complete the two-column proof below.
   Given: $\overleftrightarrow{AB} \perp \overleftrightarrow{BC}$, $m\angle 1 + m\angle 2 = 180°$
   Prove: $\overleftrightarrow{BC} \perp \overleftrightarrow{CD}$
   Proof:

Statements	Reasons
1. $\overleftrightarrow{AB} \perp \overleftrightarrow{BC}$	1. Given
2. $m\angle 1 + m\angle 2 = 180°$	2. a. ___?___ **Given**
3. $\angle 1$ and $\angle 2$ are supplementary.	3. Def. of supplementary
4. b. ___?___ $\overleftrightarrow{AB} \parallel \overleftrightarrow{CD}$	4. Converse of the Same-Side Interior Angles Theorem
5. $\overleftrightarrow{BC} \perp \overleftrightarrow{CD}$	5. c. ___?___ $\perp$ Transv. Thm.

Assignment Guide

Assign *Guided Practice* exercises as necessary.

If you finished Examples **1-3**
  Basic 6–9, 10–20 even, 23–24, 27–28, 31–35, 39–45
  Average 6–26, 28–36, 39–45
  Advanced 6–23, 25–45

Homework Quick Check
Quickly check key concepts.
Exercises: 6, 8, 9, 10, 12

Teaching Tip **Visual** For **Exercise 1**, students may find it helpful to draw a diagram.

Teaching Tip **Critical Thinking** Ask students why the Perpendicular Transversal Theorem cannot be the reason for **Step 4** in **Exercise 4**. In the theorem, parallel lines are part of the hypothesis and perpendicular lines are part of the conclusion.

⬇ TAKS Practice

Grades 9–11	Exercises
Obj. 4	10–15, 24
Obj. 6	10, 11, 31
Obj. 10	24, 34, 39

Answers

22. The Reflex. Prop. is not true for ⊥ lines because a line is not ⊥ to itself. The Sym. Prop. is true, because if ℓ ⊥ m, then ℓ and m intersect to form a 90° angle. So m ⊥ ℓ. The Trans. Prop. is not true, because if ℓ ⊥ m and m ⊥ n, then ℓ ∥ n.

23a. It is given that $\overline{QR} \perp \overline{PQ}$ and $\overline{PQ} \parallel \overline{RS}$, so $\overline{QR} \perp \overline{RS}$ by the ⊥ Transv. Thm. It is given that $\overline{PS} \parallel \overline{QR}$. Since $\overline{QR} \perp \overline{RS}$, $\overline{PS} \perp \overline{RS}$ by the ⊥ Transv. Thm.

b. It is given that $\overline{PS} \parallel \overline{QR}$ and $\overline{QR} \perp \overline{PQ}$. So $\overline{PQ} \perp \overline{PS}$ by the ⊥ Transv. Thm.

---

9. **Music** The *frets* on a guitar are all perpendicular to one of the strings. Explain why the frets must be parallel to each other.
The frets are lines that are ⊥ to the same line (the string), so the frets must be ∥ to each other.

String
Fret

For each diagram, write and solve an inequality for *x*.

10.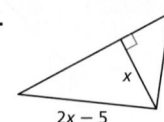
$2x - 5 > x,$
$x > 5$

11.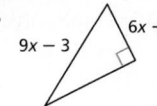
$9x - 3 > 6x + 5;$
$x > \dfrac{8}{3}$

Multi-Step Solve to find *x* and *y* in each diagram.

12. 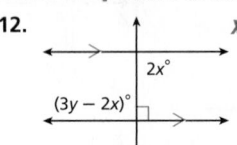 $x = 45; y = 60$

13. 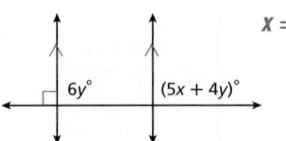 $x = 6, y = 15$

14. 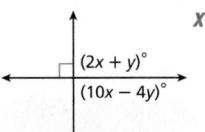 $x = 25, y = 40$

15. 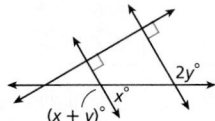 $x = 60, y = 60$

Determine if there is enough information given in the diagram to prove each statement.

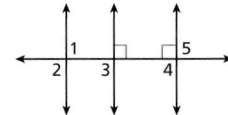

16. ∠1 ≅ ∠2 **yes**
17. ∠1 ≅ ∠3 **no**
18. ∠2 ≅ ∠3 **no**
19. ∠2 ≅ ∠4 **no**
20. ∠3 ≅ ∠4 **yes**
21. ∠3 ≅ ∠5 **yes**

22. **Critical Thinking** Are the Reflexive, Symmetric, and Transitive Properties true for perpendicular lines? Explain why or why not.
Reflexive: ℓ ⊥ ℓ
Symmetric: If ℓ ⊥ m, then m ⊥ ℓ.
Transitive: If ℓ ⊥ m and m ⊥ n, then ℓ ⊥ n.

23. This problem will prepare you for the Multi-Step TAKS Prep on page 180.

MULTI-STEP TAKS PREP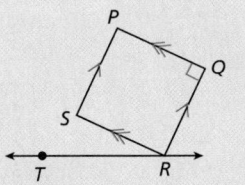

In the diagram, which represents the side view of a mystery spot, $\overline{QR} \perp \overline{PQ}$, $\overline{PQ} \parallel \overline{RS}$, and $\overline{PS} \parallel \overline{QR}$.

a. Prove $\overline{QR} \perp \overline{RS}$ and $\overline{PS} \perp \overline{RS}$.
b. Prove $\overline{PQ} \perp \overline{PS}$.

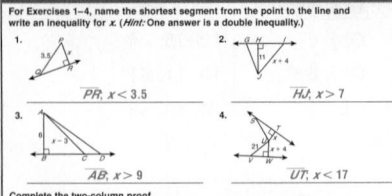
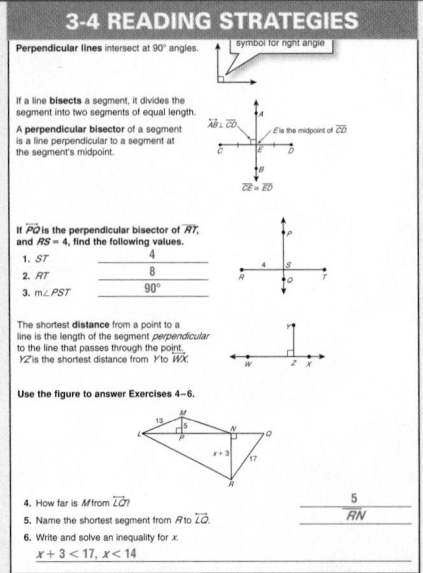
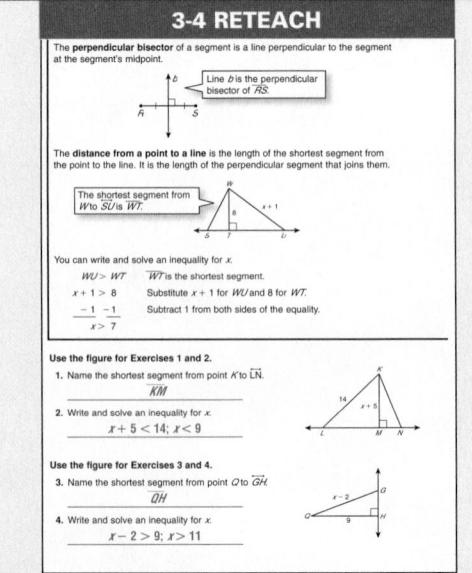

24. Geography Felton Avenue, Arlee Avenue, and Viehl Avenue are all parallel. Broadway Street is perpendicular to Felton Avenue. Use the satellite photo and the given information to determine the values of x and y. **$x = 6$; $y = 6$**

25. Estimation Copy the diagram onto a grid with 1 cm by 1 cm squares. Estimate the distance from point P to line ℓ. **Possible answer: 1.6 cm**

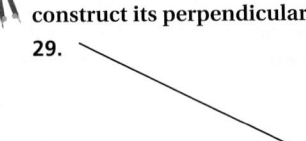

26. Critical Thinking Draw a figure to show that Theorem 3-4-3 is not true if the lines are not in the same plane.

27. Draw a figure in which $\overleftrightarrow{AB}$ is a perpendicular bisector of $\overline{XY}$ but $\overleftrightarrow{XY}$ is not a perpendicular bisector of $\overline{AB}$.

28. Write About It A ladder is formed by rungs that are perpendicular to the sides of the ladder. Explain why the rungs of the ladder are parallel.

Construction Construct a segment congruent to each given segment and then construct its perpendicular bisector.

29.

Check students' work.

30.

Check students' work.

31. Which inequality is correct for the given diagram?

Ⓐ $2x + 5 < 3x$ Ⓒ $2x + 5 > 3x$

Ⓑ $x > 1$ Ⓓ $x > 5$

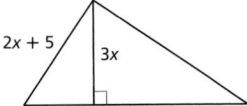

32. In the diagram, $\ell \perp m$. Find x and y.

Ⓕ $x = 5, y = 7$

Ⓖ $x = 7, y = 5$

Ⓗ $x = 90, y = 90$

Ⓙ $x = 10, y = 5$

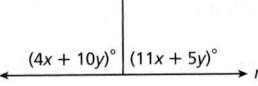

33. If $\ell \perp m$, which statement is NOT correct?

Ⓐ $m\angle 2 = 90°$

Ⓑ $m\angle 1 + m\angle 2 = 180°$

Ⓒ $\angle 1 \cong \angle 2$

Ⓓ $\angle 1 \perp \angle 2$

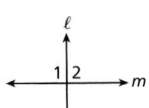

Construction

In **Exercises 29** and **30**, you may want to ask students how they can check their constructions by using paper folding.

Students who chose **D** in **Exercise 31** may need to review the Multiplication Property of Inequality. Remind students that for all real numbers a and b, if $a > b$, then $-a < -b$.

Encourage students to substitute their values for x and y in the variable expressions in **Exercise 32** before choosing their answer.

Answers

26. Possible answer: The two edges of the cube that are skew are $\perp$ to a third edge, but they are not $\parallel$.

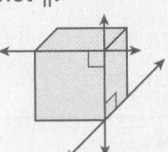

27. Possible answer:

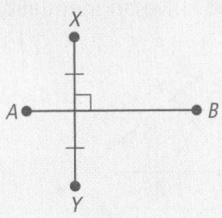

28. The rungs of the ladder are lines that are all $\perp$ to the same line, a side of the ladder, so the rungs must be $\parallel$.

3-4 PROBLEM SOLVING

A wall rack for holding CDs is shown. Use the figure for Exercises 1 and 2.

1. Explain why $\overleftrightarrow{HK}$ must be perpendicular to $\overleftrightarrow{KL}$.

   $\overleftrightarrow{HK}$ is a transversal to $\overleftrightarrow{GH}$ and $\overleftrightarrow{KL}$. $\overleftrightarrow{GH}$ and

   $\overleftrightarrow{KL}$ are parallel, and $\overleftrightarrow{HK} \perp \overleftrightarrow{GH}$. So by the

   Perpendicular Transversal Theorem, $\overleftrightarrow{HK} \perp \overleftrightarrow{KL}$.

2. If $\overleftrightarrow{JM} \perp \overleftrightarrow{HK}$, explain why $\overleftrightarrow{JM} \parallel \overleftrightarrow{GH}$.

   $\overleftrightarrow{JM} \perp \overleftrightarrow{HK}$ and $\overleftrightarrow{GH} \perp \overleftrightarrow{HK}$. If two coplanar lines are perpendicular to the

   same line, then the two lines are parallel to each other. Since $\overleftrightarrow{JM}$ and $\overleftrightarrow{GH}$

   are both perpendicular to $\overleftrightarrow{HK}$, it follows that $\overleftrightarrow{JM} \parallel \overleftrightarrow{GH}$.

3. The valve pistons on a trumpet are all perpendicular to the lead pipe. Explain why the valve pistons must be parallel to each other.

   The valve pistons are lines that are $\perp$ to the same line (the lead pipe),

   so the valve pistons must be $\parallel$ to each other.

Use the diagram of a bocce court for Exercises 4 and 5. Choose the best answer.

4. If $m\angle 1 = m\angle 2$, what can you conclude?

A $\overleftrightarrow{BH} \perp \overleftrightarrow{GJ}$ C $\overleftrightarrow{BH} \parallel \overleftrightarrow{CJ}$

B $\overleftrightarrow{AC} \perp \overleftrightarrow{BH}$ D $\overleftrightarrow{AC} \parallel \overleftrightarrow{GJ}$

5. The pitch lines are parallel, and the first pitch line is perpendicular to the long sides of the court. Which is a correct conclusion?

F $\overleftrightarrow{BH} = \overleftrightarrow{CJ}$ H $\overleftrightarrow{EL} \perp \overleftrightarrow{AF}$

G $\overleftrightarrow{BH} \parallel \overleftrightarrow{CJ}$ J $\overleftrightarrow{DK} \perp \overleftrightarrow{AF}$

3-4 CHALLENGE

Line m at right is the perpendicular bisector of $\overline{BC}$. Every triangle has three perpendicular bisectors.

Materials: ruler, compass

Trace $\triangle HJK$ at right onto a separate sheet of paper.

1. Find the midpoints of $\overline{HK}$, $\overline{KJ}$, and $\overline{HJ}$. Mark each point and label the points X, Y, and Z respectively.

2. Fold the paper at X so that $\overline{HK}$ folds onto itself. Draw the fold line. This is the perpendicular bisector of $\overline{HK}$.

3. Fold the paper at Y to construct the perpendicular bisector of $\overline{KJ}$. Then fold the paper at Z to construct the perpendicular bisector of $\overline{HJ}$.

4. The point of intersection of the perpendicular bisectors is called the **circumcenter** of the triangle. Is it possible for the circumcenter to be in the exterior of the triangle? Can it be on the triangle? Use drawings to explain.

   Yes; if one angle of the triangle is an obtuse angle, then the circumcenter

   is in the exterior. Yes; if one angle of the triangle is a right angle, then the

   circumcenter is on the hypotenuse of the triangle. Samples:

5. Make a conjecture about the distances from the vertices to the circumcenter. Then test your conjecture by measuring the segments.

   The distance from each vertex to the circumcenter is the same.

6. A circle is **circumscribed** about a polygon if the circle contains all the vertices of the polygon. Draw the circle that is circumscribed about $\triangle HJK$. Describe your procedure.

   Place the compass point at the circumcenter.

   Open the compass so that its width equals

   the distance from the circumcenter to one

   of the vertices of the triangle. Then draw

   the circle.

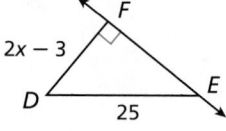
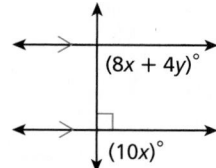
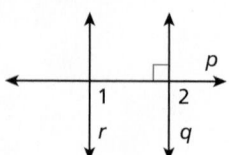
34. In a plane, both lines m and n are perpendicular to both lines p and q. Which conclusion CANNOT be made?
   Ⓐ $p \parallel q$
   Ⓑ $m \parallel n$
   Ⓒ $p \perp q$
   Ⓓ All angles formed by lines m, n, p, and q are congruent.

35. **Extended Response** Lines m and n are parallel. Line p intersects line m at A and line n at B, and is perpendicular to line m.
   a. What is the relationship between line n and line p? Draw a diagram to support your answer.
   b. What is the distance from point A to line n? What is the distance from point B to line m? Explain.
   c. How would you define the distance between two parallel lines in a plane?

CHALLENGE AND EXTEND

36. **Multi-Step** Find m$\angle 1$ in the diagram. (*Hint:* Draw a line parallel to the given parallel lines.) m$\angle 1 = 135°$

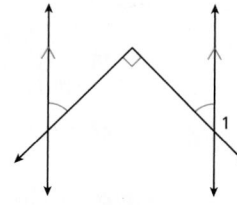

37. Label the $\cong$ $\angle$ $\angle 1$ and $\angle 2$. By def. of $\cong$ $\angle$, m$\angle 1 = $ m$\angle 2$. By the Lin. Pair Thm., m$\angle 1 + $ m$\angle 2 = 180°$. By subst., m$\angle 1 + $ m$\angle 1 = 180°$, so $2($m$\angle 1) = 180°$. By Div. Prop. of =, m$\angle 1 = 90°$, so the lines are $\perp$ by the def. of $\perp$ lines.

37. Prove Theorem 3-4-1: If two intersecting lines form a linear pair of congruent angles, then the two lines are perpendicular.

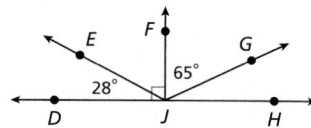

38. Prove Theorem 3-4-3: If two coplanar lines are perpendicular to the same line, then the two lines are parallel to each other. Label a pair of corr. rt. $\angle$ $\angle 1$ and $\angle 2$. By the Rt. $\angle$ $\cong$ Thm., $\angle 1 \cong \angle 2$. So $r \parallel s$ by the Conv. of the Corr. $\angle$ Post.

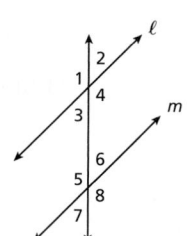

SPIRAL REVIEW

39. A soccer league has 6 teams. During one season, each team plays each of the other teams 2 times. What is the total number of games played in the league during one season? (*Previous course*) **30 games**

Find the measure of each angle. (*Lesson 1-4*)
40. the supplement of $\angle DJE$ **152°**
41. the complement of $\angle FJG$ **25°**
42. the supplement of $\angle GJH$ **155°**

For the given information, name the postulate or theorem that proves $\ell \parallel m$. (*Lesson 3-3*)
43. $\angle 2 \cong \angle 7$ **Conv. of Alt. Ext. $\angle$ Thm.**
44. $\angle 3 \cong \angle 6$ **Conv. of Alt. Int. $\angle$ Thm.**
45. m$\angle 4 + $ m$\angle 6 = 180°$ **Conv. of Same-Side Int. $\angle$ Thm.**

Answers
35a. $n \perp p$

b. AB; AB; the shortest distance from a point to a line is measured along a $\perp$ segment.

c. The distance between two $\parallel$ lines is the length of a segment that is $\perp$ to both lines and has one endpoint on each line.

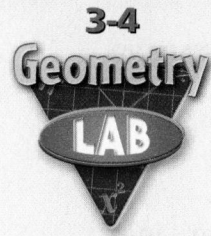

Construct Perpendicular Lines

In Lesson 3-4, you learned to construct the perpendicular bisector of a segment. This is the basis of the construction of a line perpendicular to a given line through a given point. The steps in the construction are the same whether the point is on or off the line.

 **TEKS G.2.A Geometric structure: use constructions to explore attributes of geometric figures and to make conjectures about geometric relationships. Also G.9.A**

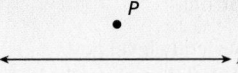

Copy the given line ℓ and point P.

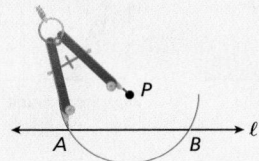

1 Place the compass point on P and draw an arc that intersects ℓ at two points. Label the points A and B.

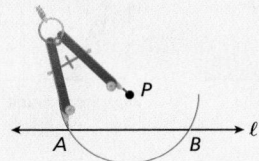

2 Construct the perpendicular bisector of $\overline{AB}$.

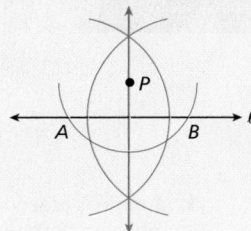

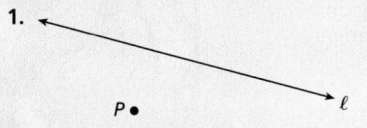

Copy each diagram and construct a line perpendicular to line ℓ through point P. Use a protractor to verify that the lines are perpendicular.

1.

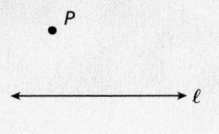

Check students' work.

2.

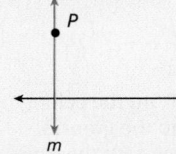

Check students' work.

3. Follow the steps below to construct two parallel lines. Explain why ℓ ∥ n.

Step 1 Given a line ℓ, draw a point P not on ℓ.

Step 2 Construct line m perpendicular to ℓ through P.

Step 3 Construct line n perpendicular to m through P.

Check students' work. The lines are ∥ because two lines that are ⊥ to the same line are ∥ to each other.

Pacing:
Traditional $\frac{1}{2}$ day
Block $\frac{1}{4}$ day

Objective: Construct a line perpendicular to a given line through a given point.

Materials: compass and protractor

 Online Edition

 Countdown to TAKS Week 5

Teach
Discuss

Relate the construction on page 172 of the perpendicular bisector of a segment to this construction.

Close
Key Concept

You can use the construction of the perpendicular bisector of a segment to construct a line perpendicular to a given line through a given point.

Assessment

Journal Have students draw a line m and a point Q not on m. Ask them to explain how to construct $\overleftrightarrow{QR} \perp m$.

 Geometry TEKS

G.2 Geometric structure*
(A) use constructions to explore attributes of geometric figures and to make conjectures about geometric relationships

G.9 Congruence and the geometry of size*
(A) formulate and test conjectures about the properties of parallel and perpendicular lines based on explorations …

* Knowledge and Skills See p. 144.

MULTI-STEP TAKS PREP

Organizer

Objective: Assess students' ability to apply concepts and skills in Lessons 3-1 through 3-4 in a real-world format.

 Online Edition

Resources

 Geometry Assessments
www.mathtekstoolkit.org

Problem	Text Reference
1	Lesson 3-1
2	Lesson 3-2
3	Lesson 3-3
4	Lesson 3-4

Answers

1–4. See p. A13.

 **TAKS Practice**

Grades 9–11	Problems
Obj. 7	1–4
Obj. 10	1–4

Parallel and Perpendicular Lines and Transversals

On the Spot Inside a mystery spot building, objects can appear to roll uphill, and people can look as if they are standing at impossible angles. This is because there is no view of the outside, so the room appears to be normal.

Suppose that the ground is perfectly level and the floor of the building forms a 25° angle with the ground. The floor and ceiling are parallel, and the walls are perpendicular to the floor.

Demonstrating the Creeping Ball

View from outside

View from inside

1. A table is placed in the room. The legs of the table are perpendicular to the floor, and the top is perpendicular to the legs. Draw a diagram and describe the relationship of the tabletop to the floor, walls, and ceiling of the room.

2. Find the angle of the table top relative to the ground. Suppose a ball is placed on the table. Describe what would happen and how it would appear to a person in the room.

3. Two people of the same height are standing on opposite ends of a board that makes a 25° angle with the floor, as shown. Explain how you know that the board is parallel to the ground. What would appear to be happening from the point of view of a person inside the room?

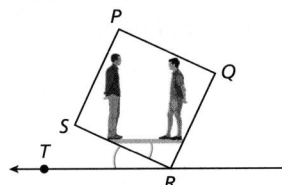

4. In the room, a lamp hangs from the ceiling along a line perpendicular to the ground. Find the angle the line makes with the walls. Describe how it would appear to a person standing in the room.

INTERVENTION

Scaffolding Questions

1. If you extended the tabletop, at what angle would it intersect the walls? 90°

2. If you extended the tabletop, would it intersect the ground? Yes Which pair of congruent corresponding angles would be formed? the angle formed by the floor and the ground and the angle formed by the tabletop and the ground

3. What is m∠SRT? 25° What type of angle pair are ∠SRT and the angle formed by the board and the floor? alternate interior angles

4. What angle do the walls make with the ground? 65° How can you use this angle to find the angle the line makes with the walls? The angles are complementary.

Extension

A ball appears to roll up a ramp on the floor of the room. What can you say about the angle that the ramp makes with the floor? The angle is less than 25°.

Quiz for Lessons 3-1 Through 3-4

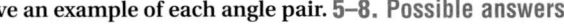

3-1 Lines and Angles

Identify each of the following. $\overline{AE} \perp \overline{AB}$

1. a pair of perpendicular segments
2. a pair of skew segments
3. a pair of parallel segments $\overline{AE} \parallel \overline{FB}$
4. a pair of parallel planes
   plane $AEF \parallel$ plane DHG

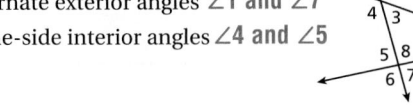

2. Possible answer: $\overline{AB}$ and $\overline{FG}$ are skew.

Give an example of each angle pair. **5–8. Possible answers:**

5. alternate interior angles
   $\angle 3$ and $\angle 5$
6. alternate exterior angles $\angle 1$ and $\angle 7$
7. corresponding angles
   $\angle 2$ and $\angle 8$
8. same-side interior angles $\angle 4$ and $\angle 5$

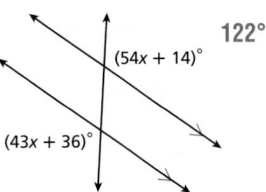

3-2 Angles Formed by Parallel Lines and Transversals

Find each angle measure.

9. **135°**

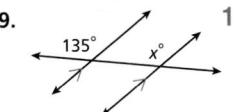

10. **23°**

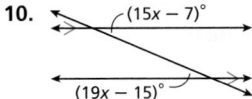

$(15x - 7)°$
$(19x - 15)°$

11. **122°**

$(54x + 14)°$
$(43x + 36)°$

3-3 Proving Lines Parallel

Use the given information and the theorems and postulates you have learned to show that $a \parallel b$.

12. $m\angle 8 = (13x + 20)°$, $m\angle 6 = (7x + 38)°$, $x = 3$
13. $\angle 1 \cong \angle 5$
14. $m\angle 8 + m\angle 7 = 180°$
15. $m\angle 8 = m\angle 4$

16. The tower shown is supported by guy wires such that $m\angle 1 = (3x + 12)°$, $m\angle 2 = (4x - 2)°$, and $x = 14$. Show that the guy wires are parallel.
    16. $m\angle 1 = 3(14) + 12 = 54°$, and $m\angle 2 = 4(14) - 2 = 54°$, so $\angle 1 \cong \angle 2$. The guy wires

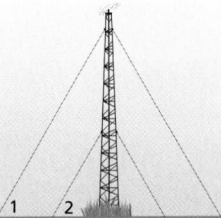

3-4 Perpendicular Lines

are $\parallel$ by the Conv. of the Corr. $\angle$ Post.

17. Write a two-column proof.
    Given: $\angle 1 \cong \angle 2$, $\ell \perp n$
    Prove: $\ell \perp p$

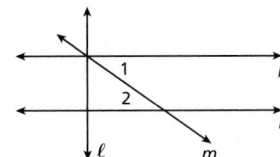

1. $\angle 1 \cong \angle 2$, $\ell \perp n$ (Given)
2. $p \parallel n$ (Conv. of Alt. Int. $\angle$ Thm.)
3. $\ell \perp p$ ($\perp$ Transv. Thm.)

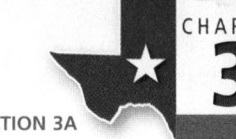 ## READY TO GO ON?

SECTION
3A

Organizer

Objective: Assess students' mastery of concepts and skills in Lessons 3-1 through 3-4.

Resources

Assessment Resources
Section 3A Quiz

Test & Practice Generator
One-Stop Planner®

INTERVENTION ◄═══►

Resources

Ready to Go On? Intervention and Enrichment Worksheets

Ready to Go On? CD-ROM

Ready to Go On? Online

my.hrw.com

Answers

12–15. See p. A13.

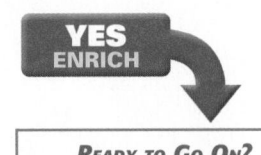

READY TO GO ON?

Diagnose and Prescribe

 **NO**
INTERVENE

YES
ENRICH

READY TO GO ON? Intervention, Section 3A			
Ready to Go On? Intervention	*Worksheets*	CD-ROM	Online
✓ Lesson 3-1	3-1 Intervention	Activity 3-1	Diagnose and Prescribe Online
✓ Lesson 3-2	3-2 Intervention	Activity 3-2	
✓ Lesson 3-3	3-3 Intervention	Activity 3-3	
✓ Lesson 3-4	3-4 Intervention	Activity 3-4	

READY TO GO ON? Enrichment, Section 3A

Worksheets
CD-ROM
Online

Coordinate Geometry

One-Minute Section Planner

Lesson	Lab Resources	Materials
Lesson 3-5 Slopes of Lines • Find the slope of a line. • Use slopes to identify parallel and perpendicular lines. ☑ Exit Level TAKS　☑ ACT　☑ SAT　☑ SAT Subject Tests	**Texas Lab Manual** 3-5 Geometry Lab	**Optional** compass and straightedge
3-6 Technology Lab Explore Parallel and Perpendicular Lines • Use a graphing calculator to graph parallel and perpendicular lines. ☑ Exit Level TAKS　☑ ACT　☑ SAT　☑ SAT Subject Tests		**Required** graphing calculator
Lesson 3-6 Lines in the Coordinate Plane • Graph lines, and write their equations in slope-intercept and point-slope form. • Classify lines as parallel, perpendicular, or coinciding. ☑ Exit Level TAKS　☑ ACT　☑ SAT　☑ SAT Subject Tests	**Texas Lab Manual** 3-6 Technology Lab (A) 3-6 Technology Lab (B)	**Optional** straws or uncooked spaghetti

MK = *Manipulatives Kit*

Section Overview

Determining the Slope of a Line

Why? Real-world situations that involve a rate of change, such the steepness of a road over a given distance, can be expressed as the ratio of rise over run.

$$\text{slope} = \frac{\text{rise}}{\text{run}} = \frac{6}{-3} = -2$$

You can also use the slope formula to determine the slope of a line.

$$m = \frac{y_2 - y_1}{x_2 - x_1}$$

$$m = \frac{7 - 1}{1 - 4} = -2$$

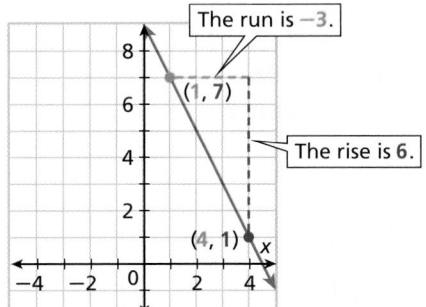

The run is -3.

$(1, 7)$

The rise is 6.

$(4, 1)$

Classifying Lines as Parallel, Intersecting, or Coinciding

Why? Two real-world situations with the same rate of change, but different initial values, can be modeled by parallel lines.

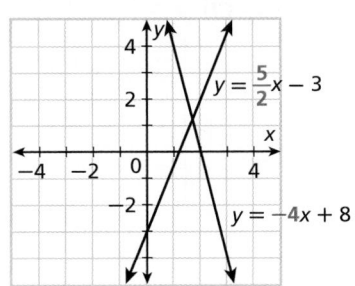

$y = \frac{5}{2}x - 3$

$y = -4x + 8$

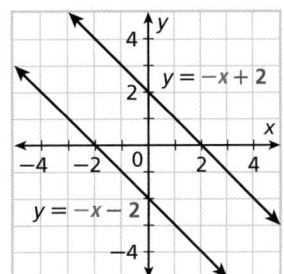

$y = -x + 2$

$y = -x - 2$

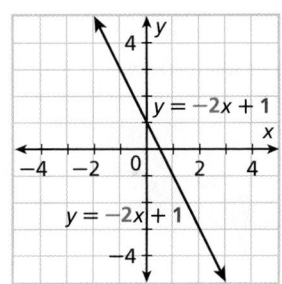

$y = -2x + 1$

$y = -2x + 1$

Intersecting lines have different slopes.

Parallel lines have the same slope but different y-intercepts.

Coinciding lines have the same slope and same y-intercepts.

Writing Equations of Lines

Why? A linear relationship between two variables can be represented by an equation in point-slope form or slope-intercept form. The equation can then be used to analyze the relationship.

A line has a slope of 2 and a y-intercept of -5, and contains the point $(3, 1)$.

Point-Slope Form of the Equation	Slope-Intercept Form of the Equation
$y - y_1 = m(x - x_1)$	$y = mx + b$
$y - 1 = 2(x - 3)$	$y = 2x - 5$

Objectives: Find the slope of a line.

Use slopes to identify parallel and perpendicular lines.

Geometry Lab
In *Texas Lab Manual*

Online Edition
Tutorial Videos

Countdown to TAKS Week 6

Power Presentations
with PowerPoint®

Warm Up

Find the value of *m*.

1. $m = \dfrac{7-5}{8-3}$ $\dfrac{2}{5}$

2. $m = \dfrac{(-3)-6}{5-(-1)}$ $-\dfrac{3}{2}$

3. $m = \dfrac{4-(-4)}{2-2}$ undefined

4. $m = \dfrac{-3+3}{1-6}$ 0

Also available on transparency

Math Humor

Q: How do the geometry teacher and track coach wake up their son?

A: It's time to rise and run!

⭐ Geometry TEKS

G.7 Dimensionality and the geometry of location*
(A) use one- and two-dimensional coordinate systems to represent points, lines, rays, line segments, and figures
(B) use slopes and equations of lines to investigate geometric relationships, including parallel lines, perpendicular lines, ...
(C) develop and use formulas involving ... slope ...

* **Knowledge and Skills** See p. 144.

3-5 Slopes of Lines

 TEKS G.7.B Dimensionality and the geometry of location: use slopes ... to investigate geometric relationships, including parallel lines, perpendicular lines, ... Also G.7.A, G.7.C

Objectives
Find the slope of a line.

Use slopes to identify parallel and perpendicular lines.

Vocabulary
rise
run
slope

Why learn this?
You can use the graph of a line to describe your rate of change, or speed, when traveling. (See Example 2.)

The *slope* of a line in a coordinate plane is a number that describes the steepness of the line. Any two points on a line can be used to determine the slope.

Know it!
.Note

Slope of a Line

DEFINITION	EXAMPLE
The **rise** is the difference in the *y*-values of two points on a line. The **run** is the difference in the *x*-values of two points on a line. The **slope** of a line is the ratio of rise to run. If (x_1, y_1) and (x_2, y_2) are any two points on a line, the slope of the line is $m = \dfrac{y_2 - y_1}{x_2 - x_1}$.	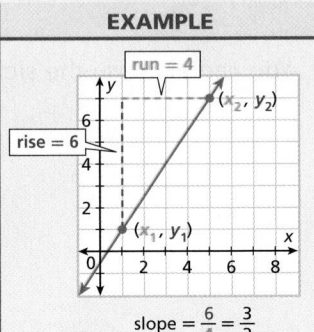 $\text{slope} = \dfrac{6}{4} = \dfrac{3}{2}$

EXAMPLE 1   **Finding the Slope of a Line**

Use the slope formula to determine the slope of each line.

 Algebra

A $\overleftrightarrow{AB}$

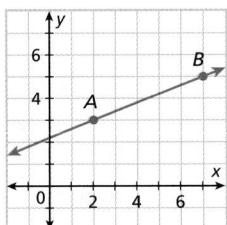

Substitute $(2, 3)$ for (x_1, y_1) and $(7, 5)$ for (x_2, y_2) in the slope formula and then simplify.

$m = \dfrac{y_2 - y_1}{x_2 - x_1} = \dfrac{5-3}{7-2} = \dfrac{2}{5}$

B $\overleftrightarrow{CD}$

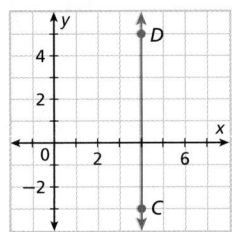

Substitute $(4, -3)$ for (x_1, y_1) and $(4, 5)$ for (x_2, y_2) in the slope formula and then simplify.

$m = \dfrac{y_2 - y_1}{x_2 - x_1} = \dfrac{5-(-3)}{4-4} = \dfrac{8}{0}$

The slope is undefined.

Remember!

A fraction with zero in the denominator is undefined because it is impossible to divide by zero.

---

1 Introduce

EXPLORATION

3-5 Slopes of Lines

Recall that the slope of a line that passes through the points (x_1, y_1) and (x_2, y_2) is given by slope $= \dfrac{\text{rise}}{\text{run}} = \dfrac{y_2 - y_1}{x_2 - x_1}$.

1. Copy line ℓ and point *P*. Use a compass and straightedge to construct a line *m* that passes through *P* and is parallel to line ℓ.
2. Find the slope of line ℓ and line *m*. How are the slopes related?
3. Construct another pair of parallel lines to see if the same result holds.
4. Use a compass and straightedge to construct a line *n* that passes through *P* and is perpendicular to line ℓ.
5. Find the slope of line ℓ and line *n*. How are the slopes related?
6. Construct another pair of perpendicular lines to see if the same result holds.

THINK AND DISCUSS

7. Discuss whether your conclusions about lines ℓ and *m* hold for horizontal and vertical lines.
8. Explain how you would find the slope of a line that is perpendicular to the line through $(-3, 1)$ and $(3, 3)$.

Motivate

Ice climbers ascend a cliff in a series of stages called *pitches*. The angle of each pitch can contribute to the difficulty of the climb. Discuss with students the difference between a section of cliff with a 30° angle and one with a 15° angle. Show the difference between the ratios of rise to run of each cliff section.

Explorations and answers are provided in the *Explorations* binder.

Use the slope formula to determine the slope of each line.

C $\overleftrightarrow{EF}$

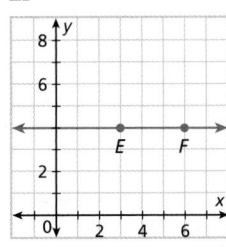

Substitute $(3, 4)$ for (x_1, y_1) and $(6, 4)$ for (x_2, y_2) in the slope formula and then simplify.

$$m = \frac{y_2 - y_1}{x_2 - x_1} = \frac{4 - 4}{6 - 3} = \frac{0}{3} = 0$$

D $\overleftrightarrow{GH}$

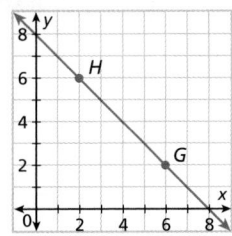

Substitute $(6, 2)$ for (x_1, y_1) and $(2, 6)$ for (x_2, y_2) in the slope formula and then simplify.

$$m = \frac{y_2 - y_1}{x_2 - x_1} = \frac{6 - 2}{2 - 6} = \frac{4}{-4} = -1$$

 **1.** Use the slope formula to determine the slope of $\overleftrightarrow{JK}$ through $J(3, 1)$ and $K(2, -1)$. $m = 2$

Summary: Slope of a Line			
Positive Slope	**Negative Slope**	**Zero Slope**	**Undefined Slope**

One interpretation of slope is a *rate of change*. If y represents miles traveled and x represents time in hours, the slope gives the rate of change in miles per hour.

EXAMPLE **2** *Transportation Application*

Tony is driving from Dallas, Texas, to Atlanta, Georgia. At 3:00 P.M., he is 180 miles from Dallas. At 5:30 P.M., he is 330 miles from Dallas. Graph the line that represents Tony's distance from Dallas at a given time. Find and interpret the slope of the line.

Use the points $(3, 180)$ and $(5.5, 330)$ to graph the line and find the slope.

$$m = \frac{330 - 180}{5.5 - 3} = \frac{150}{2.5} = 60$$

The slope is 60, which means he is traveling at an average speed of 60 miles per hour.

Distance from Dallas

 2. What if...? Use the graph above to estimate how far Tony will have traveled by 6:30 P.M. if his average speed stays the same.

390 mi

3-5 Slopes of Lines **183**

Example 1

Use the slope formula to determine the slope of each line.

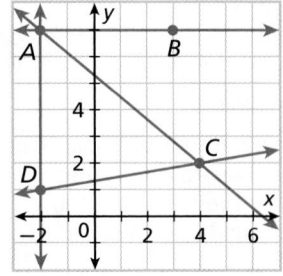

A. $\overleftrightarrow{AB}$ 0   **B.** $\overleftrightarrow{AC}$ $-\frac{5}{6}$

C. $\overleftrightarrow{AD}$ undefined   **D.** $\overleftrightarrow{CD}$ $\frac{1}{6}$

Example 2

Justin is driving from home to his college dormitory. At 4:00 P.M., he is 260 miles from home. At 7:00 P.M., he is 455 miles from home. Graph the line that represents Justin's distance from home at a given time. Find and interpret the slope of the line.

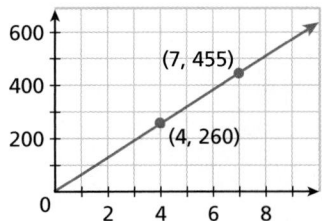

65; Justin is traveling at an average speed of 65 mi/h.

Also available on transparency

INTERVENTION ⬅➡
Questioning Strategies

EXAMPLE **1**

• How much horizontal distance does the line gain for every y units it rises?

EXAMPLE **2**

• Explain how to interpret the slope of a line.

---

2 Teach

Guided Instruction

When calculating the slope of a line through two points, encourage students to graph the line to see the relationship between the value of the slope and the graph. Graph pairs of lines with the same slope and pairs of lines whose slopes are opposite reciprocals, and ask the students to make a conjecture about the lines. Then discuss the two theorems that relate the slopes of parallel and perpendicular lines.

Reaching All Learners
Through Kinesthetic Experience

To help students remember the order for writing the slope ratio tell them that, if you are sitting at your desk, you have to get up before you can go somewhere. In other words, you have to *rise* before you can *run*. Students should place the rise in the numerator before placing the run in the denominator.

Lesson 3-5 **183**

Additional Examples

Example 3

Graph each pair of lines. Use their slopes to determine whether they are parallel, perpendicular, or neither.

A. $\overleftrightarrow{UV}$ and $\overleftrightarrow{XY}$ for $U(0, 2)$, $V(-1, -1)$, $X(3, 1)$, and $Y(-3, 3)$

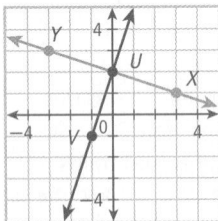

$3, -\dfrac{1}{3}$; perpendicular

B. $\overleftrightarrow{GH}$ and $\overleftrightarrow{IJ}$ for $G(-3, -2)$, m, $I(-2, 4)$, and $J(2, -4)$

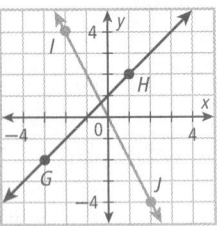

$1, -2$; neither

B. $\overleftrightarrow{CD}$ and $\overleftrightarrow{EF}$ for $C(-1, -3)$, $D(1, 1)$, $E(-1, 1)$, and $F(0, 3)$

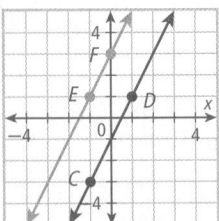

$2, 2$; parallel

Also available on transparency

Know It!
Note

Slopes of Parallel and Perpendicular Lines

3-5-1 Parallel Lines Theorem
In a coordinate plane, two nonvertical lines are parallel if and only if they have the same slope. Any two vertical lines are parallel.

3-5-2 Perpendicular Lines Theorem
In a coordinate plane, two nonvertical lines are perpendicular if and only if the product of their slopes is -1. Vertical and horizontal lines are perpendicular.

If a line has a slope of $\dfrac{a}{b}$, then the slope of a perpendicular line is $-\dfrac{b}{a}$. The ratios $\dfrac{a}{b}$ and $-\dfrac{b}{a}$ are called *opposite reciprocals*.

EXAMPLE 3

x² Algebra

Determining Whether Lines Are Parallel, Perpendicular, or Neither

Graph each pair of lines. Use slopes to determine whether the lines are parallel, perpendicular, or neither.

A $\overleftrightarrow{AB}$ and $\overleftrightarrow{CD}$ for $A(2, 1)$, $B(1, 5)$, $C(4, 2)$, and $D(5, -2)$

slope of $\overleftrightarrow{AB} = \dfrac{5 - 1}{1 - 2} = \dfrac{4}{-1} = -4$

slope of $\overleftrightarrow{CD} = \dfrac{-2 - 2}{5 - 4} = \dfrac{-4}{1} = -4$

The lines have the same slope, so they are parallel.

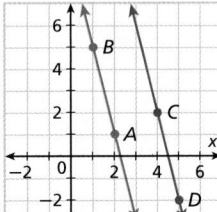

Caution!

Four given points do not always determine two lines. Graph the lines to make sure the points are not collinear.

B $\overleftrightarrow{ST}$ and $\overleftrightarrow{UV}$ for $S(-2, 2)$, $T(5, -1)$, $U(3, 4)$, and $V(-1, -4)$

slope of $\overleftrightarrow{ST} = \dfrac{-1 - 2}{5 - (-2)} = \dfrac{-3}{7} = -\dfrac{3}{7}$

slope of $\overleftrightarrow{UV} = \dfrac{-4 - 4}{-1 - 3} = \dfrac{-8}{-4} = 2$

The slopes are not the same, so the lines are not parallel. The product of the slopes is not -1, so the lines are not perpendicular.

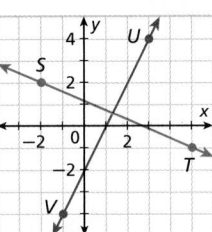

C $\overleftrightarrow{FG}$ and $\overleftrightarrow{HJ}$ for $F(1, 1)$, $G(2, 2)$, $H(2, 1)$, and $J(1, 2)$

slope of $\overleftrightarrow{FG} = \dfrac{2 - 1}{2 - 1} = \dfrac{1}{1} = 1$

slope of $\overleftrightarrow{HJ} = \dfrac{2 - 1}{1 - 2} = \dfrac{1}{-1} = -1$

The product of the slopes is $1(-1) = -1$, so the lines are perpendicular.

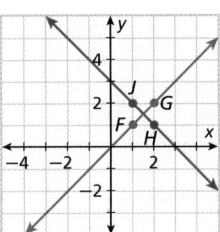

CHECK IT OUT! Graph each pair of lines. Use slopes to determine whether the lines are parallel, perpendicular, or neither.

⊥ **3a.** $\overleftrightarrow{WX}$ and $\overleftrightarrow{YZ}$ for $W(3, 1)$, $X(3, -2)$, $Y(-2, 3)$, and $Z(4, 3)$

neither **3b.** $\overleftrightarrow{KL}$ and $\overleftrightarrow{MN}$ for $K(-4, 4)$, $L(-2, -3)$, $M(3, 1)$, and $N(-5, -1)$

∥ **3c.** $\overleftrightarrow{BC}$ and $\overleftrightarrow{DE}$ for $B(1, 1)$, $C(3, 5)$, $D(-2, -6)$, and $E(3, 4)$

---

3 Close

Summarize

Remind students that the slope of a line is the ratio of the *rise* to the *run*, and describes the steepness of a line. The slope of the line can be used to classify parallel and perpendicular lines using the Parallel Lines Theorem and the Perpendicular Lines Theorem.

Answers to *Think and Discuss*

1. Subtract the first *y*-value from the second *y*-value and the first *x*-value from the second *x*-value. Divide the difference of the *y*-values by the difference of the *x*-values.

2. Any 2 points on a horiz. line have the same *y*-value, so the numerator of the slope is 0. Thus the slope of a horiz. line is 0. Any 2 points on a vert. line have the same *x*-value, so the denominator of the slope is 0. Thus the slope of a vert. line is undefined.

3. See p. A3.

THINK AND DISCUSS

1. Explain how to find the slope of a line when given two points.
2. Compare the slopes of horizontal and vertical lines.
3. **GET ORGANIZED** Copy and complete the graphic organizer.

Pairs of Lines		
Type	Slopes	Example
Parallel		
Perpendicular		

3-5 Exercises

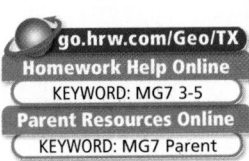

go.hrw.com/Geo/TX
Homework Help Online
KEYWORD: MG7 3-5
Parent Resources Online
KEYWORD: MG7 Parent

GUIDED PRACTICE

1. **Vocabulary** The *slope* of a line is the ratio of its __?__ to its __?__. (*rise* or *run*) **rise; run**

SEE EXAMPLE 1
p. 182

Use the slope formula to determine the slope of each line.

2. $\overleftrightarrow{MN}$
$m = \dfrac{6}{7}$

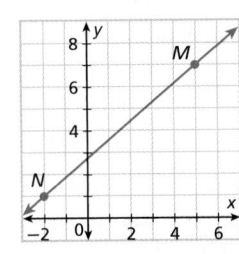

3. $\overleftrightarrow{CD}$
$m = -\dfrac{5}{9}$

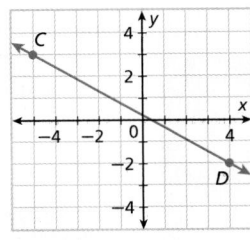

4. $\overleftrightarrow{AB}$
$m = 0$

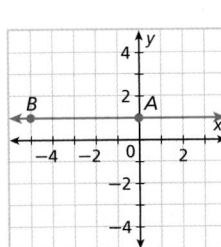

5. $\overleftrightarrow{ST}$
$m = \dfrac{5}{2}$

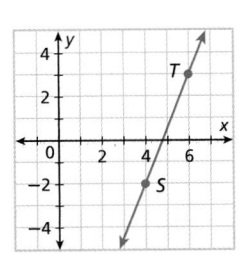

SEE EXAMPLE 2
p. 183

6. **Biology** A migrating bird flying at a constant speed travels 80 miles by 8:00 A.M. and 200 miles by 11:00 A.M. Graph the line that represents the bird's distance traveled. Find and interpret the slope of the line. $m = 40$, which means that the bird is flying at an average speed of 40 mi/h.

SEE EXAMPLE 3
p. 184

Graph each pair of lines. Use slopes to determine whether the lines are parallel, perpendicular, or neither.

7. $\overleftrightarrow{HJ}$ and $\overleftrightarrow{KM}$ for $H(3, 2)$, $J(4, 1)$, $K(-2, -4)$, and $M(-1, -5)$ ∥

8. $\overleftrightarrow{LM}$ and $\overleftrightarrow{NP}$ for $L(-2, 2)$, $M(2, 5)$, $N(0, 2)$, and $P(3, -2)$ ⊥

9. $\overleftrightarrow{QR}$ and $\overleftrightarrow{ST}$ for $Q(6, 1)$, $R(-2, 4)$, $S(5, 3)$, and $T(-3, -1)$ **neither**

3-5 Slopes of Lines **185**

Assignment Guide

Assign *Guided Practice* exercises as necessary.

If you finished Examples **1–3**
  Basic 10–14, 16–22 even, 24–28, 34–40
  Average 10–14, 16–22 even, 23–30, 34–40
  Advanced 10–14 even, 15–40

Homework Quick Check
Quickly check key concepts.
Exercises: 12, 14, 16, 18, 20

Teaching Tip **Science Link** The migration of birds is discussed in **Exercise 6.** You may want to mention that many birds have three basic flying speeds: cruising, migration, and emergency.

↘TAKS Practice

Grades 9–11	Exercises
Obj. 3	34–36
Obj. 7	18–22, 26–36
Obj. 9	25

Answers

7.

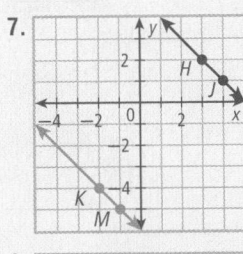

8.

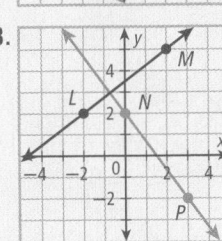

9.

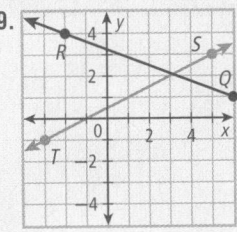

PRACTICE AND PROBLEM SOLVING

Independent Practice

For Exercises	See Example
10–13	1
14	2
15–17	3

TEKS ➡ TAKS

Skills Practice p. S9
Application Practice p. S30

Use the slope formula to determine the slope of each line.

10. $\overleftrightarrow{AB}$
m is undefined.

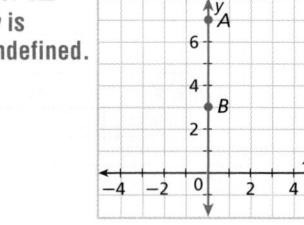

11. $\overleftrightarrow{CD}$
$m = 0$

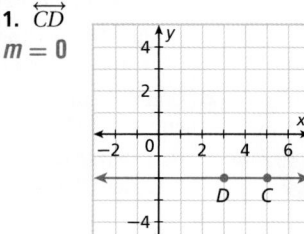

12. $\overleftrightarrow{EF}$
$m = -1$

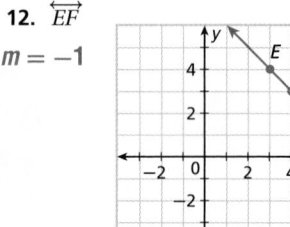

13. $\overleftrightarrow{GH}$
$m = -\frac{7}{3}$

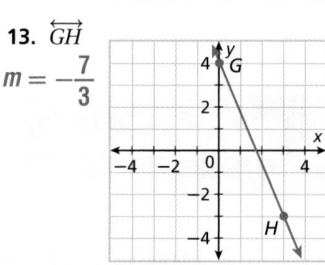

14. Aviation A pilot traveling at a constant speed flies 100 miles by 2:30 P.M. and 475 miles by 5:00 P.M. Graph the line that represents the pilot's distance flown. Find and interpret the slope of the line.

Graph each pair of lines. Use slopes to determine whether the lines are parallel, perpendicular, or neither.

15. $\overleftrightarrow{AB}$ and $\overleftrightarrow{CD}$ for $A(2, -1)$, $B(7, 2)$, $C(2, -3)$, and $D(-3, -6)$ ∥

16. $\overleftrightarrow{XY}$ and $\overleftrightarrow{ZW}$ for $X(-2, 5)$, $Y(6, -2)$, $Z(-3, 6)$, and $W(4, 0)$ **neither**

17. $\overleftrightarrow{JK}$ and $\overleftrightarrow{JL}$ for $J(-4, -2)$, $K(4, -2)$, and $L(-4, 6)$ ⊥

18. Geography The Rio Grande has an elevation of about 1150 meters above sea level in El Paso. The length of the river from that point to Brownsville where it enters the sea is about 2400 km. Find and interpret the slope of the river.

For $F(7, 6)$, $G(-3, 5)$, $H(-2, -3)$, $J(4, -2)$, and $K(6, 1)$, find each slope.

19. $\overleftrightarrow{FG}$ $m = \frac{1}{10}$ **20.** $\overleftrightarrow{GJ}$ $m = -1$ **21.** $\overleftrightarrow{HK}$ $m = \frac{1}{2}$ **22.** $\overleftrightarrow{GK}$ $m = -\frac{4}{9}$

23. Critical Thinking The slope of $\overleftrightarrow{AB}$ is greater than 0 and less than 1. Write an inequality for the slope of a line perpendicular to $\overleftrightarrow{AB}$. $m < -1$

24. Write About It Two cars are driving at the same speed. What is true about the lines that represent the distance traveled by each car at a given time?

MULTI-STEP TAKS PREP

25. This problem will prepare you for the Multi-Step TAKS Prep on page 200.

A traffic engineer calculates the speed of vehicles as they pass a traffic light. While the light is green, a taxi passes at a constant speed. After 2 s the taxi is 132 ft past the light. After 5 s it is 330 ft past the light.

a. Find the speed of the taxi in feet per second. **66 ft/s**

b. Use the fact that 22 ft/s = 15 mi/h to find the taxi's speed in miles per hour. **45 mi/h**

26. $\overleftrightarrow{AB} \perp \overleftrightarrow{CD}$ for $A(1, 3)$, $B(4, -2)$, $C(6, 1)$, and $D(x, y)$. Which are possible values of x and y?

- (A) $x = 1$, $y = -2$
- (B) $x = 3$, $y = 6$
- (C) $x = 3$, $y = -4$
- (D) $x = -2$, $y = -4$

27. Classify $\overleftrightarrow{MN}$ and $\overleftrightarrow{PQ}$ for $M(-3, 1)$, $N(1, 3)$, $P(8, 4)$, and $Q(2, 1)$.

- (F) Parallel
- (G) Perpendicular
- (H) Vertical
- (J) Skew

28. In the formula $d = rt$, d represents distance, and r represents the rate of change, or slope. Which ray on the graph represents a slope of 45 miles per hour?

- (A) A
- (B) B
- (C) C
- (D) D

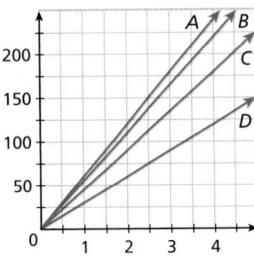

CHALLENGE AND EXTEND

Use the given information to classify $\overleftrightarrow{JK}$ for $J(a, b)$ and $K(c, d)$.

29. $a = c$ $\overleftrightarrow{JK}$ is a vert. line.

30. $b = d$ $\overleftrightarrow{JK}$ is a horiz. line.

31. The vertices of square $ABCD$ are $A(0, -2)$, $B(6, 4)$, $C(0, 10)$, $D(-6, 4)$.

a. Show that the opposite sides are parallel.

b. Show that the consecutive sides are perpendicular.

c. Show that all sides are congruent.

32. $\overleftrightarrow{ST} \parallel \overleftrightarrow{VW}$ for $S(-3, 5)$, $T(1, -1)$, $V(x, -3)$, and $W(1, y)$. Find a set of possible values for x and y. **Possible answer: $x = 3$, $y = 0$**

33. $\overleftrightarrow{MN} \perp \overleftrightarrow{PQ}$ for $M(2, 1)$, $N(-3, 0)$, $P(x, 4)$, and $Q(3, y)$. Find a set of possible values for x and y. **Possible answer: $x = 1$, $y = -6$**

SPIRAL REVIEW

Find the x- and y-intercepts of the line that contains each pair of points. *(Previous course)*

34. $(-5, 0)$ and $(0, -5)$
x-int.: −5; y-int.: −5

35. $(0, 1)$ and $(2, -7)$
x-int.: 0.25; y-int.: 1

36. $(1, -3)$ and $(3, 3)$
x-int.: 2; y-int.: −6

Use the given paragraph proof to write a two-column proof. *(Lesson 2-7)*

37.
1. ∠1 is supp. to ∠3. (Given)
2. ∠1 and ∠2 are supp. (Lin. Pair Thm.)
3. ∠2 ≅ ∠3 (≅ Supps. Thm.)

37. **Given:** ∠1 is supplementary to ∠3.
Prove: ∠2 ≅ ∠3
Proof: It is given that ∠1 is supplementary to ∠3. ∠1 and ∠2 are a linear pair by the definition of a linear pair. By the Linear Pair Theorem, ∠1 and ∠2 are supplementary. Thus ∠2 ≅ ∠3 by the Congruent Supplements Theorem.

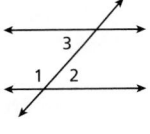

Given that m∠2 = 75°, tell whether each statement is true or false. Justify your answer with a postulate or theorem. *(Lesson 3-2)*

38. ∠1 ≅ ∠8
T; Alt. Ext. ∠ Thm.

39. ∠2 ≅ ∠6
T; Corr. ∠ Post.

40. ∠3 ≅ ∠5
F; Same-Side Int. ∠ Thm.

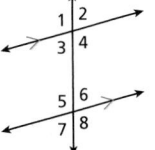

3-5 Slopes of Lines **187**

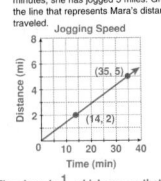
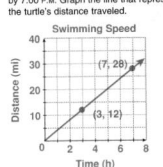

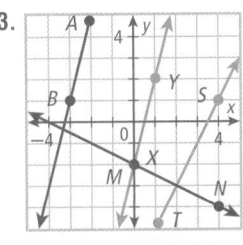

Technology Organizer

Use with Lesson 3-6

Pacing:
Traditional $\frac{1}{2}$ day
Block $\frac{1}{4}$ day

Objective: Use a graphing calculator to graph parallel and perpendicular lines.

Materials: graphing calculator

Online Edition
Graphing Calculator, TechKeys

Countdown to TAKS Week 6

Teach

Discuss

Have students use the table feature to make a table of values for $y = 3x - 4$ and $y = 3x + 1$. Use the table to find two points on each line, and calculate the slopes to verify that the lines are parallel. Then make a table of values for $y = 3x - 4$ and $y = -\frac{1}{3}x$, find two points, and calculate the slopes to verify that the lines are perpendicular.

 Geometry TEKS

G.7 Dimensionality and the geometry of location*
(B) use slopes and equations of lines to investigate geometric relationships, including parallel lines, perpendicular lines, …

* Knowledge and Skills See p. 144.

Explore Parallel and Perpendicular Lines

A graphing calculator can help you explore graphs of parallel and perpendicular lines. To graph a line on a calculator, you can enter the equation of the line in *slope-intercept form*. The slope-intercept form of the equation of a line is $y = mx + b$, where m is the slope and b is the y-intercept. For example, the line $y = 2x + 3$ has a slope of 2 and crosses the y-axis at (0, 3).

 TEKS G.7.B Dimensionality and the geometry of location: use slopes and equations of lines to investigate geometric relationships, including parallel lines, perpendicular lines, ...

go.hrw.com/Geo/TX
Lab Resources Online
KEYWORD: MG7 Lab3

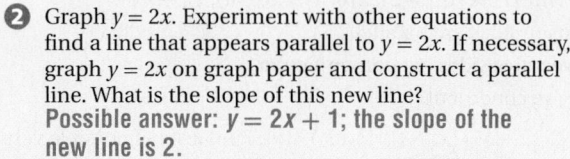 **Activity 1**

1 On a graphing calculator, graph the lines $y = 3x - 4$, $y = -3x - 4$, and $y = 3x + 1$. Which lines appear to be parallel? What do you notice about the slopes of the parallel lines?
$y = 3x - 4$ and $y = 3x + 1$ appear to be $\parallel$.
The slopes of the lines are the same.

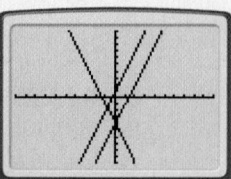

2 Graph $y = 2x$. Experiment with other equations to find a line that appears parallel to $y = 2x$. If necessary, graph $y = 2x$ on graph paper and construct a parallel line. What is the slope of this new line?
Possible answer: $y = 2x + 1$; the slope of the new line is 2.

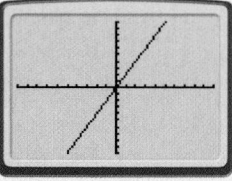

3 Graph $y = -\frac{1}{2}x + 3$. Try to graph a line that appears parallel to $y = -\frac{1}{2}x + 3$. What is the slope of this new line?
Possible answer: $y = -\frac{1}{2}x + 1$; the slope of the new line is $-\frac{1}{2}$.

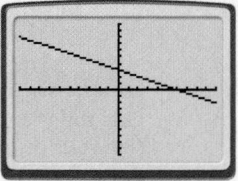

 **Try This**

2. Possible answer: Yes; the lines are still $\parallel$ if the window setting is changed; both lines appear steeper.

1. Create two new equations of lines that you think will be parallel. Graph these to confirm your conjecture. **Possible answer:** $y = x$ and $y = x + 1$

2. Graph two lines that you think are parallel. Change the window settings on the calculator. Do the lines still appear parallel? Describe your results.

3. Try changing the y-intercepts of one of the parallel lines. Does this change whether the lines appear to be parallel? **Changing the y-intercept of the lines does not change whether they are $\parallel$.**

On a graphing calculator, perpendicular lines may not appear to be perpendicular on the screen. This is because the unit distances on the *x*-axis and *y*-axis can have different lengths. To make sure that the lines appear perpendicular on the screen, use a *square window*, which shows the *x*-axis and *y*-axis as having equal unit distances.

One way to get a square window is to use the **Zoom** feature. On the **Zoom** menu, the **ZDecimal** and **ZSquare** commands change the window to a square window. The **ZStandard** command does not produce a square window.

Activity 2

1. Graph the lines $y = x$ and $y = -x$ in a square window. Do the lines appear to be perpendicular? **yes**

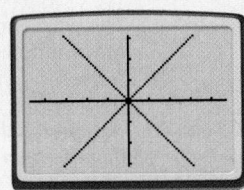

2. Graph $y = 3x - 2$ in a square window. Experiment with other equations to find a line that appears perpendicular to $y = 3x - 2$. If necessary, graph $y = 3x - 2$ on graph paper and construct a perpendicular line. What is the slope of this new line?
   Possible answer: $y = -\frac{1}{3}x + 1$; the slope of the new line is $-\frac{1}{3}$.

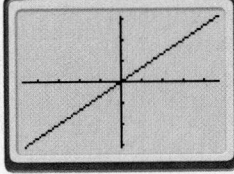

3. Graph $y = \frac{2}{3}x$ in a square window. Try to graph a line that appears perpendicular to $y = \frac{2}{3}x$. What is the slope of this new line?
   Possible answer: $y = -\frac{3}{2}x$, the slope of the new line is $-\frac{3}{2}$.

Try This

The students' equations should have slopes that are opp. reciprocals of each other. The product of the 2 slopes should be −1.

4. Create two new equations of lines that you think will be perpendicular. Graph these in a square window to confirm your conjecture.

5. Graph two lines that you think are perpendicular. Change the window settings on the calculator. Do the lines still appear perpendicular? Describe your results.
   Possible answers: No; the lines still intersect, but the ∠ does not look like a rt. ∠.

6. Try changing the *y*-intercepts of one of the perpendicular lines. Does this change whether the lines appear to be perpendicular?
   Changing the *y*-intercept of the lines does not change whether they are ⊥.

Close

Key Concepts

Parallel lines have the same slope and different *y*-intercepts.

The slopes of two perpendicular lines are opposite reciprocals of each other.

Assessment

Journal Have students explain how they can tell from the equations of two lines if the lines are parallel or perpendicular.

Pacing: Traditional 1 day
Block $\frac{1}{2}$ day

Objectives: Graph lines and write their equations in slope-intercept and point-slope form.

Classify lines as parallel, intersecting, or coinciding.

 Technology Lab
In *Texas Lab Manual*

 Online Edition
Tutorial Videos, Interactivity

 Countdown to TAKS Week 6

Power Presentations
with PowerPoint®

Warm Up

Substitute the given values of *m, x,* and *y* into the equation $y = mx + b$ and solve for *b*.

1. $m = 2$, $x = 3$, and $y = 0$
$b = -6$

2. $m = -1$, $x = 5$, and $y = -4$
$b = 1$

Solve each equation for *y*.

3. $y - 6x = 9$ $y = 6x + 9$

4. $4x - 2y = 8$ $y = 2x - 4$

 Also available on transparency

Math Humor

Q: What do two lines with the same slope do when it rains?

A: Coincide.

 Geometry TEKS

G.3 Geometric structure*
(C) use logical reasoning to prove statements are true …
(E) use deductive reasoning …

G.7 Dimensionality and the geometry of location*
(A) use … two-dimensional coordinate systems to represent points, lines, rays, line segments …
(B) use slopes and equations of lines to investigate … parallel lines, perpendicular lines, …
(C) develop 1 rand use formulas involving … slope …
* **Knowledge and Skills** See p. 144.

 TEKS G.7.B Dimensionality and the geometry of location: use… equations of lines to investigate… parallel lines, perpendicular lines, …. Also G.3.C, G.3.E, G.7.A, G.7.C

Objectives
Graph lines and write their equations in slope-intercept and point-slope form.

Classify lines as parallel, intersecting, or coinciding.

Vocabulary
point-slope form
slope-intercept form

Why learn this?

The cost of some health club plans includes a one-time enrollment fee and a monthly fee. You can use the equations of lines to determine which plan is best for you. (See Example 4.)

CLOSE TO HOME   JOHN McPHERSON

"A one-year membership is $10,000, but to encourage you to work out, we give you back $25 every time you use the facility."

©1996 John McPherson/Dist. by Universal Press Syndicate

The equation of a line can be written in many different forms. The *point-slope* and *slope-intercept* forms of a line are equivalent. Because the slope of a vertical line is undefined, these forms cannot be used to write the equation of a vertical line.

Forms of the Equation of a Line

FORM	EXAMPLE
The **point-slope form** of a line is $y - y_1 = m(x - x_1)$, where *m* is the slope and (x_1, y_1) is a given point on the line.	$y - 3 = 2(x - 4)$ $m = 2$, $(x_1, y_1) = (3, 4)$
The **slope-intercept form** of a line is $y = mx + b$, where *m* is the slope and *b* is the *y*-intercept.	$y = 3x + 6$ $m = 3$, $b = 6$
The equation of a vertical line is $x = a$, where *a* is the *x*-intercept.	$x = 5$
The equation of a horizontal line is $y = b$, where *b* is the *y*-intercept.	$y = 2$

You will prove the slope-intercept form of a line in Exercise 48.

PROOF **Point-Slope Form of a Line**

Given: The slope of a line through points (x_1, y_1) and (x_2, y_2) is $m = \frac{y_2 - y_1}{x_2 - x_1}$.
Prove: The equation of the line through (x_1, y_1) with slope *m* is
$y - y_1 = m(x - x_1)$.
Proof:
Let (x, y) be any point on the line.

$m = \frac{y_2 - y_1}{x_2 - x_1}$	*Slope formula*
$m = \frac{y - y_1}{x - x_1}$	*Substitute (x, y) for (x_2, y_2).*
$(x - x_1)m = (x - x_1)\frac{y - y_1}{x - x_1}$	*Multiply both sides by $(x - x_1)$.*
$m(x - x_1) = (y - y_1)$	*Simplify.*
$y - y_1 = m(x - x_1)$	*Sym. Prop. of =*

1 Introduce

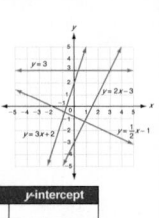

EXPLORATION
3-6 Lines in the Coordinate Plane

Use the given lines to explore equations, slopes, and *y*-intercepts.

1. Find the slope of each line. Record the slopes in the table.
2. Find the *y*-intercept of each line. Record the *y*-intercepts in the table.

Equation	Slope	*y*-intercept
$y = 3x + 2$		
$y = 2x - 3$		
$y = -\frac{1}{2}x - 1$		
$y = 3$		

3. What do you notice? How are the slopes and *y*-intercepts related to the equations?

THINK AND DISCUSS
4. **Explain** how you can identify the *y*-intercept of the line $y = -7x + 4$ without graphing it.

Motivate

Show students the instructions for baking a cake from a packaged cake mix. Point out that the baking times are different at higher altitudes because the air pressure is less at higher elevations than at sea level. Tell students that the graph of a linear equation can be used to determine how long a cake should be baked at a particular altitude.

Explorations and answers are provided in the Explorations binder.

EXAMPLE 1 Writing Equations of Lines

Write the equation of each line in the given form.

x²y Algebra

A the line with slope 3 through $(2, 1)$ in point-slope form

$y - y_1 = m(x - x_1)$ *Point-slope form*

$y - 1 = 3(x - 2)$ *Substitute 3 for m, 2 for x_1, and 1 for y_1.*

B the line through $(0, 4)$ and $(-1, 2)$ in slope-intercept form

$m = \dfrac{2 - 4}{-1 - 0} = \dfrac{-2}{-1} = 2$ *Find the slope.*

$y = mx + b$ *Slope-intercept form*

$4 = 2(0) + b$ *Substitute 2 for m, 0 for x, and 4 for y to find b.*

$4 = b$ *Simplify.*

$y = 2x + 4$ *Write in slope-intercept form using $m = 2$ and $b = 4$.*

> **Remember!**
>
> A line with y-intercept b contains the point $(0, b)$. A line with x-intercept a contains the point $(a, 0)$.

C the line with x-intercept 2 and y-intercept 3 in point-slope form

$m = \dfrac{3 - 0}{0 - 2} = -\dfrac{3}{2}$ *Use the points (2, 0) and (0, 3) to find the slope.*

$y - y_1 = m(x - x_1)$ *Point-slope form*

$y - 0 = -\dfrac{3}{2}(x - 2)$ *Substitute $-\dfrac{3}{2}$ for m, 2 for x_1, and 0 for y_1.*

              Simplify.

$y = -\dfrac{3}{2}(x - 2)$

> **CHECK IT OUT!** Write the equation of each line in the given form.
>
> **1a.** the line with slope 0 through $(4, 6)$ in slope-intercept form $y = 6$
>
> **1b.** the line through $(-3, 2)$ and $(1, 2)$ in point-slope form $y - 2 = 0$

EXAMPLE 2 Graphing Lines

Graph each line.

x²y Algebra

A $y = \dfrac{3}{2}x + 3$

The equation is given in slope-intercept form, with a slope of $\dfrac{3}{2}$ and a y-intercept of 3.

Plot the point $(0, 3)$ and then rise 3 and run 2 to find another point.

Draw the line containing the two points.

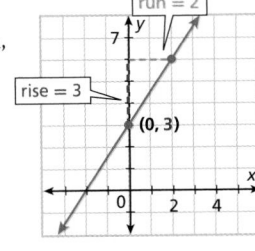

B $y + 3 = -2(x - 1)$

The equation is given in point-slope form, with a slope of $-2 = \dfrac{-2}{1}$ through the point $(1, -3)$.

Plot the point $(1, -3)$ and then rise -2 and run 1 to find another point.

Draw the line containing the two points.

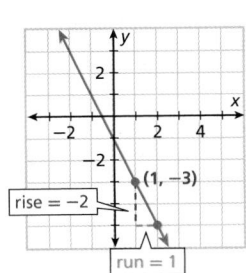

Students sometimes make errors substituting a negative coordinate into the point-slope form of an equation. Remind students that subtracting y is equivalent to adding the opposite of y.

Power Presentations with PowerPoint®

Additional Examples

Example 1

Write the equation of each line in the given form.

A. the line with slope 6 through $(3, -4)$ in point-slope form
$y + 4 = 6(x - 3)$

B. the line through $(-1, 0)$ and $(1, 2)$ in slope-intercept form
$y = x + 1$

C. the line with x-intercept 3 and y-intercept -5 in point-slope form $y = \dfrac{5}{3}(x - 3)$

Example 2

Graph each line.

A. $y = \dfrac{1}{2}x + 1$

B. $y - 3 = -2(x + 4)$

C. $y = -3$

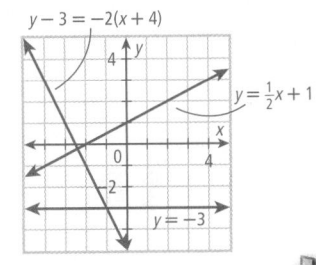

Also available on transparency

INTERVENTION

Questioning Strategies

EXAMPLE 1

- In **Example 1B**, how do you find the y-intercept b after you find the slope?

- How do you use the intercepts to find the slope in **Example 1C**?

EXAMPLE 2

- Describe how you graph each line.

---

2 Teach

ENGLISH LANGUAGE LEARNERS

Guided Instruction

Before writing equations of lines, discuss the meaning of the points (x_1, y_1) and (x_2, y_2). As you work through the lesson, relate the equations of parallel, intersecting, and coinciding lines to their graphs.

Reaching All Learners

Through Curriculum Integration

Give groups of students a thermometer showing Fahrenheit and Celsius temperatures. Ask them to write two ordered pairs (°F, °C) that relate the boiling and freezing temperatures in Fahrenheit to the corresponding temperatures in Celsius. Then have them write the slope-intercept form of the equation of the line through the two points.

INTERVENTION ◄═►
Questioning Strategies

EXAMPLE 3

• How can you tell that two lines are parallel?

• How is it helpful to solve equations for y?

• How can lines that have different equations be coinciding lines?

Answers to *Check It Out!*

2a.
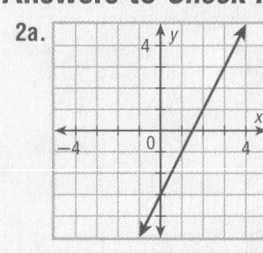

b.
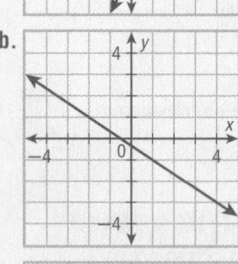

c.
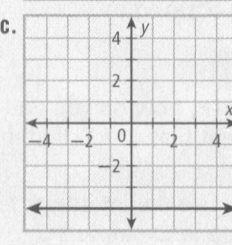

Graph the line.

C $x = 3$

The equation is given in the form for a vertical line with an x-intercept of 3. The equation tells you that the x-coordinate of every point on the line is 3. Draw the vertical line through $(3, 0)$.

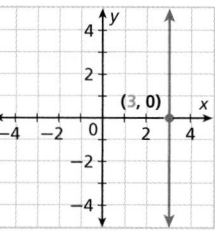

 **Graph each line.**

2a. $y = 2x - 3$ **2b.** $y - 1 = -\frac{2}{3}(x + 2)$ **2c.** $y = -4$

A system of two linear equations in two variables represents two lines. The lines can be parallel, intersecting, or coinciding. Lines that coincide are the same line, but the equations may be written in different forms.

Know it!
·*Note*

Pairs of Lines

Parallel Lines	Intersecting Lines	Coinciding Lines
$y = 5x + 8$	$y = 2x - 5$	$y = 2x - 4$
$y = 5x - 4$	$y = 4x + 3$	$y = 2x - 4$
Same slope different y-intercept	Different slopes	Same slope same y-intercept

EXAMPLE 3 Classifying Pairs of Lines

Determine whether the lines are parallel, intersect, or coincide.

A $y = 2x + 3$, $y = 2x - 1$

Both lines have a slope of 2, and the y-intercepts are different. So the lines are parallel.

B $y = 3x - 5$, $6x - 2y = 10$

Solve the second equation for y to find the slope-intercept form.
$$6x - 2y = 10$$
$$-2y = -6x + 10$$
$$y = 3x - 5$$
Both lines have a slope of 3 and a y-intercept of -5, so they coincide.

C $3x + 2y = 7$, $3y = 4x + 7$

Solve both equations for y to find the slope-intercept form.

$3x + 2y = 7$ $3y = 4x + 7$
$2y = -3x + 7$ $y = \frac{4}{3}x + \frac{7}{3}$ *The slope is $\frac{4}{3}$.*
$y = -\frac{3}{2}x + \frac{7}{2}$ *The slope is $-\frac{3}{2}$.*

The lines have different slopes, so they intersect.

 **3.** Determine whether the lines $3x + 5y = 2$ and $3x + 6 = -5y$ are parallel, intersect, or coincide. **parallel**

 Math Background An equation of the form $Ax + By = C$ can be written in slope-intercept form as $y = \frac{-A}{B}x + \frac{C}{B}$. So a quick way to check whether lines have the same slope is to find $\frac{-A}{B}$ for both lines. If the slopes are the same, then find $\frac{C}{B}$ to see if the lines coincide.

EXAMPLE 4 *Problem-Solving Application*

Audrey is trying to decide between two health club plans. After how many months would both plans' total costs be the same?

	Plan A	Plan B
Enrollment Fee	$140	$60
Monthly Fee	$35	$55

1 Understand the Problem

The **answer** is the number of months after which the costs of the two plans would be the same. Plan A costs $140 for enrollment and $35 per month. Plan B costs $60 for enrollment and $55 per month.

2 Make a Plan

Write an equation for each plan, and then graph the equations. The solution is the intersection of the two lines. Find the intersection by solving the system of equations.

3 Solve

Plan A: $y = 35x + 140$
Plan B: $y = 55x + 60$
$0 = -20x + 80$ *Subtract the second equation from the first.*

$x = 4$ *Solve for x.*
$y = 35(4) + 140 = 280$ *Substitute 4 for x in the first equation.*

The lines cross at $(4, 280)$.
Both plans cost $280 after 4 months.

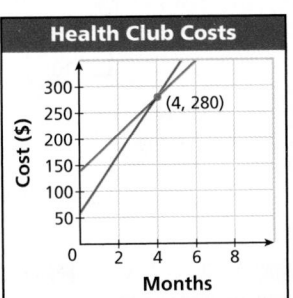

Health Club Costs

4 Look Back

Check your answer for each plan in the original problem. For 4 months, plan A costs $140 plus $35(4) = $140 + $140 = $280. Plan B costs $60 + $55(4) = $60 + $220 = $280, so the plans cost the same.

CHECK IT OUT! Use the information above to answer the following.

4. What if...? Suppose the rate for Plan B was also $35 per month. What would be true about the lines that represent the cost of each plan? **The lines would be ∥.**

THINK AND DISCUSS

1. Explain how to use the slopes and y-intercepts to determine if two lines are parallel.

2. Describe the relationship between the slopes of perpendicular lines.

3. GET ORGANIZED Copy and complete the graphic organizer.

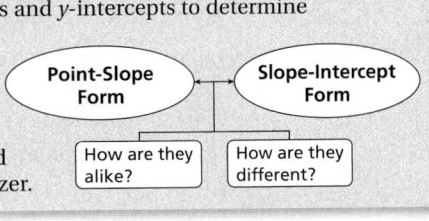

Point-Slope Form → Slope-Intercept Form

How are they alike? | How are they different?

Know it! Note

COMMON ERROR ALERT

In **Example 4,** students may forget to subtract 60 from 140, resulting in $y = -20x + 200$. Suggest that they align the equations vertically and change the sign of each term in the bottom equation, or suggest that students solve $35x + 140 = 55x + 60$ instead.

Power Presentations with PowerPoint®

Additional Examples

Example 4

Erica is trying to decide between two car rental plans. For how many miles will the plans cost the same?

	Plan A	Plan B
Initial Fee	$100.00	$85.00
Mileage Fee	$0.35/mi	$0.50

Both plans cost $135 for 100 miles.

Also available on transparency

INTERVENTION ⟸⟹
Questioning Strategies

EXAMPLE 4

• Which fee in each plan is related to the slope of the line? Which fee in each plan is related to the y-intercept of the line?

---

3 Close

Summarize

Review the point-slope and slope-intercept forms of the equations of a line and how to use each form to graph a line. Graph a line and show students how to write both the point-slope and slope-intercept forms of the equation. Compare and contrast pairs of lines that are parallel, perpendicular, or coinciding.

ONGOING ASSESSMENT

and INTERVENTION ⟸⟹

Diagnose Before the Lesson
3-6 Warm Up, TE p. 190

Monitor During the Lesson
Check It Out! Exercises, SE pp. 191–193
Questioning Strategies, TE pp. 191–193

Assess After the Lesson
3-6 Lesson Quiz, TE p. 197
Alternative Assessment, TE p. 197

Answers to *Think and Discuss*

1. If the slopes are the same and the y-intercepts are different, then the lines are ∥.

2. If the slopes of 2 ⊥ lines are multiplied, the product is −1. Each slope is the opp. reciprocal of the other slope.

3. See p. A3.

3-6 Exercises

3-6 Exercises

go.hrw.com/Geo/TX
Homework Help Online
KEYWORD: MG7 3-6
Parent Resources Online
KEYWORD: MG7 Parent

3-6 Exercises

Assignment Guide

Assign *Guided Practice* exercises as necessary.

If you finished Examples **1–2**
    Basic 13–18, 24–30
    Average 13–18, 24–31
    Advanced 13–18, 24–31, 46

If you finished Examples **1–4**
    Basic 12–23, 24–44 even,
      45–46, 53, 57–61,
      67–73
    Average 14–22 even, 23–31,
      32–52 even, 53, 54,
      56–64, 67–73
    Advanced 12–23, 24–44 even,
      47–52 even, 53–73

Homework Quick Check
Quickly check key concepts.
Exercises: 14, 16, 22, 23, 28, 36

Teaching Tip
Kinesthetic Let students use straws or uncooked spaghetti and graph paper to model a line that passes through the points in **Exercise 2**. Have them use the models to find the slope of the line and then write the equation of the line in slope-intercept form.

Answers
1, 5–7, 12, 16–18. See p. A14.
24–31. For graphs, see p. A14.

TAKS Practice

Grades 9–11	Exercises
Obj. 1	58
Obj. 3	24–32, 37–44, 47–52, 58–61
Obj. 4	45, 46, 51–53, 58, 67
Obj. 7	24–53, 59–63, 68–73
Obj. 8	62, 63
Obj. 10	45, 67

GUIDED PRACTICE

1. **Vocabulary** How can you recognize the *slope-intercept form* of an equation?

SEE EXAMPLE **1**
p. 191
  Write the equation of each line in the given form.
  2. the line through $(4, 7)$ and $(-2, 1)$ in slope-intercept form $y = x + 3$
  3. the line through $(-4, 2)$ with slope $\frac{3}{4}$ in point-slope form. $y - 2 = \frac{3}{4}(x + 4)$
  4. the line with x-intercept 4 and y-intercept -2 in slope-intercept form $y = \frac{1}{2}x - 2$

SEE EXAMPLE **2**
p. 191
  Graph each line.
  5. $y = -3x + 4$ 6. $y + 4 = \frac{2}{3}(x - 6)$ 7. $x = 5$

SEE EXAMPLE **3**
p. 192
  Determine whether the lines are parallel, intersect, or coincide.
  8. $y = -3x + 4, y = -3x + 1$ ‖
              9. $6x - 12y = -24, 3y = 2x + 18$ **intersect**
  10. $y = \frac{1}{3}x + \frac{2}{3}, 3y = x + 2$ **coincide**
           11. $4x + 2y = 10, y = -2x + 15$ ‖

SEE EXAMPLE **4**
p. 193
  12. **Transportation** A speeding ticket in Conroe costs \$115 for the first 10 mi/h over the speed limit and \$1 for each additional mi/h. In Lakeville, a ticket costs \$50 for the first 10 mi/h over the speed limit and \$10 for each additional mi/h. If the speed limit is 55 mi/h, at what speed will the tickets cost approximately the same?

PRACTICE AND PROBLEM SOLVING

Homework Help

For Exercises	See Example
13–15	1
16–18	2
19–22	3
23	4

TEKS → TAKS

Skills Practice p. S9
Application Practice p. S30

Write the equation of each line in the given form.
13. the line through $(0, -2)$ and $(4, 6)$ in point-slope form $y + 2 = 2x$
14. the line through $(5, 2)$ and $(-2, 2)$ in slope-intercept form $y = 2$
15. the line through $(6, -4)$ with slope $\frac{2}{3}$ in point-slope form $y + 4 = \frac{2}{3}(x - 6)$

Graph each line.
16. $y - 7 = x + 4$ 17. $y = \frac{1}{2}x - 2$ 18. $y = 2$

Determine whether the lines are parallel, intersect, or coincide.
19. $y = x - 7, y = -x + 3$ **intersect**
          20. $y = \frac{5}{2}x + 4, 2y = 5x - 4$ ‖
21. $x + 2y = 6, y = -\frac{1}{2}x + 3$ **coincide**
      22. $7x + 2y = 10, 3y = 4x - 5$ **intersect**

23. **Business** Chris is comparing two sales positions that he has been offered. The first pays a weekly salary of \$375 plus a 20% commission. The second pays a weekly salary of \$325 plus a 25% commission. How much must he make in sales per week for the two jobs to pay the same? **\$1000 per week**

Write the equation of each line in slope-intercept form. Then graph the line.
24. through $(-6, 2)$ and $(3, 6)$ $y = \frac{4}{9}x + \frac{14}{3}$ 25. horizontal line through $(2, 3)$ $y = 3$
$y = \frac{2}{3}x - \frac{16}{3}$ 26. through $(5, -2)$ with slope $\frac{2}{3}$ 27. x-intercept 4, y-intercept -3 $y = \frac{3}{4}x - 3$

Write the equation of each line in point-slope form. Then graph the line.
28. slope $-\frac{1}{2}$, y-intercept 2 $y - 2 = -\frac{1}{2}x$ 29. slope $\frac{3}{4}$, x-intercept -2 $y = \frac{3}{4}(x + 2)$
$y + 1 = -(x - 5)$ 30. through $(5, -1)$ with slope -1 31. through $(4, 6)$ and $(-2, -5)$
                                         31. $y - 6 = \frac{11}{6}(x - 4)$

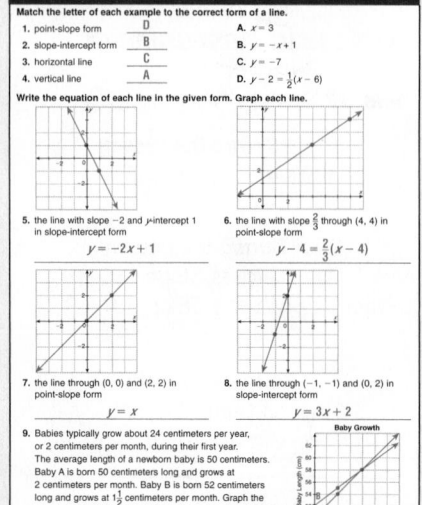

3-6 PRACTICE A

Match the letter of each example to the correct form of a line.
1. point-slope form   D   A. $x = 3$
2. slope-intercept form   B   B. $y = -x + 1$
3. horizontal line   C   C. $y = -7$
4. vertical line   A   D. $y - 2 = \frac{1}{2}(x - 6)$

Write the equation of each line in the given form. Graph each line.

5. the line with slope -2 and y-intercept 1 in slope-intercept form
$y = -2x + 1$

6. the line with slope $\frac{2}{3}$ through $(4, 4)$ in point-slope form
$y - 4 = \frac{2}{3}(x - 4)$

7. the line through $(0, 0)$ and $(2, 2)$ in point-slope form
$y = x$

8. the line through $(-1, -1)$ and $(0, 2)$ in slope-intercept form
$y = 3x + 2$

9. Babies typically grow about 24 centimeters per year, or 2 centimeters per month, during their first year. The average length of a newborn baby is 50 centimeters. Baby A is born 50 centimeters long and grows at 2 centimeters per month. Baby B is born 52 centimeters long and grows at $1\frac{1}{2}$ centimeters per month. Graph the growth of each baby. (*Hint:* The birth length is the y-intercept, and the growth rate is the slope.)

Baby Growth

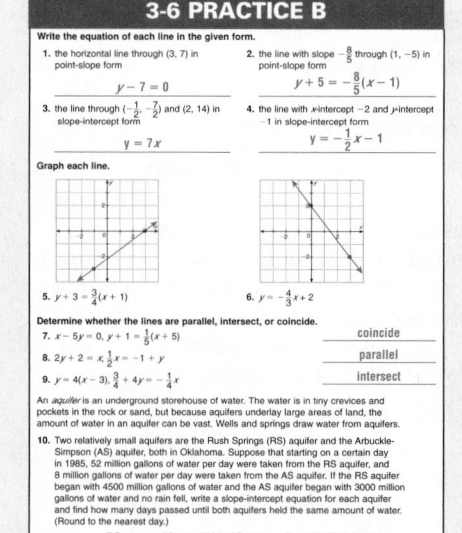

3-6 PRACTICE B

Write the equation of each line in the given form.

1. the horizontal line through $(3, 7)$ in point-slope form
$y - 7 = 0$

2. the line with slope $-\frac{8}{5}$ through $(1, -5)$ in point-slope form
$y + 5 = -\frac{8}{5}(x - 1)$

3. the line through $(-\frac{1}{2}, -\frac{7}{2})$ and $(2, 14)$ in slope-intercept form
$y = 7x$

4. the line with x-intercept -2 and y-intercept -1 in slope-intercept form
$y = -\frac{1}{2}x - 1$

Graph each line.

5. $y + 3 = \frac{3}{4}(x + 1)$ 6. $y = -\frac{4}{3}x + 2$

Determine whether the lines are parallel, intersect, or coincide.
7. $x - 5y = 0, y + 1 = \frac{1}{5}(x + 5)$ **coincide**
8. $2y + 2 = x, \frac{1}{2}x = -1 + y$ **parallel**
9. $y = 4(x - 3), \frac{3}{2} + 4y = -\frac{1}{4}x$ **intersect**

An *aquifer* is an underground storehouse of water. The water is in tiny crevices and pockets in the rock or sand, but because aquifers underlay large areas of land, the amount of water in an aquifer can be vast. Wells and springs draw water from aquifers.

10. Two relatively small aquifers are the Rush Springs (RS) aquifer and the Arbuckle-Simpson (AS) aquifer, both in Oklahoma. Suppose that starting on a certain day in 1985, 52 million gallons of water per day were taken from the RS aquifer and 8 million gallons of water per day were taken from the AS aquifer. If the RS aquifer began with 4500 million gallons of water and the AS aquifer began with 3000 million gallons of water, and no rain fell, write a slope-intercept equation for each aquifer and find how many days passed until both aquifers held the same amount of water. (Round to the nearest day.)
  RS: $y = -52x + 4500$; AS: $y = -8x + 3000$; 34 days

32. ///ERROR ANALYSIS/// Write the equation of the line with slope -2 through the point $(-4, 3)$ in slope-intercept form. Which equation is incorrect? Explain.

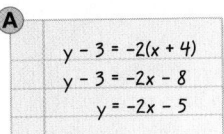

A

$$y - 3 = -2(x + 4)$$
$$y - 3 = -2x - 8$$
$$y = -2x - 5$$

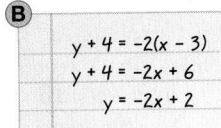

B

$$y + 4 = -2(x - 3)$$
$$y + 4 = -2x + 6$$
$$y = -2x + 2$$

B is incorrect. In B, the x- and y-values of the pt. used to find the pt.-slope form are interchanged.

Determine whether the lines are perpendicular.

33. $y = 3x - 5$, $y = -3x + 1$ **no**

34. $y = -x + 1$, $y = x + 2$ **yes**

35. $y = -\frac{2}{3}x + 5$, $y = \frac{3}{2}x - 8$, **yes**

36. $y = -2x + 4$, $y = -\frac{1}{2}x - 2$ **no**

Multi-Step Given the equation of the line and point P not on the line, find the equation of a line parallel to the given line and a line perpendicular to the given line through the given point.

37. $y = 3x + 7$, $P(2, 3)$

38. $y = -2x - 5$, $P(-1, 4)$

39. $4x + 3y = 8$, $P(4, -2)$

40. $2x - 5y = 7$, $P(-2, 4)$

Multi-Step Use slope to determine if each triangle is a right triangle. If so, which angle is the right angle?

41. $A(-5, 3)$, $B(0, -2)$, $C(5, 3)$ **yes; $\angle B$**

42. $D(1, 0)$, $E(2, 7)$, $F(5, 1)$ **no**

43. $G(3, 4)$, $H(-3, 4)$, $J(1, -2)$ **no**

44. $K(-2, 4)$, $L(2, 1)$, $M(1, 8)$ **yes; $\angle K$**

Food

In 2004, the world's largest pizza was baked in Italy. The diameter of the pizza was 5.19 m (about 17 ft) and it weighed 124 kg (about 273 lb).

45. **Food** A restaurant charges $8 for a large cheese pizza plus $1.50 per topping. Another restaurant charges $11 for a large cheese pizza plus $0.75 per topping. How many toppings does a pizza have that costs the same at both restaurants? **For 4 toppings, both pizzas will cost $14.**

46. **Estimation** Estimate the solution of the system of equations represented by the lines in the graph. **Possible answer:**
$$x = 1.2, \text{ and } y = 3.7$$

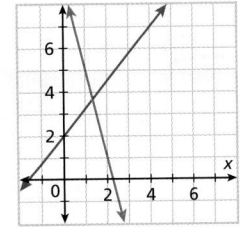

Write the equation of the perpendicular bisector of the segment with the given endpoints.

47. $(2, 5)$ and $(4, 9)$ $y = -\frac{1}{2}x + \frac{17}{2}$

48. $(1, 1)$ and $(3, 1)$ $x = 2$

49. $(1, 3)$ and $(-1, 4)$ $y = 2x + \frac{7}{2}$

50. $(-3, 2)$ and $(-3, -10)$ $y = -4$

51. Line ℓ has equation $y = -\frac{1}{2}x + 4$, and point P has coordinates $(3, 5)$. $y = 2x - 1$

   a. Find the equation of line m that passes through P and is perpendicular to ℓ.

   b. Find the coordinates of the intersection of ℓ and m. $(2, 3)$

   c. What is the distance from P to ℓ? $\sqrt{5}$ **units**

52. Line p has equation $y = x + 3$, and line q has equation $y = x - 1$. **Possible answers:**

   a. Find the equation of a line r that is perpendicular to p and q. $y = -x + 1$

   b. Find the coordinates of the intersection of p and r and the coordinates of the intersection of q and r. $(-1, 2)$; $(1, 0)$

   c. Find the distance between lines p and q. $2\sqrt{2}$ **units**

Inclusion For **Exercises** **41–44,** suggest that students first graph each triangle. Ask them if any angle looks like a right angle. Then have them verify their answer by finding the rise and run of the segments that form the angle.

Teaching Tip

Answers

37. ‖ line: $y = 3x - 3$;
   ⊥ line: $y = -\frac{1}{3}x + \frac{11}{3}$

38. ‖ line: $y = -2x + 2$;
   ⊥ line: $y = \frac{1}{2}x + \frac{9}{2}$

39. ‖ line: $y = -\frac{4}{3}x + \frac{10}{3}$;
   ⊥ line: $y = \frac{3}{4}x - 5$

40. ‖ line: $y = \frac{2}{5}x + \frac{24}{5}$;
   ⊥ line: $y = -\frac{5}{2}x - 1$

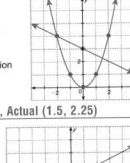
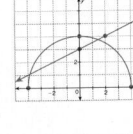

MULTI-STEP TAKS PREP **Exercise 53** involves graphing two lines and interpreting their intersection. This exercise prepares students for the Multi-Step TAKS Prep on page 200.

TEST PREP DOCTOR For **Exercise 58,** encourage students to write the equations in slope-intercept form and eliminate any graphs that have the wrong y-intercepts. This will immediately eliminate choices **B** and **C.**

Data Collecton For help with **Exercise 55,** see *Technology Lab Activities.*

Answers

53a–b.

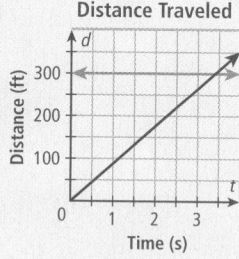

b. the time when the car has traveled 300 ft
c. Possible answer: 3.5 s

54. It is given that the eqn. of the line through (x_1, y_1) with slope m is $y - y_1 = m(x - x_1)$. Let $(0, b)$ be a pt. on the line. Then 0 is a possible value for x_1, and b is a possible value for y_1. Substitute these values into the eqn. $y - y_1 = m(x - x_1)$ to get $y - b = m(x - 0)$. Simplify to get $y - b = mx$. By the Add. Prop. of =, $y = mx + b$. Thus the eqn. of the line through $(0, b)$ with slope m is $y = mx + b$.

56. The slope of the line is $m = \dfrac{2 - 6}{2 + 4} = -\dfrac{2}{3}$. The pt-slope form of the line is $y - 6 = -\dfrac{2}{3}(x + 4)$. To see if the line crosses the x-axis at $(5, 0)$, substitute 5 for x and 0 for y:

$0 - 6 = -\dfrac{2}{3}(5 + 4)$

$-6 = -\dfrac{2}{3}(9)$

$-6 = -6$

These values make the equation true, so $(5, 0)$ is on the line.

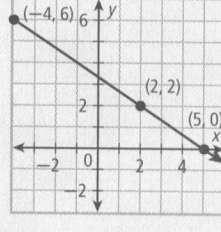

196 *Chapter 3*

MULTI-STEP TAKS PREP

53. This problem will prepare you for the Multi-Step TAKS Prep on page 200.

For a car moving at 60 mi/h, the equation $d = 88t$ gives the distance in feet d that the car travels in t seconds.

a. Graph the line $d = 88t$.

b. On the same graph you made for part **a,** graph the line $d = 300$. What does the intersection of the two lines represent?

c. Use the graph to estimate the number of seconds it takes the car to travel 300 ft.

54. Prove the slope-intercept form of a line, given the point-slope form.

Given: The equation of the line through (x_1, y_1) with slope m is $y - y_1 = m(x - x_1)$.
Prove: The equation of the line through $(0, b)$ with slope m is $y = mx + b$.
Plan: Substitute $(0, b)$ for (x_1, y_1) in the equation $y - y_1 = m(x - x_1)$ and simplify.

55. Data Collection Use a graphing calculator and a motion detector to do the following: Walk in front of the motion detector at a constant speed, and write the equation of the resulting graph. **Check students' work.**

56. Critical Thinking A line contains the points $(-4, 6)$ and $(2, 2)$. Write a convincing argument that the line crosses the x-axis at $(5, 0)$. Include a graph to verify your argument.

 **57. Write About It** Determine whether the lines are parallel. Use slope to explain your answer.

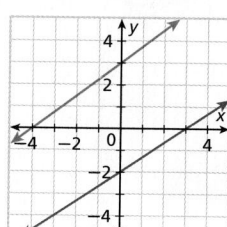

The top line passes through $(-4, 0)$ and $(0, 3)$, so its slope is $m = \dfrac{3 - 0}{0 + 4} = \dfrac{3}{4}$. The bottom line passes through $(0, -2)$ and $(3, 0)$, so its slope is $m = \dfrac{0 - (-2)}{3 - 0} = \dfrac{2}{3}$. The lines do not have the same slope, so they are not $\parallel$.

 TEST PREP

58. Which graph best represents a solution to this system of equations?

$$\begin{cases} -3x + y = 7 \\ 2x + y = -3 \end{cases}$$

Ⓐ
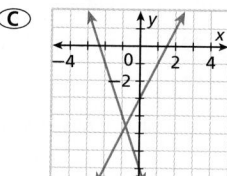

Ⓒ
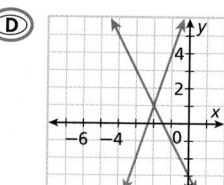

Ⓑ
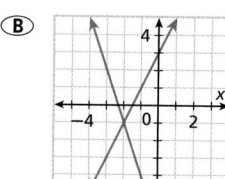

Ⓓ

196 *Chapter 3 Parallel and Perpendicular Lines*

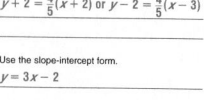

3-6 READING STRATEGIES

Equation of a line

Point-slope form | Slope-intercept form

$y - y_1 = m(x - x_1)$
m is the slope.
(x_1, y_1) is a given point.

$y = mx + b$
m is the slope.
b is the y-intercept.

1. Why do you think $y - y_1 = m(x - x_1)$ is called point-slope form?
Looking at the equation, you can see the slope and a point on the line.

2. Why do you think $y = mx + b$ is called the slope-intercept form of the line?
Looking at the equation, m is the slope and b is the y-intercept.

3. How is the point-slope form of an equation like the slope-intercept form of the equation?
They are both equations of the line, and they both plug in the slope and a point on the line.

4. If you know two points on a line, which form of the equation is easier to write?
point-slope form

Write the equations of the following lines.

5. Use the point-slope form.
$y + 2 = \frac{4}{5}(x + 2)$ or $y - 2 = \frac{4}{5}(x - 3)$

6. Use the slope-intercept form.
$y = 3x - 2$

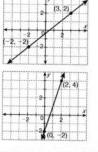

3-6 RETEACH

Slope-Intercept Form | Point-Slope Form

$y = mx + b$ | $y - y_1 = m(x - x_1)$

slope | y-intercept | slope

$y = 4x + 7$ | $y - 2 = \frac{2}{3}(x + 5)$
point on the line:
$(x_1, y_1) = (-5, 2)$

Write the equation of the line through (0, 1) and (2, 7) in slope-intercept form.

Step 1: Find the slope.
$m = \frac{y_2 - y_1}{x_2 - x_1}$ Formula for slope
$= \frac{7 - 1}{2 - 0} = \frac{6}{2} = 3$

Step 2: Find the y-intercept.
$y = mx + b$ Slope-intercept form
$1 = 3(0) + b$ Substitute 3 for m, 0 for x, and 1 for y.
$1 = b$ Simplify.

Step 3: Write the equation.
$y = mx + b$ Slope-intercept form
$y = 3x + 1$ Substitute 3 for m and 1 for b.

Write the equation of each line in the given form.

1. the line through (4, 2) and (8, 5) in slope-intercept form
$y = \frac{3}{4}x - 1$

2. the line through (4, 6) with slope $\frac{1}{2}$ in point-slope form
$y - 6 = \frac{1}{2}(x - 4)$

3. the line through (-5, 1) with slope 2 in point-slope form
$y - 1 = 2(x + 5)$

4. the line with x-intercept -5 and y-intercept 3 in slope-intercept form
$y = \frac{3}{5}x + 3$

5. the line through (8, 0) with slope $-\frac{3}{4}$ in slope-intercept form
$y = -\frac{3}{4}x + 6$

6. the line through (1, 7) and (-6, 7) in point-slope form
$y - 7 = 0$

59. Which line is parallel to the line with the equation $y = -2x + 5$?

Ⓕ $\overleftrightarrow{AB}$ through $A(2, 3)$ and $B(1, 1)$
Ⓗ $4x + 2y = 10$
Ⓖ $y = -\frac{1}{2}x - 3$
(Ⓙ) $x + \frac{1}{2}y = 1$

60. Which equation best describes the graph shown?

Ⓐ $y = -\frac{3}{2}x + 3$
Ⓒ $y = -\frac{2}{3}x + 2$
Ⓑ $y = 3x - \frac{2}{3}$
(Ⓓ) $y = -\frac{2}{3}x + 3$

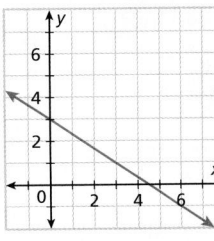

61. Which line includes the points $(-4, 2)$ and $(6, -3)$?

Ⓕ $y = 2x - 4$
Ⓗ $y = -\frac{1}{2}x - 4$
Ⓖ $y = 2x$
(Ⓙ) $y = -\frac{1}{2}x$

CHALLENGE AND EXTEND

62. $\frac{5\sqrt{5}}{2}$ units

62. A right triangle is formed by the x-axis, the y-axis, and the line $y = -2x + 5$. Find the length of the hypotenuse.

63. If the length of the hypotenuse of a right triangle is 17 units and the legs lie along the x-axis and y-axis, find a possible equation that describes the line that contains the hypotenuse. **Possible answer: $y = -\frac{8}{15}x + 8$**

64. Possible answer: $x = 0$, $y = 0$, $y = -\frac{5}{12}x + 5$

64. Find the equations of three lines that form a triangle with a hypotenuse of 13 units.

65. **Multi-Step** Are the points $(-2, -4)$, $(5, -2)$ and $(2, -3)$ collinear? Explain the method you used to determine your answer. **no**

66. For the line $y = x + 1$ and the point $P(3, 2)$, let d represent the distance from P to a point (x, y) on the line.

   a. Write an expression for d^2 in terms of x and y. Substitute the expression $x + 1$ for y and simplify. **$d^2 = 2x^2 - 8x + 10$**

   b. How could you use this expression to find the shortest distance from P to the line? Compare your result to the distance along a perpendicular line.

SPIRAL REVIEW

67. The cost of renting DVDs from an online company is \$5.00 per month plus \$2.50 for each DVD rented. Write an equation for the total cost c of renting d DVDs from the company in one month. Graph the equation. How many DVDs did Sean rent from the company if his total bill for one month was \$20.00? *(Previous course)*

Use the coordinate plane for Exercises 68–70. Find the coordinates of the midpoint of each segment. *(Lesson 1-6)*

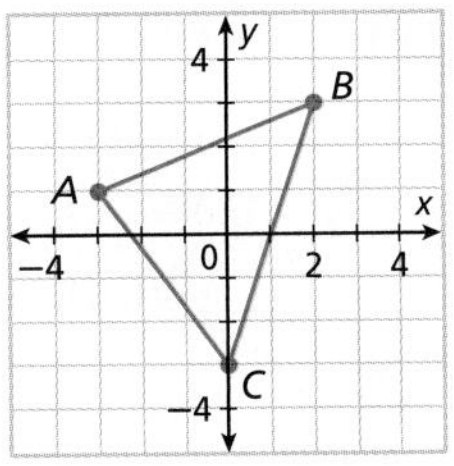

70. $\left(-\frac{3}{2}, -1\right)$

68. $\overline{AB}$ $\left(-\frac{1}{2}, 2\right)$
69. $\overline{BC}$ $(1, 0)$
70. $\overline{AC}$

Use the slope formula to find the slope of each segment. *(Lesson 3-5)*

73. $m = -\frac{4}{3}$

71. $\overline{AB}$ $m = \frac{2}{5}$
72. $\overline{BC}$ $m = 3$
73. $\overline{AC}$

COMMON ERROR ALERT

For **Exercise 57,** students may base their answers on the appearance of the lines. Remind them to calculate the slopes.

Answers

65. Possible answer: I found the equation of the line through the first 2 pts., which is $y = \frac{2}{7}x - \frac{24}{7}$. Then I substituted the x- and y-values for the third pt. to see if it lies on the line. The values did not make the equation true, so the pts. are not collinear.

Journal

Have students explain how to use two points or one point and the slope to write the equation of a line. Have them include examples.

ALTERNATIVE ASSESSMENT

Ask students to draw a pair of parallel lines, a pair of intersecting lines, and a pair of coinciding lines, and then write a system of equations for each pair.

Power Presentations with PowerPoint®

3-6 Lesson Quiz

Write the equation of each line in the given form. Then graph each line.

1. the line through $(-1, 3)$ and $(3, -5)$ in slope-intercept form $y = -2x + 1$
2. the line through $(5, -1)$ with slope $\frac{2}{5}$ in point-slope form
   $y + 1 = \frac{2}{5}(x - 5)$

1–2.

Determine whether the lines are parallel, intersect, or coincide.

3. $y - 3 = -\frac{1}{2}x$, $y - 5 = 2(x + 3)$ intersect
4. $2y = 4x + 12$, $4x - 2y = 8$ parallel

Also available on transparency

3-6 PROBLEM SOLVING

Use the following information for Exercises 1 and 2. Josh can order 1 color ink cartridge and 2 black ink cartridges for his printer for \$78. He can also order 1 color ink cartridge and 1 black ink cartridge for \$53.

1. Let x equal the cost of a color ink cartridge and y equal the cost of a black ink cartridge. Write a system of equations to represent this situation.
   $x + 2y = 78$, $x + y = 53$

2. What is the cost of each cartridge?
   color: \$28, black: \$25

3. Ms. Williams is planning to buy T-shirts for the cheerleading camp that she is running. After buying how many T-shirts would both companies' total costs be the same? Use a graph to find your solution.

	Art Creation Fee	Cost per T-shirt
Company A	\$70	\$10
Company B	\$50	\$12

Both companies total costs would be the same for 10 T-shirts.

Choose the best answer.

4. Two floats begin a parade at different times, but travel at the same speeds. Which is a true statement about the lines that represent the distance traveled by each float at a given time?
   A The lines intersect.
   (B) The lines are parallel.
   C The lines are the same.
   D The lines have a negative slope.

5. A piano teacher charges \$20 for each half hour lesson, plus an initial fee of \$50. Another teacher charges \$40 per hour, plus a fee of \$50. Which is a true statement about the lines that represent the total cost by each piano teacher?
   F The lines intersect.
   G The lines are parallel.
   (H) The lines are the same.
   J The lines have a negative slope.

6. Serina is trying to decide between two similar packages for starting her own Web site. Which is a true statement?
   A Both packages cost \$235.50 for 5 months.
   (B) Both packages cost \$295 for 10 months.
   C Both packages cost \$355 for 15 months.
   D The packages will never have the same cost.

	Design and Setup	Monthly Fee to Host
Package A	\$150.00	\$14.50
Package B	\$175.00	\$12.00

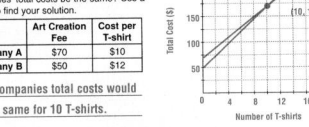

Answers

66b. See p. A15.

67c. $= 2.5d + 5$

Cost of Renting DVDs

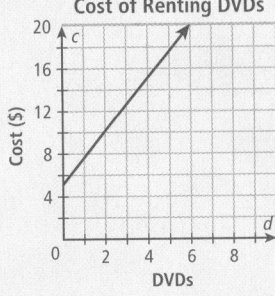

If his bill was \$20.00, Sean rented 6 DVDs.

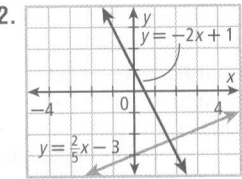

Pacing:
Traditional $\frac{1}{2}$ day
Block $\frac{1}{4}$ day

Objective: Apply linear equation skills learned in Lesson 3-6 to graphing and writing equations for lines associated with data sets.

Teach

Remember

Students review scatter plots and lines of best fit.

INTERVENTION ◄═══► For additional review and practice on finding lines of best fit, see Skills Bank page S79.

Technology A graphing calculator uses *linear regression* to find the equation of the line of best fit, which will be studied in statistics.

Close

Assess

Have students use data such as shoe size versus length of bare foot or arm span versus height to create a scatter plot, and then estimate the equation of the line of best fit.

↰TAKS *On Track for TAKS* connects TAKS objectives across the grade levels.

Grades 9–11
Obj. 2 Properties and Attributes of Functions A.2.D In solving problems, the student collects and organizes data, makes and interprets scatterplots ...; A.3.B Given situations, the student ... represents generalizations algebraically

Obj. 3 Linear Functions A.5.C ... make connections among algebraic, tabular, graphical, or verbal descriptions of linear functions; A.6.A ... determine slopes from graphs, tables, and algebraic representations; A.6.B interpret the meaning of slope ... using data, symbolic representations, or graphs; A.6.D graph and write equations of lines ...

Obj. 7 Two- and Three-Dimensional Representations G.7.A use ... coordinate systems to represent points, lines, ...; G.7.C derive and use formulas involving ... slope ...

Scatter Plots and Lines of Best Fit

Data Analysis

Recall that a line has an infinite number of points on it. You can compute the slope of a line if you can identify two distinct points on the line.

Example 1

The table shows several possible measures of an angle and its supplement. Graph the points in the table. Then draw the line that best represents the data and write the equation of the line.

x	y = 180 − x
30	150
60	120
90	90
120	60
150	30

Step 1
Use the table to write ordered pairs $(x, 180 - x)$ and then plot the points.

$(30, 150)$, $(60, 120)$, $(90, 90)$, $(120, 60)$, $(150, 30)$

Step 2
Draw a line that passes through all the points.

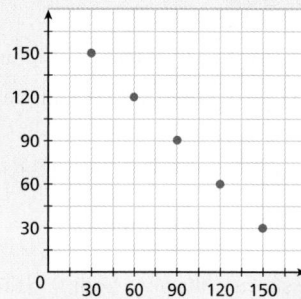

Step 3 Choose two points from the line, such as $(30, 150)$ and $(120, 60)$. Use them to find the slope.

$$m = \frac{y_2 - y_1}{x_2 - x_1}$$ *Slope formula*

$$= \frac{60 - 150}{120 - 30}$$ *Substitute $(30, 150)$ for (x_1, y_1) and $(120, 60)$ for (x_2, y_2).*

$$= \frac{-90}{90} = -1$$ *Simplify.*

Step 4 Use the point-slope form to find the equation of the line and then simplify.

$$y - y_1 = m(x - x_1)$$ *Point-slope form*

$$y - 150 = -1(x - 30)$$ *Substitute $(30, 150)$ for (x_1, y_1) and -1 for m.*

$$y = -x + 180$$ *Simplify.*

If you can draw a line through all the points in a set of data, the relationship is linear. If the points are close to a line, you can approximate the relationship with a *line of best fit*.

Example 2

A physical therapist evaluates a client's progress by measuring the angle of motion of an injured joint. The table shows the angle of motion of a client's wrist over six weeks. Estimate the equation of the line of best fit.

Week	Angle Measure
1	30
2	36
3	46
4	48
5	54
6	62

Step 1
Use the table to write ordered pairs and then plot the points.

$(1, 30), (2, 36), (3, 46), (4, 48),$
$(5, 54), (6, 62)$

Step 2
Use a ruler to estimate a line of best fit. Try to get the edge of the ruler closest to all the points on the line.

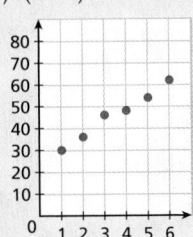
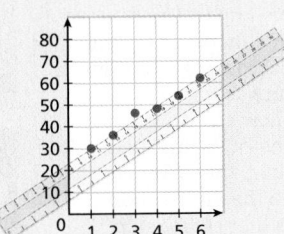

Step 3 A line passing through $(2, 36)$ and $(6, 62)$ seems to be closest to all the points. Draw this line. Use the points $(2, 36)$ and $(6, 62)$ to find the slope of the line.

$$m = \frac{y_2 - y_1}{x_2 - x_1} = \frac{62 - 36}{6 - 2} = 6.5 \qquad \text{Substitute } (2, 36) \text{ for } (x_1, y_1) \text{ and } (6, 62) \text{ for } (x_2, y_2).$$

Step 4 Use the point-slope form to find the equation of the line and then simplify.

$y - y_1 = m(x - x_1)$ *Point-slope form*

$y - 36 = 6.5(x - 2)$ *Substitute $(2, 36)$ for (x_1, y_1) and 6.5 for m.*

$y = 6.5x + 23$ *Simplify.*

Try This
TAKS Grades 9–11 Obj. 2, 3, 9

Estimate the equation of the line of best fit for each relationship. **1–2. Possible answers:**

1.
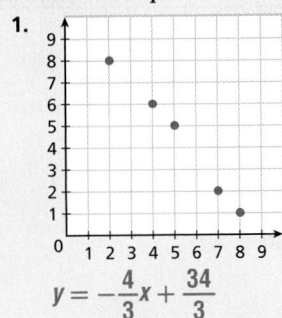
$y = -\dfrac{4}{3}x + \dfrac{34}{3}$

2. the relationship between an angle and its complement
$y = 90 - x$

3. Data Collection Use a graphing calculator and a motion detector to do the following: Set the equipment so that the graph shows distance on the y-axis and time on the x-axis. Walk in front of the motion dector while varying your speed slightly and use the resulting graph.
Check students' work.

 Data Collecton For help with **Try This 3**, see *Technology Lab Activities*.

MULTI-STEP TAKS PREP

Organizer

Objective: Assess students' ability to apply concepts and skills in Lessons 3-5 through 3-6 in a real-world format.

  Online Edition

Resources

 Geometry Assessments
www.mathtekstoolkit.org

Problem	Text Reference
1	Lesson 3-5
2	Lesson 3-6

Answers

$2. d = \frac{22}{15}(45)t$

$d = 66t$

Critical Distance

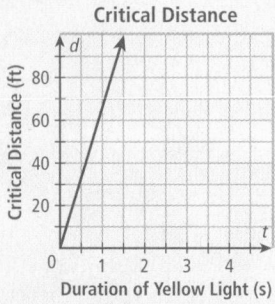

⭐TAKS Practice

Grades 9–11	Problems
Obj. 1	2
Obj. 3	2
Obj. 4	1, 2
Obj. 9	1, 2
Obj. 10	1, 2

Coordinate Geometry

Red Light, Green Light When a driver approaches an intersection and sees a yellow traffic light, she must decide if she can make it through the intersection before the light turns red. Traffic engineers use graphs and equations to study this situation.

1. Traffic engineers can set the duration of the yellow lights on Lincoln Road for any length of time t up to 10 seconds. For each value of t, there is a critical distance d. If a car moving at the speed limit is more than d feet from the light when it turns yellow, the driver will have to stop. If the car is less than d feet from the light, the driver can continue through the intersection. The graph shows the relationship between t and d. Find the speed limit on Lincoln Road in miles per hour. (*Hint:* 22 ft/s = 15 mi/h) **30 mi/h**

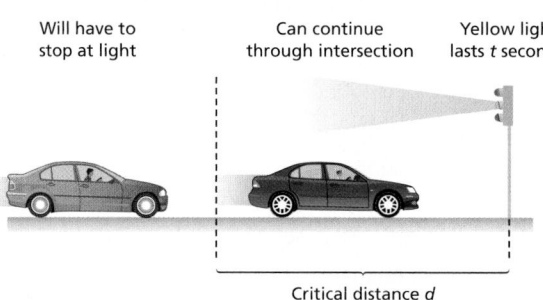

Will have to stop at light

Can continue through intersection

Yellow light lasts t seconds.

Critical distance d

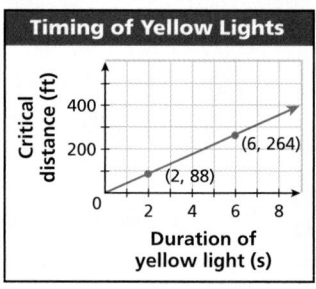

Timing of Yellow Lights

(6, 264)

(2, 88)

Duration of yellow light (s)

2. Traffic engineers use the equation $d = \frac{22}{15} st$ to determine the critical distance for various durations of a yellow light. In the equation, s is the speed limit. The speed limit on Porter Street is 45 mi/h. Write the equation of the critical distance for a yellow light on Porter Street and then graph the line. Does this line intersect the line for Lincoln Road? If so, where? Is the line for Porter Street steeper or flatter than the line for Lincoln Road? Explain how you know.

Yes, the lines intersect at (0, 0). The line for Porter Street is steeper because the slope of the line is greater.

200   *Chapter 3 Parallel and Perpendicular Lines*

INTERVENTION ⬅ ➡

Scaffolding Questions

1. In the graph, what does the slope of the line represent? the rate (i.e., the speed limit) What information do you need in order to calculate the slope of the line? coordinates of 2 points on the line If you know a speed in feet per second, how can you convert it to miles per hour? Multiply by $\frac{15}{22}$.

2. How can you simplify the equation when $s = 45$? $d = 66t$ What is the slope of the line? 66 How does this slope compare to the slope of the line in **Problem 1**? The slope is greater than in **Problem 1**.

Extension

Suppose the duration of a yellow light is 6 sec. How much greater is the critical distance for a car moving at 45 mi/h compared to that of a car moving at 30 mi/h? 132 ft

Quiz for Lesson 3-5 Through 3-6

 3-5   Slopes of Lines

Use the slope formula to determine the slope of each line.

1. $\overleftrightarrow{AC}$ $m = -1$ 2. $\overleftrightarrow{CD}$ $m = -\dfrac{1}{9}$ 3. $\overleftrightarrow{AB}$ $m = -\dfrac{2}{3}$ 4. $\overleftrightarrow{BD}$ $m = \dfrac{3}{7}$

Find the slope of the line through the given points.

5. $M(2, 3)$ and $N(0, 7)$ $m = -2$ 6. $F(-1, 4)$ and $G(5, -1)$ $m = -\dfrac{5}{6}$

7. $P(4, 0)$ and $Q(1, -3)$ $m = 1$ 8. $K(4, 2)$ and $L(-3, 2)$ $m = 0$

9. Sonia is walking 4 miles home from school. She leaves at 4:00 P.M., and gets home at 4:45 P.M. Graph the line that represents Sonia's distance from school at a given time. Find and interpret the slope of the line.

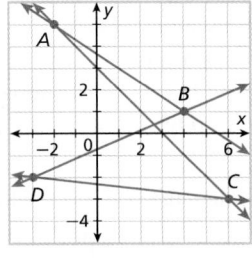

9. $m = \dfrac{16}{3} \approx 5.3$; Sonia's average speed was about 5.3 mi/h.

Graph each pair of lines and use their slopes to determine if they are parallel, perpendicular, or neither.

10. $\overleftrightarrow{EF}$ and $\overleftrightarrow{GH}$ for $E(-2, 3)$, $F(6, 1)$, $G(6, 4)$, and $H(2, 5)$ ∥

11. $\overleftrightarrow{JK}$ and $\overleftrightarrow{LM}$ for $J(4, 3)$, $K(5, -1)$, $L(-2, 4)$, and $M(3, -5)$ **neither**

12. $\overleftrightarrow{NP}$ and $\overleftrightarrow{QR}$ for $N(5, -3)$, $P(0, 4)$, $Q(-3, -2)$, and $R(4, 3)$ ⊥

13. $\overleftrightarrow{ST}$ and $\overleftrightarrow{VW}$ for $S(0, 3)$, $T(0, 7)$, $V(2, 3)$, and $W(5, 3)$ ⊥

 3-6   Lines in the Coordinate Plane

Write the equation of each line in the given form.

14. the line through $(3, 8)$ and $(-3, 4)$ in slope-intercept form $y = \dfrac{2}{3}x + 6$

15. the line through $(-5, 4)$ with slope $\dfrac{2}{3}$ in point-slope form $y - 4 = \dfrac{2}{3}(x + 5)$

16. the line with y-intercept 2 through the point $(4, 1)$ in slope-intercept form $y = -\dfrac{1}{4}x + 2$

Graph each line.

17. $y = -2x + 5$ 18. $y + 3 = \dfrac{1}{4}(x - 4)$ 19. $x = 3$

Write the equation of each line.

20.
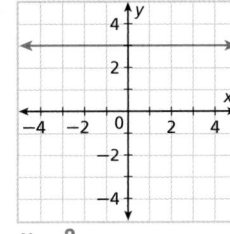
$y = 3$

21.
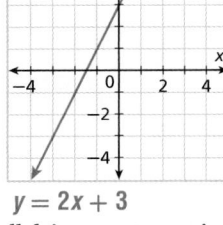
$y = 2x + 3$

22.
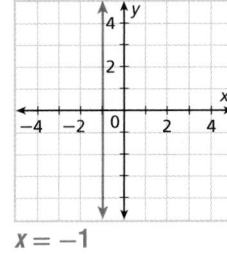
$x = -1$

Determine whether the lines are parallel, intersect, or coincide.

23. $y = -2x + 5$ ∥
   $y = -2x - 5$

24. $3x + 2y = 8$ **coincide**
   $y = -\dfrac{3}{2}x + 4$

25. $y = 4x - 5$ **intersect**
   $3x + 4y = 7$

Organizer

Objective: Assess students' mastery of concepts and skills in Lessons 3-5 through 3-6.

Resources

 **Assessment Resources**
   Section 3B Quiz

 Test & Practice Generator
 One-Stop Planner®

INTERVENTION

Resources

 ***Ready to Go On? Intervention and Enrichment Worksheets***

 Ready to Go On? CD-ROM

 Ready to Go On? Online

my.hrw.com

Answers

10–13, 17–19. See p. A15.

NO
INTERVENE

READY TO GO ON?
Diagnose and Prescribe

YES
ENRICH

Ready to Go On? Intervention	*READY TO GO ON?* Intervention, Section 3B		
	Worksheets	**CD-ROM**	**Online**
☑ Lesson 3-5	3-5 Intervention	Activity 3-5	Diagnose and Prescribe Online
☑ Lesson 3-6	3-6 Intervention	Activity 3-6	

READY TO GO ON? Enrichment, Section 3B

Worksheets
CD-ROM
Online

Organizer

Objective: Help students organize and review key concepts and skills presented in Chapter 3.

 Online Edition

Resources

 PuzzlePro One-Stop Planner®

Multilingual Glossary Online
go.hrw.com/Geo/TX
KEYWORD: MG7 Glossary

Lesson Tutorial Videos CD-ROM

Test & Practice Generator One-Stop Planner®

Answers

1. alternate interior angles
2. skew lines
3. transversal
4. point-slope form
5. rise; run
6. Possible answer: $\overline{DE}$ and $\overline{BC}$ are skew.
7. $\overline{AB} \parallel \overline{DE}$
8. $\overline{AD} \perp \overline{DE}$
9. plane ABC ∥ plane DEF

 **For a complete list of the postulates and theorems in this chapter, see p. S82.**

Vocabulary

Complete the sentences below with vocabulary words from the list above.

1. Angles on opposite sides of a transversal and between the lines it intersects are ___?___.

2. Lines that are in different planes are ___?___.

3. A(n) ___?___ is a line that intersects two coplanar lines at two points.

4. The ___?___ is used to write the equation of a line with a given slope that passes through a given point.

5. The slope of a line is the ratio of the ___?___ to the ___?___.

3-1 Lines and Angles (pp. 146–151)

EXAMPLES

Identify each of the following.

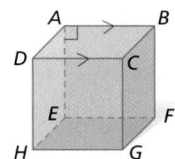

- a pair of parallel segments
  $\overline{AB} \parallel \overline{CD}$
- a pair of parallel planes
  plane ABC ∥ plane EFG
- a pair of perpendicular segments
  $\overline{AB} \perp \overline{AE}$
- a pair of skew segments
  $\overline{AB}$ and $\overline{FG}$ are skew.

EXERCISES

Identify each of the following.

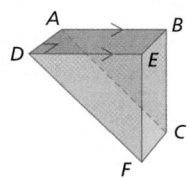

6. a pair of skew segments
7. a pair of parallel segments
8. a pair of perpendicular segments
9. a pair of parallel planes

Identify the transversal and classify each angle pair.

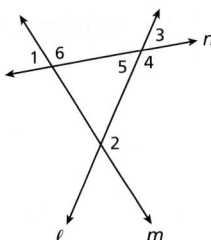

- ∠4 and ∠6

  p, corresponding angles

- ∠1 and ∠2

  q, alternate interior angles

- ∠3 and ∠4

  p, alternate exterior angles

- ∠6 and ∠7

  r, same-side interior angles

Identify the transversal and classify each angle pair.

10. ∠5 and ∠2

11. ∠6 and ∠3

12. ∠2 and ∠4

13. ∠1 and ∠2

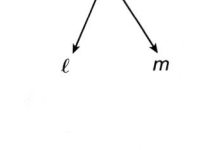

3-2 Angles Formed by Parallel Lines and Transversals (pp. 155–161) ⭐ TEKS G.2.A, G.3.C, G.3.E, G.9.A

EXAMPLES

Find each angle measure.

- m∠TUV

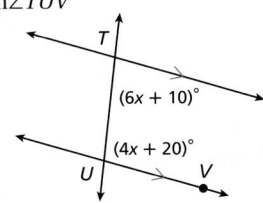

By the Same-Side Interior Angles Theorem,
$(6x + 10) + (4x + 20) = 180$.

$$x = 15 \quad \textit{Solve for x.}$$

Substitute the value for *x* into the expression for m∠TUV.
m∠TUV = $4(15) + 20 = 80°$

- m∠ABC

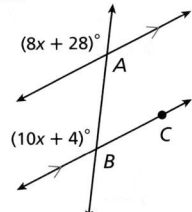

By the Corresponding Angles Postulate,
$8x + 28 = 10x + 4$.

$$x = 12 \quad \textit{Solve for x.}$$

Substitute the value for *x* into the expression for one of the obtuse angles.
$10(12) + 4 = 124°$

∠ABC is supplementary to the 124° angle, so
m∠ABC = $180 - 124 = 56°$.

EXERCISES

Find each angle measure.

14. m∠WYZ

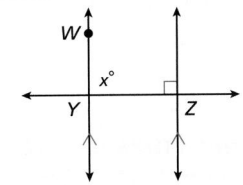

15. m∠KLM

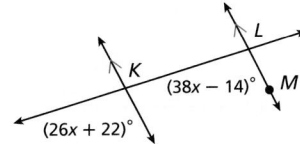

16. m∠DEF

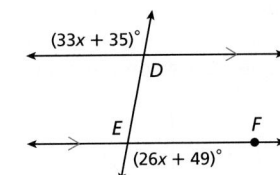

17. m∠QRS

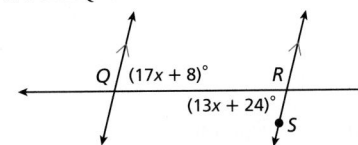

Answers

18. ∠4 ≅ ∠6, so c ∥ d by the Conv. of the Alt. Int. ∠ Thm.

19. m∠1 = 107°; and m∠5 = 107°, so ∠1 ≅ ∠5. c ∥ d by the Conv. of the Corr. ∠ Post.

20. m∠6 = 66°, m∠3 = 114°, and 66° + 114° = 180°, so ∠6 and ∠3 are supp. c ∥ d by the Conv. of the Same-Side Int. ∠ Thm.

21. m∠1 = 99°, and m∠7 = 99°, so ∠1 ≅ ∠7. c ∥ d by the Conv. of the Alt. Ext. ∠ Thm.

22. $\overline{KM}$

23. x − 5 < 8; x < 13

24. 1. $\overline{AD}$ ∥ $\overline{BC}$, $\overline{AD}$ ⊥ $\overline{AB}$, $\overline{DC}$ ⊥ $\overline{BC}$ (Given);
2. $\overline{AB}$ ⊥ $\overline{BC}$ (⊥ Transv. Thm.);
3. $\overline{AB}$ ∥ $\overline{CD}$ (2 lines ⊥ to same line → 2 lines ∥)

3-3 Proving Lines Parallel (pp. 162–169)

TEKS G.1.A, G.3.C, G.3.E, G.9.A

EXAMPLES

Use the given information and theorems and postulates you have learned to show that *p* ∥ *q*.

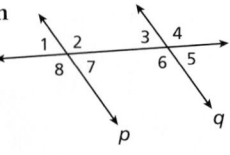

■ m∠2 + m∠3 = 180°

∠2 and ∠3 are supplementary, so *p* ∥ *q* by the Converse of the Same-Side Interior Angles Theorem.

■ ∠8 ≅ ∠6

∠8 ≅ ∠6, so *p* ∥ *q* by the Converse of the Corresponding Angles Postulate.

■ m∠1 = $(7x − 3)°$, m∠5 = $5x + 15$, x = 9

m∠1 = 60°, and m∠5 = 60°. So ∠1 ≅ ∠5. *p* ∥ *q* by the Converse of the Alternate Exterior Angles Theorem.

EXERCISES

Use the given information and theorems and postulates you have learned to show that *c* ∥ *d*.

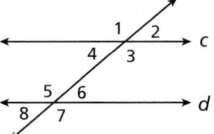

18. m∠4 = 58°, m∠6 = 58°

19. m∠1 = $(23x + 38)°$, m∠5 = $(17x + 56)°$, x = 3

20. m∠6 = $(12x + 6)°$, m∠3 = $(21x + 9)°$, x = 5

21. m∠1 = 99°, m∠7 = $(13x + 8)°$, x = 7

3-4 Perpendicular Lines (pp. 172–178)

TEKS G.1.A, G.2.A, G.3.C, G.3.E, G.9.A

EXAMPLES

■ Name the shortest segment from point X to $\overline{WY}$.
$\overline{XZ}$

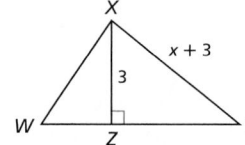

■ Write and solve an inequality for x.

x + 3 > 3

x > 0   *Subtract 3 from both sides.*

■ Given: m ⊥ p, ∠1 and ∠2 are complementary.
Prove: *p* ∥ *q*

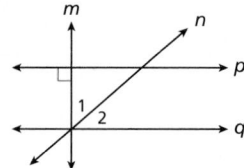

Proof:
It is given that m ⊥ p. ∠1 and ∠2 are complementary, so m∠1 + m∠2 = 90°. Thus m ⊥ q. Two lines perpendicular to the same line are parallel, so *p* ∥ *q*.

EXERCISES

22. Name the shortest segment from point K to $\overline{LN}$.

23. Write and solve an inequality for x.

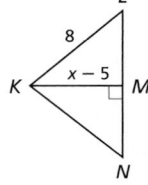

24. Given: $\overline{AD}$ ∥ $\overline{BC}$, $\overline{AD}$ ⊥ $\overline{AB}$, $\overline{DC}$ ⊥ $\overline{BC}$

Prove: $\overline{AB}$ ∥ $\overline{CD}$

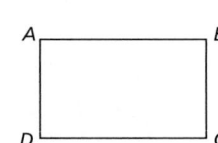

204   *Chapter 3 Parallel and Perpendicular Lines*

204   *Chapter 3*

3-5 Slopes of Lines (pp. 182–187)

EXAMPLES

- Use the slope formula to determine the slope of the line.

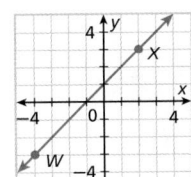

$$\text{slope of } \overleftrightarrow{WX} = \frac{y_2 - y_1}{x_2 - x_1} = \frac{3 - (-3)}{2 - (-4)} = \frac{6}{6} = 1$$

- Use slopes to determine whether $\overleftrightarrow{AB}$ and $\overleftrightarrow{CD}$ are parallel, perpendicular, or neither for $A(-1, 5)$, $B(-3, 4)$, $C(3, -1)$, and $D(4, -3)$.

$$\text{slope of } \overleftrightarrow{AB} = \frac{4 - 5}{-3 - (-1)} = \frac{1}{2}$$

$$\text{slope of } \overleftrightarrow{CD} = \frac{-3 - (-1)}{4 - 3} = \frac{-2}{1} = -2$$

The slopes are opposite reciprocals, so the lines are perpendicular.

EXERCISES

Use the slope formula to determine the slope of each line.

25.
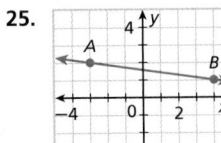

26.
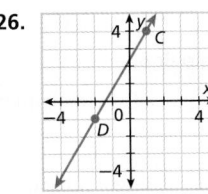

Use slopes to determine if the lines are parallel, perpendicular, or neither.

27. $\overleftrightarrow{EF}$ and $\overleftrightarrow{GH}$ for $E(8, 2)$, $F(-3, 4)$, $G(6, 1)$, and $H(-4, 3)$

28. $\overleftrightarrow{JK}$ and $\overleftrightarrow{LM}$ for $J(4, 3)$, $K(-4, -2)$, $L(5, 6)$, and $M(-3, 1)$

29. $\overleftrightarrow{ST}$ and $\overleftrightarrow{UV}$ for $S(-4, 5)$, $T(2, 3)$, $U(3, 1)$, and $V(4, 4)$

3-6 Lines in the Coordinate Plane (pp. 190–197)

EXAMPLES

- Write the equation of the line through $(5, -2)$ with slope $\frac{3}{5}$ in slope-intercept form.

$$y - (-2) = \frac{3}{5}(x - 5) \qquad \textit{Point-slope form}$$

$$y + 2 = \frac{3}{5}x - 3 \qquad \textit{Simplify.}$$

$$y = \frac{3}{5}x - 5 \qquad \textit{Solve for y.}$$

- Determine whether the lines $y = 4x + 6$ and $8x - 2y = 4$ are parallel, intersect, or coincide.

Solve the second equation for y to find the slope-intercept form.

$$8x - 2y = 4$$

$$y = 4x - 2$$

Both the lines have a slope of 4 and have different y-intercepts, so they are parallel.

EXERCISES

Write the equation of each line in the given form.

30. the line through $(6, 1)$ and $(-3, 5)$ in slope-intercept form

31. the line through $(-3, -4)$ with slope $\frac{2}{3}$ in slope-intercept form

32. the line with x-intercept 1 and y-intercept -2 in point-slope form

Determine whether the lines are parallel, intersect, or coincide.

33. $-3x + 2y = 5$, $6x - 4y = 8$

34. $y = 4x - 3$, $5x + 2y = 1$

35. $y = 2x + 1$, $2x - y = -1$

Answers

25. $m = -\frac{1}{7}$

26. $m = \frac{5}{3}$

27. neither

28. $\parallel$

29. $\perp$

30. $y = -\frac{4}{9}x + \frac{11}{3}$

31. $y = \frac{2}{3}x - 2$

32. $y - 0 = 2(x - 1)$

33. $\parallel$

34. intersect

35. coincide

Organizer

Objective: Assess students' mastery of concepts and skills in Chapter 3.

Resources

Assessment Resources

Chapter 3 Tests

- Free Response (Levels A, B, C)
- Multiple Choice (Levels A, B, C)
- Performance Assessment

IDEA Works! CD-ROM

Modified Chapter 3 Test

Test & Practice Generator
One-Stop Planner®

TAKS Practice

Grades 9–11	Items
Obj. 1	13
Obj. 3	13–15
Obj. 4	4–6
Obj. 7	10–16

Identify each of the following.

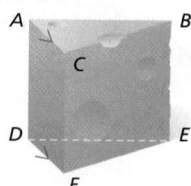

1. a pair of parallel planes
2. a pair of parallel segments $\overline{AC} \parallel \overline{DF}$
3. a pair of skew segments

Find each angle measure.

4.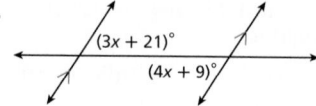
$(3x + 21)°$
$(4x + 9)°$

5.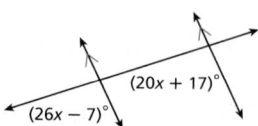
$(20x + 17)°$
$(26x - 7)°$

6.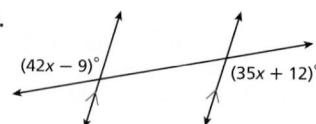
$(42x - 9)°$ $(35x + 12)°$

Use the given information and the theorems and postulates you have learned to show $f \parallel g$.

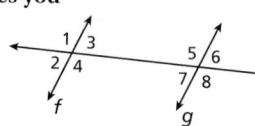

7. $m\angle 4 = (16x + 20)°$, $m\angle 5 = (12x + 32)°$, $x = 3$

8. $m\angle 3 = (18x + 6)°$, $m\angle 5 = (21x + 18)°$, $x = 4$

Write a two-column proof.

9. Given: $\angle 1 \cong \angle 2$, $n \perp \ell$

   Prove: $n \perp m$

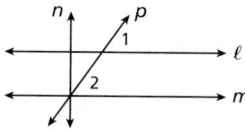

Use the slope formula to determine the slope of each line.

$m = \frac{4}{5}$

10. 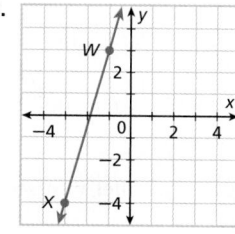 $m = \frac{7}{2}$

11. 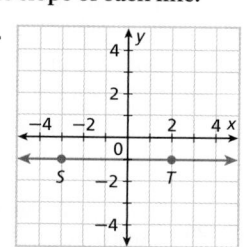 $m = 0$

12.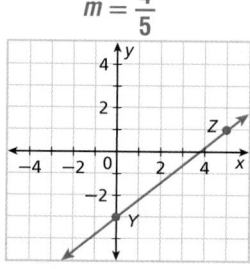

13. Greg is on a 32-mile bicycle trail from Elroy, Wisconsin, to Sparta, Wisconsin. He leaves Elroy at 9:30 A.M. and arrives in Sparta at 2:00 P.M. Graph the line that represents Greg's distance from Elroy at a given time. Find and interpret the slope of the line. $m = \frac{32}{4.5} \approx 7.1$; Greg's average speed was about 7.1 mi/h.

14. Graph $\overleftrightarrow{QR}$ and $\overleftrightarrow{ST}$ for $Q(3, 3)$, $R(6, -5)$, $S(-4, 6)$, and $T(-1, -2)$. Use slopes to determine whether the lines are parallel, perpendicular, or neither.

15. Write the equation of the line through $(-2, -5)$ with slope $-\frac{3}{4}$ in point-slope form. $y + 5 = -\frac{3}{4}(x + 2)$

16. Determine whether the lines $6x + y = 3$ and $2x + 3y = 1$ are parallel, intersect, or coincide. **intersect**

Answers

14.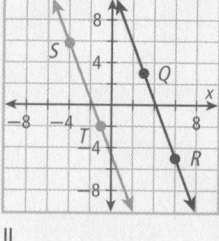

1. plane $ABC \parallel$ plane DEF

3. Possible answer: $\overline{AB}$ and $\overline{CF}$ are skew.

4. Both labeled angles measure 57°.

5. Both labeled angles measure 97°.

6. Both labeled angles measure 117°.

7. $m\angle 4 = 68°$, and $m\angle 5 = 68°$, so $\angle 4 \cong \angle 5$. $f \parallel g$ by the Conv. of Alt. Int. ∠ Thm.

8. $m\angle 3 = 78°$, and $m\angle 5 = 102°$, so $m\angle 3 + m\angle 5 = 180°$. $f \parallel g$ by the Conv. of Same-Side Int. ∠ Thm.

9. 1. $\angle 1 \cong \angle 2$, $n \perp \ell$ (Given)
   2. $\ell \parallel m$ (Conv. of Corr. ∠ Post.)
   3. $n \perp m$ (⊥ Transv. Thm.)

∥

COLLEGE ENTRANCE EXAM PRACTICE

FOCUS ON ACT

When you take the ACT Mathematics Test, you receive a separate subscore for each of the following areas:
- Pre-Algebra/Elementary Algebra,
- Intermediate Algebra/Coordinate Geometry, and
- Plane Geometry/Trigonometry.

You may want to time yourself as you take this practice test. It should take you about 5 minutes to complete.

Find out what percent of questions are from each area and concentrate on content that represents the greatest percent of questions.

---

1. Which of the following is an equation of the line that passes through the point $(2, -3)$ and is parallel to the line $4x - 5y = 1$?

   (A) $-4x + 5y = -23$
   (B) $-5x - 4y = 2$
   (C) $-2x - 5y = 11$
   (D) $-4x - 5y = 7$
   (E) $-5x + 4y = -22$

2. In the figure below, line t crosses parallel lines ℓ and m. Which of the following statements are true?

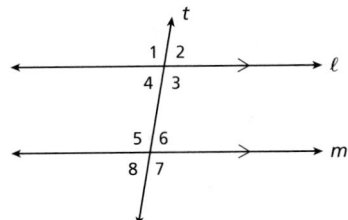

   I. $\angle 1$ and $\angle 6$ are alternate interior angles.
   II. $\angle 2 \cong \angle 4$
   III. $\angle 2 \cong \angle 8$

   (F) I only
   (G) II only
   (H) III only
   (J) I and II only
   (K) II and III only

3. In the standard (x, y) coordinate plane, the line that passes through $(1, -7)$ and $(-8, 5)$ is perpendicular to the line that passes through $(3, 6)$ and $(-1, b)$. What is the value of b?

   (A) 2
   (B) 3
   (C) 7
   (D) 9
   (E) 10

4. Lines m and n are cut by a transversal so that $\angle 2$ and $\angle 5$ are corresponding angles. If $m\angle 2 = (x + 18)°$ and $m\angle 5 = (2x - 28)°$, which value of x makes lines m and n parallel?

   (F) $3\frac{1}{3}$
   (G) $33\frac{1}{3}$
   (H) 46
   (J) $63\frac{1}{3}$
   (K) 72

5. What is the distance between point $G(4, 2)$ and the line through the points $E(1, -2)$ and $F(7, -2)$?

   (A) 3
   (B) 4
   (C) 5
   (D) 6
   (E) 7

Organizer

Objective: Provide practice for college entrance exams such as the ACT.

Online Edition

Resources

📖 *College Entrance Exam Practice*

Questions on the ACT represent the following content areas:

Pre-Algebra, 23%
Elementary Algebra, 17%
Intermediate Algebra, 15%
Coordinate Geometry, 15%
Plane Geometry, 23%
Trigonometry, 7%

Items on this page focus on:
- Parallel Lines and Transversals
- Lines in the Coordinate Plane

Text References:

Item	1	2	3	4	5
Lesson	3-5, 3-6	3-2	3-6	3-3	3-4

TEST PREP DOCTOR ✚

1. Students who chose **B** found the equation of the line perpendicular to the given line and through the given point. Remind students that parallel lines have the same slope.

2. Students who chose **G** may not recognize that $\angle 2$ and $\angle 8$ are alternate exterior angles and are therefore congruent. Students who chose **F** or **J** may not understand the definition of alternate interior angles.

3. Students who chose **A** or **E** found the equation of a line parallel to the line through the points $(1, -7)$ and $(-8, 5)$, rather than a perpendicular line. Students who chose **D** found a line such that the product of the slopes is 1 rather than -1.

4. Students who chose **B** found the value of x that makes the angles formed by lines m and n complementary. Students who chose **D** found the value of x that makes the angles formed by lines m and n supplementary. Remind students of the definition of corresponding angles.

5. Students may not know how to approach this problem. Suggest that they draw a diagram, and remind students that the distance between a point and a line is measured along a line perpendicular to the line.

Organizer

Objective: Provide students with opportunities to learn and practice common test-taking strategies.

 Online Edition

Resources

 TAKS Prep Workbook

 TAKS Prep CD-ROM

 TAKS Practice Online

 **go.hrw.com/Geo/TX**
KEYWORD: MG7 TestPrep

TAKS PREP DOCTOR This TAKS Tackler focuses on how to interpret graphs and relate the graph of a line to its equation. Review the meaning of slope and how to determine the slope and *y*-intercept of a line from its equation. Some students may want to solve the problems algebraically and not use a graph. Encourage them to use a graph to check their answers.

Any Question Type: Interpret Coordinate Graphs

When test items refer to a coordinate plane, it is important to interpret the coordinate graphs correctly. It is also important to understand the relationship between an equation and its graph.

EXAMPLE 1

Multiple Choice Which statement best describes the graph of the following equations?

$$y = 2x + 6$$
$$2y = 4x + 6$$

Ⓐ The lines are parallel.

Ⓑ The lines are perpendicular.

Ⓒ The lines coincide.

Ⓓ The lines have the same *y*-intercept.

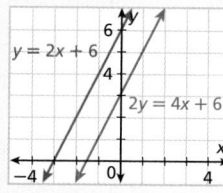

It may help to graph the lines or visualize the graph in order to answer the question. The lines appear to be parallel.

Write the equations of both lines in slope-intercept form.

$$y = 2x + 6 \qquad \text{The slope is 2 and the y-intercept is 6.}$$
$$y = 2x + 3 \qquad \text{The slope is 2 and the y-intercept is 3.}$$

The lines have the same slope and different *y*-intercepts, so they are parallel. The answer is A.

EXAMPLE 2

Gridded Response What is the rate of change of the following graph?

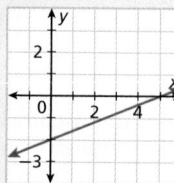

Remember that the rate of change of the graph of a line is its slope. Choose two points on the line and use their coordinates to calculate the slope of the line.

Use the points $(5, 0)$ *and* $(0, -2)$. $m = \dfrac{-2 - 0}{0 - 5} = \dfrac{2}{5}$

The slope is $\dfrac{2}{5} = 0.4$. Enter 0.4 in the answer grid.

TAKS Tip A quick look at the graph of a line can tell you whether the slope is positive or negative. This may help you eliminate answer choices.

Read each test item and answer the questions that follow.

Item A

Multiple Choice The line segment on the graph shows the altitude of a hot air balloon during a landing. Which statement best describes the slope of the line segment?

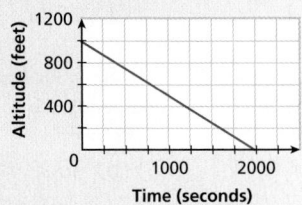

Ⓐ The balloon descends about 5 feet per 8 seconds.

Ⓑ The balloon descends about 8 feet per 5 seconds.

Ⓒ The balloon descends about 1 foot per 2 seconds.

Ⓓ The balloon descends about 2 feet per second.

1. What are the coordinates of two points on the graph?

2. How does the scale of the graph affect the appearance of the slope?

3. How is the slope of the line related to the rate of descent?

Item B

Gridded Response What is the y-intercept of the line through $(5, 2)$ that is parallel to the line $x - 4y = 8$?

4. Graph the line $x - 4y = 8$. What is its slope?

5. Write an equation in point-slope form for the line through $(5, 2)$ that is parallel to $x - 4y = 8$.

6. How would you use the equation in point-slope form to find the y-intercept of the line?

Item C

Multiple Choice Which equation describes the line through the point $(4, 2)$ that is perpendicular to the line $3x - y = 7$?

Ⓐ $y = 3x - 10$

Ⓑ $y = -3x + 14$

Ⓒ $y = \frac{1}{3}x + \frac{2}{3}$

Ⓓ $y = -\frac{1}{3}x + 3\frac{1}{3}$

7. Graph the line represented by $3x - y = 7$. What is its slope?

8. Is the slope of a line perpendicular to the line represented by $3x - y = 7$ positive or negative? Based on your answer, can you eliminate any answer choices?

9. What is the slope of a line perpendicular to the line represented by $3x - y = 7$?

Item D

Multiple Choice Which graph best represents a solution to the following system of equations?

$$-2x + y = 6$$
$$3x + y = -2$$

Ⓕ 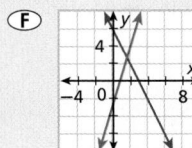 Ⓗ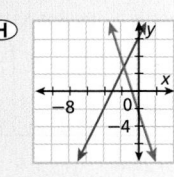

Ⓖ 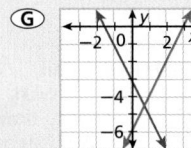 Ⓙ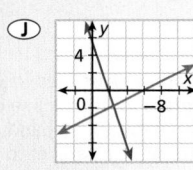

10. What is the slope of the line represented by $-2x + y = 6$? Based on your answer, can you eliminate any answer choices?

11. What is the slope of the line represented by $3x + y = -2$? Based on your answer, can you eliminate any answer choices?

Answers

1–3. Possible answers given.

1. $(2000, 0)$ and $(0, 1000)$

2. The scales on the x- and y-axes are different, so the slope appears to have a value of $-\frac{5}{2}$ when in fact the value is $-\frac{1}{2}$.

3. The slope is the rate of change. If the slope is $-\frac{1}{2}$, the balloon descends 1 foot per 2 seconds.

4.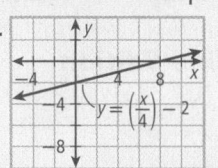

5. $y - 2 = \frac{1}{4}(x - 5)$

6. Write the equation in slope-intercept form. The constant term is the y-intercept.

7.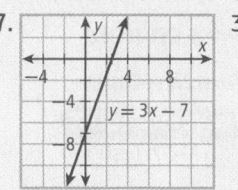

8. negative; choices **A** and **C**

9. $-\frac{1}{3}$

10. 2; choices **F** and **J**

11. -3; choices **F** and **G**

Answers to Test Items

A. C

B. 0.75

C. D

D. H

⬇TAKS Practice

Grades 9–11	Items
Obj. 3	A–D
Obj. 4	D
Obj. 7	B, D

CHAPTER
3
TAKS PREP

CHAPTER
3

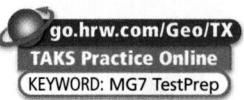
go.hrw.com/Geo/TX
TAKS Practice Online
KEYWORD: MG7 TestPrep

Organizer

Objective: Provide review and practice for Chapters 1–3 and standardized tests.

Online Edition

Resources

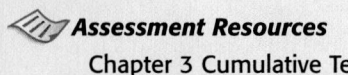
Assessment Resources
Chapter 3 Cumulative Test

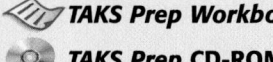
TAKS Prep Workbook

TAKS Prep CD-ROM

TAKS Practice Online
go.hrw.com/Geo/TX
KEYWORD: MG7 TestPrep

CUMULATIVE ASSESSMENT, CHAPTERS 1–3

Multiple Choice

Use the diagram below for Items 1 and 2.

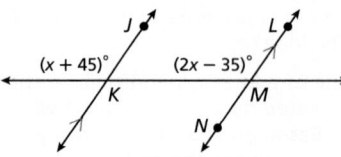

1. What type of angle pair are ∠JKM and ∠KMN?
   Ⓐ Corresponding angles
   Ⓑ Alternate exterior angles
   Ⓒ Same-side interior angles
   Ⓓ Alternate interior angles

2. What is m∠KML?
   Ⓕ 57°   Ⓗ 102°
   Ⓖ 80°   Ⓙ 125°

3. What is a possible value of x in the diagram?

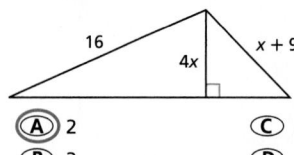

   Ⓐ 2   Ⓒ 4
   Ⓑ 3   Ⓓ 5

4. A graphic artist used a computer illustration program to draw a line connecting points with coordinates (3, −1) and (4, 6). She needs to draw a second line parallel to the first line. What slope should the second line have?
   Ⓕ $\frac{1}{7}$ Ⓗ 5
   Ⓖ $\frac{1}{5}$ **Ⓙ** 7

5. Which term describes a pair of vertical angles that are also supplementary?
   Ⓐ Acute   Ⓒ Right
   Ⓑ Obtuse   **Ⓓ** Straight

6. What is the equation of the line that passes through the points (−1, 8) and (4, −2)?
   Ⓕ $y = -2x + 6$ Ⓗ $y = \frac{1}{2}x - 4$
   Ⓖ $y = -\frac{1}{2}x$ Ⓙ $y = 2x + 10$

7. Given the points R(−5, 3), S(−5, 4), T(−3, 4), and U(−3, 1), which line is perpendicular to $\overleftrightarrow{TU}$?
   Ⓐ $\overleftrightarrow{RS}$ Ⓒ $\overleftrightarrow{ST}$
   Ⓑ $\overleftrightarrow{RT}$ Ⓓ $\overleftrightarrow{SU}$

8. Which of following is true if $\overleftrightarrow{XY}$ and $\overleftrightarrow{UV}$ are skew?
   Ⓕ $\overleftrightarrow{XY}$ and $\overleftrightarrow{UV}$ are coplanar.
   Ⓖ X, Y, and U are noncollinear.
   Ⓗ $\overleftrightarrow{XY} \parallel \overleftrightarrow{UV}$
   Ⓙ $\overleftrightarrow{XY} \perp \overleftrightarrow{UV}$

TAKS Tip Make sure that you answer the question that is asked. Some problems require more than one step. You must perform *all* of the steps to get the correct answer.

9. Point C is the midpoint of $\overline{AB}$ for A(1, −2) and B(7, 2). What is the length of $\overline{AC}$? Round to the nearest tenth.
   Ⓐ 3.0   Ⓒ 5.0
   Ⓑ 3.6   Ⓓ 7.2

Use the diagram below for Items 10 and 11.

10. $\overrightarrow{AD}$ bisects ∠CAE, and $\overrightarrow{AE}$ bisects ∠CAF. If m∠DAF = 120°, what is m∠DAE?
    Ⓕ 40°   **Ⓖ** 60°   Ⓗ 80°   Ⓙ 100°

11. What is the intersection of $\overrightarrow{AF}$ and $\overrightarrow{AD}$?
    Ⓐ A   Ⓑ F   Ⓒ $\overline{FD}$ Ⓓ ∠DAF

TAKS Practice

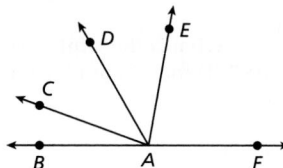
TAKS PREP DOCTOR

For **Item 9**, students who answered **D** found the length of $\overline{AB}$ rather than the length of $\overline{AC}$.

For **Item 10**, suggest that students let m∠DAE equal x°. Then they can define the measures of other angles in the figure in terms of x.

For **Item 14**, students who answered 40 determined the number of sections needed to fence all four sides of the lawn. Students who answered 180 determined the length in feet around three sides of the lawn instead of the number of sections.

12. Which statement is true by the Transitive Property of Equality?

   Ⓕ If $x + 3 = y$, then $y = x + 3$.

   Ⓖ If $k = 6$, then $2k = 12$.

   Ⓗ If $a = b$ and $b = 8$, then $a = 8$.

   Ⓙ If $m = n$, then $m + 7 = n + 7$.

13. Which condition guarantees that $r \parallel s$?

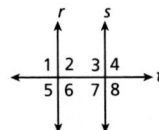

   Ⓐ $\angle 1 \cong \angle 2$ Ⓒ $\angle 2 \cong \angle 3$

   Ⓑ $\angle 2 \cong \angle 7$ Ⓓ $\angle 1 \cong \angle 4$

14. What is the converse of the following statement?

           If $x = 2$, then $x + 3 = 5$.

   Ⓕ If $x \neq 2$, then $x + 3 = 5$.

   Ⓖ If $x = 2$, then $x + 3 \neq 5$.

   Ⓗ If $x + 3 \neq 5$, then $x \neq 2$.

   Ⓙ If $x + 3 = 5$, then $x = 2$.

Gridded Response

15. Two lines a and b are cut by a transversal so that $\angle 1$ and $\angle 2$ are same-side interior angles. If $m\angle 1 = (2x + 30)°$ and $m\angle 2 = (4x - 75)°$, what value of x proves that $a \parallel b$? **37.5**

16. What is the slope of the line that passes through $(3, 7)$ and $(-5, 1)$? **0.75**

17. $\angle 1$ and $\angle 2$ form a linear pair. $m\angle 1 = (4x + 18)°$ and $m\angle 2 = (3x - 6)°$. What is the value of x? **24**

18. Points A, B, and C are collinear, and B is between A and C. $AB = 16$ and $AC = 27$. What is the distance BC? **11**

19. Ms. Nelson wants to put a chain-link fence around 3 sides of a square-shaped lawn. Chain-link fencing is sold in sections that are each 6 feet wide. If Ms. Nelson's lawn has an area of 3600 square feet, how many sections of fencing will she need? **30**

20. What is the next number in this pattern?

        67, 76, 83, 88,… **91**

Short Response

21. Given $\ell \parallel m$ with transversal t, explain why $\angle 1$ and $\angle 8$ are supplementary.

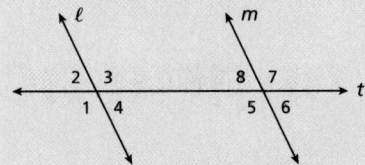

22. Read the following conditional statement.

   If two angles are vertical angles, then they are congruent.

   a. Write the converse of this conditional statement.

   b. Give a counterexample to show that the converse is false.

23. Assume that the following statements are true when the bases are loaded in a baseball game.

   If a batter hits the ball over the fence, then the batter hits a home run.
A batter hits a home run if and only if the result is four runs scored.

   a. If a batter hits the ball over the fence when the bases are loaded, can you conclude that four runs were scored? Explain your answer.

   b. If a batter hits a home run when the bases are loaded, can you conclude that the batter hit the ball over the fence? Explain your answer.

Extended Response

24. A car passes through a tollbooth at 8:00 A.M. and begins traveling east at an average speed of 45 miles per hour. A second car passes through the same tollbooth an hour later and begins traveling east at an average speed of 60 miles per hour.

   a. Write an equation for each car that relates the number of hours x since 8:00 A.M. to the distance in miles y the car has traveled. Explain what the slope of each equation represents.

   b. Graph the system of equations on the coordinate plane.

   c. If neither car stops, at what time will the second car catch up to the first car? Explain how you determined your answer.

Short-Response Rubric

Items 16–18

2 Points = The student's answer is an accurate and complete execution of the task or tasks.

1 Point = The student's answer contains attributes of an appropriate response but is flawed.

0 Points = The student's answer contains no attributes of an appropriate response.

Extended-Response Rubric

Item 19

4 Points = The student's equations are written, graphed, and analyzed correctly. Work demonstrates a thorough understanding of concepts related to equations of lines and lines in the coordinate plane.

3 Points = The student's equations, graph, and answers are correct but may contain minor flaws. Work demonstrates an understanding of major concepts.

2 Points = The student answers correctly, but explanations are missing or incomplete, or the student only answers part of the problem. Work demonstrates a limited understanding of concepts.

1 Point = The student answers incorrectly but makes a reasonable attempt to show work and write and graph the equations.

0 Points = The student does not answer correctly and does not attempt all parts of the problem.

Answers

21. Possible answer: $\angle 1 \cong \angle 5$ by the Corr. ∡ Post. $\angle 5$ is supp. to $\angle 8$ by the Lin. Pair Thm. Therefore, $\angle 1$ is supp to $\angle 8$ by the $\cong$ Supp. Thm.

22a. If 2 ∡ are $\cong$, then they are vert. ∡.

   b. Possible answer: $\angle A \cong \angle B$, but $\angle A$ and $\angle B$ are not vert. ∡ because they are not formed by 2 intersecting lines.

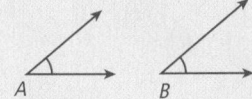

23a. Yes; possible answer: based on the given statements, if a batter hits the ball over the fence, then the batter hits a home run. If a batter hits a home run, then the batter hits in 4 runs. Therefore, by the Law of Syllogism, if a batter hits the ball over the fence, then the batter hits in 4 runs.

   b. No; possible answer: the converse of the statement, "If a batter hits the ball over the fence, then the batter hits a home run," is not necessarily true.

24a. First car: $y = 45x$; second car: $y = 60x - 60$; the slope of each equation represents the car's average speed.

b.

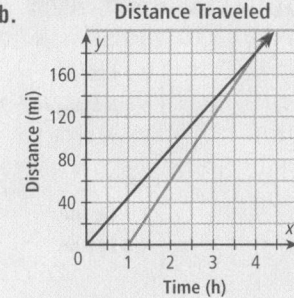

Distance Traveled

c. Noon; possible answer: the point where the lines cross represents the time when the first car catches up to the second car. The lines cross at $(4, 180)$. The first car catches up to the second car 4 hours after 8:00 A.M., when both cars have traveled 180 mi.

CHAPTER 4

Triangle Congruence

Section 4A	Section 4B
Triangles and Congruence	**Proving Triangles Congruent**

Section 4A — Triangles and Congruence

4-1 **Classifying Triangles**

4-2 **Geometry Lab** Develop the Triangle Sum Theorem

4-2 **Angle Relationships in Triangles**

4-3 **Congruent Triangles**

Section 4B — Proving Triangles Congruent

4-4 **Geometry Lab** Explore SSS and SAS Triangle Congruence

4-4 **Triangle Congruence: SSS and SAS**

4-5 **Technology Lab** Predict Other Triangle Congruence Relationships

4-5 **Triangle Congruence: ASA, AAS, and HL**

4-6 **Triangle Congruence: CPCTC**

On Track for TAKS Quadratic Equations

4-7 **Introduction to Coordinate Proof**

4-8 **Isosceles and Equilateral Triangles**

EXTENSION **Proving Constructions Valid**

Pacing Guide for 45-Minute Classes

Chapter 4

Countdown to TAKS Weeks 7, 8, 9

DAY 1	DAY 2	DAY 3	DAY 4	DAY 5
4-1 Lesson 4-2 Geometry Lab	4-2 Lesson	4-3 Lesson	Multi-Step TAKS Prep Ready to Go On?	4-4 Geometry Lab
DAY 6	**DAY 7**	**DAY 8**	**DAY 9**	**DAY 10**
4-4 Lesson	4-4 Lesson	4-5 Technology Lab	4-5 Lesson	4-5 Lesson
DAY 11	**DAY 12**	**DAY 13**	**DAY 14**	**DAY 15**
4-6 Lesson On Track for TAKS	4-7 Lesson	4-7 Lesson	4-8 Lesson	Multi-Step TAKS Prep Ready to Go On?
DAY 16	**DAY 17**	**DAY 18**		
EXTENSION	Chapter 4 Review	Chapter 4 Test		

Pacing Guide for 90-Minute Classes

Chapter 4

DAY 1	DAY 2	DAY 3	DAY 4	DAY 5
4-1 Lesson 4-2 Geometry Lab 4-2 Lesson	4-3 Lesson Multi-Step TAKS Prep Ready to Go On?	4-4 Geometry Lab 4-4 Lesson	4-4 Lesson 4-5 Technology Lab	4-5 Lesson
DAY 6	**DAY 7**	**DAY 8**	**DAY 9**	
4-6 Lesson On Track for TAKS 4-7 Lesson	4-7 Lesson 4-8 Lesson	Multi-Step TAKS Prep Ready to Go On? EXTENSION	Chapter 4 Review Chapter 4 Test	

ONGOING ASSESSMENT and INTERVENTION

	DIAGNOSE	PRESCRIBE
Assess Prior Knowledge	**Before Chapter 4**	
	Diagnose readiness for the chapter.	Prescribe intervention.
	Are You Ready? SE p. 213	**Are You Ready? Intervention** Skills 24, 58, 71
Formative Assessment	**Before Every Lesson**	
	Diagnose readiness for the lesson.	Prescribe intervention.
	Warm Up TE, every lesson	**Skills Bank** SE pp. S50–S81
		Reteach CRB, Ch. 1–4
	During Every Lesson	
	Diagnose understanding of lesson concepts.	Prescribe intervention.
	Check It Out! SE, every example	**Questioning Strategies** TE, every example
	Think and Discuss SE, every lesson	**Reading Strategies** CRB, every lesson
	Write About It SE, every lesson	**Success for ELL** pp. 41–56
	Journal TE, every lesson	
	After Every Lesson	
	Diagnose mastery of lesson concepts.	Prescribe intervention.
	Lesson Quiz TE, every lesson	**Reteach** CRB, every lesson
	Alternative Assessment TE, every lesson	**Problem Solving** CRB, every lesson
	Test Prep SE, every lesson	**Test Prep Doctor** TE, every lesson
	Test and Practice Generator	**Homework Help** Online
	Before Chapter 4 Testing	
	Diagnose mastery of concepts in the chapter.	Prescribe intervention.
	Ready to Go On? SE pp. 239, 281	**Ready to Go On? Intervention** pp. 41–56
	Multi-Step TAKS Prep SE pp. 238, 280	**Scaffolding Questions** TE pp. 238, 280
	Section Quizzes AR pp. 65–66	
	Test and Practice Generator	
	Before High Stakes Testing	
	Diagnose mastery of benchmark concepts.	Prescribe intervention.
	Ready for TAKS? Benchmark Tests	**Ready for TAKS? Intervention**
	College Entrance Exam Practice SE p. 289	**College Entrance Exam Practice**
	TAKS Prep SE pp. 292–293	**TAKS Prep Workbook**
	TAKS Prep CD-ROM	
Summative Assessment	**After Chapter 4**	
	Check mastery of chapter concepts.	Prescribe intervention.
	Multiple-Choice Tests (Forms A, B, C)	**Reteach** CRB, every lesson
	Free-Response Tests (Forms A, B, C)	**Lesson Tutorial Videos** Chapter 4
	Performance Assessment AR pp. 67–80	
	Test and Practice Generator	
	Check mastery of benchmark concepts.	Prescribe intervention.
	TAKS Tests	**State Test Prep Workbook**
	College Entrance Exams	**College Entrance Exam Practice**

KEY: **SE** = *Student Edition* **TE** = *Teacher's Edition* **CRB** = *Chapter Resource Book* **AR** = *Assessment Resources*   Available online   Available on CD-ROM   **212B**

CHAPTER 4

Supporting the Teacher

Chapter 4 Resource Book

Practice A, B, C
pp. 3–5, 11–13, 19–21, 27–29, 35–37, 43–45, 51–53, 59–61

Reading Strategies ELL
pp. 10, 18, 26, 34, 42, 50, 58, 66

Reteach
pp. 6–7, 14–15, 22–23, 30–31, 38–39, 46–47, 54–55, 62–63

Problem Solving
pp. 9, 17, 25, 33, 41, 49, 57, 65

Challenge
pp. 8, 16, 24, 32, 40, 48, 56, 64

Parent Letter   pp. 1–2

Transparencies

Lesson Transparencies, Volume 2 .... Chapter 4
• Warm Ups
• Teaching Transparencies
• Additional Examples
• Lesson Quizzes

Alternate Openers: Explorations .... pp. 21–28

Countdown to TAKS .... pp. 13–18

Know-It Notebook .... Chapter 4
• Graphic Organizers
• Key Concepts
• Vocabulary
• Chapter Review
• Big Ideas
• Postulates
• Theorems

Teacher Tools

Power Presentations®
Complete PowerPoint® presentations for Chapter 4 lessons

Lesson Tutorial Videos®
Holt authors Ed Burger and Freddie Renfro present tutorials to support the Chapter 4 lessons.

One-Stop Planner®
Easy access to all Chapter 4 resources and assessments, as well as software for lesson planning, test generation, and puzzle creation

IDEA Works!®
Key Chapter 4 resources and assessments modified to address special learning needs

Lesson Plans .... pp. 21–28

Solutions Key .... p. 247

Geometry Posters .... Chapter 4

TechKeys 🪐   **Lab Resources** 🪐

Project Teacher Support 🪐   **Parent Resources** 🪐

Workbooks

Homework and Practice Workbook
  Teacher's Guide .... pp. 21–28

Know-It Notebook
  Teacher's Guide .... pp. 49–64

Problem Solving Workbook
  Teacher's Guide .... pp. 21–28

TAKS Prep Workbook
  Teacher's Guide

Technology Highlights for the Teacher

 Power Presentations
Dynamic presentations to engage students. Complete PowerPoint® presentations for every lesson in Chapter 4.

 One-Stop Planner
Easy access to Chapter 4 resources and assessments. Includes lesson-planning, test-generation, and puzzle-creation software.

🪐 **Premier Online Edition**
Chapter 4 includes Tutorial Videos, Lesson Activities, Lesson Quizzes, Homework Help, and Chapter Project.

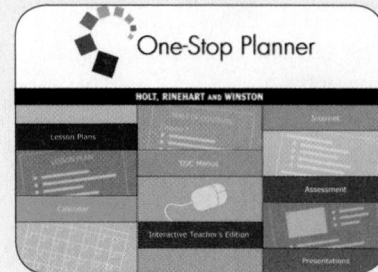

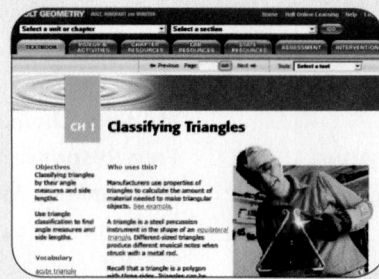

 KEY: **SE** = *Student Edition*   **TE** = *Teacher's Edition*   English Language Learners   Spanish version available    Available online   Available on CD-ROM

Reaching All Learners

Resources for All Learners

DEVELOPING LEARNERS

ON-LEVEL LEARNERS

ADVANCED LEARNERS

English Language Learners

ENGLISH
LANGUAGE
LEARNERS

Reaching All Learners Through...

Technology Highlights for Reaching All Learners

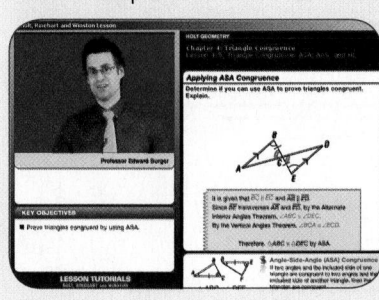

Lesson Tutorial Videos
Starring Holt authors Ed Burger and Freddie Renfro! Live tutorials to support every lesson in Chapter 4.

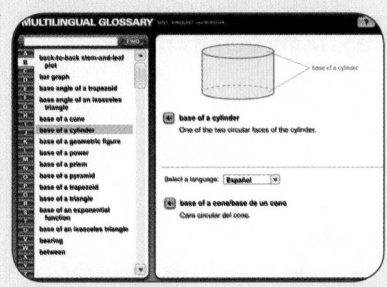

Multilingual Glossary
Searchable glossary includes definitions in English, Spanish, Vietnamese, Chinese, Hmong, Korean, and 4 other languages.

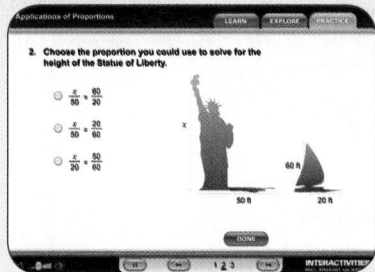

Online Interactivities
Interactive tutorials provide visually engaging alternative opportunities to learn concepts and master skills.

KEY: **SE** = *Student Edition*   **TE** = *Teacher's Edition*   **CRB** = *Chapter Resource Book*   SPANISH Spanish version available    Available online   Available on CD-ROM

212D

Ongoing Assessment

Assessing Prior Knowledge

Determine whether students have the prerequisite concepts and skills for success in Chapter 4.

Are You Ready? SPANISH 🪐 💿 .... SE p. 213
Warm Up 🖨 💿 .... TE, every lesson

Test Preparation

Provide practice and review for Chapter 4 and standardized tests.

Multi-Step TAKS Prep .... SE pp. 238, 280
Study Guide: Review .... SE pp. 284–287
TAKS Tackler .... SE pp. 290–291
TAKS Prep .... SE pp. 292–293
College Entrance Exam Practice .... SE p. 289
Countdown to TAKS Transparencies 🖨 💿 ......pp. 13–18
Ready for TAKS? 🪐 💿
TAKS Prep Workbook
TAKS Prep CD-ROM 💿
IDEA Works! 💿

Alternative Assessment

Assess students' understanding of Chapter 4 concepts and combined problem-solving skills.

Chapter 4 Project .... SE p. 212
Alternative Assessment .... TE, every lesson
Performance Assessment .... AR pp. 79–80
Portfolio Assessment .... AR p. xxxiv

Daily Assessment

Provide formative assessment for each day of Chapter 4.

Questioning Strategies .... TE, every example
Think and Discuss .... SE, every lesson
Check It Out! Exercises .... SE, every example
Write About It .... SE, every lesson
Journal .... TE, every lesson
Lesson Quiz 🖨 💿 .... TE, every lesson
Alternative Assessment .... TE, every lesson
Modified Lesson Quizzes 💿 .... *IDEA Works!*

Weekly Assessment

Provide formative assessment for each week of Chapter 4.

Multi-Step TAKS Prep .... SE pp. 238, 280
Ready to Go On? 🪐 💿 .... SE pp. 239, 281
Cumulative Assessment .... SE pp. 292–293
Test and Practice Generator SPANISH 💿 .. *One-Stop Planner*

Formal Assessment

Provide summative assessment of Chapter 4 mastery.

Section Quizzes .... AR pp. 65–66
Chapter 4 Test .... SE p. 288
Chapter Test (Levels A, B, C) .... AR pp. 67–78
    • Multiple Choice   • Free Response
Cumulative Test .... AR pp. 81–84
Test and Practice Generator SPANISH 💿 .. *One-Stop Planner*
Modified Chapter 4 Test 💿 .... *IDEA Works!*

Technology Highlights for Ongoing Assessment

 Are You Ready?

Automatically assess readiness and prescribe intervention for Chapter 4 prerequisite skills.

 Ready to Go On? SPANISH

Automatically assess understanding of and prescribe intervention for Sections 4A and 4B.

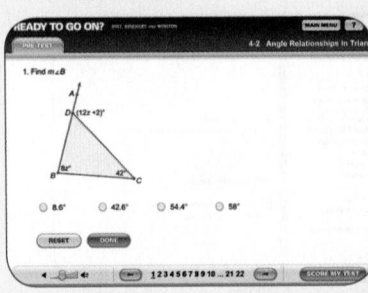

 Ready for TAKS? SPANISH

Automatically assess proficiency with and provide intervention for TAKS objectives. Grade 6 through Exit Level.

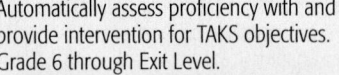
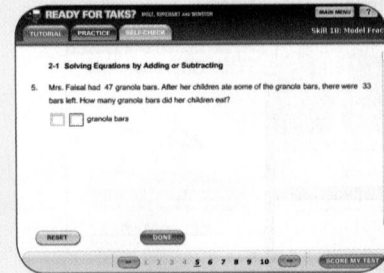

KEY: **SE** = *Student Edition*   **TE** = *Teacher's Edition*   **AR** = *Assessment Resources*   SPANISH Spanish version available   🪐 Available online   💿 Available on CD-ROM

Formal Assessment

Three levels (A, B, C) of multiple-choice and free-response chapter tests are available in the *Assessment Resources.*

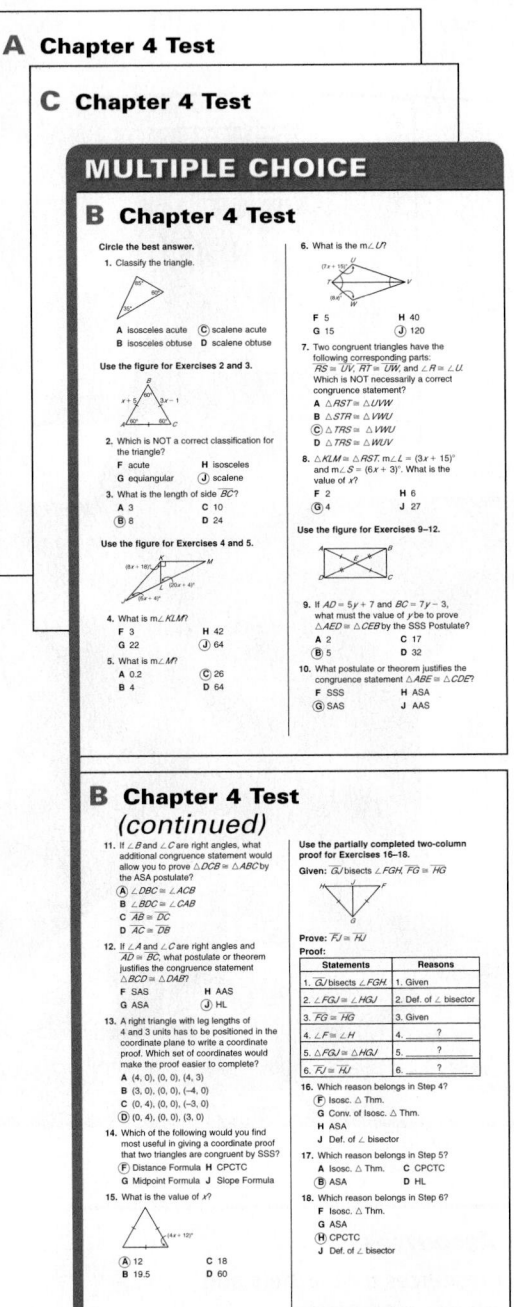

A Chapter 4 Test

C Chapter 4 Test

MULTIPLE CHOICE

B Chapter 4 Test

Circle the best answer.

1. Classify the triangle.

A isosceles acute   **C** scalene acute
B isosceles obtuse   D scalene obtuse

Use the figure for Exercises 2 and 3.

2. Which is NOT a correct classification for the triangle?
F acute   H isosceles
G equiangular   **J** scalene

3. What is the length of side $\overline{BC}$?
A 3   C 10
B 8   D 24

Use the figure for Exercises 4 and 5.

4. What is m∠KLM?
F 3   H 42
G 22   **J** 64

5. What is m∠M?
A 0.2   **C** 26
B 4   D 64

6. What is the m∠U?
F 5   H 40
G 15   **J** 120

7. Two congruent triangles have the following corresponding parts: $\overline{RS} \cong \overline{UV}$, $\overline{RT} \cong \overline{UW}$, and ∠$R \cong$ ∠U. Which is NOT necessarily a correct congruence statement?
A △$RST \cong$ △UVW
B △$STR \cong$ △VWU
C △$TRS \cong$ △VWU
D △$TRS \cong$ △WUV

8. △$KLM \cong$ △RST. m∠$L = (3x + 15)°$ and m∠$S = (6x + 3)°$. What is the value of x?
F 2   H 6
G 4   J 27

Use the figure for Exercises 9–12.

9. If $AD = 5y + 7$ and $BC = 7y - 3$, what must the value of y be to prove △$AED \cong$ △CEB by the SSS Postulate?
A 2   C 17
B 5   D 32

10. What postulate or theorem justifies the congruence statement △$ABE \cong$ △CDE?
F SSS   H ASA
G SAS   J AAS

B Chapter 4 Test
(continued)

11. If ∠B and ∠C are right angles, what additional congruence statement would allow you to prove △$DCB \cong$ △ABC by the ASA postulate?
A ∠$DBC \cong$ ∠ACB
B ∠$BDC \cong$ ∠CAB
C $\overline{AB} \cong \overline{DC}$
D $\overline{AC} \cong \overline{DB}$

12. If ∠A and ∠C are right angles and $\overline{AD} \cong \overline{BC}$, what postulate or theorem justifies the congruence statement △$BCD \cong$ △DAB?
F SAS   H AAS
G ASA   **J** HL

13. A right triangle with leg lengths of 4 and 3 units has to be positioned in the coordinate plane to write a coordinate proof. Which set of coordinates would make the proof easier to complete?
A (4, 0), (0, 0), (4, 3)
B (3, 0), (0, 0), (−4, 0)
C (0, 4), (0, 0), (−3, 0)
D (0, 4), (0, 0), (3, 0)

14. Which of the following would you find most useful in giving a coordinate proof that two triangles are congruent by SSS?
F Distance Formula   H CPCTC
G Midpoint Formula   J Slope Formula

15. What is the value of x?

A 12   C 18
B 19.5   D 60

Use the partially completed two-column proof for Exercises 16–18.

Given: $\overline{GJ}$ bisects ∠FGH, $\overline{FG} \cong \overline{HG}$

Prove: $\overline{FJ} \cong \overline{HJ}$

Proof:

Statements	Reasons
1. $\overline{GJ}$ bisects ∠FGH.	1. Given
2. ∠$FGJ \cong$ ∠HGJ	2. Def. of ∠ bisector
3. $\overline{FG} \cong \overline{HG}$	3. Given
4. ∠$F \cong$ ∠H	4. ?
5. △$FGJ \cong$ △HGJ	5. ?
6. $\overline{FJ} \cong \overline{HJ}$	6. ?

16. Which reason belongs in Step 4?
F Isosc. △ Thm.
G Conv. of Isosc. △ Thm.
H ASA
J Def. of ∠ bisector

17. Which reason belongs in Step 5?
A Isosc. △ Thm.   C CPCTC
B ASA   D HL

18. Which reason belongs in Step 6?
F Isosc. △ Thm.
G ASA
H CPCTC
J Def. of ∠ bisector

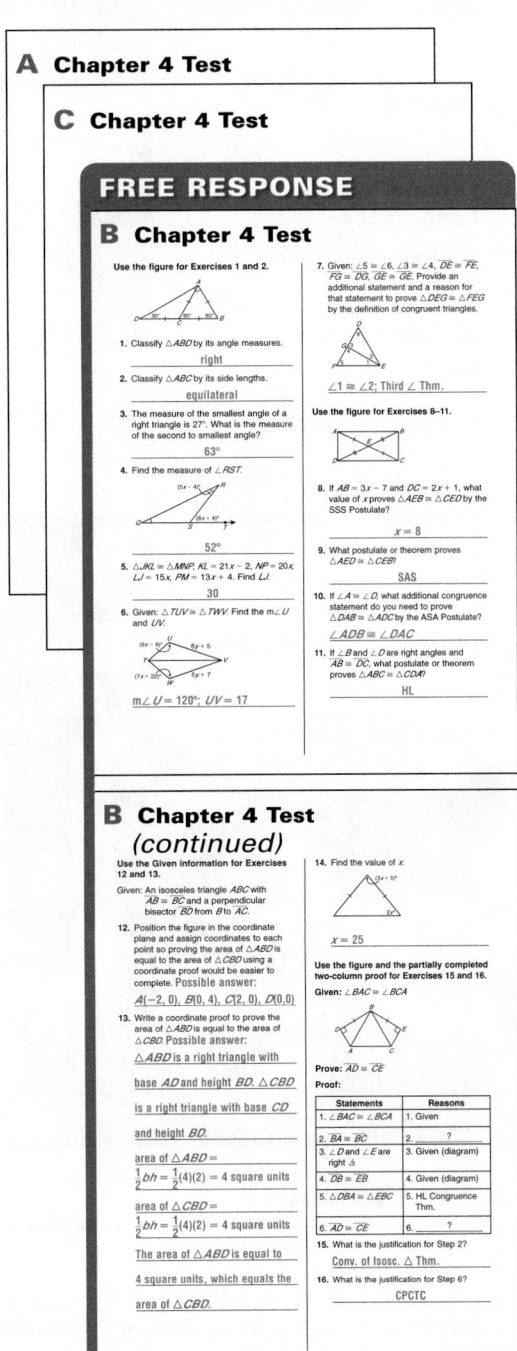

A Chapter 4 Test

C Chapter 4 Test

FREE RESPONSE

B Chapter 4 Test

Use the figure for Exercises 1 and 2.

1. Classify △ABD by its angle measures.
right

2. Classify △ABC by its side lengths.
equilateral

3. The measure of the smallest angle of a right triangle is 27°. What is the measure of the second to smallest angle?
63°

4. Find the measure of ∠RST.
52°

5. △$JKL \cong$ △MNP, $KL = 21x - 2$, $NP = 20x$, $LJ = 15x$, $PM = 13x + 4$. Find LJ.
30

6. Given: △$TUV \cong$ △TWV. Find the m∠U and UV.
m∠$U = 120°$; $UV = 17$

7. Given: ∠$5 \cong$ ∠6, ∠$3 \cong$ ∠4, $\overline{DE} \cong \overline{FE}$, $\overline{FG} \cong \overline{DG}$, $\overline{GE} \cong \overline{GE}$. Provide an additional statement and a reason for that statement to prove △$DEG \cong$ △FEG by the definition of congruent triangles.

∠$1 \cong$ ∠2; Third ∠ Thm.

Use the figure for Exercises 8–11.

8. If $AB = 3x - 7$ and $DC = 2x + 1$, what value of x proves △$AEB \cong$ △CED by the SSS Postulate?
$x = 8$

9. What postulate or theorem proves △$AED \cong$ △CEB?
SAS

10. If ∠$A \cong$ ∠D, what additional congruence statement do you need to prove △$DAB \cong$ △ADC by the ASA Postulate?
∠$ADB \cong$ ∠DAC

11. If ∠B and ∠D are right angles and $\overline{AB} \cong \overline{DC}$, what postulate or theorem proves △$ABC \cong$ △CDA?
HL

B Chapter 4 Test
(continued)

Use the Given information for Exercises 12 and 13.

Given: An isosceles triangle ABC with $\overline{AB} \cong \overline{BC}$ and a perpendicular bisector $\overline{BD}$ from B to $\overline{AC}$.

12. Position the figure in the coordinate plane and assign coordinates to each point so proving the area of △ABD is equal to the area of △CBD using a coordinate proof would be easier to complete. Possible answer:

$A(−2, 0)$, $B(0, 4)$, $C(2, 0)$, $D(0,0)$

13. Write a coordinate proof to prove the area of △ABD is equal to the area of △CBD. Possible answer:

△ABD is a right triangle with base AD and height BD. △CBD is a right triangle with base CD and height BD.

area of △ABD =
$\frac{1}{2}bh = \frac{1}{2}(4)(2) = 4$ square units

area of △CBD =
$\frac{1}{2}bh = \frac{1}{2}(4)(2) = 4$ square units

The area of △ABD is equal to 4 square units, which equals the area of △CBD.

14. Find the value of x.

$x = 25$

Use the figure and the partially completed two-column proof for Exercises 15 and 16.

Given: ∠$BAC \cong$ ∠BCA

Prove: $\overline{AD} \cong \overline{CE}$

Proof:

Statements	Reasons
1. ∠$BAC \cong$ ∠BCA	1. Given
2. $\overline{BA} \cong \overline{BC}$	2. ?
3. ∠D and ∠E are right ∠.	3. Given (diagram)
4. $\overline{DB} \cong \overline{EB}$	4. Given (diagram)
5. △$DBA \cong$ △EBC	5. HL Congruence Thm.
6. $\overline{AD} \cong \overline{CE}$	6. ?

15. What is the justification for Step 2?
Conv. of Isosc. △ Thm.

16. What is the justification for Step 6?
CPCTC

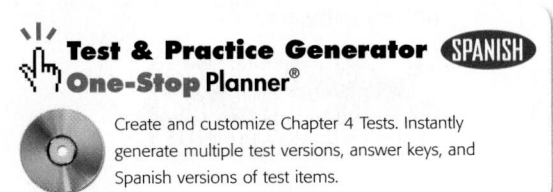

CHAPTER 4

Triangle Congruence

go.hrw.com/Geo/TX
Chapter Project Online
KEYWORD: MG7 ChProj

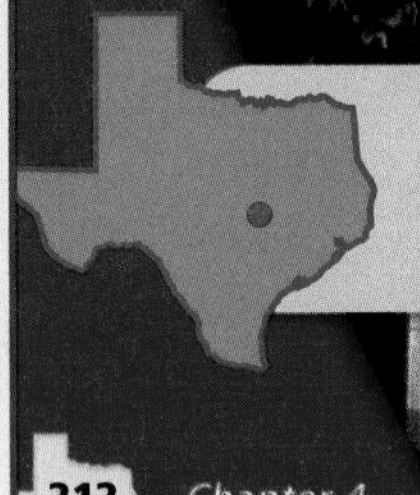

SECTION 4A

Triangles and Congruence

MULTI-STEP TAKS PREP

On page 238, students use the ancient art of paper folding to make an origami swan. They answer questions about the sides, angles, and triangles created when a square piece of paper is folded.

Exercises designed to prepare students for success on the Multi-Step TAKS Prep can be found on pages 220, 229, and 236.

SECTION 4B

Proving Triangle Congruence

MULTI-STEP TAKS PREP

On page 280, students see how geometric concepts are used to design and construct a doghouse. Students prove several facts about the triangles used in the design, including that they are congruent.

Exercises designed to prepare students for success on the Multi-Step TAKS Prep can be found on pages 247, 258, 264, 271, and 278.

The Bob Bullock Texas State History Museum opened in Austin in April 2001.

About the Project

Flexible Creations

In the Chapter Project, students fold strips of paper to form rows of congruent equilateral triangles. Then they use these strips to create their own polygonal flexagons.

Project Resources

All project resources for teachers and students are provided online.

Materials:
- paper, scissors, glue, ruler and protractor or straightedge and compass
- geometry software

go.hrw.com/Geo/TX
Project Teacher Support
KEYWORD: MG7 ProjectTS

Geometry in Texas

The 35-foot star sculpture that welcomes you to the Bob Bullock Texas State History Museum is made of congruent triangles.

ARE YOU READY?

✓ Vocabulary

Match each term on the left with a definition on the right.

1. acute angle F
2. congruent segments D
3. obtuse angle B
4. postulate A
5. triangle E

A. a statement that is accepted as true without proof
B. an angle that measures greater than 90° and less than 180°
C. a statement that you can prove
D. segments that have the same length
E. a three-sided polygon
F. an angle that measures greater than 0° and less than 90°

✓ Measure Angles

Use a protractor to measure each angle.

6.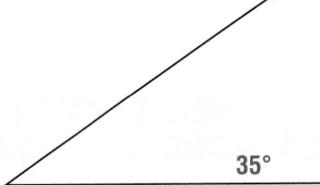
   35°

7.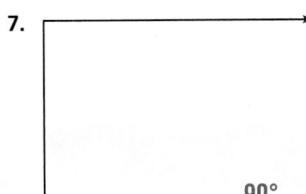
   90°

Use a protractor to draw an angle with each of the following measures.

8. 20°   9. 63°   10. 105°   11. 158°

For exercises 8–11 check students' drawings.

✓ Solve Equations with Fractions

Solve.

12. $\frac{9}{2}x + 7 = 25$ **4**

13. $3x - \frac{2}{3} = \frac{4}{3}$ $\frac{2}{3}$

14. $x - \frac{1}{5} = \frac{12}{5}$ $2\frac{3}{5}$

15. $2y = 5y - \frac{21}{2}$ $3\frac{1}{2}$

✓ Connect Words and Algebra

Write an equation for each statement.

16. Tanya's age t is three times Martin's age m. $t = 3m$

17. Twice the length of a segment x is 9 ft. $2x = 9$

18. The sum of 53° and twice an angle measure y is 90°. $53 + 2y = 90$

19. The price of a radio r is $25 less than the price of a CD player p. $r = p - 25$

20. Half the amount of liquid j in a jar is 5 oz more than the amount of liquid b in a bowl. $\frac{1}{2}j = b + 5$

Organizer

Objective: Assess students' understanding of prerequisite skills.

Prerequisite Skills

Measure Angles

Solve Equations with Fractions

Connect Words and Algebra

Assessing Prior Knowledge

INTERVENTION ◄►

Diagnose and Prescribe

Use this page to determine whether intervention is necessary or whether enrichment is appropriate.

Resources

- **Are You Ready? Intervention and Enrichment Worksheets**
- **Are You Ready? CD-ROM**
- **Are You Ready? Online**

my.hrw.com

ARE YOU READY?
Diagnose and Prescribe

NO
INTERVENE

YES
ENRICH

✓ Prerequisite Skill	🗎 Worksheets	💿 CD-ROM	🪐 Online
✓ Measure Angles	Skill 24	Activity 24	
✓ Solve Equations with Fractions	Skill 71	Activity 71	Diagnose and Prescribe Online
✓ Connect Words and Algebra	Skill 58	Activity 58	

ARE YOU READY? Intervention, Chapter 4

ARE YOU READY? Enrichment, Chapter 4
- 🗎 Worksheets
- 💿 CD-ROM
- 🪐 Online

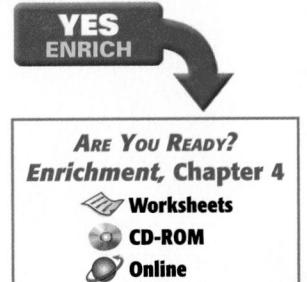

Organizer

Objective: Help students organize the new concepts they will learn in Chapter 4.

Online Edition
Multilingual Glossary

Resources

PuzzlePro
One-Stop Planner®

Multilingual Glossary Online
go.hrw.com/Geo/TX
KEYWORD: MG7 Glossary

Answers to Vocabulary Connections

1.

Possible answer: Yes, I think the △ is acute.

2. Possible answer: *Exterior* means "outside." An ext. ∠ of a △ is located outside the △.

3. Possible answer: An obtuse △ is a △ that contains an obtuse ∠.

Key Vocabulary/Vocabulario

acute triangle	triángulo acutángulo
congruent polygons	polígonos congruentes
corollary	corolario
equilateral triangle	triángulo equilátero
exterior angle	ángulo externo
interior angle	ángulo interno
isosceles triangle	triángulo isósceles
obtuse triangle	triángulo obtusángulo
right triangle	triángulo rectángulo
scalene triangle	triángulo escaleno

Vocabulary Connections

To become familiar with some of the vocabulary terms in the chapter, consider the following. You may refer to the chapter, the glossary, or a dictionary if you like.

1. The Latin word *acutus* means "pointed" or "sharp." Draw a triangle that looks pointed or sharp. Do you think this is an **acute triangle**?

2. Consider the everyday meaning of the word *exterior*. Where do you think an **exterior angle** of a triangle is located?

3. You already know the definition of an obtuse angle. Use this meaning to make a conjecture about an **obtuse triangle**.

★ Geometry TEKS

Geometry TEKS	Les. 4-1	4-2 Geo. Lab	Les. 4-2	Les. 4-3	4-4 Geo. Lab	Les. 4-4	4-5 Tech. Lab	Les. 4-5	Les. 4-6	Les. 4-7	Les. 4-8	Ext.
G.1.A Geometric structure* develop an awareness of the structure of a mathematical system …	★	★						★	★			
G.2.A Geometric structure* use constructions to explore attributes of geometric figures and to make conjectures …						★	★	★				★
G.2.B Geometric structure* make conjectures about angles, lines, polygons … and determine validity of the conjectures, choosing from a variety of approaches …				★	★					★	★	
G.5.A Geometric patterns* use … geometric patterns to develop algebraic expressions representing geometric properties	★											
G.7.A Dimensionality and the geometry of location* use one- and two-dimensional coordinate systems to represent points, lines, rays, line segments, and figures								★				
G.9.B Congruence and the geometry of size* formulate and test conjectures about the properties and attributes of polygons … based on explorations …	★			★		★	★		★			
G.10.B Congruence and the geometry of size* justify and apply triangle congruence relationships				★	★	★	★	★	★	★	★	

* *Knowledge and skills are written out completely on pages TX28–TX35.*

★ Geometry TEKS—Knowledge and Skills

G.1 Geometric structure The student understands the structure of, and relationships within, an axiomatic system.

G.2 Geometric structure The student analyzes geometric relationships in order to make and verify conjectures.

G.3 Geometric structure The student applies logical reasoning to justify and prove mathematical statements.

G.4 Geometric structure The student uses a variety of representations to describe geometric relationships and solve problems.

G.5 Geometric patterns The student uses a variety of representations to describe geometric relationships and solve problems.

G.7 Dimensionality and the geometry of location The student understands that coordinate systems provide convenient and efficient ways of representing geometric figures and uses them accordingly.

G.9 Congruence and the geometry of size The student analyzes properties and describes relationships in geometric figures.

G.10 Congruence and the geometry of size The student applies the concept of congruence to justify properties of figures and solve problems.

Reading and Writing Math

Reading Strategy: Read Geometry Symbols

In Geometry we often use symbols to communicate information. When studying each lesson, read both the symbols and the words slowly and carefully. Reading aloud can sometimes help you translate symbols into words.

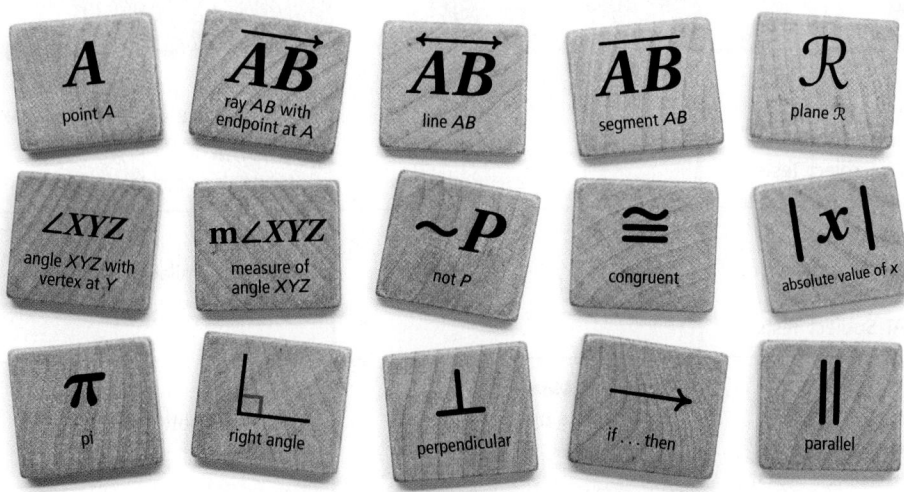

Symbol	Meaning
A	point A
$\overrightarrow{AB}$	ray AB with endpoint at A
$\overleftrightarrow{AB}$	line AB
$\overline{AB}$	segment AB
$\mathcal{R}$	plane $\mathcal{R}$
$\angle XYZ$	angle XYZ with vertex at Y
$m\angle XYZ$	measure of angle XYZ
$\sim P$	not P
$\cong$	congruent
$\lvert x \rvert$	absolute value of x
π	pi
⌐	right angle
$\perp$	perpendicular
$\rightarrow$	if . . . then
$\parallel$	parallel

Throughout this course, you will use these symbols and combinations of these symbols to represent various geometric statements.

Symbol Combinations	Translated into Words
$\overleftrightarrow{ST} \parallel \overrightarrow{UV}$	Line ST is parallel to line UV.
$\overline{BC} \perp \overline{GH}$	Segment BC is perpendicular to segment GH.
$p \rightarrow q$	If p, then q.
$m\angle QRS = 45°$	The measure of angle QRS is 45 degrees.
$\angle CDE \cong \angle LMN$	Angle CDE is congruent to angle LMN.

Try This

Rewrite each statement using symbols.

1. the absolute value of 2 times pi
2. The measure of angle 2 is 125 degrees.
3. Segment XY is perpendicular to line BC.
4. If not p, then not q.

Translate the symbols into words.

5. $m\angle FGH = m\angle VWX$
6. $\overleftrightarrow{ZA} \parallel \overrightarrow{TU}$
7. $\sim p \rightarrow q$
8. $\overrightarrow{ST}$ bisects $\angle TSU$.

Organizer

Objective: Help students apply the strategies to understand and retain key concepts.

 **Online Edition**

Resources

 **Chapter 4 Resource Book**
Reading Strategies

ENGLISH LANGUAGE LEARNERS

Reading Strategy: Read Geometry Symbols

Discuss Students benefit from reading geometric symbols and their meanings aloud. Have students listen to other students read statements containing geometric symbols. Then have them practice using symbols, not words, to write the statements. They can write these on butcher paper and post them in the classroom to use as a visual reference later.

Extend As students work through Chapter 4, have them present their proofs to the class and read the geometric symbols in them. Discuss what the symbols mean and how the meanings would differ if the symbols were changed or left out.

Answers to *Try This*

1. $\lvert 2\pi \rvert$
2. $m\angle 2 = 125°$
3. $\overline{XY} \perp \overleftrightarrow{BC}$
4. $\sim p \rightarrow \sim q$
5. The measure of angle FGH equals the measure of angle VWX.
6. Line ZA is parallel to line TU.
7. If not p, then q.
8. Ray ST bisects angle TSU.

🔲 TAKS Objectives

Grades 9–11

Obj. 2 Properties and Attributes of Functions: A.4.A
Obj. 5 Quadratic and Other Nonlinear Functions: A.10.A
Obj. 6 Geometric Relationships and Spatial Reasoning: G.5.A, G.5.B, G.5.D, G.10.B
Obj. 7 Two- and Three-Dimensional Representations: 8.7.B
Obj. 8 Measurement and Similarity: G.8.A
Obj. 10 Mathematical Processes and Tools: 8.14.A, 8.14.B

Triangles and Congruence

One-Minute Section Planner

Lesson	Lab Resources	Materials
Lesson 4-1 Classifying Triangles • Classify triangles by their angle measures and side lengths. • Use triangle classification to find angle measures and side lengths. ☑ Exit Level TAKS ☑ ACT ☑ SAT ☑ SAT Subject Tests		**Required** straightedge and compass (MK) **Optional** triangular objects
4-2 Geometry Lab Develop the Triangle Sum Theorem • Use patty paper to discover the relationship between the measures of the interior angles of a triangle. ☐ Exit Level TAKS ☑ ACT ☐ SAT ☐ SAT Subject Tests		**Required** patty or similar paper
Lesson 4-2 Angle Relationships in Triangles • Find the measures of interior and exterior angles of triangles. • Apply theorems about the interior and exterior angles of triangles. ☑ Exit Level TAKS ☑ ACT ☑ SAT ☑ SAT Subject Tests	*Texas Lab Manual* 4-2 Technology Lab	**Optional** geometry software
Lesson 4-3 Congruent Triangles • Use properties of congruent triangles. • Prove triangles congruent by using the definition of congruence. ☐ Exit Level TAKS ☑ ACT ☑ SAT ☑ SAT Subject Tests		**Optional** patterns with congruent triangles, color pencils, ruler (MK), tracing paper

MK = *Manipulatives Kit*

Section Overview

Properties and Angle Relationships in Triangles   *Lessons 4-1, 4-2*

 A knowledge of the types of triangles and their properties will be needed throughout geometry and will be helpful in real-world situations.

Triangle Classification

By Angle Measures	**By Side Lengths**

By Angle Measures

Acute Triangle

Three acute angles

Equiangular Triangle

Three congruent
acute angles

Right Triangle

One right angle

Obtuse Triangle

One obtuse angle

By Side Lengths

Equilateral Triangle

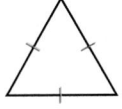

Three congruent sides

Isosceles Triangle

At least two
congruent sides

Scalene Triangle

No congruent sides

Example

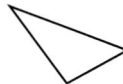

Acute isosceles

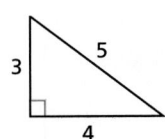

Right scalene

Theorems	**Corollaries**

Theorems

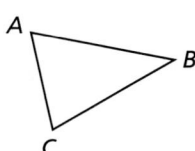

For any △*ABC*,
m∠*A* + m∠*B* + m∠*C*
= 180°.

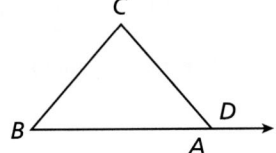

For any △*ABC* and
exterior ∠*D* adjacent to ∠*A*,
m∠*D* = m∠*B* + m∠*C*.

Corollaries

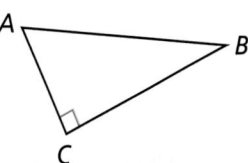

For any right △*ABC*
with right ∠*C*,
m∠*A* + m∠*B* = 90°.

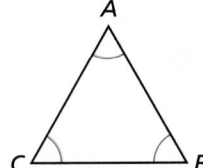

For any equiangular
△*ABC*, m∠*A* = m∠*B* =
m∠*C* = 60°.

Congruent Triangles   *Lesson 4-3*

 Properties of congruent triangles are used in mathematical proofs.

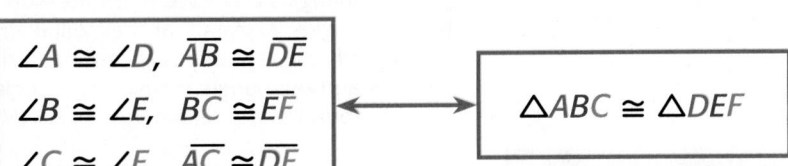

$$\angle A \cong \angle D, \ \overline{AB} \cong \overline{DE}$$
$$\angle B \cong \angle E, \ \overline{BC} \cong \overline{EF}$$
$$\angle C \cong \angle F, \ \overline{AC} \cong \overline{DF}$$

⟷ △*ABC* ≅ △*DEF*

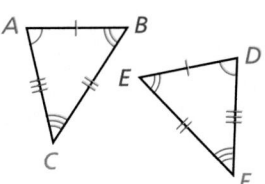

Objectives: Classify triangles by their angle measures and side lengths.

Use triangle classification to find angle measures and side lengths.

Online Edition
Tutorial Videos

Countdown to TAKS Week 7

Power Presentations
with PowerPoint®

Warm Up

Classify each angle.

1.
right

2. acute
40°

3. 150°
obtuse

4. If the perimeter is 47, find *x* and the length of each side.

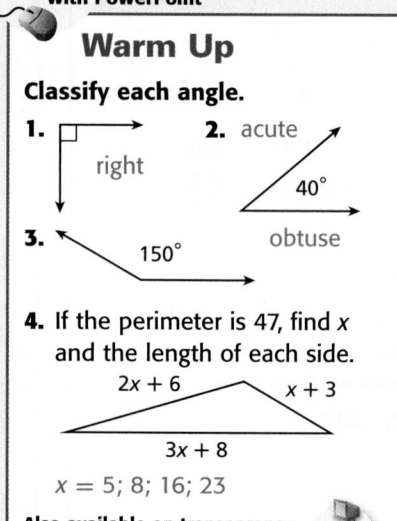

$2x + 6$ $x + 3$
      $3x + 8$

$x = 5$; 8; 16; 23

Also available on transparency

Math Humor

Q: What do you call a tall kettle on the stove?

A: Hypotenuse!

Geometry TEKS

G.1 Geometric structure*
(A) develop an awareness of the structure of a mathematical system, connecting definitions, postulates, logical reasoning, and theorems

* Knowledge and Skills See p. 214.

4-1 Classifying Triangles

★ **TEKS G.1.A Geometric structure:** develop an awareness of the structure of a mathematical system, connecting definitions, postulates, logical reasoning ...

Objectives
Classify triangles by their angle measures and side lengths.

Use triangle classification to find angle measures and side lengths.

Vocabulary
acute triangle
equiangular triangle
right triangle
obtuse triangle
equilateral triangle
isosceles triangle
scalene triangle

Who uses this?

Manufacturers use properties of triangles to calculate the amount of material needed to make triangular objects. (See Example 4.)

A triangle is a steel percussion instrument in the shape of an *equilateral triangle*. Different-sized triangles produce different musical notes when struck with a metal rod.

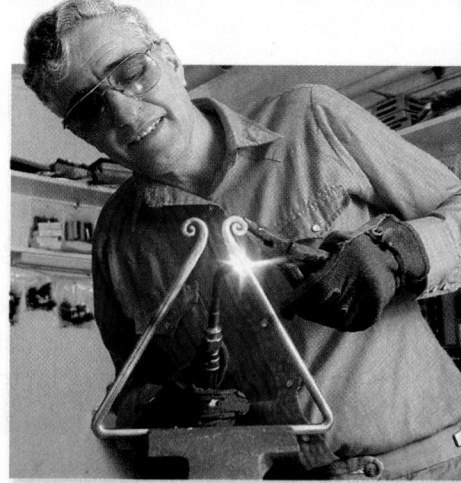

Recall that a *triangle* (△) is a polygon with three sides. Triangles can be classified in two ways: by their angle measures or by their side lengths.

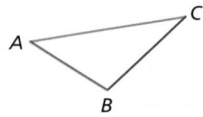

$\overline{AB}$, $\overline{BC}$, and $\overline{AC}$ are the *sides* of △ABC.
A, B, and C are the triangle's *vertices*.

Know it!
Note

Triangle Classification	**By Angle Measures**

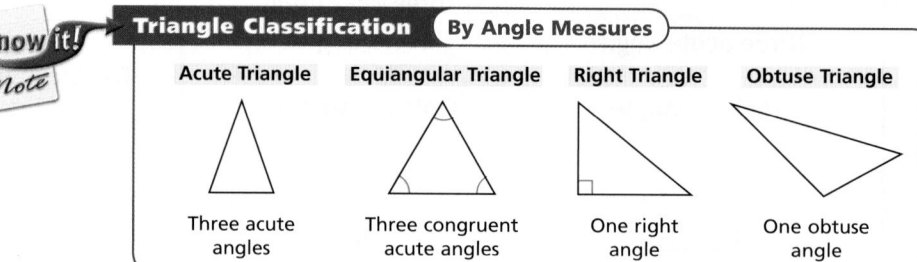

Acute Triangle	**Equiangular Triangle**	**Right Triangle**	**Obtuse Triangle**
Three acute angles	Three congruent acute angles	One right angle	One obtuse angle

EXAMPLE 1 **Classifying Triangles by Angle Measures**

Classify each triangle by its angle measures.

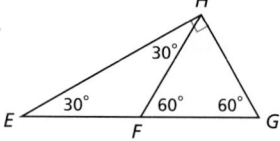

A △EHG
∠EHG is a right angle. So △EHG is a right triangle.

B △EFH
∠EFH and ∠HFG form a linear pair, so they are supplementary. Therefore m∠EFH + m∠HFG = 180°. By substitution, m∠EFH + 60° = 180°. So m∠EFH = 120°. △EFH is an obtuse triangle by definition.

CHECK IT OUT! **1.** Use the diagram to classify △FHG by its angle measures.
equiangular

---

1 Introduce

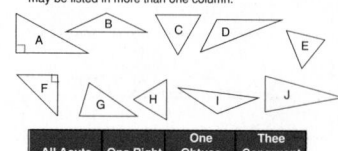
Motivate

Ask students to identify different types of triangles found in the classroom and/or in the real world, such as musical triangles, art sponges, or roof tops. Give them models of different types of triangles and have them measure the sides and angles. Explain that they will learn how to classify these triangles according to their side lengths and their angle measures. Triangle models can be found in the Manipulatives Kit (MK).

Explorations and answers are provided in the *Explorations* binder.

Triangle Classification | **By Side Lengths**

Equilateral Triangle	Isosceles Triangle	Scalene Triangle
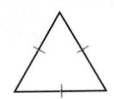		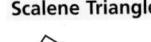 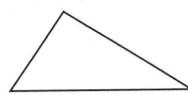
Three congruent sides	At least two congruent sides	No congruent sides

---

EXAMPLE 2 **Classifying Triangles by Side Lengths**

Classify each triangle by its side lengths.

Remember!

When you look at a figure, you cannot assume segments are congruent based on their appearance. They must be marked as congruent.

A △ABC
From the figure, $\overline{AB} \cong \overline{AC}$. So AC = 15, and △ABC is equilateral.

B △ABD
By the Segment Addition Postulate,
$BD = BC + CD = 15 + 5 = 20$.
Since no sides are congruent, △ABD is scalene.

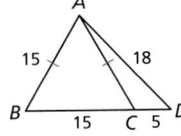

CHECK IT OUT! 2. Use the diagram to classify △ACD by its side lengths.
scalene

EXAMPLE 3 **Using Triangle Classification**

Find the side lengths of the triangle.

Algebra

Step 1 Find the value of x.

$\overline{JK} \cong \overline{KL}$	*Given*
$JK = KL$	*Def. of ≅ segs.*
$(4x - 1.3) = (x + 3.2)$	*Substitute (4x − 13) for JK and (x + 3.2) for KL.*
$3x = 4.5$	*Add 1.3 and subtract x from both sides.*
$x = 1.5$	*Divide both sides by 3.*

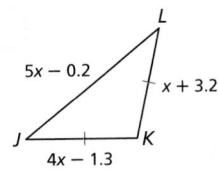

Step 2 Substitute 1.5 into the expressions to find the side lengths.
$$JK = 4x - 1.3$$
$$= 4(1.5) - 1.3 = 4.7$$
$$KL = x + 3.2$$
$$= (1.5) + 3.2 = 4.7$$
$$JL = 5x - 0.2$$
$$= 5(1.5) - 0.2 = 7.3$$

CHECK IT OUT! 3. Find the side lengths of equilateral △FGH.
17; 17; 17

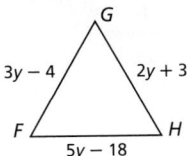

4-1 Classifying Triangles **217**

COMMON ERROR ALERT

Students sometimes think that a triangle is acute if it has one acute angle. Remind them that for a triangle to be acute, all three of its angles must be acute.

Power Presentations with PowerPoint®

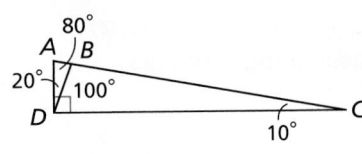
Additional Examples

Example 1

Classify each triangle by its angle measures.

A. △BDC   obtuse

B. △ABD   acute

Example 2

Classify each triangle by its side lengths.

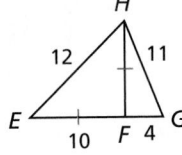

A. △EHF   isosceles

B. △EHG   scalene

Example 3

Find the side lengths of the triangle.   23.3; 23.3; 44.5

Also available on transparency

INTERVENTION
Questioning Strategies

EXAMPLE 1

• How do you find the measure of the other angles in the triangles?

EXAMPLES 2–3

• What segment length can you change so that there is an equilateral triangle?

Teaching Tip **Algebra** In **Example 3,** stress that students substitute 1.5 for x as a way to find and verify the answer to the problem.

Teach

Guided Instruction

Explain how to classify a triangle by its angles as acute, equiangular, right, or obtuse. Show that triangles can also be classified by their side lengths as equilateral, isosceles, or scalene. Then explain that some classifications can occur together. For example, a triangle can be right and isosceles.

Teaching Tip **Inclusion** Remind students that △ABC is a triangle and ∠ABC is one angle of the triangle.

Reaching All Learners
Through Auditory Cues

Have students work with a partner. Ask one student to describe a triangle classified by its angles and the other student to draw a diagram of what it would look like. Then have them reverse roles and have one student describe a triangle classified by its sides and the partner draw a diagram of what it would look like.

Lesson 4-1 **217**

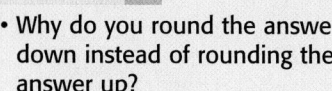

Example 4

A steel mill produces roof supports by welding pieces of steel beams into equilateral triangles. Each side of the triangle is 18 feet long. How many triangles can be formed from 420 feet of steel beam?   7

Also available on transparency

INTERVENTION ◀▬▶
Questioning Strategies

EXAMPLE 4

• Why do you round the answer down instead of rounding the answer up?

EXAMPLE 4   *Music Application*

A manufacturer produces musical triangles by bending pieces of steel into the shape of an equilateral triangle. The triangles are available in side lengths of 4 inches, 7 inches, and 10 inches. How many 4-inch triangles can the manufacturer produce from a 100 inch piece of steel?

4 in.

4 in.

4 in.

The amount of steel needed to make one triangle is equal to the perimeter P of the equilateral triangle.

$$P = 3(4)$$
$$= 12 \text{ in.}$$

To find the number of triangles that can be made from 100 inches. of steel, divide 100 by the amount of steel needed for one triangle.

$$100 \div 12 = 8\frac{1}{3} \text{ triangles}$$

There is not enough steel to complete a ninth triangle. So the manufacturer can make 8 triangles from a 100 in. piece of steel.

 Each measure is the side length of an equilateral triangle. Determine how many triangles can be formed from a 100 in. piece of steel.

4a. 7 in. 4   **4b.** 10 in. 3

THINK AND DISCUSS

1. For $\triangle DEF$, name the three pairs of consecutive sides and the vertex formed by each.

2. Sketch an example of an obtuse isosceles triangle, or explain why it is not possible to do so.

3. Is every acute triangle equiangular? Explain and support your answer with a sketch.

4. Use the Pythagorean Theorem to explain why you cannot draw an equilateral right triangle.

5. **GET ORGANIZED** Copy and complete the graphic organizer. In each box, describe each type of triangle.

Triangle Classification

By sides   By angles

---

3 Close

Summarize

Review triangle classifications by angle measures and side lengths. Draw an example of each. Emphasize what sides or angles need to be congruent to classify each triangle.

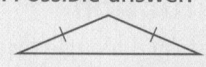
ONGOING ASSESSMENT

and INTERVENTION ◀▬▶

Diagnose Before the Lesson
4-1 Warm Up, TE p. 216

Monitor During the Lesson
Check It Out! Exercises, SE pp. 216–218
Questioning Strategies, TE pp. 217–218

Assess After the Lesson
4-1 Lesson Quiz, TE p. 221
Alternative Assessment, TE p. 221

Answers to *Think and Discuss*

1. $\overline{DE}, \overline{EF}, E; \overline{EF}, \overline{FD}, F; \overline{FD}, \overline{DE}, D$

2. Possible answer:

3. No; all 3 ∡ in an acute △ must be acute, but they do not have to have the same measure; possible answer:

4. In an equil. rt. △, all 3 sides have the same length. By the Pyth. Thm., the 3 sides lengths are related by the formula $c^2 = a^2 + b^2$, making the hyp. c greater than either a or b. So the 3 sides cannot have the same length.

5. See p. A3.

GUIDED PRACTICE

Vocabulary Apply the vocabulary from this lesson to answer each question.

1. In △JKL, JK, KL, and JL are *equal*. How does this help you classify △JKL by its side lengths? **An equilateral △ has 3 ≅ sides.**

2. △XYZ is an *obtuse* triangle. What can you say about the types of angles in △XYZ? **One of the ∠ is obtuse, and the other 2 ∠ are acute.**

SEE EXAMPLE **1**
p. 216

Classify each triangle by its angle measures.

3. △DBC **rt.**   **4.** △ABD **rt.**   **5.** △ADC **obtuse**

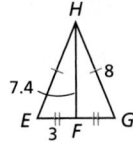

SEE EXAMPLE **2**
p. 217

Classify each triangle by its side lengths.

6. △EGH **isosc.**   **7.** △EFH **scalene**   **8.** △HFG **scalene**

SEE EXAMPLE **3**
p. 217

Multi-Step Find the side lengths of each triangle.

9. 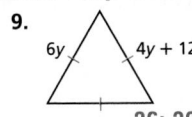 **36; 36; 36**

10. 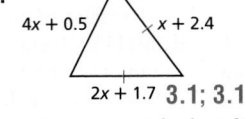 **3.1; 3.1; 3.3**

SEE EXAMPLE **4**
p. 218

11. Crafts A jeweler creates triangular earrings by bending pieces of silver wire. Each earring is an isosceles triangle with the dimensions shown. How many earrings can be made from a piece of wire that is 50 cm long? **6**

3 cm

1.5 cm

PRACTICE AND PROBLEM SOLVING

Independent Practice

For Exercises	See Example
12–14	1
15–17	2
18–20	3
21–22	4

TEKS 👍 TAKS
Skills Practice p. S10
Application Practice p. S31

Classify each triangle by its angle measures.

12. △BEA **rt.**

13. △DBC **obtuse**

14. △ABC **equiangular**

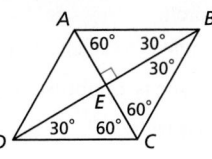

Classify each triangle by its side lengths.

15. △PST **equil.**   **16.** △RSP **isosc.**   **17.** △RPT **scalene**

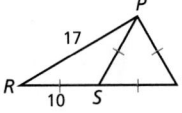

Multi-Step Find the side lengths of each triangle.

18. **8; 8; 8**
z + 5
4z − 4
3z − 1

19. **8.6; 8.6**
2x + 6.8
8x + 1.4

20. Check students' drawings.
a. $\overline{XY}$, $\overline{YZ}$, $\overline{XZ}$, ∠X, ∠Y, ∠Z
b. Possible answer: scalene obtuse

20. Draw a triangle large enough to measure. Label the vertices X, Y, and Z.
a. Name the three sides and three angles of the triangle.
b. Use a ruler and protractor to classify the triangle by its side lengths and angle measures.

Assignment Guide

Assign *Guided Practice* exercises as necessary.

If you finished Examples **1–2**
Basic 12–17, 20, 23–31, 35–37
Average 12–17, 20, 23–31, 35–37, 39
Advanced 12–17, 20, 23–31, 35–37, 39, 46

If you finished Examples **1–4**
Basic 12–29, 35, 36, 39–44, 49–58
Average 12–23, 24–32 even, 33, 34, 38–44, 48–58
Advanced 12–22, 24–30 even, 32–34, 38–58

Homework Quick Check
Quickly check key concepts.
Exercises: 12, 16, 18, 22, 24, 28

Teaching Tip **Visual** For **Exercises 15–17**, introduce the orientation of isosceles △RSP. Point out that the triangle is not "upside down" but that the orientation is just different.

For **Exercise 20**, have students use a different color for each side of the triangle so they can refer to the angles by the colors that form them.

⬇️TAKS Practice

Grades 9–11	Exercises
Obj. 3	50
Obj. 6	29–33, 40–44, 47, 48
Obj. 7	33, 55–58
Obj. 8	40
Obj. 10	33

Construction

For help with **Exercise 39,** have students first construct $\overline{AB}$. Then have them set their compasses to the width AB. Draw an arc centered at A and then another arc centered at B. Label the intersection C and draw $\triangle ABC$.

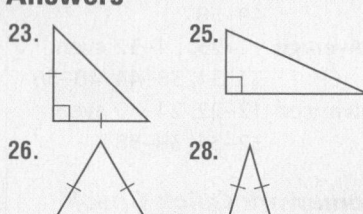

MULTI-STEP TAKS PREP Exercise 40 involves using the Pythagorean Theorem to find the length of the hypotenuse of a right triangle. This exercise prepares students for the Multi-Step TAKS Prep on page 238.

Answers

23. **25.**

26. **28.**

34. No; yes; not every isosc. $\triangle$ is equil. because only 2 of the 3 sides must be $\cong$. Every equil. $\triangle$ is isosc. because an equil. $\triangle$ has 3 $\cong$ sides, and the def. of an isosc. $\triangle$ requires that at least 2 sides be $\cong$.

35. **36.**

37.

38. $s = \frac{P}{3}$. The perimeter of an equil. $\triangle$ is 3 times the length of any 1 side, or $P = 3s$. Solve this formula for s by dividing both sides by 3.

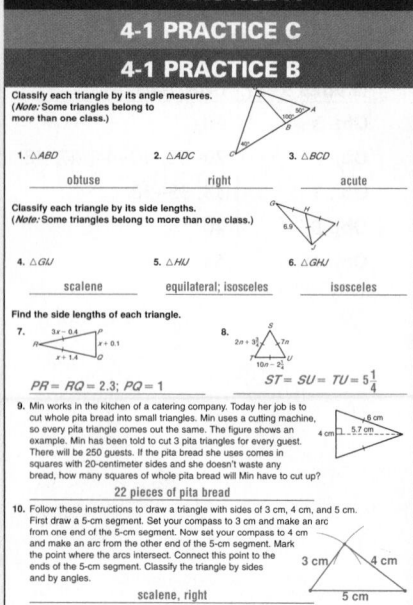

4-1 PRACTICE A
4-1 PRACTICE C
4-1 PRACTICE B

---

24. Not possible; an equiangular. $\triangle$ must contain only acute $\angle$s.

27. Not possible; an equiangular $\triangle$ must also be equil.

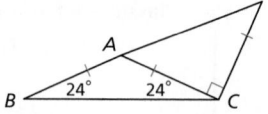

Architecture

Daniel Burnham designed and built the 22-story Flatiron Building in New York City in 1902.

Source: www.greatbuildings.com

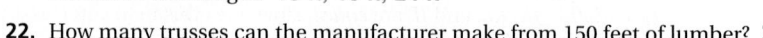

Carpentry Use the following information for Exercises 21 and 22.
A manufacturer makes trusses, or triangular supports, for the roofs of houses. Each truss is the shape of an isosceles triangle in which $\overline{PQ} \cong \overline{PR}$. The length of the base $\overline{QR}$ is $\frac{4}{3}$ the length of each of the congruent sides.

21. The perimeter of each truss is 60 ft. Find each side length. **18 ft; 18 ft; 24 ft**

22. How many trusses can the manufacturer make from 150 feet of lumber? **2**

Draw an example of each type of triangle or explain why it is not possible.

23. isosceles right **24.** equiangular obtuse **25.** scalene right

26. equilateral acute **27.** scalene equiangular **28.** isosceles acute

29. An equilateral triangle has a perimeter of 105 in. What is the length of each side of the triangle? **35 in.**

Classify each triangle by its angles and sides.

30. $\triangle ABC$ **isosc. obtuse** **31.** $\triangle ACD$ **isosc. rt.**

32. An isosceles triangle has a perimeter of 34 cm. The congruent sides measure $(4x - 1)$ cm. The length of the third side is x cm. What is the value of x? **4**

33. **Architecture** The base of the Flatiron Building is a triangle bordered by three streets: Broadway, Fifth Avenue, and East Twenty-second Street. The Fifth Avenue side is 1 ft shorter than twice the East Twenty-second Street side. The East Twenty-second Street side is 8 ft shorter than half the Broadway side. The Broadway side is 190 ft.
   a. Find the two unknown side lengths. **173 ft; 87 ft**
   b. Classify the triangle by its side lengths. **scalene**

34. **Critical Thinking** Is every isosceles triangle equilateral? Is every equilateral triangle isosceles? Explain.

Tell whether each statement is sometimes, always, or never true. Support your answer with a sketch.

35. An acute triangle is a scalene triangle. **S**

36. A scalene triangle is an obtuse triangle. **S**

37. An equiangular triangle is an isosceles triangle. **A**

38. **Write About It** Write a formula for the side length s of an equilateral triangle, given the perimeter P. Explain how you derived the formula.

39. **Construction** Use the method for constructing congruent segments to construct an equilateral triangle. **Check students' constructions.**

MULTI-STEP TAKS PREP

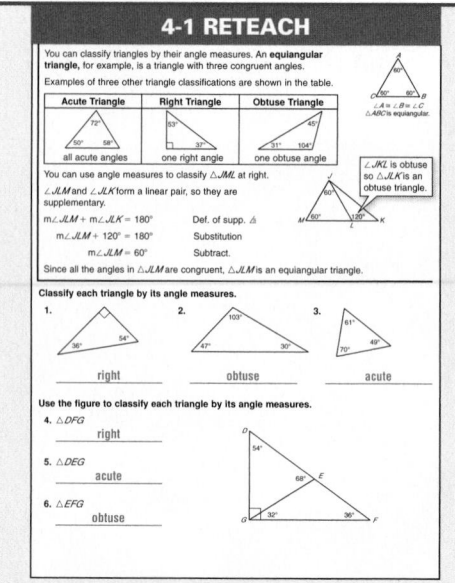

40. This problem will prepare you for the Multi-Step TAKS Prep on page 238.
Marc folded a rectangular sheet of paper, $ABCD$, in half along $\overline{EF}$. He folded the resulting square diagonally and then unfolded the paper to create the creases shown.
   a. Use the Pythagorean Theorem to find DE and CE. **$5\sqrt{2}$**
   b. What is the m$\angle DEC$? **90°**
   c. Classify $\triangle DEC$ by its side lengths and by its angle measures. **isosc. $\triangle$; rt. $\triangle$**

41. What is the side length of an equilateral triangle with a perimeter of $36\frac{2}{3}$ inches?

(A) $36\frac{2}{3}$ inches (C) $12\frac{1}{3}$ inches

(B) $18\frac{1}{3}$ inches (D) $12\frac{2}{9}$ inches

42. The vertices of $\triangle RST$ are $R(3, 2)$, $S(-2, 3)$, and $T(-2, 1)$. Which of these best describes $\triangle RST$?

(F) Isosceles (G) Scalene (H) Equilateral (J) Right

43. Which of the following is NOT a correct classification of $\triangle LMN$?

(A) Acute (C) Isosceles

(B) Equiangular (D) Right

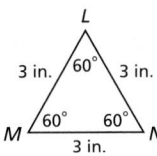

44. Gridded Response $\triangle ABC$ is isosceles, and $\overline{AB} \cong \overline{AC}$. $AB = \left(\frac{1}{2}x + \frac{1}{4}\right)$, and $BC = \left(\frac{5}{2} - x\right)$. What is the perimeter of $\triangle ABC$? **3**

CHALLENGE AND EXTEND

45. A triangle has vertices with coordinates $(0, 0)$, $(a, 0)$, and $(0, a)$, where $a \neq 0$. Classify the triangle in two different ways. Explain your answer.

46. Write a two-column proof.
Given: $\triangle ABC$ is equiangular.
  $EF \parallel AC$
Prove: $\triangle EFB$ is equiangular.

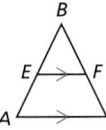

47. Two sides of an equilateral triangle measure $(y + 10)$ units and $(y^2 - 2)$ units. If the perimeter of the triangle is 21 units, what is the value of y? **−3**

48. Multi-Step The average length of the sides of $\triangle PQR$ is 24. How much longer then the average is the longest side? **8**

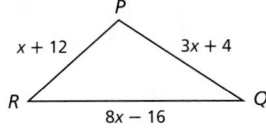

SPIRAL REVIEW

Name the parent function of each function. *(Previous course)*

49. $y = 5x^2 + 4$ $y = x^2$ **50.** $2y = 3x + 4$ $y = x$ **51.** $y = 2(x - 8)^2 + 6$ $y = x^2$

Determine if each biconditional is true. If false, give a counterexample. *(Lesson 2-4)*

52. Two lines are parallel if and only if they do not intersect.
F; skew lines do not intersect and are not parallel.
53. A triangle is equiangular if and only if it has three congruent angles. **T**

54. A number is a multiple of 20 if and only if the number ends in a 0.
F; possible answer: 30 has a 0 in the ones place, but 30 is not a multiple of 20.

Determine whether each line is parallel to, is perpendicular to, or coincides with $y = 4x$. *(Lesson 3-6)*

55. $y = 4x + 2$ $\parallel$ **56.** $4y = -x + 8$ $\perp$

57. $\frac{1}{2}y = 2x$ **coincides**   **58.** $-2y = \frac{1}{2}x$ $\perp$

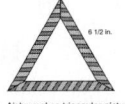
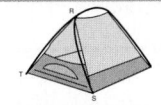
Answers

46. 1. $\triangle ABC$ is equiangular. (Given)

2. $\angle A \cong \angle B \cong \angle C$ (Def. of equiangular $\triangle$)

3. $\overline{EF} \parallel \overline{AC}$ (Given)

4. $\angle BEF \cong \angle A$, $\angle BFE \cong \angle C$, (Corr. $\angle$ Post.)

5. $\angle BEF \cong \angle B$, $\angle BFE \cong \angle B$, (Trans. Prop. of $\cong$)

6. $\angle BEF \cong \angle BFE$ ($\angle \cong$ to the same $\angle$ are $\cong$.)

7. $\triangle EFB$ is equiangular. (Def. of equiangular $\triangle$)

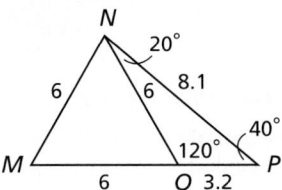
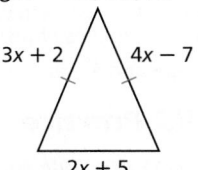

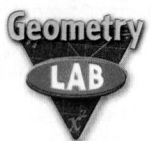

Geometry LAB — Organizer

Pacing:
Traditional $\frac{1}{2}$ day
Block $\frac{1}{4}$ day

Objective: Use patty paper to discover the relationship between the measures of the interior angles of a triangle.

Materials: patty paper

Online Edition

Countdown to TAKS Week 7

Teach

Discuss

Discuss the algebraic language used to describe the relationship between the angles of a triangle.

Alternative Approach

Have students use geometry software to draw a triangle, measure the interior angles, and drag the vertices. Lead them to the conjecture that the angle sum is always 180°.

Close

Key Concept

The sum of the measures of the angles of any triangle is 180°.

Assessment

Journal Have students draw different-shaped triangles, measure the angles, and find the sum. Then compare their results.

 Geometry TEKS

G.3 Geometric structure*
(D) use inductive reasoning …

G.4 Geometric structure*
(A) select an appropriate representation … to solve problems

G.5 Geometric patterns*
(A) use … geometric patterns to develop algebraic expressions …

G.9 Congruence and the geometry of size*
(B) formulate and test conjectures about the … attributes of polygons …

* Knowledge and Skills See p. 214.

⟲TAKS Practice

Grades 9–11	*Try This* Problems
Obj. 2	3
Obj. 6	3

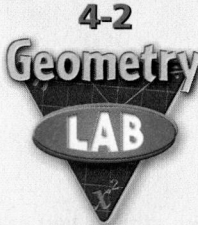
4-2 Geometry LAB

Develop the Triangle Sum Theorem

In this lab, you will use patty paper to discover a relationship between the measures of the interior angles of a triangle.

★ **TEKS G.9.B Congruence and the geometry of size:** formulate and test conjectures about the properties and attributes of polygons … based on explorations. Also G.3.D G.4.A, G.5.A

Activity

❶ Draw and label △ABC on a sheet of notebook paper.

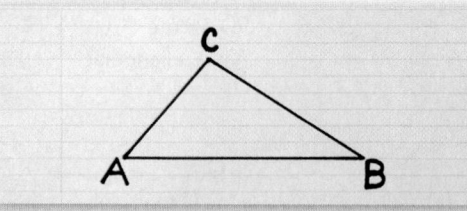

❷ On patty paper draw a line ℓ and label a point P on the line.

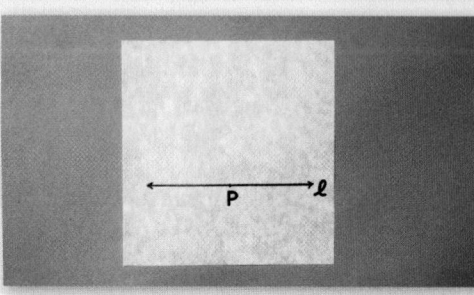

❸ Place the patty paper on top of the triangle you drew. Align the papers so that $\overline{AB}$ is on line ℓ and P and B coincide. Trace ∠B. Rotate the triangle and trace ∠C adjacent to ∠B. Rotate the triangle again and trace ∠A adjacent to ∠C. The diagram shows your final step.

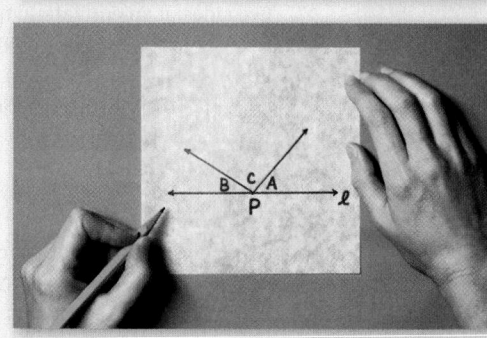

Try This

When placed together the 3 ∡ form a line.

1. What do you notice about the three angles of the triangle that you traced?

2. Repeat the activity two more times using two different triangles. Do you get the same results each time? **yes**

3. Write an equation describing the relationship among the measures of the angles of △ABC. $m\angle A + m\angle B + m\angle C = 180°$

4. Use inductive reasoning to write a conjecture about the sum of the measures of the angles of a triangle. **The sum of the measures of the ∡ of a △ is 180°.**

Teacher to Teacher

A pencil can be used to "swing" through the angles of a triangle. At the final move the pencil point will face the opposite direction—a rotation of 180°.

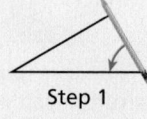
Step 1

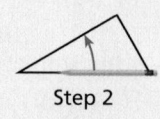
Step 2

Step 3   Step 4

Kathleen Kelly
Fairfield, ME

Angle Relationships in Triangles

TEKS G.2.B Geometric structure: make conjectures about angles, lines, polygons .... Also G.1.A

Objectives
Find the measures of interior and exterior angles of triangles.

Apply theorems about the interior and exterior angles of triangles.

Vocabulary
auxiliary line
corollary
interior
exterior
interior angle
exterior angle
remote interior angle

Who uses this?
Surveyors use triangles to make measurements and create boundaries. (See Example 1.)

Triangulation is a method used in surveying. Land is divided into adjacent triangles. By measuring the sides and angles of one triangle and applying properties of triangles, surveyors can gather information about adjacent triangles.

This engraving shows the county surveyor and commissioners laying out the town of Baltimore in 1730.

Know it! *Note*

Theorem 4-2-1 [**Triangle Sum Theorem**]

The sum of the angle measures of a triangle is 180°.

$m\angle A + m\angle B + m\angle C = 180°$

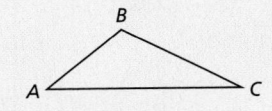

The proof of the Triangle Sum Theorem uses an *auxiliary line*. An **auxiliary line** is a line that is added to a figure to aid in a proof.

PROOF

Triangle Sum Theorem

Given: $\triangle ABC$
Prove: $m\angle 1 + m\angle 2 + m\angle 3 = 180°$

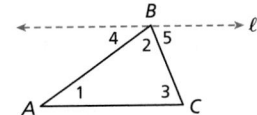

Proof:

Caution!
Whenever you draw an auxiliary line, you must be able to justify its existence. Give this as the reason: Through any two points there is exactly one line.

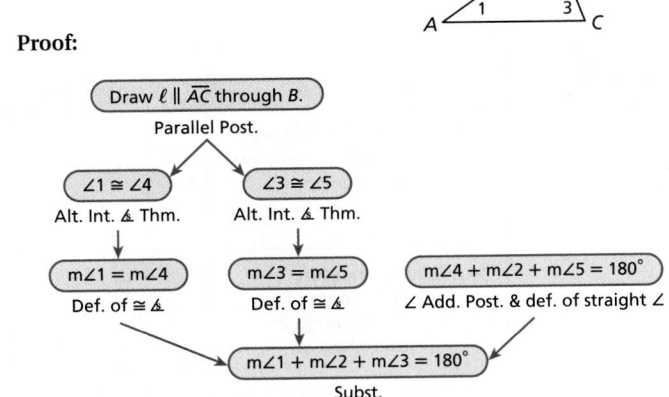

Draw $\ell \parallel \overline{AC}$ through B.
Parallel Post.

$\angle 1 \cong \angle 4$
Alt. Int. ⦟ Thm.

$\angle 3 \cong \angle 5$
Alt. Int. ⦟ Thm.

$m\angle 1 = m\angle 4$
Def. of ≅ ⦟

$m\angle 3 = m\angle 5$
Def. of ≅ ⦟

$m\angle 4 + m\angle 2 + m\angle 5 = 180°$
∠ Add. Post. & def. of straight ∠

$m\angle 1 + m\angle 2 + m\angle 3 = 180°$
Subst.

---

1 Introduce

EXPLORATION

4-2 Angle Relationships in Triangles

Use geometry software for this Exploration.

1. Construct a triangle.
2. Label the vertices *A*, *B*, and *C*.
3. Use the Measure menu to measure the three angles.
4. Use the Calculate tool to find the sum of the angle measures.

m∠CAB = 51.55°
m∠ABC = 41.17°
m∠BCA = 87.28°

m∠CAB = 51.55°
m∠ABC = 41.17°
m∠BCA = 87.28°

m∠CAB + m∠ABC + m∠BCA = 180.00°

5. Drag the vertices and sides of the triangle to change its shape. What do you notice about the sum of the angle measures?

THINK AND DISCUSS

Motivate

Have students trace a circular object to create a protractor-like shape. Then have them label their drawings with estimated angle measures every ten degrees. Have students use the protractor they created to measure and find the sum of the interior angles of a triangle. Finally have them draw an exterior angle of a triangle and measure it. Students should check their estimates with an actual protractor.

Explorations and answers are provided in the *Explorations* binder.

Pacing: Traditional 1 day
Block $\frac{1}{2}$ day

Objectives: Find the measures of interior and exterior angles of triangles.

Apply theorems about the interior and exterior angles of triangles.

 Technology Lab
In *Texas Lab Manual*

 Online Edition
PREMIER Tutorial Videos

 Countdown to TAKS Week 7

Power Presentations
with PowerPoint®

Warm Up

1. Find the measure of exterior ∠*DBA* of △*BCD*, if m∠*DBC* = 30°, m∠*C* = 70°, and m∠*D* = 80°.   150°

2. What is the complement of an angle with measure 17°?   73°

3. How many lines can be drawn through *N* parallel to $\overline{MP}$? Why?   1; Parallel Post.

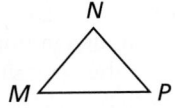

Also available on transparency

Math Humor

Q: How many feet are in a yard?

A: It depends on how many people are in the yard!

Geometry TEKS

G.1 Geometric structure*
(A) develop an awareness of the structure of a mathematical system, connecting definitions, postulates, logical reasoning, and theorems

G.2 Geometric structure*
(B) make conjectures about angles, lines, polygons ... and determine validity of the conjectures, choosing from a variety of approaches ...

* **Knowledge and Skills** See p. 214.

Example 1

After an accident, the positions of cars are measured by law enforcement to investigate the collision. Use the diagram drawn from the information collected to find the indicated angle measures.

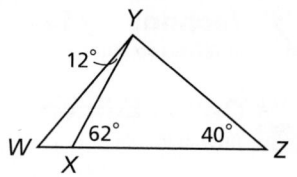

A. m∠XYZ   78°

B. m∠YWZ   50°

Also available on transparency

INTERVENTION ◄═►
Questioning Strategies

• What properties do you need to know about triangles when using the triangulation method to calculate the measures of angles?

Teaching Tip   **Language Arts** The word *auxiliary* means "giving assistance." Emphasize that an *auxiliary line* drawn from a vertex of a triangle to the opposite side may *assist* with a proof.

EXAMPLE 1   *Surveying Application*

The map of France commonly used in the 1600s was significantly revised as a result of a triangulation land survey. The diagram shows part of the survey map. Use the diagram to find the indicated angle measures.

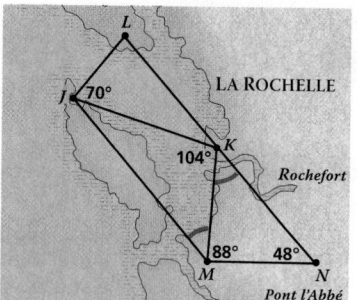

 Algebra

A   m∠NKM

m∠KMN + m∠MNK + m∠NKM = 180°	△ Sum Thm.
88 + 48 + m∠NKM = 180	Substitute 88 for m∠KMN and 48 for m∠MNK.
136 + m∠NKM = 180	Simplify.
m∠NKM = 44°	Subtract 136 from both sides.

B   m∠JLK

Step 1 Find m∠JKL.

m∠NKM + m∠MKJ + m∠JKL = 180°	Lin. Pair Thm. & ∠ Add. Post.
44 + 104 + m∠JKL = 180	Substitute 44 for m∠NKM and 104 for m∠MKJ.
148 + m∠JKL = 180	Simplify.
m∠JKL = 32°	Subtract 148 from both sides.

Step 2 Use substitution and then solve for m∠JLK.

m∠JLK + m∠JKL + m∠KJL = 180°	△ Sum Thm.
m∠JLK + 32 + 70 = 180	Substitute 32 for m∠JKL and 70 for m∠KJL.
m∠JLK + 102 = 180	Simplify.
m∠JLK = 78°	Subtract 102 from both sides.

 **1.** Use the diagram to find m∠MJK. 32°

A **corollary** is a theorem whose proof follows directly from another theorem. Here are two corollaries to the Triangle Sum Theorem.

 **Corollaries**

	COROLLARY	HYPOTHESIS	CONCLUSION
4-2-2	The acute angles of a right triangle are complementary.		∠D and ∠E are complementary. m∠D + m∠E = 90°
4-2-3	The measure of each angle of an equiangular triangle is 60°.		m∠A = m∠B = m∠C = 60°

You will prove Corollaries 4-2-2 and 4-2-3 in Exercises 24 and 25.

---

2 Teach

Guided Instruction

Review the method of constructing a parallel line before proving the Triangle Sum Theorem. Explain why an auxiliary line was added to the figure in the proof. Compare the two corollaries to the Triangle Sum Theorem. Review the meanings of interior, exterior, and remote before introducing the Exterior Angle Theorem. Show how the Third Angles Theorem is related to the Triangle Sum Theorem.

 Reaching All Learners
Through Modeling

Have students cut a triangle out of a sheet of paper and tear off all three corners. Have them place these next to each other to form a line. Then ask students to explain how this models the Triangle Sum Theorem.

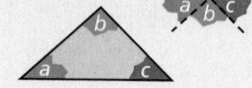

EXAMPLE  **Finding Angle Measures in Right Triangles**

x² Algebra

One of the acute angles in a right triangle measures 22.9°. What is the measure of the other acute angle?

Let the acute angles be ∠M and ∠N, with m∠M = 22.9°.

m∠M + m∠N = 90	*Acute ∠ of rt. △ are comp.*
22.9 + m∠N = 90	*Substitute 22.9 for m∠M.*
m∠N = 67.1°	*Subtract 22.9 from both sides.*

CHECK IT OUT! The measure of one of the acute angles in a right triangle is given. What is the measure of the other acute angle?

2a. 63.7° **26.3°** **2b.** $x°$ $(90 − x)°$ **2c.** $48\frac{2}{5}°$ $41\frac{3}{5}°$

The **interior** is the set of all points inside the figure. The **exterior** is the set of all points outside the figure. An **interior angle** is formed by two sides of a triangle. An **exterior angle** is formed by one side of the triangle and the extension of an adjacent side. Each exterior angle has two *remote interior angles*. A **remote interior angle** is an interior angle that is not adjacent to the exterior angle.

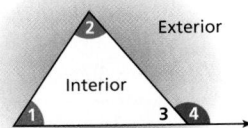

∠4 is an exterior angle.
Its remote interior
angles are ∠1 and ∠2.

Theorem 4-2-4 **Exterior Angle Theorem**

The measure of an exterior angle of a triangle is equal to the sum of the measures of its remote interior angles.

$$m∠4 = m∠1 + m∠2$$

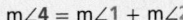

You will prove Theorem 4-2-4 in Exercise 28.

EXAMPLE  **Applying the Exterior Angle Theorem**

x² Algebra

Find m∠J.

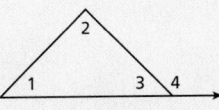

m∠J + m∠H = m∠FGH	*Ext. ∠ Thm.*
5x + 17 + 6x − 1 = 126	*Substitute 5x + 17 for m∠J, 6x − 1 for m∠H, and 126 for m∠FGH.*
11x + 16 = 126	*Simplify.*
11x = 110	*Subtract 16 from both sides.*
x = 10	*Divide both sides by 11.*
m∠J = 5x + 17 = 5(10) + 17 = 67°	

CHECK IT OUT! **3.** Find m∠ACD. **141°**

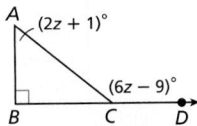

4-2 Angle Relationships in Triangles **225**

COMMON ERROR ALERT

For **Check It Out Problem 2b,** students may write $(x − 90)°$. Show them that if the given angle has a measure of 10° for example, the remaining acute angle would have measure $(90 − 10)°$, not $(10 − 90)°$.

Power Presentations with PowerPoint®

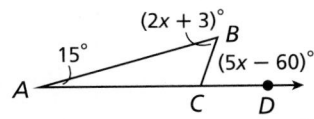

Additional Examples

Example

One of the acute angles in a right triangle measures $2x°$. What is the measure of the other acute angle? $(90 − 2x)°$

Example 3

Find m∠B. 55°

(2x + 3)° *B*
15° *(5x − 60)°*
A *C* *D*

Also available on transparency

INTERVENTION
Questioning Strategies

EXAMPLE 2

• What corollary to the Triangle Sum Theorem is used to find the acute angles of a right triangle? Does this apply to every right triangle?

EXAMPLE 3

• What is the relationship between the angle formed by extending one of the sides of a triangle and each interior angle?

Teaching Tip

Reading Math Remind students of the meanings of *interior, exterior,* and *remote.* An *interior* angle is *inside* the figure, an *exterior* angle is *outside* the figure, and a *remote interior angle* is *interior and away* from the exterior angle. Relate the idea of a remote interior angle to a television remote control that sends a signal across the room and away from you.

ENGLISH LANGUAGE LEARNERS

Lesson 4-2 **225**

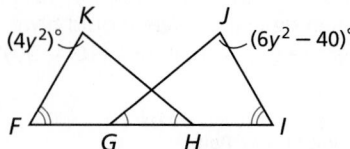
Example 4

Find m∠K and m∠J.   80°, 80°

K   J
$(4y^2)°$ $(6y^2 - 40)°$
F   G   H   I

Also available on transparency

INTERVENTION ◄═►
Questioning Strategies

EXAMPLE 4

• Why is it not necessary to solve for y to find the missing measures of the angles?

Theorem 4-2-5   **Third Angles Theorem**

THEOREM	HYPOTHESIS	CONCLUSION
If two angles of one triangle are congruent to two angles of another triangle, then the third pair of angles are congruent.	L R N S M T	∠N ≅ ∠T

You will prove Theorem 4-2-5 in Exercise 27.

EXAMPLE 4   **Applying the Third Angles Theorem**

 **Algebra**

Find m∠C and m∠F.

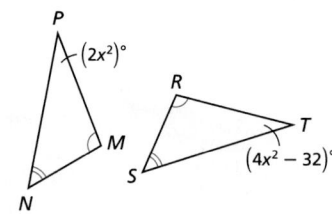

∠C ≅ ∠F	Third ∠ Thm.
m∠C = m∠F	Def. of ≅ ∠.
$y^2 = 3y^2 - 72$	Substitute y^2 for m∠C and $3y^2 - 72$ for m∠F.
$-2y^2 = -72$	Subtract $3y^2$ from both sides.
$y^2 = 36$	Divide both sides by −2.

So m∠C = 36°.
Since m∠F = m∠C, m∠F = 36°.

 **CHECK IT OUT!**   4. Find m∠P and m∠T.
    32°; 32°

P
$(2x^2)°$
M   R   T
S $(4x^2 - 32)°$
N

THINK AND DISCUSS

1. Use the Triangle Sum Theorem to explain why the supplement of one of the angles of a triangle equals in measure the sum of the other two angles of the triangle. Support your answer with a sketch.

2. Sketch a triangle and draw all of its exterior angles. How many exterior angles are there at each vertex of the triangle? How many total exterior angles does the triangle have?

3. **GET ORGANIZED** Copy and complete the graphic organizer. In each box, write each theorem in words and then draw a diagram to represent it.

Theorem	Words	Diagram
Triangle Sum Theorem		
Exterior Angle Theorem		
Third Angles Theorem		

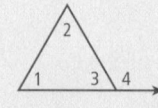

3 Close

Summarize

Review the Triangle Sum Theorem, the Exterior Angle Theorem, and the Third Angles Theorem. Have several large triangles as models for each theorem. Highlight the specific math concept on each triangle with different colors. Students should then elaborate and discuss each theorem.

ONGOING ASSESSMENT

and INTERVENTION ◄═►

Diagnose Before the Lesson
4-2 Warm Up, TE p. 223

Monitor During the Lesson
Check It Out! Exercises, SE pp. 224–226
Questioning Strategies, TE pp. 224–226

Assess After the Lesson
4-2 Lesson Quiz, TE p. 230
Alternative Assessment, TE p. 230

Answers to Think and Discuss

1. Since ∠3 and ∠4 are supp. ∠, m∠3 + m∠4 = 180° by def. ∠1 + ∠2 + ∠3 = 180° by the △ Sum Thm. By the Trans. Prop. of =, m∠3 + m∠4 = m∠1 + m∠2 + m∠3. Subtract m∠3 from both sides. Then m∠4 = m∠1 + m∠2.

2
1   3   4

2. 2; 6

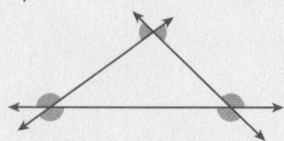

3. See p. A4.

go.hrw.com/Geo/TX
Homework Help Online
KEYWORD: MG7 4-2
Parent Resources Online
KEYWORD: MG7 Parent

GUIDED PRACTICE

Vocabulary Apply the vocabulary from this lesson to answer each question.

1. To remember the meaning of *remote interior angle*, think of a television remote control. What is another way to remember the term *remote*? **Possible answer: Think "out of the way"**

2. An *exterior angle* is drawn at vertex E of △DEF. What are its *remote interior angles*? **∠D; ∠F**

3. What do you call segments, rays, or lines that are added to a given diagram? **auxiliary lines**

SEE EXAMPLE **1**
p. 224

Astronomy Use the following information for Exercises 4 and 5.

An *asterism* is a group of stars that is easier to recognize than a constellation. One popular asterism is the Summer Triangle, which is composed of the stars Deneb, Altair, and Vega.

4. What is the value of y? **17**

5. What is the measure of each angle in the Summer Triangle? **36°; 80°; 64°**

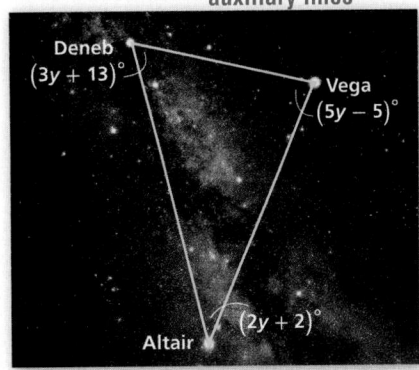

SEE EXAMPLE **2**
p. 225

The measure of one of the acute angles in a right triangle is given. What is the measure of the other acute angle?

6. 20.8° **69.2°**   7. $y°$ **$(90 - y)°$**   8. $24\frac{2}{3}°$ **$65\frac{1}{3}°$**

SEE EXAMPLE **3**
p. 225

Find each angle measure.

9. m∠M **28°**

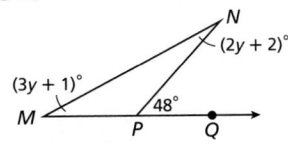

10. m∠L **41°**

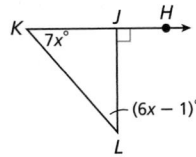

11. In △ABC, m∠A = 65°, and the measure of an exterior angle at C is 117°. Find m∠B and the m∠BCA. **52°; 63°**

SEE EXAMPLE **4**
p. 226

12. m∠C and m∠F **100°; 100°**

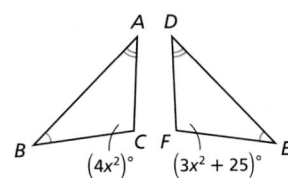

13. m∠S and m∠U **89°; 89°**

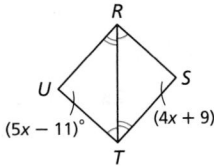

14. For △ABC and △XYZ, m∠A = m∠X and m∠B = m∠Y. Find the measures of ∠C and ∠Z if m∠C = 4x + 7 and m∠Z = 3(x + 5). **39°**

Algebra In Exercises 21 and 22, remind students that they do not have to find the value of y or x, only y^2 and x^2.

Answers

25. Possible answer:
1. $\triangle ABC$ is equiangular. (Given)
2. $m\angle A = m\angle B = m\angle C$ (Def. of equiangular)
3. $m\angle A + m\angle B + m\angle C = 180°$ ($\triangle$ Sum Thm.)
4. $m\angle A + m\angle A + m\angle A = 180°$
   $m\angle B + m\angle B + m\angle B = 180°$
   $m\angle C + m\angle C + m\angle C = 180°$
   (Subst. Prop.)
5. $3m\angle A = 180°$, $3m\angle B = 180°$, $3m\angle C = 180°$ (Simplify)
6. $m\angle A = 60°$, $m\angle B = 60°$, $m\angle C = 60°$ (Div. Prop. of =)

27.

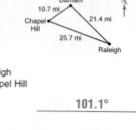

1. $\triangle ABC$, $\triangle DEF$, $\angle A \cong \angle D$, $\angle B \cong \angle E$ (Given)
2. $m\angle A + m\angle B + m\angle C = 180°$ ($\triangle$ Sum Thm.)
3. $m\angle C = 180° - m\angle A - m\angle B$ (Subtr. Prop. of =)
4. $m\angle D + m\angle E + m\angle F = 180°$ ($\triangle$ Sum Thm.)
5. $m\angle F = 180° - m\angle D - m\angle E$ (Subtr. Prop. of =)
6. $m\angle A = m\angle D$, $m\angle B = m\angle E$, (Def. of $\cong \triangle$)
7. $m\angle F = 180° - m\angle A - m\angle B$ (Subst.)
8. $m\angle F = m\angle C$ (Trans. Prop. of =)
9. $\angle F \cong \angle C$ (Def. of $\cong \triangle$)

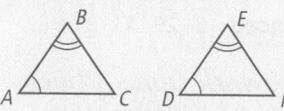

Independent Practice

For Exercises	See Example
15	1
16–18	2
19–20	3
21–22	4

TEKS ⬤ TAKS

Skills Practice p. S10
Application Practice p. S31

PRACTICE AND PROBLEM SOLVING

15. **Navigation** A sailor on ship A measures the angle between ship B and the pier and finds that it is 39°. A sailor on ship B measures the angle between ship A and the pier and finds that it is 57°. What is the measure of the angle between ships A and B? **84°**

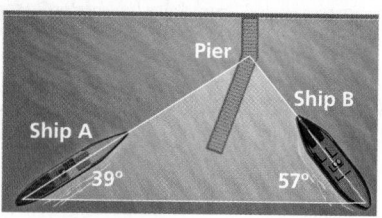

The measure of one of the acute angles in a right triangle is given. What is the measure of the other acute angle?

16. $76\frac{1}{4}°$ $\mathbf{13\frac{3}{4}°}$

17. $2x°$ $\mathbf{(90 - 2x)°}$

18. $56.8°$ **33.2°**

Find each angle measure.

19. $m\angle XYZ$ **162°**

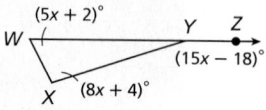

20. $m\angle C$ **61°**

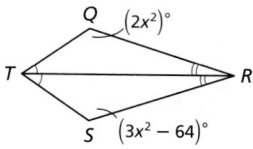

21. $m\angle N$ and $m\angle P$ **48°; 48°**

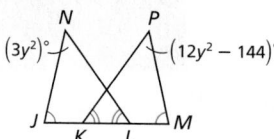

22. $m\angle Q$ and $m\angle S$ **128°; 128°**

23. **Multi-Step** The measures of the angles of a triangle are in the ratio $1:4:7$. What are the measures of the angles? (*Hint:* Let x, $4x$, and $7x$ represent the angle measures.) **15°; 60°; 105°**

24. Complete the proof of Corollary 4-2-2.
    Given: $\triangle DEF$ with right $\angle F$
    Prove: $\angle D$ and $\angle E$ are complementary.
    Proof:

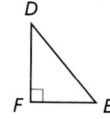

Statements	Reasons
1. $\triangle DEF$ with rt. $\angle F$	1. a. ?
2. b. ?	2. Def. of rt. $\angle$
3. $m\angle D + m\angle E + m\angle F = 180°$	3. c. ?
4. $m\angle D + m\angle E + 90° = 180°$	4. d. ?
5. e. ?	5. Subtr. Prop.
6. $\angle D$ and $\angle E$ are comp.	6. f. ?

a. Given
b. $m\angle F = 90°$
c. $\triangle$ Sum Thm.
d. Subst.
e. $m\angle D + m\angle E = 90°$
f. Def. of comp. $\triangle$

25. Prove Corollary 4-2-3 using two different methods of proof.
    Given: $\triangle ABC$ is equiangular.
    Prove: $m\angle A = m\angle B = m\angle C = 60°$

26. **Multi-Step** The measure of one acute angle in a right triangle is $1\frac{1}{4}$ times the measure of the other acute angle. What is the measure of the larger acute angle? **50°**

27. Write a two-column proof of the Third Angles Theorem.

228 Chapter 4 Triangle Congruence

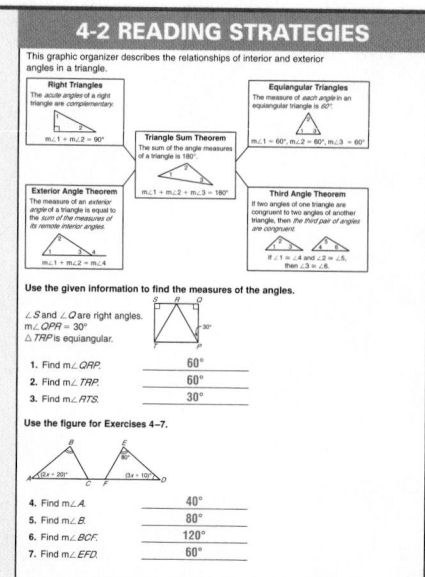
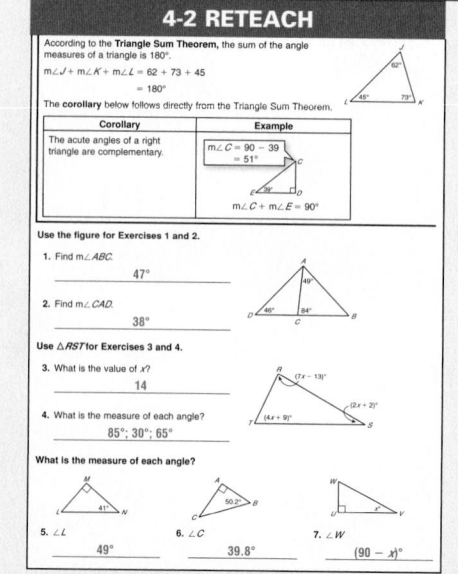

28. Prove the Exterior Angle Theorem.

  Given: $\triangle ABC$ with exterior angle $\angle ACD$
  Prove: $m\angle ACD = m\angle A + m\angle B$
  (*Hint:* $\angle BCA$ and $\angle DCA$ form a linear pair.)

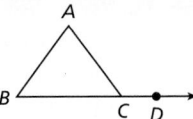

Find each angle measure.

29. $\angle UXW$ 36°   **30.** $\angle UWY$ 48°

31. $\angle WZX$ 48°   **32.** $\angle XYZ$ 42°

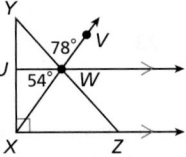

33. Critical Thinking What is the measure of any exterior angle of an equiangular triangle? What is the sum of the exterior angle measures? 120°; 360°

34. Find $m\angle SRQ$, given that $\angle P \cong \angle U$, $\angle Q \cong \angle T$, and $m\angle RST = 37.5°$. 37.5°

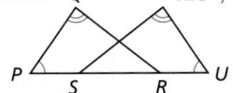

35. Multi-Step In a right triangle, one acute angle measure is 4 times the other acute angle measure. What is the measure of the smaller angle? 18°

36. Aviation To study the forces of lift and drag, the Wright brothers built a glider, attached two ropes to it, and flew it like a kite. They modeled the two wind forces as the legs of a right triangle.

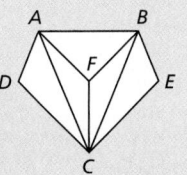

36a. hyp.
b. $x° + y° + 90° = 180°$
c. $x° + y° = 90°$; x and y are comp. $\angle$s
d. $z° = x° + 90°$
e. $53°$; $127°$

  a. What part of a right triangle is formed by each rope?

  b. Use the Triangle Sum Theorem to write an equation relating the angle measures in the right triangle.

  c. Simplify the equation from part **b.** What is the relationship between x and y?

  d. Use the Exterior Angle Theorem to write an expression for z in terms of x.

  e. If $x = 37°$, use your results from parts **c** and **d** to find y and z.

39. Check students' drawings. The measures of the ext. $\angle$s will be the sum of the pairs of remote int. $\angle$s: 155°, 65°, and 140°.

37. Estimation Draw a triangle and two exterior angles at each vertex. Estimate the measure of each angle. How are the exterior angles at each vertex related? Explain.

38. Given: $\overline{AB} \perp \overline{BD}$, $\overline{BD} \perp \overline{DC}$, $\angle A \cong \angle C$
  Prove: $\overline{AD} \parallel \overline{CB}$

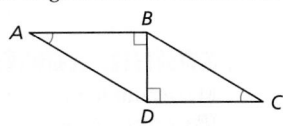

39. Write About It A triangle has angle measures of 115°, 40°, and 25°. Explain how to find the measures of the triangle's exterior angles. Support your answer with a sketch.

40. This problem will prepare you for the Multi-Step TAKS Prep on page 238.

  One of the steps in making an origami crane involves folding a square sheet of paper into the shape shown.

  a. $\angle DCE$ is a right angle. $\overline{FC}$ bisects $\angle DCE$, and $\overline{BC}$ bisects $\angle FCE$. Find $m\angle FCB$. 22.5°

  b. Use the Triangle Sum Theorem to find $m\angle CBE$. 67.5°

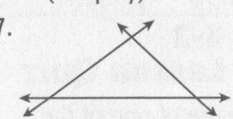

4-2 Angle Relationships in Triangles **229**

MULTI-STEP TAKS PREP **Exercise 40** involves folding a sheet of paper into a given shape. This exercise prepares students for the Multi-Step TAKS Prep on page 238.

Answers

28. 1. $\triangle ABC$ with ext. $\angle ACD$ (Given)
  2. $m\angle A + m\angle B + m\angle ACB = 180°$ ($\triangle$ Sum Thm.)
  3. $m\angle ACB + m\angle ACD = 180°$ (Lin. Pair Thm.)
  4. $m\angle ACD = 180° - m\angle ACB$ (Subtr. Prop. of $=$)
  5. $m\angle ACD = (m\angle A + m\angle B + m\angle ACB) - m\angle ACB$ (Subst.)
  6. $m\angle ACD = m\angle A + m\angle B$ (Simplify)

37.

The ext. $\angle$s at the same vertex of a $\triangle$ are vert. $\angle$s. Since vert. $\angle$s are $\cong$, the 2 ext. $\angle$s have the same measure.

38. 1. $\overline{AB} \perp \overline{BD}$, $\overline{BD} \perp \overline{DC}$, $\angle A \cong \angle C$ (Given)
  2. $\angle ABD$ and $\angle CDB$ are rt. $\angle$s. (Def. of $\perp$ lines)
  3. $m\angle ABD = m\angle CDB$ (Def. of rt. $\angle$)
  4. $\angle ABD \cong \angle CDB$ (Rt. $\angle \cong$ Thm.)
  5. $\angle ADB \cong \angle CBD$ (Third $\angle$ Thm.)
  6. $\overline{AD} \parallel \overline{CB}$ (Conv. of Alt. Int. $\angle$ Thm.)

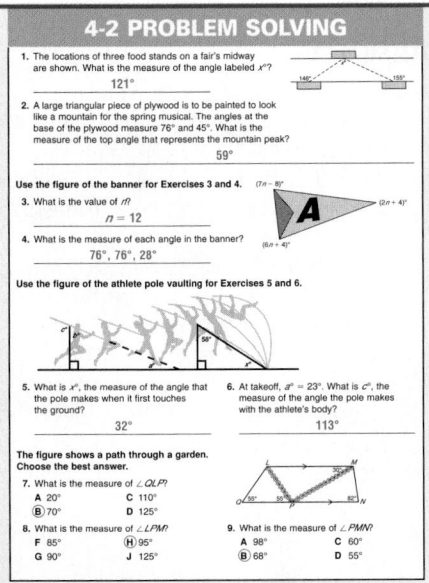

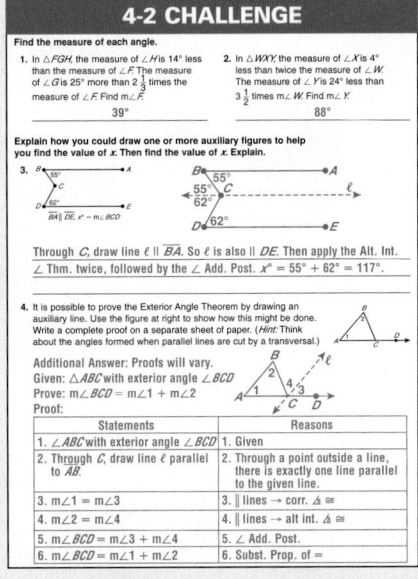

 Journal

Have students describe how they remember which angles are remote interior angles and which ones are exterior angles.

ALTERNATIVE ASSESSMENT

Have small groups of students compare answers to statements that are always, sometimes, or never true. For example, the supplement of one of the angles of a triangle is equal to the sum of the other two angles of the triangle. Then have the students write a statement to justify their answers. Encourage students to draw diagrams to support their answers.

Power Presentations
with PowerPoint®

 **4-2 Lesson Quiz**

1. The measure of one of the acute angles in a right triangle is $56\frac{2}{3}°$. What is the measure of the other acute angle?
$33\frac{1}{3}°$

2. Find m∠ABD.   124°

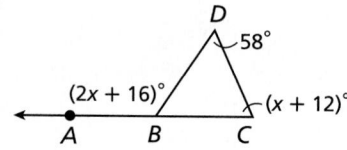

3. Find m∠N and m∠P.   75°, 75°

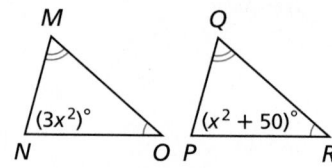

4. The diagram is a map showing John's house, Kay's house, and the grocery store. What is the angle the two houses make with the store?   30°

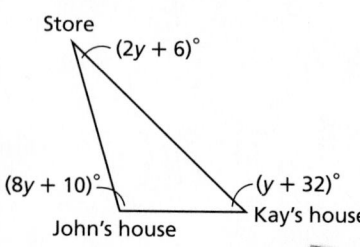

Also available on transparency

 **TEST PREP**

41. What is the value of x?
   Ⓐ 19   Ⓒ 57
   Ⓑ 52   Ⓓ 71

42. Find the value of s.
   Ⓕ 23   Ⓗ 34
   Ⓖ 28   Ⓙ 56

43. ∠A and ∠B are the remote interior angles of ∠BCD in △ABC. Which of these equations must be true?
   Ⓐ m∠A − 180° = m∠B
   Ⓑ m∠A = 90° − m∠B
   Ⓒ m∠BCD = m∠BCA − m∠A
   Ⓓ m∠B = m∠BCD − m∠A

44. **Extended Response** The measures of the angles in a triangle are in the ratio 2:3:4. Describe how to use algebra to find the measures of these angles. Then find the measure of each angle and classify the triangle.

CHALLENGE AND EXTEND

45. An exterior angle of a triangle measures 117°. Its remote interior angles measure $(2y^2 + 7)°$ and $(61 − y^2)°$. Find the value of y. **7 or −7**

46. A rt. △ is formed. The 2 same-side int. ∡ are supp., so the 2 ∡ formed by their bisectors must be comp. That means the remaining ∠ of the △ must measure 90°.

46. Two parallel lines are intersected by a transversal. What type of triangle is formed by the intersection of the angle bisectors of two same-side interior angles? Explain. (*Hint:* Use geometry software or construct a diagram of the angle bisectors of two same-side interior angles.)

47. **Critical Thinking** Explain why an exterior angle of a triangle cannot be congruent to a remote interior angle.

48. **Probability** The measure of each angle in a triangle is a multiple of 30°. What is the probability that the triangle has at least two congruent angles? $\frac{2}{3}$

49. In △ABC, m∠B is 5° less than $1\frac{1}{2}$ times m∠A. m∠C is 5° less than $2\frac{1}{2}$ times m∠A. What is m∠A in degrees? **38°**

SPIRAL REVIEW

Make a table to show the value of each function when x is −2, 0, 1, and 4.
(*Previous course*)

50. $f(x) = 3x − 4$

51. $f(x) = x^2 + 1$

52. $f(x) = (x − 3)^2 + 5$

53. Find the length of $\overline{NQ}$. Name the theorem or postulate that justifies your answer. (*Lesson 2-7*) **6 in.; Seg. Add. Post.**

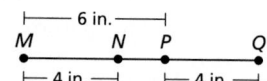

Classify each triangle by its side lengths. (*Lesson 4-1*)

54. △ACD **isosc.**   55. △BCD **scalene**   56. △ABD **scalene**

57. **What if...?** If CA = 8, What is the effect on the classification of △ACD?
   △ACD is equil.

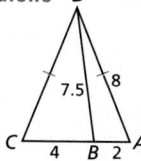

Answers

44. Let 2x, 3x, and 4x represent the ∠ measures. The sum of the ∠ measures of a △ is 180°, so 2x + 3x + 4x = 180°. Solving the eqn. for the value of x, yields x = 20. Find each measure by substituting 20 for x in each expression. 2x = 2(20) = 40; 3x = 3(20) = 60; 4x = 4(20) = 80. Since all of the ∡ measure less than 90°, they are acute ∡ by def. Thus the △ is acute.

47. Since an ext. ∠ is = to a sum of 2 remote int. ∡, it must be greater than either ∠. Therefore it cannot be ≅ to a remote int. ∠.

50–52. See p. A15.

Congruent Triangles

⭐ TEKS G.10.B Congruence and the geometry of size: justify and apply triangle congruence relationships. Also G.2.B

Objectives
Use properties of congruent triangles.

Prove triangles congruent by using the definition of congruence.

Vocabulary
corresponding angles
corresponding sides
congruent polygons

Who uses this?
Machinists used triangles to construct a model of the International Space Station's support structure.

Geometric figures are congruent if they are the same size and shape. **Corresponding angles** and **corresponding sides** are in the same position in polygons with an equal number of sides. Two polygons are **congruent polygons** if and only if their corresponding angles and sides are congruent. Thus triangles that are the same size and shape are congruent.

Know it!
Note

Helpful Hint

Two vertices that are the endpoints of a side are called consecutive vertices. For example, *P* and *Q* are consecutive vertices.

Properties of Congruent Polygons

DIAGRAM	CORRESPONDING ANGLES	CORRESPONDING SIDES
$\triangle ABC \cong \triangle DEF$	$\angle A \cong \angle D$ $\angle B \cong \angle E$ $\angle C \cong \angle F$	$\overline{AB} \cong \overline{DE}$ $\overline{BC} \cong \overline{EF}$ $\overline{AC} \cong \overline{DF}$
polygon $PQRS \cong$ polygon $WXYZ$	$\angle P \cong \angle W$ $\angle Q \cong \angle X$ $\angle R \cong \angle Y$ $\angle S \cong \angle Z$	$\overline{PQ} \cong \overline{WX}$ $\overline{QR} \cong \overline{XY}$ $\overline{RS} \cong \overline{YZ}$ $\overline{PS} \cong \overline{WZ}$

To name a polygon, write the vertices in consecutive order. For example, you can name polygon *PQRS* as *QRSP* or *SRQP*, but **not** as *PRQS*. In a congruence statement, the order of the vertices indicates the corresponding parts.

EXAMPLE 1

Naming Congruent Corresponding Parts

$\triangle RST$ and $\triangle XYZ$ represent the triangles of the space station's support structure. If $\triangle RST \cong \triangle XYZ$, identify all pairs of congruent corresponding parts.

Angles: $\angle R \cong \angle X$, $\angle S \cong \angle Y$, $\angle T \cong \angle Z$
Sides: $\overline{RS} \cong \overline{XY}$, $\overline{ST} \cong \overline{YZ}$, $\overline{RT} \cong \overline{XZ}$

$\angle L \cong \angle E$, $\angle M \cong \angle F$,
$\angle N \cong \angle G$, $\angle P \cong \angle H$,
$\overline{LM} \cong \overline{EF}$, $\overline{MN} \cong \overline{FG}$,
$\overline{NP} \cong \overline{GH}$, $\overline{LP} \cong \overline{EH}$

 CHECK IT OUT!
1. If polygon *LMNP* ≅ polygon *EFGH*, identify all pairs of corresponding congruent parts.

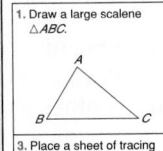

1 Introduce

Motivate

Show students a quilt or other pattern and ask them to identify all the triangles that look identical in size and shape. Explain that they will learn the properties used to prove certain triangles are identical, or congruent. Encourage students to think of examples where congruent triangles may be used or seen in the real world, such as in furniture, buildings, art, and floor tiles.

Explorations and answers are provided in the *Explorations* binder.

4-3 **Organizer**

Pacing: Traditional 1 day
Block $\frac{1}{2}$ day

Objectives: Use properties of congruent triangles.

Prove triangles congruent by using the definition of congruence.

Online Edition
Tutorial Videos, Interactivity

Countdown to TAKS Week 7

Power Presentations
with PowerPoint®

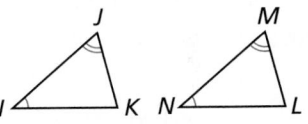

Warm Up

1. Name all sides and angles of $\triangle FGH$. $\overline{FG}, \overline{GH}, \overline{FH}, \angle F, \angle G, \angle H$

2. What is true about $\angle K$ and $\angle L$? Why? ≅; Third ∡ Thm.

3. What does it mean for two segments to be congruent? They have the same length.

Also available on transparency

Math Humor

Q: What quantity is represented by three congruent dirty trees?

A: 99. dirty tree + dirty tree + dirty tree

⭐ Geometry TEKS

G.2 Geometric structure*
(B) make conjectures about angles, lines, polygons ... and determine validity of the conjectures, choosing from a variety of approaches ...

G.10 Congruence and the geometry of size*
(B) justify and apply triangle congruence relationships
* **Knowledge and Skills** See p. 214.

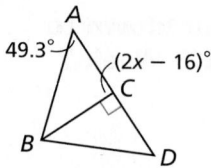
Additional Examples

Example 1

Given: △PQR ≅ △STW. Identify all pairs of congruent corresponding parts. ∠P ≅ ∠S, ∠Q ≅ ∠T, ∠R ≅ ∠W, $\overline{PQ}$ ≅ $\overline{ST}$, $\overline{PR}$ ≅ $\overline{SW}$, $\overline{QR}$ ≅ $\overline{TW}$

Example 2

Given: △ABC ≅ △DBC

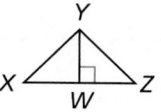

A. Find the value of x.   53

B. Find m∠DBC.   40.7°

Example 3

Given: ∠YWX and ∠YWZ are right angles. $\overline{YW}$ bisects ∠XYZ. W is the midpoint of $\overline{XZ}$. $\overline{XY}$ ≅ $\overline{YZ}$.

Prove: △XYW ≅ △ZYW

1. ∠YWX and ∠YWZ are rt. ∠. (Given)
2. ∠YWX ≅ ∠YWZ (Rt. ∠ ≅ Thm.)
3. $\overline{YW}$ bisects ∠XYZ. (Given)
4. ∠XYW ≅ ∠ZYW (Def. of ∠ bisector)
5. W is mdpt. of $\overline{XZ}$. (Given)
6. $\overline{XW}$ ≅ $\overline{ZW}$ (Def. of mdpt.)
7. $\overline{YW}$ ≅ $\overline{YW}$ (Reflex. Prop. of ≅)
8. ∠X ≅ ∠Z (Third ∠ Thm.)
9. $\overline{XY}$ ≅ $\overline{YZ}$ (Given)
10. △XYW ≅ △ZYW (Def. of ≅ △)

Also available on transparency

INTERVENTION ◀━▶
Questioning Strategies

EXAMPLE 1

• How does a triangle congruence statement indicate corresponding parts?

EXAMPLE 2

• What properties do you use to find the measure of the angle?

EXAMPLE 3

• Which proof statements could not be placed in a different order?

EXAMPLE 2 **Using Corresponding Parts of Congruent Triangles**

Given: △EFH ≅ △GFH

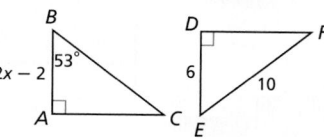

 **Algebra**

A Find the value of x.

∠FHE and ∠FHG are rt. ∠.	Def. of ⊥ lines
∠FHE ≅ ∠FHG	Rt. ∠ ≅ Thm.
m∠FHE = m∠FHG	Def. of ≅ ∠
$(6x - 12)° = 90°$	Substitute values for m∠FHE and m∠FHG.
$6x = 102$	Add 12 to both sides.
$x = 7$	Divide both sides by 6.

Helpful Hint

When you write a statement such as △ABC ≅ △DEF, you are also stating which parts are congruent.

B Find m∠GFH.

m∠EFH + m∠FHE + m∠E = 180°	△ Sum Thm.
m∠EFH + 90 + 21.6 = 180	Substitute values for m∠FHE and m∠E.
m∠EFH + 111.6 = 180	Simplify.
m∠EFH = 68.4	Subtract 111.6 from both sides.
∠GFH ≅ ∠EFH	Corr. ∠ of ≅ △ are ≅.
m∠GFH = m∠EFH	Def. of ≅ ∠
m∠GFH = 68.4°	Trans. Prop. of =

CHECK IT OUT! Given: △ABC ≅ △DEF
2a. Find the value of x.
2b. Find m∠F.
2a. 4
2b. 37°

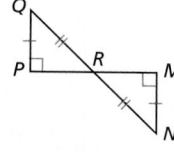

EXAMPLE 3 **Proving Triangles Congruent**

Given: ∠P and ∠M are right angles. R is the midpoint of $\overline{PM}$. $\overline{PQ}$ ≅ $\overline{MN}$, $\overline{QR}$ ≅ $\overline{NR}$
Prove: △PQR ≅ △MNR
Proof:

Statements	Reasons
1. ∠P and ∠M are rt. ∠	1. Given
2. ∠P ≅ ∠M	2. Rt. ∠ ≅ Thm.
3. ∠PRQ ≅ ∠MRN	3. Vert. ∠ Thm.
4. ∠Q ≅ ∠N	4. Third ∠ Thm.
5. R is the mdpt. of $\overline{PM}$.	5. Given
6. $\overline{PR}$ ≅ $\overline{MR}$	6. Def. of mdpt.
7. $\overline{PQ}$ ≅ $\overline{MN}$; $\overline{QR}$ ≅ $\overline{NR}$	7. Given
8. △PQR ≅ △MNR	8. Def. of ≅ △

CHECK IT OUT! 3. Given: $\overline{AD}$ bisects $\overline{BE}$. $\overline{BE}$ bisects $\overline{AD}$. $\overline{AB}$ ≅ $\overline{DE}$, ∠A ≅ ∠D
Prove: △ABC ≅ △DEC

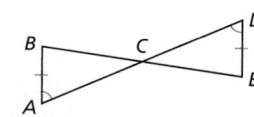

---

2 Teach

Guided Instruction

Show students how to name a polygon by writing the vertices in consecutive order. Discuss naming corresponding sides and angles of congruent polygons, including those that overlap.

Teaching Tip **Reading Math** Explain that the everyday meaning of the word *consecutive* is "following one another without interruption."

 ENGLISH LANGUAGE LEARNERS

Reaching All Learners

Through Visual Cues

Use two different-colored transparencies of congruent triangles. Demonstrate on an overhead projector or on a white board that if two triangles are congruent, you can slide one triangle exactly onto the other. Have students identify the corresponding sides and angles.

Overlapping Triangles

"With overlapping triangles, it helps me to redraw the triangles separately. That way I can mark what I know about one triangle without getting confused by the other one."

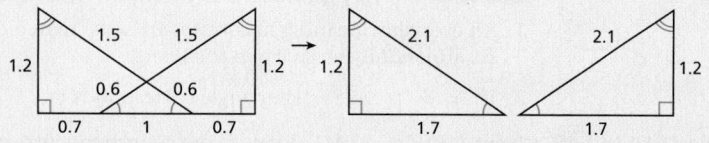

EXAMPLE 4

Engineering Application

TEXAS LINK

Engineering

The Rattler is one of the tallest wood-tracked roller coasters in the world. The ride sits on the side of a cliff at Six Flags Fiesta Texas. It is 5080 ft long and 179 ft high. The coaster travels at a speed of 65 mi/h.

The bars that give structural support to a roller coaster form triangles. Since the angle measures and the lengths of the corresponding sides are the same, the triangles are congruent.
Given: $\overline{JK} \perp \overline{KL}$, $\overline{ML} \perp \overline{KL}$, ∠KLJ ≅ ∠LKM, $\overline{JK}$ ≅ $\overline{ML}$, $\overline{JL}$ ≅ $\overline{MK}$
Prove: △JKL ≅ △MLK
Proof:

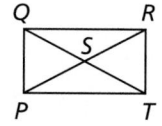

Statements	Reasons
1. $\overline{JK} \perp \overline{KL}$, $\overline{ML} \perp \overline{KL}$	1. Given
2. ∠JKL and ∠MLK are rt. ∡.	2. Def. of ⊥ lines
3. ∠JKL ≅ ∠MLK	3. Rt. ∠ ≅ Thm.
4. ∠KLJ ≅ ∠LKM	4. Given
5. ∠KJL ≅ ∠LMK	5. Third ∡ Thm.
6. $\overline{JK}$ ≅ $\overline{ML}$, $\overline{JL}$ ≅ $\overline{MK}$	6. Given
7. $\overline{KL}$ ≅ $\overline{LK}$	7. Reflex. Prop. of ≅
8. △JKL ≅ △MLK	8. Def. of ≅ ▵

 **CHECK IT OUT!**

4. Use the diagram to prove the following.
Given: $\overline{MK}$ bisects $\overline{JL}$. $\overline{JL}$ bisects $\overline{MK}$. $\overline{JK}$ ≅ $\overline{ML}$, $\overline{JK}$ ∥ $\overline{ML}$
Prove: △JKN ≅ △LMN

THINK AND DISCUSS

1. A roof truss is a triangular structure that supports a roof. How can you be sure that two roof trusses are the same size and shape?

2. **GET ORGANIZED** Copy and complete the graphic organizer. In each box, name the congruent corresponding parts.

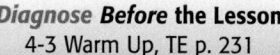

△PQR ≅ △LMN

Angles | Sides

Know it! Note

3 Close

Summarize

Review how to name corresponding angles and sides of congruent polygons. Remind students that to prove two triangles congruent, you must show all three pairs of sides and all three pairs of angles are congruent.

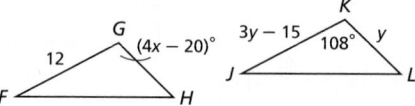

go.hrw.com/Geo/TX
Homework Help Online
KEYWORD: MG7 4-3
Parent Resources Online
KEYWORD: MG7 Parent

Answers

1. You find the ⚞ and sides that are in the same, or matching, places in the 2 △.

GUIDED PRACTICE

Vocabulary Apply the vocabulary from this lesson to answer each question.

1. An everyday meaning of *corresponding* is "matching." How can this help you find the *corresponding* parts of two triangles?

2. If $\triangle ABC \cong \triangle RST$, what angle corresponds to $\angle S$? $\angle B$

SEE EXAMPLE 1
p. 231

Given: $\triangle RST \cong \triangle LMN$. Identify the congruent corresponding parts.

3. $\overline{RS} \cong$ ___?___ $\overline{LM}$　　4. $\overline{LN} \cong$ ___?___ $\overline{RT}$　　5. $\angle S \cong$ ___?___ $\angle M$

6. $\overline{TS} \cong$ ___?___ $\overline{NM}$　　7. $\angle L \cong$ ___?___ $\angle R$　　8. $\angle N \cong$ ___?___ $\angle T$

SEE EXAMPLE 2
p. 232

Given: $\triangle FGH \cong \triangle JKL$. Find each value.

9. KL　9　　　　10. x　32

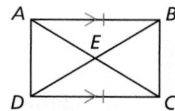

SEE EXAMPLE 3
p. 232

11. **Given:** E is the midpoint of $\overline{AC}$ and $\overline{BD}$.
　　$\overline{AB} \cong \overline{CD}$, $\overline{AB} \parallel \overline{CD}$

Prove: $\triangle ABE \cong \triangle CDE$

Proof:

Statements	Reasons
1. $\overline{AB} \parallel \overline{CD}$	1. a. ___?___
2. $\angle ABE \cong \angle CDE$, $\angle BAE \cong \angle DCE$	2. b. ___?___
3. $\overline{AB} \cong \overline{CD}$	3. c. ___?___
4. E is the mdpt. of $\overline{AC}$ and $\overline{BD}$.	4. d. ___?___
5. e. ___?___	5. Def. of mdpt.
6. $\angle AEB \cong \angle CED$	6. f. ___?___
7. $\triangle ABE \cong \triangle CDE$	7. g. ___?___

a. Given
b. Alt. Int. ⚞ Thm.
c. Given
d. Given
e. $\overline{AE} \cong \overline{CE}$, $\overline{DE} \cong \overline{BE}$
f. Vert. ⚞ Thm.
g. Def. of $\cong$ △

SEE EXAMPLE 4
p. 233

12. **Engineering** The McDonald Observatory has four research telescopes and is a leading center for astronomical study. Prove that the triangles that make up the observatory dome are congruent.

Given: $\overline{SU} \cong \overline{ST} \cong \overline{SR}$, $\overline{TU} \cong \overline{TR}$,
　　　$\angle UST \cong \angle RST$,
　　　and $\angle U \cong \angle R$
Prove: $\triangle RTS \cong \triangle UTS$

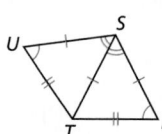

12.
1. $\angle UST \cong \angle RST$, $\angle U \cong \angle R$ (Given)
2. $\angle STU \cong \angle STR$ (Third ⚞ Thm.)
3. $\overline{SU} \cong \overline{SR}$ (Given)　　4. $\overline{ST} \cong \overline{ST}$ (Reflex. Prop. of $\cong$)
5. $\overline{TU} \cong \overline{TR}$ (Given)　　6. $\triangle RTS \cong \triangle UTS$ (Def. of $\cong$ △)

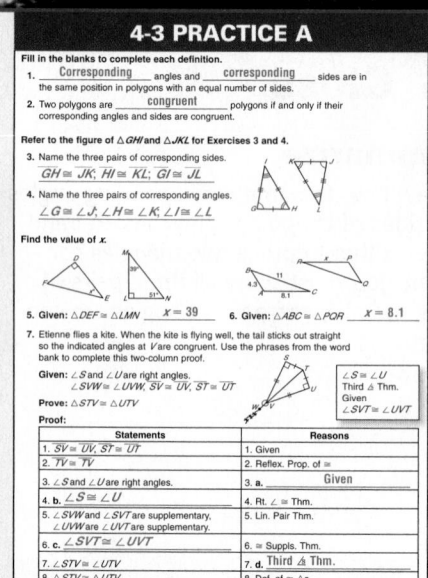

PRACTICE AND PROBLEM SOLVING

Independent Practice

For Exercises	See Example
13–16	1
17–18	2
19	3
20	4

TEKS ★ TAKS

Skills Practice p. S10
Application Practice p. S31

Given: Polygon $CDEF \cong$ **polygon** $KLMN$**. Identify the congruent corresponding parts.**

13. $\overline{DE} \cong$ ___?___ $\overline{LM}$

14. $\overline{KN} \cong$ ___?___ $\overline{CF}$

15. $\angle F \cong$ ___?___ $\angle N$

16. $\angle L \cong$ ___?___ $\angle D$

Given: $\triangle ABD \cong \triangle CBD$**. Find each value.**

17. $m\angle C$
    31°

18. y
    19

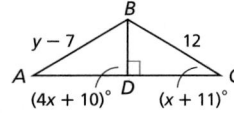

19. **Given:** $\overline{MP}$ bisects $\angle NMR$. P is the midpoint of $\overline{NR}$. $\overline{MN} \cong \overline{MR}$, $\angle N \cong \angle R$

    Prove: $\triangle MNP \cong \triangle MRP$

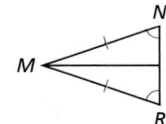

    Proof:

Statements	Reasons	
1. $\angle N \cong \angle R$	1. a. ___?___	a. Given
2. $\overline{MP}$ bisects $\angle NMR$.	2. b. ___?___	b. Given
3. c. ___?___	3. Def. of $\angle$ bisector	c. $\angle NMP \cong \angle RMP$
4. d. ___?___	4. Third $\angle$ Thm.	d. $\angle NPM \cong \angle RPM$
5. P is the mdpt. of $\overline{NR}$.	5. e. ___?___	e. Given
6. f. ___?___	6. Def. of mdpt.	f. $\overline{PN} \cong \overline{PR}$
7. $\overline{MN} \cong \overline{MR}$	7. g. ___?___	g. Given
8. $\overline{MP} \cong \overline{MP}$	8. h. ___?___	h. Reflex. Prop. of $\cong$
9. $\triangle MNP \cong \triangle MRP$	9. Def. of $\cong$ $\triangle$	

20. **Hobbies** In a garden, triangular flower beds are separated by straight rows of grass as shown.

    Given: $\angle ADC$ and $\angle BCD$ are right angles.
    $\overline{AC} \cong \overline{BD}$, $\overline{AD} \cong \overline{BC}$
    $\angle DAC \cong \angle CBD$

    Prove: $\triangle ADC \cong \triangle BCD$

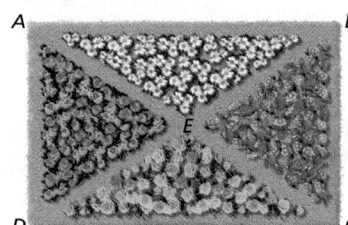

$\triangle GSR \cong \triangle KPH$;
$\triangle SRG \cong \triangle PHK$;
$\triangle RGS \cong \triangle HKP$

21. For two triangles, the following corresponding parts are given:
    $\overline{GS} \cong \overline{KP}$, $\overline{GR} \cong \overline{KH}$, $\overline{SR} \cong \overline{PH}$,
    $\angle S \cong \angle P$, $\angle G \cong \angle K$, and $\angle R \cong \angle H$.
    Write three different congruence statements.

22. The two polygons in the diagram are congruent. Complete the following congruence statement for the polygons.
    polygon R ___?___ $\cong$ polygon V ___?___
    Possible answer: $RVUTS \cong VWXZY$

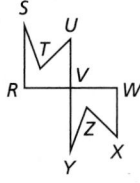

Write and solve an equation for each of the following.

23. $\triangle ABC \cong \triangle DEF$. $AB = 2x - 10$, and $DE = x + 20$. $\quad x = 30$;
    Find the value of x and AB. $\quad AB = 50$

24. $\triangle JKL \cong \triangle MNP$. $m\angle L = (x^2 + 10)°$, and $m\angle P = (2x^2 + 1)°$. What is $m\angle L$? **19°**

25. Polygon $ABCD \cong$ polygon $PQRS$. $BC = 6x + 5$, and $QR = 5x + 7$.
    Find the value of x and BC. $\quad x = 2$; $BC = 17$

MULTI-STEP TAKS PREP **Exercise 26** involves proving triangles congruent when they are formed by folding paper. This prepares students for the Multi-Step TAKS Prep on page 238.

TEST PREP DOCTOR + In **Exercise 33,** if students chose **A,** they have made the measure of ∠Y equal to the measure of ∠C instead of ∠B.

Answers

26a. $\overline{KL} \cong \overline{ML}$ by the def. of a square.

b.1. JKLM is a square. (Given)
 2. $\overline{KL} \cong \overline{ML}$ (Def. of a square)
 3. $\overline{JL}$ and $\overline{MK}$ are ⊥ bisectors of each other. (Given)
 4. $\overline{MN} \cong \overline{KN}$ (Def. of bisect)
 5. $\overline{NL} \cong \overline{NL}$ (Reflex. Prop. of ≅)
 6. ∠MNL and ∠KNL are rt. ∠. (Def. of ⊥)
 7. ∠MNL ≅ ∠KNL (Rt. ∠ ≅ Thm.)
 8. ∠NML ≅ ∠NLK (Given)
 9. ∠NLM ≅ ∠NLK (Third ∠ Thm.)
 10. △NML ≅ △NKL (Def. of ≅ △)

27.

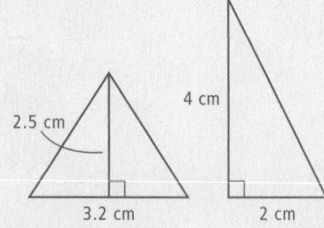

 1. $\overline{BD} \perp \overline{AC}$ (Given)
 2. ∠ADB and ∠CDB are rt. ∠ (Def. of ⊥)
 3. ∠ADB ≅ ∠CDB (Rt. ∠ ≅ Thm.)
 4. $\overline{BD}$ bisects ∠ABC. (Given)
 5. ∠ABD ≅ ∠CBD (Def. of bisect)
 6. ∠A ≅ ∠C (Third ∠ Thm.)
 7. $\overline{AB} \cong \overline{CB}$ (Given)
 8. $\overline{BD} \cong \overline{DB}$ (Reflex. Prop. of ≅)
 9. D is the mdpt. of $\overline{AC}$. (Given)
 10. $\overline{AD} \cong \overline{CD}$ (Def. of mdpt.)
 11. △ABD ≅ △CBD (Def of ≅ △)

28. Possible answer:

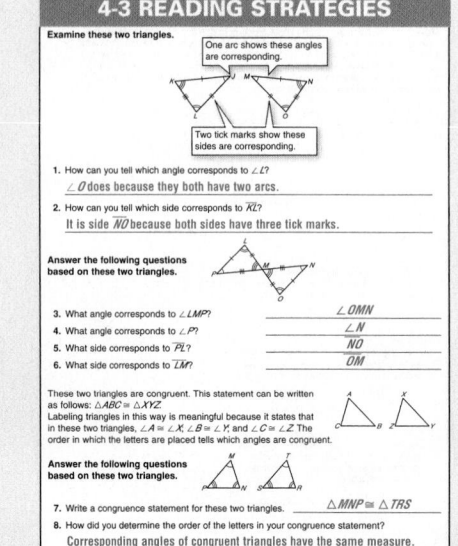

2.5 cm
4 cm
3.2 cm
2 cm

30. Yes; by the Third ∠ Thm., ∠K ≅ ∠W, so all 6 pairs of corr. parts are ≅. Therefore the △ are ≅.

236 Chapter 4

MULTI-STEP TAKS PREP

26. This problem will prepare you for the Multi-Step TAKS Prep on page 238. Many origami models begin with a square piece of paper, JKLM, that is folded along both diagonals to make the creases shown. $\overline{JL}$ and $\overline{MK}$ are perpendicular bisectors of each other, and ∠NML ≅ ∠NKL.
 a. Explain how you know that $\overline{KL}$ and $\overline{ML}$ are congruent.
 b. Prove △NML ≅ △NKL.

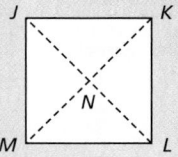

27. Draw a diagram and then write a proof.
 Given: $\overline{BD} \perp \overline{AC}$. D is the midpoint of $\overline{AC}$. $\overline{AB} \cong \overline{CB}$, and $\overline{BD}$ bisects ∠ABC.
 Prove: △ABD ≅ △CBD

28. Critical Thinking Draw two triangles that are not congruent but have an area of 4 cm² each.

29. /// **ERROR ANALYSIS** /// Given △MPQ ≅ △EDF. Two solutions for finding m∠E are shown. Which is incorrect? Explain the error.
 Solution A is incorrect.
 ∠E ≅ ∠M, so m∠E = 46°.

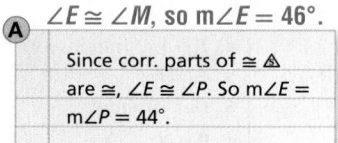

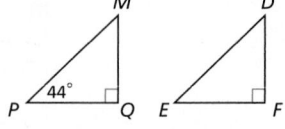

A
| Since corr. parts of ≅ △ are ≅, ∠E ≅ ∠P. So m∠E = m∠P = 44°. |

B
| Since the acute ∠ of a rt. △ are comp., m∠M = 46°. ∠E ≅ ∠M, so m∠E = 46°. |

30. Write About It Given the diagram of the triangles, is there enough information to prove that △HKL is congruent to △YWX? Explain.

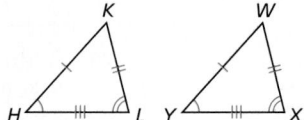

TEST PREP

31. Which congruence statement correctly indicates that the two given triangles are congruent?
 Ⓐ △ABC ≅ △EFD   Ⓒ △ABC ≅ △DEF
 Ⓑ △ABC ≅ △FDE   Ⓓ △ABC ≅ △FED

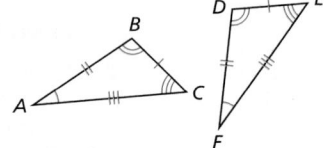

32. △MNP ≅ △RST. What are the values of x and y?
 Ⓕ $x = 26, y = 21\frac{1}{3}$ Ⓗ $x = 25, y = 20\frac{2}{3}$
 Ⓖ $x = 27, y = 20$ Ⓙ $x = 30\frac{1}{3}, y = 16\frac{2}{3}$

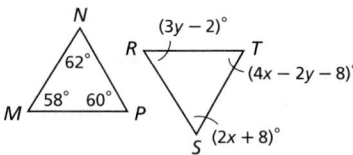

33. △ABC ≅ △XYZ. m∠A = 47.1°, and m∠C = 13.8°. Find m∠Y.
 Ⓐ 13.8   Ⓒ 76.2
 Ⓑ 42.9   Ⓓ 119.1

34. △MNR ≅ △SPQ, NL = 18, SP = 33, SR = 10, RQ = 24, and QP = 30. What is the perimeter of △MNR?
 Ⓕ 79   Ⓗ 87
 Ⓖ 85   Ⓙ 97

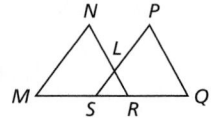

236 Chapter 4 Triangle Congruence

4-3 READING STRATEGIES

Examine these two triangles.

One arc shows these angles are corresponding.

Two tick marks show these sides are corresponding.

1. How can you tell which angle corresponds to ∠L?
 ∠O does because they both have two arcs.
2. How can you tell which side corresponds to $\overline{KL}$?
 It is side $\overline{NO}$ because both sides have three tick marks.

Answer the following questions based on these two triangles.

3. What angle corresponds to ∠LMP?   ∠OMN
4. What angle corresponds to ∠P?   ∠N
5. What side corresponds to $\overline{PL}$? $\overline{NO}$
6. What side corresponds to $\overline{LM}$? $\overline{OM}$

These two triangles are congruent. This statement can be written as follows: △ABC ≅ △XYZ. Labeling triangles in this way is meaningful because it states that in these two triangles, ∠A ≅ ∠X, ∠B ≅ ∠Y, and ∠C ≅ ∠Z. The order in which the letters are placed tells which angles are congruent.

Answer the following questions based on these two triangles.

7. Write a congruence statement for these two triangles.   △MNP ≅ △TRS
8. How did you determine the order of the letters in your congruence statement?
 Corresponding angles of congruent triangles have the same measure.

4-3 RETEACH

Triangles are **congruent** if they have the same size and shape. Their **corresponding parts,** the angles and sides that are in the same positions, are congruent.

	Corresponding Parts	
	Congruent Angles	Congruent Sides
	∠A ≅ ∠J	$\overline{AB} \cong \overline{JK}$
△ABC ≅ △JKL	∠B ≅ ∠K	$\overline{BC} \cong \overline{KL}$
	∠C ≅ ∠L	$\overline{CA} \cong \overline{LJ}$

To identify corresponding parts of congruent triangles, look at the order of the vertices in the congruence statement such as △ABC ≅ △JKL.

Given: △XYZ ≅ △NPQ. Identify the congruent corresponding parts.

1. ∠Z ≅   ∠Q   **2.** $\overline{YZ} \cong$ $\overline{PQ}$
3. ∠P ≅   ∠Y   **4.** ∠X ≅   ∠N
5. $\overline{NO} \cong$ $\overline{XY}$ **6.** $\overline{PN} \cong$ $\overline{YX}$

Given: △EFG ≅ △RST. Find each value below.

7. x =   21   **8.** y =   6
9. m∠F =   62°   **10.** ST =   10

CHALLENGE AND EXTEND

35. Multi-Step Given that the perimeter of *TUVW* is 149 units, find the value of *x*. Is △*TUV* ≅ △*TWV*? Explain.

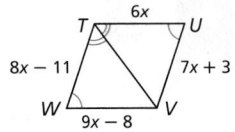

36. Multi-Step Polygon *ABCD* ≅ polygon *EFGH*. ∠*A* is a right angle. m∠*E* = $(y^2 - 10)°$, and m∠*H* = $(2y^2 - 132)°$. Find m∠*D*. **68°**

37. Given: $\overline{RS} \cong \overline{RT}$, ∠*S* ≅ ∠*T*
Prove: △*RST* ≅ △*RTS*

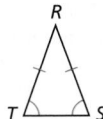

SPIRAL REVIEW

Two number cubes are rolled. Find the probability of each outcome.
(Previous course)

38. Both numbers rolled are even. $\frac{1}{4}$

39. The sum of the numbers rolled is 5. $\frac{1}{9}$

Classify each angle by its measure. *(Lesson 1-3)*

40. m∠*DOC* = 40° **acute**

41. m∠*BOA* = 90° **rt.**

42. m∠*COA* = 140° **obtuse**

Find each angle measure. *(Lesson 4-2)*

43. ∠*Q* **72°**

44. ∠*P* **74°**

45. ∠*QRS* **146°**

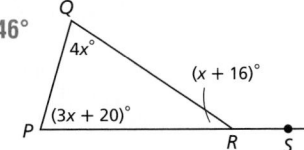

Career Path

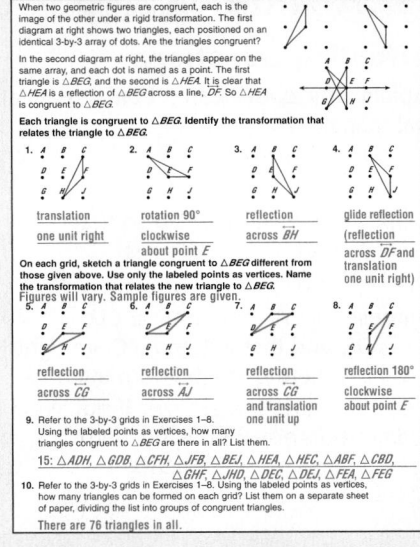

Jordan Carter
Emergency Medical
Services Program

Q: What math classes did you take in high school?

A: Algebra 1 and 2, Geometry, Precalculus

Q: What kind of degree or certification will you receive?

A: I will receive an associate's degree in applied science. Then I will take an exam to be certified as an EMT or paramedic.

Q: How do you use math in your hands-on training?

A: I calculate dosages based on body weight and age. I also calculate drug doses in milligrams per kilogram per hour or set up an IV drip to deliver medications at the correct rate.

Q: What are your future career plans?

A: When I am certified, I can work for a private ambulance service or with a fire department. I could also work in a hospital, transporting critically ill patients by ambulance or helicopter.

4-3 Congruent Triangles **237**

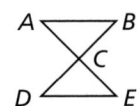

Lesson 4-3 **237**

MULTI-STEP
TAKS PREP

Organizer

Objective: Assess students' ability to apply concepts and skills in Lessons 4-1 through 4-3 in a real-world format.

 Online Edition

Resources

 Geometry Assessments
www.mathtekstoolkit.org

Problem	Text Reference
1	Lesson 4-1
2	Lesson 4-2
3	Lesson 4-3

Answers

2. m∠EBD = 45° ($\overline{DB}$ bisects rt. ∠ABC.) m∠BDE = 22.5° ($\overline{DE}$ bisects ∠ADB.) m∠DEB = 112.5° (△ Sum Thm.)

3. 1. $\overline{DB}$ bisects ∠ABC and ∠EDF. (Given)
   2. ∠EBD ≅ ∠FBD; ∠EDB ≅ ∠FDB (Def. of ∠ bisector)
   3. ∠DEB ≅ ∠DFB (Third ∠ Thm.)
   4. $\overline{BE}$ ≅ $\overline{BF}$; $\overline{DE}$ ≅ $\overline{DF}$ (Given)
   5. $\overline{DB}$ ≅ $\overline{DB}$ (Reflex. Prop. of ≅)
   6. △EDB ≅ △FDB (Def. of ≅ △)

 **TAKS Practice**

Grades 9–11	Problems
Obj. 7	1–4
Obj. 10	1–4

Triangles and Congruence

Origami Origami is the Japanese art of paper folding. The Japanese word *origami* literally means "fold paper." This ancient art form relies on properties of geometry to produce fascinating and beautiful shapes.

Each of the figures shows a step in making an origami swan from a square piece of paper. The final figure shows the creases of an origami swan that has been unfolded.

Step 1

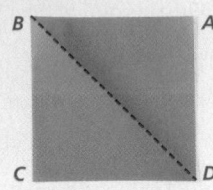

Fold the paper in half diagonally and crease it. Turn it over.

Step 2

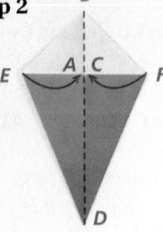

Fold corners *A* and *C* to the center line and crease. Turn it over.

Step 3

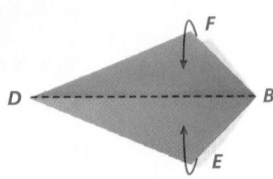

Fold in half along the center crease so that $\overline{DE}$ and $\overline{DF}$ are together.

Step 4

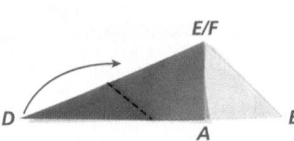

Fold the narrow point upward at a 90° angle and crease. Push in the fold so that the neck is inside the body.

Step 5

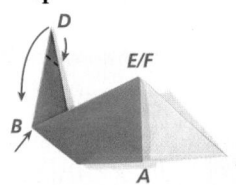

Fold the tip downward and crease. Push in the fold so that the head is inside the neck.

Step 6

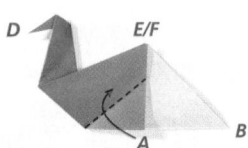

Fold up the flap to form the wing.

isosc. △;
rt. △

1. Use the fact that *ABCD* is a square to classify △*ABD* by its side lengths and by its angle measures.

2. $\overline{DB}$ bisects ∠*ABC* and ∠*ADC*. $\overline{DE}$ bisects ∠*ADB*. Find the measures of the angles in △*EDB*. Explain how you found the measures.

3. Given that $\overline{DB}$ bisects ∠*ABC* and ∠*EDF*, $\overline{BE}$ ≅ $\overline{BF}$, and $\overline{DE}$ ≅ $\overline{DF}$, prove that △*EDB* ≅ △ *FDB*.

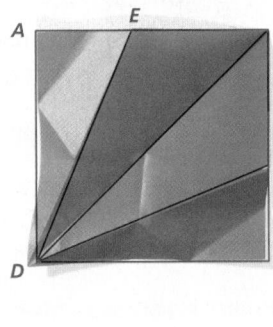

238   *Chapter 4 Triangle Congruence*

INTERVENTION ◀▶

Scaffolding Questions

1. Explain why △*ABD* cannot be an equilateral triangle. The 3 sides cannot all have equal lengths since $DB^2 = AB^2 + AD^2$ by the Pyth. Thm.

2. Suppose $\overline{DE}$ trisects ∠*ADB* so that m∠*EDB* = $\frac{1}{3}$m∠*ADB*. What is m∠*AED*? 60°

3. Suppose that $\overline{AE}$ ≅ $\overline{CF}$, $\overline{AD}$ ≅ $\overline{CD}$, $\overline{DE}$ ≅ $\overline{DF}$, and that ∠*A* and ∠*C* are right angles. Is there enough information to prove that △*ADE* ≅ △*CDF*? If not, what additional information is needed? No; you need to know ∠*ADE* ≅ ∠*CDF* or ∠*AED* ≅ ∠*CFD*.

Extension

Draw a large scalene △*ABC*. Then construct equilateral △*ABC'* outward from side $\overline{AB}$. Similarly construct equilateral △*BCA'* and △*ACB'*. Bisect each angle of the three equilateral triangles. Where the bisectors meet label the points *D*, *E*, and *F*. How would you classify △*DEF*? equilateral

READY TO GO ON?

Quiz for Lessons 4-1 Through 4-3

4-1 Classifying Triangles

Classify each triangle by its angle measures.

1. △ACD **rt.**   2. △ABD **equiangular**   3. △ADE **obtuse**

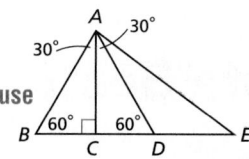

Classify each triangle by its side lengths.

4. △PQR **isosc.**   5. △PRS **equil.**   6. △PQS **scalene**

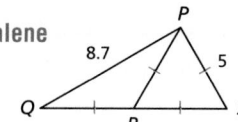

4-2 Angle Relationships in Triangles

Find each angle measure.

7. m∠M **51°**

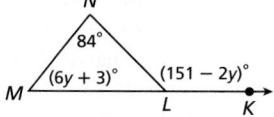

8. m∠ABC **125°**

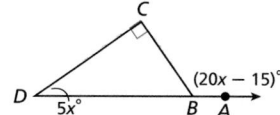

9. A carpenter built a triangular support structure for a roof. Two of the angles of the structure measure 37° and 55°. Find the measure of ∠RTP, the angle formed by the roof of the house and the roof of the patio. **92°**

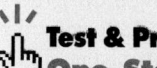

4-3 Congruent Triangles

Given: △JKL ≅ △DEF. Identify the congruent corresponding parts.

10. $\overline{KL} \cong$ ___?___ $\overline{EF}$ 11. $\overline{DF} \cong$ ___?___ $\overline{JL}$ 12. ∠K ≅ ___?___ ∠E   13. ∠F ≅ ___?___ ∠L

Given: △PQR ≅ △STU. Find each value.

14. PQ **9**   15. y **23**

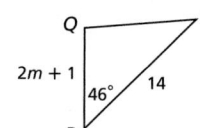 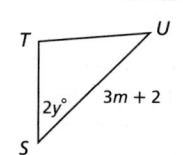

16. Given: $\overleftrightarrow{AB} \parallel \overleftrightarrow{CD}, \overline{AB} \cong \overline{CD}, \overline{AC} \cong \overline{BD},$
$\overline{AC} \perp \overline{CD}, \overline{DB} \perp \overline{AB}$
Prove: △ACD ≅ △DBA

Proof:

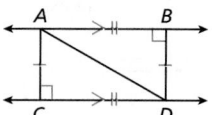

Statements	Reasons
1. $\overleftrightarrow{AB} \parallel \overleftrightarrow{CD}$	1. a. ___?___
2. ∠BAD ≅ ∠CDA	2. b. ___?___
3. $\overline{AC} \perp \overline{CD}, \overline{DB} \perp \overline{AB}$	3. c. ___?___
4. ∠ACD and ∠DBA are rt. ∡	4. d. ___?___
5. e. ___?___	5. Rt. ∠ ≅ Thm.
6. f. ___?___	6. Third ∡ Thm.
7. $\overline{AB} \cong \overline{CD}, \overline{AC} \cong \overline{BD}$	7. g. ___?___
8. h. ___?___	8. Reflex Prop. of ≅
9. △ACD ≅ △DBA	9. i. ___?___

a. Given
b. Alt. Int. ∡ Thm.
c. Given   d. Def. of ⊥
e. ∠ACD ≅ ∠DBA
f. ∠CAD ≅ ∠BDA
g. Given   h. $\overline{AD} \cong \overline{AD}$
i. Def. of ≅ ∆

READY TO GO ON?

Organizer

Objective: Assess students' mastery of concepts and skills in Lessons 4-1 through 4-3.

Resources

Assessment Resources
Section 4A Quiz

Test & Practice Generator
One-Stop Planner®

INTERVENTION

Resources

Ready to Go On?
Intervention and
Enrichment Worksheets

Ready to Go On? CD-ROM

Ready to Go On? Online

my.hrw.com

READY TO GO ON?

Diagnose and Prescribe

NO INTERVENE	*READY TO GO ON? Intervention, Section 4A*				YES ENRICH

Ready to Go On? Intervention	Worksheets	CD-ROM	Online		READY TO GO ON? Enrichment, Section 4A
✓ Lesson 4-1	4-1 Intervention	Activity 4-1	Diagnose and Prescribe Online		Worksheets
✓ Lesson 4-2	4-2 Intervention	Activity 4-2			CD-ROM
✓ Lesson 4-3	4-3 Intervention	Activity 4-3			Online

Proving Triangle Congruence

One-Minute Section Planner

Lesson	Lab Resources	Materials
4-4 Geometry Lab Explore SSS and SAS Triangle Congruence • Discover shortcuts for proving triangles are congruent. ☐ Exit Level TAKS ☐ ACT ☐ SAT ☐ SAT Subject Tests		**Required** straws, string, paper clip, and protractor (MK) **Optional** envelopes with three descriptions of parts of a triangle (MK), ruler (MK)
Lesson 4-4 Triangle Congruence: SSS and SAS • Apply SSS and SAS to construct triangles and solve problems. • Prove triangles congruent by using SSS and SAS. ☐ Exit Level TAKS ☐ ACT ☐ SAT ☐ SAT Subject Tests	**Texas Lab Manual** 4-4 Geometry Lab	**Required** straightedge, compass (MK), geometry software **Optional** magazine pictures showing triangle congruence, ruler, protractor (MK)
4-5 Technology Lab Predict Other Triangle Congruence Relationships • Use geometry software to explore triangle congruence relationships. ☐ Exit Level TAKS ☐ ACT ☑ SAT ☑ SAT Subject Tests		**Required** geometry software
Lesson 4-5 Triangle Congruence: ASA, AAS, and HL • Apply ASA, AAS, and HL to construct triangles and solve problems. • Prove triangles congruent by using ASA, AAS, and HL. ☐ Exit Level TAKS ☐ ACT ☐ SAT ☐ SAT Subject Tests		**Required** straightedge, compass (MK) **Optional** map of the area that contains your school, paper and scissors
Lesson 4-6 Triangle Congruence: CPCTC • Use CPCTC to prove parts of triangles are congruent. ☑ Exit Level TAKS ☐ ACT ☐ SAT ☐ SAT Subject Tests		**Optional** designs by M. C. Escher
Lesson 4-7 Introduction to Coordinate Proof • Position figures in the coordinate plane for use in coordinate proofs. • Prove geometric concepts by using coordinate proofs. ☐ Exit Level TAKS ☑ ACT ☑ SAT ☐ SAT Subject Tests		**Required** graph paper **Optional** scissors
Lesson 4-8 Isosceles and Equilateral Triangles • Prove theorems about isosceles and equilateral triangles. • Apply properties of isosceles and equilateral triangles. ☑ Exit Level TAKS ☑ ACT ☑ SAT ☑ SAT Subject Tests		**Required** graph paper **Optional** different examples of isosceles and equilateral triangles, poster board, ruler (MK)
Extension Proving Constructions Valid • Use congruent triangles to prove constructions valid. ☐ Exit Level TAKS ☑ ACT ☐ SAT ☐ SAT Subject Tests		

MK = *Manipulatives Kit*

Section Overview

Triangle Congruence: SSS, SAS, ASA, AAS, HL, CPCTC *Lessons 4-4, 4-5, 4-6*

 Why? Triangles have special properties that allow you to use shortcuts for proving triangles congruent.

SSS	SAS	ASA	AAS	HL
$\overline{AB} \cong \overline{DE}$ $\overline{BC} \cong \overline{EF}$ $\overline{CA} \cong \overline{FD}$	$\overline{AB} \cong \overline{DE}$ $\angle B \cong \angle E$ $\overline{BC} \cong \overline{EF}$	$\angle A \cong \angle D$ $\overline{AC} \cong \overline{DF}$ $\angle C \cong \angle F$	$\angle A \cong \angle D$ $\angle B \cong \angle E$ $\overline{BC} \cong \overline{EF}$	$\overline{BC} \cong \overline{EF}$ $\overline{AB} \cong \overline{DE}$
$\triangle ABC \cong \triangle DEF$	$\triangle ABC \cong \triangle DEF$	$\triangle ABC \cong \triangle DEF$	$\triangle ABC \cong \triangle DEF$	$\triangle ABC \cong \triangle DEF$

CPCTC = **C**orresponding **P**arts of **C**ongruent **T**riangles are **C**ongruent.
Once you know that two triangles are congruent, you know that all corresponding parts are congruent.

Introduction to Coordinate Proof *Lesson 4-7*

 Why? Coordinate proof is a style of proof that uses coordinate geometry and algebra.

Strategies for Positioning Figures in the Coordinate Plane:
- Use the origin as a vertex, keeping the figure in Quadrant 1.
- Center the figure at the origin.
- Center a side of the figure at the origin.
- Use one or both axes as sides of the figure.

Coordinate proof uses coordinates, the Midpoint Formula, the Pythagorean Theorem, and/or the Distance Formula to prove conjectures.

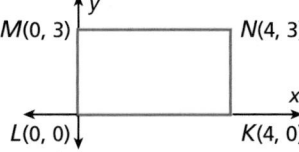

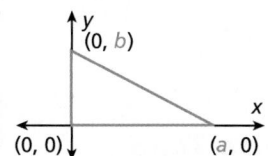

Isosceles and Equilateral Triangles *Lesson 4-8*

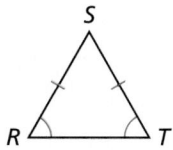 **Why?** Isosceles and equilateral triangles frequently appear in other figures, so knowing the properties of isosceles and equilateral triangles is very useful.

Equilateral △ ⟺ Equiangular △

$\overline{AB} \cong \overline{BC} \cong \overline{CA} \iff \angle A \cong \angle B \cong \angle C$

$\overline{AB} \cong \overline{BC} \cong \overline{CA}$ if and only if $\angle A \cong \angle B \cong \angle C$.

Isosceles △RST

$\overline{RS} \cong \overline{ST} \iff \angle R \cong \angle T$

$\overline{RS} \cong \overline{ST}$ if and only if $\angle R \cong \angle T$.

240 Chapter 4

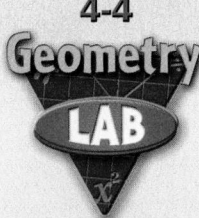

4-4

Geometry LAB

Use with Lesson 4-4

Explore SSS and SAS Triangle Congruence

In Lesson 4-3, you used the definition of congruent triangles to prove triangles congruent. To use the definition, you need to prove that all three pairs of corresponding sides and all three pairs of corresponding angles are congruent.

In this lab, you will discover some shortcuts for proving triangles congruent.

TEKS G.9.B Congruence and the geometry of size: formulate and test conjectures about the properties and attributes of polygons … based on explorations. Also G.4.A G.10.B

Activity 1

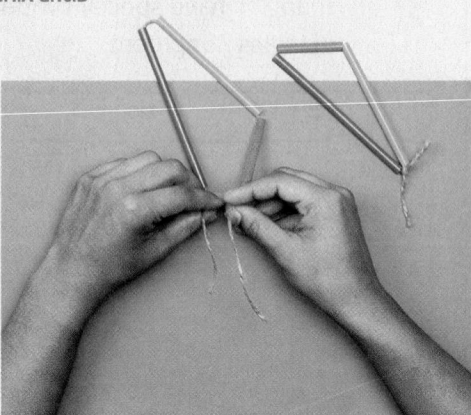

1. Measure and cut six pieces from the straws: two that are 2 inches long, two that are 4 inches long, and two that are 5 inches long.

2. Cut two pieces of string that are each about 20 inches long.

3. Thread one piece of each size of straw onto a piece of string. Tie the ends of the string together so that the pieces of straw form a triangle.

4. Using the remaining pieces, try to make another triangle with the same side lengths that is *not* congruent to the first triangle.

2. It is not possible. Once the lengths of the 3 straws are determined, only 1 △ can be formed.

Try This

3. To prove that 2 △ are ≅, check to see if the 3 pairs of corr. sides are ≅.

1. Repeat Activity 1 using side lengths of your choice. Are your results the same? **yes**

2. Do you think it is possible to make two triangles that have the same side lengths but that are not congruent? Why or why not?

3. How does your answer to Problem 2 provide a shortcut for proving triangles congruent?

4. Complete the following conjecture based on your results. Two triangles are congruent if _____?_____ . **three sides of 1 △ are ≅ to 3 sides of the other △**

240 Chapter 4 Triangle Congruence

Activity 2

1. Measure and cut two pieces from the straws: one that is 4 inches long and one that is 5 inches long.

2. Use a protractor to help you bend a paper clip to form a 30° angle.

3. Place the pieces of straw on the sides of the 30° angle. The straws will form two sides of your triangle.

4. Without changing the angle formed by the paper clip, use a piece of straw to make a third side for your triangle, cutting it to fit as necessary. Use additional paper clips or string to hold the straws together in a triangle.

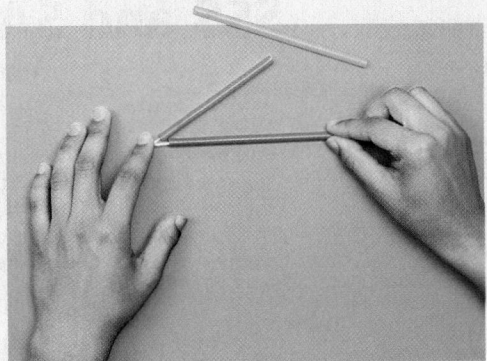

6. No; once 2 side lengths and the included ∠ measure are determined, only 1 length is possible for the remaining side.

Try This

7. To prove that 2 △ are ≅, check to see if there are 2 pairs of ≅ corr. sides and that their included ∠ are ≅.

5. Repeat Activity 2 using side lengths and an angle measure of your choice. Are your results the same? **yes**

6. Suppose you know two side lengths of a triangle and the measure of the angle between these sides. Can the length of the third side be any measure? Explain.

7. How does your answer to Problem 6 provide a shortcut for proving triangles congruent?

8. Use the two given sides and the given angle from Activity 2 to form a triangle that is not congruent to the triangle you formed. (*Hint:* One of the given sides does not have to be adjacent to the given angle.) **Check students' work.**

9. Complete the following conjecture based on your results.
Two triangles are congruent if _____?_____.

2 sides and the included ∠ of 1 △ are ≅ to 2 sides and the included ∠ of the other △

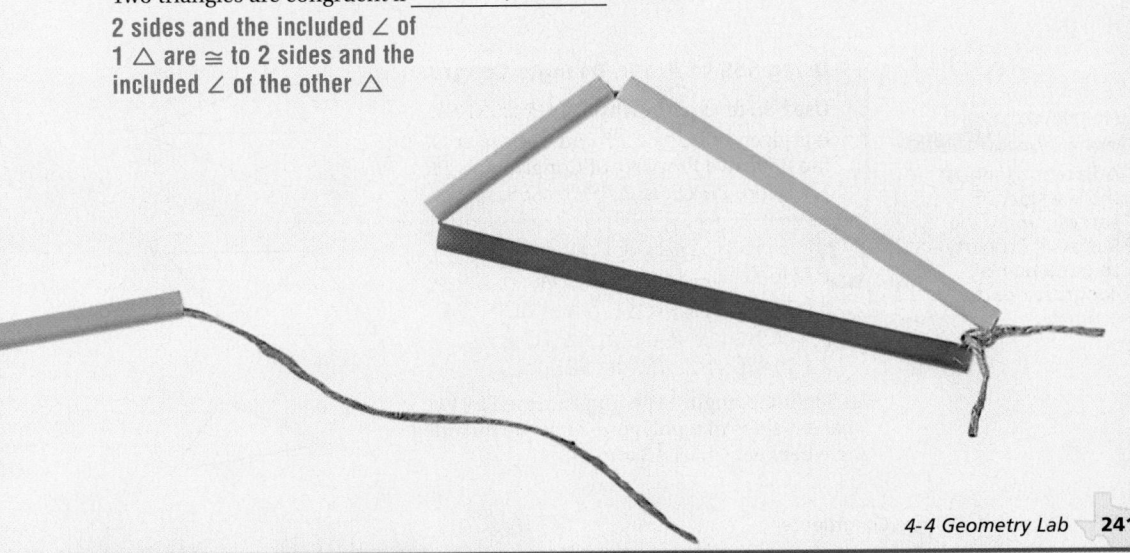

Alternative Approach

Place students in small groups. Give each student in the group an envelope containing three descriptions of parts of a triangle. For example, *AB* is 4 in., m∠A = 32°, and m∠B = 48°. At least one envelope should have the same characteristics as another envelope given to the group. The group should determine how many of the triangles are congruent and why.

Close

Key Concept

You do not need all six pairs of congruent corresponding parts to prove triangles congruent. If you know three pairs of corresponding sides are congruent (SSS) or two pairs of corresponding sides and the included angles are congruent (SAS), then you know the triangles are congruent.

Assessment

Journal Have students compare and contrast the SSS and SAS postulates and support their answers with a sketch that illustrates each postulate.

Teacher to Teacher

To save time on this lab, I have a baggie for each student with all of the supplies: 4 long straws, scissors, a protractor, a 20-inch string, and 2 paper clips. Students can use the ruler on their TAKS formula chart to measure and cut the straws. After the activity, the students place all of the supplies back in the baggie for easy collection.

Brenda Lynch
Montgomery, TX

Objectives: Apply SSS and SAS to construct triangles and solve problems.

Prove triangles congruent by using SSS and SAS.

Geometry Lab
In *Texas Lab Manual*

Online Edition
Tutorial Videos

Countdown to TAKS Week 8

Power Presentations with PowerPoint®

Warm Up

1. Name the angle formed by $\overrightarrow{AB}$ and $\overrightarrow{AC}$. Possible answer: ∠A

2. Name the three sides of △ABC. $\overline{AB}, \overline{AC}, \overline{BC}$

3. △QRS ≅ △LMN. Name all pairs of congruent corresponding parts. $\overline{QR} \cong \overline{LM}$, $\overline{RS} \cong \overline{MN}$, $\overline{QS} \cong \overline{LN}$, ∠Q ≅ ∠L, ∠R ≅ ∠M, ∠S ≅ ∠N

Also available on transparency

Math Humor

Q: Why did the greeting card come after your birthday?

A: Postulate!

Geometry TEKS

G.2 Geometric structure*
(A) use constructions to explore attributes of geometric figures and to make conjectures …

G.3 Geometric structure*
(B) construct and justify statements about geometric figures …
(E) use deductive reasoning to prove a statement

G.10 Congruence and the geometry of size*
(B) justify and apply triangle congruence relationships

* **Knowledge and Skills** See p. 214.

4-4 Triangle Congruence: SSS and SAS

⭐ TEKS G.10.B Congruence and the geometry of size: justify and apply triangle congruence relationships. Also G.2A, G.3.B, G.3.E

Objectives
Apply SSS and SAS to construct triangles and to solve problems.

Prove triangles congruent by using SSS and SAS.

Vocabulary
triangle rigidity
included angle

Who uses this?
Engineers used the property of triangle rigidity to design the internal support for the Statue of Liberty and to build bridges, towers, and other structures. (See Example 2.)

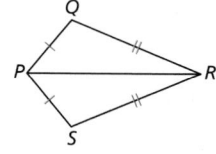

In Lesson 4-3, you proved triangles congruent by showing that all six pairs of corresponding parts were congruent.

The property of **triangle rigidity** gives you a shortcut for proving two triangles congruent. It states that if the side lengths of a triangle are given, the triangle can have only one shape.

For example, you only need to know that two triangles have three pairs of congruent corresponding sides. This can be expressed as the following postulate.

Know it! *Note*

Postulate 4-4-1	Side-Side-Side (SSS) Congruence	
POSTULATE	**HYPOTHESIS**	**CONCLUSION**
If three sides of one triangle are congruent to three sides of another triangle, then the triangles are congruent.		△ABC ≅ △FDE

EXAMPLE 1 Using SSS to Prove Triangle Congruence

Use SSS to explain why △PQR ≅ △PSR.
It is given that $\overline{PQ} \cong \overline{PS}$ and that $\overline{QR} \cong \overline{SR}$. By the Reflexive Property of Congruence, $\overline{PR} \cong \overline{PR}$. Therefore △PQR ≅ △PSR by SSS.

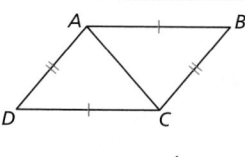

Remember!

Adjacent triangles share a side, so you can apply the Reflexive Property to get a pair of congruent parts.

✓ **CHECK IT OUT!** 1. Use SSS to explain why △ABC ≅ △CDA.
It is given that $\overline{AB} \cong \overline{CD}$ and $\overline{BC} \cong \overline{DA}$. By the Reflex. Prop. of ≅, $\overline{AC} \cong \overline{AC}$. So △ABC ≅ △CDA by SSS.

An **included angle** is an angle formed by two adjacent sides of a polygon. ∠B is the included angle between sides $\overline{AB}$ and $\overline{BC}$.

---

1 Introduce

Motivate

Use pictures from magazines to show students that triangle congruence is important in designing and building structures. Triangles can be proved congruent without using all three pairs of angles and all three pairs of sides. Explain to students that this lesson will show them how to prove triangles congruent using three pairs of congruent corresponding parts.

Explorations and answers are provided in the *Explorations* binder.

It can also be shown that only two pairs of congruent corresponding sides are needed to prove the congruence of two triangles if the included angles are also congruent.

 **Know it!** *Note*

Postulate 4-4-2 | Side-Angle-Side (SAS) Congruence

POSTULATE	HYPOTHESIS	CONCLUSION
If two sides and the included angle of one triangle are congruent to two sides and the included angle of another triangle, then the triangles are congruent.	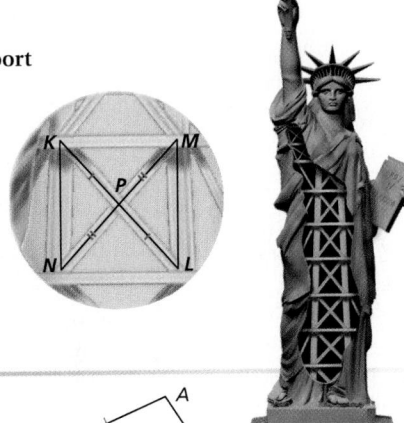	△ABC ≅ △EFD

EXAMPLE 2 *Engineering Application*

Caution!

The letters SAS are written in that order because the congruent angles must be between pairs of congruent corresponding sides.

The figure shows part of the support structure of the Statue of Liberty. Use SAS to explain why △KPN ≅ △LPM.

It is given that $\overline{KP} \cong \overline{LP}$ and that $\overline{NP} \cong \overline{MP}$. By the Vertical Angles Theorem, ∠KPN ≅ ∠LPM. Therefore △KPN ≅ △LPM by SAS.

CHECK IT OUT!

2. Use SAS to explain why △ABC ≅ △DBC.

2. It is given that $\overline{BA} \cong \overline{BD}$ and ∠ABC ≅ ∠DBC. By the Reflex. Prop. of ≅, $\overline{BC} \cong \overline{BC}$. So △ABC ≅ △DBC by SAS.

The SAS Postulate guarantees that if you are given the lengths of two sides and the measure of the included angle, you can construct one and only one triangle.

 **Construction** Congruent Triangles Using SAS

Use a straightedge to draw two segments and one angle, or copy the given segments and angle.

1	**2**	**3**
	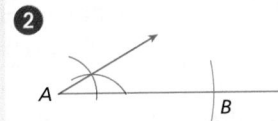	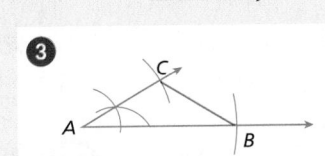
Construct $\overline{AB}$ congruent to one of the segments.	Construct ∠A congruent to the given angle.	Construct $\overline{AC}$ congruent to the other segment. Draw $\overline{CB}$ to complete △ABC.

Students may choose the wrong angle when SAS is used to prove triangles congruent. Explain that the angle must be formed by the sides. The included angle is named by the letter the segments share.

Teaching Tip **Transformations** Lead students to recognize when reflection is modeled in the examples. You can do this with a mirror (MK) or Mira.

Power Presentations with PowerPoint®

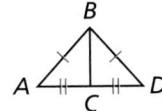 **Additional Examples**

Example 1

Use SSS to explain why △ABC ≅ △DBC.

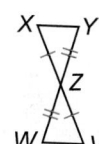

It is given that $\overline{AC} \cong \overline{DC}$ and that $\overline{AB} \cong \overline{DB}$. By the Reflex. Prop. of ≅, $\overline{BC} \cong \overline{BC}$. Therefore △ABC ≅ △DBC by SSS.

Example 2

The diagram shows part of the support structure for a tower. Use SAS to explain why △XYZ ≅ △VWZ.

It is given that $\overline{XZ} \cong \overline{VZ}$ and that $\overline{YZ} \cong \overline{WZ}$. By the Vert. ∠ Thm. ∠XZY ≅ ∠VZW. Therefore △XYZ ≅ △VWZ by SAS.

Also available on transparency

---

2 Teach

Guided Instruction

Review with students how to write congruence statements based on corresponding parts. Explain that the SSS and the SAS congruence postulates are shortcuts to verifying all six corresponding parts congruent. Draw triangles with the following measures: one side 7 cm, one side 10 cm, and a 40° angle. Explain that the triangles are not necessarily congruent. The triangles drawn with the 40° angle included between the given sides are congruent.

Reaching All Learners
Through Modeling

Introduce the SSS postulate with the following activity. Have the students draw three line segments of given lengths. Using one of the three lengths as a base and one endpoint of the base as center, draw an arc with a radius equal to a second length. Draw an arc with a radius equal to the third length, using the other endpoint as center. Join the endpoints with the intersection of the arcs. Have students compare their triangles and make a conjecture.

INTERVENTION ◄─►
Questioning Strategies

EXAMPLE 1

• What do the tick marks on the triangles show? What additional information do you need to prove the triangles congruent by SSS?

EXAMPLE 2

• Is enough information given to prove the triangles congruent by SAS? What additional information do you need?

Example 3

Show that the triangles are congruent for the given value of the variable.

A. $\triangle MNO \cong \triangle PQR$, when $x = 5$.

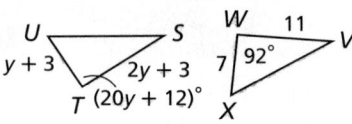

$\triangle MNO \cong \triangle PQR$ by SSS.

B. $\triangle STU \cong \triangle VWX$, when $y = 4$.

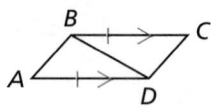

$\triangle STU \cong \triangle VWX$ by SAS.

Example 4

Given: $\overline{BC} \parallel \overline{AD}$, $\overline{BC} \cong \overline{AD}$
Prove: $\triangle ABD \cong \triangle CDB$

1. $\overline{BC} \parallel \overline{AD}$ (Given)
2. $\angle CBD \cong \angle ADB$ (Alt. Int. ∡ Thm.)
3. $\overline{BC} \cong \overline{AD}$ (Given)
4. $\overline{BD} \cong \overline{BD}$ (Reflex. Prop. of ≅)
5. $\triangle ABD \cong \triangle CDB$ (SAS Steps 3, 2, 4)

INTERVENTION ◀▶
Questioning Strategies

• How do you find the lengths of the sides of both triangles?

• How do parallel lines help you verify congruent angles?

EXAMPLE **3** **Verifying Triangle Congruence**

Show that the triangles are congruent for the given value of the variable.

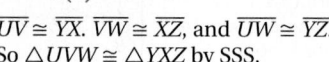 **Algebra**

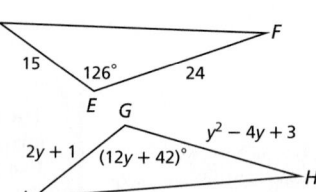

A $\triangle UVW \cong \triangle YXW$, $x = 3$

$ZY = x - 1$
$\quad = 3 - 1 = 2$
$XZ = x = 3$
$XY = 3x - 5$
$\quad = 3(3) - 5 = 4$

$\overline{UV} \cong \overline{YX}$. $\overline{VW} \cong \overline{XZ}$, and $\overline{UW} \cong \overline{YZ}$.
So $\triangle UVW \cong \triangle YXZ$ by SSS.

B $\triangle DEF \cong \triangle JGH$, $y = 7$

$JG = 2y + 1$
$\quad = 2(7) + 1$
$\quad = 15$
$GH = y^2 - 4y + 3$
$\quad = (7)^2 - 4(7) + 3$
$\quad = 24$
$m\angle G = 12y + 42$
$\quad = 12(7) + 42$
$\quad = 126°$

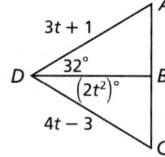

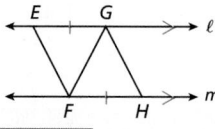

$\overline{DE} \cong \overline{JG}$. $\overline{EF} \cong \overline{GH}$, and $\angle E \cong \angle G$.
So $\triangle DEF \cong \triangle JGH$ by SAS.

CHECK IT OUT! **3.** $\triangle ADB \cong \triangle CDB$, $t = 4$

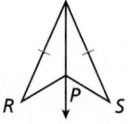

3. $DA = DC = 13$, so $\overline{DA} \cong \overline{DC}$ by def. of ≅. $m\angle ADB = m\angle CDB = 32°$, so $\angle ADB \cong \angle CDB$ by def. of ≅. $\overline{DB} \cong \overline{DB}$ by the Reflex. Prop. of ≅. Therefore $\triangle ADB \cong \triangle CDB$ by SAS.

EXAMPLE **4** **Proving Triangles Congruent**

Given: $\ell \parallel m$, $\overline{EG} \cong \overline{HF}$
Prove: $\triangle EGF \cong \triangle HFG$
Proof:

Statements	Reasons
1. $\overline{EG} \cong \overline{HF}$	1. Given
2. $\ell \parallel m$	2. Given
3. $\angle EGF \cong \angle HFG$	3. Alt. Int. ∡ Thm.
4. $\overline{FG} \cong \overline{FG}$	4. Reflex Prop. of ≅
5. $\triangle EGF \cong \triangle HFG$	5. SAS Steps 1, 3, 4

1. $\overline{QR} \cong \overline{QS}$ (Given)
2. $\overrightarrow{QP}$ bisects $\angle RQS$. (Given)
3. $\angle RQP \cong \angle SQP$ (Def. of bisector)
4. $\overline{QP} \cong \overline{QP}$ (Reflex. Prop. of ≅)
5. $\triangle RQP \cong \triangle SQP$ (SAS Steps 1, 3, 4)

CHECK IT OUT! **4.** **Given:** $\overrightarrow{QP}$ bisects $\angle RQS$. $\overline{QR} \cong \overline{QS}$
Prove: $\triangle RQP \cong \triangle SQP$

---

3 Close

Summarize

Review the SSS and SAS postulates for proving triangles congruent, and give examples of each. Remind students of the importance of the order of the letters in a congruence statement.

ONGOING ASSESSMENT

and INTERVENTION ◀▶

Diagnose Before the Lesson
4-4 Warm Up, TE p. 242

Monitor During the Lesson
Check It Out! Exercises, SE pp. 242–244
Questioning Strategies, TE pp. 243–244

Assess After the Lesson
4-4 Lesson Quiz, TE p. 249
Alternative Assessment, TE p. 249

Answers to *Think and Discuss*

1. Show that all six pairs of corr.
   parts are ≅; SSS; SAS

2. The SSS and SAS Post. are methods for proving △ ≅ without
   having to prove the congruence
   of all 6 corr. parts.

3. See p. A4

THINK AND DISCUSS

1. Describe three ways you could prove that $\triangle ABC \cong \triangle DEF$.

2. Explain why the SSS and SAS Postulates are shortcuts for proving triangles congruent.

3. **GET ORGANIZED** Copy and complete the graphic organizer. Use it to compare the SSS and SAS postulates.

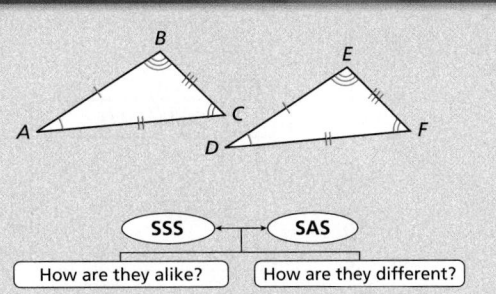

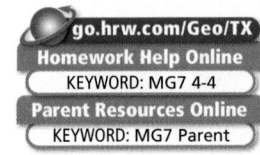

4-4 Exercises

go.hrw.com/Geo/TX
Homework Help Online
KEYWORD: MG7 4-4
Parent Resources Online
KEYWORD: MG7 Parent

4-4 Exercises

GUIDED PRACTICE

1. **Vocabulary** In $\triangle RST$ which angle is the included angle of sides $\overline{ST}$ and $\overline{TR}$? ∠T

SEE EXAMPLE 1
p. 242

Use SSS to explain why the triangles in each pair are congruent.

2. $\triangle ABD \cong \triangle CDB$

3. $\triangle MNP \cong \triangle MQP$

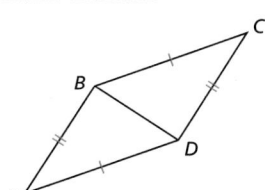

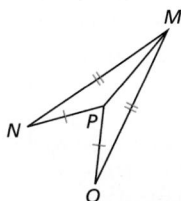

SEE EXAMPLE 2
p. 243

4. **Design** This Texas flag consists of a blue, perpendicular stripe with a white star in the center. The star consists of five triangles. $GJ = LG = 20$ in., and $GK = GH = 13$ in. Use SAS to explain why $\triangle JGK \cong \triangle LGH$.

SEE EXAMPLE 3
p. 244

Show that the triangles are congruent for the given value of the variable.

5. $\triangle GHJ \cong \triangle IHJ$, $x = 4$

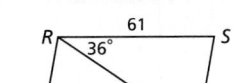

When $x = 4$, $HI = GH = 3$, and $IJ = GJ = 5$. $\overline{HJ} \cong \overline{HJ}$ by the Reflex. Prop. of ≅. Therefore $\triangle GHJ \cong \triangle IHJ$ by SSS.

6. $\triangle RST \cong \triangle TUR$, $x = 18$

When $x = 18$, $RS = UT = 61$, and m∠SRT = m∠UTR = 36°. $\overline{RT} \cong \overline{RT}$ by the Reflex. Prop. of ≅. So $\triangle RST \cong \triangle TUR$ by SAS.

4-4 Triangle Congruence: SSS and SAS **245**

Answers

2. It is given that $\overline{DA} \cong \overline{BC}$ and $\overline{AB} \cong \overline{CD}$. $\overline{BD} \cong \overline{BD}$ by the Reflex. Prop. of ≅. Thus $\triangle ABD \cong \triangle CBD$ by SSS.

3. It is given that $\overline{MN} \cong \overline{MQ}$ and $\overline{NP} \cong \overline{NQ}$. $\overline{MP} \cong \overline{MP}$ by the Reflex. Prop. of ≅. Thus $\triangle MNP \cong \triangle MQP$ by SSS.

4. It is given that $\overline{JG} \cong \overline{LG}$ and $\overline{GK} \cong \overline{GH}$. ∠$JGK \cong$ ∠LGH by the Vert. ∡ Thm. So $\triangle JGK \cong \triangle LGH$ by SAS.

Assignment Guide

Assign *Guided Practice* exercises as necessary.

If you finished Examples **1–2**
  Basic 8–10, 14–18, 27
  Average 8–10, 14–18, 24, 27
  Advanced 8–10, 14–18, 24–27

If you finished Examples **1–4**
  Basic 8–18, 21, 23, 25, 26,
      28–32, 37–45
  Average 8–19, 21, 22–31, 33,
      36–44
  Advanced 8–14, 19–44

Homework Quick Check
Quickly check key concepts.
Exercises: 8, 10, 12, 13, 14, 25

Critical Thinking In
Teaching **Exercises 5** and **6**, have
Tip students consider how they can find the value of the variable if the triangles are given as congruent.

🡇 TAKS Practice

Grades 9–11	Exercises
Obj. 2	31, 34, 35, 39–44
Obj. 4	36–41
Obj. 6	28, 29, 42–44
Obj. 7	19, 20
Obj. 10	31

Answers

8. It is given that $BC = ED = 4$ in. and $BD = EC = 3$ in. So by the def. of $\cong$, $\overline{BC} \cong \overline{ED}$, and $\overline{BD} \cong \overline{EC}$. $\overline{DC} \cong \overline{DC}$ by the Reflex. Prop. of $\cong$. Thus $\triangle BCD \cong \triangle EDC$ by SSS.

9. It is given that $\overline{KJ} \cong \overline{LJ}$ and $\overline{GK} \cong \overline{GL}$. $\overline{GJ} \cong \overline{GJ}$ by the Reflex. Prop. of $\cong$. So $\triangle GJK \cong \triangle GJL$ by SSS.

10. It is given that $\angle C$ and $\angle B$ are rt. $\angle$ and $\overline{EC} \cong \overline{DB}$. $\angle C \cong \angle B$ by the Rt. $\angle \cong$ Thm. $\overline{CB} \cong \overline{CB}$ by the Reflex. Prop. of $\cong$. So $\triangle ECB \cong \triangle DBC$ by SAS.

11. When $y = 3$, $NQ = NM = 3$, and $QP = MP = 4$. So by the def. of $\cong$, $\overline{NQ} \cong \overline{NM}$, and $\overline{QP} \cong \overline{MP}$. $m\angle M = m\angle Q = 90°$, so $\angle M \cong \angle Q$ by the def. of $\cong$. Thus $\triangle MNP \cong \triangle QNP$ by SAS.

12. When $t = 5$, $YZ = 24$, $ST = 20$, and $SU = 22$. So by the def. of $\cong$, $\overline{XY} \cong \overline{ST}$, $\overline{YZ} \cong \overline{TU}$, and $\overline{XZ} \cong \overline{SU}$. Thus $\triangle XYZ \cong \triangle STU$ by SSS.

SEE EXAMPLE 4
p. 244

7. **Given:** $\overline{JK} \cong \overline{ML}$, $\angle JKL \cong \angle MLK$
Prove: $\triangle JKL \cong \triangle MLK$

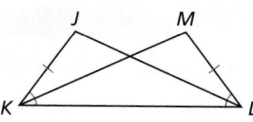

Proof:

Statements	Reasons
1. $\overline{JK} \cong \overline{ML}$	1. a. _?_
2. b. _?_	2. Given
3. $\overline{KL} \cong \overline{LK}$	3. c. _?_
4. $\triangle JKL \cong \triangle MLK$	4. d. _?_

a. Given
b. $\angle JKL \cong \angle MLK$
c. Reflex. Prop. of $\cong$
d. SAS *Steps 1, 2, 3*

PRACTICE AND PROBLEM SOLVING

Independent Practice

For Exercises	See Example
8–9	1
10	2
11–12	3
13	4

TEKS ⇨ TAKS

Skills Practice p. S11
Application Practice p. S31

Use SSS to explain why the triangles in each pair are congruent.

8. $\triangle BCD \cong \triangle EDC$

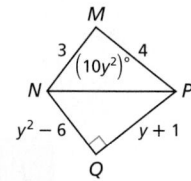

9. $\triangle GJK \cong \triangle GJL$

10. **Theater** The lights shining on a stage appear to form two congruent right triangles. Given $\overline{EC} \cong \overline{DB}$, use SAS to explain why $\triangle ECB \cong \triangle DBC$.

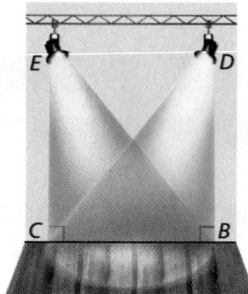

Show that the triangles are congruent for the given value of the variable.

11. $\triangle MNP \cong \triangle QNP$, $y = 3$

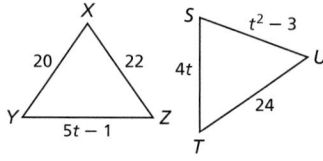

12. $\triangle XYZ \cong \triangle STU$, $t = 5$

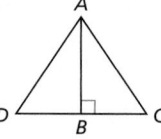

13. **Given:** B is the midpoint of $\overline{DC}$. $\overline{AB} \perp \overline{DC}$
Prove: $\triangle ABD \cong \triangle ABC$

Proof:

Statements	Reasons
1. B is the mdpt. of $\overline{DC}$.	1. a. _?_
2. b. _?_	2. Def. of mdpt.
3. c. _?_	3. Given
4. $\angle ABD$ and $\angle ABC$ are rt. $\angle$.	4. d. _?_
5. $\angle ABD \cong \angle ABC$	5. e. _?_
6. f. _?_	6. Reflex. Prop. of $\cong$
7. $\triangle ABD \cong \triangle ABC$	7. g. _?_

a. Given
b. $\overline{DB} \cong \overline{CB}$
c. $\overline{AB} \perp \overline{DC}$
d. Def. of $\perp$
e. Rt. $\angle \cong$ Thm.
f. $\overline{AB} \cong \overline{AB}$
g. SAS *Steps 2, 5, 6*

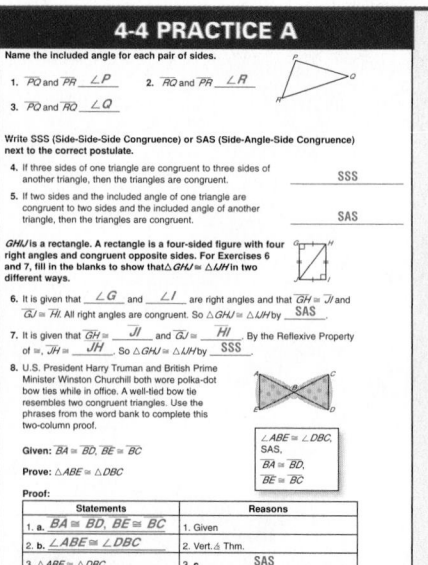

Which postulate, if any, can be used to prove the triangles congruent?

14.  SAS

15. 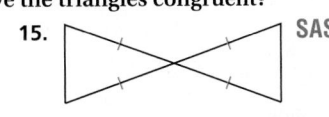 SAS

16.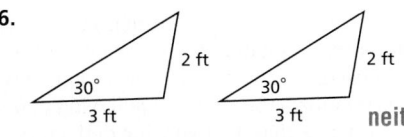

17.  neither

2 ft ... 30° ... 3 ft ... 2 ft ... 30° ... 3 ft ... neither

18a. To use SSS, you need to know that $\overline{AB} \cong \overline{DE}$ and $\overline{CB} \cong \overline{CE}$.

b. To use SAS, you need to know that $\overline{CB} \cong \overline{CE}$.

18. Explain what additional information, if any, you would need to prove $\triangle ABC \cong \triangle DEC$ by each postulate.
a. SSS b. SAS

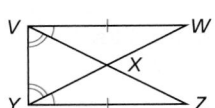

Multi-Step Graph each triangle. Then use the Distance Formula and the SSS Postulate to determine whether the triangles are congruent.

19. $\triangle QRS$ and $\triangle TUV$
$Q(-2, 0), R(1, -2), S(-3, -2)$
$T(5, 1), U(3, -2), V(3, 2)$

20. $\triangle ABC$ and $\triangle DEF$
$A(2, 3), B(3, -1), C(7, 2)$
$D(-3, 1), E(1, 2), F(-3, 5)$

21a. Given
b. Def. of $\cong$
c. $m\angle WVY = m\angle ZYV$
d. Def. of $\cong$
e. Given
f. $\overline{VY} \cong \overline{VY}$
g. SAS *Steps 6, 5, 7*

21. Given: $\angle ZVY \cong \angle WYV$,
$\angle ZVW \cong \angle WYZ$,
$\overline{VW} \cong \overline{YZ}$
Prove: $\triangle ZVY \cong \triangle WYV$
Proof:

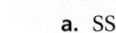

Statements	Reasons
1. $\angle ZVY \cong \angle WYV$, $\angle ZVW \cong WYZ$	1. a. ?
2. $m\angle ZVY = m\angle WYV$, $m\angle ZVW = m\angle WYZ$	2. b. ?
3. $m\angle ZVY + m\angle ZVW = m\angle WYV + m\angle WYZ$	3. Add. Prop. of =
4. c. ?	4. $\angle$ Add. Post.
5. $\angle WVY \cong \angle ZYV$	5. d. ?
6. $\overline{VW} \cong \overline{YZ}$	6. e. ?
7. f. ?	7. Reflex. Prop. of $\cong$
8. $\triangle ZVY \cong \triangle WYV$	8. g. ?

22. This problem will prepare you for the Multi-Step TAKS Prep on page 280. The diagram shows two triangular trusses that were built for the roof of a doghouse.

a. You can use a protractor to check that $\angle A$ and $\angle D$ are right angles. Explain how you could make just two additional measurements on each truss to ensure that the trusses are congruent.

b. You verify that the trusses are congruent and find that $AB = AC = 2.5$ ft. Find the length of $\overline{EF}$ to the nearest tenth. Explain.

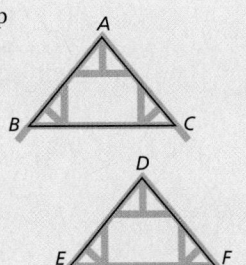

4-4 Triangle Congruence: SSS and SAS **247**

Answers

19. Check students' graphs. $QS = TV = \sqrt{5}$. $SR = VU = 4$. $QR = TU = \sqrt{13}$. The $\triangle$ are $\cong$ by SSS.

20. Check students' graphs. $AB = \sqrt{17}, BC = 5, AC = \sqrt{26}$; $DE = \sqrt{17}, EF = 5$, and $DF = 4$. The $\triangle$ are not $\cong$.

22a. Measure $\overline{AB}$ and $\overline{AC}$ on 1 truss and measure $\overline{DE}$ and $\overline{DF}$ on the other. If $\overline{AB} \cong \overline{DE}$ and $\overline{AC} \cong \overline{DF}$, then the trusses are $\cong$ by SAS.

b. 3.5 ft; by the Pyth. Thm., $BC \approx 3.5$ ft. Since the $\triangle$ are congruent, $\overline{EF} \cong \overline{BC}$.

Lesson 4-4 **247**

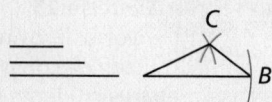

Construction

To help students construct the triangle in **Exercise 27,** have them construct $\overline{AB}$ congruent to one of the segments. Then set their compasses to the length of another segment. Have them make an arc centered at A. Next set their compasses to the length of the third segment and draw an arc centered at B. They should label the intersection of the arcs C. Finally have them draw $\triangle ABC$.

Answers

23.

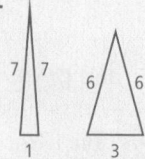

24. $x = 5.5$; by the def. of $\cong$, $\overline{AB} \cong \overline{BD}$, and $\overline{BC} \cong \overline{DC}$. $\overline{AC} \cong \overline{AC}$ by the Reflex. Prop. of $\cong$. Thus $\triangle ABC \cong \triangle ADC$ by SSS.

25. Measure the lengths of the logs. If the lengths of the logs in 1 wing deflector match the lengths of the logs in the other wing deflector, the $\triangle$ will be $\cong$ by SAS or SSS.

26. Yes; if the $\triangle$ have the same 2 side lengths and the same included $\angle$ measure, the $\triangle$ are $\cong$ by SAS.

27. Check students' constructions; yes; if each side is $\cong$ to the corr. side of the second $\triangle$, they can be in any order.

32. 1. Draw $\overline{DB}$. (Through any 2 pts. there is exactly 1 line.)
2. $\angle ADC$ and $\angle BCD$ are supp. (Given)
3. $\overline{AD} \parallel \overline{CB}$ (conv. of Same-Side Int. $\angle$ Thm.)
4. $\angle ADB \cong \angle CBD$ (Alt. Int. $\angle$ Thm.)
5. $\overline{AD} \cong \overline{CB}$ (Given)
6. $\overline{DB} \cong \overline{DB}$ (Reflex. Prop. of $\cong$)
7. $\triangle ADB \cong \triangle CBD$ (SAS Steps 5, 4, 6)

33. 1. $\angle QPS \cong \angle TPR$ (Given)
2. $\angle RPS \cong \angle RPS$ (Reflex. Prop. of $\cong$)
3. $\angle QPR \cong \angle TPS$ (Subtr. Prop. of $\cong$)
4. $\overline{PQ} \cong \overline{PT}$, $\overline{PR} \cong \overline{PS}$ (Given)
5. $\triangle PQR \cong \triangle PTS$ (SAS Steps 3, 4)

---

23. Critical Thinking Draw two isosceles triangles that are not congruent but that have a perimeter of 15 cm each.

24. $\triangle ABC \cong \triangle ADC$ for what value of x? Explain why the SSS Postulate can be used to prove the two triangles congruent.

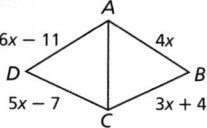

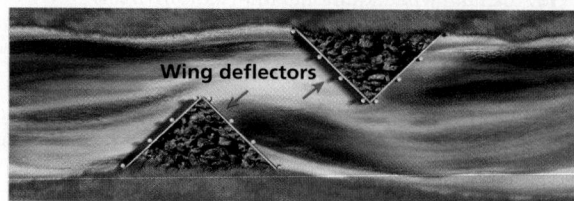
25. Ecology A *wing deflector* is a triangular structure made of logs that is filled with large rocks and placed in a stream to guide the current or prevent erosion. Wing deflectors are often used in pairs. Suppose an engineer wants to build two wing deflectors. The logs that form the sides of each wing deflector are perpendicular. How can the engineer make sure that the two wing deflectors are congruent?

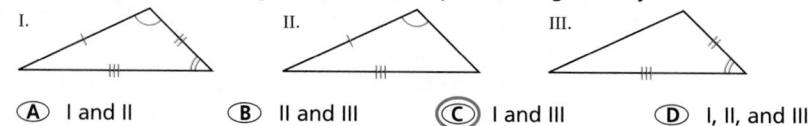

Wing deflectors

26. Write About It If you use the same two sides and included angle to repeat the construction of a triangle, are your two constructed triangles congruent? Explain.

27. Construction Use three segments (SSS) to construct a scalene triangle. Suppose you then use the same segments in a different order to construct a second triangle. Will the result be the same? Explain.

TEST PREP

28. Which of the three triangles below can be proven congruent by SSS or SAS?

I. II. III.

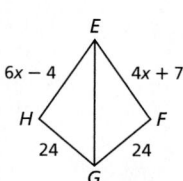

(A) I and II   (B) II and III   (C) I and III   (D) I, II, and III

29. What is the perimeter of polygon $ABCD$?
(F) 29.9 cm   (H) 49.8 cm
(G) 39.8 cm   (J) 59.8 cm

12.1 cm
10 cm
7.8 cm

30. Jacob wants to prove that $\triangle FGH \cong \triangle JKL$ using SAS. He knows that $\overline{FG} \cong \overline{JK}$ and $\overline{FH} \cong \overline{JL}$. What additional piece of information does he need?
(A) $\angle F \cong \angle J$ (C) $\angle H \cong \angle L$
(B) $\angle G \cong \angle K$ (D) $\angle F \cong \angle G$

31. What must the value of x be in order to prove that $\triangle EFG \cong \triangle EHG$ by SSS?
(F) 1.5   (H) 4.67
(G) 4.25   (J) 5.5

$6x - 4$ $4x + 7$
24   24

4-4 READING STRATEGIES

In mathematics, postulates and theorems are used to explain relationships. A **postulate** is a statement that is accepted without proof. A **theorem** is a statement that has been proven. Two postulates that can be used to prove that triangles are congruent are found in the following table:

Postulate	Hypothesis	Conclusion
SSS If three sides of one triangle are congruent to three sides of another triangle, then the triangles are congruent: Side-Side-Side Congruence	$\overline{XY} \cong \overline{QR}$ $\overline{XZ} \cong \overline{QS}$ $\overline{YZ} \cong \overline{RS}$	$\triangle XYZ \cong \triangle QRS$
SAS If two sides and the included angle of one triangle are congruent to two sides and the included angle of another triangle, then the triangles are congruent: Side-Angle-Side Congruence	$\overline{LM} \cong \overline{TU}$ $\overline{LN} \cong \overline{TV}$ $\angle NLM \cong \angle VTU$	$\triangle LMN \cong \triangle TUV$

1. How is Postulate SSS like Postulate SAS?
   Both involve the sides of the two triangles being compared.
2. How is Postulate SSS different from Postulate SAS?
   Postulate SAS involves comparing angles within the triangles, while SSS compares only the sides.
3. How is a postulate like a theorem?
   Postulates and theorems are both statements that can be used to compare geometric shapes.
4. How are postulates and theorems different?
   Postulates are accepted as being true, while a theorem has been proven.

Determine whether each pair of triangles is congruent by SSS, SAS, or neither.

5. SSS   6. SAS
7. neither   8. SAS

4-4 RETEACH

Side-Side-Side (SSS) Congruence Postulate
If three sides of one triangle are congruent to three sides of another triangle, then the triangles are congruent.
$\overline{QR} \cong \overline{TU}$, $\overline{RP} \cong \overline{US}$, and $\overline{PQ} \cong \overline{ST}$, so $\triangle PQR \cong \triangle STU$.

You can use SSS to explain why $\triangle FJH \cong \triangle FGH$.
It is given that $\overline{FJ} \cong \overline{FG}$ and that $\overline{JH} \cong \overline{GH}$. By the Reflex. Prop. of $\cong$, $\overline{FH} \cong \overline{FH}$. So $\triangle FJH \cong \triangle FGH$ by SSS.

Side-Angle-Side (SAS) Congruence Postulate
If two sides and the included angle of one triangle are congruent to two sides and the included angle of another triangle, then the triangles are congruent.

$\angle K$ is the included angle of $\overline{HK}$ and $\overline{KJ}$. $\angle N$ is the included angle of $\overline{LN}$ and $\overline{NM}$.
$\triangle HJK \cong \triangle LMN$

Use SSS to explain why the triangles in each pair are congruent.

1. $\triangle JKM \cong \triangle LKM$
   It is given that $\overline{JK} \cong \overline{LK}$ and that $\overline{JM} \cong \overline{LM}$. By the Reflex. Prop. of $\cong$, $\overline{KM} \cong \overline{KM}$. So $\triangle JKM \cong \triangle LKM$ by SSS.

2. $\triangle ABC \cong \triangle CDA$
   It is given that $\overline{AB} \cong \overline{CD}$ and that $\overline{AD} \cong \overline{CB}$. By the Reflex. Prop. of $\cong$, $\overline{AC} \cong \overline{AC}$. So $\triangle ABC \cong \triangle CDA$ by SSS.

3. Use SAS to explain why $\triangle WXY \cong \triangle WZY$.
   It is given that $\overline{ZW} \cong \overline{XW}$ and that $\angle ZWY \cong \angle XWY$. By the Reflex. Prop. of $\cong$, $\overline{WY} \cong \overline{WY}$. So $\triangle WXY \cong \triangle WZY$ by SAS.

CHALLENGE AND EXTEND

32. Given:. ∠ADC and ∠BCD are supplementary. $\overline{AD} \cong \overline{CB}$

Prove: △ADB ≅ △CBD
(*Hint:* Draw an auxiliary line.)

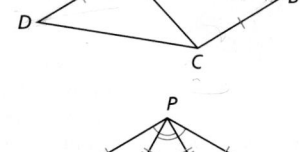

33. Given: ∠QPS ≅ ∠TPR, $\overline{PQ} \cong \overline{PT}$, $\overline{PR} \cong \overline{PS}$

Prove: △PQR ≅ △PTS

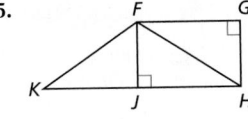

✗ᵧ Algebra Use the following information for Exercises 34 and 35.
Find the value of *x*. Then use SSS or SAS to write a paragraph proof showing that two of the triangles are congruent.

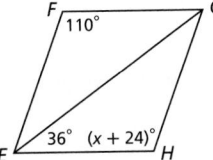

x = 16; KJ = HJ
= 72, so $\overline{KJ} \cong \overline{HJ}$
by def. of ≅.
∠FJK ≅ ∠FJH by
the Rt. ∠ ≅ Thm.
$\overline{FJ} \cong \overline{FJ}$ by the Reflex.
Prop. of ≅. So
△FJK ≅ △FJH by SAS.

34. m∠FKJ = 2x°
m∠KFJ = (3x + 10)°
KJ = 4x + 8
HJ = 6(x − 4)

35. $\overline{FJ}$ bisects ∠KFH.
m∠KFJ = (2x + 6)°
m∠HFJ = (3x − 21)°
FK = 8x − 45
FH = 6x + 9

x = 27; FK = FH = 171,
so $\overline{FK} \cong \overline{FH}$ by the def of ≅.
∠KFJ ≅ ∠HFJ by the def. of
∠ bisector. $\overline{FJ} \cong \overline{FJ}$ by the
Reflex. Prop. of ≅. So
△FJK ≅ △FJH by SAS.

SPIRAL REVIEW

Solve and graph each inequality. *(Previous course)*

36. $\frac{x}{2} - 8 \le 5$ x ≤ 26

37. 2a + 4 > 3a a < 4

38. −6m − 1 ≤ −13 m ≥ 2

Solve each equation. Write a justification for each step. *(Lesson 2-5)*

39. 4x − 7 = 21

40. $\frac{a}{4} + 5 = -8$

41. 6r = 4r + 10

Given: △EFG ≅ △GHE. Find each value. *(Lesson 4-3)*

42. x 86

43. m∠FEG 34°

44. m∠FGH 70°

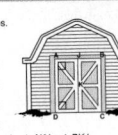

Using Technology

Use geometry software to complete the following. 1. Check students' drawings.

1. Draw a triangle and label the vertices *A*, *B*, and *C*.
Draw a point and label it *D*. Mark a vector from *A* to *B*
and translate *D* by the marked vector. Label the image *E*.
Draw $\overleftrightarrow{DE}$. Mark ∠BAC and rotate $\overleftrightarrow{DE}$ about *D* by the
marked angle. Mark ∠ABC and rotate $\overleftrightarrow{DE}$ about *E* by
the marked angle. Label the intersection *F*.

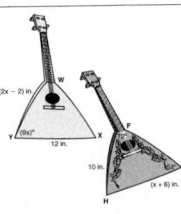

2. Drag *A*, *B*, and *C* to different locations.
What do you notice about the two triangles?

3. Write a conjecture about △ABC and △DEF. △ABC ≅ △DEF

4. Test your conjecture by measuring the sides and angles of △ABC and △DEF. Check students' measurements.

2. They stay the same size and shape.

4-4 Triangle Congruence: SSS and SAS **249**

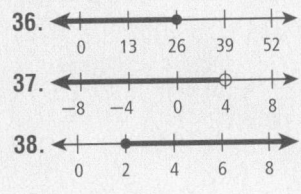
Answers

36.

0 13 26 39 52

37.

−8 −4 0 4 8

38.
0 2 4 6 8

39–41. See p. A15.

✓ 4-4 Lesson Quiz

1. Show that △ABC ≅ △DBC,
when *x* = 6.

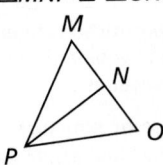

∠ABC ≅ ∠DBC, $\overline{BC} \cong \overline{BC}$, and $\overline{AB}$
≅ $\overline{DB}$. So △ABC ≅ △DBC by
SAS.

**Which postulate, if any, can
be used to prove the triangles
congruent?**

2.   none

3.   SSS

4. Given: $\overline{PN}$ bisects $\overline{MO}$.
PN ⊥ MO

Prove: △MNP ≅ △ONP

1. $\overline{PN}$ bisects $\overline{MO}$. (Given)
2. $\overline{MN} \cong \overline{ON}$ (Def. of bisect)
3. $\overline{PN} \cong \overline{PN}$ (Reflex. Prop. of ≅)
4. $\overline{PN} \perp \overline{MO}$ (Given)
5. ∠PNM and ∠PNO are rt. ∡.
   (Def. of ⊥)
6. ∠PNM ≅ ∠PNO (Rt. ∠ ≅ Thm.)
7. △MNP ≅ △ONP (SAS Steps 2, 6, 3)

Also available on transparency

Technology Organizer

LAB

Use with Lesson 4-5

Pacing:
Traditional 1 day
Block ½ day

Objective: Use geometry
software to explore triangle
congruence relationships.

Materials: geometry software

PREMIER Online Edition

Teach

Discuss

Discuss with students that ASA
makes only one triangle but that
SSA does not. Investigate and show
students that SSA makes only one
triangle for the special case when
there is a right angle. Also explain
that AAA does not make only one
triangle.

Alternative Approach

Have students work in small groups.
Each person in the group should
draw a different triangle and label it
△ABC. Have students construct $\overline{DF}$
≅ $\overline{AC}$. Students should construct an
angle congruent to ∠A at ∠D and
construct an angle congruent to ∠C
at F, and label their intersection E.
Then have them cut out △ABC and
△DEF and place △ABC over △DEF.
Have students compare the results
and make a conjecture.

 Geometry TEKS

G.2 Geometric structure*

(A) use constructions to explore
attributes of geometric figures and to
make conjectures …

G.3 Geometric structure*

(B) construct and justify statements
about geometric figures …

**G.9 Congruence and the geometry
of size***

(B) formulate and test conjectures
about the properties and attributes of
polygons … based on explorations …

**G.10 Congruence and the geometry
of size***

(B) justify and apply triangle
congruence relationships

* Knowledge and Skills See p. 214.

4-5 Technology LAB

Use with Lesson 4-5

Predict Other Triangle Congruence Relationships

Geometry software can help you investigate whether certain
combinations of triangle parts will make only one triangle.
If a combination makes only one triangle, then this arrangement
can be used to prove two triangles congruent.

 Activity 1

TEKS G.9.B Congruence and the geometry of size: formulate … conjectures about the
properties and attributes of polygons … based on explorations. Also G.2.A, G.3.B, G.10.B

1 Construct ∠CAB measuring 45° and
∠EDF measuring 110°.

2 Move ∠EDF so that $\overrightarrow{DE}$ overlays $\overrightarrow{BA}$.
Where $\overrightarrow{DF}$ and $\overrightarrow{AC}$ intersect, label the
point G. Measure ∠DGA.

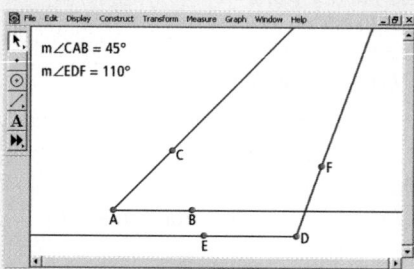

Check students' constructions.

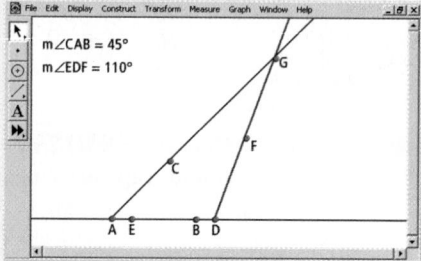

Check students' constructions.

3 Move ∠CAB to the left and right without changing the measures of the angles.
Observe what happens to the size of ∠DGA. **It stays the same.**

4 Measure the distance from A to D. Try to change the shape of the triangle
without changing AD and the measures of ∠A and ∠D. **Check students' work.**

 **Try This**

Yes; the △ stays the same
shape if you do not change AD
or the measures of ∠A and ∠D.

1. Repeat Activity 1 using angle measures of your choice. Are your results the same?
Explain.

2. Do the results change if one of the given angles measures 90°? **no**

3. What theorem proves that the measure of ∠DGA in Step 2 will always be the same? **Third ∠ Thm.**

4. In Step 3 of the activity, the angle measures in △ADG stayed the same as the size
of the triangle changed. Does Angle-Angle-Angle, like Side-Side-Side, make only
one triangle? Explain. **No; the ∠ measures may stay the same, but the side lengths can vary.**

5. Repeat Step 4 of the activity but measure the length of $\overline{AG}$ instead of $\overline{AD}$. Are your
results the same? Does this lead to a new congruence postulate or theorem?
Check students' constructions; yes; yes; AAS.

6. If you are given two angles of a triangle, what additional piece of information
is needed so that only one triangle is made? Make a conjecture based on your
findings in Step 5. **You need the length of 1 side of the △. In an AAS combination,
if 2 corr. ∠ and sides are ≅, then only 1 △ is made.**

Activity 2

① Construct $\overline{YZ}$ with a length of 6.5 cm.

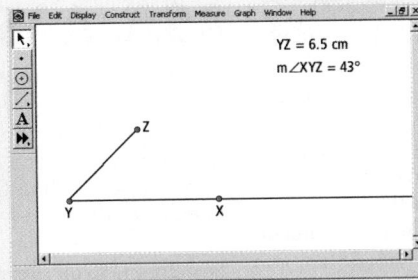

② Using $\overline{YZ}$ as a side, construct $\angle XYZ$ measuring 43°.

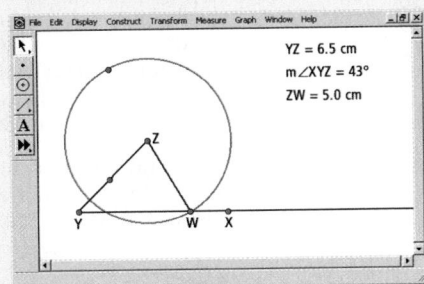

③ Draw a circle at Z with a radius of 5 cm. Construct $\overline{ZW}$, a radius of circle Z.

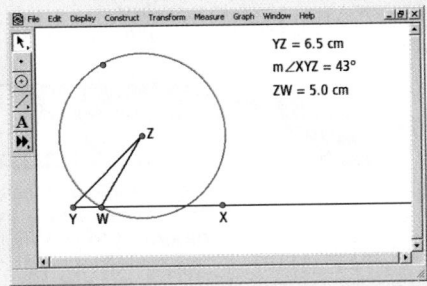

④ Move W around circle Z. Observe the possible shapes of $\triangle YZW$.

Try This

7. In Step 4 of the activity, how many different triangles were possible? Does Side-Side-Angle make only one triangle? **many; no**

8. Repeat Activity 2 using an angle measure of 90° in Step 2 and a circle with a radius of 7 cm in Step 3. How many different triangles are possible in Step 4? **1**

9. Repeat the activity again using a measure of 90° in Step 2 and a circle with a radius of 4.25 cm in Step 3. Classify the resulting triangle by its angle measures. **rt.**

10. Based on your results, complete the following conjecture. In a Side-Side-Angle combination, if the corresponding nonincluded angles are __?__ , then only one triangle is possible. **rt. ∠**

Close

Key Concept

Triangles can be proved congruent by ASA, but not by SSA or AAA. These last two methods do not always form a unique triangle. Remind students that they need to find only one counterexample. That is, students should find one triangle with the same SSA or AAA that is not congruent to the original triangle.

Assessment

Journal Have students compare and contrast ASA, AAA, and SSA. Have them show examples, including where SSA forms only one triangle.

Objectives: Apply ASA, AAS, and HL to construct triangles and solve problems.

Prove triangles congruent by using ASA, AAS, and HL.

Online Edition
Tutorial Videos

Countdown to TAKS Week 8

Power Presentations
with PowerPoint®

Warm Up

1. What are sides $\overline{AC}$ and $\overline{BC}$ called? side $\overline{AB}$?

legs; hypotenuse

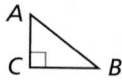

2. Which side is between $\angle A$ and $\angle C$? $\overline{AC}$

3. Given $\triangle DEF$ and $\triangle GHI$, if $\angle D \cong \angle G$ and $\angle E \cong \angle H$, why is $\angle F \cong \angle I$? Third $\angle$ Thm.

Also available on transparency

Math Fact !⋅!

Euclid thought he had proved ASA. It has since been postulated, and AAS and HL have been presented as theorems.

⭐ Geometry TEKS

G.1 Geometric structure*
(A) develop an awareness of the structure of a mathematical system, ...

G.2 Geometric structure*
(A) use constructions to explore attributes of geometric figures ...

G.3 Geometric structure*
(B) construct and justify statements about geometric figures ...
(C) use logical reasoning ...
(E) use deductive reasoning ...

G.9 Congruence and the geometry of size*
(B) formulate and test conjectures about the properties and attributes of polygons ... based on explorations ...

* Knowledge and Skills See p. 214.
Blue text indicates coverage in TE.

4-5 Triangle Congruence: ASA, AAS, and HL

⭐ TEKS G.10.B Congruence and the geometry of size: justify and apply triangle congruence relationships. Also G.1.A, G.1.B, G.2.A, G.3.B, G.3.C, G.3.E, G.9.B

Objectives
Apply ASA, AAS, and HL to construct triangles and to solve problems.

Prove triangles congruent by using ASA, AAS, and HL.

Vocabulary
included side

Why use this?
Bearings are used to convey direction, helping people find their way to specific locations.

Participants in an *orienteering* race use a map and a compass to find their way to checkpoints along an unfamiliar course. Directions are given by *bearings*, which are based on compass headings. For example, to travel along the bearing S 43° E, you face south and then turn 43° to the east.

An **included side** is the common side of two consecutive angles in a polygon. The following postulate uses the idea of an *included side*.

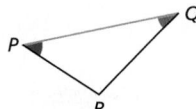

$\overline{PQ}$ is the included side of $\angle P$ and $\angle Q$.

Know it!
Note

Postulate 4-5-1	Angle-Side-Angle (ASA) Congruence	
POSTULATE	**HYPOTHESIS**	**CONCLUSION**
If two angles and the included side of one triangle are congruent to two angles and the included side of another triangle, then the triangles are congruent.		$\triangle ABC \cong \triangle DEF$

EXAMPLE 1   **Problem-Solving Application**

PROBLEM SOLVING

Organizers of an orienteering race are planning a course with checkpoints A, B, and C. Does the table give enough information to determine the location of the checkpoints?

	Bearing	Distance
A to B	N 55° E	7.6 km
B to C	N 26° W	
C to A	S 20° W	

1️⃣ Understand the Problem

The **answer** is whether the information in the table can be used to find the position of checkpoints A, B, and C. List the **important information:** The bearing from A to B is N 55° E. From B to C is N 26° W, and from C to A is S 20° W. The distance from A to B is 7.6 km.

1️⃣ Introduce

EXPLORATION

4-5 Triangle Congruence: ASA, AAS, and HL

You will need a ruler and protractor for this Exploration.

1. Draw $\triangle ABC$ with the given measurements. (*Hint:* First draw $\overline{AB}$ with the required length. Then draw $\angle A$ and $\angle B$ at the endpoints of $\overline{AB}$.)

$\triangle ABC$	
$m\angle A$	35°
$m\angle B$	80°
AB	2 in.

2. Draw $\triangle DEF$ with the given measurements.

$\triangle DEF$	
$m\angle D$	35°
$m\angle E$	80°
DE	2 in.

3. What do you notice about the two triangles you drew?

4. Is it possible to draw $\triangle DEF$ so that it is NOT congruent to $\triangle ABC$? If so, how?

5. Repeat Steps 1–4, choosing your own measures so that $m\angle A = m\angle D$, $m\angle B = m\angle E$, and $AB = DE$. Do you get the same results? Are there any restrictions on the angle measures you can choose?

6. An *included side* is the common side of two consecutive angles in a polygon. Complete the following conjecture: If two angles and the included side of one triangle are congruent to two angles and the included side of another triangle, then ___?___.

THINK AND DISCUSS

7. Explain how you could use the above conjecture to show that $\triangle KLN \cong \triangle MNL$.

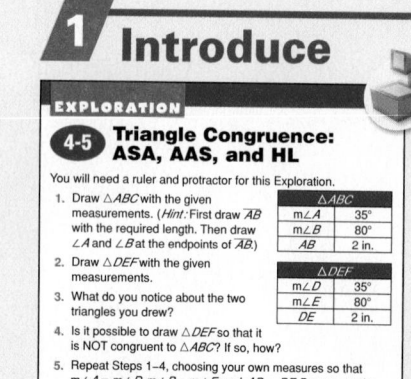

Motivate

Give students a map of the area that contains their school. Have them plot a triangle, using the school, their house, and another location as vertices. Ask them to calculate the measures of the angles of the triangle. Explain to students that angles are important in navigation where directions are given by bearings.

Explorations and answers are provided in the *Explorations* binder.

Make a Plan

Draw the course using vertical lines to show north-south directions. Then use these parallel lines and the alternate interior angles to help find angle measures of △ABC.

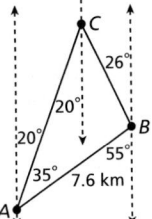

 Solve

m∠CAB = 55° − 20° = 35°

m∠CBA = 180° − (26° + 55°) = 99°

You know the measures of ∠CAB and ∠CBA and the length of the included side $\overline{AB}$. Therefore by ASA, a unique triangle ABC is determined.

 **Look Back**

One and only one triangle can be made using the information in the table, so the table does give enough information to determine the location of all the checkpoints.

CHECK IT OUT! 1. **What if...?** If 7.6 km is the distance from B to C, is there enough information to determine the location of all the checkpoints? Explain.

Yes; the △ is uniquely determined by AAS.

EXAMPLE 2 **Applying ASA Congruence**

Determine if you can use ASA to prove △UVX ≅ △WVX. Explain.

∠UXV ≅ ∠WXV as given. Since ∠WVX is a right angle that forms a linear pair with ∠UVX, ∠WVX ≅ ∠UVX. Also $\overline{VX} \cong \overline{VX}$ by the Reflexive Property. Therefore △UVX ≅ △WVX by ASA.

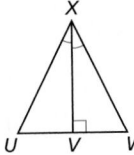

CHECK IT OUT! 2. Determine if you can use ASA to prove △NKL ≅ △LMN. Explain.

By the Alt. Int. ∠s Thm., ∠KLN ≅ ∠MNL. $\overline{LN} \cong \overline{LN}$ by the Reflex. Prop. No other congruence relationships can be determined, so ASA cannot be applied.

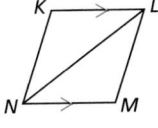

 **Construction** Congruent Triangles Using ASA

Use a straightedge to draw a segment and two angles, or copy the given segment and angles.

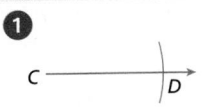

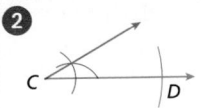

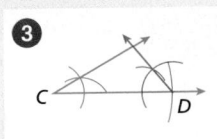

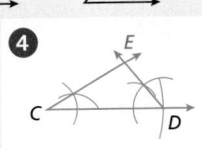

△CDE

① Construct $\overline{CD}$ congruent to the given segment.

② Construct ∠C congruent to one of the angles.

③ Construct ∠D congruent to the other angle.

④ Label the intersection of the rays as E.

 Teach

Guided Instruction

Review with students how to read bearings before presenting examples. If more explanation is needed for the drawing in Example 1, give students the following directions:

1. Draw A.
2. Find B.
3. Use a straightedge and draw $\overrightarrow{AC}$ with the bearing from A being N 20° E.

With students, practice identifying ASA, AAS, and HL from diagrams before writing proofs.

 Reaching All Learners
Through Auditory Cues

As students work through the lesson have them identify orally whether the triangles are congruent by HL, ASA, AAS, SAS, or SSS. Then have them work with a partner to identify the congruent parts and to determine if the congruent pairs of angles or sides are corresponding parts.

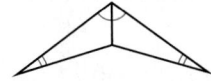

Example 3

Use AAS to prove the triangles congruent.

Given: ∠X ≅ ∠V, ∠YZW ≅ ∠YWZ, $\overline{XY} ≅ \overline{VY}$

Prove: △XYZ ≅ △VYW

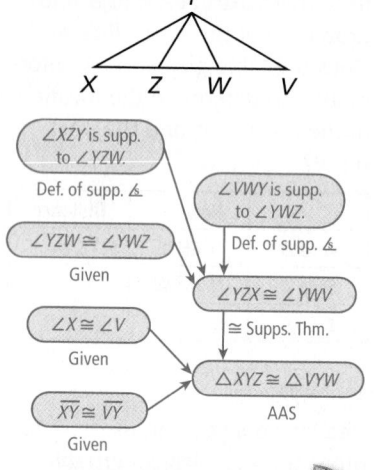

Also available on transparency

INTERVENTION ◀▶
Questioning Strategies

EXAMPLE **3**

• If AAS is used as the method of proof, can the triangles also be proved congruent using ASA?

Answers to Check It Out!

3.

```
          ┌─────────────────────┐
          │ JL bisects ∠KLM.    │
          └─────────────────────┘
                  Given
                    │
          ┌─────────────────────┐
          │  ∠KLJ ≅ ∠MLJ        │
          └─────────────────────┘
               Def. of ∠ bisector
```

```
┌─────────────┐              ┌─────────────┐
│  ∠K ≅ ∠M    │              │  JL ≅ JL    │
└─────────────┘              └─────────────┘
    Given                       Reflex.
                                Prop. of ≅
          ┌─────────────────────┐
          │  △JKL ≅ △JML        │
          └─────────────────────┘
                   AAS
```

You can use the Third Angles Theorem to prove another congruence relationship based on ASA. This theorem is Angle-Angle-Side (AAS).

Know it!
Note

Theorem 4-5-2 — **Angle-Angle-Side (AAS) Congruence**

THEOREM	HYPOTHESIS	CONCLUSION
If two angles and a nonincluded side of one triangle are congruent to the corresponding angles and nonincluded side of another triangle, then the triangles are congruent.	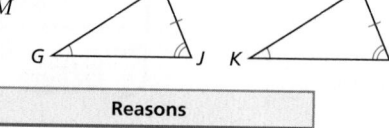	△GHJ ≅ △KLM

PROOF ▮ **Angle-Angle-Side Congruence**

Given: ∠G ≅ ∠K, ∠J ≅ ∠M, $\overline{HJ} ≅ \overline{LM}$
Prove: △GHJ ≅ △KLM
Proof:

Statements	Reasons
1. ∠G ≅ ∠K, ∠J ≅ ∠M	1. Given
2. ∠H ≅ ∠L	2. Third ∠ Thm.
3. $\overline{HJ} ≅ \overline{LM}$	3. Given
4. △GHJ ≅ △KLM	4. ASA *Steps 1, 3, and 2*

EXAMPLE 3 **Using AAS to Prove Triangles Congruent**

Use AAS to prove the triangles congruent.
Given: $\overline{AB} \parallel \overline{ED}$, $\overline{BC} ≅ \overline{DC}$
Prove: △ABC ≅ △EDC
Proof:

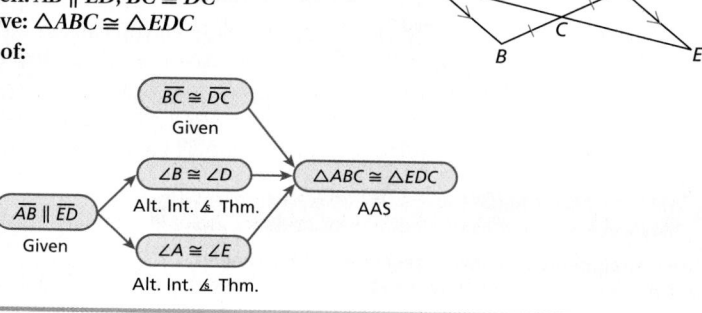

CHECK IT OUT! **3.** Use AAS to prove the triangles congruent.
Given: $\overline{JL}$ bisects ∠KLM. ∠K ≅ ∠M
Prove: △JKL ≅ △JML

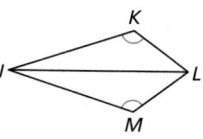

There are four theorems for right triangles that are not used for acute or obtuse triangles. They are Leg-Leg (LL), Hypotenuse-Angle (HA), Leg-Angle (LA), and Hypotenuse-Leg (HL). You will prove LL, HA, and LA in Exercises 21, 23, and 33.

Theorem 4-5-3 — Hypotenuse-Leg (HL) Congruence

THEOREM	HYPOTHESIS	CONCLUSION
If the hypotenuse and a leg of a right triangle are congruent to the hypotenuse and a leg of another right triangle, then the triangles are congruent.	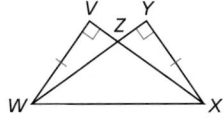	$\triangle ABC \cong \triangle DEF$

You will prove the Hypotenuse-Leg Theorem in Lesson 4-8.

EXAMPLE 4 — **Applying HL Congruence**

Determine if you can use the HL Congruence Theorem to prove the triangles congruent. If not, tell what else you need to know.

A $\triangle VWX$ and $\triangle YXW$

According to the diagram, $\triangle VWX$ and $\triangle YXW$ are right triangles that share hypotenuse $\overline{WX}$. $\overline{WX} \cong \overline{WX}$ by the Reflexive Property. It is given that $\overline{WV} \cong \overline{XY}$, therefore $\triangle VWX \cong \triangle YXW$ by HL.

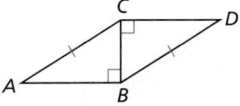

B $\triangle VWZ$ and $\triangle YXZ$

This conclusion cannot be proved by HL. According to the diagram, $\triangle VWZ$ and $\triangle YXZ$ are right triangles, and $\overline{WV} \cong \overline{XY}$. You do not know that hypotenuse $\overline{WZ}$ is congruent to hypotenuse $\overline{XZ}$.

4. Yes; it is given that $\overline{AC} \cong \overline{DB}$. $\overline{CB} \cong \overline{CB}$ by the Reflex. Prop. of $\cong$. Since $\angle ABC$ and $\angle DCB$ are rt. $\angle$s, $\triangle ABC$ and $\triangle DCB$ are rt. $\triangle$s. $\triangle ABC \cong \triangle DCB$ by HL.

CHECK IT OUT!

4. Determine if you can use the HL Congruence Theorem to prove $\triangle ABC \cong \triangle DCB$. If not, tell what else you need to know.

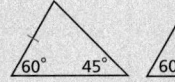

THINK AND DISCUSS

1. Could you use AAS to prove that these two triangles are congruent? Explain.

2. The arrangement of the letters in ASA matches the arrangement of what parts of congruent triangles? Include a sketch to support your answer.

3. **GET ORGANIZED** Copy and complete the graphic organizer. In each column, write a description of the method and then sketch two triangles, marking the appropriate congruent parts.

Proving Triangles Congruent						
	Def. of $\triangle \cong$	SSS	SAS	ASA	AAS	HL
Words						
Pictures						

Teaching Tip **Visual** For **Example 4**, it may be less confusing if students redraw the triangles separately and then carefully label the triangles and mark the congruent corresponding parts.

Teaching Tip **Inclusion** For **Example 4** show that AAS could be used as the method of proof. Include an illustration showing why SSA cannot be used to prove two triangles congruent. If the triangles are right triangles, then you would use HL.

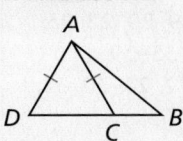

$\triangle DAB \not\cong \triangle CAB$

Power Presentations with PowerPoint®

Additional Examples

Example 4

Determine if you can use the HL Congruence Theorem to prove the triangles congruent. If not, tell what else you need to know.

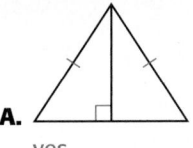

A. yes

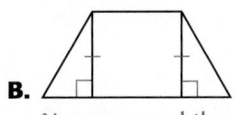

B. No; you need the hyp. $\cong$.

Also available on transparency

INTERVENTION
Questioning Strategies

EXAMPLE 4

• What type of triangle must be given to use HL as a method of proof?

Answers to *Think and Discuss*

1. No; the $\cong$ sides are not corr. sides.
2. Possible answer: corr. $\angle$ and sides

3. See p. A4.

3 Close

Summarize

Review how to identify when you should use AAS, HL, or ASA to prove triangles congruent. Remind students that three pairs of congruent corresponding parts are necessary for AAS and ASA. For HL they first must prove that the triangles are right triangles.

ONGOING ASSESSMENT
and INTERVENTION

*Diagnose **Before** the Lesson*
4-5 Warm Up, TE p. 252

*Monitor **During** the Lesson*
Check It Out! Exercises, SE pp. 253–255
Questioning Strategies, TE pp. 253–255

*Assess **After** the Lesson*
4-5 Lesson Quiz, TE p. 259
Alternative Assessment, TE p. 259

go.hrw.com/Geo/TX
Homework Help Online
KEYWORD: MG7 4-5
Parent Resources Online
KEYWORD: MG7 Parent

Assignment Guide

Assign *Guided Practice* exercises as necessary.

If you finished Examples **1–2**
   Basic 9–12, 17, 25
   Average 9–12, 17, 21, 25
   Advanced 9–12, 17, 21, 25, 32

If you finished Examples **1–4**
   Basic 9–17, 19, 20, 22, 25, 26–30, 35–39
   Average 9–20, 22, 24–30, 34, 35–39
   Advanced 9–16, 18, 19, 21–39

Homework Quick Check
Quickly check key concepts.
Exercises: 10, 12, 13, 14, 16, 22

Answers

1. The included side $\overline{BC}$ is enclosed between $\angle ABC$ and $\angle ACB$.

2.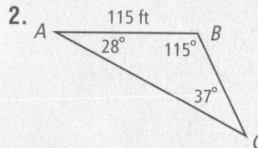

4. Yes; by the def. of bisector, $\angle TSV \cong \angle RSV$, and $\angle TVS \cong \angle RVS$. $\overline{SV} \cong \overline{SV}$ by the Reflex. Prop. of $\cong$. So $\triangle VRS \cong \triangle VTS$ by ASA.

7. Yes; it is given that $\angle D$ and $\angle B$ are rt. $\angle$ and $\overline{AD} \cong \overline{BC}$. $\triangle ABC$ and $\triangle CDA$ are rt. $\triangle$ by def. $\overline{AC} \cong \overline{CA}$ by the Reflex. Prop. of $\cong$. So $\triangle ABC \cong \triangle CDA$ by HL.

TAKS Practice

Grades 9–11	Exercises
Obj. 2	29, 31, 38, 39
Obj. 3	35–37
Obj. 5	38
Obj. 6	16, 17, 19
Obj. 7	35–37
Obj. 10	19

256   Chapter 4

GUIDED PRACTICE

1. **Vocabulary** A triangle contains $\angle ABC$ and $\angle ACB$ with $\overline{BC}$ "closed in" between them. How would this help you remember the definition of *included side*?

SEE EXAMPLE 1
p. 252

Surveying Use the table for Exercises 2 and 3.
A landscape designer surveyed the boundaries of a triangular park. She made the following table for the dimensions of the land.

	A to B	B to C	C to A
Bearing	E	S 25° E	N 62° W
Distance	115 ft	?	?

115 ft

2. Draw the plot of land described by the table. Label the measures of the angles in the triangle.

3. Does the table have enough information to determine the locations of points *A*, *B*, and *C*? Explain.
   Yes, the △ is determined by AAS.

SEE EXAMPLE 2
p. 253

Determine if you can use ASA to prove the triangles congruent. Explain.

4. $\triangle VRS$ and $\triangle VTS$, given that $\overline{VS}$ bisects $\angle RST$ and $\angle RVT$

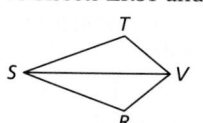

5. $\triangle DEH$ and $\triangle FGH$

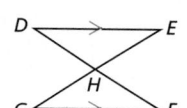
No; you need to know that a pair of corr. sides are $\cong$.

SEE EXAMPLE 3
p. 254

6. Use AAS to prove the triangles congruent.
   Given: $\angle R$ and $\angle P$ are right angles.
     $\overline{QR} \parallel \overline{SP}$
   Prove: $\triangle QPS \cong \triangle SRQ$
   Proof:

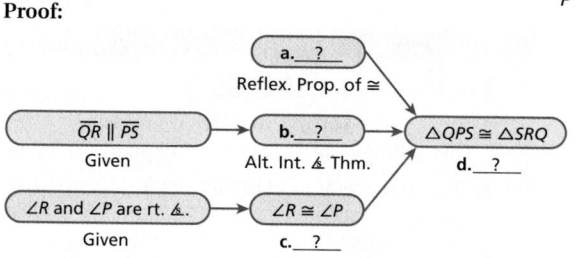

a. $\overline{QS} \cong \overline{QS}$
b. $\angle RQS \cong \angle PSQ$
c. Rt $\angle \cong$ Thm.
d. AAS

SEE EXAMPLE 4
p. 255

Determine if you can use the HL Congruence Theorem to prove the triangles congruent. If not, tell what else you need to know.

7. $\triangle ABC$ and $\triangle CDA$

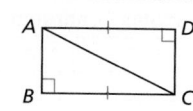

8. $\triangle XYV$ and $\triangle ZYV$

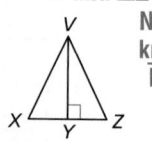
No; you need to know that $\overline{VX} \cong \overline{VZ}$.

256   Chapter 4 Triangle Congruence

PRACTICE AND PROBLEM SOLVING

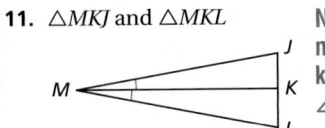

For Exercises	See Example
9–10	1
11–12	2
13	3
14–15	4

TEKS **TAKS**

Skills Practice p. S11
Application Practice p. S31

Surveying Use the table for Exercises 9 and 10.
From two different observation towers a fire is sighted. The locations of the towers are given in the following table.

	X to Y	X to F	Y to F
Bearing	E	N 53° E	N 16° W
Distance	6 km	?	?

9. Draw the diagram formed by observation tower X, observation tower Y, and the fire F. Label the measures of the angles.

10. Is there enough information given in the table to pinpoint the location of the fire? Explain. **Yes; the △ is uniquely determined by ASA.**

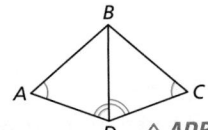

Math History

Euclid wrote the mathematical text *The Elements* around 2300 years ago. It may be the second most reprinted book in history.

Determine if you can use ASA to prove the triangles congruent. Explain.

11. △MKJ and △MKL   **No; you need to know that ∠MKJ ≅ ∠MKL.**

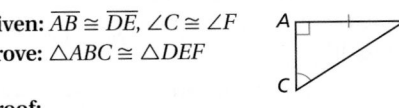

12. △RST and △TUR

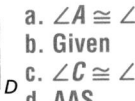

13. Given: $\overline{AB} \cong \overline{DE}$, ∠C ≅ ∠F
Prove: △ABC ≅ △DEF

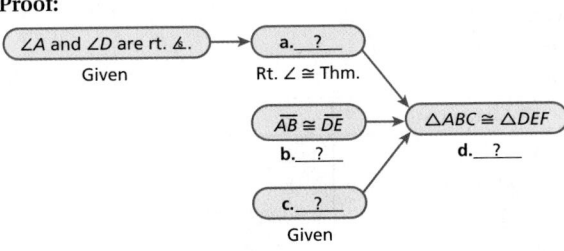

a. ∠A ≅ ∠D
b. **Given**
c. ∠C ≅ ∠F
d. **AAS**

Proof:

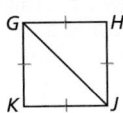 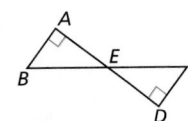

Determine if you can use the HL Congruence Theorem to prove the triangles congruent. If not, tell what else you need to know.

14. △GHJ and △JKG
No; you need to know that ∠K and ∠H are rt. ∡.

15. △ABE and △DCE, given that E is the midpoint of $\overline{AD}$ and $\overline{BC}$

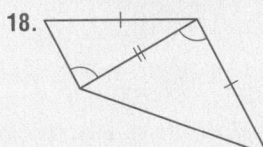

Multi-Step For each pair of triangles write a triangle congruence statement. Identify the transformation that moves one triangle to the position of the other triangle.

16.

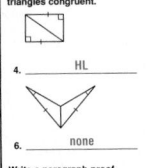

△ADB ≅ △CDB; reflection

17.

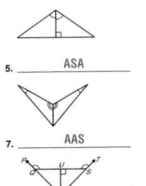

△FEG ≅ △QSR; rotation

18. Critical Thinking Side-Side-Angle (SSA) cannot be used to prove two triangles congruent. Draw a diagram that shows why this is true.

Answers

9.

12. Yes; by the Alt. Int. ∡ Thm. ∠SRT ≅ ∠UTR, and ∠STR ≅ ∠URT. $\overline{RT}$ ≅ $\overline{RT}$ by the Reflex. Prop. of ≅. So △RST ≅ △TUR by ASA.

15. Yes; E is a mdpt. So by def., $\overline{BE}$ ≅ $\overline{CE}$, and $\overline{AE}$ ≅ $\overline{DE}$. ∠A and ∠D are ≅ by the Rt. ∠ ≅ Thm. By def., △ABE and △DCE are rt. ∡. So △ABE ≅ △DCE by HL.

18.

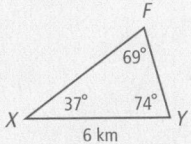

MULTI-STEP TAKS PREP **Exercise 19** involves proving that the triangles that form a truss are congruent. This exercise prepares students for the Multi-Step TAKS Prep on page 280.

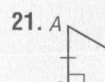 **Teaching Tip** **Construction** For **Exercise 25,** have students draw a 5 cm segment and a 10 cm segment. Have them construct $\overline{AB}$ congruent to the 5 cm segment and $\overrightarrow{AX}$ perpendicular to $\overline{AB}$ at A. Then have them set their compasses to the length of the 10 cm segment and draw an arc centered at A. Have them label the intersection of the arc and $\overrightarrow{AX}$ as C. Finally, have them draw right $\triangle ABC$.

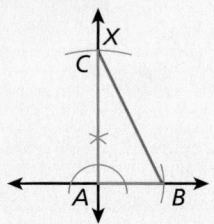

Answers

19a. No; there is not enough information given to use any of the congruence theorems.

21.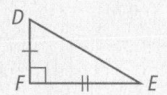

It is given that $\triangle ABC$ and $\triangle DEF$ are rt. $\triangle$. $\overline{AC} \cong \overline{DF}$, $\overline{BC} \cong \overline{EF}$, and $\angle C$ and $\angle F$ are rt. $\angle$. $\angle C \cong \angle F$ by the Rt. $\angle \cong$ Thm. Thus $\triangle ABC \cong \triangle DEF$ by SAS.

23. 1. $\overline{KM} \perp \overline{JL}$ (Given)
2. $\angle JKM$ and $\angle LKM$ are rt. $\angle$. (Def. of $\perp$)
3. $\angle JKM \cong \angle LKM$ (Rt. $\angle \cong$ Thm.)
4. $\overline{JM} \cong \overline{LM}$, $\angle JMK \cong \angle LMK$ (Given)
5. $\triangle JKM \cong \triangle LKM$ (AAS Steps 3, 4)

24. Since 2 sides and the included $\angle$ are equal in measure and therefore $\cong$, you could prove the $\triangle \cong$ using SAS. You could also use HL since the $\triangle$ are rt. $\triangle$.

31. Yes; the sum of the $\angle$ measures in each $\triangle$ must be 180°, which makes it possible to solve for x and y. The value of x is 15, and the value of y is 12. Each $\triangle$ has $\angle$ measuring 82°, 68°, and 30°. $\overline{VU} \cong \overline{VU}$ by the Reflex. Prop. of $\cong$. So $\triangle VSU \cong \triangle VTU$ by ASA or AAS.

19. This problem will prepare you for the Multi-Step TAKS Prep on page 280. A carpenter built a truss to support the roof of a doghouse.
a. The carpenter knows that $\overline{KJ} \cong \overline{MJ}$. Can the carpenter conclude that $\triangle KJL \cong \triangle MJL$? Why or why not?
b. Suppose the carpenter also knows that $\angle JLK$ is a right angle. Which theorem can be used to show that $\triangle KJL \cong \triangle MJL$? **HL**

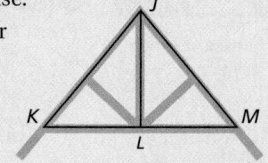

20. ///**ERROR ANALYSIS**/// Two proofs that $\triangle EFH \cong \triangle GHF$ are given. Which is incorrect? Explain the error.

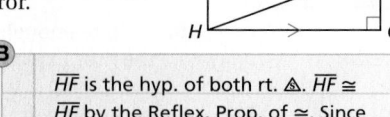

20. Proof B is incorrect. The corr. sides are not in the correct order.

A

It is given that $\overline{EF} \parallel \overline{GH}$. By the Alt. Int. $\angle$ Thm., $\angle EFH \cong \angle GHF$. $\angle E \cong \angle G$ by the Rt. $\angle \cong$ Thm. By the Reflex. Prop. of $\cong$, $\overline{HF} \cong \overline{HF}$. So by AAS, $\triangle EFH \cong \triangle GHF$.

B

$\overline{HF}$ is the hyp. of both rt. $\triangle$. $\overline{HF} \cong \overline{HF}$ by the Reflex. Prop. of $\cong$. Since the opp. sides of a rect. are $\cong$, $\overline{EF} \cong \overline{GH}$. So by HL, $\triangle EFH \cong \triangle FHG$.

21. Write a paragraph proof of the Leg-Leg (LL) Congruence Theorem. If the legs of one right triangle are congruent to the corresponding legs of another right triangle, the triangles are congruent.

22. Use AAS to prove the triangles congruent.
Given: $\overline{AD} \parallel \overline{BC}$, $\overline{AD} \cong \overline{CB}$
Prove: $\triangle AED \cong \triangle CEB$
Proof:

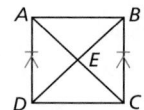

Statements	Reasons
1. $\overline{AD} \parallel \overline{BC}$	1. a. __?__
2. $\angle DAE \cong \angle BCE$	2. b. __?__
3. c. __?__	3. Vert. $\angle$ Thm.
4. d. __?__	3. Given
5. e. __?__	4. f. __?__

a. Given
b. Alt. Int. $\angle$ Thm.
c. $\angle AED \cong \angle CEB$
d. $\overline{AD} \cong \overline{CB}$
e. $\triangle AED \cong \triangle CEB$
f. AAS Steps 2, 3, 4

23. Prove the Hypotenuse-Angle (HA) Theorem.
Given: $\overline{KM} \perp \overline{JL}$, $\overline{JM} \cong \overline{LM}$, $\angle JMK \cong \angle LMK$
Prove: $\triangle JKM \cong \triangle LKM$

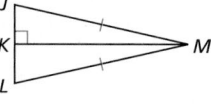

24. **Write About It** The legs of both right $\triangle DEF$ and right $\triangle RST$ are 3 cm and 4 cm. They each have a hypotenuse 5 cm in length. Describe two different ways you could prove that $\triangle DEF \cong \triangle RST$.

25.  **Construction** Use the method for constructing perpendicular lines to construct a right triangle. **Check students' constructions.**

TEST PREP

26. What additional congruence statement is necessary to prove $\triangle XWY \cong \triangle XVZ$ by ASA?
Ⓐ $\angle XVZ \cong \angle XWY$
Ⓑ $\angle VUY \cong \angle WUZ$
Ⓒ $\overline{VZ} \cong \overline{WY}$
Ⓓ $\overline{XZ} \cong \overline{XY}$

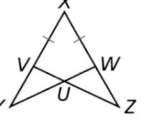

4-5 READING STRATEGIES

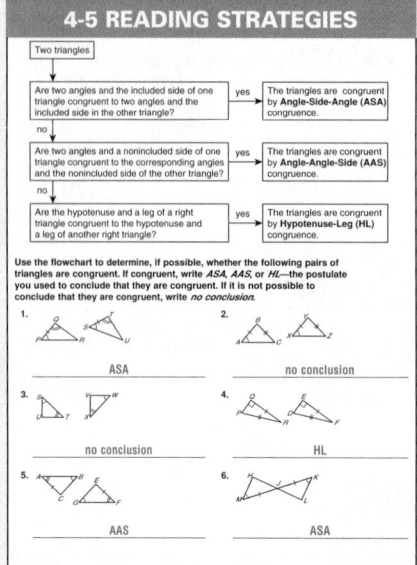

4-5 RETEACH

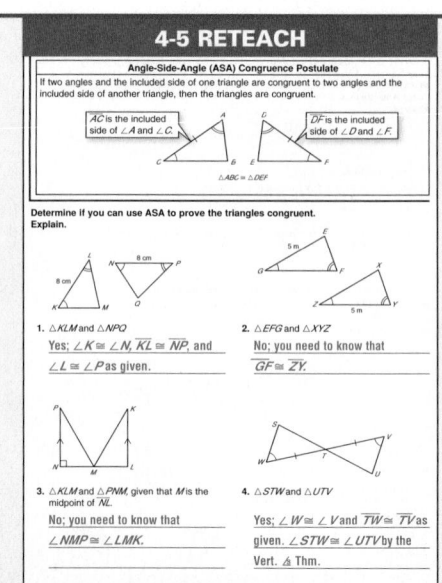

27. Which postulate or theorem justifies the congruence statement $\triangle STU \cong \triangle VUT$?

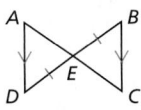

- **F** ASA
- **G** SSS
- **H** HL
- **J** SAS

28. Which of the following congruence statements is true?

- **A** $\angle A \cong \angle B$
- **B** $\overline{CE} \cong \overline{DE}$
- **C** $\triangle AED \cong \triangle CEB$
- **D** $\triangle AED \cong \triangle BEC$

29. In $\triangle RST$, $RT = 6y - 2$. In $\triangle UVW$, $UW = 2y + 7$. $\angle R \cong \angle U$, and $\angle S \cong \angle V$. What must be the value of y in order to prove that $\triangle RST \cong \triangle UVW$?

- **F** 1.25
- **G** 2.25
- **H** 9.0
- **J** 11.5

30. Extended Response Draw a triangle. Construct a second triangle that has the same angle measures but is not congruent. Compare the lengths of each pair of corresponding sides. Consider the relationship between the lengths of the sides and the measures of the angles. Explain why Angle-Angle-Angle (AAA) is not a congruence principle.

30. Check students' drawings and constructions; since the lengths of the corr. sides of the 2 △ are not equal, the 2 △ are not ≅ even if the corr. ∡ have the same measure.

CHALLENGE AND EXTEND

31. Sports This bicycle frame includes $\triangle VSU$ and $\triangle VTU$, which lie in intersecting planes. From the given angle measures, can you conclude that $\triangle VSU \cong \triangle VTU$? Explain.

$m\angle VUS = (7y - 2)^\circ$ $m\angle VUT = \left(5\frac{1}{2}x - \frac{1}{2}\right)^\circ$

$m\angle USV = 5\frac{2}{3}y^\circ$ $m\angle UTV = (4x + 8)^\circ$

$m\angle SVU = (3y - 6)^\circ$ $m\angle TVU = 2x^\circ$

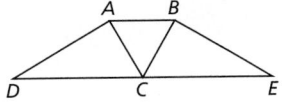

32. Given: $\triangle ABC$ is equilateral. C is the midpoint of $\overline{DE}$. $\angle DAC$ and $\angle EBC$ are congruent and supplementary.

Prove: $\triangle DAC \cong \triangle EBC$

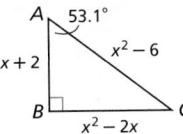

33. Write a two-column proof of the Leg-Angle (LA) Congruence Theorem. If a leg and an acute angle of one right triangle are congruent to the corresponding parts of another right triangle, the triangles are congruent. (*Hint:* There are two cases to consider.)

34. If two triangles are congruent by ASA, what theorem could you use to prove that the triangles are also congruent by AAS? Explain.

34. Third ∡ Thm.; if the third pair of ∡ are ≅, then the △ are also ≅ by AAS.

SPIRAL REVIEW

Identify the *x*- and *y*-intercepts. Use them to graph each line. *(Previous course)*

35. $y = 3x - 6$ **2; −6**

36. $y = -\frac{1}{2}x + 4$ **8; 4**

37. $y = -5x + 5$ **1; 5**

38. Find AB and BC if $AC = 10$. *(Lesson 1-6)*

$AB = 6; BC = 8$

39. Find $m\angle C$. *(Lesson 4-2)*
36.9°

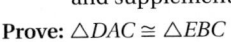

4-5 PROBLEM SOLVING

Use the following information for Exercises 1 and 2.

Melanie is at hole 6 on a miniature golf course. She walks east 7.5 meters to hole 7. She then faces south, turns 67° west, and walks to hole 8. From hole 8, she faces north, turns 35° west, and walks to hole 6.

Possible drawing:

1. Draw the section of the golf course described. Label the measures of the angles in the triangle.

2. Is there enough information given to determine the location of holes 6, 7, and 8? Explain.

Yes; the △ is uniquely determined by AAS.

3. A section of the front of an English Tudor home is shown in the diagram. If you know that $\overline{KN} \cong \overline{LN}$ and $\overline{JN} \cong \overline{MN}$, can you use HL to conclude that $\triangle JKN \cong \triangle MLN$? Explain.

No; you need to know that $\angle KJN$ and $\angle LMN$ are rt. ∡.

Use the diagram of a kite for Exercises 4 and 5.

$\overline{AE}$ is the angle bisector of $\angle DAF$ and $\angle DEF$.

4. What can you conclude about $\triangle DEA$ and $\triangle FEA$?

- **A** $\triangle DEA \cong \triangle FEA$ by HL.
- **B** $\triangle DEA \cong \triangle FEA$ by AAA.
- **C** $\triangle DEA \cong \triangle FEA$ by ASA.
- **D** $\triangle DEA \cong \triangle FEA$ by SAS.

5. Based on the diagram, what can you conclude about $\triangle BCA$ and $\triangle HGA$?

- **F** $\triangle BCA \cong \triangle HGA$ by HL.
- **G** $\triangle BCA \cong \triangle HGA$ by AAS.
- **H** $\triangle BCA \cong \triangle HGA$ by ASA.
- **J** It cannot be shown using the given information that $\triangle BCA \cong \triangle HGA$.

Answers

32. 1. $\triangle ABC$ is equil. (Given)
2. $\overline{AC} \cong \overline{BC}$ (Def. of equil.)
3. C is the mdpt. of $\overline{DE}$. (Given)
4. $\overline{DC} \cong \overline{EC}$ (Def. of mdpt.)
5. $\angle DAC$ and $\angle EBC$ are ≅ and supp. (Given)
6. $\angle DAC$ and $\angle EBC$ are rt. ∡. (∡ that are ≅ and supp. are rt. ∡.)
7. $\triangle DAC$ and $\triangle EBC$ are rt. △. (Def. of rt. △)
8. $\triangle DAC \cong \triangle EBC$ (HL Steps 4, 2)

33, 35–37. See pp. A15–A16.

4-5 Lesson Quiz

Identify the postulate or theorem that proves the triangles congruent.

1. 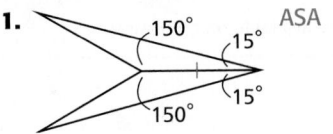 ASA

2. 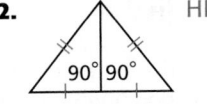 HL

3. 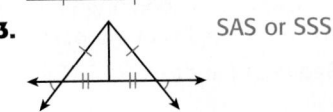 SAS or SSS

4. Given: $\angle FAB \cong \angle GED$, $\angle ACB \cong \angle DCE$, $\overline{AC} \cong \overline{EC}$

Prove: $\triangle ABC \cong \triangle EDC$

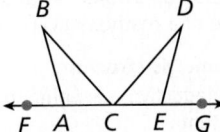

Proof:
1. $\angle FAB \cong \angle GED$ (Given)
2. $\angle BAC$ is a supp. of $\angle FAB$; $\angle DEC$ is a supp. of $\angle GED$. (Def. of supp. ∡)
3. $\angle BAC \cong \angle DEC$ (≅ Supp. Thm.)
4. $\angle ACB \cong \angle DCE$; $\overline{AC} \cong \overline{EC}$ (Given)
5. $\triangle ABC \cong \triangle EDC$ (ASA Steps 3, 4)

Also available on transparency

Objective: Use CPCTC to prove parts of triangles are congruent.

Online Edition
Tutorial Videos

Countdown to TAKS Week 8

Power Presentations
with PowerPoint®

Warm Up

1. If $\triangle ABC \cong \triangle DEF$, then $\angle A \cong$ __?__ and $\overline{BC} \cong$ __?__. $\angle D, \overline{EF}$

2. What is the distance between $(3, 4)$ and $(-1, 5)$? $\sqrt{17}$

3. If $\angle 1 \cong \angle 2$, why is $a \parallel b$?
Conv. of Alt. Int. $\angle$ Thm.

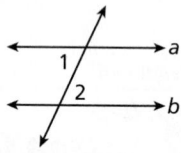

4. List methods used to prove two triangles congruent.
SSS, SAS, ASA, AAS, HL

Also available on transparency

Math Humor

Q: What do you write as the reason when using corresponding parts of congruent triangles in a proof?

A: See Peas Eat Easy! (CPCTC)

⭐ Geometry TEKS

G.1 Geometric structure*
(A) develop an awareness of the structure of a mathematical system, ...

G.3 Geometric structure*
(E) use deductive reasoning to prove a statement

G.7 Dimensionality and the geometry of location*
(A) use ... two-dimensional coordinate systems to represent ... figures

G.10 Congruence and the geometry of size*
(B) justify and apply triangle congruence relationships

* Knowledge and Skills See p. 214.

4-6 Triangle Congruence: CPCTC

⭐ **TEKS G.1.A** Geometric structure: develop an awareness of the structure of a mathematical system, connecting definitions, postulates, logical reasoning ... Also G.3.E, G.7.A, G.10.B

Objective
Use CPCTC to prove parts of triangles are congruent.

Vocabulary
CPCTC

Why learn this?
You can use congruent triangles to estimate distances.

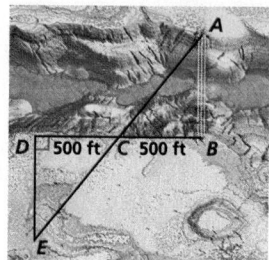

CPCTC is an abbreviation for the phrase "Corresponding Parts of Congruent Triangles are Congruent." It can be used as a justification in a proof after you have proven two triangles congruent.

EXAMPLE 1 Engineering Application

To design a bridge across a canyon, you need to find the distance from A to B. Locate points C, D, and E as shown in the figure. If $DE = 600$ ft, what is AB?

$\angle D \cong \angle B$, because they are both right angles.
$\overline{DC} \cong \overline{CB}$, because $DC = CB = 500$ ft.
$\angle DCE \cong \angle BCA$, because vertical angles are congruent. Therefore $\triangle DCE \cong \triangle BCA$ by ASA or LA. By CPCTC, $\overline{ED} \cong \overline{AB}$, so
$AB = ED = 600$ ft.

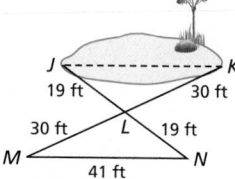

Remember!
SSS, SAS, ASA, AAS, and HL use corresponding parts to prove triangles congruent. CPCTC uses congruent triangles to prove corresponding parts congruent.

1. A landscape architect sets up the triangles shown in the figure to find the distance JK across a pond. What is JK? **41 ft**

EXAMPLE 2 Proving Corresponding Parts Congruent

Given: $\overline{AB} \cong \overline{DC}$, $\angle ABC \cong \angle DCB$
Prove: $\angle A \cong \angle D$
Proof:

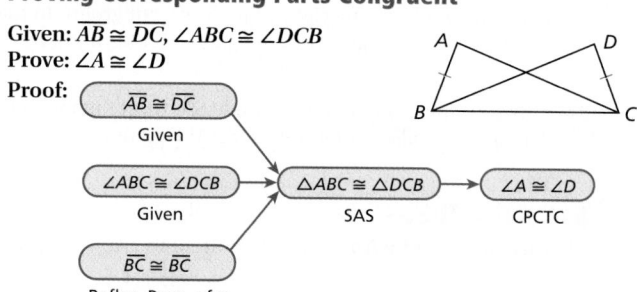

2. Given: $\overline{PR}$ bisects $\angle QPS$ and $\angle QRS$.
Prove: $\overline{PQ} \cong \overline{PS}$

---

1 Introduce

EXPLORATION

4-6 Triangle Congruence: CPCTC

Once you have proved that two triangles are congruent, you can use this fact to make some additional observations.

1. Put the statements and reasons in order to write a two-column proof.
Given: $\overline{AC} \cong \overline{AD}$; $\overline{AB}$ bisects $\angle CAD$.
Prove: $\triangle CAB \cong \triangle DAB$

Statements	Reasons
$\triangle CAB \cong \triangle DAB$	Reflex. Prop. of $\cong$
$\overline{AB} \cong \overline{AB}$	SAS
$\overline{AB}$ bisects $\angle CAD$.	Given
$\angle CAB \cong \angle DAB$	Def. of $\angle$ bisector
$\overline{AC} \cong \overline{AD}$	Given

2. Now that you have proved that $\triangle CAB \cong \triangle DAB$, what additional congruence statements can you write by looking at corresponding parts of the triangles?

THINK AND DISCUSS
3. Explain how you could

Motivate

Point out that congruent triangles can be used to find the distance between two points that is difficult to measure, such as the distance across a lake. Show designs by M. C. Escher to demonstrate that the size of one part determines the size of another. Students will learn that you can base assumptions about parts of a triangles on information about other parts.

Explorations and answers are provided in the *Explorations* binder.

EXAMPLE 3

Using CPCTC in a Proof

Given: $\overline{EG} \parallel \overline{DF}, \overline{EG} \cong \overline{DF}$
Prove: $\overline{ED} \parallel \overline{GF}$

Proof:

Statements	Reasons
1. $\overline{EG} \cong \overline{DF}$	1. Given
2. $\overline{EG} \parallel \overline{DF}$	2. Given
3. $\angle EGD \cong \angle FDG$	3. Alt. Int. ∠ Thm.
4. $\overline{GD} \cong \overline{GD}$	4. Reflex. Prop. of $\cong$
5. $\triangle EGD \cong \triangle FDG$	5. SAS *Steps 1, 3, and 4*
6. $\angle EDG \cong \angle FGD$	6. CPCTC
7. $\overline{ED} \parallel \overline{GF}$	7. Converse of Alt. Int. ∠ Thm.

CHECK IT OUT!

3. Given: J is the midpoint of $\overline{KM}$ and $\overline{NL}$.
Prove: $\overline{KL} \parallel \overline{MN}$

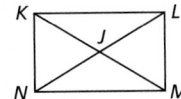

You can also use CPCTC when triangles are on a coordinate plane.
You use the Distance Formula to find the lengths of the sides of each triangle.
Then, after showing that the triangles are congruent, you can
make conclusions about their corresponding parts.

EXAMPLE 4

Using CPCTC in the Coordinate Plane

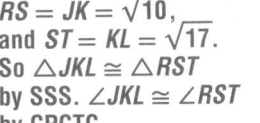

Given: $A(2, 3), B(5, -1), C(1, 0),$
$D(-4, -1), E(0, 2), F(-1, -2)$
Prove: $\angle ABC \cong \angle DEF$

x²ʸ Algebra

Step 1 Plot the points on a coordinate plane.

Step 2 Use the Distance Formula to find the
lengths of the sides of each triangle.

$$D = \sqrt{(x_2 - x_1)^2 + (y_2 - y_1)^2}$$

$$AB = \sqrt{(5-2)^2 + (-1-3)^2} \qquad DE = \sqrt{(0-(-4))^2 + (2-(-1))^2}$$
$$= \sqrt{9 + 16} = \sqrt{25} = 5 \qquad = \sqrt{16 + 9} = \sqrt{25} = 5$$

$$BC = \sqrt{(1-5)^2 + (0-(-1))^2} \qquad EF = \sqrt{(-1-0)^2 + (-2-2)^2}$$
$$= \sqrt{16 + 1} = \sqrt{17} \qquad = \sqrt{1 + 16} = \sqrt{17}$$

$$AC = \sqrt{(1-2)^2 + (0-3)^2} \qquad DF = \sqrt{(-1-(-4))^2 + (-2-(-1))^2}$$
$$= \sqrt{1 + 9} = \sqrt{10} \qquad = \sqrt{9 + 1} = \sqrt{10}$$

So $\overline{AB} \cong \overline{DE}$, $\overline{BC} \cong \overline{EF}$, and $\overline{AC} \cong \overline{DF}$. Therefore $\triangle ABC \cong \triangle DEF$ by SSS,
and $\angle ABC \cong \angle DEF$ by CPCTC.

4. $RT = JL = \sqrt{5}$,
$RS = JK = \sqrt{10}$,
and $ST = KL = \sqrt{17}$.
So $\triangle JKL \cong \triangle RST$
by SSS. $\angle JKL \cong \angle RST$
by CPCTC.

CHECK IT OUT!

4. Given: $J(-1, -2), K(2, -1), L(-2, 0), R(2, 3), S(5, 2), T(1, 1)$
Prove: $\angle JKL \cong \angle RST$

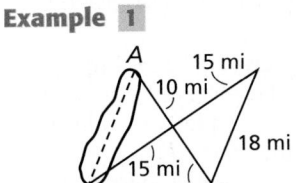

Additional Examples

Example 1

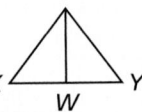

A and B are on the edges of a
ravine. What is AB?   18 mi

Example 2

Given: $\overline{YW}$ bisects
$\overline{XZ}$.
$\overline{XY} \cong \overline{YZ}$.

Prove: $\angle XYW \cong \angle ZYW$

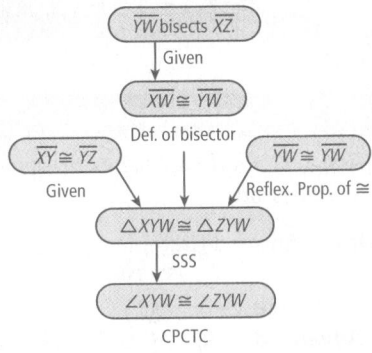

Example 3

Given: $\overline{NO} \parallel \overline{MP},$
$\angle N \cong \angle P$

Prove: $\overline{MN} \parallel \overline{OP}$

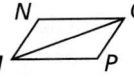

1. $\angle N \cong \angle P$; $\overline{NO} \parallel \overline{MP}$ (Given)
2. $\angle NOM \cong \angle PMO$ (Alt. Int. ∠ Thm.)
3. $\overline{MO} \cong \overline{MO}$ (Reflex. Prop of $\cong$)
4. $\triangle MNO \cong \triangle OPM$ (AAS)
5. $\angle NMO \cong \angle POM$ (CPCTC)
6. $\overline{MN} \parallel \overline{OP}$ (Conv. of Alt. Int. ∠ Thm.)

Example 4

Given: $D(-5, -5), E(-3, -1),$
$F(-2, -3), G(-2, 1),$
$H(0, 5),$ and $I(1, 3)$

Prove: $\angle DEF \cong \angle GHI$

$DE = GH = 2\sqrt{5}, EF = HI = \sqrt{5},$
$DF = GI = \sqrt{13}.$ Therefore $\triangle DEF$
$\cong \triangle GHI$ by SSS, and $\angle DEF \cong$
$\angle GHI$ by CPCTC.

Also available on transparency

Guided Instruction

Present CPCTC as a way to use congruent triangles to prove corresponding parts
congruent. Have students complete fill-in-
the-blank proofs using CPCTC. Be sure students know the importance of first proving
triangle congruence before using CPCTC to
prove parts congruent. Review the Distance
Formula before Example 4.

Teaching Tip

Auditory Have students recite
the meaning of CPCTC with
emphasis on the words congruent triangles.

Summarize

Remind students what CPCTC means.
Point out that the middle of this statement
implies that students first prove triangles
congruent and then make conclusions
about the corresponding parts. Remind
students that they can use the Distance
Formula when proving triangle congruence
in the coordinate plane.

Answers to Check It Out!

2–3. See p. A16.

INTERVENTION

Questioning Strategies

EXAMPLES 1–4

• What transformations are used to
change each triangle into the second congruent triangle?

Answers to *Think and Discuss*
1. SAS; $\overline{UW} \cong \overline{XZ}$;
   $\angle U \cong \angle X$; $\angle W \cong \angle Z$
2. See p. A4.

Teaching Tip

Critical Thinking
Emphasize that proofs in this lesson go beyond proving triangles congruent. Encourage students to work backward when using CPCTC in proofs. Remind students to first locate which triangles they need to prove congruent and then find the angles or sides needed.

THINK AND DISCUSS

1. In the figure, $\overline{UV} \cong \overline{XY}$, $\overline{VW} \cong \overline{YZ}$, and $\angle V \cong \angle Y$. Explain why $\triangle UVW \cong \triangle XYZ$. By CPCTC, which additional parts are congruent?

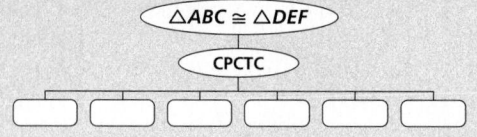

Know it!
Note

2. **GET ORGANIZED** Copy and complete the graphic organizer. Write all conclusions you can make using CPCTC.

$$\triangle ABC \cong \triangle DEF$$
$$\text{CPCTC}$$

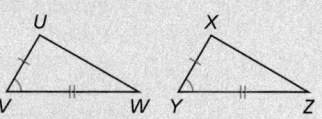

Assignment Guide

Assign *Guided Practice* exercises as necessary.

If you finished Examples **1–2**
   Basic 7–9, 17–19
   Average 7–9, 17–20
   Advanced 7–9, 17–20, 29, 32

If you finished Examples **1–4**
   Basic 7–19, 24–28, 33–37
   Average 7–16, 20–28, 30, 33–37
   Advanced 7–16, 19–37

Homework Quick Check
Quickly check key concepts.
Exercises: 7, 8, 10, 12, 14

GUIDED PRACTICE

1. **Vocabulary** You use CPCTC after proving triangles are congruent. Which parts of congruent triangles are referred to as corresponding parts? **corr. ∠ and corr. sides**

SEE EXAMPLE 1
p. 260

2. **Engineering** To find the height of a windmill, a rancher places a marker at *C* and steps off the distance from *C* to *B*. Then the rancher walks the same distance from *C* in the opposite direction and places a marker at *D*. If *DE* = 6.3 m, what is *AB*? **6.3 m**

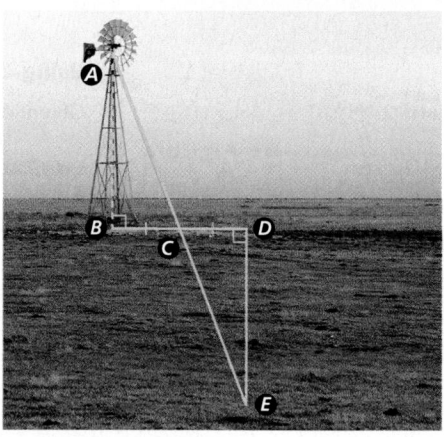

SEE EXAMPLE 2
p. 260

3. **Given:** *X* is the midpoint of $\overline{ST}$. $\overline{RX} \perp \overline{ST}$
   Prove: $\overline{RS} \cong \overline{RT}$

   Proof:

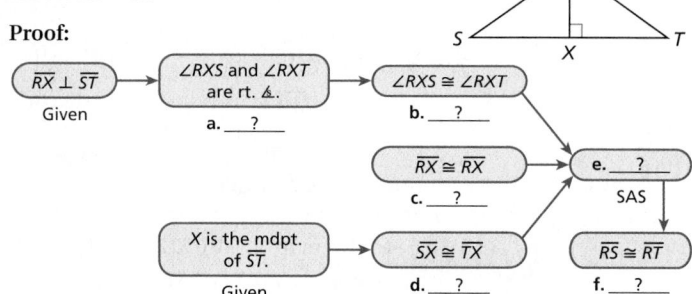

⬥TAKS Practice

Grades 9–11	Exercises
Obj. 2	17, 18, 26, 33
Obj. 4	17, 18, 26, 33, 34
Obj. 6	25, 28, 35, 36
Obj. 7	16, 25, 28, 35, 36
Obj. 10	16, 23, 33, 34

ONGOING ASSESSMENT
and INTERVENTION ⬥➡

Diagnose Before the Lesson
4-6 Warm Up, TE p. 260

Monitor During the Lesson
Check It Out! Exercises, SE pp. 260–261
Questioning Strategies, TE p. 261

Assess After the Lesson
4-6 Lesson Quiz, TE p. 265
Alternative Assessment, TE p. 265

Answers

3a. Def. of ⊥
 b. Rt. ∠ ≅ Thm.
 c. Reflex. Prop. of ≅
 d. Def. of mdpt.
 e. $\triangle RXS \cong \triangle RXT$
 f. CPCTC

4. Given: $\overline{AC} \cong \overline{AD}$, $\overline{CB} \cong \overline{DB}$
Prove: $\overline{AB}$ bisects $\angle CAD$.

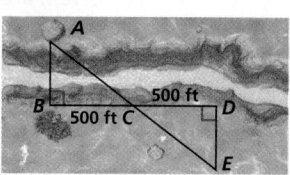

Proof:

Statements	Reasons
1. $\overline{AC} \cong \overline{AD}$, $\overline{CB} \cong \overline{DB}$	1. a. __?__
2. b. __?__	2. Reflex. Prop. of $\cong$
3. $\triangle ACB \cong \triangle ADB$	3. c. __?__
4. $\angle CAB \cong \angle DAB$	4. d. __?__
5. $\overline{AB}$ bisects $\angle CAD$	5. e. __?__

a. Given
b. $\overline{AB} \cong \overline{AB}$
c. SSS *Steps 1, 2*
d. CPCTC
e. Def. of $\angle$ bisect

Multi-Step Use the given set of points to prove each congruence statement.

5. $E(-3, 3)$, $F(-1, 3)$, $G(-2, 0)$, $J(0, -1)$, $K(2, -1)$, $L(1, 2)$; $\angle EFG \cong \angle JKL$

6. $A(2, 3)$, $B(4, 1)$, $C(1, -1)$, $R(-1, 0)$, $S(-3, -2)$, $T(0, -4)$; $\angle ACB \cong \angle RTS$

PRACTICE AND PROBLEM SOLVING

Independent Practice

For Exercises	See Example
7	1
8–9	2
10–11	3
12–13	4

TEKS ⬤ TAKS

Skills Practice p. S11
Application Practice p. S31

7. Surveying To find the distance *AB* across a river, a surveyor first locates point *C*. He measures the distance from *C* to *B*. Then he locates point *D* the same distance east of *C*. If *DE* = 420 ft, what is *AB*? **420 ft**

8. Given: *M* is the midpoint of $\overline{PQ}$ and $\overline{RS}$.
Prove: $\overline{QR} \cong \overline{PS}$

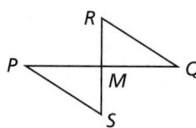

9. Given: $\overline{WX} \cong \overline{XY} \cong \overline{YZ} \cong \overline{ZW}$
Prove: $\angle W \cong \angle Y$

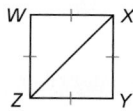

10. Given: *G* is the midpoint of $\overline{FH}$.
$\overline{EF} \cong \overline{EH}$
Prove: $\angle 1 \cong \angle 2$

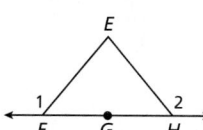

11. Given: $\overline{LM}$ bisects $\angle JLK$. $\overline{JL} \cong \overline{KL}$
Prove: *M* is the midpoint of $\overline{JK}$.

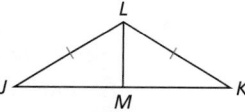

Multi-Step Use the given set of points to prove each congruence statement.

12. $R(0, 0)$, $S(2, 4)$, $T(-1, 3)$, $U(-1, 0)$, $V(-3, -4)$, $W(-4, -1)$; $\angle RST \cong \angle UVW$

13. $A(-1, 1)$, $B(2, 3)$, $C(2, -2)$, $D(2, -3)$, $E(-1, -5)$, $F(-1, 0)$; $\angle BAC \cong \angle EDF$

14. Given: $\triangle QRS$ is adjacent to $\triangle QTS$. $\overline{QS}$ bisects $\angle RQT$. $\angle R \cong \angle T$
Prove: $\overline{QS}$ bisects $\overline{RT}$.

15. Given: $\triangle ABE$ and $\triangle CDE$ with *E* the midpoint of $\overline{AC}$ and $\overline{BD}$
Prove: $\overline{AB} \parallel \overline{CD}$

12. $ST = VW = RT = UW = \sqrt{10}$. $RS = UV = 2\sqrt{5}$. So $\triangle RST \cong \triangle UVW$ by SSS. $\angle RST \cong \angle UVW$ by CPCTC.

Answers

13. $AB = DE = \sqrt{13}$, $BC = EF = 5$, and $AC = DF = \sqrt{18} = 3\sqrt{2}$. So $\triangle ABC \cong \triangle DEF$ by SSS. $\angle BAC \cong \angle EDF$ by CPCTC.

14. 1. $\triangle QRS$ is adj. to $\triangle QTS$. $\overline{QS}$ bisects $\angle RQT$. $\angle R \cong \angle T$ (Given)
2. $\angle RQS \cong \angle TQS$ (Def. of $\angle$ bisect)
3. $\overline{QS} \cong \overline{QS}$ (Reflex. Prop. of $\cong$)
4. $\triangle RSQ \cong \triangle TSQ$ (AAS Steps 1, 2, 3)
5. $\overline{RS} \cong \overline{TS}$ (CPCTC)
6. $\overline{QS}$ bisects $\overline{RT}$. (Def. of bisect)

15. 1. *E* is the mdpt. of $\overline{AC}$ and $\overline{BD}$. (Given)
2. $\overline{AE} \cong \overline{CE}$; $\overline{BE} \cong \overline{DE}$ (Def. of mdpt.)
3. $\angle AEB \cong \angle CED$ (Vert. $\angle$ Thm.)
4. $\triangle AEB \cong \triangle CED$ (SAS Steps 2, 3)
5. $\angle A \cong \angle C$ (CPCTC)
6. $\overline{AB} \parallel \overline{CD}$ (Conv. of Alt. Int. $\angle$ Thm.)

In **Exercise 11**, students may think that if a ray bisects an angle of a triangle then it also bisects the side opposite the angle. Explain that this is only true for some triangles.

Teaching Tip **Technology** For **Exercises 5, 6, 12,** and **13,** use geometry software to graph the points and to demonstrate that the corresponding angle measures in each proof statement are the same. Also address transformations after triangles are graphed.

Answers

5. $EF = JK = 2$, and $EG = FG = JL = KL = \sqrt{10}$. So $\triangle EFG \cong \triangle JKL$ by SSS. $\angle EFG \cong \angle JKL$ by CPCTC.

6. $AB = RS = 2\sqrt{2}$, $BC = ST = \sqrt{13}$, and $RT = AC = \sqrt{17}$. So $\triangle ABC \cong \triangle RST$ by SSS. $\angle ACB \cong \angle RTS$ by CPCTC.

8. 1. *M* is the mdpt. of $\overline{PQ}$ and $\overline{RS}$. (Given)
2. $\overline{PM} \cong \overline{QM}$, $\overline{RM} \cong \overline{SM}$ (Def. of mdpt.)
3. $\angle PMS \cong \angle QMR$ (Vert. $\angle$ Thm.)
4. $\triangle PMS \cong \triangle QMR$ (SAS, Steps 2, 3)
5. $\overline{QR} \cong \overline{PS}$ (CPCTC)

9. 1. $\overline{WX} \cong \overline{XY} \cong \overline{YZ} \cong \overline{ZW}$ (Given)
2. $\overline{ZX} \cong \overline{ZX}$ (Reflex. Prop. of $\cong$)
3. $\triangle WXZ \cong \triangle YZX$ (SSS)
4. $\angle W \cong \angle Y$ (CPCTC)

10. 1. *G* is the mdpt. of $\overline{FH}$. (Given)
2. $FG = HG$ (Def. of mdpt.)
3. $\overline{FG} \cong \overline{HG}$ (Def. of $\cong$)
4. Draw $\overline{EG}$. (Through any 2 pts. there is exactly 1 line.)
5. $\overline{EG} \cong \overline{EG}$ (Reflex. Prop. of $\cong$)
6. $\overline{EF} \cong \overline{EH}$ (Given)
7. $\triangle EGF \cong \triangle EGH$ (SSS Steps 3, 5, 6)
8. $\angle EFG \cong \angle EHG$ (CPCTC)
9. $\angle 1 \cong \angle 2$ ($\cong$ Supp. Thm.)

11. 1. $\overline{LM}$ bisects $\angle JLK$. (Given)
2. $\angle JLM \cong \angle KLM$ (Def. of $\angle$ bisect)
3. $\overline{JL} \cong \overline{KL}$ (Given)
4. $\overline{LM} \cong \overline{LM}$ (Reflex. Prop. of $\cong$)
5. $\triangle JLM \cong \triangle KLM$ (SAS Steps 3, 2, 4)
6. $\overline{JM} \cong \overline{KM}$ (CPCTC)
7. *M* is the mdpt. of $\overline{JK}$. (Def. of mdpt.)

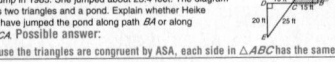
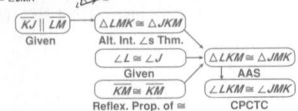
---

16. This problem will prepare you for the Multi-Step TAKS Prep on page 280.

The front of a doghouse has the dimensions shown.
a. How can you prove that $\triangle ADB \cong \triangle ADC$? **HL**
b. Prove that $\overline{BD} \cong \overline{CD}$.
c. What is the length of $\overline{BD}$ and $\overline{BC}$ to the nearest tenth? **17.3 in.; 34.6 in.**

Multi-Step Find the value of x.

17. 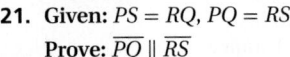 **14**
$x + 11$ $2x - 3$

18. 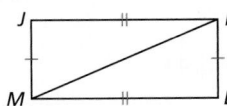 **21**
$(4x + 1)°$ $(6x - 41)°$

Use the diagram for Exercises 19–21.

19. **Given:** $PS = RQ$, $m\angle 1 = m\angle 4$
Prove: $m\angle 3 = m\angle 2$

20. **Given:** $m\angle 1 = m\angle 2$, $m\angle 3 = m\angle 4$
Prove: $PS = RS$

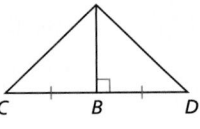

21. **Given:** $PS = RQ$, $PQ = RS$
Prove: $\overline{PQ} \parallel \overline{RS}$

22. **Critical Thinking** Does the diagram contain enough information to allow you to conclude that $\overline{JK} \parallel \overline{ML}$? Explain.

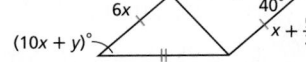

23. **Write About It** Draw a diagram and explain how a surveyor can set up triangles to find the distance across a lake. Label each part of your diagram. List which sides or angles must be congruent.

TEST PREP

24. Which of these will NOT be used as a reason in a proof of $\overline{AC} \cong \overline{AD}$?
Ⓐ SAS   Ⓒ ASA
Ⓑ CPCTC   Ⓓ Reflexive Property

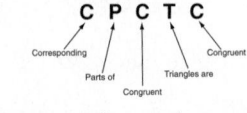

25. Given the points $K(1, 2)$, $L(0, -4)$, $M(-2, -3)$, and $N(-1, 3)$, which of these is true?
Ⓕ $\angle KNL \cong \angle MNL$ Ⓗ $\angle MLN \cong \angle KLN$
Ⓖ $\angle LNK \cong \angle NLM$ Ⓙ $\angle MNK \cong \angle NKL$

26. What is the value of y?
Ⓐ 10   Ⓒ 35
Ⓑ 20   Ⓓ 85

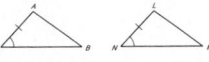
$(10x + y)°$ $6x$ $40°$ $x + \frac{5}{2}$

27. Which of these are NOT used to prove angles congruent?
Ⓕ congruent triangles   Ⓗ parallel lines
Ⓖ noncorresponding parts   Ⓙ perpendicular lines

---

28. Which set of coordinates represents the vertices of a triangle congruent to △RST? (*Hint:* Find the lengths of the sides of △RST.)

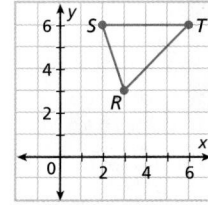

Ⓐ (3, 4), (3, 0), (0, 0)   Ⓒ (3, 1), (3, 3), (4, 6)
Ⓑ (3, 3), (0, 4), (0, 0)   Ⓓ (3, 0), (4, 4), (0, 6)

CHALLENGE AND EXTEND

29. Any diag. on any face of the cube is the hyp. of a rt. △ whose legs are edges of the cube. Any 2 of these △ are ≅ by SAS. Therefore any 2 diags. are ≅ by CPCTC.

29. All of the edges of a cube are congruent. All of the angles on each face of a cube are right angles. Use CPCTC to explain why any two diagonals on the faces of a cube (for example, $\overline{AC}$ and $\overline{AF}$) must be congruent.

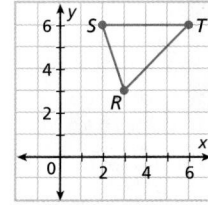

30. Given: $\overline{JK} \cong \overline{ML}$, $\overline{JM} \cong \overline{KL}$
Prove: $\angle J \cong \angle L$
(*Hint:* Draw an auxiliary line.)

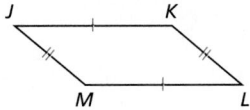

31. Given: R is the midpoint of $\overline{AB}$.
S is the midpoint of $\overline{DC}$.
$\overline{RS} \perp \overline{AB}$, $\angle ASD \cong \angle BSC$
Prove: $\triangle ASD \cong \triangle BSC$

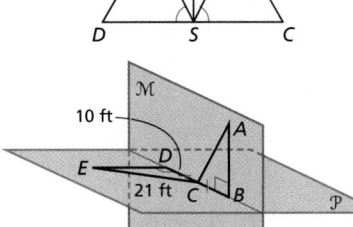

32. △ABC is in plane 𝓜. △CDE is in plane 𝓟. Both planes have C in common and ∠A ≅ ∠E. What is the height AB to the nearest foot? **18 ft**

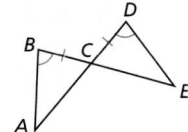

SPIRAL REVIEW

33. Lina's test scores in her history class are 90, 84, 93, 88, and 91. What is the minimum score Lina must make on her next test to have an average test score of 90? *(Previous course)* **94**

35. reflection across the x-axis

36. translation $(x, y) \rightarrow (x - 3, y - 4)$

37. Yes; it is given that $\angle B \cong \angle D$ and $\overline{BC} \cong \overline{DC}$. By the Vert. ∠ Thm., ∠BCA ≅ ∠DCE. Therefore △ABC ≅ △EDC by ASA.

34. One long-distance phone plan costs $3.95 per month plus $0.08 per minute of use. A second long-distance plan costs $0.10 per minute for the first 50 minutes used each month and then $0.15 per minute after that. Which plan is cheaper if you use an average of 75 long-distance minutes per month? *(Previous course)*
The second plan is cheaper.

A figure has vertices at $(1, 3), (2, 2), (3, 2),$ and $(4, 3)$. Identify the transformation of the figure that produces an image with each set of vertices. *(Lesson 1-7)*

35. $(1, -3), (2, -2), (3, -2), (4, -3)$

36. $(-2, -1), (-1, -2), (0, -2), (1, -1)$

37. Determine if you can use ASA to prove △ACB ≅ △ECD. Explain. *(Lesson 4-5)*

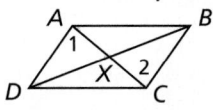

4-6 PROBLEM SOLVING

1. Two triangular plates are congruent. The area of one of the plates is 60 square inches. What is the area of the other plate? Explain.
60 in²; Since the triangles are ≅, they have the same measures. So, the triangles also have the same areas.

2. An archaeologist draws the triangles to find the distance XY across a ravine. What is XY? Explain.
82 m; △UVW ≅ △XYW by SAS, so $\overline{UV} \cong \overline{XY}$ by CPCTC. Therefore UV = XY = 82 m.

3. A city planner sets up the triangles to find the distance RS across a river. Describe the steps that she can use to find RS.
$\angle P \cong \angle R$ because they are both rt. ∡. $\overline{PQ} \cong \overline{RQ}$ because PQ = RQ = 65 ft. ∠NQP ≅ ∠SQR because vert. ∡ are ≅. Therefore △NQP ≅ △SRQ by ASA. By CPCTC, $\overline{NP} \cong \overline{SR}$. So SR = NP = 40 ft.

Choose the best answer.

4. A lighthouse and the range of its shining light are shown. What can you conclude?
Ⓐ x = y by CPCTC   C ∠AED ≅ ∠ADE by CPCTC
B x = 2y   D ∠AED ≅ ∠ACB

5. A rectangular piece of cloth 15 centimeters long is cut along a diagonal to form two triangles. One of the triangles has a side length of 9 centimeters. Which is a true statement?
F The second triangle has an angle measure of 15° by CPCTC.
Ⓖ The second triangle has a side length of 9 centimeters by CPCTC.
H You cannot make a conclusion about the side length of the second triangle.
J The triangles are not congruent.

6. Small sandwiches are cut in the shape of right triangles. The longest sides of all the sandwiches are 3 inches. One sandwich has a side length of 2 inches. Which is a true statement?
A All the sandwiches have a side length of 2 inches by CPCTC.
B All the sandwiches are isosceles triangles with side lengths of 2 inches.
C None of the other sandwiches have side lengths of 2 inches.
Ⓓ You cannot make a conclusion using CPCTC.

Answers

31. 1. R is the mdpt. of $\overline{AB}$. (Given)
2. $\overline{AR} \cong \overline{BR}$ (Def. of mdpt.)
3. $\overline{RS} \perp \overline{AB}$ (Given)
4. ∠ARS and ∠BRS are rt. ∡. (Def. of ⊥)
5. ∠ARS ≅ ∠BRS (Rt. ∠ ≅ Thm.)
6. $\overline{RS} \cong \overline{RS}$ (Reflex. Prop. of ≅)
7. △ARS ≅ △BRS (SAS *Steps* 2, 5, 6)
8. $\overline{AS} \cong \overline{BS}$ (CPCTC)
9. ∠ASD ≅ ∠BSC (Given)
10. S is the mdpt. of $\overline{DC}$. (Given)
11. $\overline{DS} = \overline{CS}$ (Def. of mdpt.)
12. △ASD ≅ △BSC (SAS *Steps* 8, 9, 11)

✓ 4-6 Lesson Quiz

1. Given: Isosceles △PQR, base $\overline{QR}$, $\overline{PA} \cong \overline{PB}$
Prove: $\overline{AR} \cong \overline{BQ}$

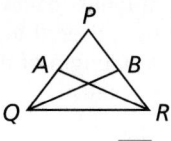

1. Isosc. △PQR, base $\overline{QR}$ (Given)
2. $\overline{PQ} = \overline{PR}$ (Def. of Isosc. △)
3. $\overline{PA} = \overline{PB}$ (Given)
4. ∠P ≅ ∠P (Reflex. Prop. of ≅)
5. △QPB ≅ △RPA (SAS *Steps* 2, 4, 3)
6. $\overline{AR} = \overline{BQ}$ (CPCTC)

2. Given: X is the midpoint of $\overline{AC}$. ∠1 ≅ ∠2
Prove: X is the midpoint of $\overline{BD}$.

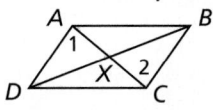

1. X is mdpt. of $\overline{AC}$. ∠1 ≅ ∠2 (Given)
2. AX = CX (Def. of mdpt.)
3. $\overline{AX} \cong \overline{CX}$ (Def. of ≅)
4. ∠AXD ≅ ∠CXB (Vert. ∡ Thm.)
5. △AXD ≅ △CXB (ASA *Steps* 1, 4, 5)
6. $\overline{DX} \cong \overline{BX}$ (CPCTC)
7. DX = BX (Def. of ≅)
8. X is mdpt. of $\overline{BD}$. (Def. of mdpt.)

3. Use the given set of points to prove △DEF ≅ △GHJ: D(-4, 4), E(-2, 1), F(-6, 1), G(3, 1), H(5, -2), J(1, -2).
$DE = GH = \sqrt{13}, DF = GJ = \sqrt{13}, EF = HJ = 4,$ and △DEF ≅ △GHJ by SSS.

Also available on transparency

Pacing:
Traditional $\frac{1}{2}$ day
Block $\frac{1}{4}$ day

Objective: Solve quadratic equations to find the length of a side of a triangle.

 Online Edition

 Countdown to TAKS Week 9

Teach

Remember

Students review and apply the methods of solving quadratic equations.

INTERVENTION ◀▬▶ For additional review and practice on factoring and using the Quadratic Formula, see Skills Bank page S66.

 Critical Thinking Have students check each solution. Even if the value of x is negative, a length of the side cannot be negative.

Close

Assess

Have students compare and contrast the two methods used for finding the value of the variable.

 **On Track for TAKS** connects TAKS objectives across the grade levels.

Grades 9–11

Obj. 5 Quadratic and Other Nonlinear Functions A.10.A solve quadratic equations using ... algebraic methods

Obj. 6 Geometric Relationships and Spatial Reasoning G.5.A use numeric and geometric patterns to develop algebraic expressions representing geometric properties; G.5.B use numeric and geometric patterns to make generalizations about geometric properties, including properties of polygons, ...

Quadratic Equations

Algebra

A quadratic equation is an equation that can be written in the form $ax^2 + bx + c = 0$.

See Skills Bank page S66

Example

Given: $\triangle ABC$ is isosceles with $\overline{AB} \cong \overline{AC}$. Solve for x.

Step 1 Set $x^2 - 5x$ equal to 6 to get $x^2 - 5x = 6$.

Step 2 Rewrite the quadratic equation by subtracting 6 from each side to get $x^2 - 5x - 6 = 0$.

Step 3 Solve for x.

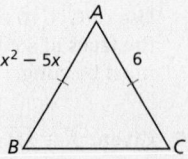

Method 1: Factoring		Method 2: Quadratic Formula	
$x^2 - 5x - 6 = 0$		$x = \dfrac{-b \pm \sqrt{b^2 - 4ac}}{2a}$	
$(x - 6)(x + 1) = 0$	*Factor.*	$x = \dfrac{-(-5) \pm \sqrt{(-5)^2 - 4(1)(-6)}}{2(1)}$	*Substitute 1 for a, −5 for b, and −6 for c.*
$x - 6 = 0$ or $x + 1 = 0$	*Set each factor equal to 0.*	$x = \dfrac{5 \pm \sqrt{49}}{2}$	*Simplify.*
$x = 6$ or $x = -1$	*Solve.*	$x = \dfrac{5 \pm 7}{2}$	*Find the square root.*
		$x = \dfrac{12}{2}$ or $x = \dfrac{-2}{2}$	*Simplify.*
		$x = 6$ or $x = -1$	

Step 4 Check each solution in the original equation.

$$\begin{array}{r|l} x^2 - 5x = 6 & \\ \hline (6)^2 - 5(6) & 6 \\ 36 - 30 & 6 \\ 6 & 6 \quad \checkmark \end{array} \qquad \begin{array}{r|l} x^2 - 5x = 6 & \\ \hline (-1)^2 - 5(-1) & 6 \\ 1 + 5 & 6 \\ 6 & 6 \quad \checkmark \end{array}$$

Try This ★ TAKS Grades 9–11 Obj. 5, 6

Solve for x in each isosceles triangle.

1. Given: $\overline{FE} \cong \overline{FG}$
6 or −3

2. Given: $\overline{JK} \cong \overline{JL}$
−6 or 2
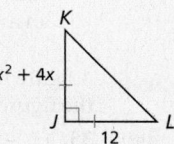

3. Given: $\overline{YX} \cong \overline{YZ}$
6 or −2
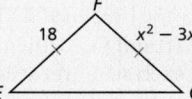

4. Given: $\overline{QP} \cong \overline{QR}$
−3 or 1
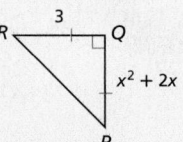

4-7 Introduction to Coordinate Proof

 TEK G.2.B Geometric structure: make conjectures about … polygons … and determine validity of the conjectures. Also G.3.B, G.9.B, G.10.B

Objectives
Position figures in the coordinate plane for use in coordinate proofs.

Prove geometric concepts by using coordinate proof.

Vocabulary
coordinate proof

Who uses this?

The Bushmen in South Africa use the Global Positioning System to transmit data about endangered animals to conservationists. (See Exercise 24.)

You have used coordinate geometry to find the midpoint of a line segment and to find the distance between two points. Coordinate geometry can also be used to prove conjectures.

A **coordinate proof** is a style of proof that uses coordinate geometry and algebra. The first step of a coordinate proof is to position the given figure in the plane. You can use any position, but some strategies can make the steps of the proof simpler.

Strategies for Positioning Figures in the Coordinate Plane

- Use the origin as a vertex, keeping the figure in Quadrant I.
- Center the figure at the origin.
- Center a side of the figure at the origin.
- Use one or both axes as sides of the figure.

EXAMPLE 1 **Positioning a Figure in the Coordinate Plane**

Position a rectangle with a length of 8 units and a width of 3 units in the coordinate plane.

Method 1 You can center the longer side of the rectangle at the origin.

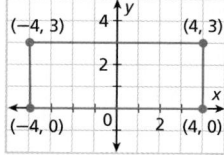

Method 2 You can use the origin as a vertex of the rectangle.

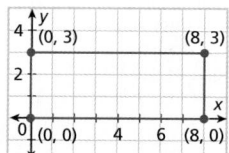

Depending on what you are using the figure to prove, one solution may be better than the other. For example, if you need to find the midpoint of the longer side, use the first solution.

 **1.** Position a right triangle with leg lengths of 2 and 4 units in the coordinate plane. (*Hint:* Use the origin as the vertex of the right angle.)

---

1 Introduce

EXPLORATION

4-7 Introduction to Coordinate Proof

You will need graph paper and scissors for this Exploration.

1. On graph paper, draw a rectangle with a length of 6 units and a width of 4 units.

2. Shade the interior of the rectangle and then cut it out.

3. Next draw a set of axes on the graph paper.

4. Place the rectangle in Quadrant I so that one vertex is at the origin. What are the coordinates of the other vertices?

5. Is there another way to position the rectangle in Quadrant I so that one vertex is at the origin? If so, what are the coordinates of the other vertices?

6. Now move the rectangle so that it is centered at the origin. What are the coordinates of the vertices in this case?

7. Position the rectangle so that one of the long sides is on the *x*-axis and is centered at the origin. What are the coordinates of the vertices?

THINK AND DISCUSS

8. Discuss which set of coordinates you would choose for the rectangle if you wanted to use the Distance Formula to find the length of a diagonal.

Motivate

Relate coordinate proofs to other methods of proofs students have used. Point out that they will use algebra and what they already know about triangles in the coordinate plane in this geometric proof. Make transparencies of graph paper so students can display their work on the overhead projector as they discuss coordinate proofs.

Explorations and answers are provided in the *Explorations* binder.

4-7 Organizer

Pacing: Traditional 2 days
Block 1 day

Objectives: Position figures in the coordinate plane for use in coordinate proofs.

Prove geometric concepts by using coordinate proof.

PREMIER **Online Edition**
Tutorial Videos

Countdown to TAKS Week 9

Power Presentations
with PowerPoint®

Warm Up

Evaluate.

1. Find the midpoint between $(0, 2x)$ and $(2y, 2z)$. $(y, x + z)$

2. One leg of a right triangle has length 12, and the hypotenuse has length 13. What is the length of the other leg?   5

3. Find the distance between $(0, a)$ and $(0, b)$, where $b > a$. $b - a$

Also available on transparency

Math Humor

Q: What do you call a broken angle?

A: A rectangle!

Answers to *Check it Out!*

1. See p. A16.

Geometry TEKS

G.2 Geometric structure*
(B) make conjectures about angles, lines, polygons … and determine validity of the conjectures, choosing from a variety of approaches …

G.9 Congruence and the geometry of size*
(B) formulate and test conjectures about the properties and attributes of polygons … based on explorations …

G.10 Congruence and the geometry of size*
(B) justify and apply triangle congruence relationships

* Knowledge and Skills See p. 214.

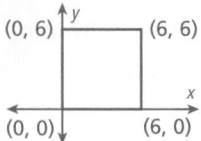
Additional Examples

Example 1

Position a square with a side length of 6 units in the coordinate plane.   Possible answer:

(0, 6) (6, 6)

(0, 0) (6, 0)

Example 2

Write a coordinate proof.

Given: Rectangle *ABCD* with *A*(0, 0), *B*(4, 0), *C*(4, 10), and *D*(0, 10)

Prove: The diagonals bisect each other.

Mdpt. of $\overline{AC}$ is (2, 5). Mdpt. of $\overline{BD}$ is also (2, 5). Therefore the diags. bisect each other.

Example 3

Position each figure in the coordinate plane and give the coordinates of each vertex.

A. rectangle with width *m* and length twice the width
Possible answer:

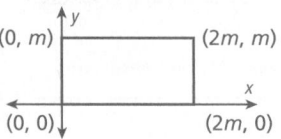
(0, m) (2m, m)

(0, 0) (2m, 0)

B. right triangle with legs of lengths *s* and *t*
Possible answer:

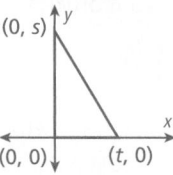
(0, s)

(0, 0) (t, 0)

Also available on transparency

---

268   *Chapter 4 Triangle Congruence*

INTERVENTION ◄►
Questioning Strategies

EXAMPLES 1-3

• How do you decide which strategy to use to position a figure in a coordinate plane? What are the advantages of each position?

Answers to *Check it Out!*

2–3. See p. A16.

Once the figure is placed in the coordinate plane, you can use slope, the coordinates of the vertices, the Distance Formula, or the Midpoint Formula to prove statements about the figure.

EXAMPLE 2   **Writing a Proof Using Coordinate Geometry**

Write a coordinate proof.
Given: Right △*ABC* has vertices *A*(0, 6), *B*(0, 0), and *C*(4, 0). *D* is the midpoint of $\overline{AC}$.
Prove: The area of △*DBC* is one half the area of △*ABC*.

Proof: △*ABC* is a right triangle with height *AB* and base *BC*.
area of △*ABC* = $\frac{1}{2}bh$
    = $\frac{1}{2}(4)(6)$ = 12 square units

By the Midpoint Formula, the coordinates of
$D = \left(\frac{0+4}{2}, \frac{6+0}{2}\right) = (2, 3)$. The *y*-coordinate of *D* is the height of △*DBC*, and the base is 4 units.
area of △*DBC* = $\frac{1}{2}bh$
    = $\frac{1}{2}(4)(3)$ = 6 square units

Since 6 = $\frac{1}{2}(12)$, the area of △*DBC* is one half the area of △*ABC*.

 **2.** Use the information in Example 2 to write a coordinate proof showing that the area of △*ADB* is one half the area of △*ABC*.

A coordinate proof can also be used to prove that a certain relationship is always true. You can prove that a statement is true for all right triangles without knowing the side lengths. To do this, assign variables as the coordinates of the vertices.

Caution!

Do not use both axes when positioning a figure unless you know the figure has a right angle.

EXAMPLE 3   **Assigning Coordinates to Vertices**

Position each figure in the coordinate plane and give the coordinates of each vertex.

A a right triangle with leg lengths *a* and *b*

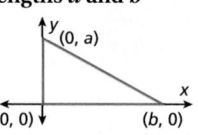
(0, a)

(0, 0) (b, 0)

B a rectangle with length *c* and width *d*

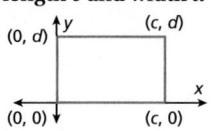
(0, d) (c, d)

(0, 0) (c, 0)

 **3.** Position a square with side length 4*p* in the coordinate plane and give the coordinates of each vertex.

If a coordinate proof requires calculations with fractions, choose coordinates that make the calculations simpler. For example, use multiples of 2 when you are to find coordinates of a midpoint. Once you have assigned the coordinates of the vertices, the procedure for the proof is the same, except that your calculations will involve variables.

 Teach

Guided Instruction

Discuss how to position figures in the coordinate plane. Show students how to assign convenient variable coordinates to vertices. Have students review the Distance and Midpoint Formulas before using them in coordinate proofs.

 **Social Studies** René Descartes, a 17th century mathematician and philosopher, first developed the coordinate plane to make it easier to describe the position of objects.

Reaching All Learners

Through Multiple Representations

Divide the class into two groups. Have one group complete a proof that a triangle with coordinates (0, 4), (0, 0), and (3, 0) is a right triangle. Have the second group use the coordinates (0, *a*), (0, 0), and (*b*, 0) and then verify that the triangle is a right triangle. Compare and contrast the two methods of proof. Emphasize that when you use variables, you prove that the statement is true for all right triangles, not just for a specific triangle.

EXAMPLE 4 Writing a Coordinate Proof

Given: $\angle B$ is a right angle in $\triangle ABC$. D is the midpoint of $\overline{AC}$.
Prove: The area of $\triangle DBC$ is one half the area of $\triangle ABC$.

Step 1 Assign coordinates to each vertex.
The coordinates of A are $(0, 2j)$,
the coordinates of B are $(0, 0)$,
and the coordinates of C are $(2n, 0)$.

Since you will use the Midpoint Formula to find the coordinates of D, use multiples of 2 for the leg lengths.

Step 2 Position the figure in the coordinate plane.

Step 3 Write a coordinate proof.

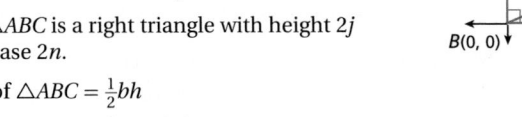

Remember!

Because the x- and y-axes intersect at right angles, they can be used to form the sides of a right triangle.

Proof: $\triangle ABC$ is a right triangle with height $2j$ and base $2n$.

$$\text{area of } \triangle ABC = \tfrac{1}{2}bh$$
$$= \tfrac{1}{2}(2n)(2j)$$
$$= 2nj \text{ square units}$$

By the Midpoint Formula, the coordinates of $D = \left(\dfrac{0 + 2n}{2}, \dfrac{2j + 0}{2}\right) = (n, j)$.

The height of $\triangle DBC$ is j units, and the base is $2n$ units.

$$\text{area of } \triangle DBC = \tfrac{1}{2}bh$$
$$= \tfrac{1}{2}(2n)(j)$$
$$= nj \text{ square units}$$

Since $nj = \tfrac{1}{2}(2nj)$, the area of $\triangle DBC$ is one half the area of $\triangle ABC$.

 **4.** Use the information in Example 4 to write a coordinate proof showing that the area of $\triangle ADB$ is one half the area of $\triangle ABC$.

THINK AND DISCUSS

1. When writing a coordinate proof why are variables used instead of numbers as coordinates for the vertices of a figure?

2. How does the way you position a figure in the coordinate plane affect your calculations in a coordinate proof?

3. Explain why it might be useful to assign $2p$ as a coordinate instead of just p.

4. GET ORGANIZED Copy and complete the graphic organizer. In each row, draw an example of each strategy that might be used when positioning a figure for a coordinate proof.

Positioning Strategy	Example
Use origin as a vertex.	
Center figure at origin.	
Center side of figure at origin.	
Use axes as sides of figure.	

4-7 Introduction to Coordinate Proof **269**

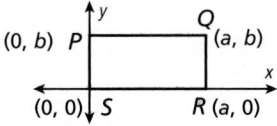

4-7 Exercises

4-7 Exercises

go.hrw.com/Geo/TX
Homework Help Online
KEYWORD: MG7 4-7
Parent Resources Online
KEYWORD: MG7 Parent

Assignment Guide

Assign *Guided Practice* exercises as necessary.

If you finished Examples 1–2
  Basic 8–10, 15–17, 21
  Average 8–10, 15–17, 20–22
  Advanced 8–10, 15–17, 20–24

If you finished Examples 1–4
  Basic 8–13, 15–21, 26–30, 35–40
  Average 8–15, 21, 22, 25–32, 35–40
  Advanced 8–15, 21–40

Homework Quick Check
Quickly check key concepts.
Exercises: 8, 10, 12, 13, 15

Answers

2. Possible answer:

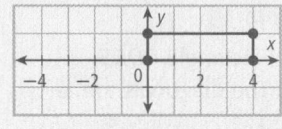

3.

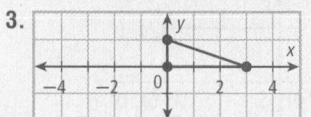

5. Possible answer:

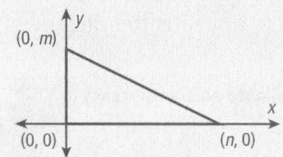

4, 6–13. See pp. A16–A17.

⬇TAKS Practice

Grades 9–11	Exercises
Obj. 2	38, 39
Obj. 5	35–37
Obj. 6	15, 18, 19, 26–32, 38, 39
Obj. 7	20, 21, 26–30, 31, 32
Obj. 8	16, 17
Obj. 10	15, 21, 26

GUIDED PRACTICE

1. **Vocabulary** What is the relationship between *coordinate geometry*, *coordinate plane*, and *coordinate proof*? **Possible answer: In coord. geometry, a coord. proof is a proof in which you place figures in the coord. plane to prove a result.**

SEE EXAMPLE 1
p. 267

Position each figure in the coordinate plane.

2. a rectangle with a length of 4 units and width of 1 unit

3. a right triangle with leg lengths of 1 unit and 3 units

SEE EXAMPLE 2
p. 268

Write a proof using coordinate geometry.

4. **Given:** Right $\triangle PQR$ has coordinates $P(0, 6)$, $Q(8, 0)$, and $R(0, 0)$. A is the midpoint of $\overline{PR}$. B is the midpoint of $\overline{QR}$.
   Prove: $AB = \frac{1}{2}PQ$

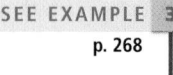

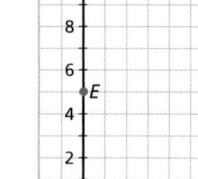

SEE EXAMPLE 3
p. 268

Position each figure in the coordinate plane and give the coordinates of each vertex.

5. a right triangle with leg lengths m and n

6. a rectangle with length a and width b

SEE EXAMPLE 4
p. 269

Multi-Step Assign coordinates to each vertex and write a coordinate proof.

7. **Given:** $\angle R$ is a right angle in $\triangle PQR$. A is the midpoint of $\overline{PR}$. B is the midpoint of $\overline{QR}$.
   Prove: $AB = \frac{1}{2}PQ$

PRACTICE AND PROBLEM SOLVING

Independent Practice
For Exercises	See Example
8–9	1
10	2
11–12	3
13	4

TEKS ✦ TAKS
Skills Practice p. S11
Application Practice p. S31

Position each figure in the coordinate plane.

8. a square with side lengths of 2 units

9. a right triangle with leg lengths of 1 unit and 5 units

Write a proof using coordinate geometry.

10. **Given:** Rectangle $ABCD$ has coordinates $A(0, 0)$, $B(0, 10)$, $C(6, 10)$, and $D(6, 0)$. E is the midpoint of $\overline{AB}$, and F is the midpoint of $\overline{CD}$.
    Prove: $EF = BC$

Position each figure in the coordinate plane and give the coordinates of each vertex.

11. a square with side length $2m$

12. a rectangle with dimensions x and $3x$

Multi-Step Assign coordinates to each vertex and write a coordinate proof.

13. **Given:** E is the midpoint of $\overline{AB}$ in rectangle $ABCD$. F is the midpoint of $\overline{CD}$.
    Prove: $EF = AD$

14. **Critical Thinking** Use variables to write the general form of the endpoints of a segment whose midpoint is $(0, 0)$. **(x, y) and $(-x, -y)$**

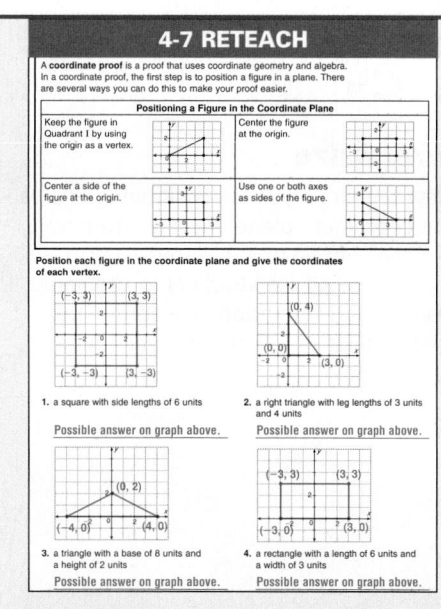

4-7 READING STRATEGIES

Figures can be positioned in a coordinate plane in one of four ways:

Use the **origin as a vertex**, which may keep the figure in Quadrant I.

Center the figure at the origin of the coordinate plane.

Center a side of the figure at the origin of the coordinate plane.

Use **one or both axes** as sides of the figure.

Using the given information, position the figure on the coordinate plane provided and answer the following questions.

1. Where would you position the triangle on the coordinate plane if you want to find the area of $\triangle ABC$?
   with one leg along one of the axes

2. Where would you position the triangle to find the midpoint of $\overline{AB}$?
   with one leg running through the origin

Indicate where on a coordinate plane each figure should be placed in order to find the following measurement.

3. the area of $\triangle ABC$ — **so that one side is along each axis**
4. the midpoint of $\overline{AB}$ — **so that the side straddles the origin**
5. the area of $\triangle ADC$ — **so that one vertex is at the origin**
6. the area of $\triangle CDB$ — **so that one side crosses through the origin**

4-7 RETEACH

A **coordinate proof** is a proof that uses coordinate geometry and algebra. In a coordinate proof, the first step is to position a figure in a plane. There are several ways you can do this to make your proof easier.

Positioning a Figure in the Coordinate Plane
Keep the figure in Quadrant I by using the origin as a vertex.	Center the figure at the origin.
Center a side of the figure at the origin.	Use one or both axes as sides of the figure.

Position each figure in the coordinate plane and give the coordinates of each vertex.

1. a square with side lengths of 6 units
   Possible answer on graph above.

2. a right triangle with leg lengths of 3 units and 4 units
   Possible answer on graph above.

3. a triangle with a base of 8 units and a height of 2 units
   Possible answer on graph above.

4. a rectangle with a length of 6 units and a width of 3 units
   Possible answer on graph above.

15. Recreation A hiking trail begins at $E(0, 0)$. Bryan hikes from the start of the trail to a waterfall at $W(3, 3)$ and then makes a 90° turn to a campsite at $C(6, 0)$.

  a. Draw Bryan's route in the coordinate plane.

  b. If one grid unit represents 1 mile, what is the total distance Bryan hiked? Round to the nearest tenth. **8.5 mi**

Find the perimeter and area of each figure.

16. a right triangle with leg lengths of a and $2a$ units $a\left(3 + \sqrt{5}\right)$ units; a^2 square units

17. a rectangle with dimensions s and t units $2s + 2t$ units; st square units

Find the missing coordinates for each figure.

18. 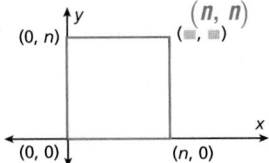 (n, n) $(\blacksquare, \blacksquare)$

19. 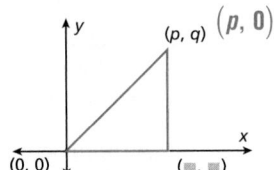 (p, q) $(p, 0)$

Conservation

The origin of the springbok's name may come from its habit of *pronking*, or bouncing. When pronking, a springbok can leap up to 13 feet in the air. Springboks can run up to 53 miles per hour.

20. Conservation The Bushmen have sighted animals at the following coordinates: $(-25, 31.5)$, $(-23.2, 31.4)$, and $(-24, 31.1)$. Prove that the distance between two of these locations is approximately twice the distance between two other.

21. Navigation Two ships depart from a port at $P(20, 10)$. The first ship travels to a location at $A(-30, 50)$, and the second ship travels to a location at $B(70, -30)$. Each unit represents one nautical mile. Find the distance to the nearest nautical mile between the two ships. Verify that the port is at the midpoint between the two.

Write a coordinate proof.

22. Given: Rectangle $PQRS$ has coordinates $P(0, 2)$, $Q(3, 2)$, $R(3, 0)$, and $S(0, 0)$. $\overline{PR}$ and $\overline{QS}$ intersect at $T(1.5, 1)$.
  Prove: The area of $\triangle RST$ is $\frac{1}{4}$ of the area of the rectangle.

23. Given: $A(x_1, y_1)$, $B(x_2, y_2)$, with midpoint $M\left(\frac{x_1 + x_2}{2}, \frac{y_1 + y_2}{2}\right)$
  Prove: $AM = \frac{1}{2}AB$

24. Plot the points on a coordinate plane and connect them to form $\triangle KLM$ and $\triangle MPK$. Write a coordinate proof.

  Given: $K(-2, 1)$, $L(-2, 3)$, $M(1, 3)$, $P(1, 1)$
  Prove: $\triangle KLM \cong \triangle MPK$

25. Write About It When you place two sides of a figure on the coordinate axes, what are you assuming about the figure? **You are assuming the figure has a rt. $\angle$.**

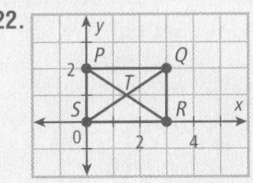
MULTI-STEP TAKS PREP

26. This problem will prepare you for the Multi-Step TAKS Prep on page 280.

Paul designed a doghouse to fit against the side of his house. His plan consisted of a right triangle on top of a rectangle.

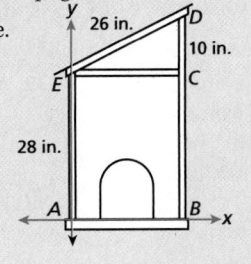
26 in.
10 in.
28 in.

  a. Find BD and CE. **BD = 38 in.; CE = 24 in.**

  b. Before building the doghouse, Paul sketched his plan on a coordinate plane. He placed A at the origin and $\overline{AB}$ on the y-axis. Find the coordinates of B, C, D, and E, assuming that each unit of the coordinate plane represents one inch.
  $B(24, 0)$; $C(24, 28)$; $D(24, 38)$; $E(0, 28)$

4-7 Introduction to Coordinate Proof **271**

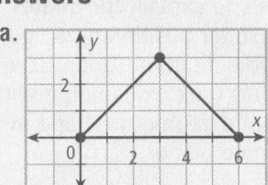
Answers

22.

The area of the rect. is $A = \ell w = 3(2)$ $= 6$ square units. For $\triangle RST$, the base is 3 units, and the height is 1 unit. So the area of $\triangle RST = \frac{1}{2}bh = \frac{1}{2}(3)(1) = 1.5$ square units. Since $\frac{1}{4}(6) = 1.5$, the area of $\triangle RST$ is $\frac{1}{4}$ the area of the rect.

23–24. See p. A17.

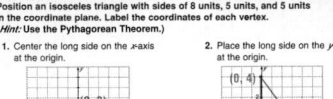 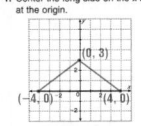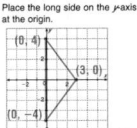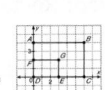
Lesson 4-7 **271**

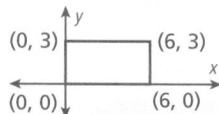
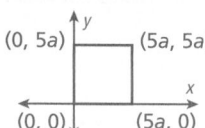
 **TEST PREP**

27. The coordinates of the vertices of a right triangle are $(0, 0)$, $(4, 0)$, and $(0, 2)$. Which is a true statement?
Ⓐ The vertex of the right angle is at $(4, 2)$.
Ⓑ The midpoints of the two legs are at $(2, 0)$ and $(0, 1)$.
Ⓒ The hypotenuse of the triangle is $\sqrt{6}$ units.
Ⓓ The shortest side of the triangle is positioned on the *x*-axis.

28. A rectangle has dimensions of 2*g* and 2*f* units. If one vertex is at the origin, which coordinates could NOT represent another vertex?
Ⓕ $(2f, g)$ Ⓖ $(2f, 0)$ Ⓗ $(2g, 2f)$ Ⓙ $(-2f, 2g)$

29. The coordinates of the vertices of a rectangle are $(0, 0)$, $(a, 0)$, (a, b), and $(0, b)$. What is the perimeter of the rectangle?
Ⓐ $a + b$ Ⓑ ab Ⓒ $\frac{1}{2}ab$ Ⓓ $2a + 2b$

30. A coordinate grid is placed over a map. City A is located at $(-1, 2)$ and city C is located at $(3, 5)$. If city C is at the midpoint between city A and city B, what are the coordinates of city B?
Ⓕ $(1, 3.5)$ Ⓖ $(-5, -1)$ Ⓗ $(7, 8)$ Ⓙ $(2, 7)$

CHALLENGE AND EXTEND

Find the missing coordinates for each figure.

31. 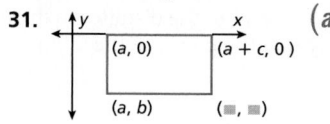 $(a + c, b)$

32. 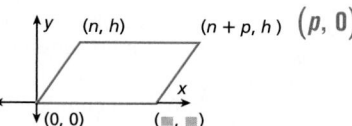 $(p, 0)$

33. Possible answer: Rotate the △ 180° and translate it vertically 2*s* units. The new coords. would be $(0, 0)$, $(0, 2s)$, and $(2s, 0)$.

33. The vertices of a right triangle are at $(-2s, 2s)$, $(0, 2s)$, and $(0, 0)$. What coordinates could be used so that a coordinate proof would be easier to complete?

34. Rectangle *ABCD* has dimensions of 2*f* and 2*g* units. The equation of the line containing $\overline{BD}$ is $y = \frac{g}{f}x$, and the equation of the line containing $\overline{AC}$ is $y = -\frac{g}{f}x + 2g$. Use algebra to show that the coordinates of *E* are (f, g).

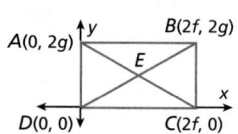

SPIRAL REVIEW

Use the quadratic formula to solve for *x*. Round to the nearest hundredth if necessary. *(Previous course)*

35. $0 = 8x^2 + 18x - 5$ **36.** $0 = x^2 + 3x - 5$ **37.** $0 = 3x^2 - x - 10$
−2.5 or 0.25   1.19 or −4.19   2 or −1.67

Find each value. *(Lesson 3-2)*

38. *x* 112

39. *y* 22

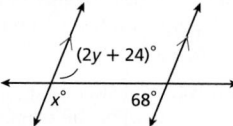

40. Use $A(-4, 3)$, $B(-1, 3)$, $C(-3, 1)$, $D(0, -2)$, $E(3, -2)$, and $F(2, -4)$ to prove $\angle ABC \cong \angle EDF$. *(Lesson 4-6)*.

Answers

34.
$\frac{g}{f}x = -\frac{g}{f}x + 2g$	Set eqns. = to each other.
$\frac{2g}{f}x = 2g$	Combine like terms.
$x = f$	Simplify.
$y = \frac{g}{f}x$	Given
$y = \frac{g}{f}(f)$	Subst.
$y = g$	Simplify.

40. $AB = 3$, $BC = 2\sqrt{2}$, $AC = \sqrt{5}$
$ED = 3$, $DF = 2\sqrt{2}$, $EF = \sqrt{5}$
$\overline{AB} \cong \overline{ED}$, $\overline{BC} \cong \overline{DF}$, and $\overline{AC} \cong \overline{EF}$.
Therefore $\triangle ABC \cong \triangle EDF$ by SSS, and $\angle ABC \cong \angle EDF$ by CPCTC.

Corollary 4-8-4 **Equiangular Triangle**

COROLLARY	HYPOTHESIS	CONCLUSION
If a triangle is equiangular, then it is equilateral. (equiangular △ → equilateral △)	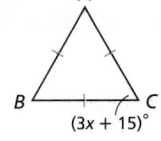	$\overline{DE} \cong \overline{DF} \cong \overline{EF}$

You will prove Corollary 4-8-4 in Exercise 37.

EXAMPLE 3 **Using Properties of Equilateral Triangles**

Find each value.

 Algebra

A x

△ABC is equiangular.   *Equilateral △ → equiangular △*

$(3x + 15)° = 60°$ *The measure of each ∠ of*
                       an equiangular △ is 60°.

      $3x = 45$ *Subtract 15 from both sides.*

       $x = 15$ *Divide both sides by 3.*

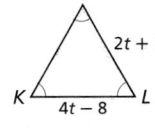

B t

△JKL is equilateral.   *Equiangular △ → equilateral △*

$4t - 8 = 2t + 1$ *Def. of equilateral △*

      $2t = 9$ *Subtract 2t and add 8 to*
                   both sides.

      $t = 4.5$ *Divide both sides by 2.*

 **3.** Use the diagram to find *JL*. 10

EXAMPLE 4 **Using Coordinate Proof**

Remember!

A coordinate proof may be easier if you place one side of the triangle along the x-axis and locate a vertex at the origin or on the y-axis.

Prove that the triangle whose vertices are the midpoints of the sides of an isosceles triangle is also isosceles.

Given: △ABC is isosceles. X is the mdpt. of $\overline{AB}$.
        Y is the mdpt. of $\overline{AC}$. Z is the mdpt. of $\overline{BC}$.

Prove: △XYZ is isosceles.

Proof:

Draw a diagram and place the coordinates of △ABC and △XYZ as shown.

By the Midpoint Formula, the coordinates of X are $\left(\frac{2a + 0}{2}, \frac{2b + 0}{2}\right) = (a, b)$,

the coordinates of Y are $\left(\frac{2a + 4a}{2}, \frac{2b + 0}{2}\right) = (3a, b)$, and the coordinates of Z

are $\left(\frac{4a + 0}{2}, \frac{0 + 0}{2}\right) = (2a, 0)$.

By the Distance Formula, $XZ = \sqrt{(2a - a)^2 + (0 - b)^2} = \sqrt{a^2 + b^2}$, and

$YZ = \sqrt{(2a - 3a)^2 + (0 - b)^2} = \sqrt{a^2 + b^2}$.

Since $XZ = YZ$, $\overline{XZ} \cong \overline{YZ}$ by definition. So △XYZ is isosceles.

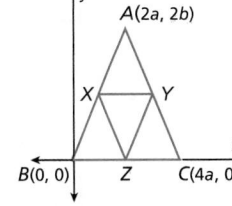

4. By the Mdpt. Formula, the coords. of X are $(-a, b)$, the coords. of Y are (a, b), and the coords. of Z are $(0, 0)$. By the Dist. Formula, $XZ = YZ = \sqrt{a^2 + b^2}$. So $\overline{XZ} \cong \overline{YZ}$ and △XYZ is isosc.

 **4.** **What if...?** The coordinates of △ABC are $A(0, 2b)$, $B(-2a, 0)$, and $C(2a, 0)$. Prove △XYZ is isosceles.

4-8 Isosceles and Equilateral Triangles **275**

---

3 Close

Summarize

Remind students that an isosceles triangle has at least two congruent sides, and its properties can be used to prove that it also has at least two congruent angles. Emphasize that an equilateral triangle has three congruent sides and angles. Review the best methods of naming the vertices of an isosceles and equilateral triangle in the coordinate plane.

ONGOING ASSESSMENT

and INTERVENTION

Diagnose Before the Lesson
4-8 Warm Up, TE p. 273

Monitor During the Lesson
Check It Out! Exercises, SE pp. 274–275
Questioning Strategies, TE pp. 274–275

Assess After the Lesson
4-8 Lesson Quiz, TE p. 279
Alternative Assessment, TE p. 279

Power Presentations
with PowerPoint®

Additional Examples

Example 3

Find each value.

A. x 14

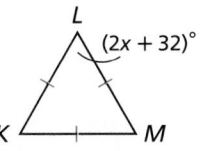

B. y 18

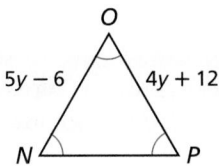

Example 4

Prove that the segment joining the midpoints of two sides of an isosceles triangle is half the base.

Given: In isosceles △ABC, X is the mdpt. of $\overline{AB}$, and Y is the mdpt. of $\overline{AC}$.

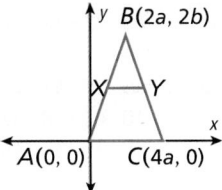

Prove: $XY = \frac{1}{2}AC$.

By the Mdpt. Formula, the coords. of X are (a, b), and Y are $(3a, b)$. By the Dist. Formula, $XY = \sqrt{4a^2} = 2a$, and $AC = 4a$. Therefore $XY = \frac{1}{2}AC$.

Also available on transparency

INTERVENTION
Questioning Strategies

EXAMPLE 3

• If the triangle is equiangular, how do you find the measure of one of its angles?

EXAMPLE 4

• Why is it not suggested that you use numerical values for the vertices in a coordinate proof?

Multiple Representations
For **Example 4**, you could also place the triangle's vertices at $(2a, 0)$, $(-2a, 0)$, and $(0, 2b)$.

Lesson 4-8 **275**

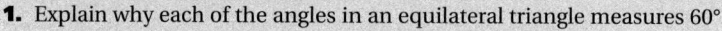

THINK AND DISCUSS

1. Explain why each of the angles in an equilateral triangle measures 60°.

2. **GET ORGANIZED** Copy and complete the graphic organizer. In each box, draw and mark a diagram for each type of triangle.

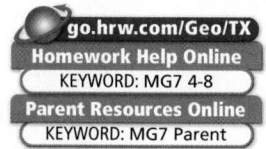

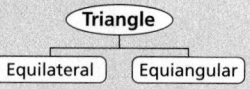

go.hrw.com/Geo/TX
Homework Help Online
KEYWORD: MG7 4-8
Parent Resources Online
KEYWORD: MG7 Parent

Assignment Guide

Assign *Guided Practice* exercises as necessary.

If you finished Examples **1–2**
  Basic 12–16, 22–25, 28, 29, 32–34
  Average 12–16, 22–25, 28, 29, 32–39
  Advanced 12–16, 22–25, 28, 29, 32–39, 41, 45

If you finished Examples **1–4**
  Basic 12–25, 28–30, 42–44, 48–54
  Average 12–23, 26–31, 33, 35, 36, 40, 42–44, 47–54
  Advanced 12–21, 26–33, 35–54

Homework Quick Check
Quickly check key concepts.
Exercises: 12, 14, 18, 21, 28, 30

Teaching Tip **Algebra** In **Exercise 11,** show students that $\sqrt{a^2 + a^2} \neq a + a$, or $2a$.

TAKS Practice

Grades 9–11	Exercises
Obj. 2	27–29, 33, 34, 42–44
Obj. 3	51–53
Obj. 5	48–50
Obj. 6	27–29, 31, 33, 34
Obj. 10	27

GUIDED PRACTICE

1. **Vocabulary** Draw isosceles △*JKL* with ∠*K* as the vertex angle. Name the legs, base, and base angles of the triangle.

SEE EXAMPLE **1**
p. 274

2. **Surveying** To find the distance *QR* across a river, a surveyor locates three points *Q*, *R*, and *S*. *QS* = 41 m, and m∠*S* = 35°. The measure of exterior ∠*PQS* = 70°. Draw a diagram and explain how you can find *QR*.

SEE EXAMPLE **2**
p. 274

Find each angle measure.

3. m∠*ECD*
  118°

4. m∠*K*
  49°

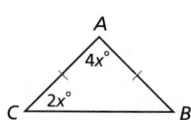

5. m∠*X*
  27°

6. m∠*A*
  90°

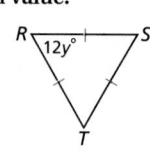

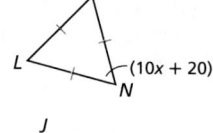

SEE EXAMPLE **3**
p. 275

Find each value.

7. *y*
  5

8. *x*
  4

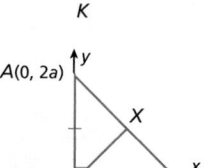

9. *BC*
  20

10. *JK*
  50

SEE EXAMPLE **4**
p. 275

11. **Given:** △*ABC* is right isosceles. *X* is the midpoint of $\overline{AC}$. $\overline{AB} \cong \overline{BC}$

  Prove: △*AXB* is isosceles.

Answers

1.

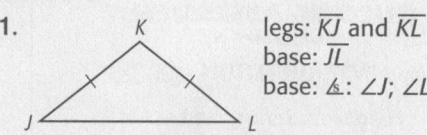

legs: $\overline{KJ}$ and $\overline{KL}$
base: $\overline{JL}$
base: ∡: ∠*J*; ∠*L*

2. By the Ext. ∠ Thm., m∠*R* = 35°. Since m∠*R* = m∠*S* by the Conv. of the Isosc. △ Thm., *QR* = *QS* = 41 m.

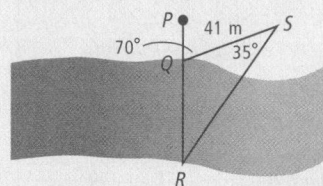

11. It is given that △*ABC* is rt. isosc., $\overline{AB} \cong \overline{BC}$, and *X* is the mdpt. of $\overline{AC}$. By the Mdpt. Formula, the coords. of *X* are (*a*, *a*). By the Dist. Formula, *AX* = *BX* = $a\sqrt{2}$. So △*AXB* is isosc. by def. of an isosc. △.

12. Aviation A plane is flying parallel to the ground along $\overrightarrow{AC}$. When the plane is at A, an air-traffic controller in tower T measures the angle to the plane as 40°. After the plane has traveled 2.4 mi to B, the angle to the plane is 80°. How can you find BT?

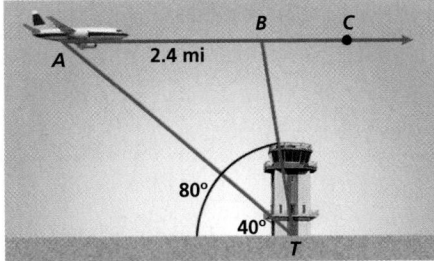

Find each angle measure.

13. m∠E
69°

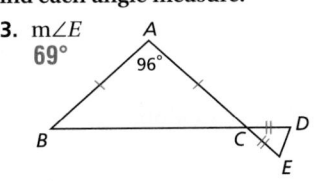

14. m∠TRU
33°

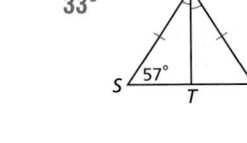

15. m∠F
130° or 172°

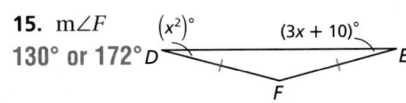

16. m∠A
31°

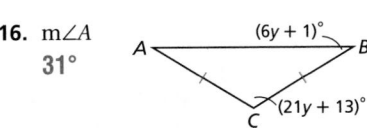

Find each value.

17. z
92

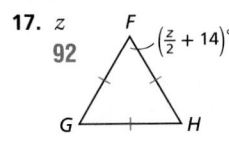

18. y
48

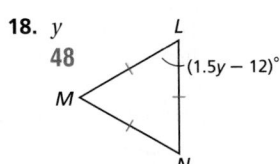

19. BC
26

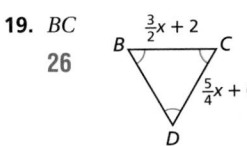

20. XZ
20

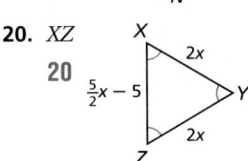

21. Given: △ABC is isosceles. P is the midpoint of $\overline{AB}$. Q is the midpoint of $\overline{AC}$.
$\overline{AB} \cong \overline{AC}$
Prove: $\overline{PC} \cong \overline{QB}$

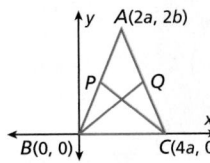

Tell whether each statement is sometimes, always, or never true. Support your answer with a sketch.

22. An equilateral triangle is an isosceles triangle. **A**

23. The vertex angle of an isosceles triangle is congruent to the base angles. **S**

24. An isosceles triangle is a right triangle. **S**

25. An equilateral triangle and an obtuse triangle are congruent. **N**

26. Critical Thinking Can a base angle of an isosceles triangle be an obtuse angle? Why or why not?

Answers

22.

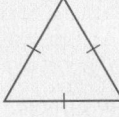

23.

24.

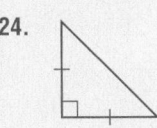

25. Possible answer:

26. No; if a base ∠ is obtuse, then the other base ∠ would also have to be obtuse since they are ≅. The sum of the measures of the ∡ of the △ cannot be greater than 180°.

Answers

12. By the ∠ Add. Post., m∠ATB = 40°. m∠BAT = 40° by the Alt. Int. ∡ Thm. ∠ATB ≅ ∠BAT by def. of ≅. Since △ABT is isosc. by the Converse of the Isosc. △ Thm., BT = BA = 2.4 mi.

21. It is given that △ABC is isosc. $\overline{AB} \cong \overline{AC}$, P is the mdpt. of $\overline{AB}$, and Q is the midpt. of $\overline{AC}$. By the Mdpt. Formula, the coords. of P are (a, b), and the coords. of Q are $(3a, b)$. By the Dist. Formula, $PC = QB = \sqrt{9a^2 + b^2}$, so $\overline{PC} \cong \overline{QB}$ by the def. of ≅.

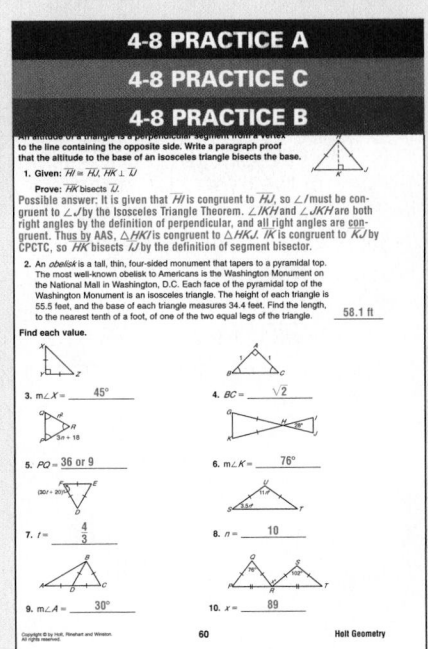

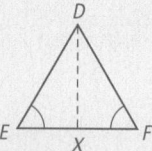

MULTI-STEP TAKS PREP Exercise 27 involves finding angle measures of an isosceles triangle. This exercise prepares students for the Multi-Step TAKS Prep on page 280.

Answers

30. It is given that △ABC is isosc. $\overline{BA} \cong \overline{BC}$, and X is the mdpt. of $\overline{AC}$. Assign the coords. A(0, 2a), B(0, 0) and C(2a, 0). By the Mdpt. Formula, the coords. of X are (a, a). By the Dist. Formula, $AX = XB = XC = a\sqrt{2}$. So △AXB ≅ △CXB by SSS.

31. Check students' drawings. The ∠ are approximately 34°, 34°, and 112°. The conjecture should be that the △ is isosc. The conjecture is correct since there are 2 ≅ ∠.

35.

1. △DEF (Given)
2. Draw the bisector of ∠EDF so that it intersects $\overline{EF}$ at X. (Every ∠ has a unique bisector.)
3. ∠EDX ≅ ∠FDX (Def. of ∠ bisector)
4. $\overline{DX} \cong \overline{DX}$ (Reflex. Prop. of ≅)
5. ∠E ≅ ∠F (Given)
6. △EDX ≅ △FDX (AAS Steps 3, 5, 4)
7. $\overline{DE} \cong \overline{DF}$ (CPCTC)

36a. ∠B ≅ ∠C
b. Isosc. △ Thm.
c. Trans. Prop. of ≅

37. △DEF with ∠D ≅ ∠E ≅ ∠F is given. Since ∠E ≅ ∠F, $\overline{DE} \cong \overline{DF}$ by the Conv. of the Isosc. △ Thm. Similarly, since ∠D ≅ ∠F, $\overline{EF} \cong \overline{DE}$. By the Trans. Prop. of ≅, $\overline{EF} \cong \overline{DF}$. Combining the ≅ statements, $\overline{DE} \cong \overline{DF} \cong \overline{EF}$, and △DEF is equil. by def.

38. By the Ext. ∠ Thm., m∠C = 45°, so ∠A ≅ ∠C. BC = AB by the Conv. of the Isosc. △ Thm. So the distance to island C is the same as the distance traveled from A to B.

39. 1. △ABC ≅ △CBA (Given)
2. $\overline{AB} \cong \overline{CB}$ (CPCTC)
3. △ABC is isosceles (Def. of Isosc. △)

27. This problem will prepare you for the Multi-Step TAKS Prep on page 280.
The diagram shows the inside view of the support structure of the back of a doghouse. $\overline{PQ} \cong \overline{PR}$, $\overline{PS} \cong \overline{PT}$, m∠PST = 71°, and m∠QPS = m∠RPT = 18°.

a. Find m∠SPT. **38°**
b. Find m∠PQR and m∠PRQ. **53°**

Multi-Step Find the measure of each numbered angle.

28.

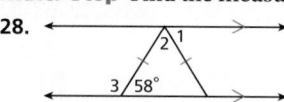

m∠1 = 58°;
m∠2 = 64°;
m∠3 = 122°

29.

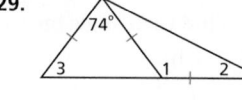

m∠1 = 127°;
m∠2 = 26.5°;
m∠3 = 53°

30. Write a coordinate proof.

Given: ∠B is a right angle in isosceles right △ABC.
X is the midpoint of $\overline{AC}$. $\overline{BA} \cong \overline{BC}$
Prove: △AXB ≅ △CXB

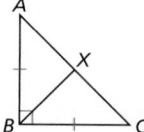

31. **Estimation** Draw the figure formed by (−2, 1), (5, 5), and (−1, −7). Estimate the measure of each angle and make a conjecture about the classification of the figure. Then use a protractor to measure each angle. Was your conjecture correct? Why or why not?

32. How many different isosceles triangles have a perimeter of 18 and sides whose lengths are natural numbers? Explain. **4 △: 5, 5, 8; 6, 6, 6; 7, 7, 4; 8, 8, 2**

Multi-Step Find the value of the variable in each diagram.

33.

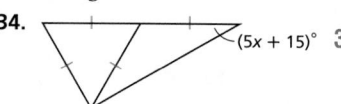

20

(3y − 5)°
40°

34.

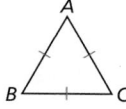

(5x + 15)° **3**

35. Prove the Converse of the Isosceles Triangle Theorem.

36. Complete the proof of Corollary 4-8-3.

Given: $\overline{AB} \cong \overline{AC} \cong \overline{BC}$
Prove: ∠A ≅ ∠B ≅ ∠C

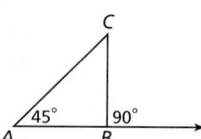

Proof: Since $\overline{AB} \cong \overline{AC}$, **a.** __?__ by the Isosceles Triangle Theorem. Since $\overline{AC} \cong \overline{BC}$, ∠A ≅ ∠B by **b.** __?__. Therefore ∠A ≅ ∠C by **c.** __?__. By the Transitive Property of ≅, ∠A ≅ ∠B ≅ ∠C.

37. Prove Corollary 4-8-4.

38. **Navigation** The captain of a ship traveling along $\overrightarrow{AB}$ sights an island C at an angle of 45°. The captain measures the distance the ship covers until it reaches B, where the angle to the island is 90°. Explain how to find the distance BC to the island.

39. **Given:** △ABC ≅ △CBA
Prove: △ABC is isosceles.

40. **Write About It** Write the Isosceles Triangle Theorem and its converse as a biconditional. **Two sides of a △ are ≅ if and only if the ∠ opp. those sides are ≅.**

Navigation

The taffrail log is dragged from the stern of a vessel to measure the speed or distance traveled during a voyage. The log consists of a rotator, recording device, and governor.

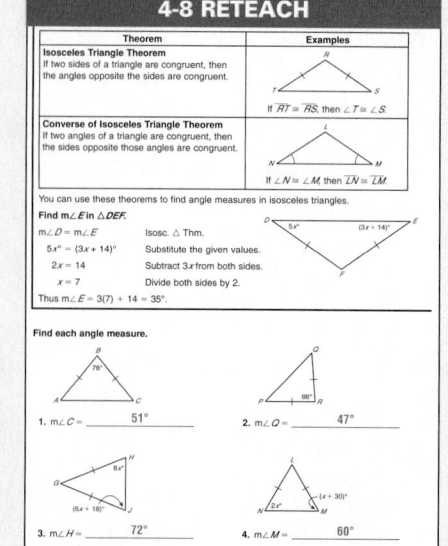

41. Rewrite the paragraph proof of the Hypotenuse-Leg (HL) Congruence Theorem as a two-column proof.

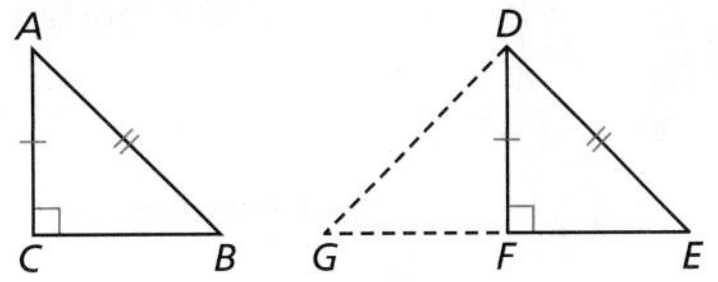

Given: $\triangle ABC$ and $\triangle DEF$ are right triangles. $\angle C$ and $\angle F$ are right angles. $\overline{AC} \cong \overline{DF}$, and $\overline{AB} \cong \overline{DE}$.

Prove: $\triangle ABC \cong \triangle DEF$

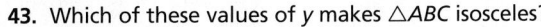

Proof: On $\triangle DEF$ draw $\overrightarrow{EF}$. Mark G so that $FG = CB$. Thus $\overline{FG} \cong \overline{CB}$. From the diagram, $\overline{AC} \cong \overline{DF}$ and $\angle C$ and $\angle F$ are right angles. $\overline{DF} \perp \overline{EG}$ by definition of perpendicular lines. Thus $\angle DFG$ is a right angle, and $\angle DFG \cong \angle C$. $\triangle ABC \cong \triangle DGF$ by SAS. $\overline{DG} \cong \overline{AB}$ by CPCTC. $\overline{AB} \cong \overline{DE}$ as given. $\overline{DG} \cong \overline{DE}$ by the Transitive Property. By the Isosceles Triangle Theorem $\angle G \cong \angle E$. $\angle DFG \cong \angle DFE$ since right angles are congruent. So $\triangle DGF \cong \triangle DEF$ by AAS. Therefore $\triangle ABC \cong \triangle DEF$ by the Transitive Property.

**TEST PREP**

42. Lorena is designing a window so that $\angle R$, $\angle S$, $\angle T$, and $\angle U$ are right angles, $\overline{VU} \cong \overline{VT}$, and m$\angle UVT = 20°$. What is m$\angle RUV$?

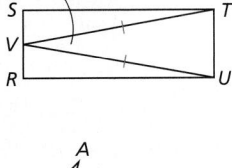

Ⓐ 10°   Ⓒ 20°

Ⓑ 70°   Ⓓ 80°

43. Which of these values of y makes $\triangle ABC$ isosceles?

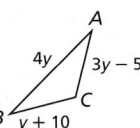

Ⓕ $1\frac{1}{4}$ Ⓗ $7\frac{1}{2}$

Ⓖ $2\frac{1}{2}$ Ⓙ $15\frac{1}{2}$

44. Gridded Response The vertex angle of an isosceles triangle measures $(6t - 9)°$, and one of the base angles measures $(4t)°$. Find t. **13.5**

CHALLENGE AND EXTEND

45. In the figure, $\overline{JK} \cong \overline{JL}$, and $\overline{KM} \cong \overline{KL}$. Let m$\angle J = x°$. Prove m$\angle MKL$ must also be $x°$.

46. An equilateral $\triangle ABC$ is placed on a coordinate plane. Each side length measures $2a$. B is at the origin, and C is at $(2a, 0)$. Find the coordinates of A. $\left(a, a\sqrt{3}\right)$

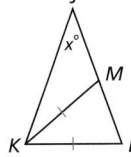

47. An isosceles triangle has coordinates $A(0, 0)$ and $B(a, b)$. What are all possible coordinates of the third vertex? $(2a, 0)$, $(0, 2b)$, or any pt. on the $\perp$ bisector of $\overline{AB}$

SPIRAL REVIEW

54. Possible answer:

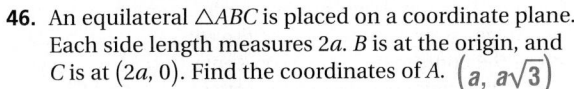

Find the solutions for each equation. *(Previous course)*

48. $x^2 + 5x + 4 = 0$ **49.** $x^2 - 4x + 3 = 0$ **50.** $x^2 - 2x + 1 = 0$
-4 or -1 3 or 1 1

Find the slope of the line that passes through each pair of points. *(Lesson 3-5)*

51. $(2, -1)$ and $(0, 5)$ **52.** $(-5, -10)$ and $(20, -10)$ **53.** $(4, 7)$ and $(10, 11)$ $\frac{2}{3}$
-3 0

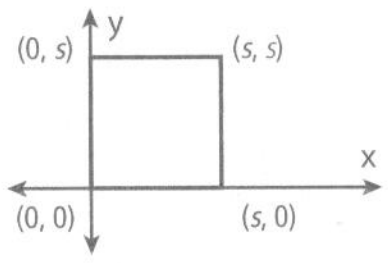

54. Position a square with a perimeter of $4s$ in the coordinate plane and give the coordinates of each vertex. *(Lesson 4-7)*

4-8 PROBLEM SOLVING

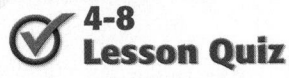

1. A "Yield" sign is an equiangular triangle. What are the lengths of the sides?
14 in.

2. The measure of $\angle C$ is 70°. What is the measure of $\angle B$?
40°

3. Samantha is swimming along $\overline{HF}$. When she is at point H, she sees a necklace straight ahead of her but on the bottom of the pool at point J. Then she swims 11 more feet to point G. Use the diagram to find GJ, the distance Samantha is from the necklace. Explain.
11 ft; m$\angle$ GJH = 72° − 36° = 36°. m$\angle$ GHJ = 36° by Alt. Int. $\angle$ Thm. By Converse of Isosceles Triangle Theorem, GJ = GH = 11 ft.

Choose the best answer.

4. A billiards triangle is equiangular. What is the perimeter?
A $5\frac{1}{8}$ in.   C $11\frac{1}{4}$ in.
B $10\frac{1}{4}$ in.   Ⓓ $33\frac{3}{4}$ in.

5. A triangular shaped trellis has angles R, S, and T that measure 73°, 73°, and 34°, respectively. If $ST = 4y + 6$ and $TR = 7y - 21$, what is the value of y?
F 5   H 11
Ⓖ 9   J 15

6. Two triangular tiles each have two sides measuring 4 inches. Which is a true statement?
A Their corresponding angles are congruent.   Ⓒ The triangles may be congruent.
B The triangles are congruent.   D The triangles cannot be congruent.

7. What is the value of x in the figure?
F 42°   Ⓗ 96°
G 90°   J 106°

Answers

41. See p. A17.

45. It is given that $\overline{JK} \cong \overline{JL}$, $\overline{KM} \cong \overline{KL}$, and m$\angle J = x°$. By the $\triangle$ Sum Thm., m$\angle JKL$ + m$\angle JLK$ + $x°$ = 180°. By the Isosc. $\triangle$ Thm., m$\angle JKL$ = m$\angle JLK$. So $2(m\angle JLK)$ + $x°$ = 180° or m$\angle JLK$ = $\left(\frac{180 - x}{2}\right)°$. Since m$\angle KML$ = m$\angle JLK$, m$\angle KML$ = $\left(\frac{180 - x}{2}\right)°$ by the Isosc. $\triangle$ Thm. By the $\triangle$ Sum Thm., m$\angle MKL$ + m$\angle JLK$ + m$\angle KML$ = 180° or m$\angle MKL$ = 180° − $\left(\frac{180 - x}{2}\right)°$ − $\left(\frac{180 - x}{2}\right)°$. Simplifying gives m$\angle MKL$ = $x°$.

Journal

Compare the hypothesis and the conclusion of the Isosceles Triangle Theorem with its converse. Support your comparison with a sketch.

ALTERNATIVE ASSESSMENT

Have students create a poster to present examples of how to find missing parts of an isosceles and an equilateral triangle, when given the measure of one angle or an algebraic expression.

Power Presentations with PowerPoint®

4-8 Lesson Quiz

Find each angle measure.

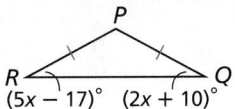

R $(5x - 17)°$ $(2x + 10)°$ Q

1. m$\angle R$ **28°**   **2.** m$\angle P$ **124°**

Find each value.

3. x **20**

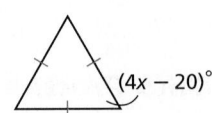
$(4x - 20)°$

4. y **6**

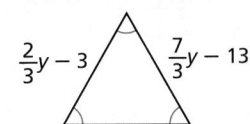
$\frac{2}{3}y - 3$ $\frac{7}{3}y - 13$

5. x **26°**

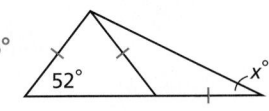
52° $x°$

6. The vertex angle of an isosceles triangle measures $(a + 15)°$, and one of the base angles measures $7a°$. Find a and each angle measure.
$a = 11$; 26°; 77°; 77°

Also available on transparency

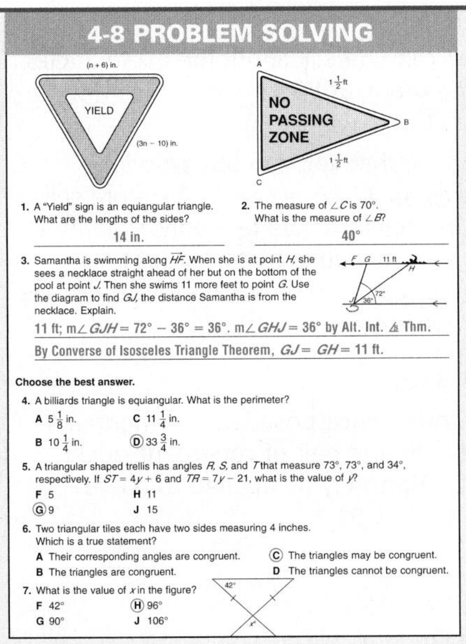

MULTI-STEP TAKS PREP

Organizer

Objective: Assess students' ability to apply concepts and skills in Lessons 4-4 through Lesson 4-8 in a real-world format.

 **Online Edition**

Resources

 *Geometry Assessments*
www.mathtekstoolkit.org

Problem	Text Reference
1	Lesson 4-4
2	Lesson 4-5
3	Lesson 4-6
4	Lesson 4-7
5	Lesson 4-8
6	Lessons 4-4 to 4-8

Answers

2. 1. $\overline{CD} \perp \overline{AB}$ (Given)
   2. $\angle CDA$ and $\angle CDB$ are rt. $\angle$s. (Def. of $\perp$)
   3. $\triangle CDA$ and $\triangle CDB$ are rt. $\triangle$s. (Def. of rt. $\triangle$)
   4. $\overline{AC} \cong \overline{BC}$ (Given)
   5. $\overline{CD} \cong \overline{CD}$ (Reflex. Prop. of $\cong$)
   6. $\triangle CDA \cong \triangle CDB$ (HL *Steps 4, 5*)

⬆️TAKS Practice

Grades 9–11	Problems
Obj. 6	1, 2

Proving Triangles Congruent

Gone to the Dogs You are planning to build a doghouse for your dog. The pitched roof of the doghouse will be supported by four trusses. Each truss will be an isosceles triangle with the dimensions shown. To determine the materials you need to purchase and how you will construct the trusses, you must first plan carefully.

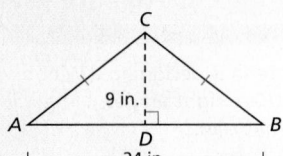

1. Measure $\overline{AB}$, $\overline{BC}$, and $\overline{CA}$. If these 3 lengths are the same for every truss, then the trusses all have the same size and shape by SSS.

1. You want to be sure that all four trusses are exactly the same size and shape. Explain how you could measure three lengths on each truss to ensure this. Which postulate or theorem are you using?

2. Prove that the two triangular halves of the truss are congruent.

3. $\overline{AD} \cong \overline{DB}$ by CPCTC. $AD = DB = 12$ in. and $AC = BC = 15$ in.

3. What can you say about $\overline{AD}$ and $\overline{DB}$? Why is this true? Use this to help you find the lengths of $\overline{AD}$, $\overline{DB}$, $\overline{AC}$, and $\overline{BC}$.

4. Possible answer: $A(0, 0)$, $B(24, 0)$, $C(12, 9)$

4. You want to make careful plans on a coordinate plane before you begin your construction of the trusses. Each unit of the coordinate plane represents 1 inch. How could you assign coordinates to vertices A, B, and C?

5. $m\angle ACB = 106°$. What is the measure of each of the acute angles in the truss? Explain how you found your answer.

5. $m\angle A = m\angle B = 37°$; the base $\angle$s of an isosc. $\triangle$ are $\cong$, so $2m\angle A + 106° = 180°$.

6. You can buy the wood for the trusses at the building supply store for $0.80 a foot. The store sells the wood in 6-foot lengths only. How much will you have to spend to get enough wood for the 4 trusses of the doghouse? (*Hint:* You need to use the Pythagorean Theorem to find the two unknown side lengths of each truss.) **$14.40**

INTERVENTION ⬅️➡️

Scaffolding Questions

1. Which postulate or theorem applies if you know that three sides of one triangle are congruent to three sides of another triangle? SSS

2. What type of triangle is formed by each half of the truss? rt.

3. Can you conclude that $\overline{AD} \cong \overline{DB}$? If so, why? Yes; CPCTC Once you know *AD*, how can you find *AC*? Pyth. Thm.

4. If you place *A* at the origin and $\overline{AB}$ along the *x*-axis, what are the coordinates of *B*? Why? $B(24, 0)$; $AB = 24$

5. What can you say about the acute angles of the triangle? Why? They are $\cong$; they are base $\angle$s of an isosc. $\triangle$.

6. Suppose that you can buy wooden boards for $1.80 per foot. The store sells the boards in whole feet only. How much will you have to spend in order to buy enough wood to make the trusses for the doghouse? $9

Extension

Which congruence postulates or theorems involve only one pair of congruent sides? ASA; AAS Can they be applied to prove $\triangle ACD \cong \triangle BCD$? Yes

Quiz for Lessons 4-4 Through 4-8

READY TO GO ON?

✓ 4-4 Triangle Congruence: SSS and SAS

1. The figure shows one tower and the cables of a suspension bridge. Given that $\overline{AC} \cong \overline{BC}$, use SAS to explain why $\triangle ACD \cong \triangle BCD$.

2. **Given:** $\overline{JK}$ bisects $\angle MJN$. $\overline{MJ} \cong \overline{NJ}$
   Prove: $\triangle MJK \cong \triangle NJK$

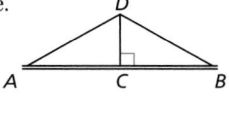

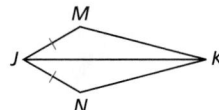

✓ 4-5 Triangle Congruence: ASA, AAS, and HL

Determine if you can use the HL Congruence Theorem to prove the triangles congruent. If not, tell what else you need to know.

3. $\triangle RSU$ and $\triangle TUS$
   yes

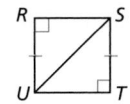

4. $\triangle ABC$ and $\triangle DCB$
   no; $\overline{AC} \cong \overline{DB}$

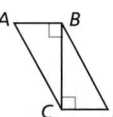

Observers in two lighthouses K and L spot a ship S.

5. Draw a diagram of the triangle formed by the lighthouses and the ship. Label each measure.

6. Is there enough data in the table to pinpoint the location of the ship? Why?
   Yes; the $\triangle$ is uniquely determined by ASA.

	K to L	K to S	L to S
Bearing	E	N 58° E	N 77° W
Distance	12 km	?	?

5.

✓ 4-6 Triangle Congruence: CPCTC

7. **Given:** $\overline{CD} \parallel \overline{BE}$, $\overline{DE} \parallel \overline{CB}$
   Prove: $\angle D \cong \angle B$

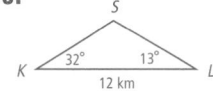

✓ 4-7 Introduction to Coordinate Proof

Check students' work; possible answer: vertices at $(0, 0)$, $(9, 0)$, $(9, 9)$, and $(0, 9)$.

8. Position a square with side lengths of 9 units in the coordinate plane

9. Assign coordinates to each vertex and write a coordinate proof.
   Given: $ABCD$ is a rectangle with M as the midpoint of $\overline{AB}$. N is the midpoint of $\overline{AD}$.
   Prove: The area of $\triangle AMN$ is $\frac{1}{8}$ the area of rectangle $ABCD$.

✓ 4-8 Isosceles and Equilateral Triangles

Find each value.

10. $m\angle C$
    100°

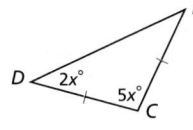

11. ST
    6

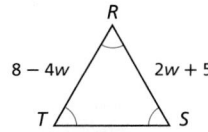

12. **Given:** Isosceles $\triangle JKL$ has coordinates $J(0, 0)$, $K(2a, 2b)$, and $L(4a, 0)$. M is the midpoint of $\overline{JK}$, and N is the midpoint of $\overline{KL}$.
    Prove: $\triangle KMN$ is isosceles.

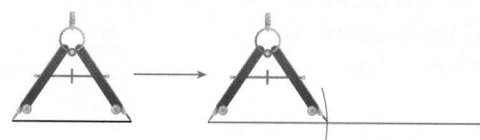

Online Edition

Using the Extension

In Chapter 4, students learn to prove triangles congruent and to use properties of congruent triangles in other proofs. In this extension, students use the properties of congruent triangles to prove constructions valid.

Answers to *Check It Out!*

1. **1.** Draw $\overline{AC}$, $\overline{BC}$, $\overline{AD}$, and $\overline{BD}$. (Through any 2 pts. there is exactly 1 line.)
   2. $\overline{AC} \cong \overline{BC} \cong \overline{AD} \cong \overline{BD}$ (Same compass setting used)
   3. $\overline{CD} \cong \overline{CD}$ (Reflex. Prop. of $\cong$)
   4. $\triangle ACD \cong \triangle BCD$ (SSS *Steps 2, 3*)
   5. $\angle ACD \cong \angle BCD$ (CPCTC)
   6. $\overline{CM} \cong \overline{CM}$ (Reflex. Prop. of $\cong$)
   7. $\triangle ACM \cong \triangle BCM$ (SAS *Steps 2, 5, 6*)
   8. $\angle AMC \cong \angle BMC$ (CPCTC)
   9. $\angle AMC$ and $\angle BMC$ are rt. $\angle$s. ($\cong$ $\angle$s supp. $\rightarrow$ rt. $\angle$s)
   10. $\overline{CD} \perp \overline{AB}$ (Def. of $\perp$)
   11. $\overline{AM} \cong \overline{BM}$ (CPCTC)
   12. $\overleftrightarrow{CD}$ bisects $\overline{AB}$. (Def. of bisector)

Proving Constructions Valid

TEK G.2.A Geometric structure: use constructions to explore attributes of geometric figures and to make conjectures about geometric relationships. **Also G.3.B**

When performing a compass and straight edge construction, the compass setting remains the same width until you change it. This fact allows you to construct a segment congruent to a given segment. You can assume that two distances constructed with the same compass setting are congruent.

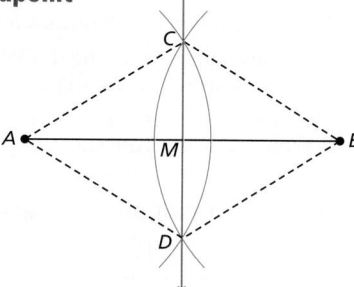

The steps in the construction of a figure can be justified by combining the assumptions of compass and straightedge constructions and the postulates and theorems that are used for proving triangles congruent.

You have learned that there exists exactly one midpoint on any line segment. The proof below justifies the construction of a midpoint.

EXAMPLE 1 **Proving the Construction of a Midpoint**

Given: diagram showing the steps in the construction
Prove: M is the midpoint of $\overline{AB}$.

Remember!

To construct a midpoint, see the construction of a perpendicular bisector on p. 172.

Proof:

Statements	Reasons
1. Draw $\overline{AC}$, $\overline{BC}$, $\overline{AD}$, and $\overline{BD}$.	**1.** Through any two pts. there is exactly one line.
2. $\overline{AC} \cong \overline{BC} \cong \overline{AD} \cong \overline{BD}$	**2.** Same compass setting used
3. $\overline{CD} \cong \overline{CD}$	**3.** Reflex. Prop. of $\cong$
4. $\triangle ACD \cong \triangle BCD$	**4.** SSS *Steps 2, 3*
5. $\angle ACD \cong \angle BCD$	**5.** CPCTC
6. $\overline{CM} \cong \overline{CM}$	**6.** Reflex. Prop. of $\cong$
7. $\triangle ACM \cong \triangle BCM$	**7.** SAS *Steps 2, 5, 6*
8. $\overline{AM} \cong \overline{BM}$	**8.** CPCTC
9. M is the midpt. of $\overline{AB}$.	**9.** Def. of mdpt.

CHECK IT OUT!
1. **Given:** above diagram
Prove: $\overleftrightarrow{CD}$ is the perpendicular bisector of $\overline{AB}$.

G.2 Geometric structure*
(A) use constructions to explore attributes of geometric figures and to make conjectures about geometric relationships

G.3 Geometric structure*
(B) construct and justify statements about geometric figures and their properties

* Knowledge and Skills See p. 214.

---

1 Introduce

Motivate

Point out to students that some assumptions made about their construction tools, such as a compass setting being fixed, could make their constructions inaccurate. Discuss what characteristics of their construction tools might make their constructions invalid. Possible answer: Compass does not hold its setting; compass does not hold the pencil firmly; straightedge is cracked or broken.

---

2 Teach

Guided Instruction

Explain that steps in a construction contain given information much like the tick marks in a diagram show that segments are congruent. Have students practice identifying what information is given from the construction marks in a diagram. Explain to students that justifying their constructions can provide a review of concepts from previous lessons.

Teaching Tip **Inclusion** Remind students to make their constructions big enough for easy use of their compass.

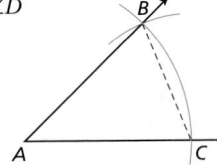
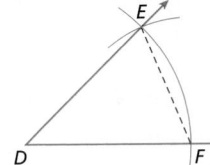

EXAMPLE **2** **Proving the Construction of an Angle**

Given: diagram showing the steps in the construction

Prove: $\angle A \cong \angle D$

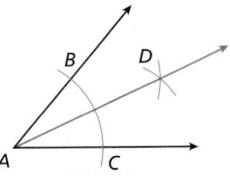

Proof: Since there is a straight line through any two points, you can draw $\overline{BC}$ and $\overline{EF}$. The same compass setting was used to construct $\overline{AC}$, $\overline{AB}$, $\overline{DF}$, and $\overline{DE}$, so $\overline{AC} \cong \overline{AB} \cong \overline{DF} \cong \overline{DE}$. The same compass setting was used to construct $\overline{BC}$ and $\overline{EF}$, so $\overline{BC} \cong \overline{EF}$. Therefore $\triangle BAC \cong \triangle EDF$ by SSS, and $\angle A \cong \angle D$ by CPCTC.

CHECK IT OUT! **2.** Prove the construction for bisecting an angle. (See page 23.)

Draw $\overline{BD}$ and $\overline{CD}$ (through any 2 pts. there is exactly 1 line). Since the same compass setting was used, $\overline{AB} \cong \overline{AC}$ and $\overline{BD} \cong \overline{CD}$. $\overline{AD} \cong \overline{AD}$ by the Reflex. Prop. of $\cong$. So $\triangle ABD \cong \triangle ACD$ by SSS, and $\angle BAD \cong \angle CAD$ by CPCTC. Therefore $\overrightarrow{AD}$ bisects $\angle BAC$ by the def. of $\angle$ bisector.

EXTENSION

Exercises

Use each diagram to prove the construction valid.

1. parallel lines
(See page 163 and page 170.)

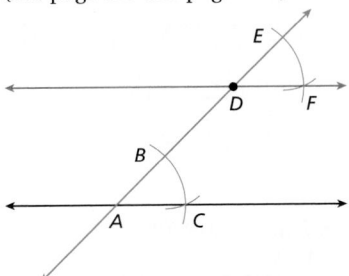

2. a perpendicular through a point not on the line (See page 179.)

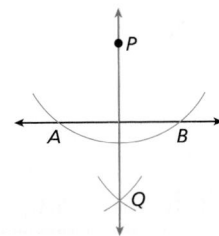

3. constructing a triangle using SAS
(See page 243.)

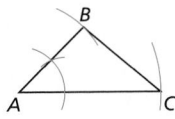
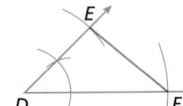

4. constructing a triangle using ASA
(See page 253.)

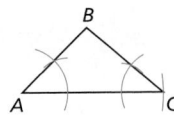
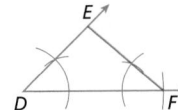

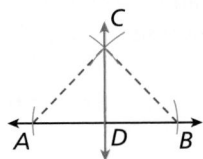
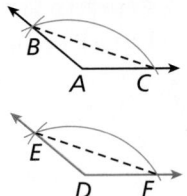
Answers

1. Draw auxiliary segments $\overline{BC}$ and $\overline{EF}$. (Through any 2 pts. there is exactly 1 line.) Since the same compass setting was used, $\overline{AB} \cong \overline{AC} \cong \overline{DE} \cong \overline{DF}$ and $\overline{BC} \cong \overline{EF}$. $\triangle BAC \cong \triangle EDF$ by SSS. $\angle BAC \cong \angle EDF$ by CPCTC. Therefore $\overleftrightarrow{DF} \parallel \overleftrightarrow{AC}$ by the Conv. of the Corr. $\angle$ Thm.

2–4. See p. A17.

Organizer

Objective: Help students organize and review key concepts and skills presented in Chapter 4.

Online Edition
Multilingual Glossary

Countdown to TAKS Week 9

Resources

PuzzlePro
One-Stop Planner®

Multilingual Glossary Online
go.hrw.com/Geo/TX
KEYWORD: MG7 Glossary

Lesson Tutorial Videos
CD-ROM

Test & Practice Generator
One-Stop Planner®

Answers

1. isosceles triangle
2. corresponding angles
3. included side
4. equiangular; equil.
5. obtuse; scalene
6. 60°
7. 66.5°

Know it!
.Note

For a complete list of the postulates and theorems in this chapter, see p. S82.

Vocabulary

Complete the sentences below with vocabulary words from the list above.

1. A(n) ___?___ is a triangle with at least two congruent sides.

2. A name given to matching angles of congruent triangles is ___?___ .

3. A(n) ___?___ is the common side of two consecutive angles in a polygon.

4-1 Classifying Triangles (pp. 216–221)

 TEKS G.1.A

EXAMPLE

■ Classify the triangle by its angle measures and side lengths.

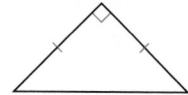

isosceles right triangle

EXERCISES

Classify each triangle by its angle measures and side lengths.

4.
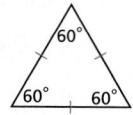

5.

4-2 Angle Relationships in Triangles (pp. 223–230)

 TEKS G.1.A, G.2.B

EXAMPLE

■ Find m∠S.

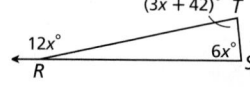

$12x = 3x + 42 + 6x$
$12x = 9x + 42$
$3x = 42$
$x = 14$
$\text{m}\angle S = 6(14) = 84°$

EXERCISES

Find m∠N.

6.

7. In △LMN, m∠L = 8x°, m∠M = (2x + 1)°, and m∠N = (6x − 1)°.

4-3 Congruent Triangles (pp. 231–237)

⭐ TEKS G.2.B, G.10.B

EXAMPLE

■ Given: $\triangle DEF \cong \triangle JKL$. Identify all pairs of congruent corresponding parts. Then find the value of x.

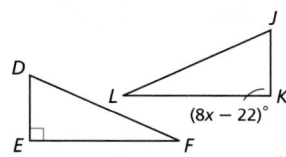

The congruent pairs follow: $\angle D \cong \angle J$, $\angle E \cong \angle K$, $\angle F \cong \angle L$, $\overline{DE} \cong \overline{JK}$, $\overline{EF} \cong \overline{KL}$, and $\overline{DF} \cong \overline{JL}$.

Since $m\angle E = m\angle K$, $90 = 8x - 22$. After 22 is added to both sides, $112 = 8x$. So $x = 14$.

EXERCISES

Given: $\triangle PQR \cong \triangle XYZ$. Identify the congruent corresponding parts.

8. $\overline{PR} \cong$ __?__

9. $\angle Y \cong$ __?__

Given: $\triangle ABC \cong \triangle CDA$
Find each value.

10. x

11. CD

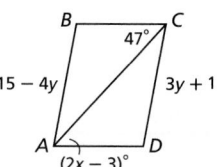

12. 1. $\overline{AB} \cong \overline{DE}$, $\overline{DB} \cong \overline{AE}$ (Given)
2. $\overline{DA} \cong \overline{DA}$ (Reflex. Prop. of $\cong$)
3. $\triangle ADB \cong \triangle DAE$ (SSS Steps 1, 2)

13. 1. $\overline{GJ}$ bisects $\overline{FH}$, and $\overline{FH}$ bisects $\overline{GJ}$. (Given)
2. $\overline{GK} \cong \overline{JK}$, $\overline{FK} \cong \overline{HK}$ (Def. of seg. bisect)
3. $\angle GKF \cong \angle JKH$ (Vert. $\angle$ Thm.)
4. $\triangle FGK \cong \triangle HJK$ (SAS Steps 2, 3)

14. $BC = (-6)^2 + 36 = 72$; $YZ = 2(-6)^2 = 72$; $\overline{BC} \cong \overline{YZ}$; $\angle C \cong \angle Z$; $\overline{AC} \cong \overline{XZ}$. So $\triangle ABC \cong \triangle XYZ$ by SAS.

15. $PQ = 25 - 1 = 24$; $QR = 25$; and $PR = 25^2 - (25 - 1)^2 - 42 = 7$; $\overline{LM} \cong \overline{PQ}$; $\overline{MN} \cong \overline{QR}$; $\overline{LN} \cong \overline{PR}$; so $\triangle LMN \cong \triangle PQR$ by SSS.

4-4 Triangle Congruence: SSS and SAS (pp. 242–249)

⭐ TEKS G.2.A, G.3.B, G.3.E, G.10.B

EXAMPLES

■ Given: $\overline{RS} \cong \overline{UT}$, and $\overline{VS} \cong \overline{VT}$. V is the midpoint of $\overline{RU}$.

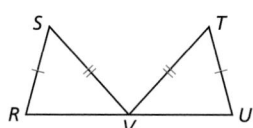

Prove: $\triangle RSV \cong \triangle UTV$

Proof:

Statements	Reasons
1. $\overline{RS} \cong \overline{UT}$	1. Given
2. $\overline{VS} \cong \overline{VT}$	2. Given
3. V is the mdpt. of $\overline{RU}$.	3. Given
4. $\overline{RV} \cong \overline{UV}$	4. Def. of mdpt.
5. $\triangle RSV \cong \triangle UTV$	5. SSS Steps 1, 2, 4

■ Show that $\triangle ADB \cong \triangle CDB$ when s = 5.

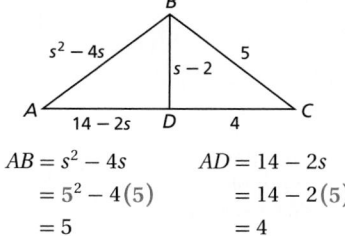

$AB = s^2 - 4s \qquad AD = 14 - 2s$
$\quad = 5^2 - 4(5) \qquad = 14 - 2(5)$
$\quad = 5 \qquad\qquad = 4$

$\overline{BD} \cong \overline{BD}$ by the Reflexive Property. $\overline{AD} \cong \overline{CD}$ and $\overline{AB} \cong \overline{CB}$. So $\triangle ADB \cong \triangle CDB$ by SSS.

EXERCISES

12. Given: $\overline{AB} \cong \overline{DE}$, $\overline{DB} \cong \overline{AE}$
Prove: $\triangle ADB \cong \triangle DAE$

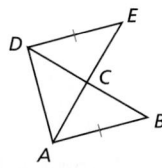

13. Given: $\overline{GJ}$ bisects $\overline{FH}$, and $\overline{FH}$ bisects $\overline{GJ}$.
Prove: $\triangle FGK \cong \triangle HJK$

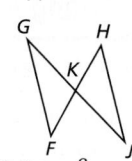

14. Show that $\triangle ABC \cong \triangle XYZ$ when $x = -6$.

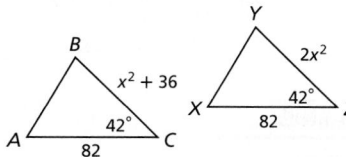

15. Show that $\triangle LMN \cong \triangle PQR$ when $y = 25$.

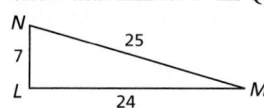

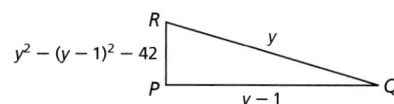

16. 1. C is the mdpt. of $\overline{AG}$. (Given)
 2. $\overline{GC} \cong \overline{AC}$ (Def. of mdpt.)
 3. $\overline{HA} \parallel \overline{GB}$ (Given)
 4. $\angle HAC \cong \angle BGC$ (Alt. Int. ∡ Thm.)
 5. $\angle HCA \cong \angle BCG$ (Vert. ∡ Thm.)
 6. $\triangle HAC \cong \triangle BGC$ (ASA Steps 4, 2, 5)

17. 1. $\overline{WX} \perp \overline{XZ}, \overline{YZ} \perp \overline{ZX}$ (Given)
 2. $\angle WXZ$ and $\angle YZX$ are rt. ∡. (Def. of $\perp$)
 3. $\triangle WZX$ and $\triangle YXZ$ are rt. △. (Def. of rt. △)
 4. $\overline{XZ} \cong \overline{XZ}$ (Reflex. Prop. of $\cong$)
 5. $\overline{WZ} \cong \overline{YX}$ (Given)
 6. $\triangle WZX \cong \triangle YXZ$ (HL Steps 5, 4)

18. 1. $\angle S$ and $\angle V$ are rt. ∡. (Given)
 2. $\angle S \cong \angle V$ (Rt. $\angle \cong$ Thm.)
 3. $RT = UW$ (Given)
 4. $\overline{RT} \cong \overline{UW}$ (Def. of $\cong$)
 5. $m\angle T = m\angle W$ (Given)
 6. $\angle T \cong \angle W$ (Def. of $\cong$)
 7. $\triangle RST \cong \triangle UVW$ (AAS Steps 2, 6, 4)

19. 1. M is the mdpt. of $\overline{BD}$. (Given)
 2. $\overline{MB} \cong \overline{DM}$ (Def. of mdpt.)
 3. $\overline{BC} \cong \overline{DC}$ (Given)
 4. $\overline{CM} \cong \overline{CM}$ (Reflex. Prop. of $\cong$)
 5. $\triangle CBM \cong \triangle CDM$ (SSS Steps 2, 3, 4)
 6. $\angle 1 \cong \angle 2$ (CPCTC)

20. 1. $\overline{PQ} \cong \overline{RQ}$ (Given)
 2. $\overline{PS} \cong \overline{RS}$ (Given)
 3. $\overline{QS} \cong \overline{QS}$ (Reflex. Prop. of $\cong$)
 4. $\triangle PQS \cong \triangle RQS$ (SSS Steps 1, 2, 3)
 5. $\angle PQS \cong \angle RQS$ (CPCTC)
 6. $\overline{QS}$ bisects $\angle PQR$. (Def. of bisect)

21. 1. H is mdpt. of $\overline{GJ}$, and L is mdpt. of $\overline{MK}$. (Given)
 2. $GH = JH$, $ML = KL$ (Def. of mdpt.)
 3. $\overline{GH} \cong \overline{JH}, \overline{ML} \cong \overline{KL}$ (Def. of $\cong$)
 4. $\overline{GJ} \cong \overline{KM}$ (Given)
 5. $\overline{GH} \cong \overline{KL}$ (Div. Prop. of $\cong$)
 6. $\overline{GM} \cong \overline{KJ}, \angle G \cong \angle K$ (Given)
 7. $\triangle GMH \cong \triangle KJL$ (SAS Steps 5, 6)
 8. $\angle GMH \cong \angle KJL$ (CPCTC)

4-5 **Triangle Congruence: ASA, AAS, and HL** *(pp. 252–259)*

TEKS G.1.A, G.1.B, G.2.A, G.3.B, G.3.C, G.3.E, G.9.B, G.10.B

EXAMPLES

■ **Given:** B is the midpoint of $\overline{AE}$.
 $\angle A \cong \angle E$,
 $\angle ABC \cong \angle EBD$
 Prove: $\triangle ABC \cong \triangle EBD$

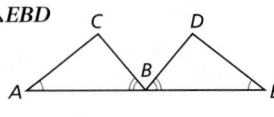

Proof:

Statements	Reasons
1. $\angle A \cong \angle E$	1. Given
2. $\angle ABC \cong \angle EBD$	2. Given
3. B is the mdpt. of $\overline{AE}$.	3. Given
4. $\overline{AB} \cong \overline{EB}$	4. Def. of mdpt.
5. $\triangle ABC \cong \triangle EBD$	5. ASA *Steps 1, 4, 2*

EXERCISES

16. Given: C is the midpoint of $\overline{AG}$.
 $\overline{HA} \parallel \overline{GB}$
 Prove: $\triangle HAC \cong \triangle BGC$

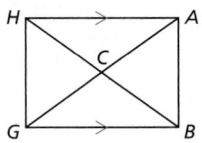

17. Given: $\overline{WX} \perp \overline{XZ}$,
 $\overline{YZ} \perp \overline{ZX}$,
 $\overline{WZ} \cong \overline{YX}$
 Prove: $\triangle WZX \cong \triangle YXZ$

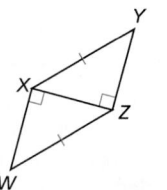

18. Given: $\angle S$ and $\angle V$ are right angles.
 $RT = UW$.
 $m\angle T = m\angle W$
 Prove: $\triangle RST \cong \triangle UVW$

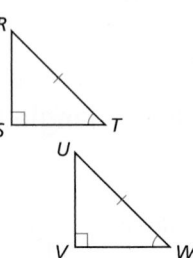

4-6 **Triangle Congruence: CPCTC** *(pp. 260–265)*

TEKS G.1.A, G.3.E, G.7.A, G.10.B

EXAMPLES

■ **Given:** $\overline{JL}$ and $\overline{HK}$ bisect each other.
 Prove: $\angle JHG \cong \angle LKG$

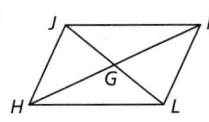

Proof:

Statements	Reasons
1. $\overline{JL}$ and $\overline{HK}$ bisect each other.	1. Given
2. $\overline{JG} \cong \overline{LG}$, and $\overline{HG} \cong \overline{KG}$.	2. Def. of bisect
3. $\angle JGH \cong \angle LGK$	3. Vert. ∡ Thm.
4. $\triangle JHG \cong \triangle LKG$	4. SAS *Steps 2, 3*
5. $\angle JHG \cong \angle LKG$	5. CPCTC

EXERCISES

19. Given: M is the midpoint of $\overline{BD}$.
 $\overline{BC} \cong \overline{DC}$
 Prove: $\angle 1 \cong \angle 2$

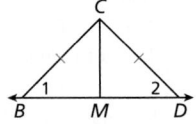

20. Given: $\overline{PQ} \cong \overline{RQ}$,
 $\overline{PS} \cong \overline{RS}$
 Prove: $\overline{QS}$ bisects $\angle PQR$.

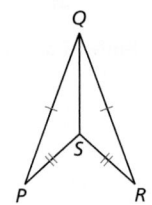

21. Given: H is the midpoint of $\overline{GL}$.
 L is the midpoint of $\overline{MK}$.
 $\overline{GM} \cong \overline{KJ}, \overline{GJ} \cong \overline{KM}$,
 $\angle G \cong \angle K$
 Prove: $\angle GMH \cong \angle KJL$

4-7 Introduction to Coordinate Proof (pp. 267–272)

 TEKS G.2.B, G.3.B, G.9.B, G.10.B

EXAMPLES

■ **Given:** $\angle B$ is a right angle in isosceles right $\triangle ABC$. E is the midpoint of $\overline{AB}$. D is the midpoint of $\overline{CB}$. $\overline{AB} \cong \overline{CB}$

Prove: $\overline{CE} \cong \overline{AD}$

Proof: Use the coordinates $A(0, 2a)$, $B(0, 0)$, and $C(2a, 0)$. Draw $\overline{AD}$ and $\overline{CE}$.

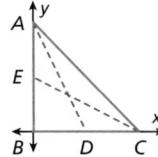

By the Midpoint Formula,
$$E = \left(\frac{0+0}{2}, \frac{2a+0}{2}\right) = (0, a) \text{ and}$$
$$D = \left(\frac{0+2a}{2}, \frac{0+0}{2}\right) = (a, 0)$$

By the Distance Formula,
$$CE = \sqrt{(2a-0)^2 + (0-a)^2}$$
$$= \sqrt{4a^2 + a^2} = a\sqrt{5}$$
$$AD = \sqrt{(a-0)^2 + (0-2a)^2}$$
$$= \sqrt{a^2 + 4a^2} = a\sqrt{5}$$

Thus $\overline{CE} \cong \overline{AD}$ by the definition of congruence.

EXERCISES

Position each figure in the coordinate plane and give the coordinates of each vertex.

22. a right triangle with leg lengths r and s

23. a rectangle with length $2p$ and width p

24. a square with side length $8m$

For exercises 25 and 26 assign coordinates to each vertex and write a coordinate proof.

25. **Given:** In rectangle $ABCD$, E is the midpoint of $\overline{AB}$, F is the midpoint of $\overline{BC}$, G is the midpoint of $\overline{CD}$, and H is the midpoint of $\overline{AD}$.
    Prove: $\overline{EF} \cong \overline{GH}$

26. **Given:** $\triangle PQR$ has a right $\angle Q$. M is the midpoint of $\overline{PR}$.
    Prove: $MP = MQ = MR$

27. Show that a triangle with vertices at $(3, 5)$, $(3, 2)$, and $(2, 5)$ is a right triangle.

4-8 Isosceles and Equilateral Triangles (pp. 273–279)

 TEKS G.2.B, G.3.C, G.10.B

EXAMPLE

■ **Find the value of x.**

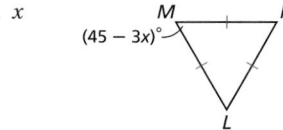

$m\angle D + m\angle E + m\angle F = 180°$
by the Triangle Sum Theorem. $m\angle E = m\angle F$
by the Isosceles Triangle Theorem.

$m\angle D + 2m\angle E = 180°$	*Substitution*
$42 + 2(3x) = 180$	*Substitute the given values.*
$6x = 138$	*Simplify.*
$x = 23$	*Divide both sides by 6.*

EXERCISES

Find each value.

28. x

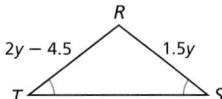

29. RS

30. **Given:** $\triangle ACD$ is isosceles with $\angle D$ as the vertex angle. B is the midpoint of $\overline{AC}$.
    $AB = x + 5$, $BC = 2x - 3$, and $CD = 2x + 6$.
    Find the perimeter of $\triangle ACD$.

Study Guide: Review **287**

Answers

22. $(0, 0)$, $(r, 0)$, $(0, s)$

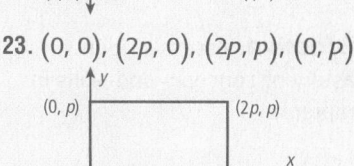

23. $(0, 0)$, $(2p, 0)$, $(2p, p)$, $(0, p)$

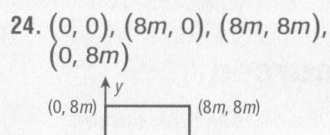

24. $(0, 0)$, $(8m, 0)$, $(8m, 8m)$, $(0, 8m)$

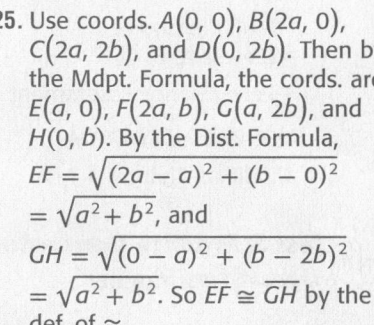

25. Use coords. $A(0, 0)$, $B(2a, 0)$, $C(2a, 2b)$, and $D(0, 2b)$. Then by the Mdpt. Formula, the cords. are $E(a, 0)$, $F(2a, b)$, $G(a, 2b)$, and $H(0, b)$. By the Dist. Formula,
$EF = \sqrt{(2a - a)^2 + (b - 0)^2}$
$= \sqrt{a^2 + b^2}$, and
$GH = \sqrt{(0 - a)^2 + (b - 2b)^2}$
$= \sqrt{a^2 + b^2}$. So $\overline{EF} \cong \overline{GH}$ by the def. of $\cong$.

26. Use coords. $P(0, 2b)$, $Q(0, 0)$, and $R(2a, 0)$. Then by the Mdpt. Formula, the cords. are $M(a, b)$. By the Dist. Formula,
$QM = \sqrt{(a - 0)^2 + (b - 0)^2}$
$= \sqrt{a^2 + b^2}$,
$PM = \sqrt{(a - 0)^2 + (b - 2b)^2}$
$= \sqrt{a^2 + b^2}$, and
$RM = \sqrt{(2a - a)^2 + (0 - b)^2}$
$= \sqrt{a^2 + b^2}$. So $QM = PM = RM$. By def. M is equidistant from the vertices of $\triangle PQR$.

27. In a rt. $\triangle$, $a^2 + b^2 = c^2$.
$\sqrt{(3 - 3)^2 + (5 - 2)^2} = 3$,
$\sqrt{(3 - 2)^2 + (2 - 5)^2} = \sqrt{10}$,
$\sqrt{(2 - 3)^2 + (5 - 5)^2} = 1$, and
$3^2 + 1^2 = \left(\sqrt{10}\right)^2$.
Since $9 + 1 = 10$, it is a rt. $\triangle$.

28. -5

29. 13.5

30. 70 units

Organizer

Objective: Assess students' mastery of concepts and skills in Chapter 4.

 Online Edition

Resources

 Assessment Resources

Chapter 4 Tests

• Free Response (Levels A, B, C)

• Multiple Choice (Levels A, B, C)

• Performance Assessment

 IDEA Works! CD-ROM

Modified Chapter 4 Test

 **Test & Practice Generator One-Stop Planner®**

Answers

10. 1. *T* is the mdpt. of $\overline{PR}$ and $\overline{SQ}$. (Given)
   2. $\overline{PT} \cong \overline{RT}$, $\overline{ST} \cong \overline{QT}$ (Def. of mdpt.)
   3. $\angle PTS \cong \angle RTQ$ (Vert. ∠ Thm.)
   4. $\triangle PTS \cong \triangle RTQ$ (SAS *Steps 2, 3*)

★ **TAKS Practice**

Grades 9–11	Items
Obj. 2	5, 16, 17
Obj. 6	1, 5, 16, 17
Obj. 10	5

288 *Chapter 4*

1. Classify $\triangle ACD$ by its angle measures. **rt.**

Classify each triangle by its side lengths.

2. $\triangle ACD$
   scalene

3. $\triangle ABC$
   isosc.

4. $\triangle ABD$
   scalene

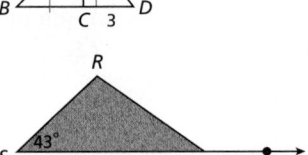

5. While surveying the triangular plot of land shown, a surveyor finds that m∠*S* = 43°. The measure of ∠*RTP* is twice that of ∠*RTS*. What is m∠*R*? **77°**

Given: $\triangle XYZ \cong \triangle JKL$
Identify the congruent corresponding parts.

6. $\overline{JL} \cong$ ___? **$\overline{XZ}$**

7. $\angle Y \cong$ ___? **$\angle K$**

8. $\angle L \cong$ ___? **$\angle Z$**

9. $\overline{YZ} \cong$ ___? **$\overline{KL}$**

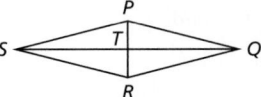

10. **Given:** *T* is the midpoint of $\overline{PR}$ and $\overline{SQ}$.
    Prove: $\triangle PTS \cong \triangle RTQ$

11. The figure represents a walkway with triangular supports. Given that $\overline{GJ}$ bisects ∠*HGK* and ∠*H* ≅ ∠*K*, use AAS to prove $\triangle HGJ \cong \triangle KGJ$

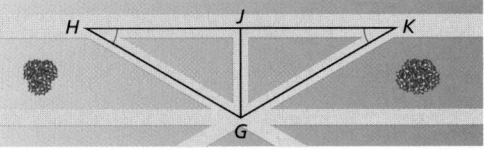

12. **Given:** $\overline{AB} \cong \overline{DC}$,
    $\overline{AB} \perp \overline{AC}$,
    $\overline{DC} \perp \overline{DB}$
    Prove: $\triangle ABC \cong \triangle DCB$

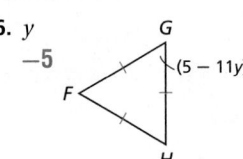

13. **Given:** $\overline{PQ} \parallel \overline{SR}$,
    ∠*S* ≅ ∠*Q*
    Prove: $\overline{PS} \parallel \overline{QR}$

14. Position a right triangle with legs 3 m and 4 m long in the coordinate plane. Give the coordinates of each vertex.

15. Assign coordinates to each vertex and write a coordinate proof.
    Given: Square *ABCD*
    Prove: $\overline{AC} \cong \overline{BD}$

Find each value.

16. *y*
    −5
    $(5 - 11y)°$

17. m∠*S*
    44°

18. **Given:** Isosceles $\triangle ABC$ has coordinates $A(2a, 0)$, $B(0, 2b)$, and $C(-2a, 0)$. *D* is the midpoint of $\overline{AC}$, and *E* is the midpoint of $\overline{AB}$.
    Prove: $\triangle AED$ is isosceles.

288 *Chapter 4 Triangle Congruence*

Answers

11. 1. ∠*H* ≅ ∠*K* (Given)
    2. $\overline{GJ}$ bisects ∠*HGK*. (Given)
    3. ∠*HGJ* ≅ ∠*KGJ* (Def. of bisect)
    4. $\overline{JG} \cong \overline{JG}$ (Reflex. Prop. of ≅)
    5. $\triangle HGJ \cong \triangle KGJ$ (AAS *Steps 1, 3, 4*)

12. 1. $\overline{AB} \perp \overline{AC}$, $\overline{DC} \perp \overline{DB}$ (Given)
    2. ∠*BAC* and ∠*CDB* are rt. ∠. (Def. of ⊥)
    3. $\triangle ABC$ and $\triangle DCB$ are rt. △. (Def. of rt. △)
    4. $\overline{AB} \cong \overline{DC}$ (Given)
    5. $\overline{BC} \cong \overline{BC}$ (Reflex. Prop. of ≅)
    6. $\triangle ABC \cong \triangle DCB$ (HL *Steps 5, 4*)

13. 1. $\overline{PQ} \parallel \overline{SR}$ (Given)
    2. ∠*QPR* ≅ ∠*SRP* (Alt. Int. ∠ Thm.)
    3. ∠*S* ≅ ∠*Q* (Given)
    4. $\overline{PR} \cong \overline{PR}$ (Reflex. Prop. of ≅)
    5. $\triangle QPR \cong \triangle SRP$ (AAS *Steps 2, 3, 4*)
    6. ∠*SPR* ≅ ∠*QRP* (CPCTC)
    7. $\overline{PS} \parallel \overline{QR}$ (Conv. of Alt. Int. ∠ Thm.)

14.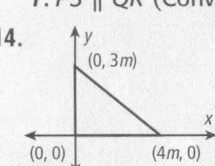

15, 18. See p. A17.

FOCUS ON ACT

The ACT Mathematics Test is one of four tests in the ACT. You are given 60 minutes to answer 60 multiple-choice questions. The questions cover material typically taught through the end of eleventh grade. You will need to know basic formulas but nothing too difficult.

You may want to time yourself as you take this practice test. It should take you about 5 minutes to complete.

There is no penalty for guessing on the ACT. If you are unsure of the correct answer, eliminate as many answer choices as possible and make your best guess. Make sure you have entered an answer for every question before time runs out.

---

1. For the figure below, which of the following must be true?

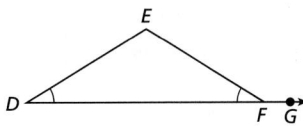

   I. m∠EFG > m∠DEF

   II. m∠EDF = m∠EFD

   III. m∠DEF + m∠EDF > m∠EFG

(A) I only

(B) II only

(C) I and II only

(D) II and III only

(E) I, II, and III

---

2. In the figure below, $\triangle ABD \cong \triangle CDB$, $m\angle A = (2x + 14)°$, $m\angle C = (3x - 15)°$, and $m\angle DBA = 49°$. What is the measure of ∠BDA?

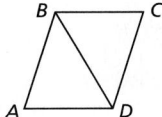

(F) 29°

(G) 49°

(H) 59°

(J) 72°

(K) 101°

---

3. Which of the following best describes a triangle with vertices having coordinates $(-1, 0)$, $(0, 3)$, and $(1, -4)$?

(A) Equilateral

(B) Isosceles

(C) Right

(D) Scalene

(E) Equiangular

---

4. In the figure below, what is the value of y?

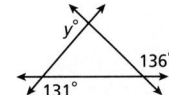

(F) 49

(G) 87

(H) 93

(J) 131

(K) 136

---

5. In $\triangle RST$, $RS = 2x + 10$, $ST = 3x - 2$, and $RT = \frac{1}{2}x + 28$. If $\triangle RST$ is equiangular, what is the value of x?

(A) 2

(B) $5\frac{1}{3}$

(C) 6

(D) 12

(E) 34

Organizer

Objective: Provide practice for college entrance exams such as the ACT.

PREMIER

Online Edition

Resources

College Entrance Exam Practice

Questions on the ACT represent the following content areas:

Pre-Algebra, 23%

Elementary Algebra, 17%

Intermediate Algebra, 15%

Coordinate Geometry, 15%

Plane Geometry, 23%

Trigonometry, 7%

Items on this page focus on:

• Elementary Algebra

• Coordinate Geometry

• Plane Geometry

Text References:

Item	1	2	3	4	5
Lesson	4-2	4-3	4-7	4-2	4-8

TEST PREP DOCTOR

1. Remind students that the sum of the angle measures of a triangle is 180° and that the measure of an exterior angle is equal to the sum of the measures of its remote interior angles. These facts, along with the diagram, lead to the conclusion that statements **I** and **II** are true but **III** is false.

2. Students may choose **G** because they mislabeled the figure or misinterpreted the names of the angles. Students may choose **F** because they only solved for *x*. Remind students to read each test item completely.

3. Encourage students to draw a rough sketch of the triangle to estimate the position of the vertices. This should eliminate choices **A** and **E**. Using the coordinates, slope, and the Distance Formula eliminates choices **B** and **C**.

4. Students may choose answer **G** because they found the measures of the remote interior angles and subtracted their sum from 180. The result is the measure of the third interior angle instead of the exterior angle labeled *y*.

5. Students may choose answer **D** because they did not answer the question being asked. Remind students to read each test item carefully.

Organizer

Objective: Provide opportunities to learn and practice common test-taking strategies.

 Online Edition

Resources

 TAKS Prep Workbook

 TAKS Prep **CD-ROM**

 TAKS Practice **Online**

> **go.hrw.com/Geo/TX**
> KEYWORD: MG7 TestPrep

 **TAKS PREP DOCTOR** This TAKS Tackler describes how to identify key words and context clues in a test item to answer it correctly. Encourage students to read a problem statement once for understanding and then to reread the statement, underlining the key words or clues. Because of the large number of vocabulary words in this chapter, students should refer to definitions in order to answer questions correctly.

Any Question Type:
Identify Key Words and Context Clues

When reading a test item, you should pay attention to key words and context clues given in the problem statement. These clues will guide you in providing a correct response.

EXAMPLE 1

Multiple Choice What is the side length of an equilateral triangle with a perimeter of $42\frac{3}{4}$ cm?

  (A) $42\frac{3}{4}$ cm   (C) $21\frac{3}{8}$ cm

  (B) $24\frac{3}{7}$ cm   (D) $14\frac{1}{4}$ cm

LOOK for key words and context clues and underline them. Identify what they mean.

What is the side length of an <u>equilateral triangle</u> with a <u>perimeter</u> of $42\frac{3}{4}$ in.?

equilateral triangle $\rightarrow$ a triangle with three congruent sides
perimeter $\rightarrow$ the distance around a figure
perimeter = 3 (length of one side)

$$42\frac{3}{4} = 3(x)$$

You find the perimeter of an equilateral triangle by multiplying the length of one side of the triangle by three.

$$\frac{42\frac{3}{4}}{3} = \frac{3(x)}{3}$$

$$\frac{171}{4} \cdot \frac{1}{3} = x$$

*The correct choice is **D** because the length of the side of the equilateral triangle is $14\frac{1}{4}$ cm.*

$$14\frac{1}{4} = x$$

EXAMPLE 2

Gridded Response The vertex angle of an isosceles triangle measures $(5t - 5)°$, and one of the base angles measures $(t + 5)°$. Find t.

isosceles triangle $\rightarrow$ a triangle with at least two congruent sides
vertex angle $\rightarrow$ the angle formed by the legs
base angles $\rightarrow$ The side opposite the vertex angle is called the base, and the base angles are the two angles that have the base as a side.

2(measure of the base angle) + (measure of the vertex angle) = 180°

$$2(t + 5) + (5t - 5) = 180$$
$$2t + 10 + 5t - 5 = 180$$
$$7t + 5 = 180$$
$$t = 25$$ *The correct value for t is 25.*

TAKS Tip If you do not understand what a word means, reread the sentences that contain the word and make a logical guess.

Read each test item and answer the questions that follow.

Item A
Multiple Choice Which value of k would make $\triangle CDE$ isosceles?

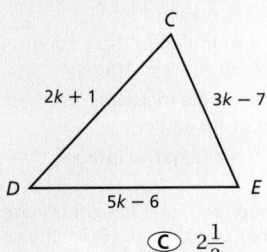

Ⓐ 7

Ⓒ $2\frac{1}{3}$

Ⓑ 6

Ⓓ $1\frac{2}{3}$

1. Whether a triangle is isosceles depends on what characteristics of the triangle?

2. What do $2k + 1$, $3k - 7$, and $5k - 6$ represent in the model?

3. How will you use the definition of an isosceles triangle to find the correct value of k?

Item B
Gridded Response What must the value of x be in order to prove that $\triangle MNQ \cong \triangle PNQ$ by SSS?

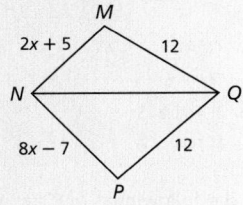

4. What statement are you trying to prove?

5. Explain the meaning of the symbol $\cong$.

6. How will you use the abbreviation SSS to help you answer the question?

Item C
Multiple Choice $\angle X$ and $\angle Y$ are the remote interior angles of $\angle YZW$ in $\triangle XYZ$. Which of these equations must be true?

Ⓕ $180° - m\angle X = m\angle YZW$

Ⓖ $m\angle X = m\angle Y + 90°$

Ⓗ $m\angle X = m\angle YZW - m\angle Y$

Ⓙ $m\angle YZW = m\angle YZX - m\angle YXZ$

7. Create a drawing that represents the situation. Label the remote interior angles.

8. What is the relationship between the remote interior angles and an exterior angle?

9. How can you manipulate the relationship given in Problem 8 to get one of the four choices?

Item D
Multiple Choice Which of the following is a correct classification of $\triangle FGH$?

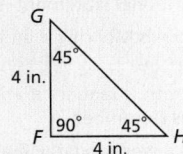

Ⓐ Acute

Ⓒ Isosceles

Ⓑ Equiangular

Ⓓ Scalene

10. What are the two ways by which triangles can be classified?

11. What must be true for the triangle to be classified as acute? as equiangular?

12. What must be true for the triangle to be classified as isosceles? as scalene?

TAKS PREP DOCTOR Read each word problem aloud as you write it on the overhead or board. Emphasize the key words and context clues. Use different-colored pens or chalk to underline each of the important parts of the problem. Be sure to review vocabulary that students may have forgotten or could easily misinterpret, such as the words *supplementary* and *complementary*.

Answers

1. An isosc. $\triangle$ has at least 2 $\cong$ sides.

2. the side lengths fo the $\triangle$

3. Substitute each choice for k into the expressions $2k + 1$, $3k - 7$, and $5k - 6$. Then simplify each expression to find the value for k that makes at least 2 of the sides the same length.

4. $\triangle MNQ \cong \triangle PNQ$

5. having the same size and shape

6. SSS refers to the Side-Side-Side Thm. Set $8x - 7$ to $2x + 5$ and solve for the value of x.

7.

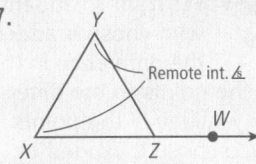

8. The measure of an ext. $\angle$ of a $\triangle$ is = to the sum of measures of its remote int. $\angle$s.

9. If you subtract 1 of the measures of the remote int. $\angle$ from the measure of the ext. $\angle$, the result is the measure of the other remote int. $\angle$.

10. by its $\angle$s or by its sides

Answers to Test Items

A. C

B. 2

C. H

D. C

Answers

11. Each of the 3 $\angle$s must measure less than 90°. Each of the 3 $\angle$s is acute.

12. At least 2 sides must be $\cong$. Each of the 3 sides must have a different length.

TAKS Practice

Grades 9–11	Items
Obj. 2	A
Obj. 5	C
Obj. 6	A, B, C
Obj. 8	C

Organizer

Objective: Provide review and practice for Chapters 1–4 and standardized tests.

 Online Edition

Resources

 Assessment Resources

Chapter 4 Cumulative Test

 TAKS Prep Workbook

 TAKS Prep CD-ROM

 TAKS Practice Online

go.hrw.com/Geo/TX
KEYWORD: MG7 TestPrep

 **TAKS PREP DOCTOR** For **Item 7,** students who chose **B** added the difference in the x-values of the points to the difference in the y-values of the points. Students who chose **C** divided by 2 when they should have found a square root.

For **Item 8,** encourage students to rule out the answer choices that do not have the correct y-intercept. This will eliminate choices **H** and **J**.

For **Item 14,** suggest that students draw a diagram. They can use the diagram to help identify corresponding parts of the congruent triangles.

TAKS Practice

Grades 9–11	Items
Obj. 2	10
Obj. 3	8, 9
Obj. 4	14, 19
Obj. 5	5, 16
Obj. 6	14, 19
Obj. 7	7–9, 15
Obj. 10	7, 15

CUMULATIVE ASSESSMENT, CHAPTERS 1–4

Multiple Choice

Use the diagram for Items 1 and 2.

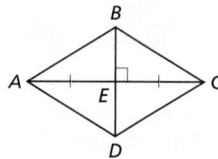

1. Which of these congruence statements can be proved from the information given in the figure?

  (A) $\triangle AEB \cong \triangle CED$

  (B) $\triangle BAC \cong \triangle DAC$

  (C) $\triangle ABD \cong \triangle BCA$

  (D) $\triangle DEC \cong \triangle DEA$

2. What other information is needed to prove that $\triangle CEB \cong \triangle AED$ by the HL Congruence Theorem?

  (F) $\overline{AD} \cong \overline{AB}$

  (G) $\overline{BE} \cong \overline{AE}$

  (H) $\overline{CB} \cong \overline{AD}$

  (J) $\overline{DE} \cong \overline{CE}$

3. Which biconditional statement is true?

  (A) Tomorrow is Monday if and only if today is not Saturday.

  (B) Next month is January if and only if this month is December.

  (C) Today is a weekend day if and only if yesterday was Friday.

  (D) This month had 31 days if and only if last month had 30 days.

4. What must be true if $\overleftrightarrow{PQ}$ intersects $\overleftrightarrow{ST}$ at more than one point?

  (F) P, Q, S, and T are collinear.

  (G) P, Q, S, and T are noncoplanar.

  (H) $\overleftrightarrow{PQ}$ and $\overleftrightarrow{ST}$ are opposite rays.

  (J) $\overleftrightarrow{PQ}$ and $\overleftrightarrow{ST}$ are perpendicular.

5. $\triangle ABC \cong \triangle DEF$, $EF = x^2 - 7$, and $BC = 4x - 2$. Find the values of x.

  (A) -1 and 5

  (B) -1 and 6

  (C) 1 and 5

  (D) 2 and 3

6. Which conditional statement has the same truth value as its inverse?

  (F) If $n < 0$, then $n^2 > 0$.

  (G) If a triangle has three congruent sides, then it is an isosceles triangle.

  (H) If an angle measures less than 90°, then it is an acute angle.

  (J) If n is a negative integer, then $n < 0$.

7. On a map, an island has coordinates (3, 5), and a reef has coordinates (6, 8). If each map unit represents 1 mile, what is the distance between the island and the reef to the nearest tenth of a mile?

  (A) 4.2 miles

  (B) 6.0 miles

  (C) 9.0 miles

  (D) 15.8 miles

8. A line has an x-intercept of -8 and a y-intercept of 3. What is the equation of the line?

  (F) $y = -8x + 3$

  (G) $y = \frac{3}{8}x + 3$

  (H) $y = \frac{8}{3}x - 8$

  (J) $y = 3x - 8$

9. $\overleftrightarrow{JK}$ passes through points $J(1, 3)$ and $K(-3, 11)$. Which of these lines is perpendicular to $\overleftrightarrow{JK}$?

  (A) $y = -\frac{1}{2}x + \frac{1}{3}$

  (B) $y = \frac{1}{2}x + 6$

  (C) $y = -2x - \frac{1}{5}$

  (D) $y = 2x - 4$

10. If $PQ = 2(RS) + 4$ and $RS = TU + 1$, which equation is true by the Substitution Property of Equality?

  (F) $PQ = TU + 5$

  (G) $PQ = TU + 6$

  (H) $PQ = 2(TU) + 5$

  (J) $PQ = 2(TU) + 6$

11. Which of the following is NOT valid for proving that triangles are congruent?

  (A) AAA

  (B) ASA

  (C) SAS

  (D) HL

Answers

20. Possible answer: Because the acute ∡ of a rt. △ are comp., ∠1 is comp. to ∠2. By the Corr. ∡ Post., ∠1 ≅ ∠3. Therefore ∠3 is also comp. to ∠2 by the ≅ Comps. Thm.

21a.
$$2x + 12 + x = 180$$
$$3x + 12 = 180 \quad \text{(Simplify.)}$$
$$3x + 12 - 12 = 180 - 12 \quad \text{(Subtr. Prop. of =)}$$
$$3x = 168 \quad \text{(Simplify.)}$$
$$\frac{3x}{3} = \frac{168}{3} \quad \text{(Div. Prop. of =)}$$
$$x = 56 \quad \text{(Simplify.)}$$

21b. Possible answer: The sum of the measures of an ∠ and its comp. is 90°. Therefore any ∠ that measures 90° or greater does not have a comp. Because m∠$H = x° = 56°$, the ∠ does have a comp. Because m∠$G = (2x + 12)° = [2(56) + 12]° = 124°$, ∠$G$ does not have a comp.

22a. 90; based on the conjecture, 60 out of 1000 parts will be defective. Express this ratio as a percent: $\frac{60}{1000} = \frac{6}{100} = 6\%$. Find 6% of 1500. $1500 \times 6\% = 1500 \times 0.06 = 90$. Based on the conjecture, 90 out of 1500 parts will be defective.

Use this diagram for Items 12 and 13.

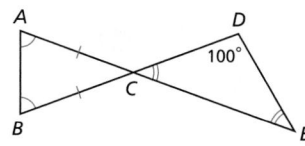

12. What is the measure of ∠ACD?

- (F) 40°
- (G) 80°
- (H) 100°
- (J) 140°

13. What type of triangle is △ABC?

- (A) Isosceles acute
- (B) Equilateral acute
- (C) Isosceles obtuse
- (D) Scalene acute

Take some time to learn the directions for filling in a grid. Check and recheck to make sure you are filling in the grid properly. You will only get credit if the ovals below the boxes are filled in correctly. To check your answer, solve the problem using a different method from the one you originally used. If you made a mistake the first time, you are unlikely to make the same mistake when you solve a different way.

Gridded Response

14. △CDE ≅ △JKL. m∠E = $(3x + 4)°$, and m∠L = $(6x − 5)°$. What is the value of x? **3**

15. Lucy, Eduardo, Carmen, and Frank live on the same street. Eduardo's house is halfway between Lucy's house and Frank's house. Lucy's house is halfway between Carmen's house and Frank's house. If the distance between Eduardo's house and Lucy's house is 150 ft, what is the distance in feet between Carmen's house and Eduardo's house? **450 ft**

16. △JKL ≅ △XYZ, and JK = 10 − 2n. XY = 2, and YZ = n^2. Find KL. **16**

17. An angle is its own supplement. What is its measure? **90°**

18. The area of a circle is 154 square inches. What is its circumference to the nearest inch? **44 in.**

19. The measure of ∠P is $3\frac{1}{2}$ times the measure of ∠Q. If ∠P and ∠Q are complementary, what is m∠P in degrees? **70**

Short Response

20. Given ℓ ∥ m with transversal n, explain why ∠2 and ∠3 are complementary.

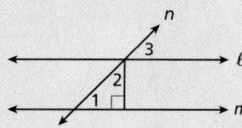

21. ∠G and ∠H are supplementary angles. m∠G = $(2x + 12)°$, and m∠H = $x°$.

  a. Write an equation that can be used to determine the value of x. Solve the equation and justify each step.

  b. Explain why ∠H has a complement but ∠G does not.

22. A manager conjectures that for every 1000 parts a factory produces, 60 are defective.

  a. If the factory produces 1500 parts in one day, how many of them can be expected to be defective based on the manager's conjecture? Explain how you found your answer.

  b. Use the data in the table below to show that the manager's conjecture is false.

Day	1	2	3	4	5
Parts	1000	2000	500	1500	2500
Defective Parts	60	150	30	90	150

23. $\overline{BD}$ is the perpendicular bisector of $\overline{AC}$.

  a. What are the conclusions you can make from this statement?

  b. Suppose $\overline{BD}$ intersects $\overline{AC}$ at D. Explain why $\overline{BD}$ is the shortest path from B to $\overline{AC}$.

Extended Response

24. △ABC and △DEF are isosceles triangles. $\overline{BC} ≅ \overline{EF}$, and $\overline{AC} ≅ \overline{DF}$. m∠C = 42.5°, and m∠E = 95°.

  a. What is m∠D? Explain how you determined your answer.

  b. Show that △ABC and △DEF are congruent.

  c. Given that EF = 2x + 7 and AB = 3x + 2, find the value for x. Explain how you determined your answer.

23a. Possible answer: ∠ABD is a rt. ∠; ∠BDC is a rt. ∠; AD = DC; D is the mdpt. of $\overline{AC}$.

23b. The shortest dist. from a pt. to a line is measured along the ⊥ from the pt. to the line.

Short-Response Rubric

Items 20–23

2 Points = The student's answer is an accurate and complete execution of the task or tasks.

1 Point = The student's answer contains attributes of an appropriate response but is flawed.

0 Points = The student's answer contains no attributes of an appropriate response.

Extended-Response Rubric

Item 24

4 Points = The student correctly finds m∠D and the value of x and shows that △ABC ≅ △DEF. Explanations are complete, and work demonstrates a thorough understanding of concepts related to isosceles and congruent triangles.

3 Point = The student answers correctly, but the explanations may contain minor flaws. Work demonstrates an understanding of major concepts related to isosceles and congruent triangles.

2 Points = The student answers correctly, but the explanations are missing or incomplete. Or the student answers part of the problem only. Work demonstrates a limited understanding of concepts.

1 Point = The student answers incorrectly but makes a reasonable attempt to show work or offer explanation.

0 Points = The student does not answer correctly and does not attempt all parts of the problem.

Answers

22b. Possible answer: Based on the manager's conjecture, 120 parts should be defective if 2000 parts are produced. However, the table shows that 150 out of 2000 parts were defective on day 2. Therefore the data for day 2 is a counterexample to the manager's conjecture. This shows that the conjecture is false.

24a. 42.5°

Possible answer: Because △DEF is an isosc. △, 2 of its sides are ≅, and the ∠ opp. these sides are ≅. ∠E is an obtuse ∠. Because a △ cannot

have more than 1 obtuse ∠, the 2 ≅ ∠ in △DEF must be ∠D and ∠F. Use this information to find m∠D. m∠D + m∠E + m∠F = 180° by the △ Sum Thm. x + 95° + x = 180°. Substitute x for m∠D and m∠F, and 95° for m∠E. 2x = 85°. Simplify and then subtract 95° from both sides. x = 42.5°. Divide both sides by 2. Thus m∠D = 42.5°.

24b. Possible answer: From part **a**, ∠F ≅ ∠D. Therefore m∠F = m∠D = 42.5°. It is given that m∠C = 42.5°. Therefore ∠C ≅ ∠F. It is also given that $\overline{BC} ≅ \overline{EF}$ and $\overline{AC} ≅ \overline{DF}$. Therefore △ABC ≅ △DEF by SAS.

24c. 5; possible answer: because ∠D ≅ ∠F, $\overline{DE} ≅ \overline{EF}$ by the Conv. of the Isosc. △ Thm.

$\overline{AB} ≅ \overline{DE}$	CPCTC
$\overline{AB} ≅ \overline{EF}$	Trans. Prop. of ≅
AB = EF	Def. of ≅ Segs.
3x + 2 = 2x + 7	Subst. Prop. of =
x = 5	Subtr. Prop. of =

Organizer

Objective: Choose appropriate problem-solving strategies and use them with skills from Chapters 3 and 4 to solve real-world problems.

Online Edition

Cavanaugh Flight Museum

Reading Strategies

ENGLISH LANGUAGE LEARNERS

Remind students to read the entire problem before trying to solve it. Have them identify all the given information first. In **Problem 1**, most of the information is given in the table. In **Problem 2**, they need to know that the wings are parallel in order to solve the problem. In **Problem 3**, information about two cameras is given, and there is a relationship between the triangles in the diagram.

Using Data Before students begin **Problem1**, briefly discuss how to find the rate of change. Then ask students to estimate the number of each type of aircraft that declines each year. Later they can compare their calculated values to these initial estimates.

TAKS *Problem Solving on Location* focuses on TAKS objectives involving the underlying mathematical processes.

Grades 9–11

Obj. 10 Mathematical processes and tools 8.14.A, 8.14.B, 8.14.C; 8.15.A; 8.16.A, 8.16.B

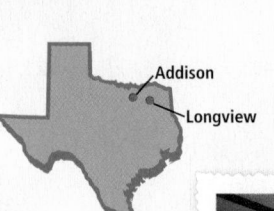

Addison

Longview

TAKS Grades 9–11 Obj. 10

Cavanaugh Flight Museum

Located on the grounds of the Addison Airport in Addison, Texas, the Cavanaugh Flight Museum offers visitors a thrilling voyage through the history of U.S. military flight. The museum exhibits aircraft and other military artifacts on almost 50,000 square feet of display area. It also features an informative self-guided tour and offers rides in two classic airplanes.

Choose one or more strategies to solve each problem.

Airplane	Number Built	Number Left in 2005	Year First Built
N2S-4 Stearman	10,346	2136	1933
Fairchild PT-19	4,889	272	1938
Spitfire Mk VIII	20,334	70	1943
F9F-2 Panther	761	9	1947

2. Visitors to the museum can see a replica of an N2S-4 Stearman "Yellow Peril," a plane used to train pilots during World War II. The plane has two parallel wings $\overline{AB}$ and $\overline{CD}$ that are connected by bracing wires. The wires are arranged such that m∠EFG = 29° and $\overline{GF}$ bisects ∠EGD. What is m∠AEG? **58°**

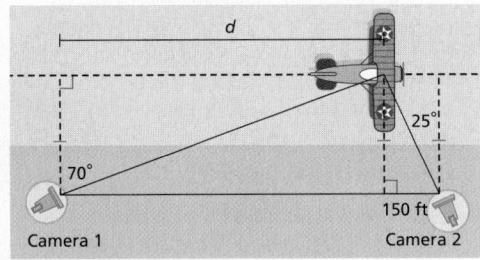

---

1. The table gives data on some of the aircraft on display in the museum. Suppose the number of each type of aircraft declines at the same rate each year. Find the yearly rate of change for each given year. Round to the nearest whole number.
114; 69; 327; 13

3. Visitors have the opportunity to ride in either the N2S-4 Stearman or the AT-6 Texan. If the airport uses two cameras mounted 1000 ft apart to determine the position of a plane during landing and takeoff, what is the distance *d* that the plane in the diagram has moved along the runway since it passed camera 1?
850 ft

Problem-Solving Focus

Encourage students to use the four-step problem-solving process for the problems. Focus on the third step: **(3) Plan.** In particular, ask students to consider the information that is given in the statement of **Problem 2** and in the accompanying diagram.

Discuss with students which pieces of information are essential in solving the problem. $\overline{AB} \parallel \overline{CD}$; m∠EFG = 29°; $\overline{GF}$ bisects ∠EGD. Then have students describe a sequence of steps they can use to find m∠AEG. First find the m∠FGD. Then add m∠FGD and m∠EGF. Finally use the Alt. Int. ∠ Thm.

The Great Texas Balloon Race

The annual Great Texas Balloon Race is one of the most exciting hot air balloon events in Texas. "Balloon Glow," in which balloons are tethered and illuminated in an evening display, was begun in Longview, the race's starting point, in 1980. Traditionally held in July, the race attracts balloonists who compete to fly the obstacle course the most accurately.

Problem Solving Strategies

Draw a Diagram
Make a Model
Guess and Test
Work Backward
Find a Pattern
Make a Table
Solve a Simpler Problem
Use Logical Reasoning
Use a Venn Diagram
Make an Organized List

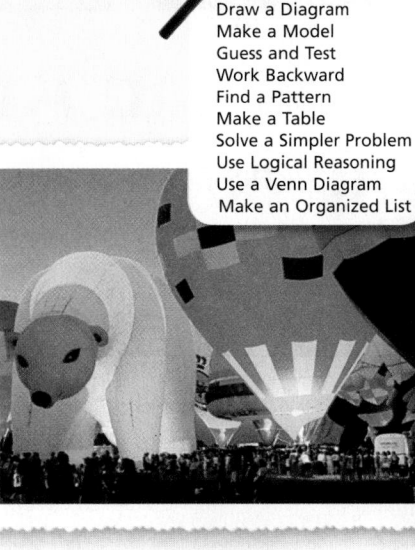

Choose one or more strategies to solve each problem.

1. The event starts in Longview, and ends near Estes, Texas. The balloons do not fly from the start to the finish in a straight line. They follow a zigzag course to take advantage of the wind. Suppose one of the balloons leaves Longview at a bearing of N 50° E and follows the course shown. At what bearing does the balloon approach Estes? **S20°E**

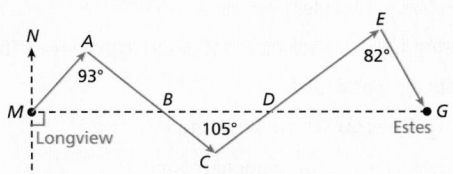

2. The speed of the balloon depends on the current wind speed. One event in The Great Texas Balloon Race requires the balloonist to fly to a pole that is 2 mi from the starting point. The balloonist must drop a small ring around the pole, which is 20 ft tall. A second target is 1 mi from the first, a third target is another 3 mi from the second, and a final target is 5 mi farther. If the wind speed is 3.5 mi/h, how long will it take the balloonist to finish the course? Round to the nearest hundredth of an hour. **3.14 h**

3. During the race, one of the balloons leaves Longview *L*, flies to *X*, and then flies to *Y*. The team discovers a problem with the balloon, so it must return directly to Longview. Does the table contain enough information to determine the return course to *L*? Explain.

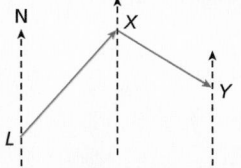

	Bearing	Distance (mi)
L to *X*	N 42° E	3.1
X to *Y*	S 59° E	2.4
Y to *L*	▮	▮

Yes; there is enough information to find m∠*MXY* (101°). *MX* and *MY* are known, so a unique △*MXY* is determined by SAS.

The Great Texas Balloon Race

Reading Strategies

Have students read **Problem 2.** Then suggest that they reread the problem, this time writing down the given information as they read.

Using Data The table for **Problem 3** contains bearings. As a review for the entire class, have one or more students explain how bearings are measured. As they do so, ask them to sketch some examples on the board.

Problem-Solving Focus

Ask students what strategies they used to solve each problem. Have them compare the different strategies they each used to solve **Problem 2.** One student might indicate that the strategy "Make a Table" may be especially useful in organizing the given information.

CHAPTER 5
Properties and Attributes of Triangles

Section 5A
Segments in Triangles

5-1 Perpendicular and Angle Bisectors
5-2 Bisectors of Triangles
5-3 Medians and Altitudes of Triangles
5-3 Technology Lab Special Points in Triangles
5-4 The Triangle Midsegment Theorem

Section 5B
Relationships in Triangles

On Track for TAKS Solving Compound Inequalities
5-5 Geometry Lab Explore Triangle Inequalities
5-5 Indirect Proof and Inequalities in One Triangle
5-6 Inequalities in Two Triangles
On Track for TAKS Simplest Radical Form
5-7 Geometry Lab Hands-on Proof of the Pythagorean Theorem
5-7 The Pythagorean Theorem
5-8 Applying Special Right Triangles
5-8 Geometry Lab Graph Irrational Numbers

Pacing Guide for 45-Minute Classes

Calendar Planner
One-Stop Planner®

Chapter 5

Countdown to TAKS Weeks ⑩, ⑪, ⑫

DAY 1	DAY 2	DAY 3	DAY 4	DAY 5
5-1 Lesson	5-2 Lesson	5-3 Lesson	5-3 Technology Lab	5-4 Lesson
DAY 6	**DAY 7**	**DAY 8**	**DAY 9**	**DAY 10**
Multi-Step TAKS Prep Ready to Go On?	On Track for TAKS 5-5 Geometry Lab	5-5 Lesson	5-6 Lesson	On Track for TAKS 5-7 Geometry Lab
DAY 11	**DAY 12**	**DAY 13**	**DAY 14**	**DAY 15**
5-7 Lesson	5-8 Lesson	5-8 Geometry Lab	Multi-Step TAKS Prep Ready to Go On?	Chapter 5 Review
DAY 16				
Chapter 5 Test				

Pacing Guide for 90-Minute Classes

Calendar Planner
One-Stop Planner®

Chapter 5

DAY 1	DAY 2	DAY 3	DAY 4	DAY 5
5-1 Lesson 5-2 Lesson	5-3 Lesson 5-3 Technology Lab	5-4 Lesson Multi-Step TAKS Prep Ready to Go On?	On Track for TAKS 5-5 Geometry Lab 5-5 Lesson	5-6 Lesson On Track for TAKS 5-7 Geometry Lab
DAY 6	**DAY 7**	**DAY 8**		
5-7 Lesson 5-8 Lesson	5-8 Geometry Lab Multi-Step TAKS Prep Ready to Go On?	Chapter 5 Review Chapter 5 Test		

ONGOING ASSESSMENT and INTERVENTION

	DIAGNOSE	PRESCRIBE

Assess Prior Knowledge

Before Chapter 5

Diagnose readiness for the chapter.	Prescribe intervention.
Are You Ready? SE p. 297	**Are You Ready? Intervention** Skills 6, 29, 53, 74, 87

Formative Assessment

Before Every Lesson

Diagnose readiness for the lesson.	Prescribe intervention.
Warm Up TE, every lesson	**Skills Bank** SE pp. S50–S81
	Reteach CRB, Ch. 1–5

During Every Lesson

Diagnose understanding of lesson concepts.	Prescribe intervention.
Check It Out! SE, every example	**Questioning Strategies** TE, every example
Think and Discuss SE, every lesson	**Reading Strategies** CRB, every lesson
Write About It SE, every lesson	*Success for ELL* pp. 57–72
Journal TE, every lesson	

After Every Lesson

Diagnose mastery of lesson concepts.	Prescribe intervention.
Lesson Quiz TE, every lesson	**Reteach** CRB, every lesson
Alternative Assessment TE, every lesson	**Problem Solving** CRB, every lesson
Test Prep SE, every lesson	**Test Prep Doctor** TE, every lesson
Test and Practice Generator	*Homework Help* Online

Before Chapter 5 Testing

Diagnose mastery of concepts in the chapter.	Prescribe intervention.
Ready to Go On? SE pp. 329, 365	*Ready to Go On? Intervention* pp. 57–75
Multi-Step TAKS Prep SE pp. 328, 364	**Scaffolding Questions** TE pp. 328, 364
Section Quizzes AR pp. 85–86	
Test and Practice Generator	

Before High Stakes Testing

Diagnose mastery of benchmark concepts.	Prescribe intervention.
Ready for TAKS? Benchmark Tests	*Ready for TAKS? Intervention*
College Entrance Exam Practice SE p. 371	*College Entrance Exam Practice*
TAKS Prep SE pp. 374–375	*TAKS Prep Workbook*
TAKS Prep CD-ROM	

Summative Assessment

After Chapter 5

Check mastery of chapter concepts.	Prescribe intervention.
Multiple-Choice Tests (Forms A, B, C)	**Reteach** CRB, every lesson
Free-Response Tests (Forms A, B, C)	*Lesson Tutorial Videos* Chapter 5
Performance Assessment AR pp. 87–100	
Test and Practice Generator	
Check mastery of benchmark concepts.	Prescribe intervention.
TAKS Tests	*TAKS Prep Workbook*
College Entrance Exams	*College Entrance Exam Practice*

KEY: **SE** = *Student Edition* **TE** = *Teacher's Edition* **CRB** = *Chapter Resource Book* **AR** = *Assessment Resources* Available online Available on CD-ROM **296B**

CHAPTER 5

Supporting the Teacher

Chapter 5 Resource Book

Practice A, B, C
pp. 3–5, 11–13, 19–21, 27–29, 35–37,
43–45, 51–53, 59–61

Reading Strategies ELL
pp. 10, 18, 26, 34, 42, 50, 58, 66

Reteach
pp. 6–7, 11–13, 19–21, 27–29, 35–37, 43–45, 51–53, 59–61

Problem Solving
pp. 9, 17, 25, 33, 41, 49, 57, 65

Challenge
pp. 8, 16, 24, 32, 40, 48, 56, 64

Parent Letter   pp. 1–2

Transparencies

Lesson Transparencies, Volume 2 .... Chapter 5
 • Warm Ups
 • Teaching Transparencies
 • Additional Examples
 • Lesson Quizzes

Alternate Openers: Explorations .... pp. 29–36

Countdown to TAKS .... pp. 19–24

Know-It Notebook .... Chapter 5
 • Graphic Organizers
 • Key Concepts
 • Vocabulary
 • Chapter Review
 • Big Ideas
 • Postulates
 • Theorems

Teacher Tools

Power Presentations®
Complete PowerPoint® presentations for Chapter 5 lessons

Lesson Tutorial Videos®
Holt authors Ed Burger and Freddie Renfro present tutorials to support the Chapter 5 lessons.

One-Stop Planner®
Easy access to all Chapter 5 resources and assessments, as well as software for lesson planning, test generation, and puzzle creation

IDEA Works!®
Key Chapter 5 resources and assessments modified to address special learning needs

Lesson Plans.. pp. 29–36

Solutions Key .... p. 329

Geometry Posters .... Chapter 5

TechKeys   **Lab Resources**

Project Teacher Support   **Parent Resources**

Workbooks

Homework and Practice Workbook
 Teacher's Guide .... pp. 29–36

Know-It Notebook
 Teacher's Guide .... pp. 65–80

Problem Solving Workbook
 Teacher's Guide .... pp. 29–36

TAKS Prep Workbook
 Teacher's Guide

Technology Highlights for the Teacher

Power Presentations
Dynamic presentations to engage students. Complete PowerPoint® presentations for every lesson in Chapter 5.

One-Stop Planner
Easy access to Chapter 5 resources and assessments. Includes lesson-planning, test-generation, and puzzle-creation software.

Premier Online Edition
Chapter 5 includes Tutorial Videos, Lesson Activities, Lesson Quizzes, Homework Help, and Chapter Project.

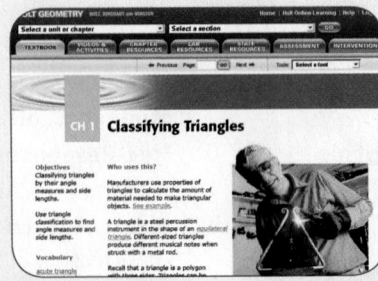

KEY: **SE** = *Student Edition*   **TE** = *Teacher's Edition*   **ELL** English Language Learners   **SPANISH** Spanish version available 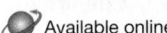 Available online 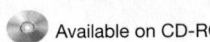 Available on CD-ROM

Reaching All Learners

Resources for All Learners

Texas Lab Manual	Chapter 5
Homework and Practice Workbook	pp. 29–36
Know-It Notebook	pp. 65–80
Problem Solving Workbook	pp. 29–36

DEVELOPING LEARNERS

Practice A	CRB, every lesson
Reteach	CRB, every lesson
Inclusion	TE pp. 303, 316, 323, 353, 360
Questioning Strategies	TE, every example
Modified Chapter 5 Resources	*IDEA Works!*
Homework Help Online	

ON-LEVEL LEARNERS

Practice B	CRB, every lesson
Multiple Representations	TE pp. 308, 338
Modeling	TE p. 315

ADVANCED LEARNERS

Practice C	CRB, every lesson
Challenge	CRB, every lesson
Reading and Writing Math EXTENSION	TE p. 299
Multi-Step TAKS Prep EXTENSION	TE pp. 328, 364
Critical Thinking	TE pp. 302, 316, 350, 358

English Language Learners

ENGLISH LANGUAGE LEARNERS

Are You Ready? Vocabulary	SE p. 297
Vocabulary Connections	SE p. 298
Lesson Vocabulary	SE pp. 300, 307, 314, 322, 332, 348
Vocabulary Exercises	SE pp. 304, 311, 317, 324, 336, 352
Vocabulary Review	SE p. 366
English Language Learners	TE pp. 299, 308, 315
Reading Strategies	CRB, every lesson
Success for English Language Learners	pp. 57–72
Multilingual Glossary	

Reaching All Learners Through...

Concrete Manipulatives	TE pp. 301, 349
Visual Cues	TE pp. 301, 312, 333, 342, 357
Critical Thinking	TE pp. 302, 316, 350, 358
Inclusion	TE pp. 303, 316, 323, 353, 360
Kinesthetic Experience	TE pp. 305, 308, 327, 334, 341
Multiple Representations	TE pp. 308, 338
Modeling	TE p. 315
Test Prep Doctor	TE pp. 306, 313, 319, 326, 338, 345, 355, 362, 371, 372, 374
Common Error Alerts	TE pp. 301, 305, 309, 315, 319, 325, 327, 333, 335, 337, 341, 349, 351, 353, 355, 357, 359, 361
Scaffolding Questions	TE pp. 328, 364

Technology Highlights for Reaching All Learners

Lesson Tutorial Videos

Starring Holt authors Ed Burger and Freddie Renfro! Live tutorials to support every lesson in Chapter 5.

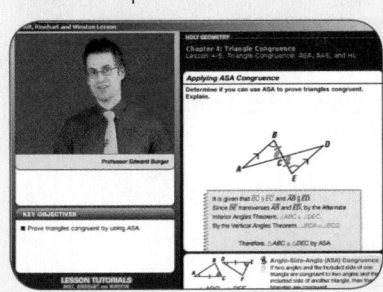

Multilingual Glossary

Searchable glossary includes definitions in English, Spanish, Vietnamese, Chinese, Hmong, Korean, and 4 other languages.

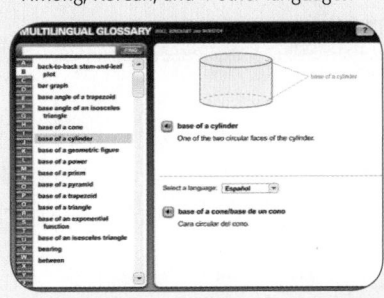

Online Interactivities

Interactive tutorials provide visually engaging alternative opportunities to learn concepts and master skills.

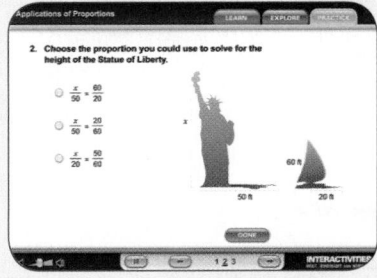

KEY: **SE** = *Student Edition*   **TE** = *Teacher's Edition*   **CRB** = *Chapter Resource Book*   **SPANISH** Spanish version available    Available online   Available on CD-ROM

CHAPTER

5

Ongoing Assessment

Assessing Prior Knowledge

Determine whether students have the prerequisite concepts and skills for success in Chapter 5.

Are You Ready? .... SE p. 297

Warm Up .... TE, every lesson

Test Preparation

Provide practice and review for Chapter 5 and standardized tests.

Multi-Step TAKS Prep .... SE pp. 328, 364

Study Guide: Review .... SE pp. 366–369

TAKS Tackler .... SE pp. 372–373

TAKS Prep .... SE pp. 374–375

College Entrance Exam Practice .... SE p. 371

Countdown to TAKS Transparencies ...... pp. 19–24

Ready for TAKS?

TAKS Prep Workbook

TAKS Prep CD-ROM

IDEA Works!

Alternative Assessment

Assess students' understanding of Chapter 5 concepts and combined problem-solving skills.

Chapter 5 Project .... SE p. 296

Alternative Assessment .... TE, every lesson

Performance Assessment .... AR pp. 99–100

Portfolio Assessment .... AR p. xxxiv

Daily Assessment

Provide formative assessment for each day of Chapter 5.

Questioning Strategies .... TE, every example

Think and Discuss .... SE, every lesson

Check It Out! Exercises .... SE, every example

Write About It .... SE, every lesson

Journal .... TE, every lesson

Lesson Quiz .... TE, every lesson

Alternative Assessment .... TE, every lesson

Modified Lesson Quizzes .... IDEA Works!

Weekly Assessment

Provide formative assessment for each week of Chapter 5.

Multi-Step TAKS Prep .... SE pp. 328, 364

Ready to Go On? .... SE pp. 329, 365

Cumulative Assessment .... SE pp. 374–375

Test and Practice Generator SPANISH .. One-Stop Planner

Formal Assessment

Provide summative assessment of Chapter 5 mastery.

Section Quizzes .... AR pp. 85–86

Chapter 5 Test .... SE p. 370

Chapter Test (Levels A, B, C) .... AR pp. 87–98
• Multiple Choice   • Free Response

Cumulative Test .... AR pp. 101–104

Test and Practice Generator SPANISH .. One-Stop Planner

Modified Chapter 5 Test .... IDEA Works!

Technology Highlights for Ongoing Assessment

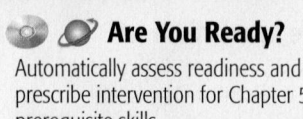

Are You Ready?
Automatically assess readiness and prescribe intervention for Chapter 5 prerequisite skills.

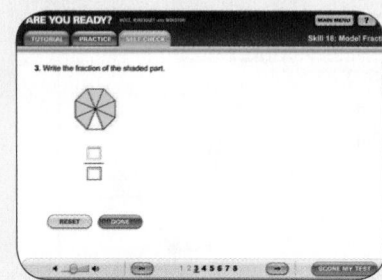

Ready to Go On? SPANISH
Automatically assess understanding of and prescribe intervention for Sections 5A and 5B.

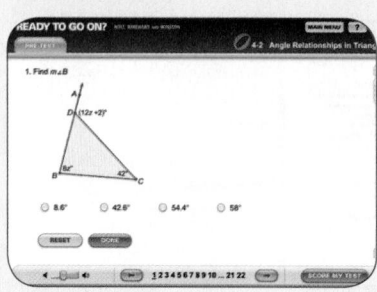

Ready for TAKS? SPANISH
Automatically assess proficiency with and provide intervention for TAKS objectives. Grade 6 through Exit Level.

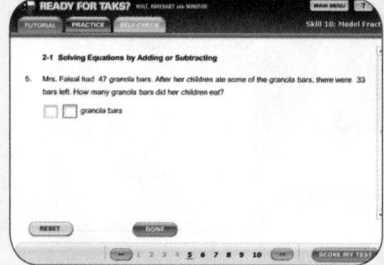

KEY: **SE** = *Student Edition*   **TE** = *Teacher's Edition*   **AR** = Assessment Resources   SPANISH Spanish version available   Available online   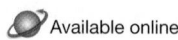 Available on CD-ROM

Formal Assessment

Three levels (A, B, C) of multiple-choice and free-response chapter tests are available in the *Assessment Resources.*

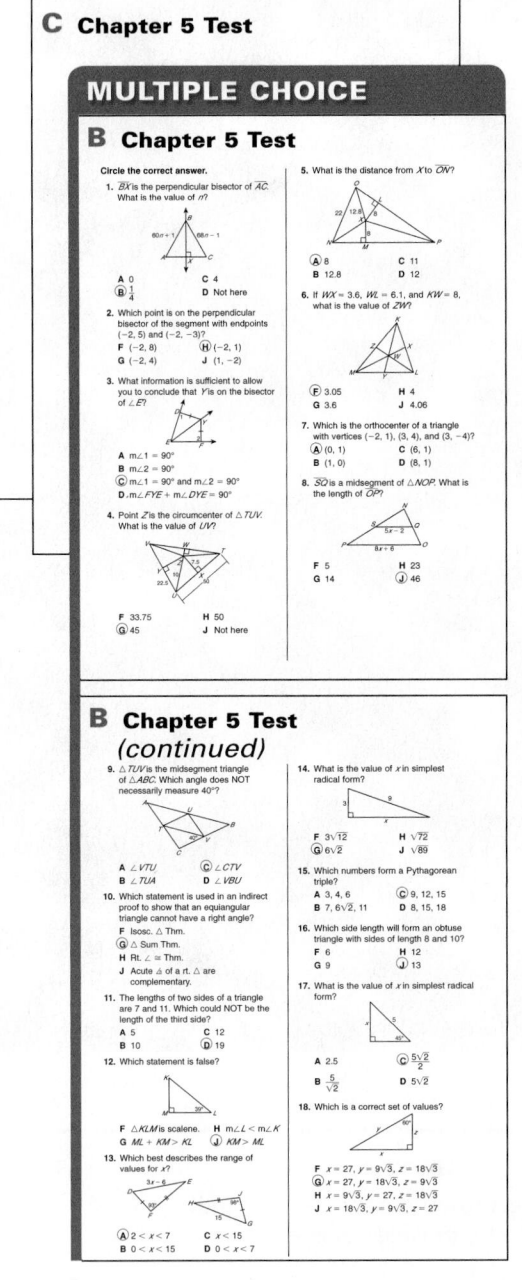

A Chapter 5 Test

C Chapter 5 Test

MULTIPLE CHOICE

B Chapter 5 Test

Circle the correct answer.

1. $\overline{BX}$ is the perpendicular bisector of $\overline{AC}$. What is the value of n?

  A 0   C 4
  B $\frac{1}{4}$ D Not here

2. Which point is on the perpendicular bisector of the segment with endpoints $(-2, 5)$ and $(-2, -3)$?
  F $(-2, 8)$ H $(-2, 1)$
  G $(-2, 4)$ J $(1, -2)$

3. What information is sufficient to allow you to conclude that Y is on the bisector of $\angle E$?
  A $m\angle 1 = 90°$
  B $m\angle 2 = 90°$
  C $m\angle 1 = 90°$ and $m\angle 2 = 90°$
  D $m\angle FYE + m\angle DYE = 90°$

4. Point Z is the circumcenter of $\triangle TUV$. What is the value of UV?
  F 33.75   H 50
  G 45   J Not here

5. What is the distance from X to $\overline{ON}$?
  A 8   C 11
  B 12.8   D 12

6. If $WX \approx 3.6$, $WL \approx 6.1$, and $KW = 8$, what is the value of ZW?
  F 3.05   H 4
  G 3.6   J 4.06

7. Which is the orthocenter of a triangle with vertices $(-2, 1)$, $(3, 4)$, and $(3, -4)$?
  A $(0, 1)$ C $(6, 1)$
  B $(1, 0)$ D $(8, 1)$

8. $\overline{SQ}$ is a midsegment of $\triangle NOP$. What is the length of $\overline{OP}$?
  F 5   H 23
  G 14   J 46

B Chapter 5 Test (continued)

9. $\triangle TUV$ is the midsegment triangle of $\triangle ABC$. Which angle does NOT necessarily measure 40°?
  A $\angle VTU$ C $\angle CTV$
  B $\angle TUA$ D $\angle VBU$

10. Which statement is used in an indirect proof to show that an equiangular triangle cannot have a right angle?
  F Isosc. $\triangle$ Thm.
  G $\triangle$ Sum Thm.
  H Rt. $\angle$ = Thm.
  J Acute $\triangle$ of a rt. $\triangle$ are complementary.

11. The lengths of two sides of a triangle are 7 and 11. Which could NOT be the length of the third side?
  A 5   C 12
  B 10   D 19

12. Which statement is false?
  F $\triangle KLM$ is scalene.   H $m\angle L < m\angle K$
  G $ML + KM > KL$ J $KM > ML$

13. Which best describes the range of values for x?
  A $2 < x < 7$ C $x < 15$
  B $0 < x < 15$ D $0 < x < 7$

14. What is the value of x in simplest radical form?
  F $3\sqrt{12}$ H $\sqrt{72}$
  G $6\sqrt{2}$ J $\sqrt{89}$

15. Which numbers form a Pythagorean triple?
  A 3, 4, 6   C 9, 12, 15
  B 7, $6\sqrt{2}$, 11   D 8, 15, 18

16. Which side length will form an obtuse triangle with sides of length 8 and 10?
  F 6   H 12
  G 9   J 13

17. What is the value of x in simplest radical form?
  A 2.5   C $\frac{5\sqrt{2}}{2}$
  B $\frac{5}{\sqrt{2}}$ D $5\sqrt{2}$

18. Which is a correct set of values?
  F $x = 27$, $y = 9\sqrt{3}$, $z = 18\sqrt{3}$
  G $x = 27$, $y = 18\sqrt{3}$, $z = 9\sqrt{3}$
  H $x = 9\sqrt{3}$, $y = 27$, $z = 18\sqrt{3}$
  J $x = 18\sqrt{3}$, $y = 9\sqrt{3}$, $z = 27$

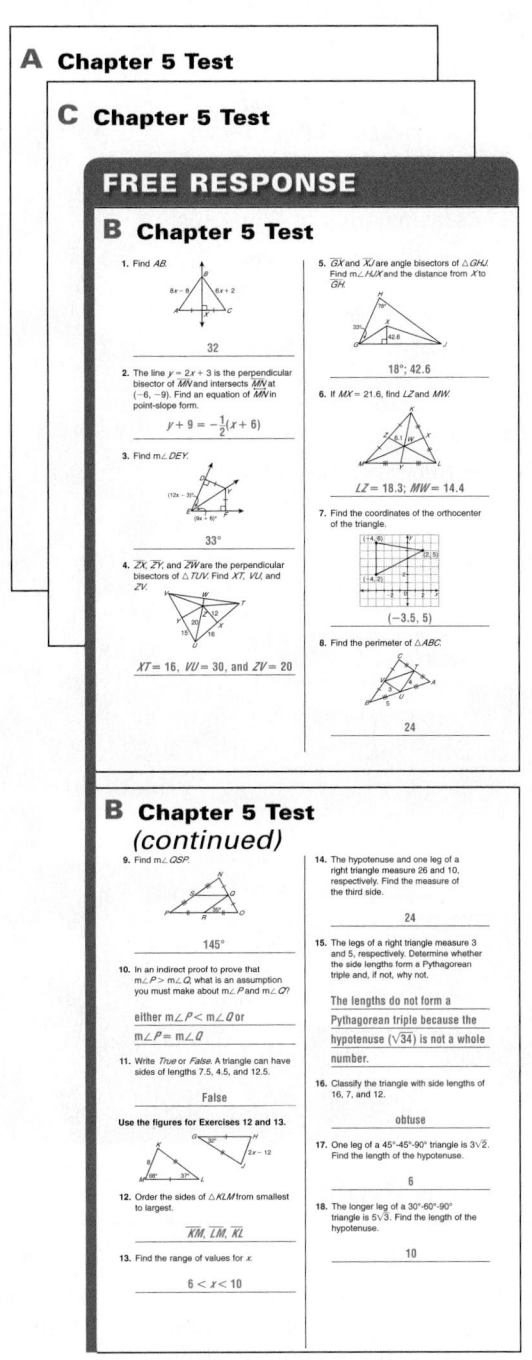

A Chapter 5 Test

C Chapter 5 Test

FREE RESPONSE

B Chapter 5 Test

1. Find AB.

  32

2. The line $y = 2x + 3$ is the perpendicular bisector of $\overline{MN}$ and intersects $\overline{MN}$ at $(-6, -9)$. Find an equation of $\overline{MN}$ in point-slope form.

  $y + 9 = -\frac{1}{2}(x + 6)$

3. Find $m\angle DEY$.

  33°

4. $\overline{ZX}$, $\overline{ZY}$, $\overline{ZW}$ are the perpendicular bisectors of $\triangle TUV$. Find XT, VU, and ZV.

  $XT = 16$, $VU = 30$, and $ZV = 20$

5. $\overline{GX}$ and $\overline{XJ}$ are angle bisectors of $\triangle GHJ$. Find $m\angle HJX$ and the distance from X to $\overline{GH}$.

  18°; 42.6

6. If $MX = 21.6$, find LZ and MW.

  $LZ = 18.3$; $MW = 14.4$

7. Find the coordinates of the orthocenter of the triangle.

  $(-3.5, 5)$

8. Find the perimeter of $\triangle ABC$.

  24

B Chapter 5 Test (continued)

9. Find $m\angle QSP$.

  145°

10. In an indirect proof to prove that $m\angle P > m\angle Q$, what is an assumption you must make about $m\angle P$ and $m\angle Q$?

  either $m\angle P < m\angle Q$ or
  $m\angle P = m\angle Q$

11. Write *True* or *False*. A triangle can have sides of lengths 7.5, 4.5, and 12.5.

  False

Use the figures for Exercises 12 and 13.

12. Order the sides of $\triangle KLM$ from smallest to largest.

  $\overline{KM}$, $\overline{LM}$, $\overline{KL}$

13. Find the range of values for x.

  $6 < x < 10$

14. The hypotenuse and one leg of a right triangle measure 26 and 10, respectively. Find the measure of the third side.

  24

15. The legs of a right triangle measure 3 and 5, respectively. Determine whether the side lengths form a Pythagorean triple and, if not, why not.

  The lengths do not form a
  Pythagorean triple because the
  hypotenuse ($\sqrt{34}$) is not a whole
  number.

16. Classify the triangle with side lengths of 16, 7, and 12.

  obtuse

17. One leg of a 45°-45°-90° triangle is $3\sqrt{2}$. Find the length of the hypotenuse.

  6

18. The longer leg of a 30°-60°-90° triangle is $5\sqrt{3}$. Find the length of the hypotenuse.

  10

Test & Practice Generator SPANISH
One-Stop Planner®

Create and customize Chapter 5 Tests. Instantly generate multiple test versions, answer keys, and Spanish versions of test items.

CHAPTER
5

Properties and Attributes of Triangles

go.hrw.com/Geo/TX
Chapter Project Online
KEYWORD: MG7 ChProj

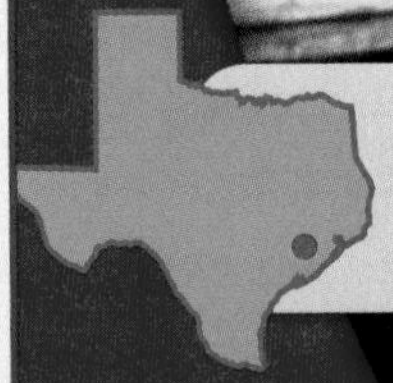

SECTION 5A
Segments in Triangles

MULTI-STEP TAKS PREP On page 328, students use special points in triangles to find possible locations for a music distribution warehouse.

Exercises designed to prepare students for success on the Multi-Step TAKS Prep can be found on pages 305, 312, 319, and 326.

SECTION 5B
Relationships in Triangles

MULTI-STEP TAKS PREP On page 364, students use relationships in triangles to analyze the possible locations for a new airport.

Exercises designed to prepare students for success on the Multi-Step TAKS Prep can be found on pages 338, 344, 354, and 361.

The Broken Obelisk in Houston was dedicated in 1971 as a memorial to Martin Luther King Jr.

About the Project

Balancing Act

In the Chapter Project, students use theorems about perpendicular bisectors to build a stand that will support a balanced triangle. Then students cut out a cardboard triangle, locate its centroid, and check to see whether the triangle will balance at this point.

Project Resources

All project resources for teachers and students are provided online.

Materials:
- cardboard
- scissors
- string
- tape

go.hrw.com/Geo/TX
Project Teacher Support
KEYWORD: MG7 ProjectTS

Geometry in Texas

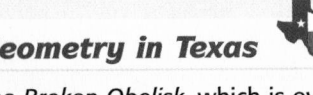

The Broken Obelisk, which is over 25 feet tall, is composed of an obelisk balancing on the vertex of a rectangular pyramid. In this chapter, students will learn about properties and special points of triangles, including the point at which a triangular region will balance.

ARE YOU READY?

☑ **Vocabulary**

Match each term on the left with a definition on the right.

1. angle bisector **E**
2. conclusion **C**
3. hypotenuse **A**
4. leg of a right triangle **D**
5. perpendicular bisector of a segment **B**

   A. the side opposite the right angle in a right triangle

   B. a line that is perpendicular to a segment at its midpoint

   C. the phrase following the word *then* in a conditional statement

   D. one of the two sides that form the right angle in a right triangle

   E. a line or ray that divides an angle into two congruent angles

   F. the phrase following the word *if* in a conditional statement

☑ **Classify Triangles**

Tell whether each triangle is acute, right, or obtuse.

6.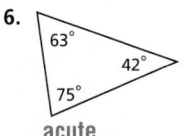
acute

7.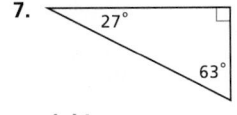
right

8.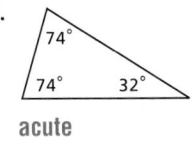
acute

9.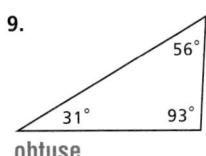
obtuse

☑ **Squares and Square Roots**

Simplify each expression.

10. 8^2 **64**
11. $(-12)^2$ **144**
12. $\sqrt{49}$ **7**
13. $-\sqrt{36}$ **−6**

☑ **Simplify Radical Expressions**

Simplify each expression.

14. $\sqrt{9 + 16}$ **5**
15. $\sqrt{100 - 36}$ **8**
16. $\sqrt{\frac{81}{25}}$ **$\frac{9}{5}$**
17. $\sqrt{2^2}$ **2**

☑ **Solve and Graph Inequalities**

Solve each inequality. Graph the solutions on a number line.

18. $d + 5 < 1$ **$d < -4$**
19. $-4 \le w - 7$ **$w \ge 3$**
20. $-3s \ge 6$ **$s \le -2$**
21. $-2 > \frac{m}{10}$ **$m < -20$**

☑ **Logical Reasoning**

Draw a conclusion from each set of true statements.

22. If two lines intersect, then they are not parallel. Lines ℓ and m intersect at P.
   Lines ℓ and m are not parallel.

23. If M is the midpoint of $\overline{AB}$, then $AM = MB$. If $AM = MB$, then $AM = \frac{1}{2}AB$ and $MB = \frac{1}{2}AB$.
   If M is the mdpt. of $\overline{AB}$, then $AM = \frac{1}{2}AB$ and $MB = \frac{1}{2}AB$.

ARE YOU READY?

Organizer

Objective: Assess students' understanding of prerequisite skills.

Prerequisite Skills

Classify Triangles

Squares and Square Roots

Simplify Radical Expressions

Solve and Graph Inequalities

Logical Reasoning

Assessing Prior Knowledge

INTERVENTION ◀ ▶

Diagnose and Prescribe

Use this page to determine whether intervention is necessary or whether enrichment is appropriate.

Resources

 ***Are You Ready? Intervention and Enrichment* Worksheets**

 ***Are You Ready?* CD-ROM**

 ***Are You Ready?* Online**

my.hrw.com

Answers

18–21. For graphs, see p. A18.

ARE YOU READY?
Diagnose and Prescribe

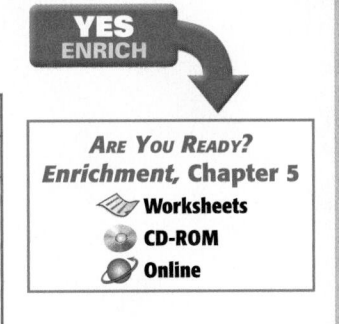

	ARE YOU READY? *Intervention, Chapter 5*		
☑ **Prerequisite Skill**	〰 **Worksheets**	💿 **CD-ROM**	🪐 **Online**
☑ Classify Triangles	Skill 29	Activity 29	
☑ Squares and Square Roots	Skill 6	Activity 6	
☑ Simplify Radical Expressions	Skill 53	Activity 53	Diagnose and Prescribe Online
☑ Solve and Graph Inequalities	Skill 74	Activity 74	
☑ Logical Reasoning	Skill 87	Activity 87	

NO INTERVENE

YES ENRICH

ARE YOU READY? *Enrichment, Chapter 5*

〰 **Worksheets**

💿 **CD-ROM**

🪐 **Online**

Organizer

Objective: Help students organize the new concepts they will learn in Chapter 5.

Online Edition
Multilingual Glossary

Resources

PuzzlePro
One-Stop Planner®

Multilingual Glossary Online
go.hrw.com/Geo/TX
KEYWORD: MG7 Glossary

Answers to Vocabulary Connections

Possible answers:

1. Lines that are concurrent "run together," or intersect, at one point.

2. Each endpoint of a midsegment of a triangle is the midpoint of one side of the triangle.

3. A median of a triangle is a segment whose endpoints are a vertex of the triangle and the midpoint of the opposite side.

4. The altitude of a triangle is the height of the triangle.

Key Vocabulary/Vocabulario

altitude of a triangle	altura de un triángulo
centroid of a triangle	centroide de un triángulo
circumcenter of a triangle	circuncentro de un triángulo
concurrent	concurrente
equidistant	equidistante
incenter of a triangle	incentro de un triángulo
median of a triangle	mediana de un triángulo
midsegment of a triangle	segmento medio de un triángulo
orthocenter of a triangle	orthocentro de un triángulo

Vocabulary Connections

To become familiar with some of the vocabulary terms in the chapter, consider the following. You may refer to the chapter, the glossary, or a dictionary if you like.

1. In Latin, *co* means "together with," and *currere* means "to run." How can you use these meanings to understand what **concurrent** lines are?

2. The endpoints of a **midsegment of a triangle** are on two sides of the triangle. Where on the sides do you think the endpoints are located?

3. The strip of concrete or grass in the middle of some roadways is called the *median*. What do you think the term **median of a triangle** means?

4. Think of the everyday meaning of *altitude*. What do you think the **altitude of a triangle** is?

Geometry TEKS

	Les. 5-1	Les. 5-2	Les. 5-3	5-3 Tech. Lab	Les. 5-4	5-5 Geo. Lab	Les. 5-5	Les. 5-6	5-7 Geo. Lab	Les. 5-7	Les. 5-8	5-8 Geo. Lab
G.2.A Geometric structure* use constructions to explore attributes of geometric figures and to make conjectures …		★	★	★	★							★
G.3.B Geometric structure* construct and justify statements about geometric figures and their properties	★	★	★		★		★	★			★	
G.5.D Geometric patterns* identify and apply patterns from right triangles … including special right triangles (45-45-90 and 30-60-90) and triangles whose sides are Pythagorean triples										★	★	
G.7.B Dimensionality and the geometry of location* … investigate geometric relationships, including … special segments of triangles …	★	★	★		★							
G.8.C Congruence and the geometry of size* derive, extend, and use the Pythagorean Theorem									★	★		
G.9.B Congruence and the geometry of size* formulate and test conjectures about … polygons and their component parts …				★	★	★			★			
G.11.C Similarity and the geometry of shape* develop, apply, and justify triangle similarity relationships, such as … Pythagorean triples …										★		

* Knowledge and skills are written out completely on pages TX28–TX35.

Geometry TEKS—Knowledge and Skills

G.1 Geometric structure The student understands the structure of, and relationships within, an axiomatic system.

G.2 Geometric structure The student analyzes geometric relationships in order to make and verify conjectures.

G.3 Geometric structure The student applies logical reasoning to justify and prove mathematical statements.

G.5 Geometric patterns The student uses a variety of representations to describe geometric relationships and solve problems.

G.7 Dimensionality and the geometry of location The student understands that coordinate systems provide convenient and efficient ways of representing geometric figures and uses them accordingly.

G.8 Congruence and the geometry of size The student uses tools to determine measurements of geometric figures and extends measurement concepts to find perimeter, area, and volume in problem situations.

G.9 Congruence and the geometry of size The student analyzes properties and describes relationships in geometric figures.

G.10 Congruence and the geometry of size The student applies the concept of congruence to justify properties of figures and solve problems.

G.11 Similarity and the geometry of shape The student applies the concepts of similarity to justify properties of figures and solve problems.

Reading and Writing Math

Reading Strategy: Learn Math Vocabulary

Mathematics has a vocabulary all its own. To learn and remember new vocabulary words, use the following study strategies.

- Try to figure out the meaning of a new word based on its context.
- Use a dictionary to look up the root word or prefix.
- Relate the new word to familiar everyday words.

Once you know what a word means, write its definition in your own words.

Term	Study Notes	Definition
Polygon	The prefix *poly* means "many" or "several."	A closed plane figure formed by three or more line segments
Bisect	The prefix *bi* means "two."	Cuts or divides something into two equal parts
Slope	Think of a ski slope.	The measure of the steepness of a line
Intersection	The root word *intersect* means "to overlap." Think of the intersection of two roads.	The set of points that two or more lines have in common

polygon = many
bisect = two
slope = ski slope
intersection = overlap

Try This

Complete the table below.

	Term	Study Notes	Definition
1.	Trinomial		
2.	Equiangular triangle		
3.	Perimeter		
4.	Deductive reasoning		

Use the given prefix and its meanings to write a definition for each vocabulary word.

5. *circum* (about, around); circumference

6. *co* (with, together); coplanar

7. *trans* (across, beyond, through); translation

Properties and Attributes of Triangles **299**

Reading and Writing Math

Organizer

Objective: Help students apply strategies to understand and retain key concepts.

 **Online Edition**

Resources

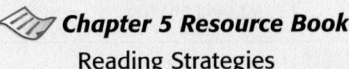 ***Chapter 5 Resource Book***
Reading Strategies

Reading Strategy: Learn Math Vocabulary

ENGLISH LANGUAGE LEARNERS

Discuss Students will remember new vocabulary words better if they understand the meanings of the parts of the words. Discuss examples of common mathematical prefixes such as "bi-" and "tri-". Review the meanings of prefixes and root words in the new terms throughout this chapter. Relate the parts of new vocabulary terms, such as *incenter, circumscribed,* and *orthocenter,* to familiar everyday words.

Extend As students prepare for each lesson throughout the chapter, have them try to write a definition for each new term based on its prefix and/or root word. Then discuss the vocabulary words with the class and review any unfamiliar terms.

Answers to *Try This*

Possible answers:

1. *Tri* means "three"; a polynomial with three terms.

2. *Equi* means "equal," and *tri* means "three"; a triangle with three equal angle measures.

3. *Peri* means "around," and *meter* implies a length; the distance around a figure.

4. Think of the root word *deduce*, which means "to infer"; the process of using logic to draw conclusions from given facts, definitions, and properties.

5. the distance around a circle

6. points that lie in the same plane

7. movement of each point of a figure across a plane the same distance in the same direction

---

⬇ TAKS Objectives

Grades 9–11

Obj. 2	Properties and Attributes of Functions A.4.B
Obj. 3	Linear Functions A.6.D
Obj. 4	Linear Equations and Inequalities A.7.B
Obj. 6	Geometric Relationships and Spatial Reasoning G.5.B, G.5.D
Obj. 7	Two- and Three-Dimensional Representations G.7.A, G.7.B, G.7.C
Obj. 8	Measurement 8.9.A, G.8.C, G.11.C

Segments in Triangles

One-Minute Section Planner

Lesson	Lab Resources	Materials
Lesson 5-1 Perpendicular and Angle Bisectors • Prove and apply theorems about perpendicular bisectors. • Prove and apply theorems about angle bisectors. ☐ Exit Level TAKS ☑ ACT ☑ SAT ☐ SAT Subject Tests	*Texas Lab Manual* 5-1 Technology Lab	**Optional** ruler (MK), protractor (MK), compass (MK), straightedge (MK), local map, patty paper
Lesson 5-2 Bisectors of Triangles • Prove and apply properties of perpendicular bisectors of a triangle. • Prove and apply properties of angle bisectors of a triangle. ☐ Exit Level TAKS ☑ ACT ☑ SAT ☐ SAT Subject Tests	*Texas Lab Manual* 5-2 Technology Lab	**Required** patty paper **Optional** compass (MK), straightedge (MK), local map, geometry software
Lesson 5-3 Medians and Altitudes of Triangles • Apply properties of medians of a triangle. • Apply properties of altitudes of a triangle. ☐ Exit Level TAKS ☑ ACT ☑ SAT ☐ SAT Subject Tests		**Required** compass (MK), straightedge (MK) **Optional** scissors, patty paper, cardboard triangles, string
5-3 Technology Lab Special Points in Triangles • Use special points in triangles to explore Euler's line. ☐ Exit Level TAKS ☐ ACT ☐ SAT ☐ SAT Subject Tests		**Required** geometry software
Lesson 5-4 The Triangle Midsegment Theorem • Prove and use properties of triangle midsegments. ☐ Exit Level TAKS ☑ ACT ☑ SAT ☑ SAT Subject Tests	*Texas Lab Manual* 5-4 Technology Lab	**Optional** compass (MK), straightedge (MK), heavy paper, scissors, geometry software

MK = *Manipulatives Kit*

Section Overview

 Professional Development

Perpendicular and Angle Bisectors

Lesson 5-1

Why? Properties of perpendicular and angle bisectors are used to solve problems involving distance.

Points on a Perpendicular Bisector

Given that m is the perpendicular bisector of $\overline{AB}$,

C is on $m \leftrightarrow CA = CB$.

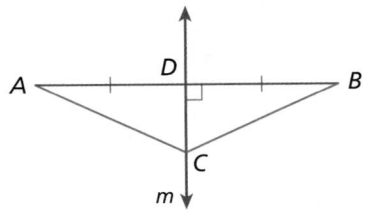

Points on an Angle Bisector

Given that G is in the interior of $\angle DEF$, n bisects $\angle DEF$, $\overline{DG} \perp \overline{ED}$, and $\overline{FG} \perp \overline{EF}$,

G is on $n \leftrightarrow GD = GF$.

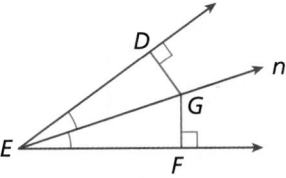

Bisectors, Medians, and Altitudes of Triangles

Lessons 5-2, 5-3

Why? A triangle's points of concurrency can be used to locate points equidistant from the vertices, points equidistant from the sides, and the center of gravity.

Perpendicular bisectors intersect at the **circumcenter** P.	Angle bisectors intersect at the **incenter** P.	Medians intersect at the **centroid** P.	Altitudes intersect at the **orthocenter** P.
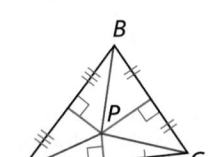	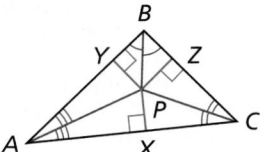	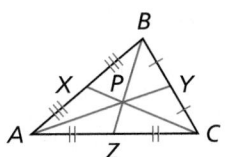	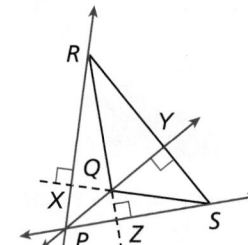
Circumcenter Theorem $PA = PB = PC$	**Incenter Theorem** $PX = PY = PZ$	**Centroid Theorem** $AP = \frac{2}{3}AY$, $BP = \frac{2}{3}BZ$, and $CP = \frac{2}{3}CX$	

The Triangle Midsegment Theorem

Lesson 5-4

Why? Triangle midsegments can be used to make indirect measurements.

Midsegment $\overline{AB} \leftrightarrow AE = AC$ and $BE = BD$

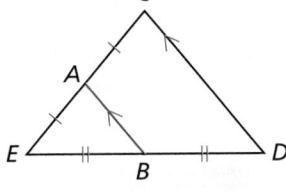

Triangle Midsegment Theorem

If $\overline{AB}$ is a midsegment, then $\overline{AB} \parallel \overline{CD}$ and $AB = \frac{1}{2}CD$.

Objectives: Prove and apply theorems about perpendicular bisectors.

Prove and apply theorems about angle bisectors.

 Technology Lab
In *Texas Lab Manual*

 Online Edition
Tutorial Videos, Interactivity

 Countdown to TAKS Week 10

Power Presentations
with PowerPoint®

Warm Up

Construct each of the following.

1. a perpendicular bisector **2.** an angle bisector

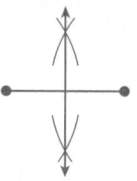 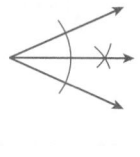

3. Find the midpoint and slope of the segment with endpoints (2, 8) and (−4, 6).

$(−1, 7), \frac{1}{3}$

Also available on transparency

Math Humor

Q: Where do math teachers shop?

A: Deci-malls (decimals)!

⭐ Geometry TEKS

G.3 Geometric structure*
(B) construct and justify statements about geometric figures …

(E) use deductive reasoning …

G.7 Dimensionality and the geometry of location*
(A) use one- and two-dimensional coordinate systems …

(B) … investigate … special segments of triangles …

(C) … use … slope, and midpoint

G.10 Congruence and the geometry of size*
(B) … apply triangle congruence relationships

* Knowledge and Skills See p. 298.

5-1 Perpendicular and Angle Bisectors

⭐ **TEKS G.3.B** Geometric structure: construct and justify statements about geometric figures and their properties. Also G.3.E, G.7.A, G.7.B, G.7.C, G.10.B

Objectives
Prove and apply theorems about perpendicular bisectors.

Prove and apply theorems about angle bisectors.

Vocabulary
equidistant
locus

Who uses this?

The suspension and steering lines of a parachute keep the sky diver centered under the parachute. (See Example 3.)

When a point is the same distance from two or more objects, the point is said to be **equidistant** from the objects. Triangle congruence theorems can be used to prove theorems about equidistant points.

Know it!
Note

Theorems	Distance and Perpendicular Bisectors		
	THEOREM	**HYPOTHESIS**	**CONCLUSION**
5-1-1	**Perpendicular Bisector Theorem** If a point is on the perpendicular bisector of a segment, then it is equidistant from the endpoints of the segment.	$\overline{XY} \perp \overline{AB}$ $\overline{YA} \cong \overline{YB}$	$XA = XB$
5-1-2	**Converse of the Perpendicular Bisector Theorem** If a point is equidistant from the endpoints of a segment, then it is on the perpendicular bisector of the segment.	$XA = XB$	$\overline{XY} \perp \overline{AB}$ $\overline{YA} \cong \overline{YB}$

You will prove Theorem 5-1-2 in Exercise 30.

PROOF **Perpendicular Bisector Theorem**

Given: ℓ is the perpendicular bisector of $\overline{AB}$.
Prove: $XA = XB$

Reading Math

The word *locus* comes from the Latin word for location. The plural of *locus* is *loci*, which is pronounced LOW-sigh.

Proof:

Since ℓ is the perpendicular bisector of $\overline{AB}$, $\ell \perp \overline{AB}$ and Y is the midpoint of $\overline{AB}$. By the definition of perpendicular, $\angle AYX$ and $\angle BYX$ are right angles and $\angle AYX \cong \angle BYX$. By the definition of midpoint, $\overline{AY} \cong \overline{BY}$. By the Reflexive Property of Congruence, $\overline{XY} \cong \overline{XY}$. So $\triangle AYX \cong \triangle BYX$ by SAS, and $\overline{XA} \cong \overline{XB}$ by CPCTC. Therefore $XA = XB$ by the definition of congruent segments.

A **locus** is a set of points that satisfies a given condition. The perpendicular bisector of a segment can be defined as the locus of points in a plane that are equidistant from the endpoints of the segment.

---

1 Introduce

EXPLORATION

5-1 Perpendicular and Angle Bisectors

You can use a ruler and protractor to explore properties of perpendicular bisectors.

1. Draw a long segment on a sheet of paper and label it $\overline{AB}$.

2. Use a ruler to find the midpoint of $\overline{AB}$. Label it P.

3. Use a protractor to draw a line ℓ through P that is perpendicular to $\overline{AB}$.

4. Draw any point X on ℓ. Measure the distance from X to A and the distance from X to B. What do you notice?

5. Mark three more points on ℓ and measure the distance from each point to both endpoints. What do you find?

6. Complete the following conjecture: If a point is on the perpendicular bisector of a segment, then ? .

THINK AND DISCUSS

7. **Explain** how you can use your conjecture and the fact that line m is the perpendicular bisector of $\overline{QR}$ to classify $\triangle PQR$.

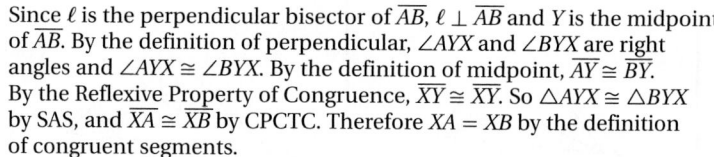

Motivate

Show students a local map marked with two locations, such as your school and a grocery store. Ask them to find places that are about the same distance from both locations. After they have found several, show them that all these places lie near the perpendicular bisector of the segment joining the two original locations. Explain that students will study properties like this in this lesson.

Explorations and answers are provided in the *Explorations* binder.

EXAMPLE 1

Applying the Perpendicular Bisector Theorem and Its Converse

Find each measure.

A *YW*

$YW = XW$	⊥ Bisector Thm.
$YW = 7.3$	Substitute 7.3 for *XW*.

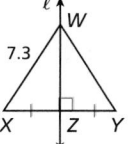

B *BC*

Since $AB = AC$ and $\ell \perp \overline{BC}$, ℓ is the perpendicular bisector of $\overline{BC}$ by the Converse of the Perpendicular Bisector Theorem.

$BC = 2CD$	Def. of seg. bisector
$BC = 2(16) = 32$	Substitute 16 for *CD*.

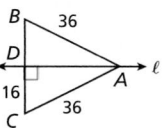

x²/y **Algebra**

C *PR*

$PR = RQ$	⊥ Bisector Thm.
$2n + 9 = 7n - 18$	Substitute the given values.
$9 = 5n - 18$	Subtract 2n from both sides.
$27 = 5n$	Add 18 to both sides.
$5.4 = n$	Divide both sides by 5.

So $PR = 2(5.4) + 9 = 19.8$.

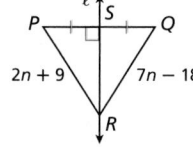

 **Find each measure.**

1a. Given that line ℓ is the perpendicular bisector of $\overline{DE}$ and $EG = 14.6$, find *DG*. **14.6**

1b. Given that $DE = 20.8$, $DG = 36.4$, and $EG = 36.4$, find *EF*. **10.4**

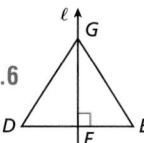

Remember that the distance between a point and a line is the length of the perpendicular segment from the point to the line.

Theorems (**Distance and Angle Bisectors**)

THEOREM	HYPOTHESIS	CONCLUSION
5-1-3 Angle Bisector Theorem If a point is on the bisector of an angle, then it is equidistant from the sides of the angle.	∠APC ≅ ∠BPC	$AC = BC$
5-1-4 Converse of the Angle Bisector Theorem If a point in the interior of an angle is equidistant from the sides of the angle, then it is on the bisector of the angle.	$AC = BC$	∠APC ≅ ∠BPC

You will prove these theorems in Exercises 31 and 40.

5-1 Perpendicular and Angle Bisectors **301**

Students sometimes confuse Theorems 5-1-1 and 5-1-2. To apply Theorem 5-1-1, they must be given a perpendicular bisector to conclude that a point on it is equidistant from the endpoints of the segment. To apply Theorem 5-1-2, they must have a point equidistant from the endpoints of a segment to conclude that the point is on the perpendicular bisector of that segment.

Power Presentations
with PowerPoint®

Additional Examples

Example 1

Find each measure.

A. *MN*   2.6

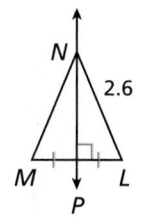

B. *BC*   24

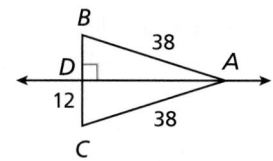

C. *TU*   28.5

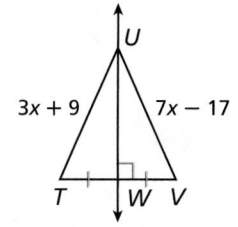

Also available on transparency

INTERVENTION
Questioning Strategies

EXAMPLE 1

• How do you know which theorem to use in each part of the example?

Teaching Tip **Visual** For **Example 1B**, draw counterexamples showing that $\overline{BC} \not\perp \overline{AD}$ to demonstrate why you must know that $\overline{BC} \perp \overline{AD}$ to conclude that ℓ is the perpendicular bisector.

---

2 Teach

Guided Instruction

Review the definitions and constructions of perpendicular and angle bisectors. Discuss the Perpendicular Bisector Theorem and its converse, and illustrate them with algebraic examples. Discuss the Angle Bisector Theorem and its converse. Before covering **Example 4,** review how to find the midpoint and slope of a segment when given the coordinates of the endpoints, and then review the relationship between the slopes of perpendicular lines.

Reaching All Learners

Through Concrete Manipulatives

Have students draw a segment $\overline{AB}$ on a piece of patty paper and then fold the paper so that *A* and *B* coincide. Point out that the fold is the perpendicular bisector of the segment. Have students mark several points on the fold and measure the distance from each of these points to *A* and to *B*. Students should note that these distances are the same in each case. A similar exploration can be done with angle bisectors or by using a Mira.

Lesson 5-1 **301**

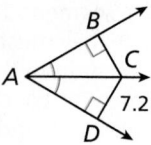
Example 2

Find each measure.

A. BC 7.2

B. m∠EFH, given that m∠EFG = 50°   25°

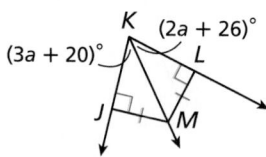

C. m∠MKL   38°

Example 3

John wants to hang a spotlight along the back of a display case. Wires $\overline{AD}$ and $\overline{CD}$ are the same length, and A and C are equidistant from B. How do the wires keep the spotlight centered?

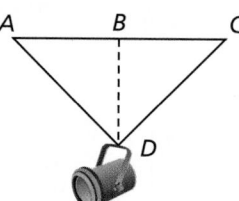

Since $\overline{AD} \cong \overline{CD}$, D is on the ⊥ bisector of $\overline{AC}$. B is the mdpt. of $\overline{AC}$, so $\overline{BD}$ is the ⊥ bisector of $\overline{AC}$. Thus D is centered below B.

Also available on transparency

Based on these theorems, an angle bisector can be defined as the locus of all points in the interior of the angle that are equidistant from the sides of the angle.

EXAMPLE 2   **Applying the Angle Bisector Theorems**

Find each measure.

A LM

$LM = JM$ ∠ Bisector Thm.
$LM = 12.8$ Substitute 12.8 for JM.

B m∠ABD, given that m∠ABC = 112°

Since $AD = DC$, $\overline{AD} \perp \overline{BA}$, and $\overline{DC} \perp \overline{BC}$, $\overrightarrow{BD}$ bisects ∠ABC by the Converse of the Angle Bisector Theorem.

$m\angle ABD = \frac{1}{2}m\angle ABC$ Def. of ∠ bisector

$m\angle ABD = \frac{1}{2}(112°) = 56°$ Substitute 112° for m∠ABC.

 **Algebra**

C m∠TSU

Since $RU = UT$, $\overline{RU} \perp \overline{SR}$, and $\overline{UT} \perp \overline{ST}$, $\overrightarrow{SU}$ bisects ∠RST by the Converse of the Angle Bisector Theorem.

$m\angle RSU = m\angle TSU$ Def. of ∠ bisector
$6z + 14 = 5z + 23$ Substitute the given values.
$z + 14 = 23$ Subtract 5z from both sides.
$z = 9$ Subtract 14 from both sides.

So $m\angle TSU = [5(9) + 23]° = 68°$.

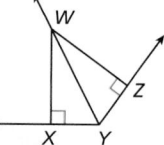

CHECK IT OUT!   Find each measure.

2a. Given that $\overrightarrow{YW}$ bisects ∠XYZ and $WZ = 3.05$, find WX.   3.05

2b. Given that m∠WYZ = 63°, XW = 5.7, and ZW = 5.7, find m∠XYZ.   126°

EXAMPLE 3   *Parachute Application*

Each pair of suspension lines on a parachute are the same length and are equally spaced from the center of the chute. How do these lines keep the sky diver centered under the parachute?

It is given that $\overline{PQ} \cong \overline{RQ}$. So Q is on the perpendicular bisector of $\overline{PR}$ by the Converse of the Perpendicular Bisector Theorem. Since S is the midpoint of $\overline{PR}$, $\overline{QS}$ is the perpendicular bisector of $\overline{PR}$. Therefore the sky diver remains centered under the chute.

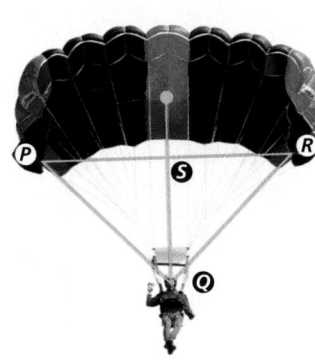

INTERVENTION ◄═►
Questioning Strategies

EXAMPLE 2

• How do you know which theorem to use in each part of the example?

EXAMPLE 3

• How can the Perpendicular Bisector Theorem be used to center a real-life object?

 Teaching Tip   **Critical Thinking** Ask students "Does the Converse of the Angle Bisector Theorem apply if the point is in the exterior of the angle?" Lead students to see that an angle bisector must be in the interior of the angle it bisects. Therefore a point equidistant from the sides must also be in the angle's interior in order to be on the bisector.

 Teaching Tip   **Reading Math** Remind students that in the converse of a statement, the hypothesis and conclusion are switched.

 **CHECK IT OUT!**
3. S is equidistant from each pair of suspension lines. What can you conclude about $\overrightarrow{QS}$? $\overrightarrow{QS}$ bisects $\angle PQR$.

EXAMPLE **4** **Writing Equations of Bisectors in the Coordinate Plane**

 **Algebra**

Write an equation in point-slope form for the perpendicular bisector of the segment with endpoints $A(-1, 6)$ and $B(3, 4)$.

Step 1 Graph $\overline{AB}$.

The perpendicular bisector of $\overline{AB}$ is perpendicular to $\overline{AB}$ at its midpoint.

Step 2 Find the midpoint of $\overline{AB}$.

$\left(\dfrac{x_1 + x_2}{2}, \dfrac{y_1 + y_2}{2}\right)$ *Midpoint formula*

mdpt. of $\overline{AB} = \left(\dfrac{-1 + 3}{2}, \dfrac{6 + 4}{2}\right) = (1, 5)$

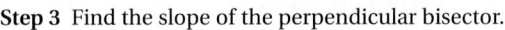

Step 3 Find the slope of the perpendicular bisector.

slope $= \dfrac{y_2 - y_1}{x_2 - x_1}$ *Slope formula*

slope of $\overline{AB} = \dfrac{4 - 6}{3 - (-1)} = \dfrac{-2}{4} = -\dfrac{1}{2}$

Since the slopes of perpendicular lines are opposite reciprocals, the slope of the perpendicular bisector is 2.

Step 4 Use point-slope form to write an equation.

The perpendicular bisector of $\overline{AB}$ has slope 2 and passes through $(1, 5)$.

$y - y_1 = m(x - x_1)$ *Point-slope form*

$y - 5 = 2(x - 1)$ *Substitute 5 for y_1, 2 for m, and 1 for x_1.*

 **CHECK IT OUT!**

4. Write an equation in point-slope form for the perpendicular bisector of the segment with endpoints $P(5, 2)$ and $Q(1, -4)$.

$y + 1 = -\dfrac{2}{3}(x - 3)$

THINK AND DISCUSS

1. Is line ℓ a bisector of $\overline{PQ}$? Is it a perpendicular bisector of $\overline{PQ}$? Explain.

2. Suppose that M is in the interior of $\angle JKL$ and $MJ = ML$. Can you conclude that $\overrightarrow{KM}$ is the bisector of $\angle JKL$? Explain.

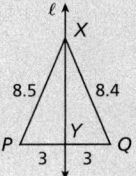

 **Know it! Note**

3. GET ORGANIZED Copy and complete the graphic organizer. In each box, write the theorem or its converse in your own words.

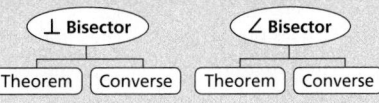

Inclusion Before **Example 4,** review how to find the opposite reciprocal of a number. For example, the opposite reciprocal of 3 is $-\dfrac{1}{3}$.

Power Presentations with PowerPoint®

Additional Examples

Example 4

Write an equation in point-slope form for the perpendicular bisector of the segment with endpoints $C(6, -5)$ and $D(10, 1)$.

$y + 2 = -\dfrac{2}{3}(x - 8)$

Also available on transparency

INTERVENTION ◄—►
Questioning Strategies

EXAMPLE **4**

• How do you use the endpoints of the segment to write the equation of its perpendicular bisector?

---

3 Close

Summarize

Discuss how to construct a perpendicular bisector and an angle bisector. Review the theorems from the lesson, illustrating each with a diagram. Explain the method for writing the equation of the perpendicular bisector of a segment when given the coordinates of the endpoints.

ONGOING ASSESSMENT

and INTERVENTION ◄—►

Diagnose Before the Lesson
5-1 Warm Up, TE p. 300

Monitor During the Lesson
Check It Out! Exercises, SE pp. 301–303
Questioning Strategies, TE pp. 301–303

Assess After the Lesson
5-1 Lesson Quiz, TE p. 306
Alternative Assessment, TE p. 306

Answers to Think and Discuss

1. Yes; no; since $PY = QY = 3$, Y is the mdpt. of $\overline{PQ}$, and thus by the def. of bisect, ℓ is a bisector of $\overline{PQ}$. If ℓ were the $\perp$ bisector of $\overline{PQ}$, then PX would equal QX by the $\perp$ Bisector Thm. However, $PX = 8.5$ and $QX = 8.4$, so ℓ is not the $\perp$ bisector of $\overline{PQ}$.

2. No; although $MJ = ML$, to apply the Conv. of the $\angle$ Bisector Thm., you must know that $\overline{MJ} \perp \overrightarrow{KJ}$ and $\overline{ML} \perp \overrightarrow{KL}$.

3. See p. A4.

---

go.hrw.com/Geo/TX
Homework Help Online
KEYWORD: MG7 5-1
Parent Resources Online
KEYWORD: MG7 Parent

Assignment Guide

Assign *Guided Practice* exercises as necessary.

If you finished Examples **1–2**
Basic 12–17, 23–28
Average 12–17, 22–29
Advanced 12–17, 22–30, 39, 41

If you finished Examples **1–4**
Basic 12–29, 33, 35–37, 42–48
Average 12–29, 32–38, 42–48
Advanced 12–21, 24–28 even, 29–48

Homework Quick Check
Quickly check key concepts.
Exercises: 14, 16, 18, 20, 24, 26

Answers

8. The braces can be installed so that $\overline{PK} \perp \overline{JL}$, $\overline{PM} \perp \overline{NL}$, and $PK = PM$. Then by the Conv. of the ∠ Bisector Thm., P will be on the bisector of ∠*JLN*.

18. They can position Main St. so that the ∠ formed by Elm St. and Main St. is congruent to the ∠ formed by Grove St. and Main St. Then by the ∠ Bisector Thm., every point on Main St. will be equidistant from Elm St. and Grove St.

19. $y + 3 = -\frac{1}{2}(x + 2)$
20. $y - 2 = x + 4$
21. $y + 3 = \frac{5}{2}(x - 2)$

⬧TAKS Practice

GUIDED PRACTICE

1. **Vocabulary** A ___?___ is the *locus* of all points in a plane that are *equidistant* from the endpoints of a segment. (*perpendicular bisector* or *angle bisector*) **perpendicular bisector**

SEE EXAMPLE **1**
p. 301

Use the diagram for Exercises 2–4.

2. Given that $PS = 53.4$, $QT = 47.7$, and $QS = 53.4$, find PQ. **95.4**

3. Given that m is the perpendicular bisector of $\overline{PQ}$ and $SQ = 25.9$, find SP. **25.9**

4. Given that m is the perpendicular bisector of $\overline{PQ}$, $PS = 4a$, and $QS = 2a + 26$, find QS. **52**

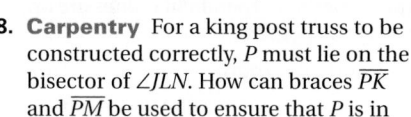

SEE EXAMPLE **2**
p. 302

Use the diagram for Exercises 5–7.

5. Given that $\overrightarrow{BD}$ bisects ∠*ABC* and $CD = 21.9$, find AD. **21.9**

6. Given that $AD = 61$, $CD = 61$, and m∠*ABC* = 48°, find m∠*CBD*. **24°**

7. Given that $DA = DC$, m∠*DBC* = $(10y + 3)°$, and m∠*DBA* = $(8y + 10)°$, find m∠*DBC*. **38°**

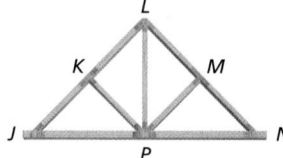

SEE EXAMPLE **3**
p. 302

8. **Carpentry** For a king post truss to be constructed correctly, P must lie on the bisector of ∠*JLN*. How can braces $\overline{PK}$ and $\overline{PM}$ be used to ensure that P is in the proper location?

SEE EXAMPLE **4**
p. 303

Write an equation in point-slope form for the perpendicular bisector of the segment with the given endpoints.

9. $M(-5, 4), N(1, -2)$
$y - 1 = x + 2$

10. $U(2, -6), V(4, 0)$
$y + 3 = -\frac{1}{3}(x - 3)$

11. $J(-7, 5), K(1, -1)$
$y - 2 = \frac{4}{3}(x + 3)$

PRACTICE AND PROBLEM SOLVING

Independent Practice	
For Exercises	**See Example**
12–14	1
15–17	2
18	3
19–21	4

TEKS ⬧ TAKS

Skills Practice p. S12
Application Practice p. S32

Use the diagram for Exercises 12–14.

12. Given that line t is the perpendicular bisector of $\overline{JK}$ and $GK = 8.25$, find GJ. **8.25**

13. Given that line t is the perpendicular bisector of $\overline{JK}$, $JG = x + 12$, and $KG = 3x - 17$, find KG. **26.5**

14. Given that $GJ = 70.2$, $JH = 26.5$, and $GK = 70.2$, find JK. **53**

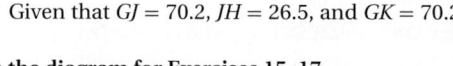

Use the diagram for Exercises 15–17.

15. Given that m∠*RSQ* = m∠*TSQ* and $TQ = 1.3$, find RQ. **1.3**

16. Given that m∠*RSQ* = 58°, $RQ = 49$, and $TQ = 49$, find m∠*RST*. **116°**

17. Given that $RQ = TQ$, m∠*QSR* = $(9a + 48)°$, and m∠*QST* = $(6a + 50)°$, find m∠*QST*. **54°**

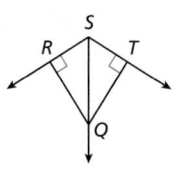

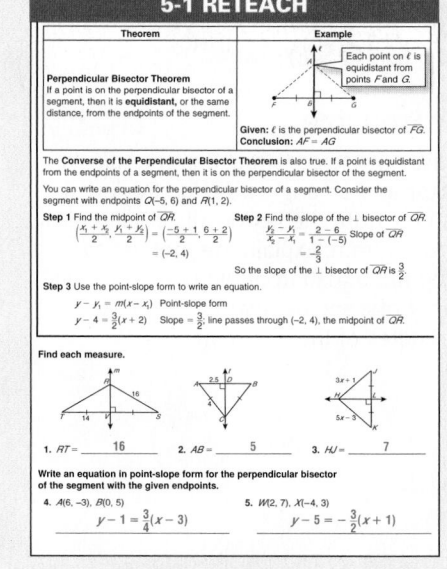

18. City Planning The planners for a new section of the city want every location on Main Street to be equidistant from Elm Street and Grove Street. How can the planners ensure that this is the case?

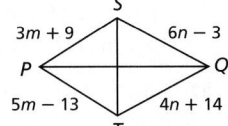

Elm Street / Main Street / Grove Street

Write an equation in point-slope form for the perpendicular bisector of the segment with the given endpoints.

19. $E(-4, -7)$, $F(0, 1)$ **20.** $X(-7, 5)$, $Y(-1, -1)$ **21.** $M(-3, -1)$, $N(7, -5)$

22. $\overline{PQ}$ is the perpendicular bisector of $\overline{ST}$. Find the values of m and n.
$m = 11$; $n = 8.5$

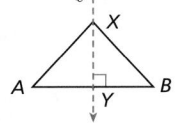
$3m + 9$ $6n - 3$ $5m - 13$ $4n + 14$

Shuffleboard Use the diagram of a shuffleboard and the following information to find each length in Exercises 23–28.

$\overline{KZ}$ is the perpendicular bisector of $\overline{GN}$, $\overline{HM}$, and $\overline{JL}$.

23. JK 38   **24.** GN 72   **25.** ML 38

26. HY 24   **27.** JL 24   **28.** NM 38

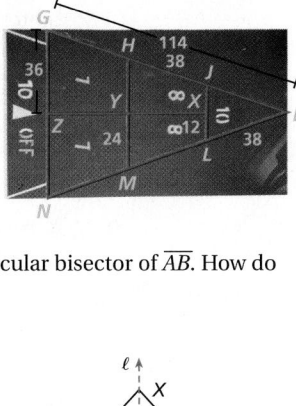

29. Multi-Step The endpoints of $\overline{AB}$ are $A(-2, 1)$ and $B(4, -3)$. Find the coordinates of a point C other than the midpoint of $\overline{AB}$ that is on the perpendicular bisector of $\overline{AB}$. How do you know it is on the perpendicular bisector?

30. Write a paragraph proof of the Converse of the Perpendicular Bisector Theorem.

Given: $AX = BX$
Prove: X is on the perpendicular bisector of $\overline{AB}$.

Plan: Draw ℓ perpendicular to $\overline{AB}$ through X. Show that $\triangle AYX \cong \triangle BYX$ and thus $\overline{AY} \cong \overline{BY}$. By definition, ℓ is the perpendicular bisector of $\overline{AB}$.

31. Write a two-column proof of the Angle Bisector Theorem.

Given: $\overrightarrow{PS}$ bisects $\angle QPR$. $\overline{SQ} \perp \overrightarrow{PQ}$, $\overline{SR} \perp \overrightarrow{PR}$
Prove: $SQ = SR$

Plan: Use the definitions of angle bisector and perpendicular to identify two pairs of congruent angles. Show that $\triangle PQS \cong \triangle PRS$ and thus $\overline{SQ} \cong \overline{SR}$.

32. Critical Thinking In the Converse of the Angle Bisector Theorem, why is it important to say that the point must be in the interior of the angle?

33. This problem will prepare you for the Multi-Step TAKS Prep on page 328.

A music company has stores in Abby $(-3, -2)$ and Cardenas $(3, 6)$. Each unit in the coordinate plane represents 1 mile. $y = -\dfrac{3}{4}x + 2$

a. The company president wants to build a warehouse that is equidistant from the two stores. Write an equation that describes the possible locations.

b. A straight road connects Abby and Cardenas. The warehouse will be located exactly 4 miles from the road. How many locations are possible? 2

c. To the nearest tenth of a mile, how far will the warehouse be from each store?
6.4 mi

COMMON ERROR ALERT

In **Exercise 22**, students may solve the equations $3m + 9 = 6n - 3$ and $5m - 13 = 4n + 14$ instead of $3m + 9 = 5m - 13$ and $6n - 3 = 4n + 14$. Discuss which segments are equal when $\overline{PQ}$ is the perpendicular bisector of $\overline{ST}$.

Teaching Tip
Kinesthetic For **Exercise 18**, have students copy the drawing and then fold their sketches so that Elm Street and Grove Street coincide. Show them that Main Street is on the fold and is therefore the bisector of the angle formed by Elm Street and Grove Street.

MULTI-STEP TAKS PREP **Exercise 33** involves using the equation of the perpendicular bisector of a segment when given the coordinates of the segment's endpoints. This exercise prepares students for the Multi-Step TAKS Prep on page 328.

Answers

29. Possible answer: $C(3, 2)$; $AC = \sqrt{26}$; $BC = \sqrt{26}$; so $AC = BC$, and by the Conv. of the $\perp$ Bisector Thm., C is on the $\perp$ bisector of $\overline{AB}$.

30–32. See p. A18.

 Journal

Have students write the Angle Bisector Theorem and its converse in their own words and explain the difference between the two, using examples.

ALTERNATIVE ASSESSMENT

Have students construct the perpendicular bisector of a segment and the bisector of an angle. Then have them illustrate that points on the perpendicular bisector are equidistant from the endpoints of the segment and that points on the angle bisector are equidistant from the sides of the angle.

Power Presentations with PowerPoint®

 5-1 Lesson Quiz

Use the diagram for Items 1–2.

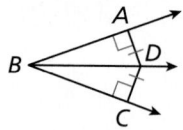

1. Given that m∠ABD = 16°, find m∠ABC.   32°

2. Given that m∠ABD = $(2x + 12)$° and m∠CBD = $(6x - 18)$°, find m∠ABC.   54°

Use the diagram for Items 3–4.

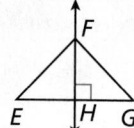

3. Given that $\overline{FH}$ is the perpendicular bisector of $\overline{EG}$, EF = $4y - 3$, and FG = $6y - 37$, find FG.   65

4. Given that EF = 10.6, EH = 4.3, and FG = 10.6, find EG.   8.6

5. Write an equation in point-slope form for the perpendicular bisector of the segment with endpoints X(7, 9) and Y(−3, 5). $y - 7 = -\frac{5}{2}(x - 2)$

Also available on transparency

306 *Chapter 5*

34. Write About It How is the construction of the perpendicular bisector of a segment related to the Converse of the Perpendicular Bisector Theorem?

35. If $\overrightarrow{JK}$ is perpendicular to $\overline{XY}$ at its midpoint M, which statement is true?

Ⓐ JX = KY　　Ⓑ JX = KX　　Ⓒ JM = KM　　Ⓓ JX = JY

36. What information is needed to conclude that $\overrightarrow{EF}$ is the bisector of ∠DEG?

Ⓕ m∠DEF = m∠DEG

Ⓖ m∠FEG = m∠DEF

Ⓗ m∠GED = m∠GEF

Ⓙ m∠DEF = m∠EFG

37. Short Response The city wants to build a visitor center in the park so that it is equidistant from Park Street and Washington Avenue. They also want the visitor center to be equidistant from the museum and the library. Find the point V where the visitor center should be built. Explain your answer.

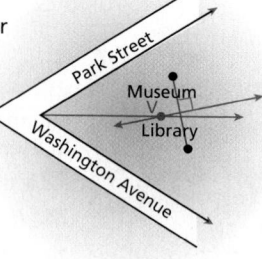

CHALLENGE AND EXTEND

38. Consider the points $P(2, 0)$, $A(-4, 2)$, $B(0, -6)$, and $C(6, -3)$.

　a. Show that P is on the bisector of ∠ABC.

　b. Write an equation of the line that contains the bisector of ∠ABC.

39. Find the locus of points that are equidistant from the *x*-axis and *y*-axis.
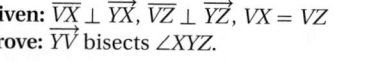 the lines $y = x$ and $y = -x$

40. Write a two-column proof of the Converse of the Angle Bisector Theorem.

　Given: $\overrightarrow{VX} \perp \overrightarrow{YX}$, $\overrightarrow{VZ} \perp \overrightarrow{YZ}$, VX = VZ

　Prove: $\overrightarrow{YV}$ bisects ∠XYZ.

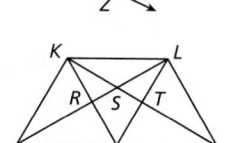

41. Write a paragraph proof.

　Given: $\overline{KN}$ is the perpendicular bisector of $\overline{JL}$.
　　　$\overline{LN}$ is the perpendicular bisector of $\overline{KM}$.
　　　$\overline{JR} \cong \overline{MT}$

　Prove: ∠JKM ≅ ∠MLJ

SPIRAL REVIEW

42. Lyn bought a sweater for $16.95. The change *c* that she received can be described by $c = t - 16.95$, where *t* is the amount of money Lyn gave the cashier. What is the dependent variable? *(Previous course)* c

For the points $R(-4, 2)$, $S(1, 4)$, $T(3, -1)$, and $V(-7, -5)$, determine whether the lines are parallel, perpendicular, or neither. *(Lesson 3-5)*

43. $\overleftrightarrow{RS}$ and $\overleftrightarrow{VT}$ **parallel**　　**44.** $\overleftrightarrow{RV}$ and $\overleftrightarrow{ST}$ **neither**　　**45.** $\overleftrightarrow{RT}$ and $\overleftrightarrow{VR}$ **perpendicular**

Write the equation of each line in slope-intercept form. *(Lesson 3-6)*

46. the line through the points $(1, -1)$ and $(2, -9)$ $y = -8x + 7$

47. the line with slope -0.5 through $(10, -15)$ $y = -\frac{1}{2}x - 10$

48. the line with *x*-intercept -4 and *y*-intercept 5 $y = \frac{5}{4}x + 5$

Answers

34. In the construction of the ⊥ bisector of $\overline{AB}$, the same compass setting is used to draw an arc from each endpoint of the segment. So in the diagram, AX = BX and AY = BY. By the Conv. of the ⊥ Bisector Thm., both X and Y lie on the ⊥ bisector of $\overline{AB}$. So ℓ is the ⊥ bisector of $\overline{AB}$.

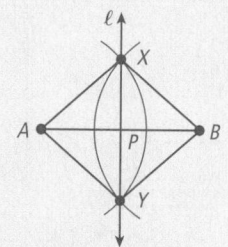

37. Possible answer: All locations that are equidistant from Park St. and Washington Ave. lie on the bisector of the ∠ formed by the 2 streets. All locations that are equidistant from the museum and the library lie on the ⊥ bisector of the seg. formed by the museum and the library. So the visitor center should be built at the point V, where the 2 bisectors intersect.

38a. The dist. from P to $\overrightarrow{BA}$ is $2\sqrt{5}$, and the dist. from P to $\overrightarrow{BC}$ is $2\sqrt{5}$. So P is equidistant from $\overrightarrow{BA}$ and $\overrightarrow{BC}$, and therefore, by the Conv. of the ∠ Bisector Thm., P is on the bisector of ∠ABC.

　b. Possible answer: $y = 3x - 6$

40–41. See p. A18.

5-2 Bisectors of Triangles

TEKS G.3.B Geometric structure: construct and justify statements about geometric figures and their properties. Also G.2A, G.2.B, G.7.A, G.7.B

Objectives
Prove and apply properties of perpendicular bisectors of a triangle.

Prove and apply properties of angle bisectors of a triangle.

Vocabulary
concurrent
point of concurrency
circumcenter of a triangle
circumscribed
incenter of a triangle
inscribed

Who uses this?
An event planner can use perpendicular bisectors of triangles to find the best location for a fireworks display. (See Example 4.)

Since a triangle has three sides, it has three perpendicular bisectors. When you construct the perpendicular bisectors, you find that they have an interesting property.

Helpful Hint

The perpendicular bisector of a side of a triangle does not always pass through the opposite vertex.

Construction Circumcenter of a Triangle

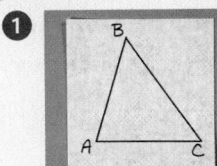 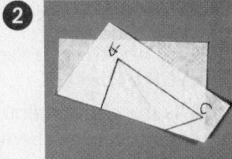 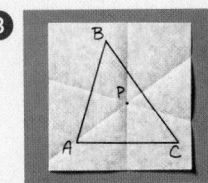

① Draw a large scalene acute triangle ABC on a piece of patty paper.

② Fold the perpendicular bisector of each side.

③ Label the point where the three perpendicular bisectors intersect as P.

When three or more lines intersect at one point, the lines are said to be **concurrent**. The **point of concurrency** is the point where they intersect. In the construction, you saw that the three perpendicular bisectors of a triangle are concurrent. This point of concurrency is the **circumcenter of the triangle**.

Theorem 5-2-1 (Circumcenter Theorem)

The circumcenter of a triangle is equidistant from the vertices of the triangle.

$$PA = PB = PC$$

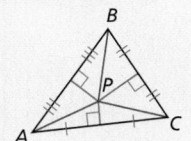

The circumcenter can be inside the triangle, outside the triangle, or on the triangle.

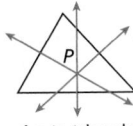 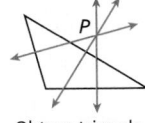 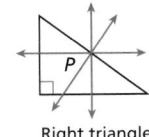

Acute triangle   Obtuse triangle   Right triangle

---

1 Introduce

Motivate

Give students a city map with three houses marked on it. Ask students to find a location equidistant from all three houses where three friends should meet. Explain that this point is the intersection of the perpendicular bisectors of the sides of the triangle formed by the three houses. It is called the circumcenter. Explain that in this lesson students will learn how to find the circumcenter and the incenter of a triangle.

Explorations and answers are provided in the *Explorations* binder.

5-2 Organizer

Pacing: Traditional 1 day
Block ½ day

Objectives: Prove and apply properties of perpendicular bisectors of a triangle.

Prove and apply properties of angle bisectors of a triangle.

Technology Lab
In *Texas Lab Manual*

Online Edition
Tutorial Videos

Countdown to TAKS Week 10

Power Presentations
with PowerPoint®

Warm Up

1. Draw a triangle and construct the bisector of one angle.

2. $\overline{JK}$ is perpendicular to $\overline{ML}$ at its midpoint K. List the congruent segments. $\overline{JM} \cong \overline{JL}$, $\overline{MK} \cong \overline{ML}$

Also available on transparency

Math Humor

Teacher: How many sides does a circle have?

Student: Two—inside and outside!

Geometry TEKS

G.2 Geometric structure*
(A) use constructions to explore attributes of geometric figures and to make conjectures …
(B) make conjectures about … polygons … and determine the validity of the conjectures …

G.3 Geometric structure*
(B) construct and justify statements about geometric figures …

G.7 Dimensionality and the geometry of location*
(A) use … coordinate systems to represent … figures
(B) … investigate … special segments of triangles …

* **Knowledge and Skills** See p. 298.

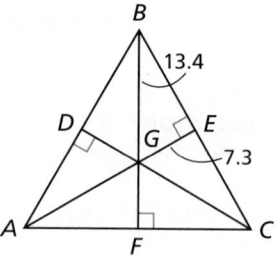

Additional Examples

Example 1

$\overline{DG}$, $\overline{EG}$, and $\overline{FG}$ are the perpendicular bisectors of $\triangle ABC$. Find GC.   13.4

Example 2

Find the circumcenter of $\triangle HJK$ with vertices $H(0, 0)$, $J(10, 0)$, and $K(0, 6)$.   (5, 3)

Also available on transparency

INTERVENTION ◄══►
Questioning Strategies

EXAMPLE 1

• What is true of the circumcenter of a triangle?

• Which measure given for the triangle is unnecessary?

EXAMPLE 2

• How do you find the circumcenter of a triangle when given the coordinates of the three vertices?

Reading Math To help students remember the meanings of the words *incenter, inscribed, circumcenter,* and *circumscribed,* remind them of the meanings of the prefixes. The prefix *in-* means "inside" or "within," and the prefix *circum-* means "around."

ENGLISH
LANGUAGE
LEARNERS

Kinesthetic Have students construct perpendicular bisectors to circumscribe a circle about a triangle. This will help students remember the meaning of *circumscribe.*

The circumcenter of $\triangle ABC$ is the center of its *circumscribed* circle. A circle that contains all the vertices of a polygon is **circumscribed** about the polygon.

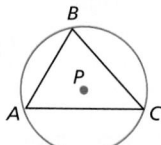

PROOF ■ **Circumcenter Theorem**

Given: Lines ℓ, m, and n are the perpendicular bisectors of $\overline{AB}$, $\overline{BC}$, and $\overline{AC}$, respectively.
Prove: $PA = PB = PC$

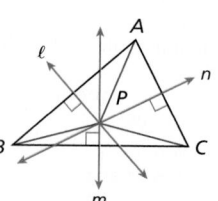

Proof:

P is the circumcenter of $\triangle ABC$. Since P lies on the perpendicular bisector of $\overline{AB}$, $PA = PB$ by the Perpendicular Bisector Theorem. Similarly, P also lies on the perpendicular bisector of $\overline{BC}$, so $PB = PC$. Therefore $PA = PB = PC$ by the Transitive Property of Equality.

EXAMPLE 1 **Using Properties of Perpendicular Bisectors**

$\overline{KZ}$, $\overline{LZ}$, and $\overline{MZ}$ are the perpendicular bisectors of $\triangle GHJ$. Find HZ.

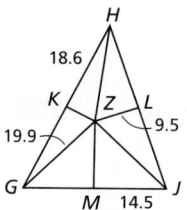

Z is the circumcenter of $\triangle GHJ$. By the Circumcenter Theorem, Z is equidistant from the vertices of $\triangle GHJ$.

$HZ = GZ$	Circumcenter Thm.
$HZ = 19.9$	Substitute 19.9 for GZ.

CHECK IT OUT! Use the diagram above. Find each length.
1a. *GM* 14.5   1b. *GK* 18.6   1c. *JZ* 19.9

EXAMPLE 2 **Finding the Circumcenter of a Triangle**

x^2 **Algebra**

Find the circumcenter of $\triangle RSO$ with vertices $R(-6, 0)$, $S(0, 4)$, and $O(0, 0)$.

Step 1 Graph the triangle.

Step 2 Find equations for two perpendicular bisectors.
Since two sides of the triangle lie along the axes, use the graph to find the perpendicular bisectors of these two sides. The perpendicular bisector of $\overline{RO}$ is $x = -3$, and the perpendicular bisector of $\overline{OS}$ is $y = 2$.

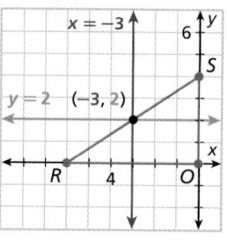

Step 3 Find the intersection of the two equations.
The lines $x = -3$ and $y = 2$ intersect at $(-3, 2)$, the circumcenter of $\triangle RSO$.

308 *Chapter 5 Properties and Attributes of Triangles*

---

2 Teach

Guided Instruction

Have students construct the circumcenter of a triangle by paper folding. Discuss the point of concurrency and the Circumcenter Theorem. Remind students of the properties of perpendicular bisectors from the previous lesson. Show them how to find the circumcenter of a triangle in the coordinate plane. Discuss the Incenter Theorem and explain how the properties of angle bisectors can be used to find segment lengths and angle measures in a triangle.

Reaching All Learners
Through Multiple Representations

Have students use geometry software to construct a triangle and the perpendicular bisectors of the sides. Have them drag a vertex of the triangle to change its shape and note that the perpendicular bisectors are still concurrent. Have them construct the circumscribed circle. Then have them construct the angle bisectors of the triangle. Have students drag a vertex to notice that the angle bisectors are still concurrent. Finally have students construct the inscribed circle.

 **2.** Find the circumcenter of $\triangle GOH$ with vertices $G(0, -9)$, $O(0, 0)$, and $H(8, 0)$. $(4, -4.5)$

A triangle has three angles, so it has three angle bisectors. The angle bisectors of a triangle are also concurrent. This point of concurrency is the **incenter of the triangle**.

Theorem 5-2-2 (**Incenter Theorem**)

The incenter of a triangle is equidistant from the sides of the triangle.

$PX = PY = PZ$

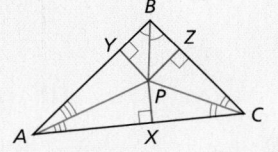

You will prove Theorem 5-2-2 in Exercise 35.

You will prove Theorem 5-2-2 in Exercise 35.

Unlike the circumcenter, the incenter is always inside the triangle.

Remember!

The distance between a point and a line is the length of the perpendicular segment from the point to the line.

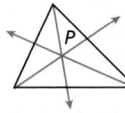

Acute triangle

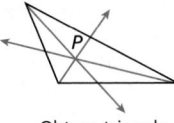

Obtuse triangle

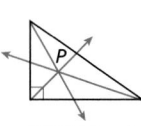

Right triangle

The incenter is the center of the triangle's *inscribed circle*. A circle **inscribed** in a polygon intersects each line that contains a side of the polygon at exactly one point.

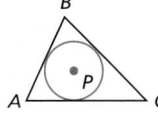

EXAMPLE 3 **Using Properties of Angle Bisectors**

$\overline{JV}$ and $\overline{KV}$ are angle bisectors of $\triangle JKL$. Find each measure.

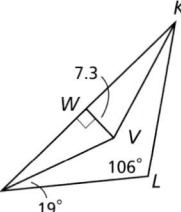

A the distance from V to $\overline{KL}$

V is the incenter of $\triangle JKL$. By the Incenter Theorem, V is equidistant from the sides of $\triangle JKL$.

The distance from V to $\overline{JK}$ is 7.3.
So the distance from V to $\overline{KL}$ is also 7.3.

B $m\angle VKL$

$m\angle KJL = 2m\angle VJL$	$\overline{JV}$ is the bisector of $\angle KJL$.
$m\angle KJL = 2(19°) = 38°$	Substitute 19° for $m\angle VJL$.
$m\angle KJL + m\angle JLK + m\angle JKL = 180°$	$\triangle$ Sum Thm.
$38 + 106 + m\angle JKL = 180$	Substitute the given values.
$m\angle JKL = 36°$	Subtract 144° from both sides.
$m\angle VKL = \frac{1}{2}m\angle JKL$	$\overline{KV}$ is the bisector of $\angle JKL$.
$m\angle VKL = \frac{1}{2}(36°) = 18°$	Substitute 36° for $m\angle JKL$.

Power Presentations with PowerPoint®

Additional Examples

Example 3

$\overline{MP}$ and $\overline{LP}$ are angle bisectors of $\triangle LMN$. Find each measure.

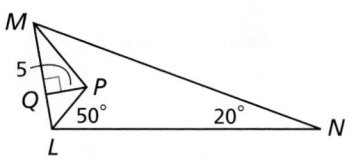

A. the distance from P to $\overline{MN}$ 5

B. $m\angle PMN$ 30°

Also available on transparency

INTERVENTION
Questioning Strategies

EXAMPLE 3

• How do you use the angle bisectors to find the indicated measures?

Teaching Tip **Technology** Have students use geometry software to draw an angle, construct its bisector, and draw a point on the bisector. Have them construct perpendicular segments from the point to the sides of the angle. Then have them measure the distances and confirm that they are equal.

Teaching Tip **Math Background** *Inscribed* is usually defined in terms of tangency, which is covered in Chapter 11.

Example 4

A city planner wants to build a new library between a school, a post office, and a hospital. Draw a sketch to show where the library should be placed so it is the same distance from all three buildings.

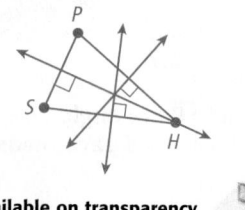

Also available on transparency

INTERVENTION ◄►
Questioning Strategies

EXAMPLE **4**

• How many perpendicular bisectors do you need to construct to find the circumcenter of a triangle?

CHECK IT OUT! $\overline{QX}$ and $\overline{RX}$ are angle bisectors of △PQR. Find each measure.
3a. the distance from X to $\overline{PQ}$ **19.2**
3b. m∠PQX **52°**

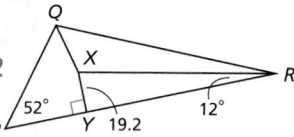

EXAMPLE · 4 **Community Application**

The city of Odessa will host a fireworks display for the next Fourth of July celebration. Draw a sketch to show where the display should be positioned so that it is the same distance from all three viewing locations *A, B,* and *C* on the map. Justify your sketch.

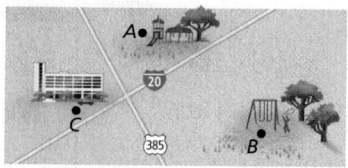

Let the three viewing locations be vertices of a triangle. By the Circumcenter Theorem, the circumcenter of the triangle is equidistant from the vertices.

Trace the map. Draw the triangle formed by the viewing locations. To find the circumcenter, find the perpendicular bisectors of each side. The position of the display is the circumcenter, *F.*

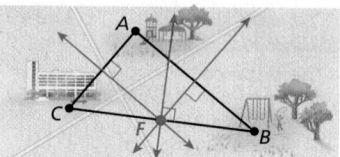

CHECK IT OUT! **4.** A city plans to build a firefighters' monument in the park between three streets. Draw a sketch to show where the city should place the monument so that it is the same distance from all three streets. Justify your sketch.

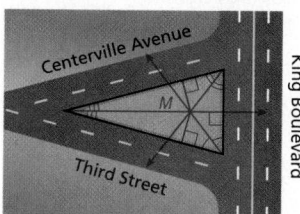

4. By the Incenter Thm., the incenter of a △ is equidistant from the sides of the △. Draw the △ formed by the streets and draw the ∠ bisectors to find the incenter, point *M.* The city should place the monument at point *M.*

THINK AND DISCUSS

1. Sketch three lines that are concurrent.

2. *P* and *Q* are the circumcenter and incenter of △RST, but not necessarily in that order. Which point is the circumcenter? Which point is the incenter? Explain how you can tell without constructing any of the bisectors.

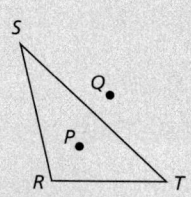

Know it!
Note

3. GET ORGANIZED Copy and complete the graphic organizer. Fill in the blanks to make each statement true.

	Circumcenter	Incenter
Definition	The point of concurrency of the _?_	The point of concurrency of the _?_
Distance	Equidistant from the _?_	Equidistant from the _?_
Location (Inside, Outside, or On)	Can be _?_ the triangle	_?_ the triangle

---

3 Close

Summarize

Discuss how to find the circumcenter and incenter of a triangle. Point out that the circumcenter is equidistant from the vertices of the triangle, while the incenter is equidistant from the sides. Illustrate the Circumcenter and Incenter Theorems with diagrams.

Answers to *Think and Discuss*
1. Possible answer:

2. *Q; P;* possible answer: the incenter is always inside the △, so *Q* cannot be the incenter. Therefore *P* must be the incenter, and *Q* must be the circumcenter.

3. See p. A4.

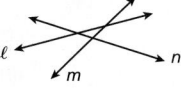
GUIDED PRACTICE

Vocabulary Apply the vocabulary from this lesson to answer each question.

1. Explain why lines ℓ, m, and n are NOT *concurrent*.
They do not intersect at a single point.

2. A circle that contains all the vertices of a polygon is ___?___ the polygon. (*circumscribed about* or *inscribed in*)
circumscribed about

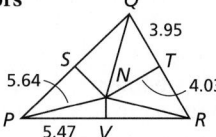

SEE EXAMPLE **1**
p. 308

$\overline{SN}$, $\overline{TN}$, and $\overline{VN}$ are the perpendicular bisectors of $\triangle PQR$. Find each length.

3. NR **5.64**   **4.** RV **5.47**

5. TR **3.95**   **6.** QN **5.64**

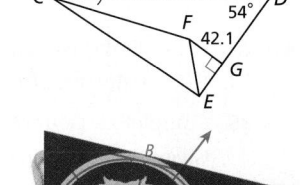

SEE EXAMPLE **2**
p. 308

Multi-Step Find the circumcenter of a triangle with the given vertices.

7. $O(0, 0)$, $K(0, 12)$, $L(4, 0)$ $(2, 6)$

8. $A(-7, 0)$, $O(0, 0)$, $B(0, -10)$ $(-3.5, -5)$

SEE EXAMPLE **3**
p. 309

$\overline{CF}$ and $\overline{EF}$ are angle bisectors of $\triangle CDE$. Find each measure.

9. the distance from F to $\overline{CD}$ **42.1**

10. $m\angle FED$ **46°**

SEE EXAMPLE **4**
p. 310

11. Design The designer of the Newtown High School pennant wants the circle around the bear emblem to be as large as possible. Draw a sketch to show where the center of the circle should be located. Justify your sketch.

PRACTICE AND PROBLEM SOLVING

Independent Practice

For Exercises	See Example
12–15	1
16–17	2
18–19	3
20	4

TEKS ⟶ TAKS

Skills Practice p. S12
Application Practice p. S32

$\overline{DY}$, $\overline{EY}$, and $\overline{FY}$ are the perpendicular bisectors of $\triangle ABC$. Find each length.

12. CF **59.7**   **13.** YC **63.9**

14. DB **62.8**   **15.** AY **63.9**

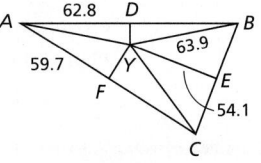

Multi-Step Find the circumcenter of a triangle with the given vertices.

16. $M(-5, 0)$, $N(0, 14)$, $O(0, 0)$ $(-2.5, 7)$ **17.** $O(0, 0)$, $V(0, 19)$, $W(-3, 0)$ $(-1.5, 9.5)$

$\overline{TJ}$ and $\overline{SJ}$ are angle bisectors of $\triangle RST$. Find each measure.

18. the distance from J to $\overline{RS}$ **8.37**

19. $m\angle RTJ$ **55°**

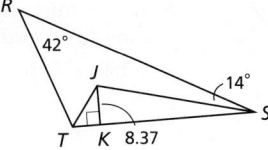

Assignment Guide

Assign *Guided Practice* exercises as necessary.

If you finished Examples **1–2**
   Basic 12–17, 30, 32–34
   Average 12–17, 30, 32–34, 36, 43
   Advanced 12–17, 30, 32–34, 36, 43, 44

If you finished Examples **1–4**
   Basic 12–20, 22–35, 37, 40–42, 45–53
   Average 12–21, 22–28 even, 30–43, 45–53
   Advanced 12–21, 22–28 even, 29–53

Homework Quick Check
Quickly check key concepts.
Exercises: 12, 16, 18, 20, 22, 32

Answers

11. The largest possible ○ in the int. of the △ is its inscribed ○, and the center of the inscribed ○ is the incenter. Draw the △ and its ∠ bisectors. Center the ○ at E, the pt. of concurrency of the ∠ bisectors.

⬇TAKS Practice

Grades 9–11	Exercises
Obj. 2	42
Obj. 7	33, 34, 37, 41, 51–53
Obj. 9	45–47
Obj. 10	22–32

22. angle bisector; m∠BAE = m∠EAC

23. perpendicular bisector; AD = BD, $\overline{AD} \perp \overline{DG}$, and $\overline{BD} \perp \overline{DG}$

24. angle bisector; m∠ABG = m∠GBC

25. Angle bisector; since $\overline{AE}$ and $\overline{BG}$ are ∠ bisectors, *R* is the incenter. $\overline{CR}$ intersects the incenter, so it is an ∠ bisector.

35 a. ∠ Bisector Thm.
b. the bisector of ∠B
c. PX = PZ

20. **Business** A company repairs photocopiers in Harbury, Gaspar, and Knowlton. Draw a sketch to show where the company should locate its office so that it is the same distance from each city. Justify your sketch.

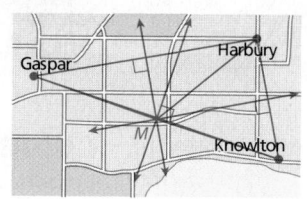

21. **Critical Thinking** If *M* is the incenter of △*JKL*, explain why ∠*JML* cannot be a right angle.

Tell whether each segment lies on a perpendicular bisector, an angle bisector, or neither. Justify your answer.

22. $\overline{AE}$ 23. $\overline{DG}$ 24. $\overline{BG}$

25. $\overline{CR}$ 26. $\overline{FR}$ neither   27. $\overline{DR}$ neither

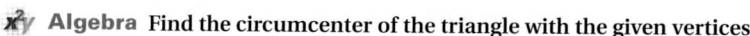

Tell whether each statement is sometimes, always, or never true. Support your answer with a sketch.

28. The angle bisectors of a triangle intersect at a point outside the triangle. **N**

29. An angle bisector of a triangle bisects the opposite side. **S**

30. A perpendicular bisector of a triangle passes through the opposite vertex. **S**

31. The incenter of a right triangle is on the triangle. **N**

32. The circumcenter of a scalene triangle is inside the triangle. **S**

x^2 **Algebra** Find the circumcenter of the triangle with the given vertices.

33. *O*(0, 0), *A*(4, 8), *B*(8, 0) **(4, 3)**   34. *O*(0, 0), *Y*(0, 12), *Z*(6, 6) **(0, 6)**

35. Complete this proof of the Incenter Theorem by filling in the blanks.
Given: $\overrightarrow{AP}$, $\overrightarrow{BP}$, and $\overrightarrow{CP}$ bisect ∠*A*, ∠*B*, and ∠*C*, respectively.
$\overline{PX} \perp \overline{AC}$, $\overline{PY} \perp \overline{AB}$, $\overline{PZ} \perp \overline{BC}$
Prove: *PX* = *PY* = *PZ*

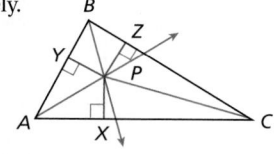

Proof: Let *P* be the incenter of △*ABC*. Since *P* lies on the bisector of ∠*A*, *PX* = *PY* by **a.** __?__ . Similarly, *P* also lies on **b.** __?__ , so *PY* = *PZ*. Therefore **c.** __?__ by the Transitive Property of Equality.

36. Prove that the bisector of the vertex angle of an isosceles triangle is the perpendicular bisector of the base.
Given: $\overleftrightarrow{QS}$ bisects ∠*PQR*. $\overline{PQ} \cong \overline{RQ}$
Prove: $\overleftrightarrow{QS}$ is the perpendicular bisector of $\overline{PR}$.
Plan: Show that △*PQS* ≅ △*RQS*. Then use CPCTC to show that *S* is the midpoint of $\overline{PR}$ and that $\overleftrightarrow{QS} \perp \overline{PR}$.

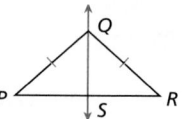

MULTI-STEP TAKS PREP

37. This problem will prepare you for the Multi-Step TAKS Prep on page 328.
A music company has stores at *A*(0, 0), *B*(8, 0), and *C*(4, 3), where each unit of the coordinate plane represents one mile.

a. A new store will be built so that it is equidistant from the three existing stores. Find the coordinates of the new store's location. $\left(4, -\frac{7}{6}\right)$

b. Where will the new store be located in relation to △*ABC*? **outside**

c. To the nearest tenth of a mile, how far will the new store be from each of the existing stores? **4.2 mi**

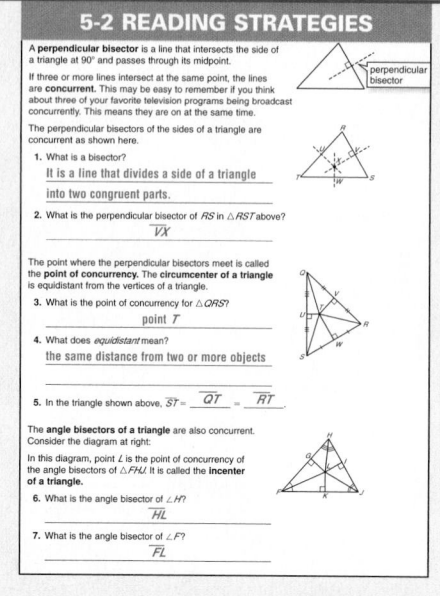
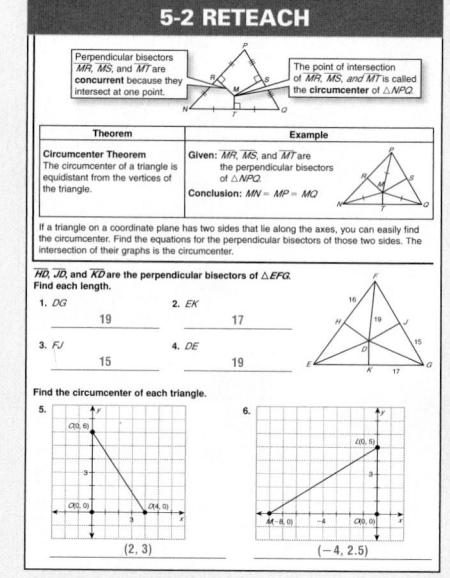

38. Write About It How are the inscribed circle and the circumscribed circle of a triangle alike? How are they different?

39. Construction Draw a large scalene acute triangle.

   a. Construct the angle bisectors to find the incenter. Inscribe a circle in the triangle. **Check students' constructions.**

   b. Construct the perpendicular bisectors to find the circumcenter. Circumscribe a circle around the triangle. **Check students' constructions.**

 **TEST PREP**

40. *P* is the incenter of △*ABC*. Which must be true?

   (A) $PA = PB$ (C) $YA = YB$
   (B) $PX = PY$ (D) $AX = BZ$

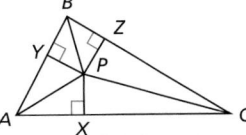

41. Lines *r*, *s*, and *t* are concurrent. The equation of line *r* is $x = 5$, and the equation of line *s* is $y = -2$. Which could be the equation of line *t*?

   (F) $y = x - 7$ (H) $y = x + 3$
   (G) $y = x - 3$ (J) $y = x + 7$

42. Gridded Response Lines *a*, *b*, and *c* are the perpendicular bisectors of △*KLM*. Find *LN*. **14.75**

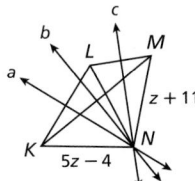

CHALLENGE AND EXTEND

43. Use the right triangle with the given coordinates.

   a. Prove that the midpoint of the hypotenuse of a right triangle is equidistant from all three vertices.

   b. Make a conjecture about the circumcenter of a right triangle.

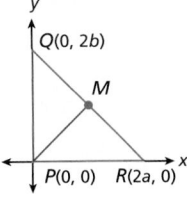

44. Design A *trefoil* is created by constructing a circle at each vertex of an equilateral triangle. The radius of each circle equals the distance from each vertex to the circumcenter of the triangle. If the distance from one vertex to the circumcenter is 14 cm, what is the distance *AB* across the trefoil? **42 cm**

Design LINK

The trefoil shape, as seen in this stained glass window, has been used in design for centuries.

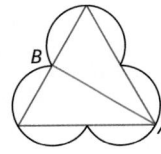

SPIRAL REVIEW

Solve each proportion. *(Previous course)*

45. $\dfrac{t}{26} = \dfrac{10}{65}$ $t = 4$ **46.** $\dfrac{2.5}{1.75} = \dfrac{6}{x}$ $x = 4.2$ **47.** $\dfrac{420}{y} = \dfrac{7}{2}$ $y = 120$

Find each angle measure. *(Lesson 2-6)*

48. m∠*BFE* **125°**   **49.** m∠*BFC* **35°**   **50.** m∠*CFE* **90°**

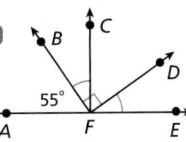

Determine whether each point is on the perpendicular bisector of the segment with endpoints $S(0, 8)$ and $T(4, 0)$. *(Lesson 5-1)*

51. $X(0, 3)$ **yes**   **52.** $Y(-4, 1)$ **yes**   **53.** $Z(-8, -2)$ **no**

Journal

Have students describe how they remember that the circumcenter is the intersection of the perpendicular bisectors and that the incenter is the intersection of the angle bisectors.

ALTERNATIVE ASSESSMENT

Give the students a map of your town. Have them mark their home and two other locations on the map to form a triangle. Have them use perpendicular bisectors to label the circumcenter and use angle bisectors to label the incenter.

Power Presentations with PowerPoint®

5-2 Lesson Quiz

1. $\overline{ED}$, $\overline{FD}$, and $\overline{GD}$ are the perpendicular bisectors of △*ABC*. Find *BD*. **17**

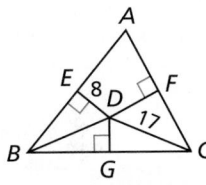

2. $\overline{JP}$, $\overline{KP}$, and $\overline{HP}$ are angle bisectors of △*HJK*. Find the distance from *P* to $\overline{HK}$. **3**

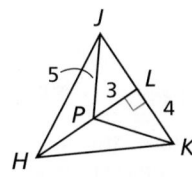

3. Lee's job requires him to travel to *X*, *Y*, and *Z*. Draw a sketch to show where he should buy a home so it is the same distance from all three places.

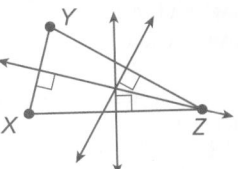

Also available on transparency

5-2 PROBLEM SOLVING

1. A new dog park is being planned. Describe how to find a location for the park so that it is the same distance from three suburbs.
Draw a triangle that has the suburbs as its vertices. Find the circumcenter of the triangle by drawing the perpendicular bisector of each side.

2. A fountain is in a triangular sitting area of a mall, △*ABC*. A diagram shows that the fountain is at the point where the angle bisectors of △*ABC* are concurrent. If the distance from the fountain to one wall is 15 feet, what is the distance from the fountain to another wall? Explain.
15 ft; By the Incenter Thm., the incenter of a triangle is equidistant from the sides of the triangle.

3. A water tower is to be built so that it is the same distance from the cities at *X*, *Y*, and *Z*. Draw a sketch on △*XYZ* to show the location *W* where the water tower should be built. Justify your sketch.
Draw the perpendicular bisectors of $\overline{XY}$, $\overline{YZ}$, and $\overline{ZX}$. By the Circumcenter Thm., *W* is equidistant from *X*, *Y*, and *Z*.

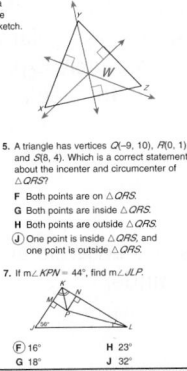

Choose the best answer.

4. The circumcenter of △*FGH* is at (4, −5). If *G* is at (0, 0), which of the following are possible coordinates of *F* and *H*?
  A *F*(0, −8), *H*(10, 0)
  B *F*(0, 8), *H*(−10, 0)
  C *F*(0, −10), *H*(8, 0)
  D *F*(0, 10), *H*(−8, 0)

5. A triangle has vertices *Q*(−9, 10), *R*(0, 1), and *S*(8, 4). Which is a correct statement about the incenter and circumcenter of △*QRS*?
  F Both points are on △*QRS*.
  G Both points are inside △*QRS*.
  H Both points are outside △*QRS*.
  J One point is inside △*QRS*, and one point is outside △*QRS*.

6. $\overline{RT}$ and $\overline{TS}$ are perpendicular bisectors of △*ABC*. What is the perimeter of △*ATC*?
  A 17.2 units
  B 19.4 units
  C 20.9 units
  D 22.4 units

7. If m∠*KPN* = 44°, find m∠*JLP*.
  F 16°   H 23°
  G 18°   J 32°

5-2 CHALLENGE

In Lesson 5-2, you investigated the three perpendicular bisectors of the sides of a triangle and discovered some surprising facts about them. On this page, you will see how coordinate methods can help you prove those facts.

1. Refer to the figure at right. Follow these steps to prove that the perpendicular bisectors of the sides of △*RST* are concurrent. That is, you will prove that all three perpendicular bisectors intersect at a single point.

  a. Write equations for the perpendicular bisectors of $\overline{RS}$, $\overline{ST}$, and $\overline{RT}$. (Hint: If a line having slope *m* passes through a point $P(x_1, y_1)$, then an equation of the line is $y - y_1 = m(x - x_1)$.)

$\overline{RS}$: $y - \dfrac{b}{2} = -\left(\dfrac{a}{b}\right)\left(x - \dfrac{a}{2}\right)$; $\overline{ST}$: $y - \dfrac{b}{2} = -\left(\dfrac{a - c}{b}\right)\left(x - \dfrac{a + c}{2}\right)$;
$\overline{RT}$: $x = \dfrac{c}{2}$

  b. Use a system of equations to find the coordinates of the point where the perpendicular bisectors of $\overline{RS}$ and $\overline{RT}$ intersect.
$\left(\dfrac{c}{2}, \dfrac{a^2 + b^2 - ac}{2b}\right)$

  c. Use a system of equations to find the coordinates of the point where the perpendicular bisectors of $\overline{ST}$ and $\overline{RT}$ intersect.
$\left(\dfrac{c}{2}, \dfrac{a^2 + b^2 - ac}{2b}\right)$

  d. Use the results of parts *b* and *c* to complete the proof.
Since the perpendicular bisectors of $\overline{RS}$ and $\overline{RT}$ intersect in the same point as the perpendicular bisectors of $\overline{ST}$ and $\overline{RT}$, all three lines intersect the same point. Thus the perpendicular bisectors of the sides of △*RST* are concurrent.

2. Let point *Z* be the point of concurrency of the three perpendicular bisectors of the sides of △*RST* above. Follow these steps to prove that *Z* is equidistant from the vertices of △*RST*. In other words, prove that $RZ = SZ = TZ$. Use the Distance Formula to write expressions for $(RZ)^2$, $(SZ)^2$, and $(TZ)^2$.

$(RZ)^2$: $\left(\dfrac{c}{2}\right)^2 + \left(\dfrac{a^2 + b^2 - ac}{2b}\right)^2$;

$(SZ)^2$: $\left(a - \dfrac{c}{2}\right)^2 + \left(b - \dfrac{a^2 + b^2 - ac}{2b}\right)^2$;

$(TZ)^2$: $\left(c - \dfrac{c}{2}\right)^2 + \left(\dfrac{a^2 + b^2 - ac}{2b}\right)^2$

5-3 Organizer

Warm Up

1. What is the name of the point where the angle bisectors of a triangle intersect?   incenter

Find the midpoint of the segment with the given endpoints.

2. $(-1, 6)$ and $(3, 0)$ $(1, 3)$

3. $(-7, 2)$ and $(-3, -8)$ $(-5, -3)$

4. Write an equation of the line containing the points $(3, 1)$ and $(2, 10)$ in point-slope form. $y - 1 = -9(x - 3)$

Also available on transparency

Math Humor

Q: What do you do when it rains?

A: Coincide!

⭐ Geometry TEKS

G.2 Geometric structure*
(A) use constructions to explore attributes of geometric figures ...
(B) make conjectures about ... polygons ...

G.3 Geometric structure*
(B) construct and justify statements about geometric figures ...

G.7 Dimensionality and the geometry of location*
(A) use ... coordinate systems to represent ... figures
(B) ... investigate ... special segments of triangles ...
(C) ... use formulas involving length, slope, and midpoint

* Knowledge and Skills See p. 298.

5-3 Medians and Altitudes of Triangles

⭐ TEKS G.3.B Geometric structure: construct and justify statements about geometric figures and their properties. Also G.2.A, G.2.B, G.7.A, G.7.B, G.7.C

Objectives
Apply properties of medians of a triangle.
Apply properties of altitudes of a triangle.

Vocabulary
median of a triangle
centroid of a triangle
altitude of a triangle
orthocenter of a triangle

Who uses this?
Sculptors who create mobiles of moving objects can use centers of gravity to balance the objects. (See Example 2.)

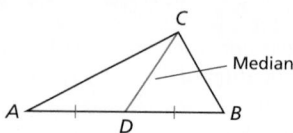

A **median of a triangle** is a segment whose endpoints are a vertex of the triangle and the midpoint of the opposite side.

Median

Every triangle has three medians, and the medians are concurrent, as shown in the construction below.

Construction   Centroid of a Triangle

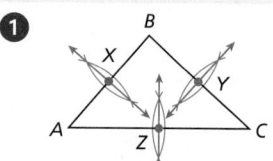
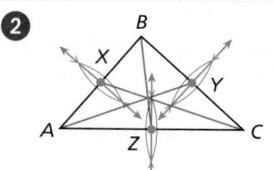
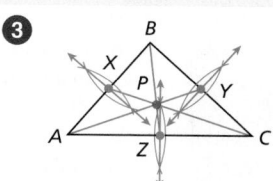

Draw △ABC. Construct the midpoints of $\overline{AB}$, $\overline{BC}$, and $\overline{AC}$. Label the midpoints of the sides X, Y, and Z, respectively.

Draw $\overline{AY}$, $\overline{BZ}$, and $\overline{CX}$. These are the three medians of △ABC.

Label the point where $\overline{AY}$, $\overline{BZ}$, and $\overline{CX}$ intersect as P.

The point of concurrency of the medians of a triangle is the **centroid of the triangle**. The centroid is always inside the triangle. The centroid is also called the *center of gravity* because it is the point where a triangular region will balance.

Know it! Note

Theorem 5-3-1   Centroid Theorem

The centroid of a triangle is located $\frac{2}{3}$ of the distance from each vertex to the midpoint of the opposite side.

$$AP = \frac{2}{3}AY \qquad BP = \frac{2}{3}BZ \qquad CP = \frac{2}{3}CX$$

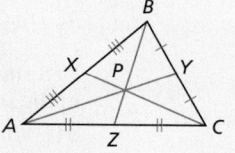

---

1 Introduce

EXPLORATION

5-3 Medians and Altitudes of Triangles

A *median of a triangle* is a segment whose endpoints are a vertex of the triangle and the midpoint of the opposite side.

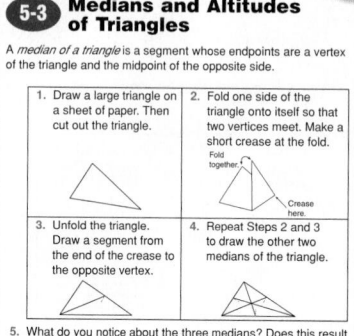

1. Draw a large triangle on a sheet of paper. Then cut out the triangle.

2. Fold one side of the triangle onto itself so that two vertices meet. Make a short crease at the fold.

3. Unfold the triangle. Draw a segment from the end of the crease to the opposite vertex.

4. Repeat Steps 2 and 3 to draw the other two medians of the triangle.

5. What do you notice about the three medians? Does this result apply to your classmates' triangles?

THINK AND DISCUSS

6. **Discuss** whether the intersection of the medians of a triangle (which is called the *centroid*) can be located outside the ...

Motivate

Give groups of students triangles cut out of heavy construction paper. Have each group find the center of gravity of the triangular region by balancing it on the end of a pencil. Explain that this point is the *centroid* of the triangle and that in this lesson they will learn how to find two more points of concurrency—the centroid and the orthocenter.

Explorations and answers are provided in the *Explorations* binder.

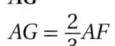 **Using the Centroid to Find Segment Lengths**

In $\triangle ABC$, $AF = 9$, and $GE = 2.4$. Find each length.

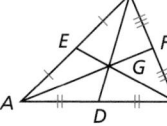

A AG

$AG = \frac{2}{3}AF$	*Centroid Thm.*
$AG = \frac{2}{3}(9)$	*Substitute 9 for AF.*
$AG = 6$	*Simplify.*

B CE

$CG = \frac{2}{3}CE$	*Centroid Thm.*
$CG + GE = CE$	*Seg. Add. Post.*
$\frac{2}{3}CE + GE = CE$	*Substitute $\frac{2}{3}$CE for CG.*
$GE = \frac{1}{3}CE$	*Subtract $\frac{2}{3}$CE from both sides.*
$2.4 = \frac{1}{3}CE$	*Substitute 2.4 for GE.*
$7.2 = CE$	*Multiply both sides by 3.*

 CHECK IT OUT! In $\triangle JKL$, $ZW = 7$, and $LX = 8.1$. Find each length.

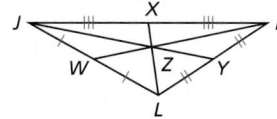

1a. KW **21**

1b. LZ **5.4**

 **Problem-Solving Application**

The diagram shows the plan for a triangular piece of a mobile. Where should the sculptor attach the support so that the triangle is balanced?

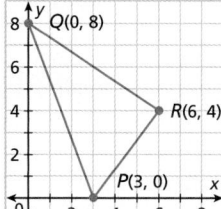

1 Understand the Problem

The **answer** will be the coordinates of the centroid of $\triangle PQR$. The **important information** is the location of the vertices, $P(3, 0)$, $Q(0, 8)$, and $R(6, 4)$.

2 Make a Plan

The centroid of the triangle is the point of intersection of the three medians. So write the equations for two medians and find their point of intersection.

3 Solve

Let M be the midpoint of $\overline{QR}$ and N be the midpoint of $\overline{QP}$.

$$M = \left(\frac{0 + 6}{2}, \frac{8 + 4}{2}\right) = (3, 6) \qquad N = \left(\frac{0 + 3}{2}, \frac{8 + 0}{2}\right) = (1.5, 4)$$

$\overline{PM}$ is vertical. Its equation is $x = 3$. $\overline{RN}$ is horizontal. Its equation is $y = 4$. The coordinates of the centroid are $S(3, 4)$.

COMMON ERROR ALERT

When using the Centroid Theorem, students may identify the wrong part of the median as $\frac{2}{3}$ of the total length. Remind them that the centroid is closer to each side than to the vertex.

Power Presentations with PowerPoint®

Additional Examples

Example 1

In $\triangle LMN$, $RL = 21$, and $SQ = 4$. Find each length.

A. LS **14**

B. NQ **12**

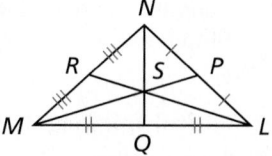

Example 2

A sculptor is shaping a triangular piece of iron that will balance on the point of a cone. At what coordinates will the triangular region balance? **(8, 5)**

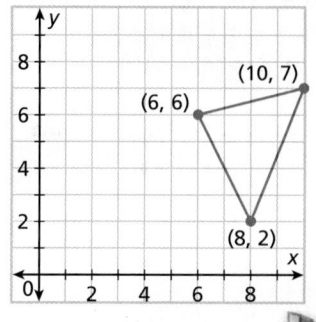

Also available on transparency

INTERVENTION ↔
Questioning Strategies

EXAMPLE 1

• What is the ratio of the segment lengths of each median?

EXAMPLE 2

• How do you find the point at which a triangular region will balance?

 Reading Math The prefix *ortho-* means "perpendicular" or "straight." To help students remember this, explain that an orthodontist straightens teeth with braces. The altitude of a triangle is straight (vertical) in relation to the side it is perpendicular to.

---

2 Teach

Guided Instruction

Define the median of a triangle and discuss that every triangle has three medians, which intersect at the centroid. Explain that the centroid is also called the *center of gravity* and that the Centroid Theorem can be used to find segment lengths in triangles. Define the altitude of a triangle and explain how every triangle has three altitudes, which intersect at the orthocenter. Show students how to find the orthocenter of a triangle when given its vertices.

Reaching All Learners
Through Modeling

Have students cut out a large scalene acute triangle. Have them construct the centroid and the orthocenter. Then have students hang the triangle from string at each point to demonstrate which one allows the triangular region to balance.

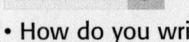

INTERVENTION ◀▬▶
Questioning Strategies

EXAMPLE **3**

- How do you write the equations of a horizontal line and a vertical line?

Teaching Tip **Inclusion** Remind students that two of the altitudes of a right triangle are its legs.

Teaching Tip **Critical Thinking** To find the point that is $\frac{2}{3}$ of the distance from (2, 7) to (5, −11), find the difference between the x-coordinates (3) and the y-coordinates (−18). Multiply each difference by $\frac{2}{3}$ and add this to the coordinates of the first point. $\frac{2}{3}(3) = 2$, and $\frac{2}{3}(−18) = −12$. Since 2 + 2 = 4 and 7 + −12 = −5, the point is (4, −5).

---

4 Look Back

Let L be the midpoint of $\overline{PR}$. The equation for $\overline{QL}$ is $y = -\frac{4}{3}x + 8$, which intersects x = 3 at S(3, 4).

 **CHECK IT OUT!** **2.** Find the average of the x-coordinates and the average of the y-coordinates of the vertices of △PQR. Make a conjecture about the centroid of a triangle.

Helpful Hint

The height of a triangle is the length of an altitude.

An **altitude of a triangle** is a perpendicular segment from a vertex to the line containing the opposite side. Every triangle has three altitudes. An altitude can be inside, outside, or on the triangle.

In △QRS, altitude $\overline{QY}$ is inside the triangle, but $\overline{RX}$ and $\overline{SZ}$ are not. Notice that the lines containing the altitudes are concurrent at P. This point of concurrency is the **orthocenter of the triangle**.

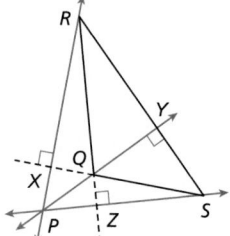

EXAMPLE 3 **Finding the Orthocenter**

Find the orthocenter of △JKL with vertices J(−4, 2), K(−2, 6), and L(2, 2).

 **Algebra**

Step 1 Graph the triangle.

Step 2 Find an equation of the line containing the altitude from K to $\overline{JL}$.

Since $\overleftrightarrow{JL}$ is horizontal, the altitude is vertical. The line containing it must pass through K(−2, 6), so the equation of the line is x = −2.

2. 3; 4; possible answer: the x-coordinate of the centroid is the average of the x-coordinates of the vertices of the △, and the y-coordinate of the centroid is the average of the y-coordinates of the vertices of the △.

3. Possible answer: An equation of the altitude to $\overline{JK}$ is $y = -\frac{1}{2}x + 3$. It is true that $4 = -\frac{1}{2}(−2) + 3$, so (−2, 4) is a solution of this equation. Therefore this altitude passes through the orthocenter.

Step 3 Find an equation of the line containing the altitude from J to $\overline{KL}$.

$$\text{slope of } \overleftrightarrow{KL} = \frac{2 - 6}{2 - (-2)} = -1$$

The slope of a line perpendicular to $\overleftrightarrow{KL}$ is 1. This line must pass through J(−4, 2).

$y - y_1 = m(x - x_1)$	*Point-slope form*
$y - 2 = 1[x - (-4)]$	*Substitute 2 for y_1, 1 for m, and −4 for x_1.*
$y - 2 = x + 4$	*Distribute 1.*
$y = x + 6$	*Add 2 to both sides.*

Step 4 Solve the system to find the coordinates of the orthocenter.

$$\begin{cases} x = -2 \\ y = x + 6 \end{cases}$$

$y = -2 + 6 = 4$ *Substitute −2 for x.*

The coordinates of the orthocenter are (−2, 4).

 **CHECK IT OUT!** **3.** Show that the altitude to $\overline{JK}$ passes through the orthocenter of △JKL.

---

3 Close

Summarize

Review with students that the centroid of a triangle is the point of concurrency of the medians of the triangle. Remind students that by the Centroid Theorem, the centroid is located $\frac{2}{3}$ of the distance from each vertex to the midpoint of the opposite side. Discuss that the three altitudes of a triangle intersect at the orthocenter of the triangle.

ONGOING ASSESSMENT

and INTERVENTION ◀▬▶

Diagnose Before the Lesson
5-3 Warm Up, TE p. 314

Monitor During the Lesson
Check It Out! Exercises, SE pp. 315–316
Questioning Strategies, TE pp. 315–316

Assess After the Lesson
5-3 Lesson Quiz, TE p. 320
Alternative Assessment, TE p. 320

THINK AND DISCUSS

1. Draw a triangle in which a median and an altitude are the same segment. What type of triangle is it?

2. Draw a triangle in which an altitude is also a side of the triangle. What type of triangle is it?

3. The centroid of a triangle divides each median into two segments. What is the ratio of the two lengths of each median?

4. **GET ORGANIZED** Copy and complete the graphic organizer. Fill in the blanks to make each statement true.

	Centroid	Orthocenter
Definition	The point of concurrency of the _?_	The point of concurrency of the _?_
Location (Inside, Outside, or On)	_?_ the triangle	Can be _?_ the triangle

Answers to *Think and Discuss*

1. Possible answer: The △ is isosc.

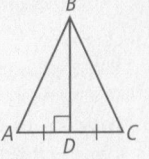

2. Possible answer: The △ is a rt △.

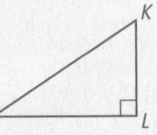

3. The ratio of the length of the longer seg. to the length of the shorter seg. is 2:1.

4. See p. A5.

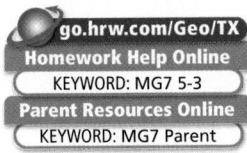

go.hrw.com/Geo/TX
Homework Help Online
KEYWORD: MG7 5-3
Parent Resources Online
KEYWORD: MG7 Parent

5-3 Exercises

GUIDED PRACTICE

Vocabulary Apply the vocabulary from this lesson to answer each question.

1. The ___?___ of a triangle is located $\frac{2}{3}$ of the distance from each vertex to the midpoint of the opposite side. (*centroid* or *orthocenter*) **centroid**

2. The ___?___ of a triangle is perpendicular to the line containing a side. (*altitude* or *median*) **altitude**

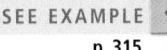
SEE EXAMPLE **1**
p. 315

$VX = 204$, and $RW = 104$. Find each length.

3. VW **136**   **4.** WX **68**

5. RY **156**   **6.** WY **52**

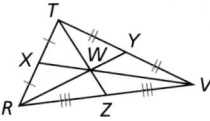

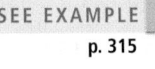
SEE EXAMPLE **2**
p. 315

7. **Design** The diagram shows a plan for a piece of a mobile. A chain will hang from the centroid of the triangle. At what coordinates should the artist attach the chain? **(4, 2)**

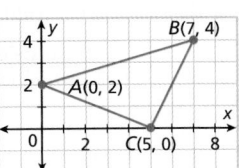

SEE EXAMPLE **3**
p. 316

Multi-Step Find the orthocenter of a triangle with the given vertices.

8. $K(2, -2)$, $L(4, 6)$, $M(8, -2)$ **(4, −1)**

9. $U(-4, -9)$, $V(-4, 6)$, $W(5, -3)$ **(2, −3)**

10. $P(-5, 8)$, $Q(4, 5)$, $R(-2, 5)$ **(−5, −4)**

11. $C(-1, -3)$, $D(-1, 2)$, $E(9, 2)$ **(−1, 2)**

Assignment Guide

Assign *Guided Practice* exercises as necessary.

If you finished Examples **1–3**
Basic 12–32, 34–37, 40–43, 46–51
Average 12–37, 39–43, 45–51
Advanced 12–51

Homework Quick Check
Quickly check key concepts.
Exercises: 12, 16, 18, 22, 28

 TAKS Practice

Grades 9–11	Exercises
Obj. 2	29–32
Obj. 4	46
Obj. 7	27, 28, 40, 45
Obj. 8	26
Obj. 10	34–37, 46

33. Possible answer:

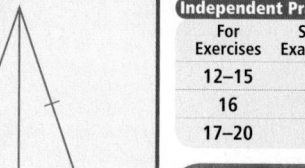

⊥ bisector of the base; bisector of the vertex ∠; median to the base; altitude to the base

34.

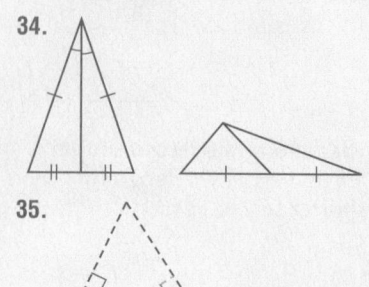

35.

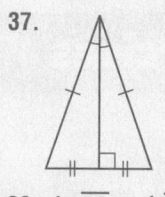

37.

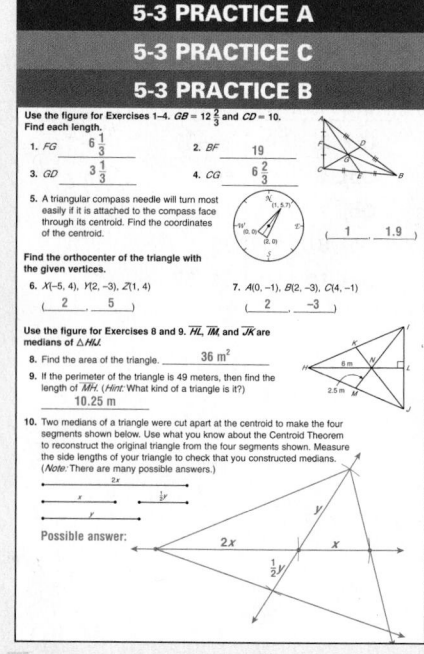

38. 1. $\overline{PS}$ and $\overline{RT}$ are medians of △PQR. $\overline{PS} \cong \overline{RT}$ (Given)
2. $PS = RT$ (Def. of ≅ segs.)
3. $\frac{2}{3}PS = \frac{2}{3}RT$ (Mult. Prop. of =)
4. $PZ = \frac{2}{3}PS$, $RZ = \frac{2}{3}RT$ (Centroid Thm.)
5. $PZ = RZ$ (Subst.)
6. $\overline{PZ} \cong \overline{RZ}$ (Def. of ≅ segs.)
7. $\angle SPR \cong \angle TRP$ (Isosc. △ Thm.)
8. $\overline{PR} \cong \overline{PR}$ (Reflex. Prop. of ≅)
9. △PTR ≅ △RSP (SAS)
10. $\angle QPR \cong \angle QRP$ (CPCTC)
11. $\overline{PQ} \cong \overline{RQ}$ (Conv. of Isosc. △ Thm.)
12. △PQR is an isosc. △. (Def. of isosc. △)

39. See p. A19.

5-3 PRACTICE A

5-3 PRACTICE C

5-3 PRACTICE B

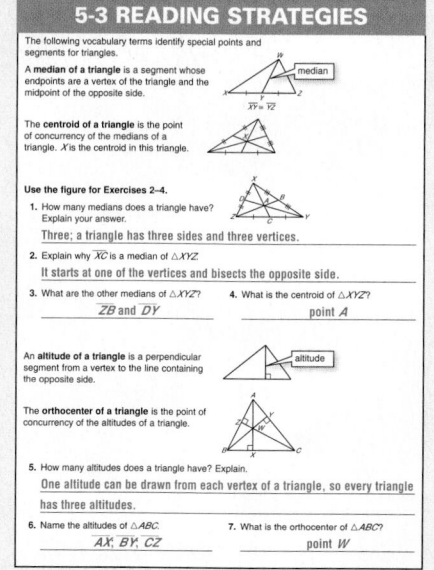

PRACTICE AND PROBLEM SOLVING

$PA = 2.9$, and $HC = 10.8$. Find each length.

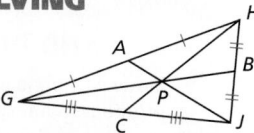

12. PC **3.6**   **13.** HP **7.2**

14. JA **8.7**   **15.** JP **5.8**

16. Design In the plan for a table, the triangular top has coordinates $(0, 10)$, $(4, 0)$, and $(8, 14)$. The tabletop will rest on a single support placed beneath it. Where should the support be attached so that the table is balanced? **(4, 8)**

Multi-Step Find the orthocenter of a triangle with the given vertices.

17. $X(-2, -2)$, $Y(6, 10)$, $Z(6, -6)$ **(0, −2)**   **18.** $G(-2, 5)$, $H(6, 5)$, $J(4, -1)$ **(4, 3)**

19. $R(-8, 9)$, $S(-2, 9)$, $T(-2, 1)$ **(−2, 9)**   **20.** $A(4, -3)$, $B(8, 5)$, $C(8, -8)$ **(−2, −3)**

Find each measure.

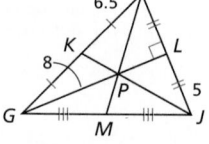

21. GL **12**   **22.** PL **4**

23. HL **5**   **24.** GJ **13**

25. perimeter of △GHJ   **26.** area of △GHJ
36 units   **60 square units**

Algebra Find the centroid of a triangle with the given vertices.

27. $A(0, -4)$, $B(14, 6)$, $C(16, -8)$ **(10, −2)**   **28.** $X(8, -1)$, $Y(2, 7)$, $Z(5, -3)$ **(5, 1)**

Find each length.

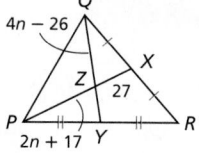

29. PZ **54**   **30.** PX **81**

31. QZ **48**   **32.** YZ **24**

33. Critical Thinking Draw an isosceles triangle and its line of symmetry. What are four other names for this segment?

Tell whether each statement is *sometimes, always,* or *never* true. Support your answer with a sketch.

34. A median of a triangle bisects one of the angles. **S**

35. If one altitude of a triangle is in the triangle's exterior, then a second altitude is also in the triangle's exterior. **A**

36. The centroid of a triangle lies in its exterior. **N**

37. In an isosceles triangle, the altitude and median from the vertex angle are the same line as the bisector of the vertex angle. **A**

38. Write a two-column proof.

Given: $\overline{PS}$ and $\overline{RT}$ are medians of △PQR. $\overline{PS} \cong \overline{RT}$
Prove: △PQR is an isosceles triangle.

Plan: Show that △PTR ≅ △RSP and use CPCTC to conclude that $\angle QPR \cong \angle QRP$.

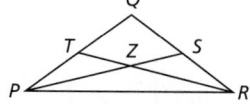

39. Write About It Draw a large triangle on a sheet of paper and cut it out. Find the centroid by paper folding. Try to balance the shape on the tip of your pencil at a point other than the centroid. Now try to balance the shape at its centroid. Explain why the centroid is also called the center of gravity.

Math History

In 1678, Giovanni Ceva published his famous theorem that states the conditions necessary for three *Cevians* (segments from a vertex of a triangle to the opposite side) to be concurrent. The medians and altitudes of a triangle meet these conditions.

5-3 READING STRATEGIES

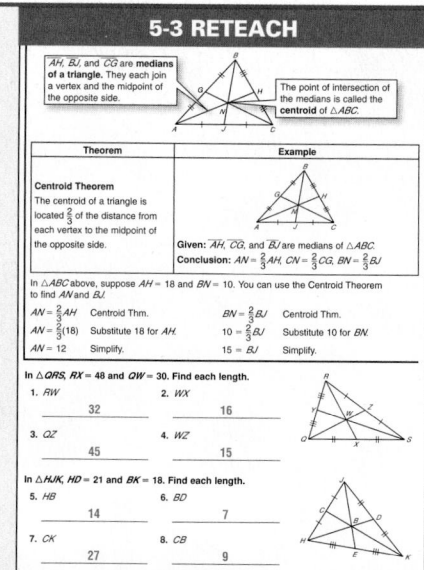

The following vocabulary terms identify special points and segments for triangles.

A **median of a triangle** is a segment whose endpoints are a vertex of the triangle and the midpoint of the opposite side.

The **centroid of a triangle** is the point of concurrency of the medians of a triangle. X is the centroid in this triangle.

Use the figure for Exercises 2–4.

1. How many medians does a triangle have? Explain your answer.
   Three; a triangle has three sides and three vertices.

2. Explain why $\overline{XC}$ is a median of △XYZ.
   It starts at one of the vertices and bisects the opposite side.

3. What are the other medians of △XYZ?   4. What is the centroid of △XYZ?
   $\overline{ZB}$ and $\overline{DY}$ **point A**

An **altitude of a triangle** is a perpendicular segment from a vertex to the line containing the opposite side.

The **orthocenter of a triangle** is the point of concurrency of the altitudes of a triangle.

5. How many altitudes does a triangle have? Explain.
   One altitude can be drawn from each vertex of a triangle, so every triangle has three altitudes.

6. Name the altitudes of △ABC.   7. What is the orthocenter of △ABC?
   $\overline{AX}$, $\overline{BY}$, $\overline{CZ}$ **point W**

5-3 RETEACH

$\overline{AH}$, $\overline{BJ}$, and $\overline{CG}$ are **medians of a triangle.** They each join a vertex and the midpoint of the opposite side.

The point of intersection of the medians is called the **centroid** of △ABC.

Theorem	Example
Centroid Theorem The centroid of a triangle is located $\frac{2}{3}$ of the distance from each vertex to the midpoint of the opposite side.	**Given:** $\overline{AH}$, $\overline{CG}$, and $\overline{BJ}$ are medians of △ABC. **Conclusion:** $AN = \frac{2}{3}AH$, $CN = \frac{2}{3}CG$, $BN = \frac{2}{3}BJ$

In △ABC above, suppose $AH = 18$ and $BN = 10$. You can use the Centroid Theorem to find AN and BN.

$AN = \frac{2}{3}AH$ Centroid Thm. $BN = \frac{2}{3}BJ$ Centroid Thm.
$AN = \frac{2}{3}(18)$ Substitute 18 for AH. $10 = \frac{2}{3}BJ$ Substitute 10 for BN.
$AN = 12$ Simplify. $15 = BJ$ Simplify.

In △QRS, $RX = 48$ and $QW = 30$. Find each length.

1. RW   **32**   2. WX   **16**

3. QZ   **45**   4. WZ   **15**

In △HJK, $HD = 21$ and $BK = 18$. Find each length.

5. HB   **14**   6. BD   **7**

7. CK   **27**   8. CB   **9**

MULTI-STEP TAKS PREP

40. This problem will prepare you for the Multi-Step TAKS Prep on page 328.

The towns of Davis, El Monte, and Fairview have the coordinates shown in the table, where each unit of the coordinate plane represents one mile. A music company has stores in each city and a distribution warehouse at the centroid of △DEF.

City	Location
Davis	D(0, 0)
El Monte	E(0, 8)
Fairview	F(8, 0)

a. What are the coordinates of the warehouse?

b. Find the distance from the warehouse to the Davis store. Round your answer to the nearest tenth of a mile. **3.8 mi**

c. A straight road connects El Monte and Fairview. What is the distance from the warehouse to the road? **1.9 mi**

a. $\left(2\frac{2}{3}, 2\frac{2}{3}\right)$

TEST PREP

41. $\overline{QT}$, $\overline{RV}$, and $\overline{SW}$ are medians of △QRS. Which statement is NOT necessarily true?

Ⓐ $QP = \frac{2}{3}QT$ Ⓒ $RT = ST$

Ⓑ $RP = 2PV$ Ⓓ $QT = SW$

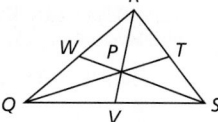

42. Suppose that the orthocenter of a triangle lies outside the triangle. Which points of concurrency are inside the triangle?

I. incenter **II.** circumcenter **III.** centroid

Ⓕ I and II only Ⓗ II and III only

Ⓖ I and III only Ⓙ I, II, and III

43. In the diagram, which of the following correctly describes $\overleftrightarrow{LN}$?

Ⓐ Altitude Ⓒ Median

Ⓑ Angle bisector Ⓓ Perpendicular bisector

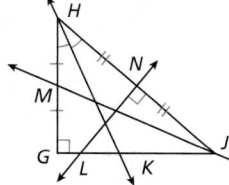

CHALLENGE AND EXTEND

44. Draw an equilateral triangle.

a. Explain why the perpendicular bisector of any side contains the vertex opposite that side.

b. Explain why the perpendicular bisector through any vertex also contains the median, the altitude, and the angle bisector through that vertex.

c. Explain why the incenter, circumcenter, centroid, and orthocenter are the same point.

45. Use coordinates to show that the lines containing the altitudes of a triangle are concurrent.

a. Find the slopes of $\overline{RS}$, $\overline{ST}$, and $\overline{RT}$.

b. Find the slopes of lines ℓ, m, and n.

c. Write equations for lines ℓ, m, and n.

d. Solve a system of equations to find the point P where lines ℓ and m intersect.

e. Show that line n contains P.

f. What conclusion can you draw?

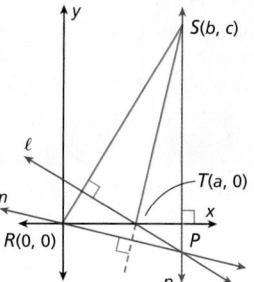

5-3 Medians and Altitudes of Triangles **319**

5-3 PROBLEM SOLVING

1. The diagram shows the coordinates of the vertices of a triangular patio umbrella. The umbrella will rest on a pole that will support it. Where should the pole be attached so that the umbrella is balanced?

$\left(4, \frac{14}{3}\right)$

2. In a plan for a triangular wind chime, the coordinates of the vertices are J(10, 2), K(7, 6), and L(12, 10). At what coordinates should the manufacturer attach the chain from which it will hang in order for the chime to be balanced?

$\left(\frac{29}{3}, 6\right)$

3. Triangle PQR has vertices at P(−3, 5), Q(−1, 7), and R(3, 1). Find the coordinates of the orthocenter and the centroid.

$\left(-1\frac{4}{5}, 5\frac{4}{5}\right); \left(-\frac{1}{3}, 4\frac{1}{3}\right)$

Choose the best answer.

4. A triangle has coordinates at A(0, 6), B(8, 6), and C(5, 0). $\overline{CD}$ is a median of the triangle, and $\overline{CE}$ is an altitude of the triangle. Which is a true statement?

A The coordinates of D and E are the same.

B The distance between D and E is 1 unit.

C The distance between D and E is 2 units.

D D is on the triangle, and E is outside the triangle.

5. Lines j and k contain medians of △DEF. Find y and z.

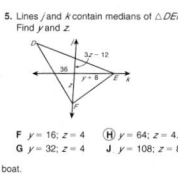

F y = 16; z = 4 **H** y = 64; z = 4.8

G y = 32; z = 4 J y = 108; z = 8

6. An inflatable triangular raft is towed behind a boat. The raft is an equilateral triangle. To maintain balance, the seat is at the centroid B of the triangle. What is AB, the distance from the seat to the tow rope? Round to the nearest tenth.

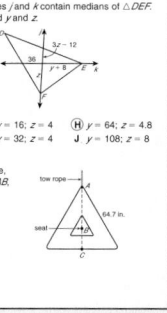

A 18.7 in.

B 37.4 in.

C 43.1 in.

D 56.0 in.

5-3 CHALLENGE

The **Fermat point**, named after seventeenth century mathematician Pierre de Fermat, is a special point in an acute triangle that can be found by using the following steps.

Step 1 Draw an acute triangle ABC.

Step 2 Construct an equilateral triangle on each side of △ABC and label the new vertices A′, B′, C′ as shown.

Step 3 Connect the opposite vertices by drawing $\overline{AA'}$, $\overline{BB'}$, and $\overline{CC'}$.

Step 4 The point of concurrency of these segments is the Fermat point of △ABC. Label this point F.

Use the figure above for Exercises 1 and 2.

1. Make a conjecture comparing the lengths of $\overline{AA'}$, $\overline{BB'}$, and $\overline{CC'}$. Verify your conjecture by measuring the segments.

The segments have equal lengths.

2. Find the sum of AF, BF, and CF. Compare this sum to the lengths of the segments that you found in Exercise 1.

The sum equals the segment lengths.

Point F is the Fermat point in △GHJ.

3. Find the sum of the distances from the Fermat point to each vertex of △GHJ. Round to the nearest tenth of a centimeter.

Possible answer: 5.8 cm

4. Draw two more points inside △GHJ and label the points X and Y. Then find each sum: GX + HX + JX and GY + HY + JY. Compare the sums to the sum you found by using the Fermat point.

These sums are both greater than the sum found by using the Fermat point.

5. Make a conjecture about the sum of the distances from the Fermat point to the vertices of a triangle, compared to the sum of the distances from any point to the vertices of a triangle.

It is the least sum that is possible from any point in a triangle to each of the three vertices.

6. Draw an acute triangle. Locate the Fermat point. Repeat Exercises 3 and 4. How do the results compare to the conjecture you made in Exercise 5?

The sums found using X and Y are both greater than the sum found by using the Fermat point. This verifies the conjecture.

COMMON ERROR
ALERT

For **Exercises 29–32**, students may assume that the medians $\overline{PX}$ and $\overline{QY}$ are congruent. Remind them that this is true only if $\overline{QR} \cong \overline{PR}$. They cannot assume from the diagram that the triangle is isosceles.

MULTI-STEP TAKS PREP **Exercise 40** involves finding the centroid of a triangle. This exercise prepares students for the Multi-Step TAKS Prep on page 328.

TEST PREP DOCTOR ⊕ If students have difficulty with **Exercise 42**, have them draw a triangle whose orthocenter is in the exterior and then sketch the other points of concurrency.

Answers

44.

a. Possible answer: △ABC is equil., and ℓ is the ⊥ bisector of $\overline{BC}$. Since △ABC is equil., $\overline{AB} \cong \overline{AC}$ by def. So AB = AC by the def. of ≅ segs. Therefore by the Conv. of the ⊥ Bisector Thm., A is on line ℓ. Similarly, B is on the ⊥ bisector of $\overline{AC}$, and C is on the ⊥ bisector of $\overline{AB}$.

b. Possible answer: By the def. of ⊥ bisector, $\overline{BD} \cong \overline{CD}$. So D is the mdpt. of $\overline{BC}$ by def., and $\overline{AD}$ is a median of △ABC by the def. of median. Therefore ℓ contains the median of △ABC through A. Also by the def. of ⊥ bisector, $\overline{AD} \perp \overline{BC}$. So $\overline{AD}$ is an altitude of △ABC by the def. Therefore ℓ contains the altitude of △ABC through A. Again by the def. of ⊥ bisector, $\overline{BD} \cong \overline{CD}$. $\overline{AB} \cong \overline{AC}$ by the def. of equil., and $\overline{AD} \cong \overline{AD}$ by the Reflex. Prop. of ≅. So △ABD ≅ △ACD by SSS. Then ∠DAB ≅ ∠DAC by CPCTC, and $\overrightarrow{AD}$ is the bisector of ∠BAC by the def. of ∠ bisector. Therefore ℓ contains the ∠ bisector of △ABC through A. The same reasoning can be applied to the other 2 ⊥ bisectors.

44c, 45. See p. A19.

Lesson 5-3 **319**

Teaching Tip **Communicating Math** In Exercises 47 and 48, remind students that for a biconditional to be true, both the conditional and its converse must be true.

Journal

Have students explain how to find the distance from the centroid to the side of a triangle when the length of the median to that side is given.

ALTERNATIVE ASSESSMENT

Pair students. Have each student write the coordinates of the vertices of a right triangle. Have them exchange papers and find the coordinates of the centroid and orthocenter of their partner's triangle. Then have them use the coordinates to verify the Centroid Theorem.

Power Presentations with PowerPoint®

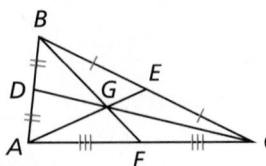
5-3 Lesson Quiz

Use the figure for Items 1–3. In △ABC, AE = 12, DG = 7, and BG = 9. Find each length.

1. AG   8

2. GC   14

3. BF   13.5

For Items 4 and 5, use △MNP with vertices M(−4, −2), N(6, −2), and P(−2, 10). Find the coordinates of each point.

4. the centroid   (0, 2)

5. the orthocenter $\left(-2, -\frac{2}{3}\right)$

Also available on transparency

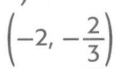

SPIRAL REVIEW

46. At a baseball game, a bag of peanuts costs $0.75 more than a bag of popcorn. If a family purchases 5 bags of peanuts and 3 bags of popcorn for $21.75, how much does one bag of peanuts cost? *(Previous course)* **$3.00**

Determine if each biconditional is true. If false, give a counterexample. *(Lesson 2-4)*

47. F; possible answer: a rectangle with width 5 and length 8

47. The area of a rectangle is 40 cm² if and only if the length of the rectangle is 4 cm and the width of the rectangle is 10 cm.

48. A nonzero number n is positive if and only if $-n$ is negative. **T**

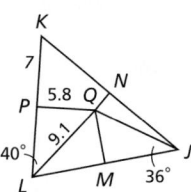

$\overline{NQ}$, $\overline{QP}$, and $\overline{QM}$ are perpendicular bisectors of △JKL. Find each measure. *(Lesson 5-2)*

49. KL **14.0**   **50.** QJ **9.1**   **51.** m∠JQL **108°**

Construction Orthocenter of a Triangle

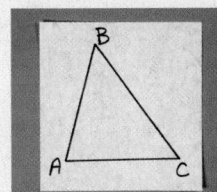
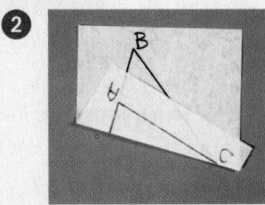
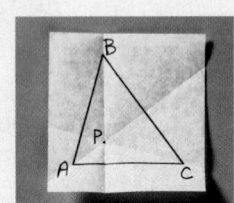

① Draw a large scalene acute triangle ABC on a piece of patty paper.

② Find the altitude of each side by folding the side so that it overlaps itself and so that the fold intersects the opposite vertex.

③ Mark the point where the three lines containing the altitudes intersect and label it P. P is the orthocenter of △ABC.

1. Repeat the construction for a scalene obtuse triangle and a scalene right triangle.
Check students' constructions.

2. Make a conjecture about the location of the orthocenter in an acute, an obtuse, and a right triangle.

Career Path

go.hrw.com/Geo/TX
Career Resources Online
KEYWORD: MG7 Career

Q: What high school math classes did you take?
A: Algebra 1, Geometry, and Statistics.

Q: What type of training did you receive?
A: In high school, I took classes in electricity, electronics, and drafting. I began an apprenticeship program last year to prepare for the exam to get my license.

Q: How do you use math?
A: Determining the locations of outlets and circuits on blueprints requires good spatial sense. I also use ratios and proportions, calculate distances, work with formulas, and estimate job costs.

Alex Peralta
Electrician

Answers to Construction

2. Possible answer: The orthocenter of an acute △ is inside the △. The orthocenter of an obtuse △ is outside the △. The orthocenter of a rt. △ is the vertex of the rt. ∠.

5-3 Technology LAB

Special Points in Triangles

In this lab you will use geometry software to explore properties of the four points of concurrency you have studied.

 TEKS G.2.A Geometric structure: use constructions to explore attributes of geometric figures and to make conjectures about geometric relationships. Also G.9.B

Use with Lesson 5-3

go.hrw.com/Geo/TX
Lab Resources Online
KEYWORD: MG7 Lab5

Activity

1. Construct a triangle.

2. Construct the perpendicular bisector of each side of the triangle. Construct the point of intersection of these three lines. This is the circumcenter of the triangle. Label it *U* and hide the perpendicular bisectors.

3. In the same triangle, construct the bisector of each angle. Construct the point of intersection of these three lines. This is the incenter of the triangle. Label it *I* and hide the angle bisectors.

4. In the same triangle, construct the midpoint of each side. Then construct the three medians. Construct the point of intersection of these three lines. Label the centroid *C* and hide the medians.

5. In the same triangle, construct the altitude to each side. Construct the point of intersection of these three lines. Label the orthocenter *O* and hide the altitudes.

6. Move a vertex of the triangle and observe the positions of the four points of concurrency. In 1765, Swiss mathematician Leonhard Euler showed that three of these points are always collinear. The line containing them is called the *Euler line*.

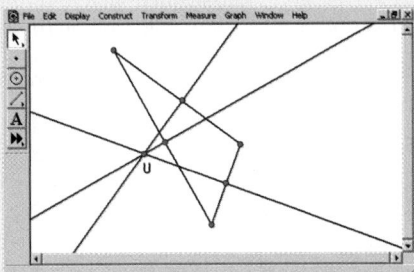

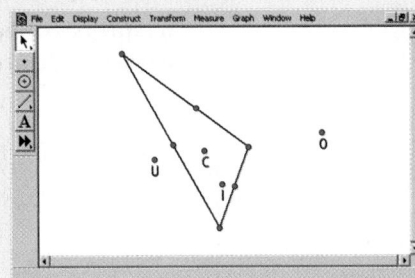

Try This

1. Which three points of concurrency lie on the Euler line? the circumcenter, the orthocenter, and the centroid

2. **Make a Conjecture** Which point on the Euler line is always between the other two? Measure the distances between the points. Make a conjecture about the relationship of the distances between these three points.

3. **Make a Conjecture** Move a vertex of the triangle until all four points of concurrency are collinear. In what type of triangle are all four points of concurrency on the Euler line? isosceles triangle

4. **Make a Conjecture** Find a triangle in which all four points of concurrency coincide. What type of triangle has this special property? equilateral triangle

Answers to *Try This*

2. The centroid; possible answer: the distance from the centroid to the orthocenter is twice the distance from the centroid to the circumcenter; that is, $CO = 2CU$.

Technology LAB Organizer
Use with Lesson 5-3

Pacing:
Traditional 1 day
Block $\frac{1}{2}$ day

Objective: Use special points in triangles to explore Euler's line.

Materials: geometry software

 **Online Edition**
PREMIER **TechKeys**

 Countdown to TAKS Week 10

Teach
Discuss

Discuss what the four points of concurrency are and have students make a conjecture about which of them lie on the Euler line.

Close
Key Concept

The circumcenter, centroid, and orthocenter of a triangle are always collinear.

Assessment

Journal Have students explain which points of concurrency lie on the Euler line.

 Geometry TEKS

G.2 Geometric structure*
(A) use constructions to explore attributes of geometric figures and to make conjectures …

G.9 Congruence and the geometry of size*
(B) formulate and test conjectures about … polygons and their component parts …

***Knowledge and Skills** See p. 298.

Objective: Prove and use properties of triangle midsegments.

Technology Lab
In *Texas Lab Manual*

Online Edition
Tutorial Videos

Countdown to TAKS Week 11

Power Presentations
with PowerPoint®

Warm Up

Use the points $A(2, 2)$, $B(12, 2)$, and $C(4, 8)$ for Exercises 1–5.

1. Find X and Y, the midpoints of $\overline{AC}$ and $\overline{CB}$. $(3, 5)$, $(8, 5)$

2. Find XY.   5

3. Find AB.   10

4. Find the slope of $\overline{AB}$.   0

5. Find the slope of $\overline{XY}$.   0

6. What is the slope of a line parallel to $3x + 2y = 12$?
$-\frac{3}{2}$

Also available on transparency

Math Humor

Q: What did the visitor from Planet Metric demand?

A: "Take me to your liter!"

★ Geometry TEKS

G.5 Geometric patterns*
(A) … develop … expressions representing geometric properties

G.7 Dimensionality and the geometry of location*
(B) … investigate … special segments of triangles …

G.9 Congruence and the geometry of size*
(B) formulate and test conjectures about … polygons … based on … concrete models
Also G.2.A, G.2.B, G.3.B
* **Knowledge and Skills** See p. 298.
Blue text indicates coverage in TE.

5-4 The Triangle Midsegment Theorem

TEKS G.7.B Dimensionality and the geometry of location: use slopes and equations of lines to investigate… special segments of triangles and other polygons.

Objective
Prove and use properties of triangle midsegments.

Vocabulary
midsegment of a triangle

Also G.2.A, G.2.B, G.3.B, G.5.A, G.9.B

Why learn this?

You can use triangle midsegments to make indirect measurements of distances, such as the distance across a volcano. (See Example 3.)

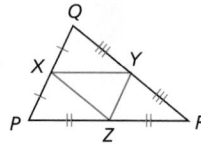

A **midsegment of a triangle** is a segment that joins the midpoints of two sides of the triangle. Every triangle has three midsegments, which form the *midsegment triangle*.

Midsegments: $\overline{XY}$, $\overline{YZ}$, $\overline{ZX}$
Midsegment triangle: $\triangle XYZ$

EXAMPLE 1   Examining Midsegments in the Coordinate Plane

In $\triangle GHJ$, show that midsegment $\overline{KL}$ is parallel to $\overline{GJ}$ and that $KL = \frac{1}{2}GJ$.

Step 1 Find the coordinates of K and L.

$$\text{mdpt. of } \overline{GH} = \left(\frac{-7 + (-5)}{2}, \frac{-2 + 6}{2}\right)$$
$$= (-6, 2)$$

$$\text{mdpt. of } \overline{HJ} = \left(\frac{-5 + 1}{2}, \frac{6 + 2}{2}\right) = (-2, 4)$$

Step 2 Compare the slopes of $\overline{KL}$ and $\overline{GJ}$.

$$\text{slope of } \overline{KL} = \frac{4 - 2}{-2 - (-6)} = \frac{1}{2}$$

$$\text{slope of } \overline{GJ} = \frac{2 - (-2)}{1 - (-7)} = \frac{1}{2}$$

Since the slopes are the same, $\overline{KL} \parallel \overline{GJ}$.

Step 3 Compare the lengths of $\overline{KL}$ and $\overline{GJ}$.

$$KL = \sqrt{\left[-2 - (-6)\right]^2 + (4 - 2)^2} = 2\sqrt{5}$$

$$GJ = \sqrt{\left[1 - (-7)\right]^2 + \left[2 - (-2)\right]^2} = 4\sqrt{5}$$

Since $2\sqrt{5} = \frac{1}{2}\left(4\sqrt{5}\right)$, $KL = \frac{1}{2}GJ$.

1. $M(1, 1)$; $N(3, 4)$;
slope of $\overline{MN} = \frac{3}{2}$;
slope of $\overline{RS} = \frac{3}{2}$;
since the slopes are the same, $\overline{MN} \parallel \overline{RS}$.
$MN = \sqrt{13}$;
$RS = \sqrt{52} = 2\sqrt{13}$;
the length of $\overline{MN}$ is half the length of $\overline{RS}$.

CHECK IT OUT!   **1.** The vertices of $\triangle RST$ are $R(-7, 0)$, $S(-3, 6)$, and $T(9, 2)$. M is the midpoint of $\overline{RT}$, and N is the midpoint of $\overline{ST}$. Show that $\overline{MN} \parallel \overline{RS}$ and $MN = \frac{1}{2}RS$.

---

1 Introduce

EXPLORATION

5-4 The Triangle Midsegment Theorem

A *midsegment* of a triangle is a segment that joins the midpoints of two sides of the triangle. Use geometry software to explore triangle midsegments.

1. Construct a triangle. Label the vertices A, B, and C.

2. Select $\overline{AB}$ and construct its midpoint. Do the same for $\overline{AC}$. Label the midpoints as shown.

3. Draw the midsegment $\overline{DE}$. Measure the lengths of $\overline{DE}$ and $\overline{BC}$.

4. Measure $\angle ADE$ and $\angle ABC$.

5. Drag the sides and vertices of $\triangle ABC$ to change its shape. How are the lengths of $\overline{DE}$ and $\overline{BC}$ related?

6. What do you notice about m$\angle ADE$ and m$\angle ABC$?

THINK AND DISCUSS

7. Describe how the length of a midsegment is related to the

Motivate

Have students cut a large scalene triangle from heavy paper. Have them construct the midpoints of two sides and connect them, forming a *midsegment*. Then have them cut along this segment to form a triangle and a trapezoid. Have them rotate the small triangle and place it next to the trapezoid to form a parallelogram. Ask students to make conjectures about the relationship between the midsegment and the base of the triangle.

Explorations and answers are provided in the *Explorations* binder.

The relationship shown in Example 1 is true for the three midsegments of every triangle.

Theorem 5-4-1 **Triangle Midsegment Theorem**

A midsegment of a triangle is parallel to a side of the triangle, and its length is half the length of that side.

$$\overline{DE} \parallel \overline{AC}, \ DE = \frac{1}{2}AC$$

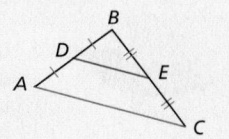

You will prove Theorem 5-4-1 in Exercise 38.

EXAMPLE 2 **Using the Triangle Midsegment Theorem**

Find each measure.

A *UW*

$UW = \frac{1}{2}ST$	△ *Midsegment Thm.*
$UW = \frac{1}{2}(7.4)$	*Substitute 7.4 for ST.*
$UW = 3.7$	*Simplify.*

B m∠*SVU*

$\overline{UW} \parallel \overline{ST}$	△ *Midsegment Thm.*
m∠*SVU* = m∠*VUW*	*Alt. Int. ∡ Thm.*
m∠*SVU* = 41°	*Substitute 41° for m∠VUW.*

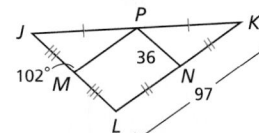

CHECK IT OUT! Find each measure.

2a. *JL* **2b.** *PM* **2c.** m∠*MLK*
  72   48.5   102°

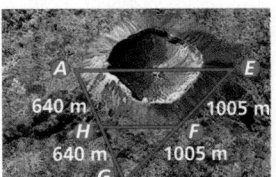

EXAMPLE 3 *Indirect Measurement Application*

Anna wants to find the distance across the base of Capulin Volcano, an extinct volcano in New Mexico. She measures a triangle at one side of the volcano as shown in the diagram. What is *AE*?

$BD = \frac{1}{2}AE$	△ *Midsegment Thm.*
$775 = \frac{1}{2}AE$	*Substitute 775 for BD.*
$1550 = AE$	*Multiply both sides by 2.*

The distance *AE* across the base of the volcano is about 1550 meters.

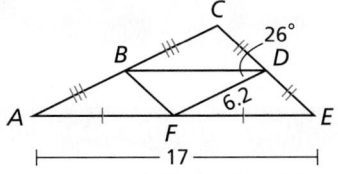

CHECK IT OUT! **3. What if...?** Suppose Anna's result in Example 3 is correct. To check it, she measures a second triangle. How many meters will she measure between *H* and *F*? 775 m

5-4 The Triangle Midsegment Theorem **323**

---

2 Teach

Guided Instruction

Define a midsegment of a triangle. Explain the Triangle Midsegment Theorem and how the theorem can be used to indirectly find the side lengths of a triangle.

Teaching Tip **Inclusion** Remind students that two lines with equal slopes are parallel and that the slope of a segment is the difference of its *y*-coordinates divided by the difference of its *x*-coordinates. Also remind them to subtract the coordinates in the same order.

3 Close

Summarize

Ask students the following questions.

• How many midsegments does a triangle have? 3

• What is the relationship between a midsegment of a triangle and the sides of the triangle? Possible answer: The midsegment connects the mdpts. of 2 sides and is ∥ to the third side.

Answers to *Think and Discuss*

1. The endpoints of $\overline{XY}$ are not mdpts. of the sides of the △.

2. See p. A5.

THINK AND DISCUSS

1. Explain why $\overline{XY}$ is NOT a midsegment of the triangle.

2. **GET ORGANIZED** Copy and complete the graphic organizer. Write the definition of a triangle midsegment and list its properties. Then draw an example and a nonexample.

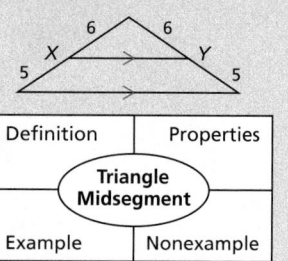

Definition	Properties
Triangle Midsegment	
Example	Nonexample

5-4 Exercises

5-4 Exercises

go.hrw.com/Geo/TX
Homework Help Online
KEYWORD: MG7 5-4
Parent Resources Online
KEYWORD: MG7 Parent

Assignment Guide

Assign *Guided Practice* exercises as necessary.

If you finished Examples **1-3**
  Basic 10–27, 29–41, 48–55
  Average 10–44, 47–55
  Advanced 10–26, 28–55

Homework Quick Check
Quickly check key concepts.
Exercises: 10, 12, 17, 18, 22

Answers

2. $S(-1, 4)$; $T(4, 6)$; slope of $\overline{ST}$ $= \frac{2}{5}$; slope of $\overline{PR} = \frac{2}{5}$; since the slopes are the same, $\overline{ST} \parallel \overline{PR}$. $ST = \sqrt{29}$; $PR = \sqrt{116} = 2\sqrt{29}$; the length of $\overline{ST}$ is half the length of $\overline{PR}$.

GUIDED PRACTICE

1. **Vocabulary** The *midsegment of a triangle* joins the __?__ of two sides of the triangle. (*endpoints* or *midpoints*) **midpoints**

SEE EXAMPLE **1**
p. 322

2. The vertices of $\triangle PQR$ are $P(-4, -1)$, $Q(2, 9)$, and $R(6, 3)$. S is the midpoint of $\overline{PQ}$, and T is the midpoint of $\overline{QR}$. Show that $\overline{ST} \parallel \overline{PR}$ and $ST = \frac{1}{2}PR$.

SEE EXAMPLE **2**
p. 323

Find each measure.

3. *NM* **5.1**   4. *XZ* **11.2**

5. *NZ* **5.6**   6. m∠*LMN* **29°**

7. m∠*YXZ* **29°**   8. m∠*XLM* **151°**

SEE EXAMPLE **3**
p. 323

9. **Architecture** In this A-frame house, the width of the first floor $\overline{XZ}$ is 30 feet. The second floor $\overline{CD}$ is slightly above and parallel to the midsegment of $\triangle XYZ$. Is the width of the second floor more or less than 5 yards? Explain.

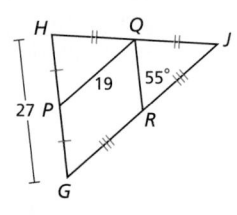

PRACTICE AND PROBLEM SOLVING

Independent Practice

For Exercises	See Example
10	1
11–16	2
17	3

TEKS TAKS

Skills Practice p. S12
Application Practice p. S32

10. The vertices of $\triangle ABC$ are $A(-6, 11)$, $B(6, -3)$, and $C(-2, -5)$. D is the midpoint of $\overline{AC}$, and E is the midpoint of $\overline{AB}$. Show that $\overline{DE} \parallel \overline{CB}$ and $DE = \frac{1}{2}CB$.

Find each measure.

11. *GJ* **38**   12. *RQ* **13.5**

13. *RJ* **19**   14. m∠*PQR* **55°**

15. m∠*HGJ* **55°** 16. m∠*GPQ* **125°**

TAKS Practice

Grades 9–11	Exercises
Obj. 2	21–26, 39, 47
Obj. 5	44, 45
Obj. 6	47, 50–52
Obj. 7	38, 42, 50–52
Obj. 9	48, 49
Obj. 10	37

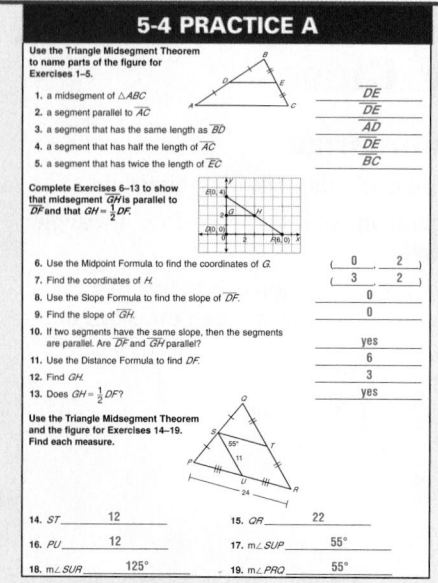

5-4 PRACTICE A

Use the Triangle Midsegment Theorem to name parts of the figure for Exercises 1–5.

1. a midsegment of △ABC _____ $\overline{DE}$
2. a segment parallel to $\overline{AC}$ _____ $\overline{DE}$
3. a segment that has the same length as $\overline{BD}$ _____ $\overline{AD}$
4. a segment that has half the length of $\overline{AC}$ _____ $\overline{DE}$
5. a segment that has twice the length of $\overline{EC}$ _____ $\overline{BC}$

Complete Exercises 6–13 to show that midsegment $\overline{GH}$ is parallel to $\overline{DF}$ and that $GH = \frac{1}{2}DF$.

6. Use the Midpoint Formula to find the coordinates of G. (0 , 2)
7. Find the coordinates of H. (3 , 2)
8. Use the Slope Formula to find the slope of $\overline{DF}$. 0
9. Find the slope of $\overline{GH}$. 0
10. If two segments have the same slope, then the segments are parallel. Are $\overline{DF}$ and $\overline{GH}$ parallel? yes
11. Use the Distance Formula to find DF. 6
12. Find GH. 3
13. Does $GH = \frac{1}{2}DF$? yes

Use the Triangle Midsegment Theorem and the figure for Exercises 14–19. Find each measure.

14. *ST* _____ 12
15. *QR* _____ 22
16. *PU* _____ 12
17. m∠*SUP* _____ 55°
18. m∠*SUR* _____ 125°
19. m∠*PRQ* _____ 55°

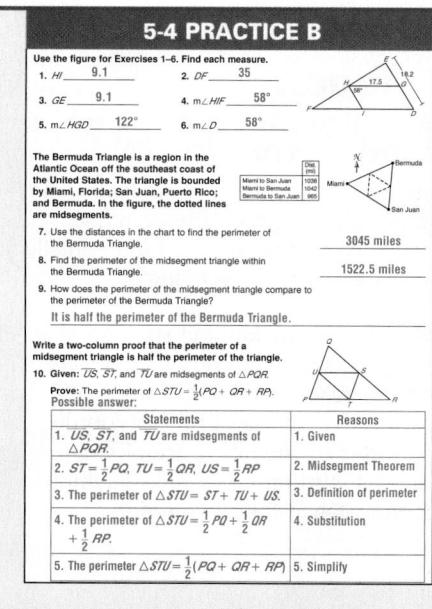

5-4 PRACTICE B

Use the figure for Exercises 1–6. Find each measure.

1. *HI* _____ 9.1
2. *DF* _____ 35
3. *GE* _____ 9.1
4. m∠*HJF* _____ 58°
5. m∠*HGD* _____ 122°
6. m∠*D* _____ 58°

The Bermuda Triangle is a region in the Atlantic Ocean off the southeast coast of the United States. The triangle is bounded by Miami, Florida; San Juan, Puerto Rico; and Bermuda. In the figure, the dotted lines are midsegments.

	Dist. (mi)
Miami to San Juan	1038
Miami to Bermuda	1042
Bermuda to San Juan	965

7. Use the distances in the chart to find the perimeter of the Bermuda Triangle. 3045 miles

8. Find the perimeter of the midsegment triangle within the Bermuda Triangle. 1522.5 miles

9. How does the perimeter of the midsegment triangle compare to the perimeter of the Bermuda Triangle? It is half the perimeter of the Bermuda Triangle.

Write a two-column proof that the perimeter of a midsegment triangle is half the perimeter of the triangle.

10. **Given:** $\overline{US}$, $\overline{ST}$, and $\overline{TU}$ are midsegments of △PQR.

Prove: The perimeter of $\triangle STU = \frac{1}{2}(PQ + QR + RP)$.

Possible answer:

Statements	Reasons
1. $\overline{US}$, $\overline{ST}$, and $\overline{TU}$ are midsegments of △PQR.	1. Given
2. $ST = \frac{1}{2}PQ$, $TU = \frac{1}{2}QR$, $US = \frac{1}{2}RP$	2. Midsegment Theorem
3. The perimeter of $\triangle STU = ST + TU + US$.	3. Definition of perimeter
4. The perimeter of $\triangle STU = \frac{1}{2}PQ + \frac{1}{2}QR + \frac{1}{2}RP$.	4. Substitution
5. The perimeter $\triangle STU = \frac{1}{2}(PQ + QR + RP)$	5. Simplify

17. Yes; $\overline{DE}$ is a midsegment of $\triangle ABC$, so its length is half of $4\frac{1}{2}$ ft, or $2\frac{1}{4}$ ft, which is 27 in. This is less than 30 in., so the carpenter can use the 30 in. timber to make the crossbar.

17. Carpentry In each support for the garden swing, the crossbar $\overline{DE}$ is attached at the midpoints of legs $\overline{BA}$ and $\overline{BC}$. The distance AC is $4\frac{1}{2}$ feet. The carpenter has a timber that is 30 inches long. Is this timber long enough to be used as one of the crossbars? Explain.

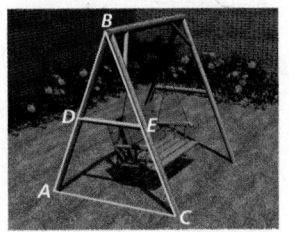

$\triangle KLM$ is the midsegment triangle of $\triangle GHJ$.

18. What is the perimeter of $\triangle GHJ$? **34**

19. What is the perimeter of $\triangle KLM$? **17**

20. What is the relationship between the perimeter of $\triangle GHJ$ and the perimeter of $\triangle KLM$?
The perimeter of $\triangle GHJ$ is twice the perimeter of $\triangle KLM$.

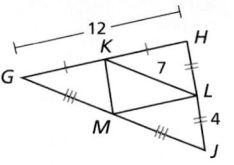

Algebra Find the value of n in each triangle.

21.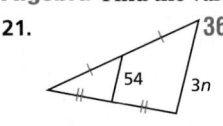

22.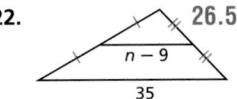

23.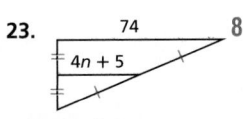

24.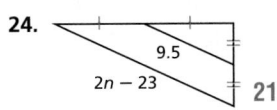

25.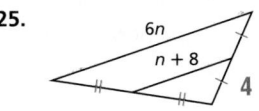

26.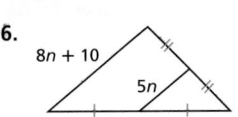

27. B; possible answer: in $\triangle ABC$, $\overline{DE}$ is a midsegment and $\overline{BC}$ is the side $\parallel$ to it. By the $\triangle$ Midsegment Thm., the length of a midsegment is half the length of the $\parallel$ side, so $DE = \frac{1}{2}BC$.

27. ///ERROR ANALYSIS/// Below are two solutions for finding BC. Which is incorrect? Explain the error.

A
$$DE = 0.5BC$$
$$47 = 0.5BC$$
$$94 = BC$$

B
$$BC = 0.5DE$$
$$BC = 0.5(47)$$
$$BC = 23.5$$

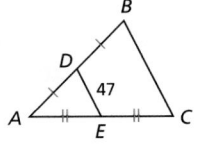

28. Critical Thinking Draw scalene $\triangle DEF$. Label X as the midpoint of $\overline{DE}$, Y as the midpoint of $\overline{EF}$, and Z as the midpoint of $\overline{DF}$. Connect the three midpoints. List all of the congruent angles in your drawing.

29. Estimation The diagram shows the sketch for a new street. Parallel parking spaces will be painted on both sides of the street. Each parallel parking space is 23 feet long. About how many parking spaces can the city accommodate on both sides of the new street? Explain your answer.

$\overline{CG}$, $\overline{EH}$, and $\overline{FJ}$ are midsegments of $\triangle ABD$, $\triangle GCD$, and $\triangle GHE$, respectively. Find each measure.

30. CG **16.5**

31. EH **11**

32. FJ **4.125**

33. $m\angle DCG$ **57°**

34. $m\angle GHE$ **57°**

35. $m\angle FJH$ **123°**

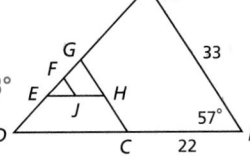

36. Write About It An isosceles triangle has two congruent sides. Does it also have two congruent midsegments? Explain.

5-4 The Triangle Midsegment Theorem **325**

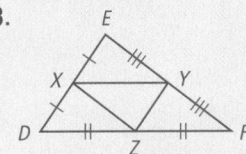
Answers

9. Less than 5 yd; possible answer: the length of the midsegment is half the length of $\overline{XZ}$. So the midsegment is 15 ft, or 5 yd. $\overline{CD}$ is shorter than the midsegment, so the width of the second floor will be less than 5 yd.

10. $D(-4, 3)$; $E(0, 4)$; slope of $\overline{DE} = \frac{1}{4}$; slope of $\overline{CB} = \frac{1}{4}$; since the slopes are the same, $\overline{DE} \parallel \overline{CB}$. $DE = \sqrt{17}$; $CB = \sqrt{68} = 2\sqrt{17}$; the length of $\overline{DE}$ is half the length of $\overline{CB}$.

28.

$\angle D \cong \angle FZY \cong \angle YXE \cong \angle ZYX$;
$\angle E \cong \angle ZYF \cong \angle DXZ \cong \angle XZY$;
$\angle F \cong \angle XYE \cong \angle DZX \cong \angle ZXY$

29. Possible answer: about 18 parking spaces; the new street is along the midsegment of the triangular plot of land. The length of the street is half of 440 ft, or 220 ft. Estimate the quotient $220 \div 23$ by rounding 220 to 225 and 23 to 25. Since $225 \div 25 = 9$, the city can put about 9 parking spaces on 1 side of the street. So the total number of parking spaces is about $2(9)$, or 18.

36. Yes; possible answer: let x be the length of each congruent side of an isosceles triangle. By the Triangle Midsegment Theorem, the length of the midsegment parallel to each of those sides is $\frac{1}{2}x$. Since these 2 midsegments are equal in length, they are congruent to each other.

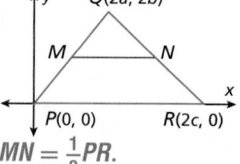

37. This problem will prepare you for the Multi-Step TAKS Prep on page 328.
The figure shows the roads connecting towns A, B, and C.
A music company has a store in each town and a distribution warehouse W at the midpoint of road $\overline{XY}$.

a. What is the distance from the warehouse to point X? **2.25 mi**

b. A truck starts at the warehouse, delivers instruments to the stores in towns A, B, and C (in this order) and then returns to the warehouse. What is the total length of the trip, assuming the driver takes the shortest possible route? **28.5 mi**

38. Use coordinates to prove the Triangle Midsegment Theorem.

(a, b) **a.** M is the midpoint of $\overline{PQ}$. What are its coordinates?

$(a + c, b)$ **b.** N is the midpoint of $\overline{QR}$. What are its coordinates?

38c. 0; 0; the slopes of $\overline{MN}$ and $\overline{PR}$ are equal, so $\overline{MN} \parallel \overline{PR}$.

c. Find the slopes of $\overline{PR}$ and $\overline{MN}$. What can you conclude?

d. Find PR and MN. What can you conclude?
$2c$; c; the length of $\overline{PR}$ is twice the length of $\overline{MN}$, so $MN = \frac{1}{2}PR$.

TEST PREP

39. $\overline{PQ}$ is a midsegment of $\triangle RST$. What is the length of $\overline{RT}$?

Ⓐ 9 meters

Ⓑ 21 meters

Ⓒ 45 meters

Ⓓ 63 meters

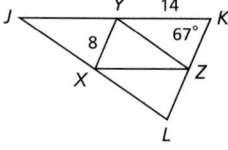

40. In $\triangle UVW$, M is the midpoint of $\overline{VU}$, and N is the midpoint of $\overline{VW}$. Which statement is true?

Ⓕ $VM = VN$

Ⓗ $VU = 2VM$

Ⓖ $MN = UV$

Ⓙ $VW = \frac{1}{2}VN$

41. $\triangle XYZ$ is the midsegment triangle of $\triangle JKL$, $XY = 8$, $YK = 14$, and $m\angle YKZ = 67°$. Which of the following measures CANNOT be determined?

Ⓐ KL

Ⓒ $m\angle XZL$

Ⓑ JY

Ⓓ $m\angle KZY$

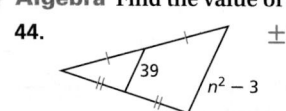
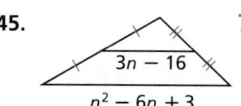

CHALLENGE AND EXTEND

$(-8, -1)$, $(-4, 7)$, $(8, -5)$

42. Multi-Step The midpoints of the sides of a triangle are $A(-6, 3)$, $B(2, 1)$, and $C(0, -3)$. Find the coordinates of the vertices of the triangle.

43. Critical Thinking Classify the midsegment triangle of an equilateral triangle by its side lengths and angle measures. **equilateral and equiangular**

x^2 **Algebra** Find the value of n in each triangle.

44. ± 9 **45.** 7

39; $n^2 - 3$

$3n - 16$; $n^2 - 6n + 3$

Answers to Construction

2. Possible answer: Find $m\angle BXY$ and $m\angle BAC$ and confirm that they are equal. This means the two segments are $\parallel$ by the Conv. of the Corr. $\angle$ Post.

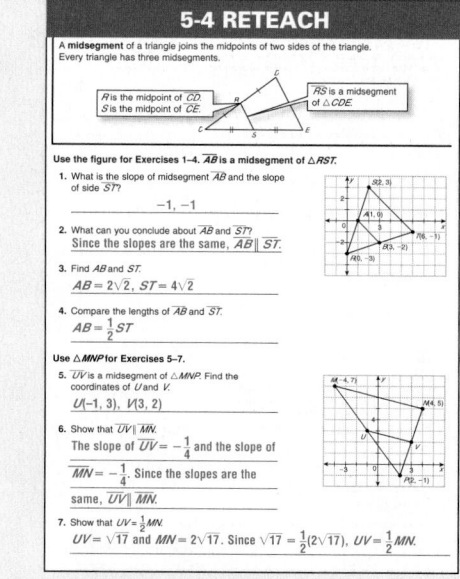

5-4 READING STRATEGIES

The **midsegment** of a triangle is a segment that joins the midpoints of two sides of the triangle.

A **midsegment triangle** is formed from the three midsegments of a triangle.

1. Name the midsegments in $\triangle QRS$.
   $\overline{LM}, \overline{MN}, \overline{NL}$

2. What is the midsegment triangle in $\triangle QRS$?
   $\triangle LMN$

The **Triangle Midsegment Theorem:** A midsegment of a triangle is parallel to a side of the triangle, and its length is half the length of that side.

3. Which midsegment is parallel to side $\overline{QS}$?
   $\overline{MN}$

4. If side $\overline{RS}$ is 12 cm, how long is $\overline{LM}$?
   6 cm

5. $\overline{LN} = \underline{NM} = \underline{ML}$

6. Draw the midsegments in $\triangle ABC$.

7. What are the names of the midsegments?
   Answers will vary based on students' choice of letters: $\overline{QR}$, $\overline{RS}$, $\overline{RQ}$.

8. What is the midsegment triangle?
   $\triangle QRS$

5-4 RETEACH

A **midsegment** of a triangle joins the midpoints of two sides of the triangle. Every triangle has three midsegments.

R is the midpoint of $\overline{CD}$.
S is the midpoint of $\overline{CE}$.
$\overline{RS}$ is a midsegment of $\triangle CDE$.

Use the figure for Exercises 1–4. $\overline{AB}$ is a midsegment of $\triangle RST$.

1. What is the slope of midsegment $\overline{AB}$ and the slope of side $\overline{ST}$?
   $-1, -1$

2. What can you conclude about $\overline{AB}$ and $\overline{ST}$?
   Since the slopes are the same, $\overline{AB} \parallel \overline{ST}$.

3. Find AB and ST.
   $AB = 2\sqrt{2}, ST = 4\sqrt{2}$

4. Compare the lengths of $\overline{AB}$ and $\overline{ST}$.
   $AB = \frac{1}{2} ST$

Use $\triangle MNP$ for Exercises 5–7.

5. $\overline{UV}$ is a midsegment of $\triangle MNP$. Find the coordinates of U and V.
   $U(-1, 3), V(3, 2)$

6. Show that $\overline{UV} \parallel \overline{MN}$.
   The slope of $\overline{UV} = -\frac{1}{4}$ and the slope of $\overline{MN} = -\frac{1}{4}$. Since the slopes are the same, $\overline{UV} \parallel \overline{MN}$.

7. Show that $UV = \frac{1}{2} MN$.
   $UV = \sqrt{17}$ and $MN = 2\sqrt{17}$. Since $\sqrt{17} = \frac{1}{2}(2\sqrt{17})$, $UV = \frac{1}{2} MN$.

$\triangle QXY \cong \triangle XPZ \cong$
$\triangle YZR \cong \triangle ZYX$;
area of $\triangle XYZ = \frac{1}{4}$
(area of $\triangle PQR$)

46. $\triangle XYZ$ is the midsegment triangle of $\triangle PQR$. Write a congruence statement involving all four of the smaller triangles. What is the relationship between the area of $\triangle XYZ$ and $\triangle PQR$?

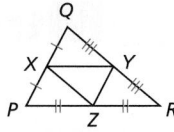

47. $\overline{AB}$ is a midsegment of $\triangle XYZ$. $\overline{CD}$ is a midsegment of $\triangle ABZ$. $\overline{EF}$ is a midsegment of $\triangle CDZ$, and $\overline{GH}$ is a midsegment of $\triangle EFZ$.

a. Copy and complete the table.

Number of Midsegment	1	2	3	4
Length of Midsegment	32	16	8	4

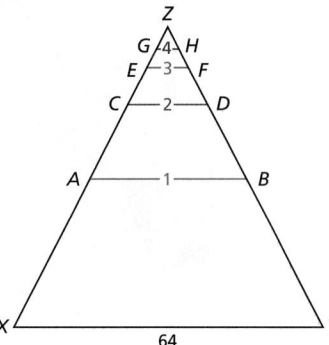

47b. $\frac{1}{4}$

47c. $64\left(\frac{1}{2}\right)^n = 2^{6-n}$

b. If this pattern continues, what will be the length of midsegment 8?

c. Write an algebraic expression to represent the length of midsegment n. (*Hint:* Think of the midsegment lengths as powers of 2.)

SPIRAL REVIEW

Suppose a 2% acid solution is mixed with a 3% acid solution. Find the percent of acid in each mixture. (*Previous course*)

48. a mixture that contains an equal amount of 2% acid solution and 3% acid solution **2.5%**

49. a mixture that contains 3 times more 2% acid solution than 3% acid solution **2.25%**

A figure has vertices $G(-3, -2)$, $H(0, 0)$, $J(4, 1)$, and $K(1, -2)$. Given the coordinates of the image of G under a translation, find the coordinates of the images of H, J, and K. (*Lesson 1-7*)

50. $(-3, 2)$
$(0, 4)$, $(4, 5)$, $(1, 2)$

51. $(1, -4)$
$(4, -2)$, $(8, -1)$, $(5, -4)$

52. $(3, 0)$
$(6, 2)$, $(10, 3)$, $(7, 0)$

Find each length. (*Lesson 5-3*)

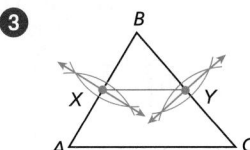

53. NX **6**

54. MR **8.25**

55. NP **9**

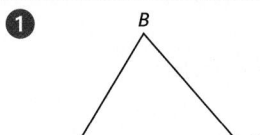

Construction Midsegment of a Triangle

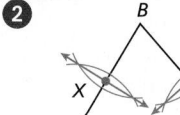

1
Draw a large triangle. Label the vertices A, B, and C.

2
Construct the midpoints of $\overline{AB}$ and $\overline{BC}$. Label the midpoints X and Y, respectively.

3
Draw the midsegment $\overline{XY}$.

1. Using a ruler, measure $\overline{XY}$ and $\overline{AC}$. How are the two lengths related?
$$XY = \frac{1}{2}AC$$

2. How can you use a protractor to verify that $\overline{XY}$ is parallel to $\overline{AC}$?

5-4 The Triangle Midsegment Theorem **327**

5-4 PROBLEM SOLVING

1. The vertices of $\triangle JKL$ are $J(-9, 2)$, $K(10, 1)$, and $L(5, 6)$. $\overline{CD}$ is the midsegment parallel to $\overline{JK}$. What is the length of $\overline{CD}$? Round to the nearest tenth.

9.5

2. In $\triangle QRS$, $QR = 2x + 5$, $RS = 3x - 1$, and $SQ = 5x$. What is the perimeter of the midsegment triangle of $\triangle QRS$?

5x + 2

3. Is $\overline{XY}$ a midsegment of $\triangle LMN$ if its endpoints are $X(8, 2.5)$ and $Y(6.5, -2)$? Explain.

Yes; X is the midpoint of $\overline{LN}$, and Y is the midpoint of $\overline{ML}$.

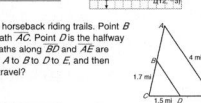

4. The diagram at right shows horseback riding trails. Point B is the halfway point along path $\overline{AC}$. Point D is the halfway point along path $\overline{CE}$. The paths along $\overline{BD}$ and $\overline{AE}$ are parallel. If riders travel from A to B to D to E, and then back to A, how far do they travel?

9.2 mi

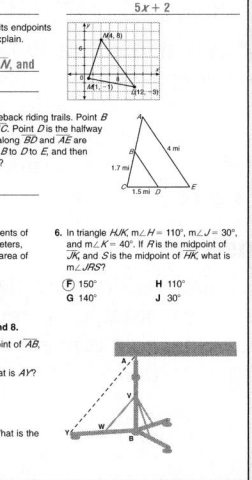

Choose the best answer.

5. Right triangle FGH has midsegments of length 10 centimeters, 24 centimeters, and 26 centimeters. What is the area of $\triangle FGH$?

A 60 cm²   C 240 cm²
B 120 cm²   **D 480 cm²**

6. In triangle HJK, $m\angle H = 110°$, $m\angle J = 30°$, and $m\angle K = 40°$. If R is the midpoint of $\overline{JK}$, and S is the midpoint of $\overline{HK}$, what is $m\angle JRS$?

F 150°   H 110°
G 140°   J 30°

Use the diagram for Exercises 7 and 8.

On the balance beam, V is the midpoint of $\overline{AB}$, and W is the midpoint of $\overline{YB}$.

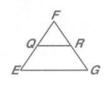

7. The length of $\overline{VW}$ is $1\frac{7}{8}$ feet. What is AY?

A $\frac{7}{8}$ ft   C $3\frac{3}{4}$ ft
B $\frac{15}{16}$ ft   D $7\frac{1}{2}$ ft

8. The measure of $\angle AYW$ is 50°. What is the measure of $\angle VWB$?

F 45°   H 90°
G 50°   J 130°

5-4 CHALLENGE

When solving a problem, it is sometimes necessary to consider more than one possible case. It is helpful to make a drawing of each case.

Triangle EFG is an isosceles triangle with $EF = FG$ and with the perimeter equal to 22 units. A midsegment, $\overline{QR}$, of $\triangle EFG$ is equal to 4 units.

1. Describe two possible cases and make a drawing of each.

Case 1: The midsegment connects the two congruent sides $\overline{EF}$ and $\overline{FG}$.

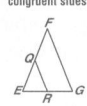

Case 2: The midsegment connects the base $\overline{EG}$ and one of the congruent sides of $\triangle EFG$.

2. Find the lengths of the triangle's sides for each of the cases in Exercise 1.

case 1: $EF = FG = 7$ and $EG = 8$; case 2: $EF = FG = 8$ and $EG = 6$

Use $\triangle ABC$ for Exercises 4 and 5. A midsegment of the triangle is 9.

3. How many cases are there to consider when making a conclusion about the third side of the triangle? Explain.

Two cases; the midsegment joins the sides with lengths 12 and 18. The midsegment joins the side with lengths 12 and x.

4. Find the length of the third side of $\triangle ABC$ by considering both cases.

If the midsegment joins the sides with lengths 12 and 18, then the third side is 18. If the midsegment joins the side with lengths 12 and x, then it is impossible to find the length of the third side.

Journal
Have students explain how to find the length of a midsegment when given the length of the parallel side.

ALTERNATIVE ASSESSMENT

Have students use geometry software to construct the midsegment of a triangle. Have them measure the midsegment and the sides of the triangle. Ask them to use the angle measures to show that the midsegment is parallel to the third side of the triangle.

Power Presentations
with PowerPoint®

5-4
Lesson Quiz

Use the diagram for Items 1–3. Find each measure.

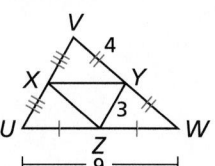

1. ED **10**

2. AB **14**

3. $m\angle BFE$ **44°**

4. Find the value of n.   **16**

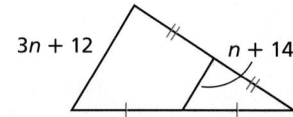

$3n + 12$ $n + 14$

5. $\triangle XYZ$ is the midsegment triangle of $\triangle WUV$. What is the perimeter of $\triangle XYZ$?   **11.5**

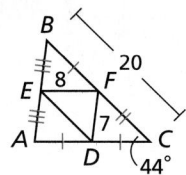

Also available on transparency

MULTI-STEP TAKS PREP

Organizer

Objective: Assess students' ability to apply concepts and skills in Lessons 5-1 through 5-4 in a real-world format.

 Online Edition

Resources

 Geometry Assessments
www.mathtekstoolkit.org

Problem	Text Reference
1	Lesson 5-3
2	Lesson 5-3
3	Lesson 5-3
4	Lesson 5-3
5	Lesson 5-2
6	Lesson 5-2
7	Lesson 5-2

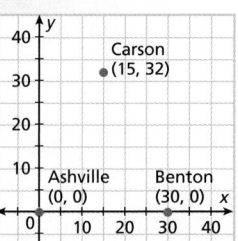

Segments in Triangles

Location Contemplation
A chain of music stores has locations in Ashville, Benton, and Carson. The directors of the company are using a coordinate plane to decide on the location for a new distribution warehouse. Each unit on the plane represents one mile.

$\left(15, 10\frac{2}{3}\right)$ **1.** A plot of land is available at the centroid of the triangle formed by the three cities. What are the coordinates for this location?

2. If the directors build the warehouse at the centroid, about how far will it be from each of the cities?
about 21.3 mi from Carson; about 18.4 mi from Benton and Ashville

$\left(15, 7\frac{1}{32}\right)$ **3.** Another plot of land is available at the orthocenter of the triangle. What are the coordinates for this location?

4. About how far would the warehouse be from each city if it were built at the orthocenter?
about 25 mi from Carson; about 16.6 mi from Benton and Ashville

$\left(15, 12\frac{31}{64}\right)$ **5.** A third option is to build the warehouse at the circumcenter of the triangle. What are the coordinates for this location?

6. About how far would the warehouse be from each city if it were built at the circumcenter? **about 19.5 mi from all 3 cities**

7. The directors decide that the warehouse should be equidistant from each city. Which location should they choose? **circumcenter**

328 *Chapter 5 Properties and Attributes of Triangles*

INTERVENTION

Scaffolding Questions

1–2. What type of triangle is formed by the three cities? Which of the medians has an equation that is easy to find? isosc.; the median through Carson

3–4. What is the definition of orthocenter? Which of the altitudes has an equation that is easy to find? pt. of intersection of the altitudes; the altitude through Carson

5. How do you find the coordinates of the circumcenter? Find the pt. of intersection of the perp. bisectors of the sides.

6–7. What is always true about the circumcenter of a triangle? It is equidistant from the vertices of the △. Once you find the distance from the circumcenter to the origin, is it necessary to find the distances to the other vertices? No

Extension

Where should the directors place the warehouse if they want it to be equidistant from the three roads that connect the cities?
at the incenter of the △

READY TO GO ON?

Quiz for Lessons 5-1 Through 5-4

5-1 Perpendicular and Angle Bisectors

Find each measure.

1. PQ **9.6**

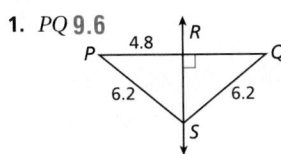

2. JM **58**

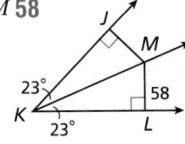

3. AC **51**

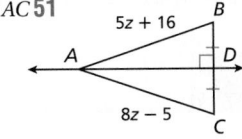

4. Write an equation in point-slope form for the perpendicular bisector of the segment with endpoints $M(-1, -3)$ and $N(7, 1)$. $y + 1 = -2(x - 3)$

5-2 Bisectors of Triangles

5. $\overline{PX}$, $\overline{PY}$, and $\overline{PZ}$ are the perpendicular bisectors of $\triangle RST$. Find PS and XT.

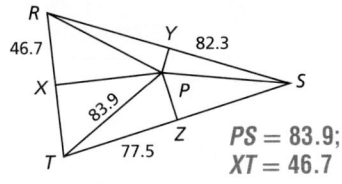

$PS = 83.9$;
$XT = 46.7$

6. $\overline{JK}$ and $\overline{HK}$ are angle bisectors of $\triangle GHJ$. Find $m\angle GJK$ and the distance from K to $\overline{HJ}$.

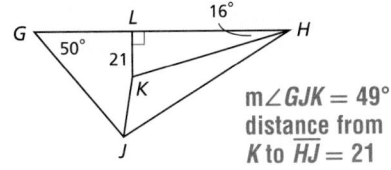

$m\angle GJK = 49°$;
distance from
K to $\overline{HJ} = 21$

7. Find the circumcenter of $\triangle TVO$ with vertices $T(9, 0)$, $V(0, -4)$, and $O(0, 0)$.
$(4.5, -2)$

5-3 Medians and Altitudes of Triangles

$BW = 29$; $CW = 19$;

8. In $\triangle DEF$, $BD = 87$, and $WE = 38$. Find BW, CW, and CE. $CE = 57$

9. Paula cuts a triangle with vertices at coordinates $(0, 4)$, $(8, 0)$, and $(10, 8)$ from grid paper. At what coordinates should she place the tip of a pencil to balance the triangle? $(6, 4)$

10. Find the orthocenter of $\triangle PSV$ with vertices $P(2, 4)$, $S(8, 4)$, and $V(4, 0)$. $(4, 2)$

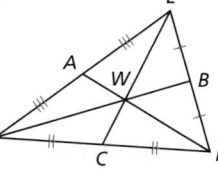

5-4 The Triangle Midsegment Theorem

11. Find ZV, PM, and $m\angle RZV$ $ZV = 45$; in $\triangle JMP$. $PM = 106$; $m\angle RZV = 36°$

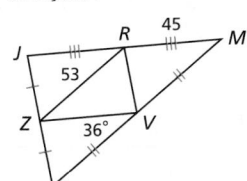

12. What is the distance XZ across the pond? **78 m**

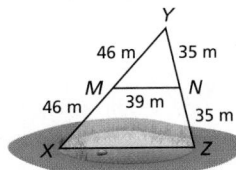

SECTION 5A

READY TO GO ON?

Organizer

Objective: Assess students' mastery of concepts and skills in Lessons 5-1 through 5-4.

Resources

Assessment Resources
Section 5A Quiz

Test & Practice Generator
One-Stop Planner®

INTERVENTION ◀▶

Resources

Ready to Go On? Intervention and Enrichment Worksheets

Ready to Go On? CD-ROM

Ready to Go On? Online

my.hrw.com

READY TO GO ON?

Diagnose and Prescribe

NO INTERVENE

YES ENRICH

READY TO GO ON? Intervention, Section 5A			
Ready to Go On? Intervention	Worksheets	CD-ROM	Online
✔ Lesson 5-1	5-1 Intervention	Activity 5-1	
✔ Lesson 5-2	5-2 Intervention	Activity 5-2	Diagnose and Prescribe Online
✔ Lesson 5-3	5-3 Intervention	Activity 5-3	
✔ Lesson 5-4	5-4 Intervention	Activity 5-4	

READY TO GO ON?
Enrichment, Section 5A

Worksheets
CD-ROM
Online

Relationships in Triangles

 One-Minute Section Planner

Lesson	Lab Resources	Materials
5-5 Geometry Lab Explore Triangle Inequalities • Explore the relationships between side lengths and angle measures in a triangle. ☐ Exit Level TAKS ☑ ACT ☐ SAT ☐ SAT Subject Tests		**Required** protractor (MK), ruler (MK), straws
Lesson 5-5 Indirect Proof and Inequalities in One Triangle • Write indirect proofs. • Apply inequalities in one triangle. ☐ Exit Level TAKS ☑ ACT ☐ SAT ☐ SAT Subject Tests		**Optional** geometry software, colored pencils, raw spaghetti, ruler (MK), protractor (MK)
Lesson 5-6 Inequalities in Two Triangles • Apply inequalities in two triangles. ☐ Exit Level TAKS ☑ ACT ☐ SAT ☐ SAT Subject Tests		**Optional** geometry software, book or scissors, straws or raw spaghetti, ruler (MK), protractor (MK), colored pencils
5-7 Geometry Lab Hands-on Proof of the Pythagorean Theorem • Use area to justify the Pythagorean Theorem. ☐ Exit Level TAKS ☐ ACT ☑ SAT ☐ SAT Subject Tests		**Required** graph paper, scissors **Optional** transparency
Lesson 5-7 The Pythagorean Theorem • Use the Pythagorean Theorem and its converse to solve problems. • Use Pythagorean inequalities to classify triangles. ☑ Exit Level TAKS ☐ ACT ☑ SAT ☐ SAT Subject Tests	*Texas Lab Manual* 5-7 Technology Lab	**Optional** geometry software, straws or raw spaghetti, protractor (MK), ruler (MK)
Lesson 5-8 Applying Special Right Triangles • Justify and apply properties of 45°-45°-90° triangles. • Justify and apply properties of 30°-60°-90° triangles. ☑ Exit Level TAKS ☑ ACT ☑ SAT ☐ SAT Subject Tests	*Texas Lab Manual* 5-8 Geometry Lab	**Optional** 45°-45°-45° plastic triangle (MK), 30°-60°-90° plastic triangle (MK), geometry software, protractor (MK), ruler (MK)
5-8 Geometry Lab Graph Irrational Numbers • Graph irrational numbers on a number line. ☐ Exit Level TAKS ☐ ACT ☐ SAT ☐ SAT Subject Tests		**Required** compass (MK), straightedge (MK)

MK = *Manipulatives Kit*

Section Overview

Indirect Proof

 Indirect proof uses indirect reasoning and is often used to prove statements that cannot be proved directly.

Indirect Proof of a Conjecture

1. Conjecture: $p \rightarrow q$
2. Assume: $\sim q$
3. Show: $\sim q \rightarrow \sim p$
4. Conclude: $p \rightarrow q$ (logically equivalent to $\sim q \rightarrow \sim p$)

Indirect proof is also known as **proof by contradiction.**

Inequalities in One and Two Triangles

 Inequalities in one and two triangles can be used to find a reasonable range of values for an unknown distance.

Inequalities in One Triangle

Triangle Inequality Theorem

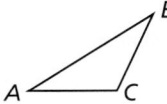

$AB + BC > AC$
$BC + AC > AB$
$AC + AB > BC$

Inequalities in Two Triangles

Hinge Theorem

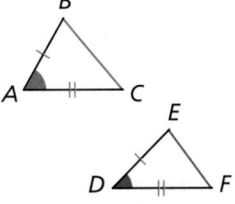

$m\angle A > m\angle D \rightarrow BC > EF$

Converse to the Hinge Theorem

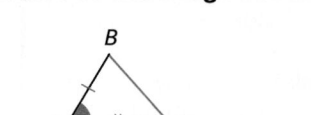

$BC > EF \rightarrow m\angle A > m\angle D$

Pythagorean Theorem and Special Right Triangles

 The Pythagorean Theorem and special right triangles have many applications in real-world situations.

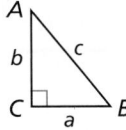

The Pythagorean Theorem

If $c^2 = a^2 + b^2$,
then $\triangle ABC$ is a **right triangle**

45°-45°-90° Triangle Theorem

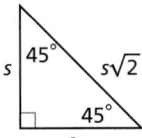

Pythagorean Inequalities

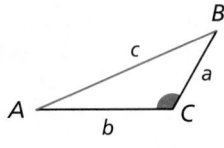

If $c^2 > a^2 + b^2$
then $\triangle ABC$ is an
obtuse triangle.

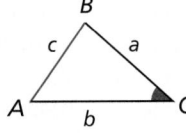

If $c^2 < a^2 + b^2$
then $\triangle ABC$ is an
acute triangle.

30°-60°-90° Triangle Theorem

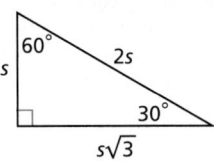

Pythagorean triple: a set of three nonzero whole numbers a, b, c such that $a^2 + b^2 = c^2$

Examples: 3, 4, 5; 5, 12, 13; 8, 15, 17; and 7, 24, 25

Pacing:
Traditional $\frac{1}{2}$ day
Block $\frac{1}{4}$ day

Objective: Apply algebra skills to solving compound inequalities.

 Online Edition

 Countdown to TAKS Week 11

Teach

Remember

Students review how to solve compound inequalities.

INTERVENTION ◄═══► For additional review and practice on solving inequalities, see Skills Bank page S60.

Teaching Tip **Number Sense** Have students write a numeric inequality, such as 10 > 2. Have them add and subtract positive and negative numbers from each side. Repeat this exercise with multiplication and division so students can see that they must reverse the inequality symbol when multiplying or dividing by a negative number.

Close

Assess

Have students write a compound inequality and present their solutions to the class.

 TAKS On Track for TAKS connects TAKS objectives across the grade levels.

Grades 9–11
Obj. 4 Linear Equations and Inequalities A.7.B investigate methods for solving linear equations and inequalities using concrete models, graphs, and the properties of equality, select a method, and solve the equations and inequalities

---

Solving Compound Inequalities

Algebra

To solve an inequality, you use the Properties of Inequality and inverse operations to undo the operations in the inequality one at a time.

See Skills Bank page S60

Properties of Inequality

PROPERTY	ALGEBRA
Addition Property	If $a < b$, then $a + c < b + c$.
Subtraction Property	If $a < b$, then $a - c < b - c$.
Multiplication Property	If $a < b$ and $c > 0$, then $ac < bc$. If $a < b$ and $c < 0$, then $ac > bc$.
Division Property	If $a < b$ and $c > 0$, then $\frac{a}{c} < \frac{b}{c}$. If $a < b$ and $c < 0$, then $\frac{a}{c} > \frac{b}{c}$.
Transitive Property	If $a < b$ and $b < c$, then $a < c$.
Comparison Property	If $a + b = c$ and $b > 0$, then $a < c$.

A compound inequality is formed when two simple inequalities are combined into one statement with the word *and* or *or*. To solve a compound inequality, solve each simple inequality and find the intersection or union of the solutions. The graph of a compound inequality may represent a line, a ray, two rays, or a segment.

Example

Solve the compound inequality $5 < 20 - 3a \leq 11$. What geometric figure does the graph represent?

$5 < 20 - 3a$	AND	$20 - 3a \leq 11$	*Rewrite the compound inequality as two simple inequalities.*
$-15 < -3a$	AND	$-3a \leq -9$	*Subtract 20 from both sides.*
$5 > a$	AND	$a \geq 3$	*Divide both sides by −3 and reverse the inequality symbols.*

$$3 \leq a < 5$$

Combine the two solutions into a single statement.

0 1 2 3 4 5 6 7

The graph represents a segment.

Try This 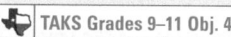 TAKS Grades 9–11 Obj. 4

Solve. What geometric figure does each graph represent?

1. $-4 + x > 1$ OR $-8 + 2x < -6$
2. $2x - 3 \geq -5$ OR $x - 4 > -1$
3. $-6 < 7 - x \leq 12$ $-5 \leq x < 13$; segment
4. $22 < -2 - 2x \leq 54$ $-28 \leq x < -12$; segment
5. $3x \geq 0$ OR $x + 5 < 7$ $x \geq 0$ OR $x < 2$; line
6. $2x - 3 \leq 5$ OR $-2x + 3 \leq -9$ $x \leq 4$ OR $x \geq 6$; two rays

1. $x < 1$ OR $x > 5$; 2 rays
2. $x \geq -1$ OR $x > 3$; ray

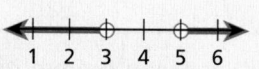

Teacher to Teacher

I have students draw a number line for each problem. They can see the answer a lot more clearly. This also helps them see when there is no solution or infinitely many solutions. For example, suppose the numeric answer ends up being $a > 5$ AND $a < 3$. When the students graph this on a number line, they can see that there is no solution.

1 2 3 4 5 6

Without graphing this, many students wouldn't realize that the numeric solution ends up meaning no solution at all.

Stephanie Turner
Colleyville, Texas

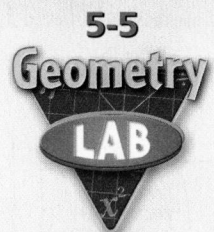

5-5

Geometry LAB

Explore Triangle Inequalities

Use with Lesson 5-5

Many of the triangle relationships you have learned so far involve a statement of equality. For example, the circumcenter of a triangle is equidistant from the vertices of the triangle, and the incenter is equidistant from the sides of the triangle. Now you will investigate some triangle relationships that involve inequalities.

 TEKS G.9.B Congruence and the geometry of size: formulate and test conjectures about ... polygons and their component parts based on explorations and concrete models. Also G.5.B

Activity 1

1 Draw a large scalene triangle. Label the vertices *A*, *B*, and *C*.

2 Measure the sides and the angles. Copy the table below and record the measures in the first row.

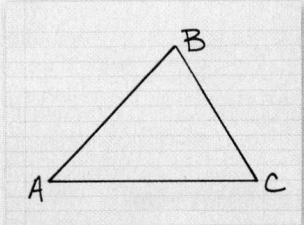

	BC	AC	AB	m∠A	m∠B	m∠C
Triangle 1						
Triangle 2						
Triangle 3						
Triangle 4						

Try This

1. In the table, draw a circle around the longest side length, and draw a circle around the greatest angle measure of △*ABC*. Draw a square around the shortest side length, and draw a square around the least angle measure. **Check students' work.**

2. **Make a Conjecture** Where is the longest side in relation to the largest angle? Where is the shortest side in relation to the smallest angle?

3. Draw three more scalene triangles and record the measures in the table. Does your conjecture hold? **Check students' work.**

Activity 2

1 Cut three sets of chenille stems to the following lengths.
   - 3 inches, 4 inches, 6 inches
   - 3 inches, 4 inches, 7 inches
   - 3 inches, 4 inches, 8 inches

2 Try to make a triangle with each set of chenille stems.

Try This

only the set with lengths 3 in., 4 in., and 6 in.

4. Which sets of chenille stems make a triangle?

5. **Make a Conjecture** For each set of chenille stems, compare the sum of any two lengths with the third length. What is the relationship?

6. Select a different set of three lengths and test your conjecture. Does your conjecture hold? **Check students' work.**

Teacher to Teacher

For **Activity 2** of this lab, students can also use raw spaghetti. Have them break it into pieces of different lengths, figure out which sets of 3 pieces make a triangle, and then measure their lengths. Students can then find out which sets of 3 pieces *cannot* make a triangle and measure those lengths.

Another idea for this activity is to copy ruler markings onto paper strips and cut those into pieces. Then the lengths of the pieces are visible as students are trying to build the triangles.

Robert Brouhle
Huntington Beach, CA

Geometry Organizer LAB

Use with Lesson 5-5

Pacing:
Traditional $\frac{1}{2}$ day
Block $\frac{1}{4}$ day

Objective: Explore the relationships between side lengths and angle measures in a triangle.

Materials: protractor, ruler, straws

PREMIER
Online Edition

Teach

Discuss

Discuss with students how the side lengths of a triangle are related to the angle measures and to each other.

Close

Key Concept

The larger angle of a triangle is opposite the longer side and vice versa. The sum of any two sides of a triangle is greater than the third side.

Assessment

Journal Have students draw and label a triangle and then write three inequalities to represent the possible side lengths.

Answers to *Try This*

2, 5. See p. A19.

 Geometry TEKS

G.5 Geometric patterns*
(B) use numeric and geometric patterns to make generalizations about geometric properties, including properties of polygons ... and angle relationships in polygons ...

G.9 Congruence and the geometry of size*
(B) formulate and test conjectures about ... polygons and their component parts ...

* **Knowledge and Skills** See p. 298.

Pacing: Traditional 1 day
Block $\frac{1}{2}$ day

Objectives: Write indirect proofs.

Apply inequalities in one triangle.

PREMIER Online Edition
Tutorial Videos

Countdown to TAKS Week 11

Power Presentations
with PowerPoint®

Warm Up

1. Write a conditional from the sentence "An isosceles triangle has two congruent sides." If a △ is isosc., then it has 2 ≅ sides.

2. Write the contrapositive of the conditional "If it is Tuesday, then John has a piano lesson." If John does not have a piano lesson, then it is not Tuesday.

3. Show that the conjecture "If $x > 6$, then $2x > 14$" is false by finding a counterexample. $x = 7$

Also available on transparency

Math Humor

Q: What do you call a prisoner's poem?

A: A converse

Geometry TEKS

G.3 Geometric structure*
(B) construct and justify statements about geometric figures …
(C) use logical reasoning to prove statements are true and find counter examples to disprove statements …
(E) use deductive reasoning to prove a statement

G.5. Geometric patterns*
(B) use numeric and geometric patterns to make generalizations about … properties of polygons … and angle relationships in polygons …

* Knowledge and Skills See p. 298.

5-5 Indirect Proof and Inequalities in One Triangle

TEKS G.3.B Geometric structure: construct and justify statements about geometric figures and their properties. Also G.3.C, G.3.E, G.5.B

Objectives
Write indirect proofs.

Apply inequalities in one triangle.

Vocabulary
indirect proof

Why learn this?
You can use a triangle inequality to find a reasonable range of values for an unknown distance. (See Example 5.)

So far you have written proofs using *direct reasoning*. You began with a true hypothesis and built a logical argument to show that a conclusion was true. In an **indirect proof**, you begin by assuming that the conclusion is false. Then you show that this assumption leads to a contradiction. This type of proof is also called a *proof by contradiction*.

THERE. THE RECLINER IS THE PERFECT DISTANCE FROM THE TV, AND I CAN REACH THE REMOTE WITHOUT STRAINING.

Getting in shape for the Summer Olympics.

1996 ©GarLanCo/Distributed by Universal Press Syndicate

Helpful Hint
When writing an indirect proof, look for a contradiction of one of the following: the given information, a definition, a postulate, or a theorem.

Writing an Indirect Proof
1. Identify the conjecture to be proven.
2. Assume the opposite (the negation) of the conclusion is true.
3. Use direct reasoning to show that the assumption leads to a contradiction.
4. Conclude that since the assumption is false, the original conjecture must be true.

EXAMPLE 1 Writing an Indirect Proof

Write an indirect proof that a right triangle cannot have an obtuse angle.

Step 1 Identify the conjecture to be proven.
Given: △JKL is a right triangle.
Prove: △JKL does not have an obtuse angle.

Step 2 Assume the opposite of the conclusion.
Assume △JKL has an obtuse angle. Let ∠K be obtuse.

Step 3 Use direct reasoning to lead to a contradiction.

$m\angle K + m\angle L = 90°$	*The acute ∠s of a rt. △ are comp.*
$m\angle K = 90° - m\angle L$	*Subtr. Prop. of =*
$m\angle K > 90°$	*Def. of obtuse ∠*
$90° - m\angle L > 90°$	*Substitute $90° - m\angle L$ for $m\angle K$.*
$m\angle L < 0°$	*Subtract 90° from both sides and solve for $m\angle L$.*

However, by the Protractor Postulate, a triangle cannot have an angle with a measure less than 0°.

Step 4 Conclude that the original conjecture is true.
The assumption that △JKL has an obtuse angle is false.
Therefore △JKL does not have an obtuse angle.

CHECK IT OUT!

1. Write an indirect proof that a triangle cannot have two right angles.

---

1 Introduce

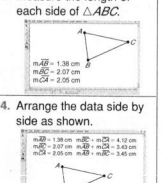
Motivate

Present the following scenario to students: Janet arrives home and wonders if her brother is already there. She knows that he always picks up the newspaper from the porch when he gets home. The newspaper is still on the porch, so she concludes that her brother is not yet home. Explain that Janet has used indirect reasoning. She reaches her conclusion without going inside to see if her brother is home.

Explorations and answers are provided in the *Explorations* binder.

The positions of the longest and shortest sides of a triangle are related to the positions of the largest and smallest angles.

 **Know it! Note**

THEOREM	HYPOTHESIS	CONCLUSION
5-5-1 If two sides of a triangle are not congruent, then the larger angle is opposite the longer side. (In △, larger ∠ is opp. longer side.)	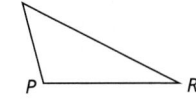 $AB > BC$	$m\angle C > m\angle A$
5-5-2 If two angles of a triangle are not congruent, then the longer side is opposite the larger angle. (In △, longer side is opp. larger ∠.)	$m\angle Z > m\angle Y$	$XY > XZ$

You will prove Theorem 5-5-1 in Exercise 67.

PROOF █ **Theorem 5-5-2**

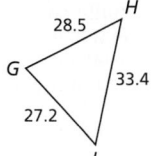

Given: $m\angle P > m\angle R$
Prove: $QR > QP$

Indirect Proof:
Assume $QR \not> QP$. This means that either $QR < QP$ or $QR = QP$.

Caution! ////////
Consider all cases when you assume the opposite. If the conclusion is $QR > QP$, the negation includes $QR < QP$ and $QR = QP$.

Case 1 If $QR < QP$, then $m\angle P < m\angle R$ because the larger angle is opposite the longer side. This contradicts the given information. So $QR \not< QP$.

Case 2 If $QR = QP$, then $m\angle P = m\angle R$ by the Isosceles Triangle Theorem. This also contradicts the given information, so $QR \neq QP$.

The assumption $QR \not> QP$ is false. Therefore $QR > QP$.

EXAMPLE 2 **Ordering Triangle Side Lengths and Angle Measures**

A Write the angles in order from smallest to largest.
The shortest side is $\overline{GJ}$, so the smallest angle is $\angle H$.
The longest side is $\overline{HJ}$, so the largest angle is $\angle G$.
The angles from smallest to largest are $\angle H$, $\angle J$, and $\angle G$.

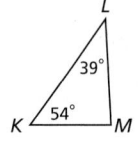

B Write the sides in order from shortest to longest.
$m\angle M = 180° - (39° + 54°) = 87°$ △ Sum Thm.
The smallest angle is $\angle L$, so the shortest side is $\overline{KM}$.
The largest angle is $\angle M$, so the longest side is $\overline{KL}$.
The sides from shortest to longest are $\overline{KM}$, $\overline{LM}$, and $\overline{KL}$.

 **CHECK IT OUT!**

2a. Write the angles in order from smallest to largest.

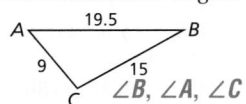

$\angle B$, $\angle A$, $\angle C$

2b. Write the sides in order from shortest to longest.
$\overline{EF}$, $\overline{DF}$, $\overline{DE}$

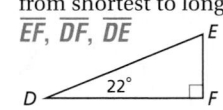

5-5 Indirect Proof and Inequalities in One Triangle **333**

Additional Examples

Example 1

Write an indirect proof that if $a > 0$, then $\frac{1}{a} > 0$.

Given: $a > 0$

Prove: $\frac{1}{a} > 0$

Proof: Assume $\frac{1}{a} \leq 0$. It is given that $a > 0$, so $a\left(\frac{1}{a}\right) \leq a(0)$. This simplifies to $1 \leq 0$, which is false. Therefore the assumption that $\frac{1}{a} \leq 0$ must be false, and thus $\frac{1}{a} > 0$.

Example 2

A. Write the angles in order from smallest to largest. $\angle F$, $\angle H$, $\angle G$

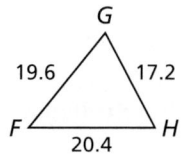

B. Write the sides in order from shortest to longest. $\overline{PQ}$, $\overline{QR}$, $\overline{PR}$

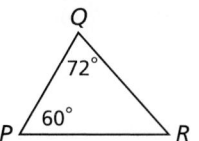

Also available on transparency

INTERVENTION ◄─►
Questioning Strategies

EXAMPLE 1
• What is the negation?
• What is the contradiction?

EXAMPLE 2
• How do you order the sides or angles of a triangle?

Answers to Check It Out!
1. See p. A19.

---

2 Teach

Guided Instruction
Remind students that a conditional statement is logically equivalent to its contrapositive. Have students practice writing negations and identifying statements that contradict each other. Explain the steps for an indirect proof. Point out that problems containing the word *not* are good candidates for an indirect proof. Discuss angle and side relationships in triangles and how to apply the Triangle Inequality Theorem.

Reaching All Learners
Through Visual Cues
Use colors to identify the steps in an indirect proof. Write each of the four steps on page 332 in a different color. Then place colored boxes around the parts of the proof that correspond to each step. For example, write the step "Assume the opposite of the conclusion is true" in blue and put a blue box around the assumption made in the indirect proof.

3a. No; 8 + 13 = 21, which is not greater than the third side length.

3b. Yes; the sum of each pair of 2 lengths is greater than the third length.

A triangle is formed by three segments, but not every set of three segments can form a triangle.

Segments with lengths of 7, 4, and 4 can form a triangle.

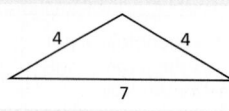

Segments with lengths of 7, 3, and 3 cannot form a triangle.

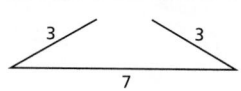

A certain relationship must exist among the lengths of three segments in order for them to form a triangle.

Know it!
Note

Theorem 5-5-3   **Triangle Inequality Theorem**

The sum of any two side lengths of a triangle is greater than the third side length.

$$AB + BC > AC$$
$$BC + AC > AB$$
$$AC + AB > BC$$

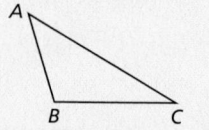

You will prove Theorem 5-5-3 in Exercise 68.

EXAMPLE **3**   **Applying the Triangle Inequality Theorem**

Tell whether a triangle can have sides with the given lengths. Explain.

A 3, 5, 7

| $3 + 5 \overset{?}{>} 7$ | $3 + 7 \overset{?}{>} 5$ | $5 + 7 \overset{?}{>} 3$ |
| $8 > 7$ ✓ | $10 > 5$ ✓ | $12 > 3$ ✓ |

Yes—the sum of each pair of lengths is greater than the third length.

Helpful Hint

To show that three lengths cannot be the side lengths of a triangle, you only need to show that one of the three triangle inequalities is false.

B 4, 6.5, 11

$4 + 6.5 \overset{?}{>} 11$
$10.5 \not> 11$

No—by the Triangle Inequality Theorem, a triangle cannot have these side lengths.

C $n + 5$, n^2, $2n$, when $n = 3$

Step 1 Evaluate each expression when $n = 3$.

$n + 5$	n^2	$2n$
$3 + 5$	3^2	$2(3)$
8	9	6

Step 2 Compare the lengths.

| $8 + 9 \overset{?}{>} 6$ | $8 + 6 \overset{?}{>} 9$ | $9 + 6 \overset{?}{>} 8$ |
| $17 > 6$ ✓ | $14 > 9$ ✓ | $15 > 8$ ✓ |

Yes—the sum of each pair of lengths is greater than the third length.

 **CHECK IT OUT!**   **Tell whether a triangle can have sides with the given lengths. Explain.**

3a. 8, 13, 21   **3b.** 6.2, 7, 9   **3c.** $t - 2$, $4t$, $t^2 + 1$, when $t = 4$

Answers to *Check It Out!*

3c. Yes; when $t = 4$, the value of $t - 2$ is 2, the value of $4t$ is 16, and the value of $t^2 + 1$ is 17. The sum of each pair of 2 lengths is greater than the third length.

EXAMPLE 4

Finding Side Lengths

The lengths of two sides of a triangle are 6 centimeters and 11 centimeters. Find the range of possible lengths for the third side.

Let s represent the length of the third side. Then apply the Triangle Inequality Theorem.

$s + 6 > 11$	$s + 11 > 6$	$6 + 11 > s$
$s > 5$	$s > -5$	$17 > s$

Combine the inequalities. So $5 < s < 17$. The length of the third side is greater than 5 centimeters and less than 17 centimeters.

 4. The lengths of two sides of a triangle are 22 inches and 17 inches. Find the range of possible lengths for the third side.
greater than 5 in. and less than 39 in.

 **Travel Application**

The map shows the approximate distances from San Antonio to Mason and from San Antonio to Austin. What is the range of distances from Mason to Austin?

Let d be the distance from Mason to Austin.

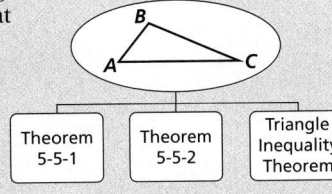

$d + 111 > 78$	$d + 78 > 111$	$111 + 78 > d$	△ Inequal. Thm.
$d > -33$	$d > 33$	$189 > d$	Subtr. Prop. of Inequal.
	$33 < d < 189$		Combine the inequalities.

The distance from Mason to Austin is greater than 33 miles and less than 189 miles.

 **5.** The distance from San Marcos to Johnson City is 50 miles, and the distance from Seguin to San Marcos is 22 miles. What is the range of distances from Seguin to Johnson City?
28 mi < d < 72 mi

THINK AND DISCUSS

1. To write an indirect proof that an angle is obtuse, a student assumes that the angle is acute. Is this the correct assumption? Explain.

2. Give an example of three measures that can be the lengths of the sides of a triangle. Give an example of three lengths that cannot be the sides of a triangle.

3. **GET ORGANIZED** Copy and complete the graphic organizer. In each box, explain what you know about △ABC as a result of the theorem.

Theorem 5-5-1	Theorem 5-5-2	Triangle Inequality Theorem

If students have trouble with compound inequalities, have them write the inequalities separately and then use a number line to combine them into one.

Power Presentations with PowerPoint®

Additional Examples

Example 4

The lengths of two sides of a triangle are 8 in. and 13 in. Find the range of possible lengths for the third side. 5 in. $< x < 21$ in.

Example 5

The figure shows the approximate distances between cities in California. What is the range of distances from San Francisco to Oakland? 5 mi $< x < 97$ mi

Also available on transparency

INTERVENTION
Questioning Strategies

EXAMPLE 4

• How do you find the range for the length of the third side of a triangle?

EXAMPLE 5

• Could you find a range of distances between the cities if they were in a straight line? Explain.

---

3 Close

Summarize

Review the process of an indirect proof: You begin by assuming the opposite of the desired conclusion, and then you write the proof until you reach a contradiction. Review the angle and side relationships in a triangle and the Triangle Inequality Theorem.

ONGOING ASSESSMENT
and INTERVENTION

Diagnose Before the Lesson
5-5 Warm Up, TE p. 332

Monitor During the Lesson
Check It Out! Exercises, SE pp. 332–335
Questioning Strategies, TE pp. 333–335

Assess After the Lesson
5-5 Lesson Quiz, TE p. 339
Alternative Assessment, TE p. 339

Answers to Think and Discuss

1. No; possible answer: the student must consider 2 cases and assume that either the ∠ is acute or the ∠ is rt.

2. Possible answers: 2 cm, 4 cm, 5 cm; 2 cm, 4 cm, 8 cm

3. See p. A5.

5-5 Exercises

5-5 Exercises

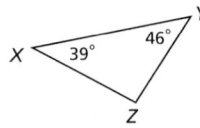
go.hrw.com/Geo/TX
Homework Help Online
KEYWORD: MG7 5-5
Parent Resources Online
KEYWORD: MG7 Parent

Assignment Guide

Assign *Guided Practice* exercises as necessary.

If you finished Examples **1–3**
Basic 16–25, 36–39, 42–57
Average 16–25, 34, 36–57, 66, 67, 73
Advanced 16–25, 34–57, 66–68, 73, 75

If you finished Examples **1–5**
Basic 16–32, 36–39, 42–57, 59–65, 70–72, 76–81
Average 16–34, 40–52, 54–73, 76–81
Advanced 16–35, 40–52, 54–81

Homework Quick Check
Quickly check key concepts.
Exercises: 16, 18, 20, 26, 32, 48, 62

Answers

1–3. See p. A19.

6. Yes; the sum of each pair of 2 lengths is greater than the third length.

7. No; $2 + 9 = 11$, which is not greater than the third side length.

8. Yes; the sum of each pair of 2 lengths is greater than the third length.

9. No; $1.1 + 1.7 = 2.8$, which is not greater than the third side length.

10–17. See p. A19.

🔶 TAKS Practice

Grades 9–11	Exercises
Obj. 1	34, 35, 42–53, 70
Obj. 2	34, 35, 60–65
Obj. 3	76, 77
Obj. 7	54–57, 80, 81
Obj. 9	73

GUIDED PRACTICE

1. **Vocabulary** Describe the process of an *indirect proof* in your own words.

SEE EXAMPLE **1**
p. 332

Write an indirect proof of each statement.

2. A scalene triangle cannot have two congruent angles.

3. An isosceles triangle cannot have a base angle that is a right angle.

SEE EXAMPLE **2**
p. 333

4. Write the angles in order from smallest to largest. $\angle R$, $\angle P$, $\angle Q$

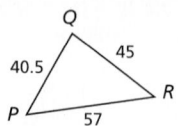

5. Write the sides in order from shortest to longest. $\overline{YZ}$, $\overline{XZ}$, $\overline{XY}$

SEE EXAMPLE **3**
p. 334

Tell whether a triangle can have sides with the given lengths. Explain.

6. 4, 7, 10   7. 2, 9, 12   8. $3\frac{1}{2}, 3\frac{1}{2}, 6$ 9. 3, 1.1, 1.7

10. $3x, 2x - 1, x^2$, when $x = 5$ 11. $7c + 6, 10c - 7, 3c^2$, when $c = 2$

SEE EXAMPLE **4**
p. 335

The lengths of two sides of a triangle are given. Find the range of possible lengths for the third side.

12. 8 mm, 12 mm   13. 16 ft, 16 ft   14. 11.4 cm, 12 cm

SEE EXAMPLE **5**
p. 335

15. **Design** The refrigerator, stove, and sink in a kitchen are at the vertices of a path called the work triangle.

a. If the angle at the sink is the largest, which side of the work triangle will be the longest?

b. The designer wants the longest side of this triangle to be 9 feet long. Can the lengths of the other sides be 5 feet and 4 feet? Explain.

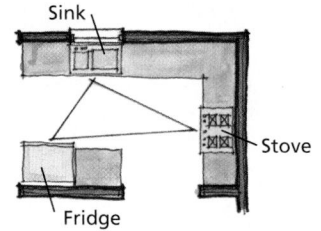
Sink
Stove
Fridge

PRACTICE AND PROBLEM SOLVING

Independent Practice

For Exercises	See Example
16–17	1
18–19	2
20–25	3
26–31	4
32	5

TEKS 🔶 TAKS
Skills Practice p. S13
Application Practice p. S32

Write an indirect proof of each statement.

16. A scalene triangle cannot have two congruent midsegments.

17. Two supplementary angles cannot both be obtuse angles.

18. Write the angles in order from smallest to largest. $\angle J$, $\angle L$, $\angle K$

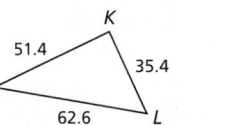

19. Write the sides in order from shortest to longest. $\overline{RS}$, $\overline{ST}$, $\overline{RT}$

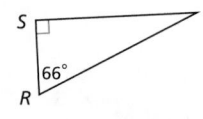

Tell whether a triangle can have sides with the given lengths. Explain.

20. 6, 10, 15   21. 14, 18, 32   22. 11.9, 5.8, 5.8   23. 103, 41.9, 62.5

24. $z + 8, 3z + 5, 4z - 11$, when $z = 6$ 25. $m + 11, 8m, m^2 + 1$, when $m = 3$

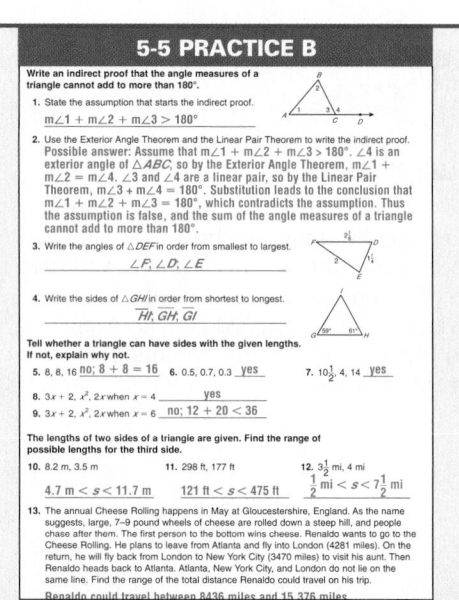

TEXAS LINK

Bicycles

Lance Armstrong, of Austin, broke his own record in 2005 and became the first person to win seven consecutive titles in the Tour de France cycling competition. Only one other person has won five consecutive times.

The lengths of two sides of a triangle are given. Find the range of possible lengths for the third side.

26. 4 yd, 19 yd

27. 28 km, 23 km

28. 9.2 cm, 3.8 cm

29. 3.07 m, 1.89 m

30. $2\frac{1}{8}$ in., $3\frac{5}{8}$ in.

31. $3\frac{5}{6}$ ft, $6\frac{1}{2}$ ft

32. **Bicycles** The five steel tubes of this mountain bike frame form two triangles. List the five tubes in order from shortest to longest. Explain your answer.

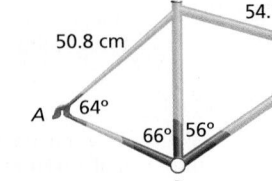

33. **Critical Thinking** The length of the base of an isosceles triangle is 15. What is the range of possible lengths for each leg? Explain.

List the sides of each triangle in order from shortest to longest.

34.

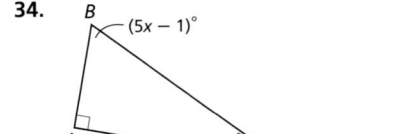

$\overline{AB}, \overline{AC}, \overline{BC}$

35. $\overline{EF}, \overline{DE}, \overline{DF}$

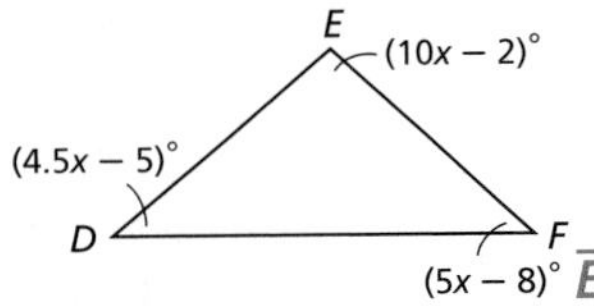

In each set of statements, name the two that contradict each other.

36. ⬭△PQR is a right triangle.
△PQR is a scalene triangle.
⬭△PQR is an acute triangle.

37. ∠Y is supplementary to ∠Z.
⬭m∠Y < 90°
⬭∠Y is an obtuse angle.

38. ⬭△JKL is isosceles with base $\overline{JL}$.
In △JKL, m∠K > m∠J
⬭In △JKL, JK > LK

39. ⬭$\overline{AB} \perp \overline{BC}$
$\overline{AB} \cong \overline{CD}$
⬭$\overline{AB} \parallel \overline{BC}$

40. Figure A is a polygon.
⬭Figure A is a triangle.
⬭Figure A is a quadrilateral.

41. x is even.
⬭x is a multiple of 4.
⬭x is prime.

Compare. Write <, >, or =.

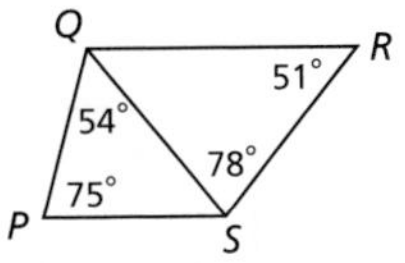

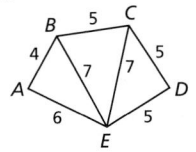

42. QS ▨ PS >

43. PQ ▨ QS <

44. QS ▨ QR <

45. QS ▨ RS =

46. PQ ▨ RS <

47. RS ▨ PS >

48. m∠ABE ▨ m∠BEA >

49. m∠CBE ▨ m∠CEB >

50. m∠DCE ▨ m∠DEC =

51. m∠DCE ▨ m∠CDE <

52. m∠ABE ▨ m∠EAB <

53. m∠EBC ▨ m∠ECB =

List the angles of △JKL in order from smallest to largest.

54. J(−3, −2), K(3, 6), L(8, −2)   ∠J, ∠L, ∠K

55. J(−5, −10), K(−5, 2), L(7, −5)   ∠L, ∠K, ∠J

56. J(−4, 1), K(−3, 8), L(3, 4)   ∠L, ∠J, ∠K

57. J(−10, −4), K(0, 3), L(2, −8)   ∠J, ∠L, ∠K

58. **Critical Thinking** An attorney argues that her client did not commit a burglary because a witness saw her client in a different city at the time of the burglary. Explain how this situation is an example of indirect reasoning.

5-5 Indirect Proof and Inequalities in One Triangle **337**

COMMON ERROR ALERT

In **Exercise 32**, students may think $\overline{BD}$ is the shortest side because it is opposite the 50° angle, which is the smallest angle labeled in the figure. Have them order the sides in each triangle separately, using the given numeric measurements. This will help them see that $\overline{AD}$ is shorter than $\overline{BD}$, and $\overline{AD}$ is thus the shortest segment.

Answers

20. Yes; the sum of each pair of 2 lengths is greater than the third length.

21. No; 14 + 18 = 32, which is not greater than the third side length.

22. No; 5.8 + 5.8 = 11.6, which is not greater than the third side length.

23. Yes; the sum of each pair of 2 lengths is greater than the third length.

24. Yes; when z = 6, the value of z + 8 is 14, the value of 3z + 5 is 23, and the value of 4z − 11 is 13. The sum of each pair of 2 lengths is greater than the third length.

25. No; when m = 3, the value of m + 11 is 14, the value of 8m is 24, and the value of m² + 1 is 10. The sum of 14 and 10 is 24, which is not greater than the third side length.

26. greater than 15 yd and less than 23 yd

27. greater than 5 km and less than 51 km

28. greater than 5.4 cm and less than 13 cm

29. greater than 1.18 m and less than 4.96 m

30. greater than $1\frac{1}{2}$ in. and less than $5\frac{3}{4}$ in.

31. greater than $2\frac{2}{3}$ ft and less than $10\frac{1}{3}$ ft

32. $\overline{AD}, \overline{BD}, \overline{AB}, \overline{BC}, \overline{CD}$; possible answer: in △ABD, m∠ABD = 50°. In △BCD, m∠DBC = 74°. In △ABD, the order of the tubes from shortest to longest is $\overline{AD}$, $\overline{BD}, \overline{AB}$. In △BCD, the order of the tubes from shortest to longest is $\overline{BD}, \overline{BC}, \overline{CD}$. So AD < BD < AB, and BD < BC < CD. Since AB = 50.8 and BC = 54.1, it is also true that AB < BC. So $\overline{AD} < \overline{BD} < \overline{AB} < \overline{BC} < \overline{CD}$.

5-5 PRACTICE C

Indirect proofs work by finding a contradiction that leads to the proof of a statement. For Exercises 1–7, rewrite each statement. Use the symbol → for an "if, then" statement and the symbol ~ for "not," the negation of a statement. Use *a* to stand for "The two angles are a linear pair." Use *b* to stand for "The two angles are supplementary."

Example: If the two angles are a linear pair, then the two angles are supplementary.
a → b

1. If the two angles are supplementary, then the two angles are a linear pair.   b → a

2. If the two angles are not supplementary, then the two angles are a linear pair.   ~b → a

3. If the two angles are a linear pair, then the two angles are not supplementary.   a → ~b

4. If the two angles are not a linear pair, then the two angles are not supplementary.   ~a → ~b

5. If the two angles are not supplementary, then the two angles are not a linear pair.   ~b → ~a

6. If the two angles are not a linear pair, then the two angles are not a linear pair.   ~a → b

7. If the two angles are supplementary, then the two angles are not a linear pair.   b → ~a

8. Suppose the example statement (a → b) is to be proven. Give the number of the statement you would begin with (knowing it would lead to a contradiction) in order to prove the example statement by indirect proof.   2

9. Suppose then the contradiction negates the conclusion. Give the number of the statement that the contradiction leads you to believe must be true.   5

10. Name the logical relationship between the answer to Exercise 9 and the example statement.   contrapositive

11. Name the shortest segment(s) in the figure and explain your reasoning. Do not use a ruler. (*Note:* The figure may not be drawn to scale.)

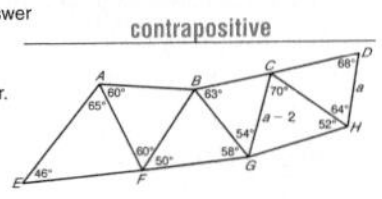

Possible answer: The shortest side in a triangle is opposite the shortest angle. The shortest side in △AEF is $\overline{AF}$. △ABF is equiangular, so $\overline{AF}$ has the same length as $\overline{BF}$. But $\overline{BG}$ is the shortest side in △BGF, so $\overline{AF}, \overline{AB},$ and $\overline{BF}$ cannot be the shortest segments in the figure. $\overline{CG}$ is the shortest segment in △CHG, but $\overline{BC}$ is the shortest segment in △BCG. So $\overline{BC}$ is shorter than $\overline{CG}$. The shortest segment in △CDH is $\overline{DH}$. $\overline{DH}$ has length *a* and $\overline{CG}$ has length a − 2, so $\overline{CG}$ is shorter than $\overline{DH}$. Therefore $\overline{BC}$ is the shortest segment in the figure.

33. a > 7.5, where a is the length of a leg. Possible answer: By the △ Inequal. Thm., a + a > 15 and a + 15 > a. The solution of the first inequality is a > 7.5. The second inequality simplifies to 15 > 0, which is always a true statement.

58. Possible answer: Assume that the client committed the burglary. A person who commits a burglary must be present at the scene at the time the crime is committed. However, a witness saw the client in a different city at the time the burglary was committed. This means the assumption that the client committed the burglary is false. Therefore the client did not commit the burglary.

Lesson 5-5 **337**

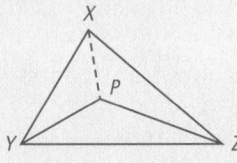
Answers

66. Possible answer:

X

P

Y   Z

Given: P is in the int. of △XYZ.
Prove: XY + XP + PZ > YZ
Proof:
By the △ Inequal. Thm., PY + PZ > YZ and XY + XP > YP. Since PZ > 0, the second inequality is equivalent to XY + XP + PZ > YP + PZ. But then YP + PZ > YZ, so XY + XP + PZ > YZ by the Trans. Prop. of Inequal.

69, 75. See p. A20.

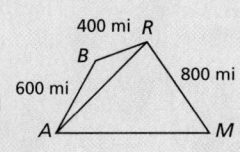

59. This problem will prepare you for the Multi-Step TAKS Prep on page 364. The figure shows an airline's routes between four cities.

400 mi R
B
600 mi   800 mi
A   M

a. The airline's planes fly at an average speed of 500 mi/h. What is the range of time it might take to fly from Auburn (A) to Raymond (R)? **0.4 h < t < 2 h**

b. The airline offers one frequent-flier mile for every mile flown. Is it possible to earn 1800 miles by flying from Millford (M) to Auburn (A)? Explain. **No; AR < 1000, so by the △ Inequal. Thm., AM must be less than 1800.**

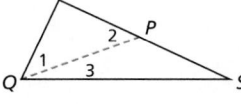

Multi-Step Each set of expressions represents the lengths of the sides of a triangle. Find the range of possible values of n.

60. $n, 6, 8$ **$2 < n < 14$**   61. $2n, 5, 7$ **$1 < n < 6$**   62. $n + 1, 3, 6$ **$2 < n < 8$**

63. $n + 1, n + 2, n + 3$ **$n > 0$** 64. $n + 2, n + 3, 3n - 2$ **$1 < n < 7$** 65. $n, n + 2, 2n + 1$ **$n > 0.5$**

66. Given that P is in the interior of $\triangle XYZ$, prove that $XY + XP + PZ > YZ$.

67. Complete the proof of Theorem 5-5-1 by filling in the blanks.

Given: $RS > RQ$
Prove: m∠RQS > m∠S

R
2 P
1   3
Q   S

a. def. of ≅ segs.
b. Isosc. △ Thm.
c. def. of ≅ ∡
d. m∠1 + m∠3
e. subst.
f. m∠S
g. Trans. Prop. of Inequal.

Proof:
Locate P on $\overline{RS}$ so that $RP = RQ$. So $\overline{RP} \cong \overline{RQ}$ by a. __?__ . Then ∠1 ≅ ∠2 by b. __?__ , and m∠1 = m∠2 by c. __?__ . By the Angle Addition Postulate, m∠RQS = d. __?__ . So m∠RQS > m∠1 by the Comparison Property of Inequality. Then m∠RQS > m∠2 by e. __?__ . By the Exterior Angle Theorem, m∠2 = m∠3 + f. __?__ . So m∠2 > m∠S by the Comparison Property of Inequality. Therefore m∠RQS > m∠S by g. __?__ .

68. Complete the proof of the Triangle Inequality Theorem.

Given: $\triangle ABC$
Prove: $AB + BC > AC$, $AB + AC > BC$, $AC + BC > AB$

B
3 2
A   1 D
C

a. △ABC
b. AD
c. Isosc. △ Thm.
d. Def. of ≅ ∡
e. m∠3
f. Subst.
g. In △, longer side is opp. larger ∠.
h. Subst.
i. AC + BC > AB

Proof:
One side of $\triangle ABC$ is as long as or longer than each of the other sides. Let this side be $\overline{AB}$. Then $AB + BC > AC$, and $AB + AC > BC$. Therefore what remains to be proved is $AC + BC > AB$.

Statements	Reasons
1. a. __?__	1. Given
2. Locate D on $\overrightarrow{AC}$ so that $BC = DC$.	2. Ruler Post.
3. $AC + DC =$ b. __?__	3. Seg. Add. Post.
4. ∠1 ≅ ∠2	4. c. __?__
5. m∠1 = m∠2	5. d. __?__
6. m∠ABD = m∠2 + e. __?__	6. ∠ Add. Post.
7. m∠ABD > m∠2	7. Comparison Prop. of Inequal.
8. m∠ABD > m∠1	8. f. __?__
9. $AD > AB$	9. g. __?__
10. $AC + DC > AB$	10. h. __?__
11. i. __?__	11. Subst.

69. Write About It Explain why the hypotenuse is always the longest side of a right triangle. Explain why the diagonal of a square is longer than each side.

5-5 READING STRATEGIES

Indirect proofs can be written by following these steps:

1. Identify the conjecture to be proven.
2. Assume the opposite of the conclusion is true.
3. Use direct reasoning to show the assumption leads to a contradiction.
4. Conclude that since the assumption is false, the original conjecture must be true.

Find the two statements in each set that contradict each other or are opposites.

1. $\overline{XY} \| \overline{AB}$
   $\overline{AB} \perp \overline{XY}$
   $\overline{AB} = \overline{XZ}$
   $\overline{XY} \| \overline{AB}, \overline{AB} \perp \overline{XY}$ _____

2. In △ABC, m∠A > m∠B.
   In △ABC, m∠C = 60°.
   In △ABC, m∠A = 50° and m∠B = 70°.
   In △ABC, m∠A > m∠B. In △ABC, m∠A = 50° and m∠B = 70°. _____

3. △PQR is a right triangle.
   ∠P is an acute angle.
   ∠Q is an obtuse angle.
   △PQR is a right triangle. ∠Q is an obtuse angle. _____

Write True or False. Explain your answer.

4. Two supplementary angles can both be obtuse.
   False; supplementary angles have measures that add up to 180°, so both angles cannot be obtuse (greater than 90°). _____

5. A scalene triangle can have two congruent sides.
   False; a scalene triangle has three unequal sides by definition. _____

5-5 RETEACH

In a direct proof, you begin with a true hypothesis and prove that a conclusion is true. In an **indirect proof,** you begin by assuming that the conclusion is false (that is, that the opposite of the conclusion is true). You then show that this assumption leads to a contradiction.

Consider the statement "Two acute angles do not form a linear pair."

	Writing an Indirect Proof	
Steps		Example
1. Identify the conjecture to be proven.		**Given:** ∠1 and ∠2 are acute angles. **Prove:** ∠1 and ∠2 do not form a linear pair.
2. Assume the opposite of the conclusion is true.		Assume ∠1 and ∠2 form a linear pair.
3. Use direct reasoning to show that the assumption leads to a contradiction.		m∠1 + m∠2 = 180° by def. of linear pair. Since m∠1 < 90° and m∠2 < 90°, m∠1 + m∠2 < 180°. This is a contradiction.
4. Conclude that the assumption that ∠1 and ∠2 form a linear pair is false. Therefore ∠1 and ∠2 do not form a linear pair.		The assumption that ∠1 and ∠2 form a linear pair is false. Therefore ∠1 and ∠2 do not form a linear pair.

Use the following statement for Exercises 1–4.
An obtuse triangle cannot have a right angle.

1. Identify the conjecture to be proven.
   Given: △ABC is an obtuse △, ∠B is an obtuse angle; **Prove:** △ABC does not have a right angle. _____

2. Assume the opposite of the conclusion. Write this assumption.
   Assume △ABC does have a right angle. Let ∠A be a right angle. _____

3. Use direct reasoning to arrive at a contradiction.
   Possible answer: If ∠A is a right angle, then m∠B + m∠C = 90°. But m∠B > 90°, since ∠B is obtuse. So this is a contradiction. _____

4. What can you conclude?
   The assumption that △ABC does have a right angle is false. Therefore △ABC does not have a right angle. _____

70. The lengths of two sides of a triangle are 3 feet and 5 feet. Which could be the length of the third side?

Ⓐ 3 feet   Ⓑ 8 feet   Ⓒ 15 feet   Ⓓ 16 feet

71. Which statement about △GHJ is false?

Ⓕ $GH < GJ$

Ⓖ $m\angle H > m\angle J$

Ⓗ $GH + HJ < GJ$

Ⓙ △GHJ is a scalene triangle.

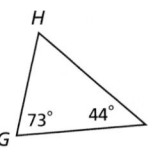

72. In △RST, $m\angle S = 92°$. Which is the longest side of △RST?

Ⓐ $\overline{RS}$ Ⓒ $\overline{RT}$

Ⓑ $\overline{ST}$ Ⓓ Cannot be determined

CHALLENGE AND EXTEND

$\dfrac{3}{10}$, or 30%   **73. Probability** A bag contains five sticks. The lengths of the sticks are 1 inch, 3 inches, 5 inches, 7 inches, and 9 inches. Suppose you pick three sticks from the bag at random. What is the probability you can form a triangle with the three sticks?

a. $\sqrt{2}$ is rational

b. $\dfrac{p^2}{q^2}$

c. $2q^2$

d. $(2x)^2 = 4x^2$

e. $q^2 = \dfrac{1}{2}p^2$ and p^2 is divisible by 4

74. Complete this indirect argument that $\sqrt{2}$ is irrational. Assume that **a.** ___?___ . Then $\sqrt{2} = \dfrac{p}{q}$, where p and q are positive integers that have no common factors. Thus $2 =$ **b.** ___?___ , and $p^2 =$ **c.** ___?___ . This implies that p^2 is even, and thus p is even. Since p^2 is the square of an even number, p^2 is divisible by 4 because **d.** ___?___ . But then q^2 must be even because **e.** ___?___ , and so q is even. Then p and q have a common factor of 2, which contradicts the assumption that p and q have no common factors.

75. Prove that the perpendicular segment from a point to a line is the shortest segment from the point to the line.

Given: $\overline{PX} \perp \ell$. Y is any point on ℓ other than X.

Prove: $PY > PX$

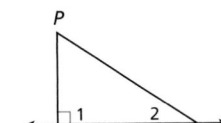

Plan: Show that $\angle 2$ and $\angle P$ are complementary. Use the Comparison Property of Inequality to show that $90° > m\angle 2$. Then show that $m\angle 1 > m\angle 2$ and thus $PY > PX$.

SPIRAL REVIEW

Write the equation of each line in standard form. *(Previous course)*

76. the line through points $(-3, 2)$ and $(-1, -2)$ $2x + y = -4$

77. the line with slope 2 and x-intercept of -3 $-2x + y = 6$

Show that the triangles are congruent for the given value of the variable. *(Lesson 4-4)*

78. $QP = 3$, $ST = 6$, and $SU = 4$, so △PQR ≅ △TUS by SSS.

78. △PQR ≅ △TUS, when $x = -1$

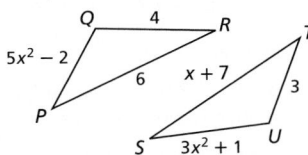

79. $BC = 10$, $EF = 11$, and $m\angle ABC = 102°$, so △ABC ≅ △EFD by SAS.

79. △ABC ≅ △EFD, when $p = 6$

Find the orthocenter of a triangle with the given vertices. *(Lesson 5-3)*

80. $R(0, 5)$, $S(4, 3)$, $T(0, 1)$ $(1, 3)$

81. $M(0, 0)$, $N(3, 0)$, $P(0, 5)$ $(0, 0)$

5-5 PROBLEM SOLVING

1. A charter plane travels from Barrow, Alaska, to Fairbanks. From Fairbanks, it flies to Nome, and then back to its starting point in Barrow. Which of the three legs of the trip is the longest?

Fairbanks to Nome

2. Three cell phone towers are shown at right. The measure of ∠M is 10° less than the measure of ∠K. The measure of ∠L is 1° greater than the measure of ∠K. Which two towers are closest together?

towers K and L

Use the figure for Exercises 3 and 4.

In disc golf, a player tries to throw a disc into a metal basket target. Four disc golf targets on a course are shown at right.

3. Which two targets are closest together?

targets 2 and 3

4. Which two targets are farthest apart?

targets 1 and 4

Choose the best answer.

5. The distance from Jacksonville to Tampa is 171 miles. The distance from Tampa to Miami is 206 miles. Use the Triangle Inequality Theorem to find the range for the distance from Jacksonville to Miami.

A 0 mi < d < 35 mi

B 0 mi < d < 377 mi

Ⓒ 35 mi < d < 377 mi

D -35 mi < d < 377 mi

6. In Jessica's room, the distance from the door D to the closet C is 4 feet. The distance from the closet to the window W is 6 feet. The distance from the window to the door is 8 feet. On a floor plan of her room, △CDW is drawn. Order the angles from least to greatest measure.

F ∠C, ∠D, ∠W   H ∠W, ∠C, ∠D

G ∠D, ∠C, ∠W   Ⓙ ∠W, ∠D, ∠C

7. Walking paths at a park are shown. Which route represents the greatest distance?

Ⓐ A to B to D   C C to B to D

B A to D to B   D C to D to B

5-5 CHALLENGE

The Triangle Inequality Theorem describes a relationship among the lengths of the sides of a triangle. The following two theorems relate the lengths of the sides to the measures of the angles.

UNEQUAL SIDES THEOREM	UNEQUAL ANGLES THEOREM
If one side of a triangle is longer than another side, then the angle opposite the longer side is larger than the angle opposite the shorter side.	If one angle of a triangle is larger than another angle, then the side opposite the larger angle is longer than the side opposite the smaller angle.

1. In △XYZ, $XY = 9.3$, $YZ = 7.6$, and $XZ = 8.05$. Name the largest and smallest angles of △XYZ.

largest angle: ∠Z, smallest angle: ∠X

2. In △JKL, $m\angle J = 62°$ and $m\angle K = 57°$. Name the longest and shortest sides of △JKL.

longest side: $\overline{KL}$; shortest side: $\overline{JL}$

In each figure, list the segments in order from longest to shortest.

3. CD, BC, BD, AB, AD

4. PT, PQ, QT, QR, RT, ST, RS

5. YZ, XY, XZ, WX, WZ, VW, VZ

On a separate sheet of paper, write a proof of each theorem.

6. *Unequal Sides Theorem*

Given: △ABC with $BC > AB$

Prove: $m\angle BAC > m\angle C$.

Plan for proof: Locate point D on $\overline{BC}$ such that $BD = BA$. Draw $\overline{AD}$. Explain why $m\angle BAC > m\angle 3$, $m\angle 3 > m\angle C$, and so $m\angle BAC > m\angle C$.

7. *Unequal Angles Theorem*

Given: △PQR with $m\angle P > m\angle R$

Prove: $QR > QP$

Plan for proof: The three possible relationships between QR and QP are $QR = QP$, $QR < QP$, and $QR > QP$. Show that the first two relationships listed are impossible.

Proofs may vary.

5-5 Lesson Quiz

1. Write the angles in order from smallest to largest. ∠C, ∠B, ∠A

2. Write the sides in order from shortest to longest. $\overline{DE}$, $\overline{EF}$, $\overline{DF}$

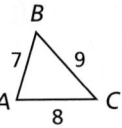

3. The lengths of two sides of a triangle are 17 cm and 12 cm. Find the range of possible lengths for the third side. 5 cm < x < 29 cm

4. Tell whether a triangle can have sides with lengths 2.7, 3.5, and 9.8. Explain. No; 2.7 + 3.5 is not greater than 9.8.

5. Ray wants to place a chair so it is 10 ft from his television set. Can the other two distances shown be 8 ft and 6 ft? Explain. Yes; the sum of any two lengths is greater than the third length.

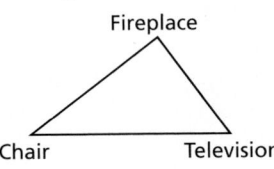

Fireplace

Chair   Television

Also available on transparency

Objective: Apply inequalities in two triangles.

Online Edition
Tutorial Videos

Countdown to TAKS Week 11

Power Presentations
with PowerPoint®

Warm Up

1. Write the angles in order from smallest to largest. ∠X, ∠Z, ∠Y

2. The lengths of two sides of a triangle are 12 cm and 9 cm. Find the range of possible lengths for the third side.
3 cm < s < 21 cm

Also available on transparency

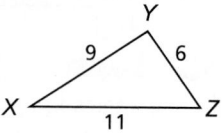

Teacher: Today we will study the Hinge Theorem.
Student: Do we need tools?

⭐ **Geometry TEKS**

G.3 Geometric structure*
(B) construct and justify statements about geometric figures and their properties
(E) use deductive reasoning to prove a statement

* **Knowledge and Skills** See p. 298.

5-6 Inequalities in Two Triangles

⭐ TEKS G.3.B Geometric structure: construct and justify statements about geometric figures and their properties. Also G.3.E

Objective
Apply inequalities in two triangles.

Who uses this?
Designers of this circular swing ride can use the angle of the swings to determine how high the chairs will be at full speed. (See Example 2.)

In this lesson, you will apply inequality relationships between two triangles.

Know it!
Note

Theorems — Inequalities in Two Triangles

THEOREM	HYPOTHESIS	CONCLUSION
5-6-1 Hinge Theorem If two sides of one triangle are congruent to two sides of another triangle and the included angles are not congruent, then the longer third side is across from the larger included angle.	m∠A > m∠D	BC > EF
5-6-2 Converse of the Hinge Theorem If two sides of one triangle are congruent to two sides of another triangle and the third sides are not congruent, then the larger included angle is across from the longer third side.	GH > KL	m∠J > m∠M

You will prove Theorem 5-6-1 in Exercise 35.

PROOF ▌ **Converse of the Hinge Theorem**

Given: $\overline{PQ} \cong \overline{XY}$, $\overline{PR} \cong \overline{XZ}$, QR > YZ
Prove: m∠P > m∠X

Indirect Proof:
Assume m∠P ≯ m∠X. So either m∠P < m∠X, or m∠P = m∠X.

Case 1 If m∠P < m∠X, then QR < YZ by the Hinge Theorem. This contradicts the given information that QR > YZ. So m∠P ≮ m∠X.

Case 2 If m∠P = m∠X, then ∠P ≅ ∠X. So △PQR ≅ △XYZ by SAS. Then $\overline{QR} \cong \overline{YZ}$ by CPCTC, and QR = YZ. This also contradicts the given information. So m∠P ≠ m∠X.
The assumption m∠P ≯ m∠X is false. Therefore m∠P > m∠X.

---

1 Introduce

EXPLORATION

5-6 Inequalities in Two Triangles

Use geometry software for this Exploration.

1. Construct a triangle. Label the vertices A, B, and C.

2. Measure the length of each side of △ABC and measure ∠BAC.

3. Copy and paste △ABC to make a congruent triangle △DEF. Measure the length of each side of △DEF and measure ∠EDF.

4. Drag point E so that m∠EDF < m∠BAC, but do not change the length of $\overline{DE}$. (Hint: Construct a circle centered at D with $\overline{DE}$ as its radius.) How do BC and EF compare?

5. Drag point E to different positions so that m∠EDF < m∠BAC, but do not change the length of $\overline{DE}$. How do BC and EF compare?

Motivate

Open the classroom door and show students that as the angle between the door and the doorway increases, the distance across the floor from the door to the door jamb also increases. This geometric relationship is summarized in the Hinge Theorem and its converse. Explain that in this lesson, students will study inequality relationships in two triangles.

Explorations and answers are provided in the *Explorations* binder.

EXAMPLE 1 Using the Hinge Theorem and Its Converse

A Compare m∠PQS and m∠RQS.

Compare the side lengths in △PQS and △RQS.

$$PQ = RQ \qquad QS = QS \qquad PS > RS$$

By the Converse of the Hinge Theorem,
m∠PQS > m∠RQS.

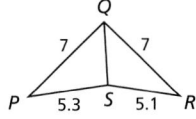

B Compare KL and MN.

Compare the sides and angles in △KLN and △MNL.

$$KN = ML \qquad LN = LN \qquad m∠LNK < m∠NLM$$

By the Hinge Theorem, KL < MN.

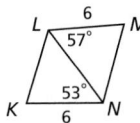

x² Algebra

C Find the range of values for z.

Step 1 Compare the side lengths in △TUV and △TWV.

$$TV = TV \qquad VU = VW \qquad TU < TW$$

By the Converse of the Hinge Theorem,
m∠UVT < m∠WVT.

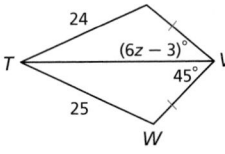

$6z - 3 < 45$	*Substitute the given values.*
$z < 8$	*Add 3 to both sides and divide both sides by 6.*

Step 2 Since ∠UVT is in a triangle, m∠UVT > 0°.

$6z - 3 > 0$	*Substitute the given value.*
$z > 0.5$	*Add 3 to both sides and divide both sides by 6.*

Step 3 Combine the inequalities.

The range of values for z is $0.5 < z < 8$.

CHECK IT OUT! Compare the given measures.

1a. m∠EGH and m∠EGF **1b.** BC and AB

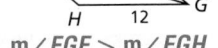

m∠EGF > m∠EGH BC > AB

EXAMPLE 2 Entertainment Application

The angle of the swings in a circular swing ride changes with the speed of the ride. The diagram shows the position of one swing at two different speeds. Which rider is farther from the base of the swing tower? Explain.

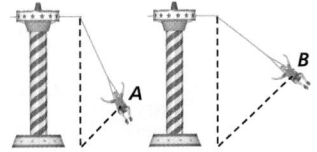

The height of the tower and the length of the cable holding the chair are the same in both triangles.

The angle formed by the swing in position A is smaller than the angle formed by the swing in position B. So rider B is farther from the base of the tower than rider A by the Hinge Theorem.

Power Presentations with PowerPoint®

Additional Examples

Example 1

A. Compare m∠BAC and m∠DAC. m∠BAC > m∠DAC

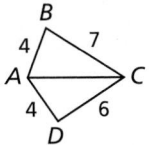

B. Compare EF and FG. EF < FG

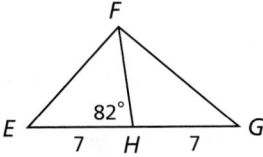

C. Find the range of values for k.

$$2.4 < k < 10$$

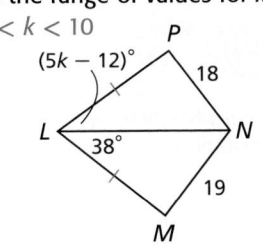

Example 2

John and Luke leave school at the same time. John rides his bike 3 blocks west and then 4 blocks north. Luke rides 4 blocks east and then 3 blocks at a bearing of N 10° E. Who is farther from school? Explain. The angle formed by John's route (90°) is less than the angle formed by Luke's route (100°), so Luke is farther from the school.

Also available on transparency

---

2 Teach

Guided Instruction

Explain the Hinge Theorem and its converse by using visual aids, such as a book or a pair of scissors. Show how the theorems are used to compare angle measures in two triangles by comparing their side lengths.

Teaching Tip **Kinesthetic** Have students place the tips of their thumbs together in a line and touch their index fingers to form a triangle. Have them observe the angle at their index fingers as they pull their thumbs apart.

Reaching All Learners

Through Kinesthetic Experience

Have students use straws, raw spaghetti, or strips of paper to build triangles with side lengths of 4 in. and 5 in. and an included angle measure of 30°, 60°, and 80°. Have students measure and compare the lengths of the third sides of their triangles. Discuss how the third side increases as the angle increases.

INTERVENTION
Questioning Strategies

EXAMPLE 1

• Which theorem did you use for each example? Explain why.

EXAMPLE 2

• How do you know whether to use the Hinge Theorem or the Converse of the Hinge Theorem?

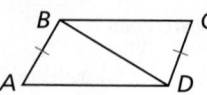

3a. 1. *C* is the mdpt. of $\overline{BD}$. $m\angle 1 = m\angle 2$, $m\angle 3 > m\angle 4$ (Given)
2. $\overline{BC} \cong \overline{DC}$ (Def. of mdpt.) 3. $\angle 1 \cong \angle 2$ (Def. of $\cong \angle$)
4. $\overline{AC} \cong \overline{EC}$ (Conv. of Isosc. $\triangle$ Thm.)
5. $AB > ED$ (Hinge Thm.)

3b. 1. $\angle SRT \cong \angle STR$, $TU > RU$ (Given)
2. $\overline{ST} \cong \overline{SR}$ (Conv. of Isosc. $\triangle$ Thm.)
3. $\overline{SU} \cong \overline{SU}$ (Reflex. Prop. of $\cong$)
4. $m\angle TSU > m\angle RSU$, (Conv. of Hinge Thm.)

 **2.** When the swing ride is at full speed, the chairs are farthest from the base of the swing tower. What can you conclude about the angles of the swings at full speed versus low speed? Explain. The ∠ of the swing at full speed is greater than the ∠ at low speed.

EXAMPLE **3** **Proving Triangle Relationships**

Write a two-column proof.
Given: $\overline{KL} \cong \overline{NL}$
Prove: $KM > NM$

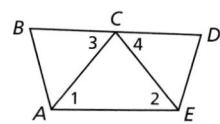

Proof:

Statements	Reasons
1. $\overline{KL} \cong \overline{NL}$	1. Given
2. $\overline{LM} \cong \overline{LM}$	2. Reflex. Prop. of $\cong$
3. $m\angle KLM = m\angle NLM + m\angle KLN$	3. $\angle$ Add. Post.
4. $m\angle KLM > m\angle NLM$	4. Comparison Prop. of Inequal.
5. $KM > NM$	5. Hinge Thm.

 Write a two-column proof.
3a. Given: *C* is the midpoint of $\overline{BD}$.
  $m\angle 1 = m\angle 2$
  $m\angle 3 > m\angle 4$
Prove: $AB > ED$

3b. Given: $\angle SRT \cong \angle STR$
  $TU > RU$
Prove: $m\angle TSU > m\angle RSU$

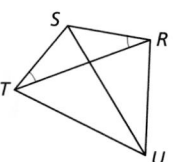

THINK AND DISCUSS

1. Describe a real-world object that shows the Hinge Theorem or its converse.

2. Can you make a conclusion about the triangles shown at right by applying the Hinge Theorem? Explain.

3. GET ORGANIZED Copy and complete the graphic organizer. In each box, use the given triangles to write a statement for the theorem.

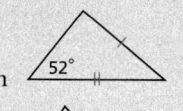

Inequalities in Two Triangles

| Hinge Theorem | Converse of Hinge Theorem |

 Know it! *Note*

Answers to *Think and Discuss*

1. Possible answer: kitchen tongs

2. No; in this case, 2 sides of one $\triangle$ are $\cong$ to 2 sides of the second $\triangle$, but the given $\angle$ measures are not the measures of the $\angle$ included between the $\cong$ sides. Thus you cannot apply the Hinge Thm.

3. See p. A5.

go.hrw.com/Geo/TX
Homework Help Online
KEYWORD: MG7 5-6
Parent Resources Online
KEYWORD: MG7 Parent

5-6 **Exercises**

GUIDED PRACTICE

SEE EXAMPLE 1
p. 341

Compare the given measures.

1. AC and XZ

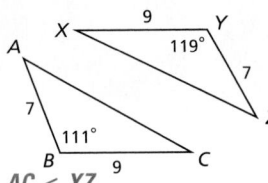

$AC < XZ$

2. m∠SRT and m∠QRT

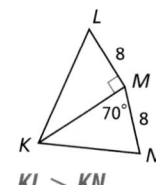

m∠SRT > m∠QRT

3. KL and KN

L, 8, M, 70°, 8, K, N

$KL > KN$

Find the range of values for x.

4.

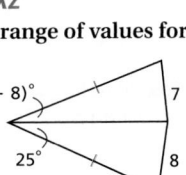

$(2x + 8)°$, 7, 25°, 8

$-4 < x < 8.5$

5.

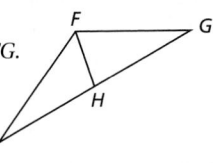

9, 53°, 62°, $5x - 6$

$1.2 < x < 3$

6.

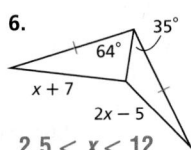

35°, 64°, $x + 7$, $2x - 5$

$2.5 < x < 12$

SEE EXAMPLE 2
p. 341

7. Health A therapist can take measurements to gauge the flexibility of a patient's elbow joint. In which position is the angle measure at the elbow joint greater? Explain.

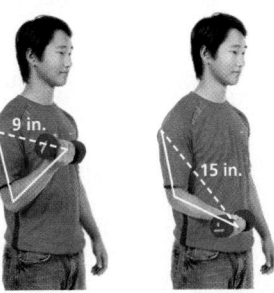

9 in. 15 in.

SEE EXAMPLE 3
p. 342

8. Write a two-column proof.
Given: $\overline{FH}$ is a median of △DFG.
m∠DHF > m∠GHF
Prove: $DF > GF$

F, G, H, D

PRACTICE AND PROBLEM SOLVING

Compare the given measures.

9. m∠DCA and m∠BCA

B, 7, 10, C, 7, A, 11, D

m∠DCA > m∠BCA

10. m∠GHJ and m∠KLM

H, 8, J, 6, 10, G, K, 11, 6, M, 8, L

m∠GHJ < m∠KLM

11. TU and SV

S, 47°, 21, T, 39°, V, 21, U

$TU > SV$

Find the range of values for z.

12.

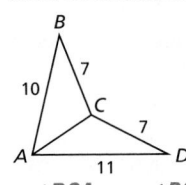

65°, 16, $4z - 12$, 54°

$3 < z < 7$

13.

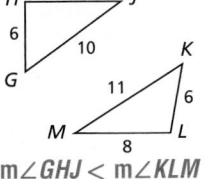

$(2z + 7)°$, 72°, 19, 30

$-3.5 < z < 32.5$

14.

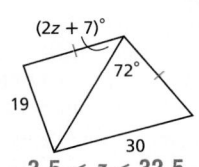

$z + 11$, 122°, $4z - 6$

$\dfrac{3}{2} < z < \dfrac{17}{3}$

Assignment Guide

Assign *Guided Practice* exercises as necessary.

If you finished Examples **1–3**
  Basic 9–16, 18–28, 30–33, 36–43
  Average 9–34, 36–43
Advanced 9–43

Homework Quick Check
Quickly check key concepts.
Exercises: 10, 15, 16, 18, 24

Answers

7. The second position; the lengths of the upper and lower arm are the same in both positions, but the distance from the shoulder to the wrist is greater in the second position. So the included ∠ measure is greater by the Conv. of the Hinge Thm.

8. 1. $\overline{FH}$ is a median of △DFG. m∠DHF > m∠GHF (Given)
   2. H is the midpoint of $\overline{DG}$. (Def. of median)
   3. $\overline{DH} \cong \overline{GH}$ (Def. of mdpt.)
   4. $\overline{FH} \cong \overline{FH}$ (Reflex. Prop. of ≅)
   5. $DF > GF$ (Hinge Thm.)

🦵TAKS Practice

Grades 9–11	Exercises
Obj. 1	18–23, 31
Obj. 2	34

15. **Industry** The operator of a backhoe changes the distance between the cab and the bucket by changing the angle formed by the arms. In which position is the distance from the cab to the bucket greater? Explain.

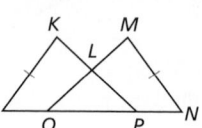

16. Write a two-column proof.
Given: $\overline{JK} \cong \overline{NM}$, $\overline{KP} \cong \overline{MQ}$, $JQ > NP$
Prove: $m\angle K > m\angle M$

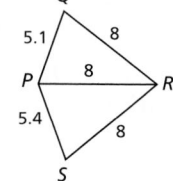

17. **Critical Thinking** ABC is an isosceles triangle with base $\overline{BC}$. XYZ is an isosceles triangle with base $\overline{YZ}$. Given that $\overline{AB} \cong \overline{XY}$ and $m\angle A = m\angle X$, compare BC and YZ. **$BC = YZ$**

Compare. Write <, >, or =.

18. $m\angle QRP$ ▨ $m\angle SRP$ **<**   19. $m\angle QPR$ ▨ $m\angle QRP$ **>**

20. $m\angle PRS$ ▨ $m\angle RSP$ **<**   21. $m\angle RSP$ ▨ $m\angle RPS$ **=**

22. $m\angle QPR$ ▨ $m\angle RPS$ **>**   23. $m\angle PSR$ ▨ $m\angle PQR$ **<**

Make a conclusion based on the Hinge Theorem or its converse. (Hint: Draw a sketch.)

24. In $\triangle ABC$ and $\triangle DEF$, $\overline{AB} \cong \overline{DE}$, $\overline{BC} \cong \overline{EF}$, $m\angle B = 59°$, and $m\angle E = 47°$. **$AC > DF$**

25. $\triangle RST$ is isosceles with base $\overline{RT}$. The endpoints of $\overline{SV}$ are vertex S and a point V on $\overline{RT}$. $RV = 4$, and $TV = 5$. **$m\angle RSV < m\angle TSV$**

26. In $\triangle GHJ$ and $\triangle KLM$, $\overline{GH} \cong \overline{KL}$, and $\overline{GJ} \cong \overline{KM}$. $\angle G$ is a right angle, and $\angle K$ is an acute angle. **$HJ > LM$**

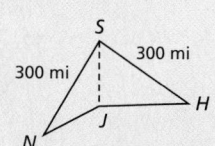

27. In $\triangle XYZ$, $\overline{XM}$ is the median to $\overline{YZ}$, and $YX > ZX$. **$m\angle YMX > m\angle ZMX$**

28. **Write About It** The picture shows a door hinge in two different positions. Use the picture to explain why Theorem 5-6-1 is called the Hinge Theorem.

29. **Write About It** Compare the Hinge Theorem to the SAS Congruence Postulate. How are they alike? How are they different?

30a. Newton Springs; $NJ < JH$ by the Hinge Thm.

30. **MULTI-STEP TAKS PREP** This problem will prepare you for the Multi-Step TAKS Prep on page 364.
The solid lines in the figure show an airline's routes between four cities.
a. A traveler wants to fly from Jackson (J) to Shelby (S), but there is no direct flight between these cities. Given that $m\angle NSJ < m\angle HSJ$, should the traveler first fly to Newton Springs (N) or to Hollis (H) if he wants to minimize the number of miles flown? Why?
b. The distance from Shelby (S) to Jackson (J) is 182 mi. What is the minimum number of miles the traveler will have to fly? **418 mi**

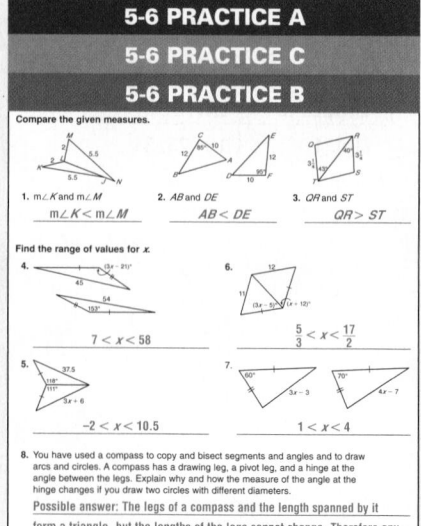
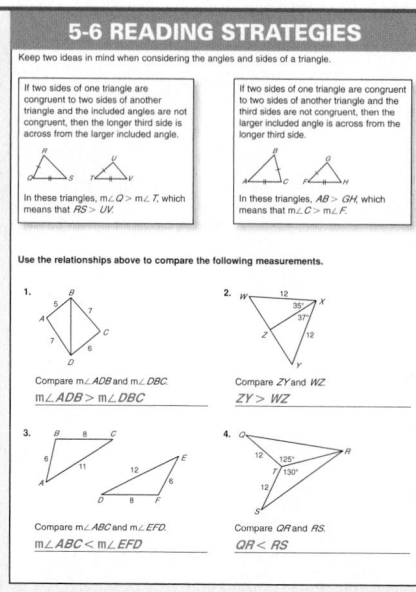
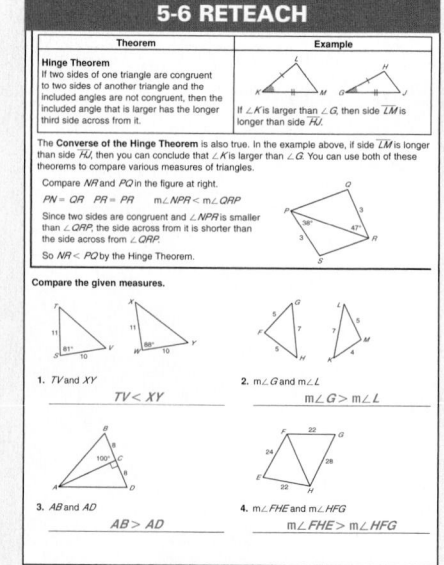
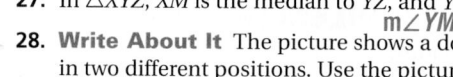

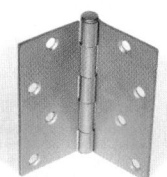

31. $\overline{ML}$ is a median of $\triangle JKL$. Which inequality best describes the range of values for *x*?

Ⓐ $x > 2$　　Ⓒ $3 < x < 4\frac{2}{3}$

Ⓑ $x > 10$　　Ⓓ $3 < x < 10$

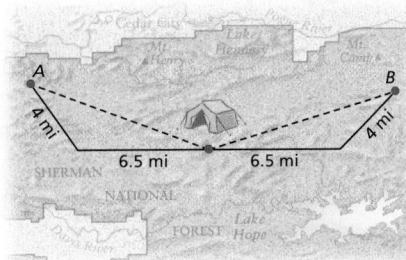

32. $\overline{DC}$ is a median of $\triangle ABC$. Which of the following statements is true?

Ⓕ $BC < AC$　　Ⓖ $BC > AC$　　Ⓗ $AD = DB$　　Ⓙ $DC = AB$

33. Short Response Two groups start hiking from the same camp. Group A hikes 6.5 miles due west and then hikes 4 miles in the direction N 35° W. Group B hikes 6.5 miles due east and then hikes 4 miles in the direction N 45° E. At this point, which group is closer to the camp? Explain.

CHALLENGE AND EXTEND

34. Multi-Step In $\triangle XYZ$, $XZ = 5x + 15$, $XY = 8x - 6$, and $m\angle XVZ > m\angle XVY$. Find the range of values for *x*.
$0.75 < x < 7$

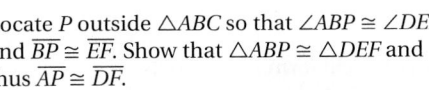

35. Use these steps to write a paragraph proof of the Hinge Theorem.

Given: $\overline{AB} \cong \overline{DE}$, $\overline{BC} \cong \overline{EF}$, $m\angle ABC > m\angle DEF$
Prove: $AC > DF$

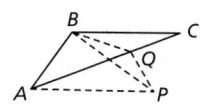

a. Locate *P* outside $\triangle ABC$ so that $\angle ABP \cong \angle DEF$ and $\overline{BP} \cong \overline{EF}$. Show that $\triangle ABP \cong \triangle DEF$ and thus $\overline{AP} \cong \overline{DF}$.

b. Locate *Q* on $\overline{AC}$ so that $\overline{BQ}$ bisects $\angle PBC$. Draw $\overline{QP}$. Show that $\triangle BQP \cong \triangle BQC$ and thus $\overline{QP} \cong \overline{QC}$.

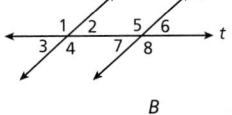

c. Justify the statements $AQ + QP > AP$, $AQ + QC = AC$, $AQ + QC > AP$, $AC > AP$, and $AC > DF$.

SPIRAL REVIEW

Find the range and mode, if any, of each set of data. *(Previous course)*

36. 2, 5, 1, 0.5, 0.75, 2
4.5; 2

37. 95, 97, 89, 87, 85, 99
14; none

38. 5, 5, 7, 9, 4, 4, 8, 7
5; 4, 5, 7

39. $m\angle 2 = m\angle 6 = 36°$; $m\|n$ by the Conv. of the Corr. ∡ Post.

40. $m\angle 4 = 48°$, $m\angle 7 = 132°$; $m\|n$ by the Conv. of the Same-Side Int. ∡ Thm.

For the given information, show that $m \| n$. State any postulates or theorems used. *(Lesson 3-3)*

39. $m\angle 2 = (3x + 21)°$, $m\angle 6 = (7x + 1)°$, $x = 5$

40. $m\angle 4 = (2x + 34)°$, $m\angle 7 = (15x + 27)°$, $x = 7$

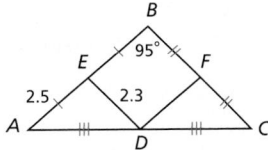

Find each measure. *(Lesson 5-4)*

41. DF **2.5**　　**42.** BC **4.6**　　**43.** $m\angle BFD$ **85°**

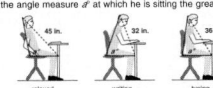
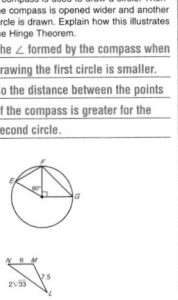

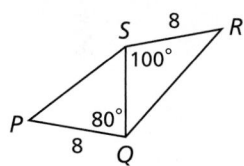
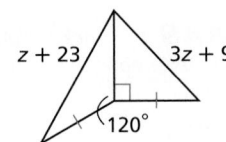
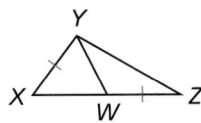

Simplest Radical Form

Algebra

When a problem involves square roots, you may be asked to give the answer in simplest radical form. Recall that the radicand is the expression under the radical sign.

See Skills Bank page S55

Simplest Form of a Square-Root Expression

An expression containing square roots is in simplest form when

- the radicand has no perfect square factors other than 1.
- the radicand has no fractions.
- there are no square roots in any denominator.

To simplify a radical expression, remember that the square root of a product is equal to the product of the square roots. Also, the square root of a quotient is equal to the quotient of the square roots.

$$\sqrt{ab} = \sqrt{a} \cdot \sqrt{b}, \text{ when } a \geq 0 \text{ and } b \geq 0$$

$$\sqrt{\frac{a}{b}} = \frac{\sqrt{a}}{\sqrt{b}}, \text{ when } a \geq 0 \text{ and } b > 0$$

Examples

Write each expression in simplest radical form.

Ⓐ $\sqrt{216}$

$\sqrt{216}$ *216 has a perfect-square factor of 36, so the expression is not in simplest radical form.*

$\sqrt{(36)(6)}$ *Factor the radicand.*

$\sqrt{36} \cdot \sqrt{6}$ *Product Property of Square Roots*

$6\sqrt{6}$ *Simplify.*

Ⓑ $\dfrac{6}{\sqrt{2}}$

$\dfrac{6}{\sqrt{2}}$ *There is a square root in the denominator, so the expression is not in simplest radical form.*

$\dfrac{6}{\sqrt{2}}\left(\dfrac{\sqrt{2}}{\sqrt{2}}\right)$ *Multiply by a form of 1 to eliminate the square root in the denominator.*

$\dfrac{6\sqrt{2}}{2}$ *Simplify.*

$3\sqrt{2}$ *Divide.*

 Try This   🔷 TAKS Grades 9–11 Obj. 2

Write each expression in simplest radical form.

1. $\sqrt{720}$ $12\sqrt{5}$
2. $\sqrt{\dfrac{3}{16}}$ $\dfrac{\sqrt{3}}{4}$
3. $\dfrac{10}{\sqrt{2}}$ $5\sqrt{2}$
4. $\sqrt{\dfrac{1}{3}}$ $\dfrac{\sqrt{3}}{3}$
5. $\sqrt{45}$ $3\sqrt{5}$

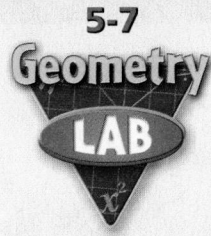
Hands-on Proof of the Pythagorean Theorem

In Lesson 1-6, you used the Pythagorean Theorem to find the distance between two points in the coordinate plane. In this activity, you will build figures and compare their areas to justify the Pythagorean Theorem.

Use with Lesson 5-7

 TEKS G.8.C Congruence and the geometry of size: derive, extend, and use the Pythagorean Theorem. Also G.9.B

Activity

1. Draw a large scalene right triangle on graph paper. Draw three copies of the triangle. On each triangle, label the shorter leg a, the longer leg b, and the hypotenuse c.

2. Draw a square with a side length of $b - a$. Label each side of the square.

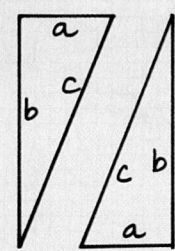 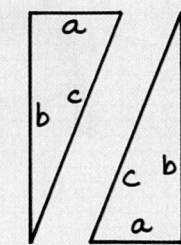 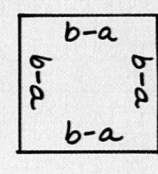

3. Cut out the five figures. Arrange them to make the composite figure shown at right.

4. You can think of this composite figure as being made of the two squares outlined in red. What are the side length and area of the small red square? of the large red square? a; a^2; b; b^2

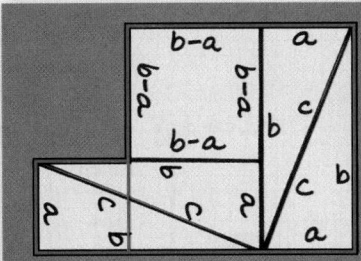

5. Use your results from Step 4 to write an algebraic expression for the area of the composite figure. $a^2 + b^2$

6. Now rearrange the five figures to make a single square with side length c. Write an algebraic expression for the area of this square. $area = c^2$

Try This

1. Since the composite figure and the square with side length c are made of the same five shapes, their areas are equal. Write and simplify an equation to represent this relationship. What conclusion can you make? $a^2 + b^2 = c^2$

2. Draw a scalene right triangle with different side lengths. Repeat the activity. Do you reach the same conclusion? **Check students' work.**

Answers to *Activity*

6.
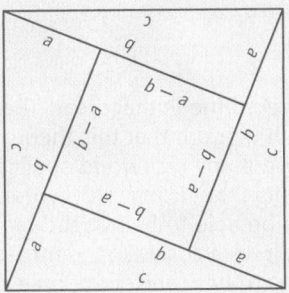

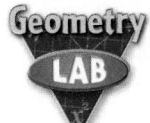

Geometry LAB **Organizer**

Use with Lesson 5-7

Pacing:
Traditional $\frac{1}{2}$ day
Block $\frac{1}{4}$ day

Objective: Use area to justify the Pythagorean Theorem.

Materials: graph paper, scissors

 Online Edition

 Countdown to TAKS Week 12

Teach

Discuss

Emphasize that the area of the composite figure students have made is equal to the sum of the areas of the five smaller figures. Remind students how to square a binomial.

Alternative Approach

Use pieces cut from a transparency to demonstrate this lab on an overhead projector.

Close

Key Concept

In a right triangle, the sum of the squares of the lengths of the legs equals the square of the hypotenuse.

Assessment

Journal Have students explain how they used area to justify the Pythagorean Theorem in this lab.

 Geometry TEKS

G.8 Congruence and the geometry of size*

(C) derive, extend, and use the Pythagorean Theorem

G.9 Congruence and the geometry of size*

(B) formulate and test conjectures about … polygons and their component parts …

* Knowledge and Skills See p. 298.

Pacing: Traditional 1 day
Block $\frac{1}{2}$ day

Objectives: Use the Pythagorean Theorem and its converse to solve problems.

Use Pythagorean inequalities to classify triangles.

Technology Lab
In *Texas Lab Manual*

Online Edition
Tutorial Videos

Countdown to TAKS Week 12

Power Presentations
with PowerPoint®

Warm Up

Classify each triangle by its angle measures.

1.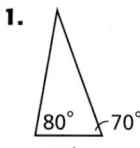
acute

2.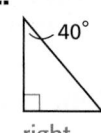
right

3. Simplify $\left(2\sqrt{3}\right)^2$.   12

4. If $a = 6$, $b = 7$, and $c = 12$, find $a^2 + b^2$ and find c^2. Which value is greater?   85; 144; c^2

Also available on transparency

Geometry TEKS

G.1 Geometric structure*
(B) recognize the historical development of geometric systems ...

G.5 Geometric patterns*
(B) use ... patterns to make generalizations about ... polygons ...
(D) identify and apply patterns from ... triangles whose sides are Pythagorean triples

G.8 Congruence and the geometry of size*
(C) derive, extend, and use the Pythagorean Theorem

G.11 Similarity and the geometry of shape*
(C) develop, apply, and justify ... Pythagorean triples ...

***Knowledge and Skills** See p. 298.

5-7 The Pythagorean Theorem

⭐ TEKS G.8.C Congruence and the geometry of size: derive, extend, and use the Pythagorean Theorem. Also G.1.B, G.5.B, G.5.D, G.11.C

Objectives
Use the Pythagorean Theorem and its converse to solve problems.

Use Pythagorean inequalities to classify triangles.

Vocabulary
Pythagorean triple

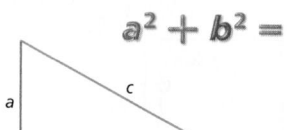
Math Builders

For more on the Pythagorean Theorem, see the Theorem Builder on page xxvi.

Why learn this?
You can use the Pythagorean Theorem to determine whether a ladder is in a safe position. (See Example 2.)

The Pythagorean Theorem is probably the most famous mathematical relationship. As you learned in Lesson 1-6, it states that in a right triangle, the sum of the squares of the lengths of the legs equals the square of the length of the hypotenuse.

$$a^2 + b^2 = c^2$$

The Pythagorean Theorem is named for the Greek mathematician Pythagoras, who lived in the sixth century B.C.E. However, this relationship was known to earlier people, such as the Babylonians, Egyptians, and Chinese.

There are many different proofs of the Pythagorean Theorem. The one below uses area and algebra.

PROOF

Remember!

The area A of a square with side length s is given by the formula $A = s^2$.

The area A of a triangle with base b and height h is given by the formula $A = \frac{1}{2}bh$.

Pythagorean Theorem

Given: A right triangle with leg lengths a and b and hypotenuse of length c

Prove: $a^2 + b^2 = c^2$

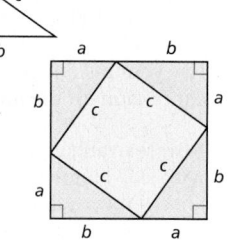

Proof: Arrange four copies of the triangle as shown. The sides of the triangles form two squares.

The area of the outer square is $(a + b)^2$. The area of the inner square is c^2. The area of each blue triangle is $\frac{1}{2}ab$.

area of outer square = area of 4 blue triangles + area of inner square

$$(a + b)^2 = 4\left(\frac{1}{2}ab\right) + c^2 \qquad \textit{Substitute the areas.}$$

$$a^2 + 2ab + b^2 = 2ab + c^2 \qquad \textit{Simplify.}$$

$$a^2 + b^2 = c^2 \qquad \textit{Subtract 2ab from both sides.}$$

The Pythagorean Theorem gives you a way to find unknown side lengths when you know a triangle is a right triangle.

---

1 Introduce

EXPLORATION

5-7 The Pythagorean Theorem

Use geometry software to explore some inequalities related to the Pythagorean Theorem.

1. Construct a triangle. Label its vertices *A*, *B*, and *C*.

2. Measure $\overline{AB}$, $\overline{CB}$, $\overline{CA}$, and $\angle BCA$. If necessary, drag the vertices so that $\overline{AB}$ is the longest side of the triangle.

3. Calculate AB^2 and $CB^2 + CA^2$.

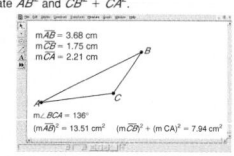

4. Drag point *C* to change the size of $\angle BCA$, keeping $\overline{AB}$ as the longest side of the triangle. When $AB^2 > CB^2 + CA^2$, what type of angle is $\angle BCA$?

5. When $AB^2 = CB^2 + CA^2$, what type of angle is $\angle BCA$?

6. When $AB^2 < CB^2 + CA^2$, what type of angle is $\angle BCA$?

Motivate

Ask students to recall the Pythagorean Theorem from Lesson 1-6. Point out that this theorem and its corollaries have many real-world applications. Explain to students that ancient surveyors and architects had to be able to build right angles without having a protractor. Ask students to brainstorm for ideas as to how ancient people might have done this. Explain that they will learn some methods in this lesson.

Explorations and answers are provided in the *Explorations* binder.

EXAMPLE 1 **Using the Pythagorean Theorem**

Find the value of *x*. Give your answer in simplest radical form.

A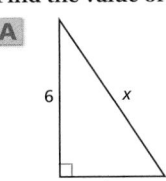

$a^2 + b^2 = c^2$ *Pythagorean Theorem*
$6^2 + 4^2 = x^2$ *Substitute 6 for a, 4 for b, and x for c.*
$52 = x^2$ *Simplify.*
$\sqrt{52} = x$ *Find the positive square root.*
$x = \sqrt{(4)(13)} = 2\sqrt{13}$ *Simplify the radical.*

B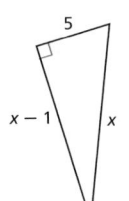

$a^2 + b^2 = c^2$ *Pythagorean Theorem*
$5^2 + (x-1)^2 = x^2$ *Substitute 5 for a, x − 1 for b, and x for c.*
$25 + x^2 - 2x + 1 = x^2$ *Multiply.*
$-2x + 26 = 0$ *Combine like terms.*
$26 = 2x$ *Add 2x to both sides.*
$x = 13$ *Divide both sides by 2.*

CHECK IT OUT! Find the value of *x*. Give your answer in simplest radical form.

1a.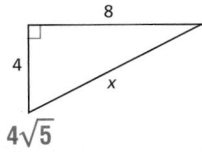

$4\sqrt{5}$

1b.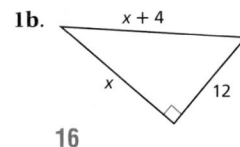

16

EXAMPLE 2 *Safety Application*

To prevent a ladder from shifting, safety experts recommend that the ratio of $a:b$ be $4:1$. How far from the base of the wall should you place the foot of a 10-foot ladder? Round to the nearest inch.

Let *x* be the distance in feet from the foot of the ladder to the base of the wall. Then $4x$ is the distance in feet from the top of the ladder to the base of the wall.

$a^2 + b^2 = c^2$ *Pythagorean Theorem*
$(4x)^2 + x^2 = 10^2$ *Substitute.*
$17x^2 = 100$ *Multiply and combine like terms.*
$x^2 = \dfrac{100}{17}$ *Divide both sides by 17.*
$x = \sqrt{\dfrac{100}{17}} \approx 2\text{ ft }5\text{ in.}$ *Find the positive square root and round it.*

CHECK IT OUT! 2. **What if...?** According to the recommended ratio, how high will a 30-foot ladder reach when placed against a wall? Round to the nearest inch. **29 ft 1 in.**

A set of three nonzero whole numbers *a*, *b*, and *c* such that $a^2 + b^2 = c^2$ is called a **Pythagorean triple** .

Common Pythagorean Triples
3, 4, 5   5, 12, 13,   8, 15, 17   7, 24, 25

Power Presentations
with PowerPoint®

Additional Examples

Example 1

Find the value of *x*. Give your answer in simplest radical form.

A. 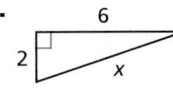 $2\sqrt{10}$

B. 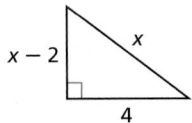   5

Example 2

Randy is building a rectangular picture frame. He wants the ratio of the length to the width to be 3:1 and the diagonal to be 12 cm. How wide should the frame be? Round to the nearest tenth of a centimeter.   **3.8 cm**

Also available on transparency

INTERVENTION
Questioning Strategies

EXAMPLE 1

• How do you know which side length to substitute for *a*, *b*, and *c* in the Pythagorean Theorem?

EXAMPLE 2

• How do you solve for the hypotenuse when you are given the ratio of the side lengths?

Teaching Tip   **Diversity** The dimensions of an American football field are 100 yd by 53.3 yd. A Canadian football field is 110 yd by 65 yd. Have students calculate how much longer the diagonal of a Canadian field is than that of an American field. about 14.5 yd

Teaching Tip   **Auditory** As a class, write a short list of common Pythagorean triples. Have students recite them out loud so they will remember the values.

---

2 Teach

Guided Instruction

Review the Pythagorean Theorem and how to use it to find an unknown side length in a right triangle. Review how to simplify square roots and square radicals. Discuss Pythagorean triples and how to identify them by using the Converse of the Pythagorean Theorem. Then explain how to use the Pythagorean Inequalities Theorem to classify triangles by their angle measures.

Reaching All Learners
Through Concrete Manipulatives

Have students use raw spaghetti or straws to build triangles with side lengths of 3, 4, and 5 in., 3, 4, and 6 in., and 4, 5, and 6 in. Have them use a protractor (MK) to classify each triangle by its angle measures. right, obtuse, acute Then have them use the theorems from the lesson to classify the triangles mathematically.

Example 3

Find the missing side length. Tell if the side lengths form a Pythagorean triple. Explain.

A.

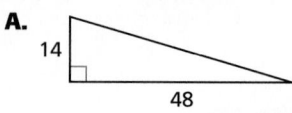

50; yes; the 3 side lengths are nonzero whole numbers that satisfy $a^2 + b^2 = c^2$, so they form a Pythagorean triple.

B.

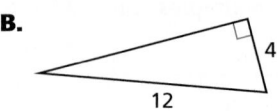

$8\sqrt{2}$; no; $8\sqrt{2}$ is not a whole number.

Also available on transparency

INTERVENTION ⬅➡
Questioning Strategies

EXAMPLE **3**

• Do the values 0.3, 0.4, and 0.5 satisfy the Pythagorean Theorem? Do they form a Pythagorean triple? Explain.

3a. $2\sqrt{41}$; no; $2\sqrt{41}$ is not a whole number.

3b. 10; yes; the 3 side lengths are nonzero whole numbers that satisfy the equation $a^2 + b^2 = c^2$.

3c. 2.6; no; 2.4 and 2.6 are not whole numbers.

3d. 34; yes; the 3 side lengths are nonzero whole numbers that satisfy the equation $a^2 + b^2 = c^2$.

EXAMPLE **3** **Identifying Pythagorean Triples**

Find the missing side length. Tell if the side lengths form a Pythagorean triple. Explain.

A

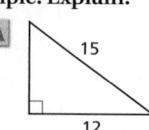

$a^2 + b^2 = c^2$	*Pythagorean Theorem*
$12^2 + b^2 = 15^2$	*Substitute 12 for a and 15 for c.*
$b^2 = 81$	*Multiply and subtract 144 from both sides.*
$b = 9$	*Find the positive square root.*

The side lengths are nonzero whole numbers that satisfy the equation $a^2 + b^2 = c^2$, so they form a Pythagorean triple.

B

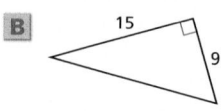

$a^2 + b^2 = c^2$	*Pythagorean Theorem*
$9^2 + 15^2 = c^2$	*Substitute 9 for a and 15 for b.*
$306 = c^2$	*Multiply and add.*
$c = \sqrt{306} = 3\sqrt{34}$	*Find the positive square root and simplify.*

The side lengths do not form a Pythagorean triple because $3\sqrt{34}$ is not a whole number.

CHECK IT OUT! Find the missing side length. Tell if the side lengths form a Pythagorean triple. Explain.

3a.

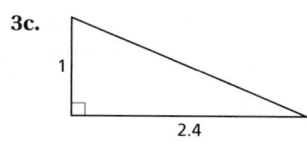

3b.

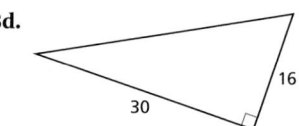

3c.

3d.

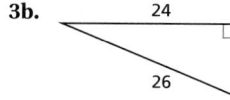

The converse of the Pythagorean Theorem gives you a way to tell if a triangle is a right triangle when you know the side lengths.

Know it! Note

Theorems 5-7-1 (Converse of the Pythagorean Theorem)

THEOREM	HYPOTHESIS	CONCLUSION
If the sum of the squares of the lengths of two sides of a triangle is equal to the square of the length of the third side, then the triangle is a right triangle.	$a^2 + b^2 = c^2$	△ABC is a right triangle.

You will prove Theorem 5-7-1 in Exercise 45.

Teaching Tip **Social Studies Link** Pythagoras was born around 569 B.C.E. on the Greek island of Samos. He studied mathematics, astronomy, and philosophy. Though it is believed that he did in fact prove the Pythagorean Theorem, the ancient Egyptians were familiar with the relationship long before Pythagoras's lifetime.

Teaching Tip **Critical Thinking** Ask students "If you multiply each value in a Pythagorean triple by 5, what is true of the resulting values?" They also form a Pythagorean triple.

You can also use side lengths to classify a triangle as acute or obtuse.

Theorems 5-7-2 | **Pythagorean Inequalities Theorem**

In △ABC, c is the length of the longest side.

If $c^2 > a^2 + b^2$, then △ABC is an **obtuse** triangle.

If $c^2 < a^2 + b^2$, then △ABC is an **acute** triangle.

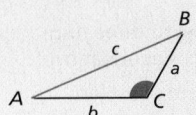
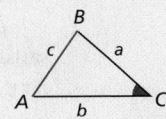

To understand why the Pythagorean inequalities are true, consider △ABC.

If $c^2 = a^2 + b^2$, then △ABC is a right triangle by the Converse of the Pythagorean Theorem. So m∠C = 90°.

If $c^2 > a^2 + b^2$, then c has increased. By the Converse of the Hinge Theorem, m∠C has also increased. So m∠C > 90°.

If $c^2 < a^2 + b^2$, then c has decreased. By the Converse of the Hinge Theorem, m∠C has also decreased. So m∠C < 90°.

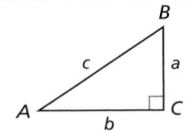
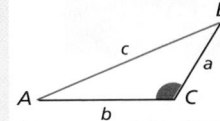
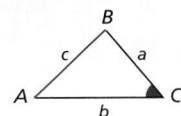

EXAMPLE 4 | **Classifying Triangles**

Tell if the measures can be the side lengths of a triangle. If so, classify the triangle as acute, obtuse, or right.

A 8, 11, 13

Step 1 Determine if the measures form a triangle.

By the Triangle Inequality Theorem, 8, 11, and 13 can be the side lengths of a triangle.

Step 2 Classify the triangle.

$c^2 \overset{?}{=} a^2 + b^2$ *Compare c^2 to $a^2 + b^2$.*

$13^2 \overset{?}{=} 8^2 + 11^2$ *Substitute the longest side length for c.*

$169 \overset{?}{=} 64 + 121$ *Multiply.*

$169 < 185$ *Add and compare.*

Since $c^2 < a^2 + b^2$, the triangle is **acute**.

B 5.8, 9.3, 15.6

Step 1 Determine if the measures form a triangle.

Since 5.8 + 9.3 = 15.1 and 15.1 ≯ 15.6, these cannot be the side lengths of a triangle.

 CHECK IT OUT! Tell if the measures can be the side lengths of a triangle. If so, classify the triangle as acute, obtuse, or right.

4a. 7, 12, 16
  yes; obtuse

4b. 11, 18, 34
  no

4c. 3.8, 4.1, 5.2
  yes, acute

5-7 The Pythagorean Theorem **351**

Remember!

By the Triangle Inequality Theorem, the sum of any two side lengths of a triangle is greater than the third side length.

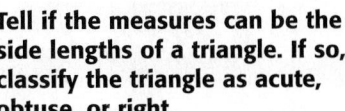
Lesson 5-7 **351**

Answers to *Think and Discuss*

1. The greatest number is substituted for c. The other 2 numbers are substituted for a and b in any order.

2. Possible answer: The sum of the areas of the 2 smaller squares equals the area of the largest square. So $3^2 + 4^2 = 5^2$, or $9 + 16 = 25$.

3. must be nonzero whole numbers and must satisfy the equation $a^2 + b^2 = c^2$

4. See p. A5.

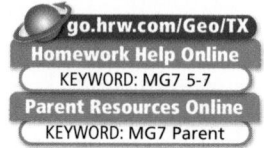

| 5-7 | **Exercises** |

| 5-7 | **Exercises** |

Assignment Guide

Assign *Guided Practice* exercises as necessary.

If you finished Examples **1–2**
 Basic 15–18, 30–36, 38–40
 Average 15–18, 30–36, 38–43, 45, 46
Advanced 15–18, 30–36, 38–43, 45, 46, 53, 54

If you finished Examples **1–4**
 Basic 15–36, 38–44, 47–51, 56–61
 Average 15–51, 55–61
Advanced 15–28, 30–61

Homework Quick Check
Quickly check key concepts.
Exercises: 16, 18, 20, 22, 30, 36

⊕TAKS Practice

Grades 9–11	Exercises
Obj. 2	51, 56–58, 60, 61
Obj. 6	49, 55
Obj. 7	52
Obj. 8	30–36, 38–43, 47–52
Obj. 10	36, 47

GUIDED PRACTICE

1. **Vocabulary** Do the numbers 2.7, 3.6, and 4.5 form a *Pythagorean triple*? Explain why or why not.

SEE EXAMPLE **1**
p. 349

Find the value of x. Give your answer in simplest radical form.

2.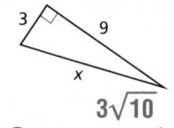
$3\sqrt{10}$

3.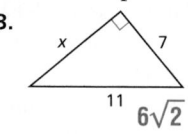
$6\sqrt{2}$

4.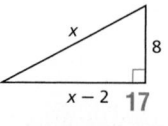

SEE EXAMPLE **2**
p. 349

5. **Computers** The size of a computer monitor is usually given by the length of its diagonal. A monitor's aspect ratio is the ratio of its width to its height. This monitor has a diagonal length of 19 inches and an aspect ratio of 5:4. What are the width and height of the monitor? Round to the nearest tenth of an inch.
width: 14.8 in.; height: 11.9 in.

SEE EXAMPLE **3**
p. 350

Find the missing side length. Tell if the side lengths form a Pythagorean triple. Explain.

6.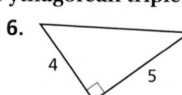

7.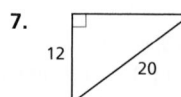

8.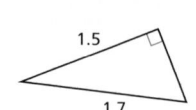

SEE EXAMPLE **4**
p. 351

Multi-Step Tell if the measures can be the side lengths of a triangle. If so, classify the triangle as acute, obtuse, or right.

9. 7, 10, 12 triangle; acute 10. 9, 11, 15 triangle; obtuse 11. 9, 40, 41 triangle; right

12. $1\frac{1}{2}, 1\frac{3}{4}, 3\frac{1}{4}$
not a triangle

13. 5.9, 6, 8.4
triangle; acute

14. 11, 13, $7\sqrt{6}$
triangle; obtuse

352 Chapter 5 *Properties and Attributes of Triangles*

Answers

1. No; although it is true that $(2.7)^2 + (3.6)^2 = (4.5)^2$, the numbers 2.7, 3.6, and 4.5 are not whole numbers.

6. $\sqrt{41}$; no; $\sqrt{41}$ is not a whole number.

7. 16; yes; the 3 side lengths are nonzero whole numbers that satisfy the equation $a^2 + b^2 = c^2$.

8. 0.8; no; the 3 side lengths are not whole numbers.

PRACTICE AND PROBLEM SOLVING

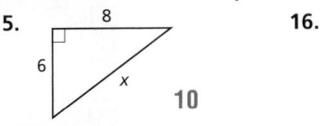

Independent Practice	
For Exercises	See Example
15–17	1
18	2
19–21	3
22–27	4

TEKS ● TAKS

Skills Practice p. S13
Application Practice p. S32

Find the value of *x*. Give your answer in simplest radical form.

15.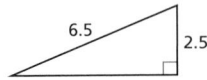

16.

17.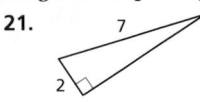

18. Safety The safety rules for a playground state that the height of the slide and the distance from the base of the ladder to the front of the slide must be in a ratio of 3:5. If a slide is about 8 feet long, what are the height of the slide and the distance from the base of the ladder to the front of the slide? Round to the nearest inch.
4 ft 1 in.; 6 ft 10 in.

Find the missing side length. Tell if the side lengths form a Pythagorean triple. Explain.

19.

20.

21.

Multi-Step Tell if the measures can be the side lengths of a triangle. If so, classify the triangle as acute, obtuse, or right.

22. 10, 12, 15 **triangle; acute** **23.** 8, 13, 23 **not a triangle** **24.** 9, 14, 17 **triangle; obtuse**

25. $1\frac{1}{2}$, 2, $2\frac{1}{2}$ **triangle; right** **26.** 0.7, 1.1, 1.7 **triangle; obtuse** **27.** 7, 12, $6\sqrt{5}$ **triangle; acute**

Surveying

Ancient Egyptian surveyors were referred to as *rope-stretchers*. The standard surveying rope was 100 royal cubits. A cubit is 52.4 cm long.

28. Surveying It is believed that surveyors in ancient Egypt laid out right angles using a rope divided into twelve sections by eleven equally spaced knots. How could the surveyors use this rope to make a right angle?

29. ///ERROR ANALYSIS/// Below are two solutions for finding *x*. Which is incorrect? Explain the error.

A
$a^2 + 4^2 = 13^2$
$a^2 = 169 - 16 = 153$
$a \approx 12.4$
$x + 3 \approx 12.4$
$x \approx 9.4$

B
$(x + 3)^2 + 4^2 = 13^2$
$x^2 + 9 + 16 = 169$
$x^2 = 144$
$x = 12$

Find the value of *x*. Give your answer in simplest radical form.

30. $5\sqrt{10}$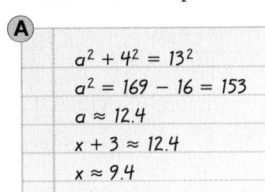

31. 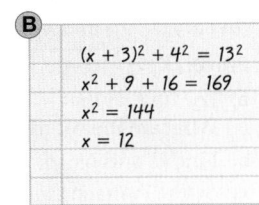 $8 + \sqrt{13}$

32. 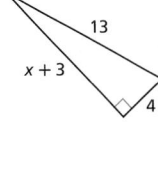 $2\sqrt{5}$

33. $4\sqrt{6}$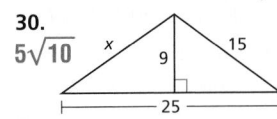

34. 11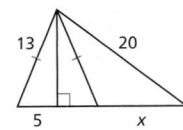

35. $6\sqrt{13}$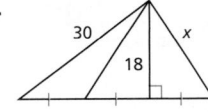

Answers

19. 6; no; 2.5 and 6.5 are not whole numbers.

20. 25; yes; the 3 side lengths are nonzero whole numbers that satisfy the equation $a^2 + b^2 = c^2$.

21. $3\sqrt{5}$; no; $3\sqrt{5}$ is not a whole number.

28. Possible answer: Shape the rope into a △ with side lengths of 3, 4, and 5. Because $3^2 + 4^2 = 5^2$, the △ is a rt. △ with the rt. ∠ across from the side with length 5.

29. B; $(x + 3)^2 + 4^2 = (x^2 + 6x + 9) + 16$. In the solution shown, the 6x term was omitted.

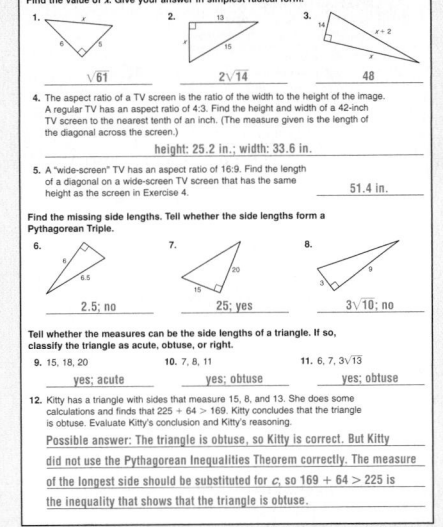

Math Background For Exercises 38–43, review how to find the area and perimeter of a triangle and a trapezoid.

MULTI-STEP TAKS PREP Exercise 47 involves using the Pythagorean Theorem to find distances between cities. This exercise prepares students for the Multi-Step TAKS Prep on page 364.

Answers

37. Possible answer: Outer figure: The length of each side is $a + b$, so the outer figure has 4 $\cong$ sides. Each $\angle$ is a rt. $\angle$ from 1 of the rt. $\triangle$s, so the outer figure has 4 rt. $\angle$s. By def., it is a square. Inner figure: The length of each side is c, so the inner figure has 4 $\cong$ sides. The 2 acute $\angle$s of a rt. $\triangle$ are comp., so the measure of each $\angle$ in the inner figure is 90°. Therefore the inner figure has 4 rt. $\angle$s. By def., it is a square.

44. Possible answer: When you use the Pythagorean Theorem, you know that the triangle is a right triangle. You substitute the known values into $a^2 + b^2 = c^2$ and solve for the unknown side length. When you use the Converse of the Pythagorean Theorem, you are trying to find out whether a given triangle is a right triangle. Usually all the side lengths are known. You substitute all the values into $a^2 + b^2 = c^2$ to determine whether the resulting equation is true. If it is true, then you know that the triangle is a right triangle.

45. Draw $\triangle PQR$ with $\angle R$ as the rt. $\angle$, leg lengths of a and b, and hyp. length of x. In $\triangle ABC$, it is given that $a^2 + b^2 = c^2$. In $\triangle PQR$, $a^2 + b^2 = x^2$ by the Pyth. Thm. Since $a^2 + b^2 = c^2$ and $a^2 + b^2 = x^2$, it follows by subst. that $x^2 = c^2$. Take the positive square root of both sides, and $x = c$. So $AB = PQ$, $BC = QR$, and $AC = PR$. By the def. of $\cong$ segs., $\overline{AB} \cong \overline{PQ}$, $\overline{BC} \cong \overline{QR}$, and $\overline{AC} \cong \overline{PR}$. Then $\triangle ABC \cong \triangle PQR$ by SSS, and $\angle C \cong \angle R$ by CPCTC. By the def. of rt. $\angle$, m$\angle R$ = 90°. So by the def. of $\cong$ $\angle$s, m$\angle C$ = 90°. Therefore $\angle C$ is a rt. $\angle$ by def., and $\triangle ABC$ is a rt. $\triangle$ by def.

51, 53, 55, 59. See p. A20.

38. perimeter: 40 units; area: 60 square units

39. perimeter: $16 + 4\sqrt{7}$ units; area: $12\sqrt{7}$ square units

40. perimeter: 32 units; area: $32\sqrt{2}$ square units

41. perimeter: $14 + 2\sqrt{13}$ units; area: 18 square units

42. perimeter: $30 + 6\sqrt{5}$ units; area: 90 square units

43. perimeter: 22 units; area: 26 square units

36. **Space Exploration** The International Space Station orbits at an altitude of about 250 miles above Earth's surface. The radius of Earth is approximately 3963 miles. How far can an astronaut in the space station see to the horizon? Round to the nearest mile. **1430 mi**

37. **Critical Thinking** In the proof of the Pythagorean Theorem on page 348, how do you know the outer figure is a square? How do you know the inner figure is a square?

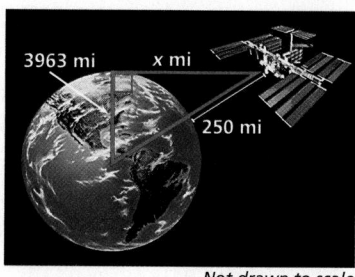

Not drawn to scale

Multi-Step Find the perimeter and the area of each figure. Give your answer in simplest radical form.

38.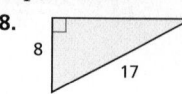

39.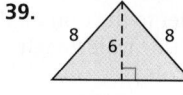

40.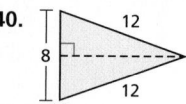

41.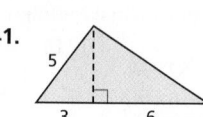

42.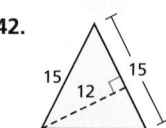

43.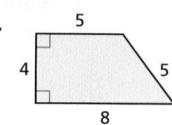

 44. **Write About It** When you apply both the Pythagorean Theorem and its converse, you use the equation $a^2 + b^2 = c^2$. Explain in your own words how the two theorems are different.

45. Use this plan to write a paragraph proof of the Converse of the Pythagorean Theorem.

Given: $\triangle ABC$ with $a^2 + b^2 = c^2$
Prove: $\triangle ABC$ is a right triangle.

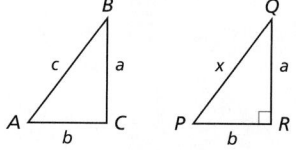

Plan: Draw $\triangle PQR$ with $\angle R$ as the right angle, leg lengths of a and b, and a hypotenuse of length x. By the Pythagorean Theorem, $a^2 + b^2 = x^2$. Use substitution to compare x and c. Show that $\triangle ABC \cong \triangle PQR$ and thus $\angle C$ is a right angle.

46. Complete these steps to prove the Distance Formula.

Given: $J(x_1, y_1)$ and $K(x_2, y_2)$ with $x_1 \neq x_2$ and $y_1 \neq y_2$
Prove: $JK = \sqrt{(x_2 - x_1)^2 + (y_2 - y_1)^2}$

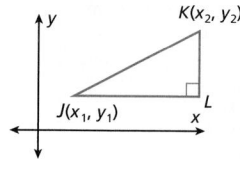

a. Locate L so that $\overline{JK}$ is the hypotenuse of right $\triangle JKL$. What are the coordinates of L? (x_2, y_1)

b. Find JL and LK. $JL = x_2 - x_1$, $LK = y_2 - y_1$

c. By the Pythagorean Theorem, $JK^2 = JL^2 + LK^2$. Find JK.
$$JK = \sqrt{(x_2 - x_1)^2 + (y_2 - y_1)^2}$$

MULTI-STEP TAKS PREP

King City

47. This problem will prepare you for the Multi-Step TAKS Prep on page 364.

The figure shows an airline's routes between four cities.

a. A traveler wants to go from Sanak (S) to Manitou (M). To minimize the total number of miles traveled, should she first fly to King City (K) or to Rice Lake (R)?

b. The airline decides to offer a direct flight from Sanak (S) to Manitou (M). Given that the length of this flight is more than 1360 mi, what can you say about m$\angle SRM$? **m$\angle SRM > 90°$**

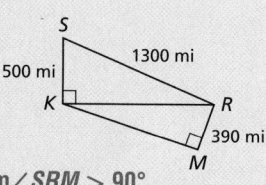

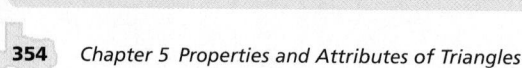

5-7 READING STRATEGIES

5-7 RETEACH

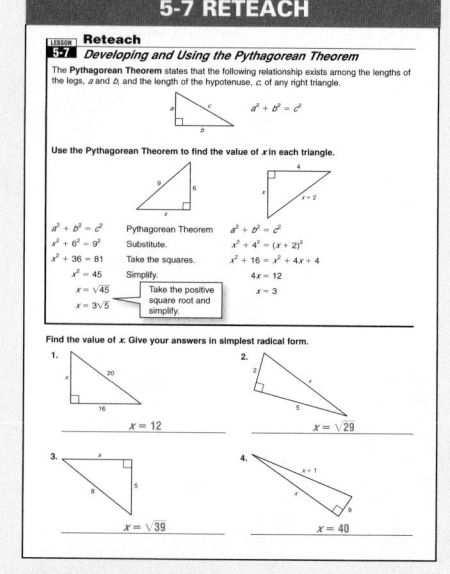

48. Gridded Response $\overline{KX}$, $\overline{LX}$, and $\overline{MX}$ are the perpendicular bisectors of $\triangle GHJ$. Find GJ to the nearest tenth of a unit. **8.9**

49. Which number forms a Pythagorean triple with 24 and 25?

Ⓐ 1   Ⓑ 7   Ⓒ 26   Ⓓ 49

50. The lengths of two sides of an obtuse triangle are 7 meters and 9 meters. Which could NOT be the length of the third side?

Ⓕ 4 meters   Ⓖ 5 meters   Ⓗ 11 meters   Ⓙ 12 meters

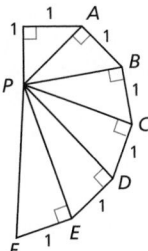

51. Extended Response The figure shows the first six triangles in a pattern of triangles.

a. Find PA, PB, PC, PD, PE, and PF in simplest radical form.

b. If the pattern continues, what would be the length of the hypotenuse of the ninth triangle? Explain your answer.

c. Write a rule for finding the length of the hypotenuse of the nth triangle in the pattern. Explain your answer.

CHALLENGE AND EXTEND

 52. Algebra Find all values of k so that $(-1, 2)$, $(-10, 5)$, and $(-4, k)$ are the vertices of a right triangle. $k = -7, -1, 8,$ or 23

53. Critical Thinking Use a diagram of a right triangle to explain why $a + b > \sqrt{a^2 + b^2}$ for any positive numbers a and b.

$h = \dfrac{ab}{\sqrt{a^2 + b^2}}$

54. In a right triangle, the leg lengths are a and b, and the length of the altitude to the hypotenuse is h. Write an expression for h in terms of a and b. (*Hint*: Think of the area of the triangle.)

55. Critical Thinking Suppose the numbers a, b, and c form a Pythagorean triple. Is each of the following also a Pythagorean triple? Explain.

a. $a + 1, b + 1, c + 1$

b. $2a, 2b, 2c$

c. a^2, b^2, c^2

d. $\sqrt{a}, \sqrt{b}, \sqrt{c}$

SPIRAL REVIEW

Solve each equation. (*Previous course*)

56. $(4 + x)12 - (4x + 1)6 = 0$
$x = 3.5$

57. $\dfrac{2x - 5}{3} = x$
$x = -5$

58. $4x + 3(x + 2) = -3(x + 3)$
$x = -\dfrac{3}{2}$

Write a coordinate proof. (*Lesson 4-7*)

59. Given: $ABCD$ is a rectangle with $A(0, 0)$, $B(0, 2b)$, $C(2a, 2b)$, and $D(2a, 0)$. M is the midpoint of $\overline{AC}$.
Prove: $AM = MB$

Find the range of values for x. (*Lesson 5-6*)

60. 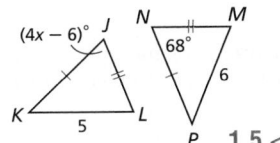 $1.5 < x < 18.5$

61. 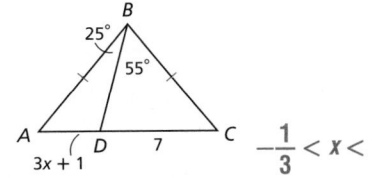 $-\dfrac{1}{3} < x < 2$

 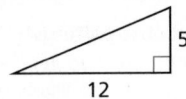

5-8 Organizer

Pacing: Traditional 1 day
Block $\frac{1}{2}$ day

Objectives: Justify and apply properties of 45°-45°-90° triangles.

Justify and apply properties of 30°-60°-90° triangles.

Geometry Lab
In *Texas Lab Manual*

Online Edition
Tutorial Videos, Interactivity

Countdown to TAKS Week 12

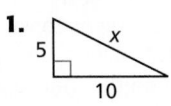

Power Presentations
with PowerPoint®

Warm Up

For Exercises 1 and 2, find the value of x. Give your answer in simplest radical form.

1.
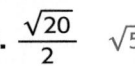

$5\sqrt{5}$

2.

$\sqrt{13}$

Simplify each expression.

3. $\dfrac{12}{\sqrt{3}}$ $4\sqrt{3}$ **4.** $\dfrac{\sqrt{20}}{2}$ $\sqrt{5}$

Also available on transparency

Math Humor

Q: How do you rationalize a denominator?

A: Ask it to be reasonable.

★ Geometry TEKS

G.3 Geometric structure*
(B) construct and justify statements about geometric figures …

G.5 Geometric patterns*
(A) use numeric and geometric patterns to develop algebraic expressions representing geometric properties
(D) identify and apply patterns from right triangles … including special right triangles (45-45-90 and 30-60-90) …

G.7 Dimensionality and the geometry of location*
(A) use … coordinate systems to represent … figures

* Knowledge and Skills See p. 298.

5-8 Applying Special Right Triangles

★ TEKS G.5.D Geometric patterns: identify and apply patterns from right triangles to solve meaningful problems, including special right triangles (45-45-90 and 30-60-90)...

Objectives
Justify and apply properties of 45°-45°-90° triangles.

Justify and apply properties of 30°-60°-90° triangles.

★ Also G.3.B, G.5.A, G.7.A

Who uses this?
You can use properties of special right triangles to calculate the correct size of a bandana for your dog. (See Example 2.)

A diagonal of a square divides it into two congruent isosceles right triangles. Since the base angles of an isosceles triangle are congruent, the measure of each acute angle is 45°. So another name for an isosceles right triangle is a 45°-45°-90° triangle.

A 45°-45°-90° triangle is one type of *special right triangle*. You can use the Pythagorean Theorem to find a relationship among the side lengths of a 45°-45°-90° triangle.

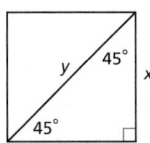

$a^2 + b^2 = c^2$	*Pythagorean Theorem*
$x^2 + x^2 = y^2$	*Substitute the given values.*
$2x^2 = y^2$	*Simplify.*
$\sqrt{2x^2} = \sqrt{y^2}$	*Find the square root of both sides.*
$x\sqrt{2} = y$	*Simplify.*

Know it!
Note

Theorem 5-8-1 — **45°-45°-90° Triangle Theorem**

In a 45°-45°-90° triangle, both legs are congruent, and the length of the hypotenuse is the length of a leg times $\sqrt{2}$.

$AC = BC = \ell$ $AB = \ell\sqrt{2}$

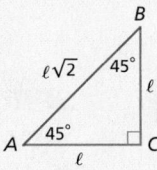

EXAMPLE 1 **Finding Side Lengths in a 45°-45°-90° Triangle**

Find the value of *x*. Give your answer in simplest radical form.

A

By the Triangle Sum Theorem, the measure of the third angle of the triangle is 45°. So it is a 45°-45°-90° triangle with a leg length of 7.

$x = 7\sqrt{2}$ *Hypotenuse = leg$\sqrt{2}$*

---

1 Introduce

EXPLORATION

5-8 Applying Special Right Triangles

You can use the Pythagorean Theorem to explore the relationships between the side lengths of some special right triangles.

1. △*ABC* is a 45°-45°-90° triangle. In the table, the length of one leg is given. Use the fact that △*ABC* is isosceles to find the length of the other leg. Then find the length of the hypotenuse. Simplify any radicals and look for a pattern.

Leg: *AB*	Leg: *BC*	Hypotenuse: *AC*
1		
2		
3		

2. △*DEF* is a 30°-60°-90° triangle. In the table, the length of the hypotenuse is given. Use the fact that △*DEF* is half of an equilateral triangle to find the length of one leg. Then find the length of the other leg. Simplify any radicals and look for a pattern.

Leg: *DE*	Leg: *FE*	Hypotenuse: *DF*
		2
		4
		6

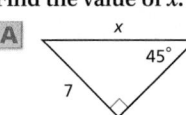

Motivate

Special right triangles appear in squares, equilateral triangles, hexagons, and other figures. They are used in three-dimensional shapes and also in trigonometry. Explain to students that they will learn about side relationships in special right triangles. The theorems covered in this lesson can be used to find unknown lengths without having to use the Pythagorean Theorem.

Explorations and answers are provided in the *Explorations* binder.

Find the value of *x*. Give your answer in simplest radical form.

 B

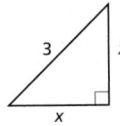

The triangle is an isosceles right triangle, which is a 45°-45°-90° triangle. The length of the hypotenuse is 3.

$$3 = x\sqrt{2} \qquad \text{Hypotenuse} = \text{leg}\sqrt{2}$$

$$\frac{3}{\sqrt{2}} = x \qquad \text{Divide both sides by } \sqrt{2}.$$

$$\frac{3\sqrt{2}}{2} = x \qquad \text{Rationalize the denominator.}$$

 **CHECK IT OUT!** **Find the value of *x*. Give your answer in simplest radical form.**

1a.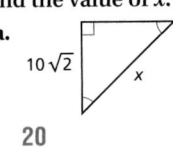

20

1b.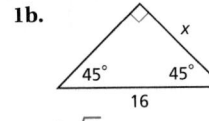

8√2

EXAMPLE 2 *Craft Application*

Tessa wants to make a bandana for her dog by folding a square of cloth into a 45°-45°-90° triangle. Her dog's neck has a circumference of about 32 cm. The folded bandana needs to be an extra 16 cm long so Tessa can tie it around her dog's neck. What should the side length of the square be? Round to the nearest centimeter.

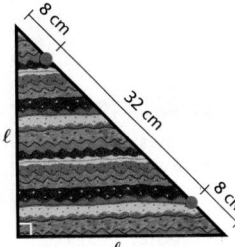

Tessa needs a 45°-45°-90° triangle with a hypotenuse of 48 cm.

$$48 = \ell\sqrt{2} \qquad \text{Hypotenuse} = \text{leg}\sqrt{2}$$

$$\ell = \frac{48}{\sqrt{2}} \approx 34 \text{ cm} \qquad \text{Divide by } \sqrt{2} \text{ and round.}$$

 **CHECK IT OUT!** **2. What if...?** Tessa's other dog is wearing a square bandana with a side length of 42 cm. What would you expect the circumference of the other dog's neck to be? Round to the nearest centimeter. **43 cm**

A 30°-60°-90° triangle is another special right triangle. You can use an equilateral triangle to find a relationship between its side lengths.

Draw an altitude in △*PQR*. Since △*PQS* ≅ △*RQS*, $\overline{PS} \cong \overline{RS}$. Label the side lengths in terms of *x*, and use the Pythagorean Theorem to find *y*.

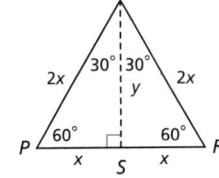

$$a^2 + b^2 = c^2 \qquad \text{Pythagorean Theorem}$$

$$x^2 + y^2 = (2x)^2 \qquad \text{Substitute x for a, y for b, and 2x for c.}$$

$$y^2 = 3x^2 \qquad \text{Multiply and combine like terms.}$$

$$\sqrt{y^2} = \sqrt{3x^2} \qquad \text{Find the square root of both sides.}$$

$$y = x\sqrt{3} \qquad \text{Simplify.}$$

5-8 Applying Special Right Triangles **357**

 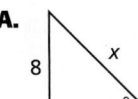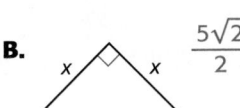
 2 Teach

Guided Instruction

Discuss the relationships between the side lengths of a 45°-45°-90° and a 30°-60°-90° triangle by using the Pythagorean Theorem. Show students how they can use these relationships to find unknown side lengths of special right triangles.

Teaching Tip **Visual** Remind students to draw and label a diagram if they forget the formulas for the side lengths of a special right triangle (MK).

 **Reaching All Learners**

Through Auditory Cues

Have students practice the formulas for the side lengths of special right triangles by quizzing each other out loud. For example, have them fill in the blanks in the following statements. "The side of a 45°-45°-90° triangle is 8√2 if the hypotenuse is ___?___." 16 "In a 30°-60°-90° triangle, the side opposite the 60° angle is 6√3 if the side opposite the 30° angle is ___?___." 6

INTERVENTION ◀▬▶
Questioning Strategies

EXAMPLE 1
- What is the relationship between the side lengths of a 45°-45°-90° triangle?

EXAMPLE 2
- What type of special right triangle is formed by the diagonal of a square?

Lesson 5-8 **357**

 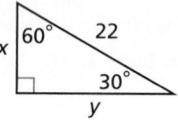
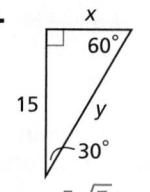
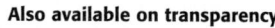 

Theorem 5-8-2 (**30°-60°-90° Triangle Theorem**)

In a 30°-60°-90° triangle, the length of the hypotenuse is is 2 times the length of the shorter leg, and the length of the longer leg is the length of the shorter leg times $\sqrt{3}$.

$$AC = s \qquad AB = 2s \qquad BC = s\sqrt{3}$$

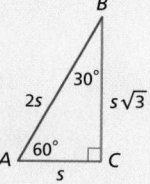

EXAMPLE 3 **Finding Side Lengths in a 30°-60°-90° Triangle**

Find the values of x and y. Give your answers in simplest radical form.

 A

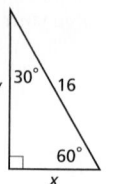

$16 = 2x$	*Hypotenuse = 2(shorter leg)*
$8 = x$	*Divide both sides by 2.*
$y = x\sqrt{3}$	*Longer leg = (shorter leg)$\sqrt{3}$*
$y = 8\sqrt{3}$	*Substitute 8 for x.*

 B

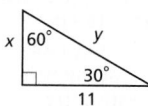

$11 = x\sqrt{3}$	*Longer leg = (shorter leg) $\sqrt{3}$*
$\dfrac{11}{\sqrt{3}} = x$	*Divide both sides by $\sqrt{3}$.*
$\dfrac{11\sqrt{3}}{3} = x$	*Rationalize the denominator.*
$y = 2x$	*Hypotenuse = 2(shorter leg)*
$y = 2\left(\dfrac{11\sqrt{3}}{3}\right)$	*Substitute $\dfrac{11\sqrt{3}}{3}$ for x.*
$y = \dfrac{22\sqrt{3}}{3}$	*Simplify.*

CHECK IT OUT! Find the values of x and y. Give your answers in simplest radical form.

3a. $x = 9\sqrt{3}; y = 27$

3b. $x = 5\sqrt{3}; y = 10$

3c. $x = 12; y = 12\sqrt{3}$

3d. $x = 6\sqrt{3}; y = 3\sqrt{3}$

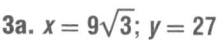

3a.

3b.

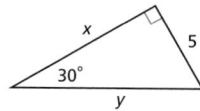

3c.

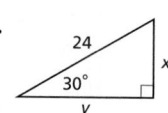

3d.

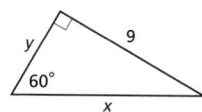

To remember the side relationships in a 30°-60°-90° triangle, I draw a simple "1-2-√3" triangle like this.

$2 = 2(1)$, so
hypotenuse $= 2$(shorter leg).

$\sqrt{3} = \sqrt{3}(1)$, so
longer leg $= \sqrt{3}$(shorter leg).

Marcus Maiello
Johnson High School

EXAMPLE 4 **Using the 30°-60°-90° Triangle Theorem**

The frame of the clock shown is an equilateral triangle. The length of one side of the frame is 20 cm. Will the clock fit on a shelf that is 18 cm below the shelf above it?

Step 1 Divide the equilateral triangle into two 30°-60°-90° triangles.

The height of the frame is the length of the longer leg.

Step 2 Find the length x of the shorter leg.

$20 = 2x$ Hypotenuse = 2(shorter leg)

$10 = x$ Divide both sides by 2.

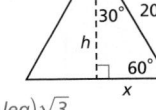

Step 3 Find the length h of the longer leg.

$h = 10\sqrt{3} \approx 17.3$ cm   Longer leg = (shorter leg)$\sqrt{3}$

The frame is approximately 17.3 centimeters tall. So the clock will fit on the shelf.

 **CHECK IT OUT!** **4.** **What if...?** A manufacturer wants to make a larger clock with a height of 30 centimeters. What is the length of each side of the frame? Round to the nearest tenth. **34.6 cm**

THINK AND DISCUSS

1. Explain why an isosceles right triangle is a 45°-45°-90° triangle.

2. Describe how finding x in triangle I is different from finding x in triangle II.

I.
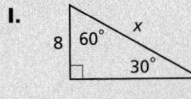

II.

Know it! Note

3. **GET ORGANIZED** Copy and complete the graphic organizer. In each box, sketch the special right triangle and label its side lengths in terms of s.

Special Right Triangles
- 45°-45°-90° triangle
- 30°-60°-90° triangle

5-8 Applying Special Right Triangles   **359**

Power Presentations with PowerPoint®

Additional Examples

Example 4

An ornamental pin is in the shape of an equilateral triangle. The length of each side is 6 cm. Josh will attach the fastener to the back along $\overline{AB}$. Will the fastener fit if it is 4 cm long? Yes; $AB = 3\sqrt{3}$ cm, which is greater than 4 cm.

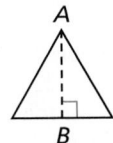

Also available on transparency

INTERVENTION ◀▶
Questioning Strategies

EXAMPLE **4**

• What kind of special right triangles are formed when an equilateral triangle is divided in half by a median?

---

3 Close

Summarize

Review with students the 45°-45°-90° and 30°-60°-90° Triangle Theorems, illustrating each with a diagram and numeric example. Emphasize that these relationships between the side lengths apply only to these two special right triangles.

Answers to Think and Discuss

1. Possible answer: The △ is a rt. △, so the measure of 1 ∠ is 90°, and the other 2 acute ∡ are comp. The △ is isosc., so its base ∡ are ≅. So the measure of each of the base ∡ is 45°.

2. In figure I, use the relationship $x = 2(8)$. In figure II, first use the relationship $8 = \sqrt{3}$(shorter leg), and then use the relationship $x = 2$(shorter leg).

3. See p. A5.

go.hrw.com/Geo/TX
Homework Help Online
KEYWORD: MG7 5-8
Parent Resources Online
KEYWORD: MG7 Parent

Assignment Guide

Assign *Guided Practice* exercises as necessary.

If you finished **Examples 1–2**
  Basic 9–12, 17, 19, 22
  Average 9–12, 17, 19, 22, 24, 25
  Advanced 9–12, 17, 19, 22, 24, 25, 34

If you finished **Examples 1–4**
  Basic 9–22, 24–33, 38–46
  Average 9–35, 38–46
  Advanced 9–46

Homework Quick Check
Quickly check key concepts.
Exercises: 10, 12, 14, 16, 17, 18

Teaching Tip **Inclusion** In **Exercise 15**, some students may find it easier to solve the equation $x\sqrt{3} = 2$ by multiplying both sides by $\sqrt{3}$ first. So $3x = 2\sqrt{3}$, and thus $x = \frac{2\sqrt{3}}{3}$.

GUIDED PRACTICE

SEE EXAMPLE 1
p. 356

Find the value of x. Give your answer in simplest radical form.

1. 45°, 14, x, $14\sqrt{2}$

2. 12, x, x, $6\sqrt{2}$

3. x, 45°, $9\sqrt{2}$, 9
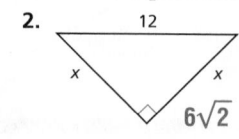

SEE EXAMPLE 2
p. 357

4. Transportation The two arms of the railroad sign are perpendicular bisectors of each other. In Pennsylvania, the lengths marked in red must be 19.5 inches. What is the distance labeled d? Round to the nearest tenth of an inch. **27.6 in.**

SEE EXAMPLE 3
p. 358

Find the values of x and y. Give your answers in simplest radical form.

5. y, 30°, x, 60°, 6, $x = 3; y = 3\sqrt{3}$

6. y, 30°, x, 15, $x = 5\sqrt{3}; y = 10\sqrt{3}$

7. x, $7\sqrt{3}$, 30°, 60°, y, $x = 21; y = 14\sqrt{3}$
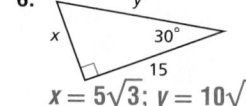

SEE EXAMPLE 4
p. 359

8. Entertainment Regulation billiard balls are $2\frac{1}{4}$ inches in diameter. The rack used to group 15 billiard balls is in the shape of an equilateral triangle. What is the approximate height of the triangle formed by the rack? Round to the nearest quarter of an inch. **9.75 in.**
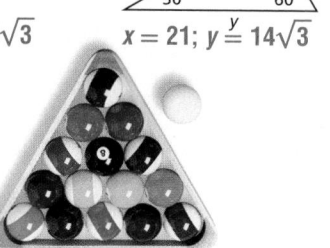

PRACTICE AND PROBLEM SOLVING

Independent Practice

For Exercises	See Example
9–11	1
12	2
13–15	3
16	4

TEKS ✏ TAKS

Skills Practice p. S13
Application Practice p. S32

Find the value of x. Give your answer in simplest radical form.

9. x, $\frac{15\sqrt{2}}{2}$, 45°, 15

10. x, 45°, 45°, 8, $4\sqrt{2}$

11. 18, x, $18\sqrt{2}$
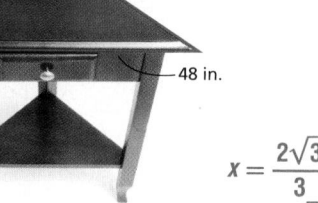

12. Design This tabletop is an isosceles right triangle. The length of the front edge of the table is 48 inches. What is the length w of each side edge? Round to the nearest tenth of an inch. **33.9 in.**
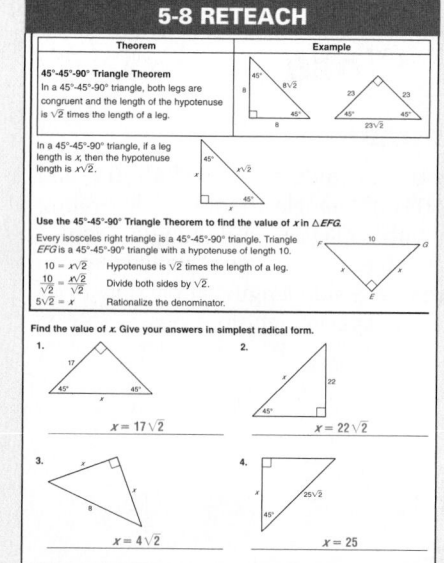

Find the value of x and y. Give your answers in simplest radical form.

13. 24, y, 60°, x, $x = 48; y = 24\sqrt{3}$

14. y, 30°, $10\sqrt{3}$, x, $x = 5\sqrt{3}; y = 15$

15. 60°, y, 30°, x, 2, $x = \frac{2\sqrt{3}}{3}; y = \frac{4\sqrt{3}}{3}$

TAKS Practice

Grades 9–11	Exercises
Obj. 2	34, 35
Obj. 5	38–40
Obj. 6	17–22, 24–27, 29–36
Obj. 7	24–27
Obj. 8	17–21, 33
Obj. 10	22, 29

5-8 READING STRATEGIES

To make a 45°-45°-90° triangle, start with a simple square.
Draw a diagonal through the square to form two 45° angles:

Now consider the Pythagorean Theorem: $a^2 + b^2 = c^2$
Use the Pythagorean Theorem to find the length of the hypotenuse of one of the triangles formed by drawing a diagonal on this square.

$10^2 + 10^2 = c^2$
$200 = c^2$
$c^2 = 10\sqrt{2}$

1. What is the length of a diagonal of a square with a side length of 8? $\quad 8\sqrt{2}$

Now consider the following equilateral triangle.

2. What is the measurement of each angle in this triangle? $\quad 60°$

3. Draw an altitude in this triangle.

4. What are the angle measurements of the two triangles you have formed?
Students should say that they have created two 30°-60°-90° triangles.

5. Use the Pythagorean Theorem to find the length of the altitude.
The altitude is $5\sqrt{3}$.

5-8 RETEACH

Theorem	Example
45°-45°-90° Triangle Theorem In a 45°-45°-90° triangle, both legs are congruent and the length of the hypotenuse is $\sqrt{2}$ times the length of a leg.	

In a 45°-45°-90° triangle, if a leg length is x, then the hypotenuse length is $x\sqrt{2}$.

Use the 45°-45°-90° Triangle Theorem to find the value of x in $\triangle EFG$.
Every isosceles right triangle is a 45°-45°-90° triangle. Triangle EFG is a 45°-45°-90° triangle with a hypotenuse of length 10.

$10 = x\sqrt{2}$ Hypotenuse is $\sqrt{2}$ times the length of a leg.
$\frac{10}{\sqrt{2}} = \frac{x\sqrt{2}}{\sqrt{2}}$ Divide both sides by $\sqrt{2}$.
$5\sqrt{2} = x$ Rationalize the denominator.

Find the value of x. Give your answers in simplest radical form.

1. $x = 17\sqrt{2}$

2. $x = 22\sqrt{2}$

3. $x = 4\sqrt{2}$

4. $x = 25$

TEXAS LINK

Pets

Agility courses test the skill of both the dog and the dog's handler. Dog agility competitions in the United States are regulated by the U.S. Dog Agility Association, headquartered in Garland, Texas.

16. Pets A dog walk is used in dog agility competitions. In this dog walk, each ramp makes an angle of 30° with the ground.

12 ft · 4.5 ft · 30° · 30°

   a. How long is one ramp? **9 ft**

   b. How long is the entire dog walk, including both ramps? **30 ft**

Multi-Step Find the perimeter and area of each figure. Give your answers in simplest radical form.

17. a 45°-45°-90° triangle with hypotenuse length 12 inches

18. a 30°-60°-90° triangle with hypotenuse length 28 centimeters

19. a square with diagonal length 18 meters

20. an equilateral triangle with side length 4 feet

21. an equilateral triangle with height 30 yards

22. Estimation The triangle loom is made from wood strips shaped into a 45°-45°-90° triangle. Pegs are placed every $\frac{1}{2}$ inch along the hypotenuse and every $\frac{1}{4}$ inch along each leg. Suppose you make a loom with an 18-inch hypotenuse. Approximately how many pegs will you need? **about 138 nails**

23. Critical Thinking The angle measures of a triangle are in the ratio 1:2:3. Are the side lengths also in the ratio 1:2:3? Explain your answer.

19. perimeter: $\left(36\sqrt{2}\right)$ m; area: 162 m²

20. perimeter: 12 ft; area: $4\sqrt{3}$ ft²

21. perimeter: $60\sqrt{3}$ yd; area: $300\sqrt{3}$ yd²

Find the coordinates of point P under the given conditions. Give your answers in simplest radical form.

24. $\triangle PQR$ is a 45°-45°-90° triangle with vertices $Q(4, 6)$ and $R(-6, -4)$, and m$\angle P = 90°$. P is in Quadrant II. $\left(-6, 6\right)$

25. $\triangle PST$ is a 45°-45°-90° triangle with vertices $S(4, -3)$ and $T(-2, 3)$, and m$\angle S = 90°$. P is in Quadrant I. $\left(10, 3\right)$

26. $\triangle PWX$ is a 30°-60°-90° triangle with vertices $W(-1, -4)$ and $X(4, -4)$, and m$\angle W = 90°$. P is in Quadrant II. $\left(-1, -4 + 5\sqrt{3}\right)$

27. $\triangle PYZ$ is a 30°-60°-90° triangle with vertices $Y(-7, 10)$ and $Z(5, 10)$, and m$\angle Z = 90°$. P is in Quadrant IV. $\left(5, 10 - 12\sqrt{3}\right)$

28. Write About It Why do you think 30°-60°-90° triangles and 45°-45°-90° triangles are called *special right triangles*?

MULTI-STEP TAKS PREP

29. This problem will prepare you for the Multi-Step TAKS Prep on page 364.

The figure shows an airline's routes among four cities. The airline offers one frequent-flier mile for each mile flown (rounded to the nearest mile). How many frequent-flier miles do you earn for each flight?

   a. Nelson (N) to Belton (B) **640 m**

   b. Idria (I) to Nelson (N) **453 m**

   c. Belton (B) to Idria (I) **234 m**

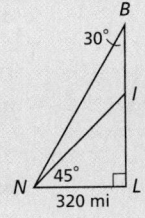

B · 30° · I · 45° · N · L · 320 mi

Answers

23. No; possible answer: if the $\angle$ measures are in the ratio 1:2:3, then the measures of the $\angle$ are 30°, 60°, and 90°, and the $\triangle$ is a 30°-60°-90° $\triangle$. Assume the length of the shortest leg is 1. Then the length of the hyp. is 2, and the length of the longer leg is $\sqrt{3}$. So the side lengths would be in the ratio $1:\sqrt{3}:2$.

28. Possible answer: Both types of triangles are right triangles. In each 1, there is a unique relationship among the side lengths. For each type of triangle, if you know 1 side length, you can find the other 2.

5-8 PRACTICE A
5-8 PRACTICE C
5-8 PRACTICE B

Find the value of x in each figure. Give your answer in simplest radical form.

1. $8\sqrt{3}$ 45°

2.

3. $2\sqrt{2}$

16 · $\frac{7\sqrt{2}}{2}$ · 2

Find the values of x and y. Give your answers in simplest radical form.

4. $x = $ **30** $y = $ **$20\sqrt{3}$**   5. $x = $ **$4\sqrt{3}$** $y = $ **$8\sqrt{3}$**   6. $x = $ **$\sqrt{3}$** $y = $ **3**

Lucia is an archaeologist trekking through the jungle of the Yucatan Peninsula. She stumbles upon a stone structure covered with creeper vines and ferns. She immediately begins taking measurements of her discovery. (*Hint:* Drawing some figures may help.)

7. Around the perimeter of the building, Lucia finds small alcoves at regular intervals carved into the stone. The alcoves are triangular in shape with a horizontal base and two sloped equal-length sides that meet at a right angle. Each of the sloped sides measures $14\frac{1}{4}$ inches. Lucia has also found several stone tablets inscribed with characters. The stone tablets measure $22\frac{1}{8}$ inches long. Lucia hypothesizes that the alcoves once held the stone tablets. Tell whether Lucia's hypothesis may be correct. Explain your answer.
Possible answer: Lucia's hypothesis cannot be correct. The base of the alcove is just over 20 inches long, so a $22\frac{1}{8}$-inch tablet could not fit.

8. Lucia also finds several statues around the building. The statues measure $9\frac{7}{16}$ inches tall. She wonders whether the statues might have been placed in the alcoves. Tell whether this is possible. Explain your answer.
Possible answer: To find the height of a 45°-45°-90° triangle, draw a perpendicular to the hypotenuse. This makes another smaller 45°-45°-90° triangle whose hypotenuse is the length of one of the legs of the larger triangle. The height of the alcove is about 10 inches, so the statues could have been placed in the alcoves.

5-8 PROBLEM SOLVING

For Exercises 1–6, give your answers in simplest radical form.

1. In bowling, the pins are arranged in a pattern based on equilateral triangles. What is the distance between pins 1 and 5?
$12\sqrt{3}$ in.

2. To secure an outdoor canopy, a 64-inch cord is extended from the top of a vertical pole to the ground. If the cord makes a 60° angle with the ground, how tall is the pole?
$32\sqrt{3}$ in.

Find the length of $\overline{AB}$ in each quilt pattern.

3.
$3\sqrt{2}$ in.

4.
$\frac{8\sqrt{3}}{3}$ in.

Choose the best answer.

5. An equilateral triangle has an altitude of 21 inches. What is the side length of the triangle?
$14\sqrt{3}$ in.

6. A shelf is an isosceles right triangle, and the longest side is 38 centimeters. What the length of each of the other two sides?
$19\sqrt{2}$

Use the figure for Exercises 7 and 8. Assume $\triangle JKL$ is in the first quadrant, with m$\angle K = 90°$.

7. Suppose that $\overline{JK}$ is a leg of $\triangle JKL$, a 45°-45°-90° triangle. What are the coordinates of point L?
Ⓐ (6, 4.5)   C (6, 2)
B (7, 2)   D (8, 7)

8. Suppose $\triangle JKL$ is a 30°-60°-90° triangle and $\overline{JK}$ is the side opposite the 60° angle. What are the approximate coordinates of point L?
F (4.9, 2)   H (8.7, 2)
G (4.5, 2)   J (7.1, 2)

5-8 CHALLENGE

Use the properties of special right triangles to solve each problem. Give your answers in simplest radical form.

1. The circumference of circle J is 14π. What is the value of x?
$7\sqrt{2}$

2. The area of semicircle D is 18π. What is the perimeter of $\triangle ABC$?
$18 + 6\sqrt{3}$

3. Find the perimeter of quadrilateral $WXYZ$.
$86 + 18\sqrt{2}$

4. Find the perimeter of quadrilateral $QRST$.
$108 + 36\sqrt{3}$

5. Find a, b, c, and d.
$a = 7$, $b = 4\sqrt{3}$, $c = 11$, $d = 0$

6. Find w, x, y, and z.
$w = 13$, $x = 13$, $y = 20$, $z = 20 + 13\sqrt{3}$

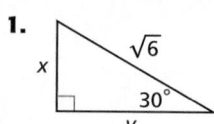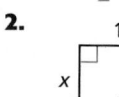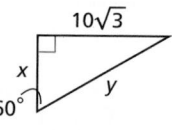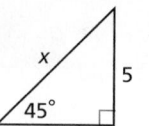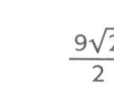

TEST PREP

30. Which is a true statement?
    (A) $AB = BC\sqrt{2}$ (C) $AC = BC\sqrt{3}$
    (B) $AB = BC\sqrt{3}$ (D) $AC = AB\sqrt{2}$

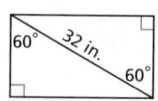

31. An 18-foot pole is broken during a storm.
    The top of the pole touches the ground 12 feet
    from the base of the pole. How tall is the
    part of the pole left standing?
    (F) 5 feet   (H) 13 feet
    (G) 6 feet   (J) 22 feet

32. The length of the hypotenuse of an isosceles right triangle is 24 inches. What is the
    length of one leg of the triangle, rounded to the nearest tenth of an inch?
    (A) 13.9 inches   (C) 33.9 inches
    (B) 17.0 inches   (D) 41.6 inches

33. **Gridded Response** Find the area of the rectangle
    to the nearest tenth of a square inch. **443.4**

CHALLENGE AND EXTEND

Multi-Step Find the value of x in each figure.

34.   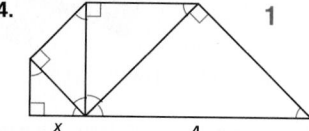   35.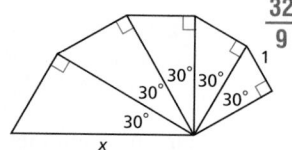

36a. When
$e = 1, d = \sqrt{3}$.
When $e = 2$,
$d = 2\sqrt{3}$. When
$e = 3, d = 3\sqrt{3}$.

36b. $d = e\sqrt{3}$

36. Each edge of the cube has length e.
    a. Find the diagonal length d when $e = 1$, $e = 2$, and $e = 3$.
    Give the answers in simplest radical form.
    b. Write a formula for d for any positive value of e.

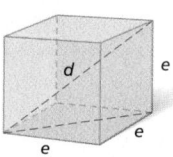

37. Write a paragraph proof to show that the altitude to the
    hypotenuse of a 30°-60°-90° triangle divides the hypotenuse
    into two segments, one of which is 3 times as long as the other.

SPIRAL REVIEW

Rewrite each function in the form $y = a(x - h)^2 - k$ and find the axis of symmetry.
(Previous course)

38. $y = (x + 2)^2$
$- 4; x = -2$

39. $y = (x - 5)^2$
$- 27; x = 5$

40. $y = (x + 3.5)^2$
$+ 2.75; x = -3.5$

38. $y = x^2 + 4x$ 39. $y = x^2 - 10x - 2$ 40. $y = x^2 + 7x + 15$

Classify each triangle by its angle measures. *(Lesson 4-1)*
41. $\triangle ADB$ **obtuse**   42. $\triangle BDC$ **acute**   43. $\triangle ABC$ **right**

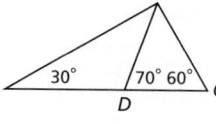

Use the diagram for Exercises 44–46. *(Lesson 5-1)*
44. Given that $PS = SR$ and m$\angle PSQ = 65°$, find m$\angle PQR$. **50°**
45. Given that $UT = TV$ and m$\angle PQS = 42°$, find m$\angle VTS$. **132°**
46. Given that $\angle PQS \cong \angle SQR$, $SR = 3TU$, and $PS = 7.5$, find TV.
    2.5

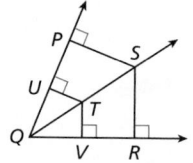

Answers

37. Possible answer:

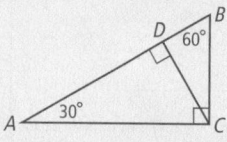

Given: $\triangle ABC$ is a 30°-60°-90° $\triangle$ with
m$\angle A = 30°$ and m$\angle B = 60°$. $\overline{CD}$
is the altitude to the hyp.

Prove: $AD = 3DB$
Proof: It is given that $\overline{CD}$ is the altitude
to the hyp. Thus $\overline{CD} \perp \overline{AB}$ by the def.
of altitude. So $\angle ADC$ and $\angle BDC$ are
rt. $\angle$ by the def. of $\perp$, and $\triangle ADC$ and

$\triangle BDC$ are rt. $\angle$ by def. It is given that
m$\angle A = 30°$ and m$\angle B = 60°$. Since the
acute $\angle$ of a rt. $\triangle$ are comp., m$\angle DCA$
$= 60°$ and m$\angle DCB = 30°$ by the Subtr.
Prop. of =. So $\triangle ADC$ and $\triangle BDC$ are
both 30°-60°-90° $\triangle$. By the 30°-60°-90°
$\triangle$ Thm., $AD = \sqrt{3}(DC)$ and $DC =$
$\sqrt{3}(DB)$. By subst., $AD = \sqrt{3}[\sqrt{3}(DB)]$.
This simplifies to $AD = 3DB$.

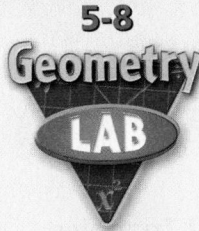

5-8 Geometry LAB

Graph Irrational Numbers

Numbers such as $\sqrt{2}$ and $\sqrt{3}$ are irrational. That is, they cannot be written as the ratio of two integers. In decimal form, they are infinite nonrepeating decimals. You can round the decimal form to estimate the location of these numbers on a number line, or you can use right triangles to construct their locations exactly.

Use with Lesson 5-8

TEKS G.2.A Geometric structure: use constructions to explore attributes of geometric figures and to make conjectures about geometric relationships. Also G.5.B

Activity

1 Draw a line. Mark two points near the left side of the line and label them 0 and 1. The distance from 0 to 1 is 1 unit.

2 Set your compass to 1 unit and mark increments at 2, 3, 4, and 5 units to construct a number line.

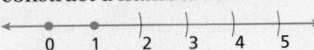

3 Construct a perpendicular to the line through 1.

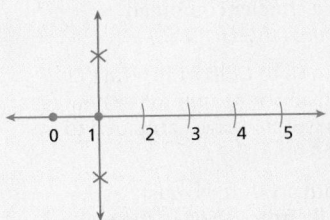

4 Using your compass, mark 1 unit up from the number line and then draw a right triangle. The legs both have length 1, so by the Pythagorean Theorem, the hypotenuse has a length of $\sqrt{2}$.

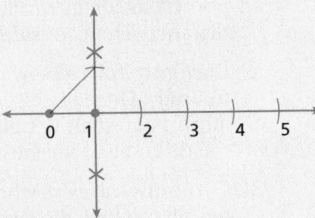

5 Set your compass to the length of the hypotenuse. Draw an arc centered at 0 that intersects the number line at $\sqrt{2}$.

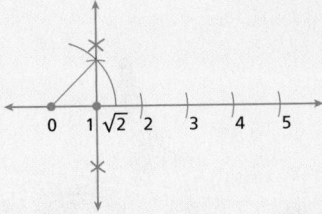

6 Repeat Steps 3 through 5, starting at $\sqrt{2}$, to construct a segment of length $\sqrt{3}$.

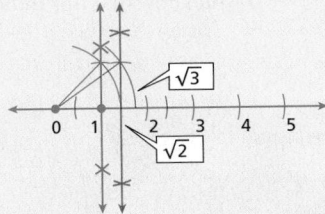

Try This

1. Sketch the two right triangles from Step 6. Label the side lengths and use the Pythagorean Theorem to show why the construction is correct.

2. Construct $\sqrt{4}$ and verify that it is equal to 2.

3. Construct $\sqrt{5}$ through $\sqrt{9}$ and verify that $\sqrt{9}$ is equal to 3.

4. Set your compass to the length of the segment from 0 to $\sqrt{2}$. Mark off another segment of length $\sqrt{2}$ to show that $\sqrt{8}$ is equal to $2\sqrt{2}$.

Answers to Try This

1.

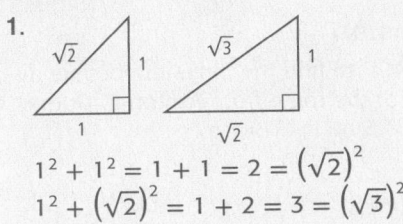

$1^2 + 1^2 = 1 + 1 = 2 = \left(\sqrt{2}\right)^2$

$1^2 + \left(\sqrt{2}\right)^2 = 1 + 2 = 3 = \left(\sqrt{3}\right)^2$

2. Check students' constructions to confirm that $\sqrt{4}$ lies at 2 on the number line.

3. Check students' constructions to confirm that $\sqrt{9}$ lies at 3 on the number line.

4. Check students' constructions to confirm that $2\sqrt{2}$ lies at $\sqrt{8}$ on the number line.

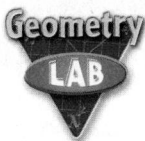

Organizer

Objective: Assess students' ability to apply concepts and skills in Lessons 5-5 through 5-8 in a real-world format.

 Online Edition

Resources

 Geometry Assessments
www.mathtekstoolkit.org

Problem	Text Reference
1	Lesson 5-5
2	Lesson 5-8
3	Lesson 5-8
4	Lesson 5-5, 5-6

Answers

1, 4. See p. A21.

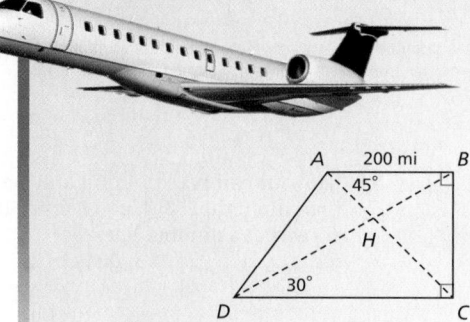

Relationships in Triangles

Fly Away! A commuter airline serves the four cities of Ashton, Brady, Colfax, and Dumas, located at points A, B, C, and D, respectively. The solid lines in the figure show the airline's existing routes. The airline is building an airport at H, which will serve as a hub. This will add four new routes to their schedule: $\overline{AH}$, $\overline{BH}$, $\overline{CH}$, and $\overline{DH}$.

1. The airline wants to locate the airport so that the combined distance to the cities $(AH + BH + CH + DH)$ is as small as possible. Give an indirect argument to explain why the airline should locate the airport at the intersection of the diagonals $\overline{AC}$ and $\overline{BD}$. (*Hint:* Assume that a different point X inside quadrilateral $ABCD$ results in a smaller combined distance. Then consider how $AX + CX$ compares to $AH + CH$.)

2. Currently, travelers who want to go from Ashton to Colfax must first fly to Brady. Once the airport is built, they will fly from Ashton to the new airport and then to Colfax. How many miles will this save compared to the distance of the current trip? **about 117.2 mi**

3. Currently, travelers who want to go from Brady to Dumas must first fly to Colfax. Once the airport is built, they will fly from Brady to the new airport and then to Dumas. How many miles will this save? **about 146.4 mi**

4. Once the airport is built, the airline plans to serve a meal only on its longest flight. On which route should they serve the meal? How do you know that this route is the longest?

INTERVENTION

Scaffolding Questions

1. How can you use the Triangle Inequality Theorem to write an inequality involving AX and CX? $AX + CX > AC$ How can you rewrite this inequality to include AH and CH? $AX + CX > AH + CH$

2. How can you find AC? It is the hyp. of a 45°-45°-90° triangle with leg length 200. So multiply 200 by $\sqrt{2}$.

3. How are $\overline{DB}$ and $\overline{DC}$ related? They are the hyp. and longer leg of a 30°-60°-90° triangle with a shorter leg length of 200.

4. Which route appears to be the longest? $\overline{DC}$ How can you show that this route is longer than $\overline{AD}$? Hinge Thm.

Extension

Use △ACD to find the range of possible distances for the route from Ashton to Dumas. about 63.6 mi to 629.2 mi

SECTION 5B

CHAPT **5**

SECTION **5B**

Quiz for Lessons 5-5 Through 5-8

✓ **5-5** **Indirect Proof and Inequalities in One Triangle**

1. Write an indirect proof that the supplement of an acute angle cannot be an acute angle.

2. Write the angles of △KLM in order from smallest to largest. ∠L, ∠K, ∠M

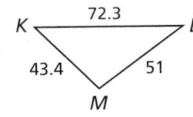

3. Write the sides of △DEF in order from shortest to longest. $\overline{EF}$, $\overline{DE}$, $\overline{DF}$

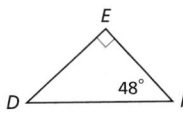

Tell whether a triangle can have sides with the given lengths. Explain.

4. 8.3, 10.5, 18.8

5. $4s$, $s + 10$, s^2, when $s = 4$

6. The distance from Kara's school to the theater is 9 km. The distance from her school to the zoo is 16 km. If the three locations form a triangle, what is the range of distances from the theater to the zoo? **greater than 7 km and less than 25 km**

✓ **5-6** **Inequalities in Two Triangles**

7. Compare PR and SV.

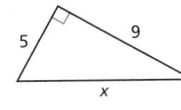

PR > SV

8. Compare m∠KJL and m∠MJL.

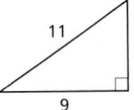

m∠KJL < m∠MJL

9. Find the range of values for x.

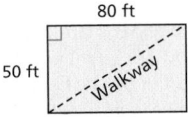

3.25 < x < 7

✓ **5-7** **The Pythagorean Theorem**

10. Find the value of x. Give the answer in simplest radical form. $\sqrt{106}$

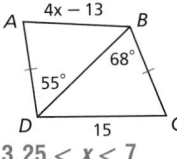

11. Find the missing side length. Tell if the side lengths form a Pythagorean triple. Explain.

12. Tell if the measures 10, 12, and 16 can be the side lengths of a triangle. If so, classify the triangle as acute, obtuse, or right. **triangle; obtuse**

13. A landscaper wants to place a stone walkway from one corner of the rectangular lawn to the opposite corner. What will be the length of the walkway? Round to the nearest inch. **94 ft 4 in.**

✓ **5-8** **Applying Special Right Triangles**

14. A yield sign is an equilateral triangle with a side length of 36 inches. What is the height h of the sign? Round to the nearest inch. **31 in.**

Find the values of the variables. Give your answers in simplest radical form.

15.

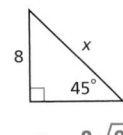

$x = 8\sqrt{2}$

16.

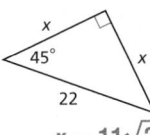

$x = 11\sqrt{2}$

17.

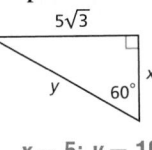

$x = 5$; $y = 10$

Ready to Go On? 365

READY TO GO ON?

GO ON?

Organizer

Objective: Assess students' mastery of concepts and skills in Lessons 5-5 through 5-8.

Resources

✏ **Assessment Resources**
　Section 5B Quiz

🖐 **Test & Practice Generator**
One-Stop Planner®

INTERVENTION ◀▶

Resources

✏ **Ready to Go On? Intervention and Enrichment** Worksheets

💿 **Ready to Go On? CD-ROM**

🪐 **Ready to Go On? Online**

my.hrw.com

Answers

1, 4, 5, 11. See p. A21.

READY TO GO ON?
Diagnose and Prescribe

NO INTERVENE

YES ENRICH

READY TO GO ON? Intervention, Section 5B			
Ready to Go On? Intervention	✏ **Worksheets**	💿 **CD-ROM**	🪐 **Online**
✓ Lesson 5-5	5-5 Intervention	Activity 5-5	Diagnose and Prescribe Online
✓ Lesson 5-6	5-6 Intervention	Activity 5-6	
✓ Lesson 5-7	5-7 Intervention	Activity 5-7	
✓ Lesson 5-8	5-8 Intervention	Activity 5-8	

READY TO GO ON? **Enrichment, Section 5B**

✏ **Worksheets**
💿 **CD-ROM**
🪐 **Online**

Ready to Go On? **365**

Organizer

Objective: Help students organize and review key concepts and skills presented in Chapter 5.

Online Edition
Multilingual Glossary

Resources

PuzzlePro
One-Stop Planner®

Multilingual Glossary Online
go.hrw.com/Geo/TX
KEYWORD: MG7 Glossary

Lesson Tutorial Videos
CD-ROM

Test & Practice Generator
One-Stop Planner®

Answers

1. equidistant
2. midsegment
3. incenter
4. locus
5. 7.4
6. 13.4
7. 5.8
8. 52°
9. $y = x - 1$
10. $y - 6 = -0.25(x - 4)$
11. No; to apply the Conv. of the ∠ Bisector Thm., you need to know that $\overline{AP} \perp \overline{AB}$ and $\overline{CP} \perp \overline{CB}$.
12. Yes; because $\overline{AP} \perp \overline{AB}$, $\overline{CP} \perp \overline{CB}$, and $\overline{AP} \cong \overline{CP}$, P is on the bisector of ∠ABC by the Conv. of the ∠ Bisector Thm.

Know it!
Note

For a complete list of the postulates and theorems in this chapter, see p. S82.

Vocabulary

Complete the sentences below with vocabulary words from the list above.

1. A point that is the same distance from two or more objects is __?__ from the objects.

2. A __?__ is a segment that joins the midpoints of two sides of the triangle.

3. The point of concurrency of the angle bisectors of a triangle is the __?__ .

4. A __?__ is a set of points that satisfies a given condition.

5-1 Perpendicular and Angle Bisectors (pp. 300–306)

 TEKS G.3.B, G.3.E, G.7.A, G.7.B, G.7.C, G.10.B

EXAMPLES

Find each measure.

■ *JL*

Because $\overline{JM} \cong \overline{MK}$ and $\overline{ML} \perp \overline{JK}$, $\overline{ML}$ is the perpendicular bisector of $\overline{JK}$.

$JL = KL$ ⊥ Bisector Thm.

$JL = 7.9$ Substitute 7.9 for KL.

■ m∠PQS, given that m∠PQR = 68°

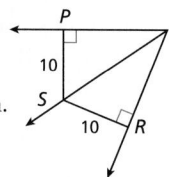

Since $SP = SR$, $\overline{SP} \perp \overline{QP}$, and $\overline{SR} \perp \overline{QR}$, $\overline{QS}$ bisects ∠PQR by the Converse of the Angle Bisector Theorem.

$m\angle PQS = \frac{1}{2}m\angle PQR$ Def. of ∠ bisector

$m\angle PQS = \frac{1}{2}(68°) = 34°$ Substitute 68° for m∠PQR.

EXERCISES

Find each measure.

5. *BD*

6. *YZ*

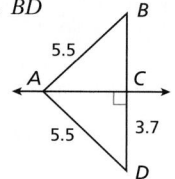

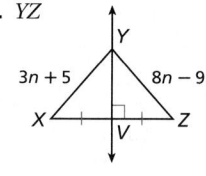

7. *HT*

8. m∠MNP

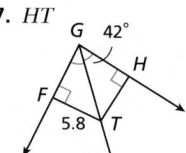

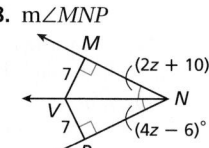

Write an equation in point-slope form for the perpendicular bisector of the segment with the given endpoints.

9. $A(-4, 5)$, $B(6, -5)$ **10.** $X(3, 2)$, $Y(5, 10)$

Tell whether the given information allows you to conclude that P is on the bisector of ∠ABC.

11.

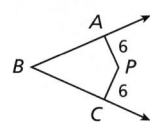

12.

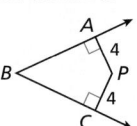

5-2 Bisectors of Triangles (pp. 307–313)

TEKS G.2.A, G.2.B, G.3.B, G.7.A, G.7.B

EXAMPLES

■ $\overline{DG}$, $\overline{EG}$, and $\overline{FG}$ are the perpendicular bisectors of $\triangle ABC$. Find AG.

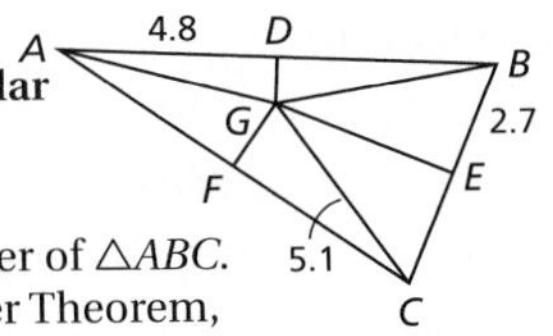

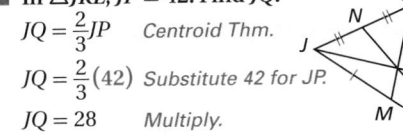

G is the circumcenter of $\triangle ABC$. By the Circumcenter Theorem, G is equidistant from the vertices of $\triangle ABC$.

$AG = CG$ Circumcenter Thm.

$AG = 5.1$ Substitute 5.1 for CG.

■ $\overline{QS}$ and $\overline{RS}$ are angle bisectors of $\triangle PQR$. Find the distance from S to $\overline{PR}$.

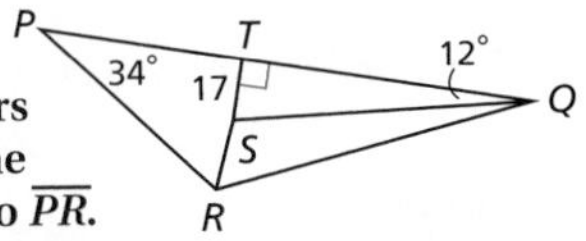

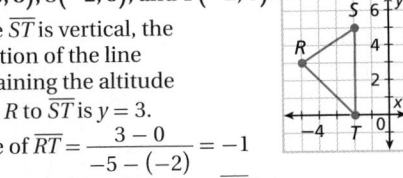

S is the incenter of $\triangle PQR$. By the Incenter Theorem, S is equidistant from the sides of $\triangle PQR$. The distance from S to $\overline{PQ}$ is 17, so the distance from S to $\overline{PR}$ is also 17.

EXERCISES

$\overline{PX}$, $\overline{PY}$, and $\overline{PZ}$ are the perpendicular bisectors of $\triangle GHJ$. Find each length.

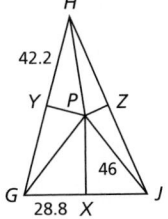

13. GY **14.** GP

15. GJ **16.** PH

$\overline{UA}$ and $\overline{VA}$ are angle bisectors of $\triangle UVW$. Find each measure.

17. the distance from A to $\overline{UV}$

18. $m\angle WVA$

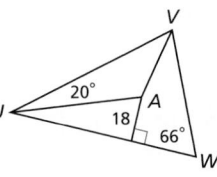

Find the circumcenter of a triangle with the given vertices.

19. $M(0, 6)$, $N(8, 0)$, $O(0, 0)$

20. $O(0, 0)$, $R(0, -7)$, $S(-12, 0)$

Answers

13. 42.2

14. 46

15. 57.6

16. 46

17. 18

18. 37°

19. $(4, 3)$

20. $(-6, -3.5)$

21. 16.4

22. 8.2

23. 5.8

24. 17.4

25. $(-6, 0)$

26. $(1, 2)$

27. $(7, 4)$

28. $(3, 0)$

29. $(3, 4)$

5-3 Medians and Altitudes of Triangles (pp. 314–320)

TEKS G.2.A, G.2.B, G.3.B, G.7.A, G.7.B, G.7.C

EXAMPLES

■ In $\triangle JKL$, $JP = 42$. Find JQ.

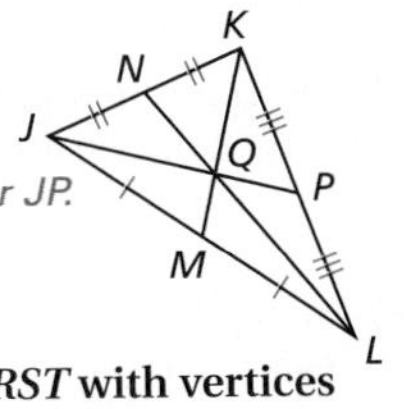

$JQ = \dfrac{2}{3}JP$ Centroid Thm.

$JQ = \dfrac{2}{3}(42)$ Substitute 42 for JP.

$JQ = 28$ Multiply.

■ Find the orthocenter of $\triangle RST$ with vertices $R(-5, 3)$, $S(-2, 5)$, and $T(-2, 0)$.

Since $\overline{ST}$ is vertical, the equation of the line containing the altitude from R to $\overline{ST}$ is $y = 3$.

slope of $\overline{RT} = \dfrac{3 - 0}{-5 - (-2)} = -1$

The slope of the altitude to $\overline{RT}$ is 1. This line must pass through $S(-2, 5)$.

$y - y_1 = m(x - x_1)$ Point-slope form

$y - 5 = 1(x + 2)$ Substitution

Solve the system $\begin{cases} y = 3 \\ y = x + 7 \end{cases}$ to find that the coordinates of the orthocenter are $(-4, 3)$.

EXERCISES

In $\triangle DEF$, $DB = 24.6$, and $EZ = 11.6$. Find each length.

21. DZ **22.** ZB

23. ZC **24.** EC

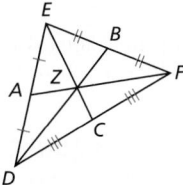

Find the orthocenter of a triangle with the given vertices.

25. $J(-6, 7)$, $K(-6, 0)$, $L(-11, 0)$

26. $A(1, 2)$, $B(6, 2)$, $C(1, -8)$

27. $R(2, 3)$, $S(7, 8)$, $T(8, 3)$

28. $X(-3, 2)$, $Y(5, 2)$, $Z(3, -4)$

29. The coordinates of a triangular piece of a mobile are $(0, 4)$, $(3, 8)$, and $(6, 0)$. The piece will hang from a chain so that it is balanced. At what coordinates should the chain be attached?

30. 35.1
31. 64.8
32. 32.4
33. 42°
34. 138°
35. 42°
36. $V(-1, -1)$; $W(6, 1)$; slope of $\overline{VW} = \frac{2}{7}$; slope of $\overline{GJ} = \frac{2}{7}$; since the slopes are the same, $\overline{VW} \parallel \overline{GJ}$. $VW = \sqrt{53}$; $GJ = 2\sqrt{53}$; since $\sqrt{53} = \frac{1}{2}(2\sqrt{53})$, $VW = \frac{1}{2}GJ$.
37. $\overline{BC}, \overline{AC}, \overline{AB}$
38. $\angle F, \angle H, \angle G$
39. greater than 9 cm and less than 18 cm
40. Yes; possible answer: the sum of each pair of 2 lengths is greater than the third length.
41. No; possible answer: when $z = 5$, the value of $3z$ is 15. So the 3 lengths are 5, 5, and 15. The sum of 5 and 5 is 10, which is not greater than 15. By the △ Inequality Thm., a △ cannot have these side lengths.
42. Possible answer:
Given: $\triangle ABC$
Prove: $\triangle ABC$ cannot have 2 obtuse ∡.
Proof: Assume that $\triangle ABC$ has 2 obtuse ∡. Let $\angle A$ and $\angle B$ be the obtuse ∡. By the def. of obtuse, $m\angle A > 90°$ and $m\angle B > 90°$. If the 2 inequalities are added, $m\angle A + m\angle B > 180°$. However, by the △ Sum Thm., $m\angle A + m\angle B + m\angle C = 180°$. So $m\angle A + m\angle B = 180° - m\angle C$. But then $180° - m\angle C > 180°$ by subst., and thus $m\angle C < 0°$. A △ cannot have an ∠ with a measure less than 0°. So the assumption that $\triangle ABC$ has 2 obtuse ∡ is false. Therefore a △ cannot have 2 obtuse ∡.
43. $PS < RS$
44. $m\angle BCA < m\angle DCA$
45. $-1.4 < n < 3$
46. $2.75 < n < 12.5$

5-4 The Triangle Midsegment Theorem (pp. 322–327)

TEKS G.2.A, G.2.B, G.3.B, G.5.A, G.7.B, G.9.B

EXAMPLES

Find each measure.

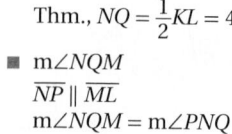

- NQ

By the △ Midsegment Thm., $NQ = \frac{1}{2}KL = 45.7$.

- $m\angle NQM$

$\overline{NP} \parallel \overline{ML}$	△ Midsegment Thm.
$m\angle NQM = m\angle PNQ$	Alt. Int. ∡ Thm.
$m\angle NQM = 37°$	Substitution

EXERCISES

Find each measure.

30. BC 31. XZ
32. XC 33. $m\angle BCZ$
34. $m\angle BAX$ 35. $m\angle YXZ$

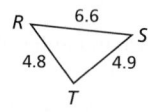

36. The vertices of $\triangle GHJ$ are $G(-4, -7)$, $H(2, 5)$, and $J(10, -3)$. V is the midpoint of $\overline{GH}$, and W is the midpoint of $\overline{HJ}$. Show that $\overline{VW} \parallel \overline{GJ}$ and $VW = \frac{1}{2}GJ$.

5-5 Indirect Proof and Inequalities in One Triangle (pp. 332–339)

TEKS G.3.B, G.3.C, G.3.E, G.5.B

EXAMPLES

- Write the angles of $\triangle RST$ in order from smallest to largest.

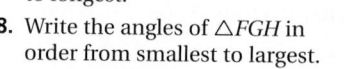

The smallest angle is opposite the shortest side. In order, the angles are $\angle S$, $\angle R$, and $\angle T$.

- The lengths of two sides of a triangle are 15 inches and 12 inches. Find the range of possible lengths for the third side.

Let s be the length of the third side.

$s + 15 > 12$	$s + 12 > 15$	$15 + 12 > s$
$s > -3$	$s > 3$	$27 > s$

By the Triangle Inequality Theorem, 3 in. $< s < 27$ in.

EXERCISES

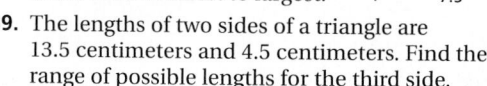

37. Write the sides of $\triangle ABC$ in order from shortest to longest.
38. Write the angles of $\triangle FGH$ in order from smallest to largest.
39. The lengths of two sides of a triangle are 13.5 centimeters and 4.5 centimeters. Find the range of possible lengths for the third side.

Tell whether a triangle can have sides with the given lengths. Explain.

40. 6.2, 8.1, 14.2   41. $z, z, 3z$, when $z = 5$
42. Write an indirect proof that a triangle cannot have two obtuse angles.

5-6 Inequalities in Two Triangles (pp. 340–345)

TEKS G.3.B, G.3.E

EXAMPLES

Compare the given measures.

- KL and ST

$KJ = RS$, $JL = RT$, and $m\angle J > m\angle R$. By the Hinge Theorem, $KL > ST$.

- $m\angle ZXY$ and $m\angle XZW$

$XY = WZ$, $XZ = XZ$, and $YZ < XW$. By the Converse of the Hinge Theorem, $m\angle ZXY < m\angle XZW$.

EXERCISES

Compare the given measures.

43. PS and RS 44. $m\angle BCA$ and $m\angle DCA$

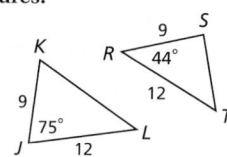 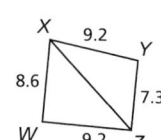 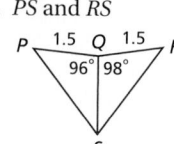 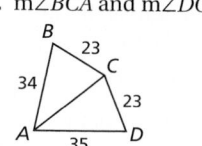

Find the range of values for n.

45.   46.

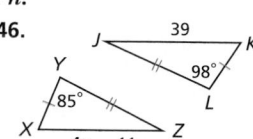

5-7 The Pythagorean Theorem (pp. 348–355)

 TEKS G.1.B, G.5.B, G.5.D, G.8.C, G.11.C

EXAMPLES

■ Find the value of x. Give your answer in simplest radical form.

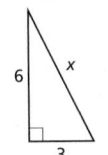

$$a^2 + b^2 = c^2 \quad \text{Pyth. Thm.}$$
$$6^2 + 3^2 = x^2 \quad \text{Substitution}$$
$$45 = x^2 \quad \text{Simplify.}$$
$$x = 3\sqrt{5} \quad \text{Find the positive}$$
$$\text{square root}$$
$$\text{and simplify.}$$

■ Find the missing side length. Tell if the sides form a Pythagorean triple. Explain.

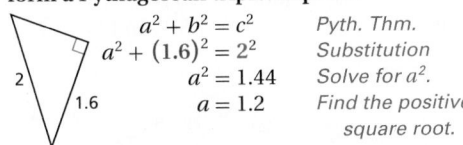

$$a^2 + b^2 = c^2 \quad \text{Pyth. Thm.}$$
$$a^2 + (1.6)^2 = 2^2 \quad \text{Substitution}$$
$$a^2 = 1.44 \quad \text{Solve for } a^2.$$
$$a = 1.2 \quad \text{Find the positive}$$
$$\text{square root.}$$

The side lengths do not form a Pythagorean triple because 1.2 and 1.6 are not whole numbers.

EXERCISES

Find the value of x. Give your answer in simplest radical form.

47.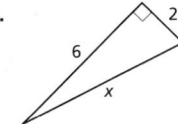

48.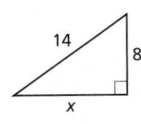

Find the missing side length. Tell if the sides form a Pythagorean triple. Explain.

49.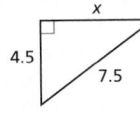

50.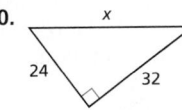

Tell if the measures can be the side lengths of a triangle. If so, classify the triangle as acute, obtuse, or right.

51. 9, 12, 16   **52.** 11, 14, 27

53. 1.5, 3.6, 3.9   **54.** 2, 3.7, 4.1

5-8 Applying Special Right Triangles (pp. 356–362)

 TEKS G.3.B, G.5.A, G.5.D, G.7.A

EXAMPLES

Find the values of the variables. Give your answers in simplest radical form.

■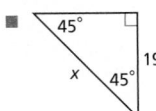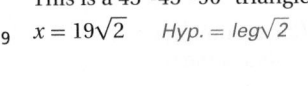

This is a 45°-45°-90° triangle.

$x = 19\sqrt{2}$ $Hyp. = leg\sqrt{2}$

■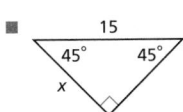

This is a 45°-45°-90° triangle.

$15 = x\sqrt{2}$ $Hyp. = leg\sqrt{2}$

$\dfrac{15}{\sqrt{2}} = x$ Divide both sides by $\sqrt{2}$.

$\dfrac{15\sqrt{2}}{2} = x$ Rationalize the denominator.

■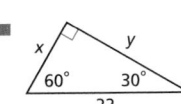

This is a 30°-60°-90° triangle.

$22 = 2x$ $Hyp. = 2(shorter\ leg)$

$11 = x$ Divide both sides by 2.

$y = 11\sqrt{3}$ Longer leg = (shorter leg)$\sqrt{3}$

EXERCISES

Find the values of the variables. Give your answers in simplest radical form.

55.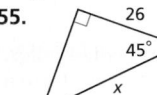

56.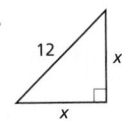

57.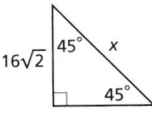

58.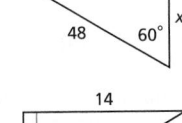

59.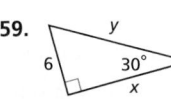

60.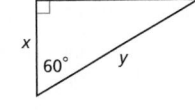

Find the value of each variable. Round to the nearest inch.

61.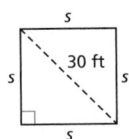

62.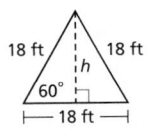

Answers

47. $x = 2\sqrt{10}$

48. $x = 2\sqrt{33}$

49. 6; the lengths do not form a Pythagorean triple because 4.5 and 7.5 are not whole numbers.

50. 40; the lengths do form a Pythagorean triple because they are nonzero whole numbers that satisfy the equation $a^2 + b^2 = c^2$.

51. triangle; obtuse

52. not a triangle

53. triangle; right

54. triangle; acute

55. $x = 26\sqrt{2}$

56. $x = 6\sqrt{2}$

57. $x = 32$

58. $x = 24; y = 24\sqrt{3}$

59. $x = 6\sqrt{3}; y = 12$

60. $x = \dfrac{14\sqrt{3}}{3}; y = \dfrac{28\sqrt{3}}{3}$

61. 21 ft 3 in.

62. 15 ft 7 in.

Organizer

Objective: Assess students' mastery of concepts and skills in Chapter 5.

Online Edition

Resources

Assessment Resources

Chapter 5 Tests
- Free Response
  (Levels A, B, C)
- Multiple Choice
  (Levels A, B, C)
- Performance Assessment

IDEA Works! CD-ROM

Modified Chapter 5 Test

Test & Practice Generator
One-Stop Planner®

Find each measure.

1. KL **9.8**

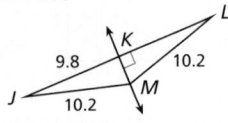

2. $m\angle WXY$ **34°**

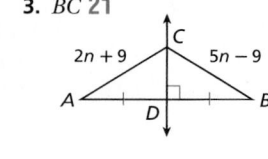

3. BC **21**

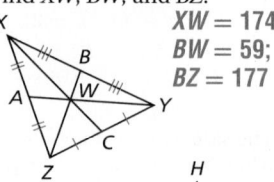

4. $\overline{MQ}$, $\overline{NQ}$, and $\overline{PQ}$ are the perpendicular bisectors of $\triangle RST$. Find RS and RQ.

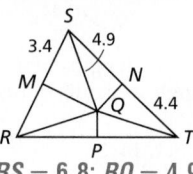

$RS = 6.8$; $RQ = 4.9$

5. $\overline{EG}$ and $\overline{FG}$ are angle bisectors of $\triangle DEF$. Find $m\angle GEF$ and the distance from G to $\overline{DF}$.

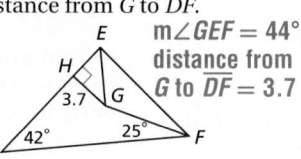

$m\angle GEF = 44°$; distance from G to $\overline{DF} = 3.7$

6. In $\triangle XYZ$, $XC = 261$, and $ZW = 118$. Find XW, BW, and BZ.

$XW = 174$; $BW = 59$; $BZ = 177$

7. Find the orthocenter of $\triangle JKL$ with vertices $J(-5, 2)$, $K(-5, 10)$, and $L(1, 4)$. $(-3, 4)$

8. In $\triangle GHJ$ at right, find PR, GJ, and $m\angle GRP$. $PR = 51$; $GJ = 148$; $m\angle GRP = 71°$

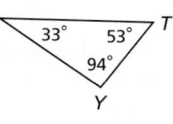

9. Write an indirect proof that two obtuse angles cannot form a linear pair.

10. Write the angles of $\triangle BEH$ in order from smallest to largest. $\angle E, \angle B, \angle H$

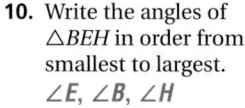

11. Write the sides of $\triangle RTY$ in order from shortest to longest. $\overline{TY}$, $\overline{RY}$, $\overline{RT}$

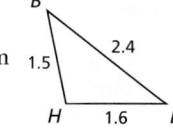

12. The distance from Arville to Branton is 114 miles. The distance from Branton to Camford is 247 miles. If the three towns form a triangle, what is the range of distances from Arville to Camford?

13. Compare $m\angle SPV$ and $m\angle ZPV$.

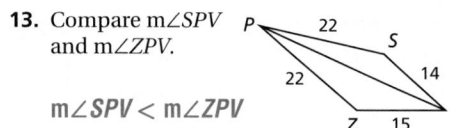

$m\angle SPV < m\angle ZPV$

14. Find the range of values for x.

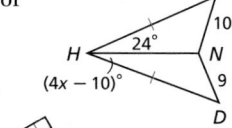

$2.5 < x < 8.5$

15. Find the missing side length in the triangle. Tell if the side lengths form a Pythagorean triple. Explain.

16. Tell if the measures 18, 20, and 27 can be the side lengths of a triangle. If so, classify the triangle as acute, obtuse, or right. **triangle; obtuse**

17. An IMAX screen is 62 feet tall and 82 feet wide. What is the length of the screen's diagonal? Round to the nearest inch. **102 ft 10 in.**

Find the values of the variables. Give your answers in simplest radical form.

18. 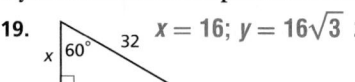 $x = 10\sqrt{2}$

19. $x = 16$; $y = 16\sqrt{3}$

20. 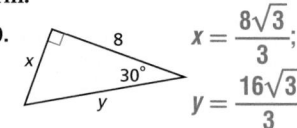 $x = \dfrac{8\sqrt{3}}{3}$; $y = \dfrac{16\sqrt{3}}{3}$

370 *Chapter 5 Properties and Attributes of Triangles*

TAKS Practice

Grades 9–11	Items
Obj. 1	10, 11, 13
Obj. 2	3, 12, 14
Obj. 6	15, 18–20
Obj. 7	7
Obj. 8	15, 17

Answers

9. Possible answer:
   Given: $\angle 1$ and $\angle 2$ form a lin. pair.
   Prove: $\angle 1$ and $\angle 2$ cannot both be obtuse ∡.

   Proof: Assume $\angle 1$ and $\angle 2$ are both obtuse ∡. By the def. of obtuse, $m\angle 1 > 90°$ and $m\angle 2 > 90°$. If the 2 inequalities are added, $m\angle 1 + m\angle 2 > 180°$. However, by the Lin. Pair Thm., $\angle 1$ and $\angle 2$ are supp. By the def. of supp. ∡, this means that $m\angle 1 + m\angle 2 = 180°$. So $m\angle 1 + m\angle 2 > 180°$ contradicts the given information. The assumption that $\angle 1$ and $\angle 2$ are both obtuse ∡ is false. Therefore $\angle 1$ and $\angle 2$ cannot both be obtuse.

12. greater than 133 mi and less than 361 mi

15. $3\sqrt{15}$; the side lengths do not form a Pythagorean triple because $3\sqrt{15}$ is not a whole number.

COLLEGE ENTRANCE EXAM PRACTICE

FOCUS ON SAT MATHEMATICS SUBJECT TESTS

Some questions on the SAT Mathematics Subject Tests require the use of a calculator. You can take the test without one, but it is not recommended. The calculator you use must meet certain criteria. For example, calculators that make noise or have typewriter-like keypads are not allowed.

 If you have both a scientific and a graphing calculator, bring the graphing calculator to the test. Make sure you spend time getting used to a new calculator before the day of the test.

You may want to time yourself as you take this practice test. It should take you about 6 minutes to complete.

1. In $\triangle ABC$, $m\angle C = 2m\angle A$, and $CB = 3$ units. What is AB to the nearest hundredth unit?

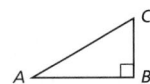

   (A) 1.73 units
   (B) 4.24 units
   (C) 5.20 units
   (D) 8.49 units
   (E) 10.39 units

2. What is the perimeter of $\triangle ABC$ if D is the midpoint of $\overline{AB}$, E is the midpoint of $\overline{BC}$, and F is the midpoint of $\overline{AC}$?

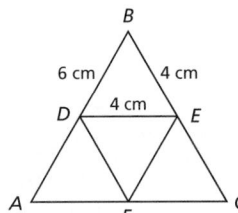

   Note: Figure not drawn to scale.

   (A) 8 centimeters
   (B) 14 centimeters
   (C) 20 centimeters
   (D) 28 centimeters
   (E) 35 centimeters

3. The side lengths of a right triangle are 2, 5, and c, where $c > 5$. What is the value of c?

   (A) $\sqrt{21}$
   (B) $\sqrt{29}$
   (C) 7
   (D) 9
   (E) $\sqrt{145}$

4. In the triangle below, which of the following CANNOT be the length of the unknown side?

   (A) 2.2
   (B) 6
   (C) 12.8
   (D) 17.2
   (E) 18.1

5. Which of the following points is on the perpendicular bisector of the segment with endpoints $(3, 4)$ and $(9, 4)$?

   (A) $(4, 2)$
   (B) $(4, 5)$
   (C) $(5, 4)$
   (D) $(6, -1)$
   (E) $(7, 4)$

Organizer

Objective: Provide practice for college entrance exams such as the SAT Mathematics Subject Tests.

 **Online Edition**

Resources

College Entrance Exam Practice

Questions on the SAT Mathematics Subject Tests Levels 1 and 2 represent the following math content areas:

	Level	
	1	2
Algebra	30%	18%
Plane Euclidean Geometry	20%	0%
Coordinate Geometry	12%	12%
Three-dimensional Geometry	6%	8%
Trigonometry	8%	20%
Functions	12%	24%
Statistics/Probability	6%	6%
Miscellaneous	6%	12%

Items on this page focus on:
• Plane Euclidean Geometry
• Coordinate Geometry

Text References:

Item	1	2	3	4	5
Lesson	5-8	5-4	5-7	5-5	5-1

TEST PREP DOCTOR

1. Students who chose **E** applied the properties of a 30°-60°-90° triangle incorrectly and found the value of $6\sqrt{3}$. Students who chose **B** applied the properties of a 45°-45°-90° triangle and found the value of $3\sqrt{2}$.

2. Students who chose **A** found AC but did not answer the question. Students who chose **B** found the perimeter of $\triangle DEF$. Students who chose **E** might have confused properties of midsegments and centroids and used a factor of $\frac{2}{3}$.

3. Students who chose **A** did not consider the given fact that $c > 5$. They used the Pythagorean Theorem with 5 as the hypotenuse. Remind students to read test items carefully.

4. Students who did not choose **E** did not apply the Triangle Inequality Theorem. Remind students not to rely on the relative lengths in the diagram.

5. Suggest that students graph the given points on a coordinate plane. They should quickly see that the segment is horizontal, so its perpendicular bisector is vertical through the midpoint. This should allow students to quickly find the correct answer, **D.**

Organizer

Objective: Provide opportunities to learn and practice common test-taking strategies.

 Online Edition

Resources

 TAKS Prep Workbook

 TAKS Prep CD-ROM

 TAKS Practice Online

go.hrw.com/Geo/TX
KEYWORD: MG7 TestPrep

TAKS PREP DOCTOR ✚ This TAKS Tackler focuses on using a different method to check the answer to a test problem. If students work a problem two ways and get the same answer both times, they can be fairly certain that their work is correct. Review with students the various problem-solving methods they have learned, as summarized in the table on the student page.

Any Question Type: Check with a Different Method

It is important to check all of your answers on a test. An effective way to do this is to use a different method to answer the question a second time. If you get the same answer with two different methods, then your answer is probably correct.

EXAMPLE **1**

Multiple Choice What are the coordinates of the centroid of $\triangle ABC$ with $A(-2, 4)$, $B(4, 6)$, and $C(1, -1)$?

Ⓕ $(1, 5)$ Ⓗ $(1, 3)$

Ⓖ $(2.5, 2.5)$ Ⓙ $(3, 1)$

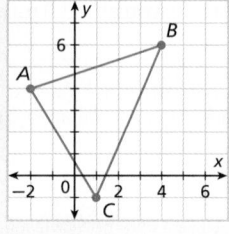

Method 1: The centroid of a triangle is the point of concurrency of the medians. Write the equations of two medians and find their point of intersection.

Let *D* be the midpoint of $\overline{AB}$ and let *E* be the midpoint of $\overline{BC}$.

$$D = \left(\frac{-2 + 4}{2}, \frac{4 + 6}{2}\right) = (1, 5) \qquad E = \left(\frac{4 + 1}{2}, \frac{6 + (-1)}{2}\right) = (2.5, 2.5)$$

The median from *C* to *D* contains $C(1, -1)$ and $D(1, 5)$. It is vertical, so its equation is $x = 1$.

The median from *A* to *E* contains $A(-2, 4)$ and $E(2.5, 2.5)$.

$$\text{slope of } \overline{AE} = \frac{4 - 2.5}{-2 - 2.5} = \frac{1.5}{-4.5} = -\frac{1}{3}$$

$y - y_1 = m(x - x_1)$ *Point-slope form*

$y - 4 = -\frac{1}{3}(x + 2)$ *Substitute 4 for y_1, $-\frac{1}{3}$ for m, and -2 for x_1.*

Solve the system $\begin{cases} x = 1 \\ y - 4 = -\frac{1}{3}(x + 2) \end{cases}$ *to find the point of intersection.*

$y - 4 = -\frac{1}{3}(1 + 2)$ *Substitute 1 for x.*

$y = 3$ *Simplify.*

The coordinates of the centroid are $(1, 3)$. So choice H is the correct answer.

Method 2: To check this answer, use a different method. By the Centroid Theorem, the centroid of a triangle is $\frac{2}{3}$ of the distance from each vertex to the midpoint of the opposite side. $\overline{CD}$ is vertical with a length of 6 units. $\frac{2}{3}(6) = 4$, and the coordinates of the point that is 4 units up from C is $(1, 3)$.

This method confirms that choice H is the correct answer.

Problem Solving Strategies

- Draw a Diagram
- Make a Model
- Guess and Test
- Work Backward
- Find a Pattern
- Make a Table
- Solve a Simpler Problem
- Use Logical Reasoning
- Use a Venn Diagram
- Make an Organized List

Read each test item and answer the questions that follow.

Item A

Multiple Choice Given that ℓ is the perpendicular bisector of $\overline{AB}$, $AC = 3n + 1$, and $BC = 6n - 11$, what is the value of n?

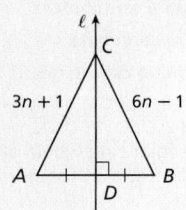

Ⓐ -4 Ⓒ $\frac{4}{3}$

Ⓑ $\frac{3}{4}$ Ⓓ 4

1. How can you use the given answer choices to solve this problem?

2. Describe how to solve this problem directly.

Item B

Multiple Choice Which number forms a Pythagorean triple with 15 and 17?

Ⓕ 5   Ⓗ 8

Ⓖ 7   Ⓙ 10

3. How can you use the given answer choices to find the answer?

4. Describe a different method you can use to check your answer.

Item C

Gridded Response Find the area of the square in square centimeters.

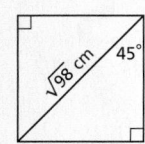

5. How can you use special right triangles to answer this question?

6. Explain how you can check your answer by using the Pythagorean Theorem.

Item D

Multiple Choice Which coordinates for point Z form a right triangle with the points $X(-8, 4)$ and $Y(0, -2)$?

Ⓐ $Z(4, 4)$ Ⓒ $Z(3, 2)$

Ⓑ $Z(4, 6)$ Ⓓ $Z(8, 4)$

7. Explain how to use slope to determine if $\triangle XYZ$ is a right triangle.

8. How can you use the Converse of the Pythagorean Theorem to check your answer?

Item E

Multiple Choice What are the coordinates of the orthocenter of $\triangle RST$?

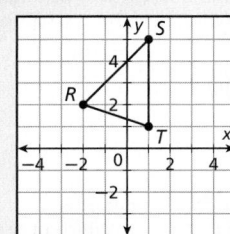

Ⓕ $(0, 2)$ Ⓗ $(-1, 3)$

Ⓖ $(0, 1)$ Ⓙ $(1, 2)$

9. Describe how you would solve this problem directly.

10. How can you use the third altitude of the triangle to confirm that your answer is correct?

TAKS Tackler **373**

Answers to Test Items

A. D

B. H

C. 49

D. C

E. F

Answers

Possible answers:

1. Substitute each answer choice into the equation $3n + 1 = 6n - 11$ to determine which choice makes the equation true.

2. Solve the equation $3n + 1 = 6n - 11$ for n.

3. Substitute each answer choice into the Pyth. Thm. as a leg length, along with a leg length of 15 and hypotenuse of 17, to determine which answer choice results in a true equation.

4. Solve the equation $x^2 + (15)^2 = (17)^2$ for x.

5. Since this is a 45°-45°-90° $\triangle$, the hyp. is equal to the product of the side length and $\sqrt{2}$. Solve $\sqrt{98} = s\sqrt{2}$ for s, and then use the formula $A = s^2$ to find the area.

6. Confirm that $s^2 + s^2 = 98$.

7. Find the slope of $\overline{XY}$, $\overline{XZ}$, and $\overline{YZ}$ for each point Z and determine if any 2 slopes are negative reciprocals of each other.

8. Find XY, XZ, and YZ for each point Z and check whether these 3 lengths satisfy the equation $a^2 + b^2 = c^2$.

9. Write equations for 2 of the altitudes of the $\triangle$, and find their point of intersection.

10. Write the equation for the third altitude of the $\triangle$, and confirm that it passes through the point of intersection of the first 2 altitudes.

TAKS Practice

Grades 9–11	Items
Obj. 2	A
Obj. 6	B
Obj. 7	D, E
Obj. 8	C, D

Organizer

Objective: Provide review and practice for Chapters 1–5 and standardized tests.

 Online Edition

Resources

 Assessment Resources
　　Chapter 5 Cumulative Test

 TAKS Prep Workbook

 TAKS Prep CD-ROM

 TAKS Practice Online
　　go.hrw.com/Geo/TX
　　KEYWORD: MG7 TestPrep

🌵 **TAKS Practice**

Grades 9–11	Items
Obj. 2	1, 2, 5, 11, 13, 15, 16
Obj. 7	5
Obj. 8	6, 11

CUMULATIVE ASSESSMENT, CHAPTERS 1–5

Multiple Choice

1. $\overline{GJ}$ is a midsegment of $\triangle DEF$, and $\overline{HK}$ is a midsegment of $\triangle GFJ$. What is the length of $\overline{HK}$?

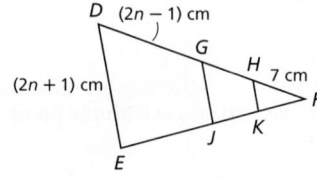

- (A) 2.25 centimeters
- (B) 4 centimeters
- (C) 7.5 centimeters
- (D) 9 centimeters

2. In $\triangle RST$, $SR < ST$, and $RT > ST$. If $m\angle R = (2x + 10)°$ and $m\angle T = (3x - 25)°$, which is a possible value of x?
- (F) 25
- (H) 35
- (G) 30
- (J) 40

3. The vertex angle of an isosceles triangle measures $(7a - 2)°$, and one of the base angles measures $(4a + 1)°$. Which term best describes this triangle?
- (A) Acute
- (B) Equiangular
- (C) Right
- (D) Obtuse

4. The lengths of two sides of an acute triangle are 8 inches and 10 inches. Which of the following could be the length of the third side?
- (F) 5 inches
- (H) 12 inches
- (G) 6 inches
- (J) 13 inches

5. For the coordinates $M(-1, 0)$, $N(-2, 2)$, $P(10, y)$, and $Q(4, 6)$, $\overline{MN} \parallel \overline{PQ}$. What is the value of y?
- (A) −18
- (C) 6
- (B) −6
- (D) 18

6. What is the area of an equilateral triangle that has a perimeter of 18 centimeters?
- (F) 9 square centimeters
- (G) $9\sqrt{3}$ square centimeters
- (H) 18 square centimeters
- (J) $18\sqrt{3}$ square centimeters

7. In $\triangle ABC$ and $\triangle DEF$, $\overline{AC} \cong \overline{DE}$, and $\angle A \cong \angle E$. Which of the following would allow you to conclude by SAS that these triangles are congruent?
- (A) $\overline{AB} \cong \overline{DF}$
- (B) $\overline{AC} \cong \overline{EF}$
- (C) $\overline{BA} \cong \overline{FE}$
- (D) $\overline{CB} \cong \overline{DF}$

8. For the segment below, $AB = \frac{1}{2}AC$, and $CD = 2BC$. Which expression is equal to the length of $\overline{AD}$?

- (F) $2AB + BC$
- (G) $2AC + AB$
- (H) $3AB$
- (J) $4BC$

9. In $\triangle DEF$, $m\angle D = 2(m\angle E + m\angle F)$. Which term best describes $\triangle DEF$?
- (A) Acute
- (B) Equiangular
- (C) Right
- (D) Obtuse

10. Which point of concurrency is always located inside the triangle?
- (F) The centroid of an obtuse triangle
- (G) The circumcenter of an obtuse triangle
- (H) The circumcenter of a right triangle
- (J) The orthocenter of a right triangle

TAKS PREP DOCTOR ✚

For **Item 2,** students who answered **G** did not check the measure of the third angle, $\angle S$. If $x = 30$, then $m\angle R = 70°$, and $m\angle T = 65°$. This satisfies $SR < ST$. However, by the Triangle Sum Theorem, $m\angle S = 45°$, which does not satisfy the condition $ST < RT$.

For **Item 4,** remind students that the variable c in the Pythagorean Inequalities Theorem is the length of the longest side. For choices **F** and **G,** 10 is the length of the longest side, but for choices **H** and **J,** 10 is not c.

If a diagram is not provided, draw your own. Use the given information to label the diagram.

11. The length of one leg of a right triangle is 3 times the length of the other, and the length of the hypotenuse is 10. What is the length of the longest leg?

   Ⓐ 3   Ⓒ $\sqrt{10}$

   Ⓑ $3\sqrt{10}$ Ⓓ $12\sqrt{5}$

12. Which statement is true by the Transitive Property of Congruence?

   Ⓕ If $\angle A \cong \angle T$, then $\angle T \cong \angle A$.

   Ⓖ If $m\angle L = m\angle S$, then $\angle L \cong \angle S$.

   Ⓗ $5QR + 10 = 5(QR + 2)$

   Ⓙ If $\overline{BD} \cong \overline{DE}$ and $\overline{DE} \cong \overline{EF}$, then $\overline{BD} \cong \overline{EF}$.

Gridded Response

13. P is the incenter of $\triangle JKL$. The distance from P to $\overline{KL}$ is $2y - 9$. What is the distance from P to $\overline{JK}$?   **2**

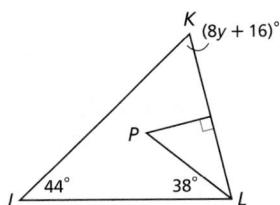

14. In a plane, $r \parallel s$, and $s \perp t$. How many right angles are formed by the lines r, s, and t? **8**

15. What is the measure, in degrees, of $\angle H$? **71**

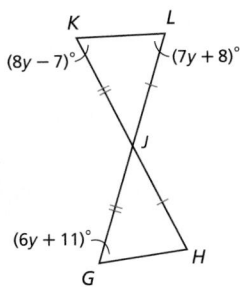

16. The point T is in the interior of $\angle XYZ$. If $m\angle XYZ = (25x + 10)°$, $m\angle XYT = 90°$, and $m\angle TYZ = (9x)°$, what is the value of x? **5**

Short Response

17. In $\triangle RST$, S is on the perpendicular bisector of $\overline{RT}$, $m\angle S = (4n + 16)°$, and $m\angle R = (3n - 18)°$. Find $m\angle R$. Show your work and explain how you determined your answer.

18. Given that $\overline{BD} \parallel \overline{AC}$ and $\overline{AB} \cong \overline{BD}$, explain why $AC < DC$.

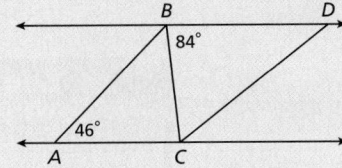

19. Write an indirect proof that an acute triangle cannot contain a pair of complementary angles.

   Given: $\triangle XYZ$ is an acute triangle.

   Prove: $\triangle XYZ$ does not contain a pair of complementary angles.

20. Find the coordinates of the orthocenter of $\triangle JKL$. Show your work and explain how you found your answer.

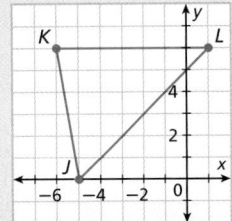

Extended Response

21. Consider the statement "If a triangle is equiangular, then it is acute."

   a. Write the converse, inverse, and contrapositive of this conditional statement.

   b. Write a biconditional statement from the conditional statement.

   c. Determine the truth value of the biconditional statement. If it is false, give a counterexample.

   d. Determine the truth value of each statement below. Give an example or counterexample to justify your reasoning.

   "For any conditional, if the inverse and contrapositive are true, then the biconditional is true."

   "For any conditional, if the inverse and converse are true, then the biconditional is true."

Short-Response Rubric

Items 17–20

2 Points = The student's answer is an accurate and complete execution of the task or tasks.

1 Point = The student's answer contains attributes of an appropriate response but is flawed.

0 Points = The student's answer contains no attributes of an appropriate response.

Extended-Response Rubric

Item 21

4 Points = The student's answers and counterexamples are correct, and explanations are complete. Work demonstrates a thorough understanding of concepts related to conditional statements, biconditional statements, and their truth values.

3 Points = The student correctly answers parts **a**, **b**, and **c**, but explanations or counterexamples may contain minor flaws. Work demonstrates an understanding of major concepts.

2 Points = The student answers correctly, but explanations are missing or incomplete. Work demonstrates a limited understanding of concepts related to conditional and biconditional statements.

1 Point = The student answers incorrectly but makes a reasonable attempt to explain the answers.

0 Points = The student does not answer correctly and does not attempt all parts of the problem.

Answers

17. 42°; since S is on the $\perp$ bisector of $\overline{RT}$, $RS = RT$. By the Isosc. $\triangle$ Thm., $\angle R \cong \angle T$, so $m\angle R = m\angle T$. By the $\triangle$ Sum Thm., $(4n + 16) + 2(3n - 18) = 180$, and thus $n = 20$. So $m\angle R = 3(20) - 18 = 42°$.

18. Since $\overline{BD} \parallel \overline{AC}$, $\angle BCA \cong \angle DBC$ by the Alt. Int. $\angle$ Thm. So $m\angle BCA = m\angle DBC = 84°$. By the $\triangle$ Sum Thm., $m\angle ABC = 50°$. Since $\overline{AB} \cong \overline{BD}$, $\overline{BC} \cong \overline{BC}$, and $m\angle ABC < m\angle DBC$, by the Hinge Thm., $AC < DC$.

19. Assume the opposite, that $\triangle XYZ$ has a pair of comp. $\angle$. Let $\angle X$ and $\angle Y$ be comp. So $m\angle X + m\angle Y = 90°$ by the def. of comp. $\angle$. By the $\triangle$ Sum Thm., $m\angle X + m\angle Y + m\angle Z = 180°$. But then by the Subtr. Prop. of =, $m\angle Z = 90°$. This contradicts the given information that $\triangle XYZ$ is acute. So the assumption is false, and $\triangle XYZ$ cannot contain a pair of comp. $\angle$.

20. Since $\overline{KL}$ is horizontal, the altitude from J to $\overline{KL}$ is vertical. It must pass through $J(-5, 0)$. So the equation of the altitude is $y = -5$. The slope of $\overline{JL}$ is $\frac{6}{1 - (-5)} = 1$, so the slope of a line $\perp$ to $\overline{JL}$ is -1. This line must pass through $K(-6, 6)$. In point-slope form, the equation of the line is $y - 6 = -1[x - (-6)]$, which simplifies to $y = -x$. The intersection of $y = -5$ and $y = -x$ is $(5, -5)$, which is the orthocenter of $\triangle JKL$.

21a. Converse: If a $\triangle$ is acute, then it is equiangular. Inverse: If a $\triangle$ is not equiangular, then it is not acute. Contrapositive: If a $\triangle$ is not acute, then it is not equiangular.

   b. A $\triangle$ is equiangular if and only if it is acute.

   c. F; a $\triangle$ with angle measures of 50°, 60°, and 70° is acute, but not equiangular.

   d. See p. A21.

CHAPTER 6

Polygons and Quadrilaterals

Section 6A
Polygons and Parallelograms

6-1 Geometry Lab Construct Regular Polygons

6-1 Properties and Attributes of Polygons

On Track for TAKS Relations and Functions

6-2 Geometry Lab Explore Properties of Parallelograms

6-2 Properties of Parallelograms

6-3 Conditions for Parallelograms

Section 6B
Other Special Quadrilaterals

6-4 Properties of Special Parallelograms

6-5 Technology Lab Predict Conditions for Special Parallelograms

6-5 Conditions for Special Parallelograms

6-6 Technology Lab Explore Isosceles Trapezoids

6-6 Properties of Kites and Trapezoids

Pacing Guide for 45-Minute Classes

Chapter 6

Countdown to TAKS Weeks ⑬, ⑭

DAY 1	DAY 2	DAY 3	DAY 4	DAY 5
6-1 Geometry Lab	6-1 Lesson	On Track for TAKS 6-2 Geometry Lab	6-2 Lesson	6-3 Lesson

DAY 6	DAY 7	DAY 8	DAY 9	DAY 10
Multi-Step TAKS Prep Ready to Go On?	6-4 Lesson	6-5 Technology Lab	6-5 Lesson	6-6 Technology Lab

DAY 11	DAY 12	DAY 13	DAY 14
6-6 Lesson	Multi-Step TAKS Prep Ready to Go On?	Chapter 6 Review	Chapter 6 Test

Pacing Guide for 90-Minute Classes

Chapter 6

DAY 1	DAY 2	DAY 3	DAY 4	DAY 5
6-1 Technology Lab 6-1 Lesson	On Track for TAKS 6-2 Geometry Lab 6-2 Lesson	6-3 Lesson Multi-Step TAKS Prep Ready to Go On?	6-4 Lesson 6-5 Technology Lab	6-5 Lesson 6-6 Technology Lab

DAY 6	DAY 7
6-6 Lesson Multi-Step TAKS Prep Ready to Go On?	Chapter 6 Review Chapter 6 Test

ONGOING ASSESSMENT and INTERVENTION

	DIAGNOSE	PRESCRIBE

Assess Prior Knowledge

Before Chapter 6

Diagnose readiness for the chapter.

Are You Ready? SE p. 377

Prescribe intervention.

Are You Ready? Intervention Skills 26, 30, 32, 88

Formative Assessment

Before Every Lesson

Diagnose readiness for the lesson.

Warm Up TE, every lesson

Prescribe intervention.

Skills Bank SE pp. S50–S81

Reteach CRB, Ch. 1–6

During Every Lesson

Diagnose understanding of lesson concepts.

Check It Out! SE, every example
Think and Discuss SE, every lesson
Write About It SE, every lesson
Journal TE, every lesson

Prescribe intervention.

Questioning Strategies TE, every example
Reading Strategies CRB, every lesson
Success for ELL pp. 73–84

After Every Lesson

Diagnose mastery of lesson concepts.

Lesson Quiz TE, every lesson
Alternative Assessment TE, every lesson
Test Prep SE, every lesson
Test and Practice Generator

Prescribe intervention.

Reteach CRB, every lesson
Problem Solving CRB, every lesson
Test Prep Doctor TE, every lesson
Homework Help Online

Before Chapter 6 Testing

Diagnose mastery of concepts in the chapter.

Ready to Go On? SE pp. 407, 437
Multi-Step TAKS Prep SE pp. 406, 436
Section Quizzes AR pp. 105–106
Test and Practice Generator

Prescribe intervention.

Ready to Go On? Intervention pp. 76–91
Scaffolding Questions TE pp. 406, 436

Before High Stakes Testing

Diagnose mastery of benchmark concepts.

Ready for TAKS? Benchmark Tests
College Entrance Exam Practice SE p. 443
TAKS Prep SE pp. 446–447
TAKS Prep CD-ROM

Prescribe intervention.

Ready for TAKS? Intervention
College Entrance Exam Practice
TAKS Prep Workbook

Summative Assessment

After Chapter 6

Check mastery of chapter concepts.

Multiple-Choice Tests (Forms A, B, C)
Free-Response Tests (Forms A, B, C)
Performance Assessment AR pp. 107–120
Test and Practice Generator

Prescribe intervention.

Reteach CRB, every lesson
Lesson Tutorial Videos Chapter 6

Check mastery of benchmark concepts.

TAKS Tests
College Entrance Exams

Prescribe intervention.

TAKS Prep Workbook
College Entrance Exam Practice

CHAPTER 6

Supporting the Teacher

Chapter 6 Resource Book

Practice A, B, C
pp. 3–5, 11–13, 19–21, 27–29, 35–37, 43–45

Reading Strategies ELL
pp. 10, 18, 26, 34, 42, 50

Reteach
pp. 6–7, 14–15, 22–23, 30–31, 38–39, 46–47

Problem Solving
pp. 9, 17, 25, 33, 41, 49

Challenge
pp. 8, 16, 24, 32, 40, 48

Parent Letter   pp. 1–2

Transparencies

Lesson Transparencies, Volume 2 .... Chapter 6
• Warm Ups
• Teaching Transparencies
• Additional Examples
• Lesson Quizzes

Alternate Openers: Explorations .... pp. 37–42

Countdown to TAKS .... pp. 25–28

Know-It Notebook .... Chapter 6
• Graphic Organizers
• Key Concepts
• Vocabulary
• Chapter Review
• Big Ideas
• Postulates
• Theorems

Teacher Tools

Power Presentations®
Complete PowerPoint® presentations for Chapter 6 lessons

Lesson Tutorial Videos®
Holt authors Ed Burger and Freddie Renfro present tutorials to support the Chapter 6 lessons.

One-Stop Planner®
Easy access to all Chapter 6 resources and assessments, as well as software for lesson planning, test generation, and puzzle creation

IDEA Works!®
Key Chapter 6 resources and assessments modified to address special learning needs

Lesson Plans .... pp. 37–42

Solutions Key .... p. 411

Geometry Posters .... Chapter 6

TechKeys   **Lab Resources**

Project Teacher Support   **Parent Resources**

Workbooks

Homework and Practice Workbook
Teacher's Guide .... pp. 37–42

Know-It Notebook
Teacher's Guide .... pp. 81–94

Problem Solving Workbook
Teacher's Guide .... pp. 37–42

TAKS Prep Workbook
Teacher's Guide

Technology Highlights for the Teacher

Power Presentations
Dynamic presentations to engage students. Complete PowerPoint® presentations for every lesson in Chapter 6.

One-Stop Planner
Easy access to Chapter 6 resources and assessments. Includes lesson-planning, test-generation, and puzzle-creation software.

Premier Online Edition
Chapter 6 includes Tutorial Videos, Lesson Activities, Lesson Quizzes, Homework Help, and Chapter Project.

KEY: **SE** = *Student Edition*   **TE** = *Teacher's Edition*   ELL English Language Learners   Spanish version available    Available online   Available on CD-ROM

Reaching All Learners

Resources for All Learners

Texas Lab Manual .... Chapter 6
Homework and Practice Workbook .... pp. 37–42
Know-It Notebook .... pp. 81–94
Problem Solving Workbook .... pp. 37–42

DEVELOPING LEARNERS
Practice A .... CRB, every lesson
Reteach .... CRB, every lesson
Inclusion .... TE p. 384
Questioning Strategies .... TE, every example
Modified Chapter 6 Resources 💿 .... *IDEA Works!*
Homework Help Online 🪐

ON-LEVEL LEARNERS
Practice B .... CRB, every lesson
Multiple Representations .... TE p. 428
Modeling .... TE p. 409

ADVANCED LEARNERS
Practice C .... CRB, every lesson
Challenge .... CRB, every lesson
Reading and Writing Math EXTENSION .... TE p. 379
Multi-Step TAKS Prep EXTENSION .... TE pp. 406, 436
Critical Thinking .... TE pp. 383, 395, 419, 421, 431

English Language Learners

ENGLISH
LANGUAGE
LEARNERS

Are You Ready? Vocabulary .... SE p. 377
Vocabulary Connections .... SE p. 378
Lesson Vocabulary .... SE pp. 382, 391, 408, 427
Vocabulary Exercises .... SE pp. 386, 395, 412, 432
Vocabulary Review .... SE p. 438
English Language Learners ..... TE pp. 399, 419, 431, 449
Reading Strategies .... CRB, every lesson
Success for English Language Learners .... pp. 73–84
Multilingual Glossary 🪐

Reaching All Learners Through...

Concrete Manipulatives .... TE p. 383
Critical Thinking .... TE pp. 383, 395, 419, 421, 431
Inclusion .... TE p. 384
Visual Cues .... TE pp. 389, 392, 396
Diversity .... TE p. 392
Kinesthetic Experience .... TE pp. 399, 409
Auditory Cues .... TE pp. 403, 419
Communication .... TE p. 419
Modeling .... TE p. 409
Multiple Representations .... TE p. 428
Test Prep Doctor .... TE pp. 388, 397, 405, 414,
                                                    425, 434, 443, 444, 446
Common Error Alerts .... TE pp. 385, 387, 393, 399, 403
                                                    411, 413, 421, 431, 433
Scaffolding Questions .... TE pp. 406, 436

Technology Highlights for Reaching All Learners

🔘 Lesson Tutorial Videos
Starring Holt authors Ed Burger and Freddie Renfro! Live tutorials to support every lesson in Chapter 6.

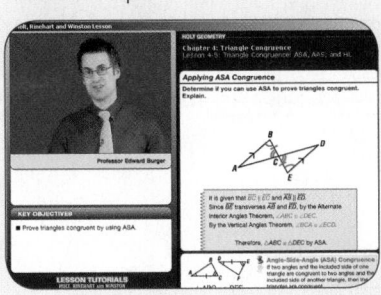

🪐 Multilingual Glossary
Searchable glossary includes definitions in English, Spanish, Vietnamese, Chinese, Hmong, Korean, and 4 other languages.

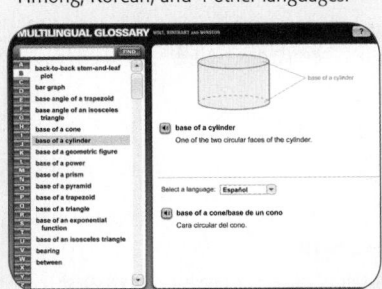

🪐 Online Interactivities
Interactive tutorials provide visually engaging alternative opportunities to learn concepts and master skills.

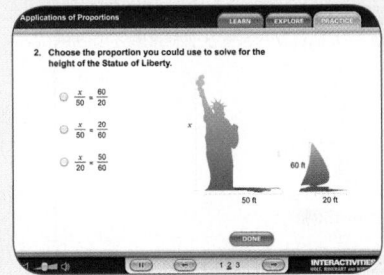

KEY: SE = *Student Edition*   **TE** = *Teacher's Edition*   **CRB** = *Chapter Resource Book*    **SPANISH** Spanish version available   🪐 Available online   🔘 Available on CD-ROM

CHAPTER

6

Ongoing Assessment

Assessing Prior Knowledge

Determine whether students have the prerequisite concepts and skills for success in Chapter 6.

Are You Ready? 	SE p. 377
Warm Up	TE, every lesson

Test Preparation

Provide practice and review for Chapter 6 and standardized tests.

Multi-Step TAKS Prep	SE pp. 406, 436
Study Guide: Review	SE pp. 438–441
TAKS Tackler	SE pp. 444–445
TAKS Prep	SE pp. 446–447
College Entrance Exam Practice	SE p. 443
Countdown to TAKS **Transparencies**	pp. 25–28
Ready for TAKS?	
TAKS Prep Workbook	
TAKS Prep CD-ROM	
IDEA Works!	

Alternative Assessment

Assess students' understanding of Chapter 6 concepts and combined problem-solving skills.

Chapter 6 Project	SE p. 376
Alternative Assessment	TE, every lesson
Performance Assessment	AR pp. 119–120
Portfolio Assessment	AR p. xxxiv

Daily Assessment

Provide formative assessment for each day of Chapter 6.

Questioning Strategies	TE, every example
Think and Discuss	SE, every lesson
Check It Out! Exercises	SE, every example
Write About It	SE, every lesson
Journal	TE, every lesson
Lesson Quiz	TE, every lesson
Alternative Assessment	TE, every lesson
Modified Lesson Quizzes	*IDEA Works!*

Weekly Assessment

Provide formative assessment for each week of Chapter 6.

Multi-Step TAKS Prep	SE pp. 406, 436
Ready to Go On?	SE pp. 407, 437
Cumulative Assessment	SE pp. 446–447
Test and Practice Generator **SPANISH**	*One-Stop Planner*

Formal Assessment

Provide summative assessment of Chapter 6 mastery.

Section Quizzes	AR pp. 105–106
Chapter 6 Test	SE p. 442
Chapter Test (Levels A, B, C)	AR pp. 107–118
• Multiple Choice • Free Response	
Cumulative Test	AR pp. 121–124
Test and Practice Generator **SPANISH**	*One-Stop Planner*
Modified Chapter 6 Test	*IDEA Works!*

Technology Highlights for Ongoing Assessment

 **Are You Ready?**

Automatically assess readiness and prescribe intervention for Chapter 6 prerequisite skills.

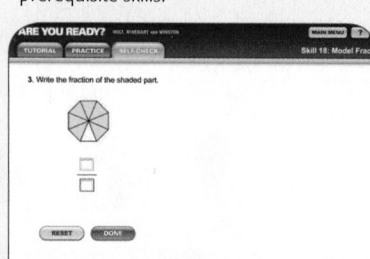

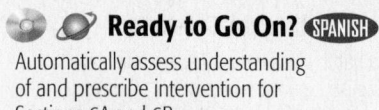 **Ready to Go On?** **SPANISH**

Automatically assess understanding of and prescribe intervention for Sections 6A and 6B.

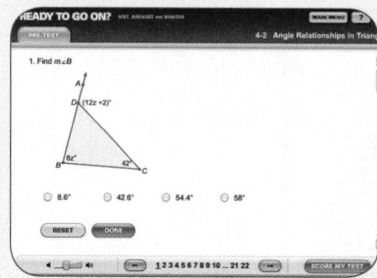

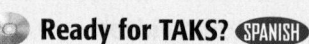 **Ready for TAKS?** **SPANISH**

Automatically assess proficiency with and provide intervention for TAKS objectives. Grade 6 through Exit Level.

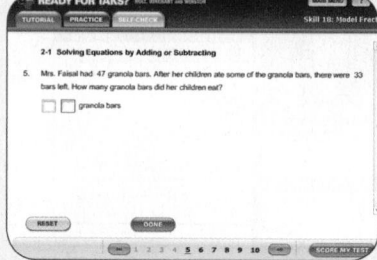

KEY: **SE** = *Student Edition* **TE** = *Teacher's Edition* **AR** = *Assessment Resources* **SPANISH** Spanish version available   Available online   Available on CD-ROM

Formal Assessment

Three levels (A, B, C) of multiple-choice and free-response chapter tests are available in the *Assessment Resources.*

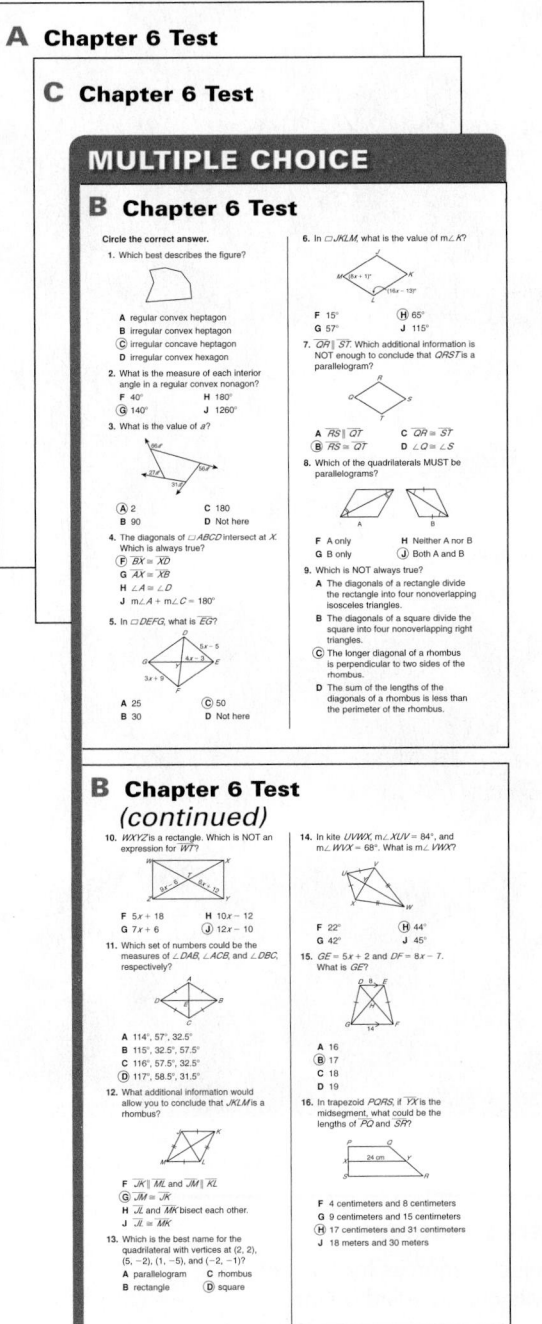

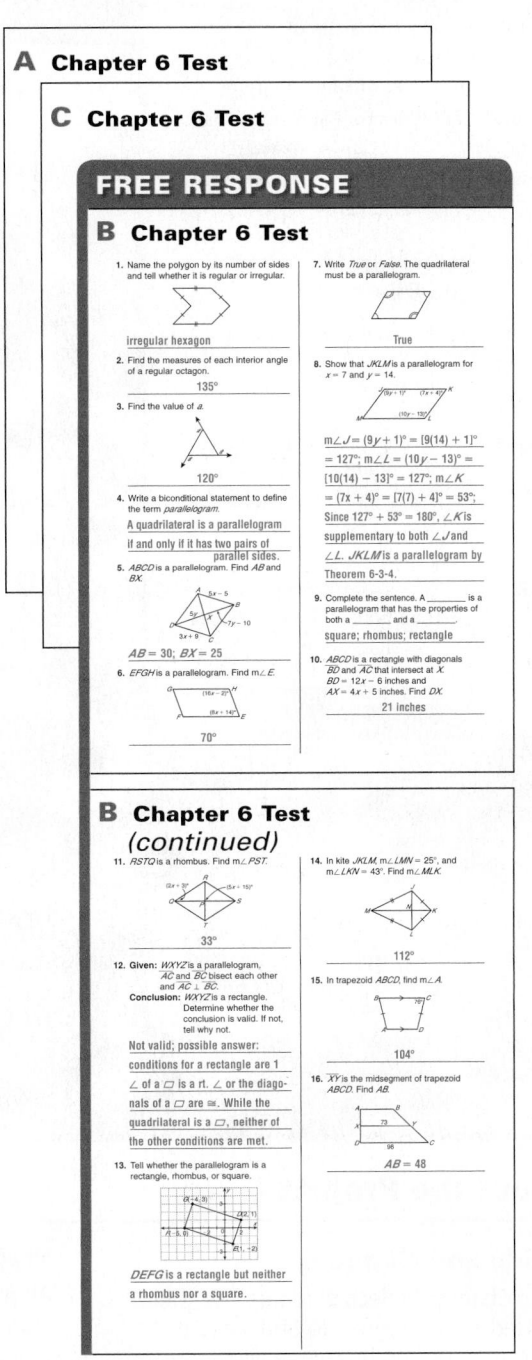

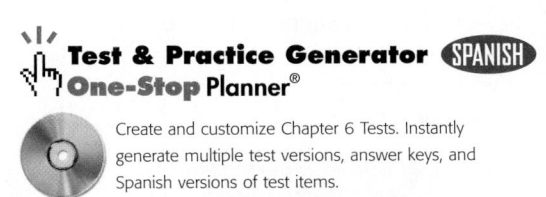

Test & Practice Generator SPANISH
One-Stop Planner®

Create and customize Chapter 6 Tests. Instantly
generate multiple test versions, answer keys, and
Spanish versions of test items.

376F

Polygons and Quadrilaterals

SECTION 6A
Polygons and Parallelograms

On page 406, students use the properties of polygons and parallelograms to investigate the faces of crystals.

Exercises designed to prepare students for success on the Multi-Step TAKS Prep can be found on pages 387, 396, and 404.

SECTION 6B
Other Special Quadrilaterals

On page 436, students use special quadrilaterals in the coordinate plane to plan the layout for a county fair.

Exercises designed to prepare students for success on the Multi-Step TAKS Prep can be found on pages 414, 424, and 434.

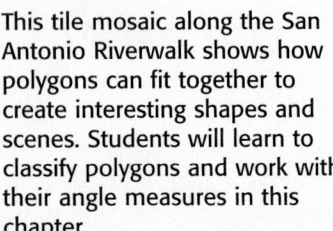

go.hrw.com/Geo/TX
Chapter Project Online
KEYWORD: MG7 ChProj

This tile mosaic showing the Alamo and surrounding buildings is on the Riverwalk in San Antonio.

About the Project

Divide and Conquer

In the Chapter Project, students use their knowledge of polygons to find ways to divide squares and hexagons according to given rules. Students also use squares, rectangles, parallelograms, trapezoids, and triangles to make a puzzle of their own.

Project Resources

All project resources for teachers and students are provided online.

Materials:
- graph paper
- isometric dot paper
- patterned wrapping paper or magazine photo
- scissors
- glue

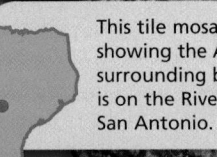

Geometry in Texas

This tile mosaic along the San Antonio Riverwalk shows how polygons can fit together to create interesting shapes and scenes. Students will learn to classify polygons and work with their angle measures in this chapter.

go.hrw.com/Geo/TX
Project Teacher Support
KEYWORD: MG7 ProjectTS

ARE YOU READY?

✓ Vocabulary

Match each term on the left with a definition on the right.

1. exterior angle **F**
2. parallel lines **B**
3. perpendicular lines **A**
4. polygon **D**
5. quadrilateral **E**

   A. lines that intersect to form right angles

   B. lines in the same plane that do not intersect

   C. two angles of a polygon that share a side

   D. a closed plane figure formed by three or more segments that intersect only at their endpoints

   E. a four-sided polygon

   F. an angle formed by one side of a polygon and the extension of a consecutive side

✓ Triangle Sum Theorem

Find the value of x.

6. 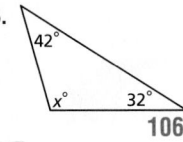 **106**
7. 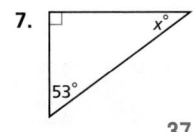 **37**
8. 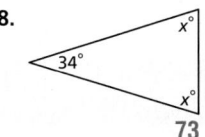 **73**
9. 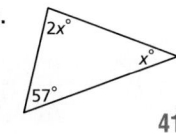 **41**

✓ Parallel Lines and Transversals

Find the measure of each numbered angle.

10.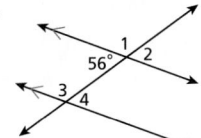
11.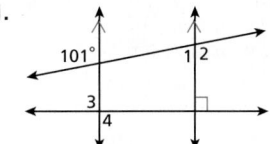
12.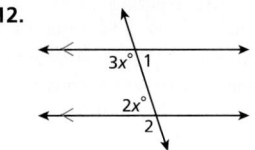

✓ Special Right Triangles

Find the value of x. Give the answer in simplest radical form.

13. 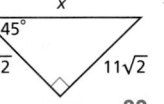 **22**
14. 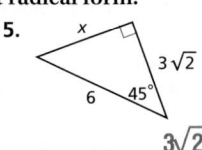 **7**
15. 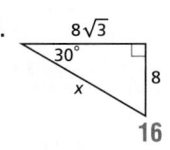 $3\sqrt{2}$
16. **16**

✓ Conditional Statements

Tell whether the given statement is true or false. Write the converse. Tell whether the converse is true or false.

17. If two angles form a linear pair, then they are supplementary.
 T; if 2 ∠ are supp., then they form a lin. pair; F.
18. If two angles are congruent, then they are right angles.
 F; if 2 ∠ are rt. ∠, then they are ≅; T.
19. If a triangle is a scalene triangle, then it is an acute triangle.
 F; if a △ is an acute △, then it is a scalene △; F.

ARE YOU READY?
Diagnose and Prescribe

✓ Prerequisite Skill	📝 Worksheets	💿 CD-ROM	🪐 Online
✓ Triangle Sum Theorem	Skill 30	Activity 30	
✓ Parallel Lines and Transversals	Skill 26	Activity 26	Diagnose and Prescribe Online
✓ Special Right Triangles	Skill 32	Activity 32	
✓ Conditional Statements	Skill 88	Activity 88	

Organizer

Objective: Help students organize the new concepts they will learn in Chapter 6.

Online Edition
Multilingual Glossary

Resources

PuzzlePro
One-Stop Planner®

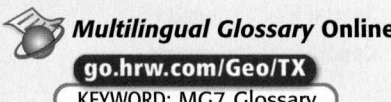
Multilingual Glossary **Online**
go.hrw.com/Geo/TX
KEYWORD: MG7 Glossary

Answers to *Vocabulary Connections*

Possible answers:

1.

2. A diag. is a seg. that goes across a polygon from ∠ to ∠.

3. It has 2 ≅ legs.

Key Vocabulary/Vocabulario

concave	cóncavo
diagonal	diagonal
isosceles trapezoid	trapecio isósceles
kite	cometa
parallelogram	paralelogramo
rectangle	rectángulo
regular polygon	polígono regular
rhombus	rombo
square	cuadrado
trapezoid	trapecio

Vocabulary Connections

To become familiar with some of the vocabulary terms in the chapter, consider the following. You may refer to the chapter, the glossary, or a dictionary if you like.

1. The word **concave** is made up of two parts: *con* and *cave*. Sketch a polygon that looks like it caves in.

2. If a triangle is *isosceles*, then it has two congruent legs. What do you think is a special property of an **isosceles trapezoid**?

3. A **parallelogram** has four sides. What do you think is a special property of the sides of a parallelogram?

Geometry TEKS

	6-1 Geo. Lab	Les. 6-1	6-2 Geo. Lab	Les. 6-2	Les. 6-3	Les. 6-4	6-5 Tech. Lab	Les. 6-5	6-6 Tech. Lab	Les. 6-6
G.2.A Geometric structure* use constructions to explore attributes of geometric figures and to make conjectures about geometric relationships	★			★	★	★	★	★	★	★
G.2.B Geometric structure* make conjectures about … polygons … and determine the validity of the conjectures, choosing from a variety of approaches …	★	★	★	★	★	★	★	★	★	★
G.3.B Geometric structure* construct and justify statements about geometric figures and their properties	★	★	★	★	★	★	★	★	★	★
G.3.E Geometric structure* use deductive reasoning to prove a statement					★	★	★		★		★
G.5.B Geometric patterns* use numeric and geometric patterns to make generalizations about geometric properties, including properties of polygons,… and angle relationships in polygons …	★	★								
G.7.A Dimensionality and the geometry of location* use one- and two-dimensional coordinate systems to represent … figures		★		★	★	★		★		★
G.7.B Dimensionality and the geometry of location* use slopes and equations of lines to investigate geometric relationships …					★	★	★		★		★
G.7.C Dimensionality and the geometry of location* … use formulas involving length, slope, and midpoint					★	★	★		★		★
G.9.B Congruence and the geometry of size* formulate and test conjectures about the properties and attributes of polygons and their component parts based on explorations and concrete models	★		★				★		★	

* Knowledge and skills are written out completely on pages TX28–TX35.

Geometry TEKS—Knowledge and Skills

G.2 Geometric structure The student analyzes geometric relationships in order to make and verify conjectures.

G.3 Geometric structure The student applies logical reasoning to justify and prove mathematical statements.

G.4 Geometric structure The student uses a variety of representations to describe geometric relationships and solve problems.

G.5 Geometric patterns The student uses a variety of representations to describe geometric relationships and solve problems.

G.7 Dimensionality and the geometry of location The student understands that coordinate systems provide convenient and efficient ways of representing geometric figures and uses them accordingly.

G.9 Congruence and the geometry of size The student analyzes properties and describes relationships in geometric figures.

G.10 Congruence and the geometry of size The student applies the concept of congruence to justify properties of figures and solve problems.

 **Reading** and **Writing Math**

Writing Strategy: Write a Convincing Argument

Throughout this book, the ✐ icon identifies exercises that require you to write an explanation or argument to support an idea. Your response to a Write About It exercise shows that you have a solid understanding of the mathematical concept.

To be effective, a written argument should contain

- a clear statement of your mathematical claim.
- evidence or reasoning that supports your claim.

 **Example**

From Lesson 5-4

✐ **36. Write About It**
An isosceles triangle has two congruent sides. Does it also have two congruent midsegments? Explain.

Step 1 Make a statement of your mathematical claim.

Draw a sketch to investigate the properties of the midsegments of an isosceles triangle. You will find that the midsegments parallel to the legs of the isosceles triangle are congruent.

Claim: The midsegments parallel to the legs of an isosceles triangle are congruent.

Step 2 Give evidence to support your claim.

Identify any properties or theorems that support your claim. In this case, the Triangle Midsegment Theorem states that the length of a midsegment of a triangle is $\frac{1}{2}$ the length of the parallel side.

To clarify your argument, label your diagram and use it in your response.

Step 3 Write a complete response.

Yes, the two midsegments parallel to the legs of an isosceles triangle are congruent. Suppose $\triangle ABC$ is isosceles with $\overline{AB} \cong \overline{AC}$. $\overline{XZ}$ and $\overline{YZ}$ are midsegments of $\triangle ABC$. By the Triangle Midsegment Theorem, $XZ = \frac{1}{2}AC$ and $YZ = \frac{1}{2}AB$. Since $\overline{AB} \cong \overline{AC}$, $AB = AC$. So $\frac{1}{2}AB = \frac{1}{2}AC$ by the Multiplication Property of Equality. By substitution, $XZ = YZ$, so $\overline{XZ} \cong \overline{YZ}$.

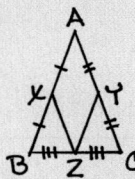

Try This

Write a convincing argument.

1. Compare the circumcenter and the incenter of a triangle.

2. If you know the side lengths of a triangle, how do you determine which angle is the largest?

⬥ TAKS Objectives

Grades 9–11

Obj. 1	Functional Relationships A.1.C
Obj. 2	Properties and Attributes of Functions A.2.B, A.4.A
Obj. 3	Linear Functions A.6.D
Obj. 6	Geometric Relationships and Spatial Reasoning G.5.A, G.5.B
Obj. 7	Two- and Three-Dimensional Representations G.7.A, G.7.B, G.7.C, 8.7.B
Obj. 10	Mathematical Processes and Tools 8.14.A, 8.14.B, 8.14.C

Organizer

Objective: Help students apply strategies to understand and retain key concepts.

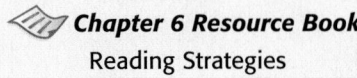 **Online Edition**

Resources

📖 ***Chapter 6 Resource Book***
Reading Strategies

Writing Strategy: Write a Convincing Argument

Discuss Though students may think of persuasive writing as a language arts skill, it is critical for effective communication in math as well. Just as it is important to show your work in a computation problem, students should be able to explain their reasoning for a critical thinking or writing question. By writing a clear, convincing argument, students demonstrate their mastery of new concepts.

Extend After completing each lesson, have individual students present their responses to the Write About It exercises to the class. Have classmates provide feedback as to whether the students' arguments are complete, clear, and convincing.

Answers to *Try This*

Possible answers:

1. The circumcenter and the incenter are points of concurrency in a triangle. The circumcenter is the point of concurrency of the perpendicular bisectors. The incenter is the point of concurrency of the angle bisectors. The circumcenter is equidistant from the vertices of the triangle. The incenter is equidistant from the sides of the triangle. The circumcenter is the center of the circumscribed circle, and the incenter is the center of the inscribed circle.

2. You can apply the angle-side relationships to conclude that the largest angle is opposite the longest side.

Polygons and Parallelograms

One-Minute Section Planner

Lesson	Lab Resources	Materials
6-1 Geometry Lab Construct Regular Polygons • Use a compass and straightedge to construct regular polygons. ☐ Exit Level TAKS ☐ ACT ☑ SAT ☐ SAT Subject Tests		**Required** compass (MK), straightedge (MK), protractor (MK) **Optional** geometry software
Lesson 6-1 Properties and Attributes of Polygons • Classify polygons based on their sides and angles. • Find and use the measures of interior and exterior angles of polygons. ☑ Exit Level TAKS ☐ ACT ☑ SAT ☐ SAT Subject Tests		**Optional** straightedge (MK), protractor (MK), picture frame, hexagonal nut, pennant, paper plate, ball, polygons cut out of construction paper
6-2 Geometry Lab Explore Properties of Parallelograms • Explore properties of parallelograms. ☐ Exit Level TAKS ☑ ACT ☑ SAT ☐ SAT Subject Tests		**Required** index cards, patty paper, ruler (MK) **Optional** cutouts of congruent parallelograms
Lesson 6-2 Properties of Parallelograms • Prove and apply properties of parallelograms. • Use properties of parallelograms to solve problems. ☑ Exit Level TAKS ☑ ACT ☐ SAT ☐ SAT Subject Tests		**Optional** geometry software, tangram puzzle (MK), colored pencils
Lesson 6-3 Conditions for Parallelograms • Prove that a given quadrilateral is a parallelogram. ☐ Exit Level TAKS ☑ ACT ☐ SAT ☐ SAT Subject Tests	*Texas Lab Manual* 6-3 Geometry Lab	**Optional** scissors, ruler (MK), chenile stems, compass (MK), straightedge (MK), heavy construction paper, hole punch, brads, raw spaghetti, straws

MK = *Manipulatives Kit*

Section Overview

Properties and Attributes of Polygons

Lesson 6-1

  Understanding properties of polygons and their angle sums is fundamental to successful work with quadrilaterals.

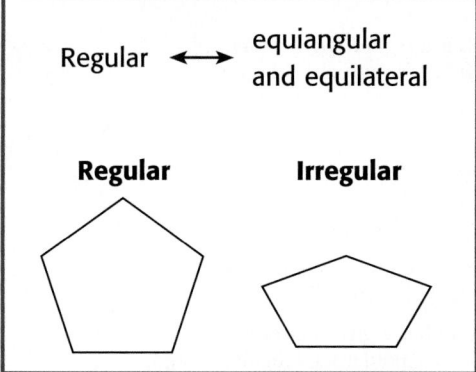

Regular ⟷ equiangular and equilateral

Regular   Irregular

If any diagonal contains points in the exterior, the polygon is **concave.** Otherwise, it is **convex.**

Convex   Concave

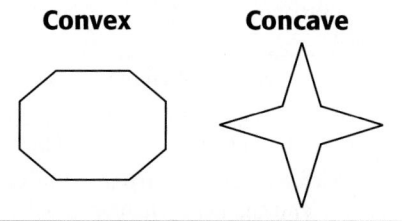

Theorem
The sum of the interior angle measures of a convex polygon with *n* sides is $(n - 2)180°$.

Theorem
The sum of the exterior angle measures, one angle at each vertex, of a convex polygon is 360°.

Properties of Parallelograms

Lesson 6-2

  The properties of parallelograms make these figures useful in mechanics and construction.

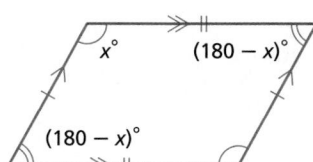

A quadrilateral is a parallelogram → all of these properties are true.
- Opposite sides are parallel.
- Opposite sides are congruent.
- Opposite angles are congruent.
- Consecutive angles are supplementary.
- Diagonals bisect each other.

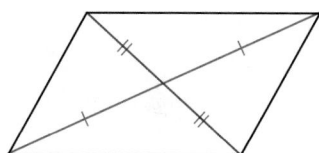

Conditions for Parallelograms

Lesson 6-3

  Understanding the conditions for parallelograms allows manufacturers to use those properties in their products.

One of these conditions is met → the quadrilateral is a parallelogram.

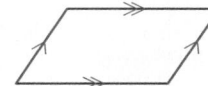

Both pairs of opposite sides are parallel.

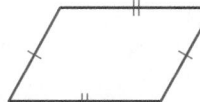

Both pairs of opposite sides are congruent.

Both pairs of opposite angles are congruent.

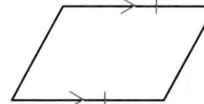

One pair of opposite sides are parallel and congruent.

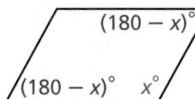

One angle is supplementary to both of its consecutive angles.

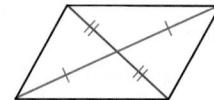

Diagonals bisect each other.

Pacing:
Traditional 1 day
Block $\frac{1}{2}$ day

Objective: Use a compass and straightedge to construct regular polygons.

Materials: compass, straightedge, protractor

Online Edition

Countdown to TAKS Week 13

Teach

Discuss

Discuss with students the different procedures that are used to construct each regular polygon. Ask students to draw connections between the construction procedure and the number of sides of the polygon. Explain that the construction of a pentagon is justified with theorems in Chapter 11.

Alternative Approach

Use geometry software to construct the regular polygons in the lab and investigate their angle measures.

 Geometry TEKS

G.2 Geometric structure*
(A) use constructions ... to make conjectures about geometric relationships
(B) make conjectures about ... polygons ... and determine the validity ...

G.3 Geometric structure*
(B) construct and justify statements about geometric figures ...
(D) use inductive reasoning to formulate a conjecture

G.5 Geometric patterns*
(B) use ... patterns to make generalizations about ... angle relationships in polygons ...

G.9 Congruence and the geometry of size*
(B) formulate and test conjectures about ... polygons ... based on explorations and concrete models

* Knowledge and Skills See p. 378.

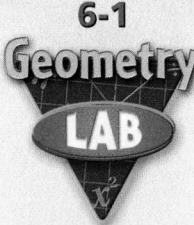

Construct Regular Polygons

In Chapter 4, you learned that an equilateral triangle is a triangle with three congruent sides. You also learned that an equilateral triangle is equiangular, meaning that all its angles are congruent.

In this lab, you will construct polygons that are both equilateral and equiangular by inscribing them in circles.

 TEKS G.2.A Geometric structure: use constructions to explore attributes of geometric figures and to make conjectures .... Also G.2.B, G.3.B, G.3.D, G.5.B, G.9.B

Activity 1

❶ Construct circle P. Draw a diameter $\overline{AC}$.

❷ Construct the perpendicular bisector of $\overline{AC}$. Label the intersections of the bisector and the circle as B and D.

❸ Draw $\overline{AB}$, $\overline{BC}$, $\overline{CD}$, and $\overline{DA}$. The polygon $ABCD$ is a *regular quadrilateral*. This means it is a four-sided polygon that has four congruent sides and four congruent angles.

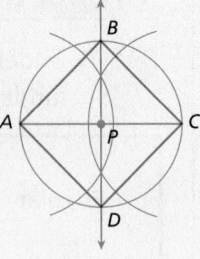

Try This

1. Describe a different method for constructing a regular quadrilateral.

2. The regular quadrilateral in Activity 1 is inscribed in the circle. What is the relationship between the circle and the regular quadrilateral?

3. A *regular octagon* is an eight-sided polygon that has eight congruent sides and eight congruent angles. Use angle bisectors to construct a regular octagon from a regular quadrilateral.

Activity 2

❶ Construct circle P. Draw a point A on the circle.

❷ Use the same compass setting. Starting at A, draw arcs to mark off equal parts along the circle. Label the other points where the arcs intersect the circle as B, C, D, E, and F.

❸ Draw $\overline{AB}$, $\overline{BC}$, $\overline{CD}$, $\overline{DE}$, $\overline{EF}$, and $\overline{FA}$. The polygon $ABCDEF$ is a *regular hexagon*. This means it is a six-sided polygon that has six congruent sides and six congruent angles.

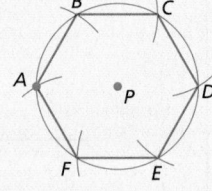

Try This

4. Justify the conclusion that $ABCDEF$ is a regular hexagon. (*Hint:* Draw diameters $\overline{AD}$, $\overline{BE}$, and $\overline{CF}$. What types of triangles are formed?)

5. A *regular dodecagon* is a 12-sided polygon that has 12 congruent sides and 12 congruent angles. Use the construction of a regular hexagon to construct a regular dodecagon. Explain your method.

Answers to *Try This*

1. Possible answer: Draw a line ℓ. Draw A and D on ℓ. Construct $m \perp$ to ℓ through A. Construct $n \perp$ to ℓ through D. Set the compass to the length AD. With the compass point at A, draw an arc that intersects m above ℓ. Label the pt. of intersection B. With the compass point at D, draw an arc that intersects n above ℓ. Label the pt. of intersection C. Draw $\overline{BC}$. The polygon $ABCD$ is a reg. quad.

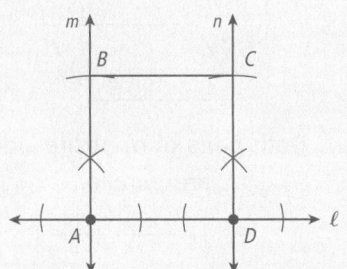

2. The circle is circumscribed about the polygon.

Activity 3

1 Construct circle *P*. Draw a diameter $\overline{AB}$.

2 Construct the perpendicular bisector of $\overline{AB}$. Label one point where the bisector intersects the circle as point *E*.

3 Construct the midpoint of radius $\overline{PB}$. Label it as point *C*.

4 Set your compass to the length *CE*. Place the compass point at *C* and draw an arc that intersects $\overline{AB}$. Label the point of intersection *D*.

5 Set the compass to the length *ED*. Starting at *E*, draw arcs to mark off equal parts along the circle. Label the other points where the arcs intersect the circle as *F*, *G*, *H*, and *J*.

6 Draw $\overline{EF}$, $\overline{FG}$, $\overline{GH}$, $\overline{HJ}$, and $\overline{JE}$. The polygon *EFGHJ* is a *regular pentagon*. This means it is a five-sided polygon that has five congruent sides and five congruent angles.

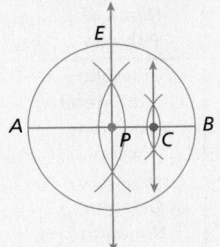 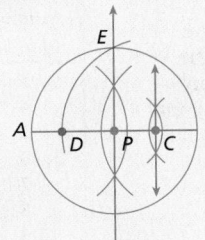 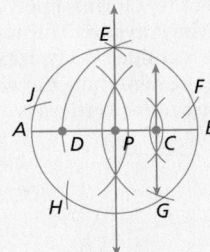 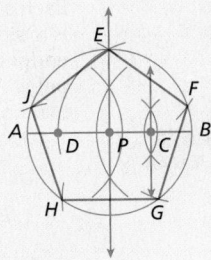

| Steps 1–3 | Step 4 | Step 5 | Step 6 |

Try This

6. A *regular decagon* is a ten-sided polygon that has ten congruent sides and ten congruent angles. Use the construction of a regular pentagon to construct a regular decagon. Explain your method.

7. Measure each angle of the regular polygons in Activities 1–3 and complete the following table.

REGULAR POLYGONS				
Number of Sides	3	4	5	6
Measure of Each Angle	60°	90°	108°	120°
Sum of Angle Measures	180°	360°	540°	720°

8. **Make a Conjecture** What is a general rule for finding the sum of the angle measures in a regular polygon with *n* sides? $(n-2)180°$

9. **Make a Conjecture** What is a general rule for finding the measure of each angle in a regular polygon with *n* sides? $\dfrac{(n-2)180°}{n}$

Teacher to Teacher

I like the emphasis on traditional construction in this lab, but I think that technology can be used to complement compass-and-straightedge construction methods.

For example, when students use geometry software for one or more of these activities, they can make the polygon larger or smaller and see that the angle measures remain the same.

Loralea Wright
Mauldin, SC

Close

Key Concept

Students should recognize that there is a relationship between the number of sides a polygon has and the sum of the angle measures of the polygon.

Assessment

Journal Have students explain how to use a compass and straightedge to construct regular polygons with 4, 6, and 8 sides.

Answers to *Try This*

3. Check students' work. Possible answer:

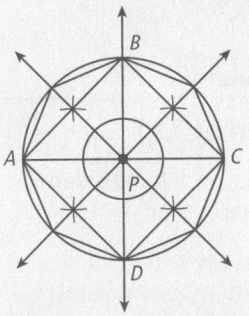

4. Possible answer: The 6 sides of *ABCDEF* were marked off with the same compass setting, so they are ≅. When $\overline{AD}$, $\overline{BE}$, and $\overline{CF}$ are drawn, the 6 △ formed are ≅ and equil. The measure of each ∠ of an equil. △ is 60°. Each ∠ of the hexagon is formed by 2 of these 60° ∡, so the 6 ∡ of *ABCDEF* are ≅. Since it has 6 ≅ sides and 6 ≅ ∡, *ABCDEF* is a reg. hexagon.

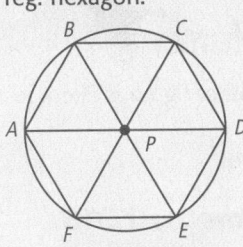

5. Check students' work. Possible answer: Draw $\overline{AD}$, $\overline{BE}$, and $\overline{CF}$. Construct the bisectors of ∠*APB*, ∠*BPC*, ∠*CPD*, ∠*DPE*, ∠*EPF*, and ∠*FPA*. Connect the 6 pts. where the ∠ bisectors intersect the circle to pts. *A*, *B*, *C*, *D*, *E*, and *F* in order around the circle.

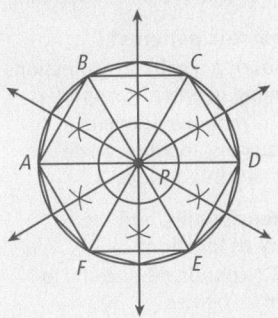

6. See p. A21.

6-1 Geometry Lab **381**

6-1 Organizer

Pacing: Traditional 1 day
Block $\frac{1}{2}$ day

Objectives: Classify polygons based on their sides and angles.

Find and use the measures of interior and exterior angles of polygons.

Online Edition
Tutorial Videos, Interactivity

Countdown to TAKS Week 13

Power Presentations
with PowerPoint®

Warm Up

1. A ___?___ is a three-sided polygon.   triangle

2. A ___?___ is a four-sided polygon.   quadrilateral

Evaluate each expression for $n = 6$.

3. $(n - 4)12$ 24

4. $(n - 3)90$ 270

Solve for a.

5. $12a + 4a + 9a = 100$ 4

Also available on transparency

Math Humor

Q: What type of figure is like a lost parrot?

A: A polygon!

 ### Geometry TEKS

G.2 Geometric structure*
(B) … determine the validity of … conjectures [about polygons] …

G.3 Geometric structure*
(B) construct and justify statements …

G.4 Geometric structure*
(A) select an appropriate representation … to solve problems

G.5 Geometric patterns*
(A) … develop algebraic expressions representing geometric properties
(B) use … patterns to make generalizations about … angle relationships in polygons …

G.7 Dimensionality and the geometry of location*
(A) use … coordinate systems to represent … figures

* Knowledge and Skills See p. 378.

6-1 Properties and Attributes of Polygons

 TEKS G.5.B Geometric patterns: use … patterns to make generalizations about … properties of … and angle relationships in polygons ….

Objectives
Classify polygons based on their sides and angles.

Find and use the measures of interior and exterior angles of polygons.

Vocabulary
side of a polygon
vertex of a polygon
diagonal
regular polygon
concave
convex

Also G.2.B, G.3.B, G.4.A, G.5.A, G.7.A

Why learn this?
The opening that lets light into a camera lens is created by an aperture, a set of blades whose edges may form a polygon. (See Example 5.)

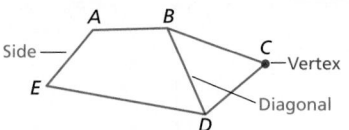

In Lesson 2-4, you learned the definition of a polygon. Now you will learn about the parts of a polygon and about ways to classify polygons.

Each segment that forms a polygon is a **side of the polygon**. The common endpoint of two sides is a **vertex of the polygon**. A segment that connects any two nonconsecutive vertices is a **diagonal**.

You can name a polygon by the number of its sides. The table shows the names of some common polygons. Polygon *ABCDE* is a pentagon.

Number of Sides	Name of Polygon
3	Triangle
4	Quadrilateral
5	Pentagon
6	Hexagon
7	Heptagon
8	Octagon
9	Nonagon
10	Decagon
12	Dodecagon
n	n-gon

EXAMPLE 1 **Identifying Polygons**

Tell whether each figure is a polygon. If it is a polygon, name it by the number of its sides.

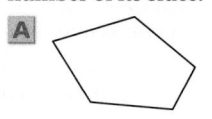  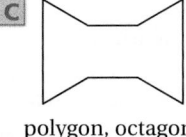

polygon, pentagon   not a polygon   polygon, octagon

 **CHECK IT OUT!** Tell whether each figure is a polygon. If it is a polygon, name it by the number of its sides.

1a.   1b.   1c.

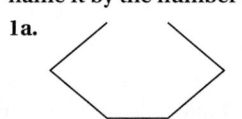

not a polygon   polygon, nonagon   not a polygon

All the sides are congruent in an equilateral polygon. All the angles are congruent in an equiangular polygon. A **regular polygon** is one that is both equilateral and equiangular. If a polygon is not regular, it is called irregular.

---

 1 Introduce

EXPLORATION
6-1 **Properties and Attributes of Polygons**

A *convex polygon* is a polygon in which no diagonal contains points in the exterior of the polygon.

Convex   Not Convex

1. Use a straightedge to draw a convex polygon with five sides.

2. Use the straightedge to extend consecutive sides of the polygon, as shown. This forms five exterior angles, ∠1 through ∠5.

3. Use a protractor to measure the exterior angles. What is the sum of the measures of the exterior angles?

4. Repeat the process with convex polygons that have 3, 4, and 6 sides. Record your results in the table.

Number of Sides	3	4	5	6
Sum of Exterior Angle Measures				

5. Compare your results with those of other students. What do you notice?

THINK AND DISCUSS

Motivate

Bring objects to class that show polygons, such as a picture frame, a hexagonal nut, or a pennant. Also bring items with shapes that are not polygons, such as a paper plate or a ball. Ask students to compare both sets of objects. Explain that students will learn properties of polygons in this lesson.

Explorations and answers are provided in the *Explorations* binder.

A polygon is **concave** if any part of a diagonal contains points in the exterior of the polygon. If no diagonal contains points in the exterior, then the polygon is **convex**. A regular polygon is always convex.

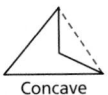
Concave quadrilateral

Convex quadrilateral

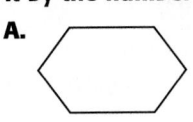

EXAMPLE 2 · Classifying Polygons

Tell whether each polygon is regular or irregular. Tell whether it is concave or convex.

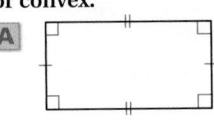
A

B

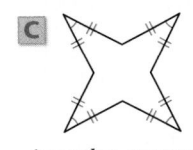
C

irregular, convex   regular, convex   irregular, concave

 **CHECK IT OUT!** Tell whether each polygon is regular or irregular. Tell whether it is concave or convex.

2a.
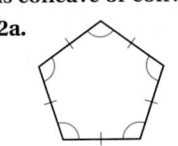
regular, convex

2b.

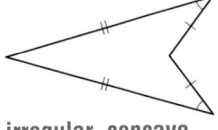
irregular, concave

To find the sum of the interior angle measures of a convex polygon, draw all possible diagonals from one vertex of the polygon. This creates a set of triangles. The sum of the angle measures of all the triangles equals the sum of the angle measures of the polygon.

Remember!

By the Triangle Sum Theorem, the sum of the interior angle measures of a triangle is 180°.

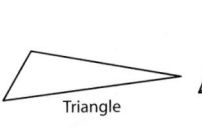
Triangle

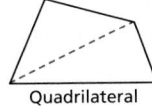
Quadrilateral

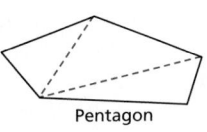
Pentagon

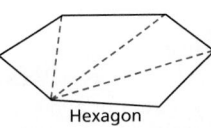
Hexagon

Polygon	Number of Sides	Number of Triangles	Sum of Interior Angle Measures
Triangle	3	1	$(1)180° = 180°$
Quadrilateral	4	2	$(2)180° = 360°$
Pentagon	5	3	$(3)180° = 540°$
Hexagon	6	4	$(4)180° = 720°$
n-gon	n	$n - 2$	$(n - 2)180°$

In each convex polygon, the number of triangles formed is two less than the number of sides n. So the sum of the angle measures of all these triangles is $(n - 2)180°$.

 **Know it! Note**

Theorem 6-1-1 (**Polygon Angle Sum Theorem**)

The sum of the interior angle measures of a convex polygon with n sides is $(n - 2)180°$.

Power Presentations with PowerPoint®

Additional Examples

Example 1

Tell whether each figure is a polygon. If it is a polygon, name it by the number of sides.

A.
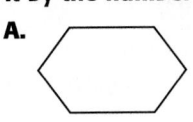
polygon, hexagon

B.
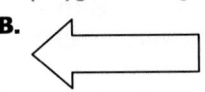
polygon, heptagon

C.
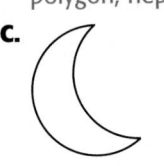
not a polygon

Example 2

Tell whether each polygon is regular or irregular. Tell whether it is concave or convex.

A.
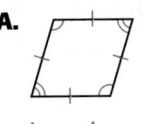
irregular, convex

B.
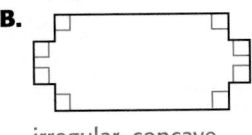
irregular, concave

C.
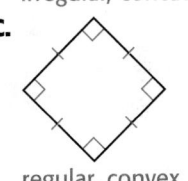
regular, convex

Also available on transparency

INTERVENTION
Questioning Strategies

EXAMPLE 1
• How can you tell whether a figure is a polygon?

EXAMPLE 2
• Explain how you know if a polygon is regular, irregular, concave, or convex.

Teaching Tip **Critical Thinking** Point out the angles larger than 180° in the figure in **Example 2C.**

---

2 Teach

Guided Instruction

Review the definition of *polygon,* and discuss with students why the figures in Example 1 are or are not polygons. Walk students through the development of both sum formulas, while having them verify the given angle measures with a protractor (MK).

Teaching Tip **Algebra** Review with students how to evaluate algebraic expressions and how to use inverse operations to solve equations.

Reaching All Learners

 Through Concrete Manipulatives

Have students fold and crease the four corners of a sheet of paper. Next, ask them to open the folds to reveal a creased polygon shape. Have students classify the polygon. octagon Ask them to find the sum of the interior and exterior angle measures. 1080°; 360° Then have students measure the interior and exterior angles to verify their sums.

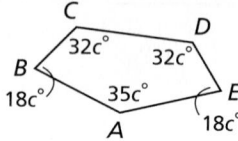
Example 3

A. Find the sum of the interior angle measures of a convex heptagon.   900°

B. Find the measure of each interior angle of a regular decagon.   144°

C. Find the measure of each interior angle of pentagon *ABCDE*.

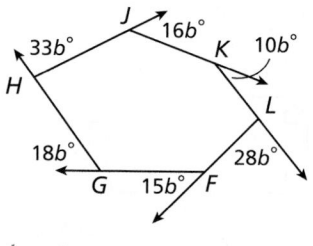

m∠A = 140°; m∠B = m∠E = 72°; m∠C = m∠D = 128°

Example 4

A. Find the measure of each exterior angle of a regular dodecagon.   30°

B. Find the value of *b* in polygon *FGHJKL*.

b = 3

Also available on transparency

INTERVENTION ◀▬▶
Questioning Strategies

EXAMPLE 3

• How do you use the sum of the interior angle measures of a regular polygon to find the measure of each interior angle?

EXAMPLE 4

• How does finding the measure of an exterior angle differ from finding the measure of an interior angle?

EXAMPLE 3   Finding Interior Angle Measures and Sums in Polygons

A Find the sum of the interior angle measures of a convex octagon.
$(n - 2)180°$ *Polygon ∠ Sum Thm.*
$(8 - 2)180°$ *An octagon has 8 sides, so substitute 8 for n.*
$1080°$ *Simplify.*

B Find the measure of each interior angle of a regular nonagon.
Step 1 Find the sum of the interior angle measures.
$(n - 2)180°$ *Polygon ∠ Sum Thm.*
$(9 - 2)180° = 1260°$ *Substitute 9 for n and simplify.*

Step 2 Find the measure of one interior angle.
$\frac{1260°}{9} = 140°$ *The int. ∠ are ≅, so divide by 9.*

 **Algebra**

C Find the measure of each interior angle of quadrilateral *PQRS*.

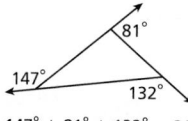

$(4 - 2)180° = 360°$ *Polygon ∠ Sum Thm.*
$m∠P + m∠Q + m∠R + m∠S = 360°$ *Polygon ∠ Sum Thm.*
$c + 3c + c + 3c = 360$ *Substitute.*
$8c = 360$ *Combine like terms.*
$c = 45$ *Divide both sides by 8.*

$m∠P = m∠R = 45°$
$m∠Q = m∠S = 3(45°) = 135°$

3a. 2340° ✓ **CHECK IT OUT!**   **3a.** Find the sum of the interior angle measures of a convex 15-gon.
3b. Find the measure of each interior angle of a regular decagon.
144°

In the polygons below, an exterior angle has been measured at each vertex. Notice that in each case, the sum of the exterior angle measures is 360°.

Remember!

An exterior angle is formed by one side of a polygon and the extension of a consecutive side.

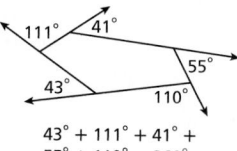

$147° + 81° + 132° = 360°$

$43° + 111° + 41° + 55° + 110° = 360°$

Know it!
Note

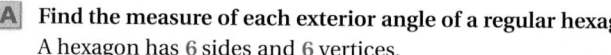

Theorem 6-1-2   Polygon Exterior Angle Sum Theorem

The sum of the exterior angle measures, one angle at each vertex, of a convex polygon is 360°.

EXAMPLE 4   Finding Exterior Angle Measures in Polygons

A Find the measure of each exterior angle of a regular hexagon.
A hexagon has 6 sides and 6 vertices.
sum of ext. ∠ = 360°   *Polygon Ext. ∠ Sum Thm.*
measure of one ext. $∠ = \frac{360°}{6} = 60°$ *A regular hexagon has 6 ≅ ext. ∠,*
                                              so divide the sum by 6.
The measure of each exterior angle of a regular hexagon is 60°.

Teaching Tip   **Inclusion** To clarify the words *concave* and *convex,* provide the class with several polygons cut out of heavyweight construction paper. Have students use a straightedge (MK) as a diagonal to determine if the polygons are *concave* or *convex.*

x² Algebra

B Find the value of a in polygon *RSTUV*.

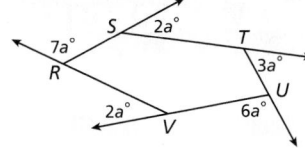

$$7a° + 2a° + 3a° + 6a° + 2a° = 360°$$ *Polygon Ext. ∠ Sum Thm.*
$$20a = 360$$ *Combine like terms.*
$$a = 18$$ *Divide both sides by 20.*

CHECK IT OUT!

4a. Find the measure of each exterior angle of a regular dodecagon. **30°**

4b. Find the value of r in polygon *JKLM*. **$r = 15$**

EXAMPLE **5** *Photography Application*

The aperture of the camera is formed by ten blades. The blades overlap to form a regular decagon. What is the measure of ∠CBD?

∠CBD is an exterior angle of a regular decagon. By the Polygon Exterior Angle Sum Theorem, the sum of the exterior angle measures is 360°.

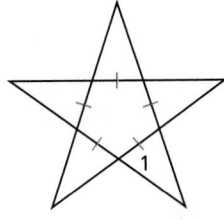

$$m∠CBD = \frac{360°}{10} = 36°$$ *A regular decagon has 10 ≅ ext. ∡, so divide the sum by 10.*

CHECK IT OUT!

5. What if...? Suppose the shutter were formed by 8 blades. What would the measure of each exterior angle be? **45°**

THINK AND DISCUSS

1. Draw a concave pentagon and a convex pentagon. Explain the difference between the two figures.

2. Explain why you cannot use the expression $\frac{360°}{n}$ to find the measure of an exterior angle of an irregular n-gon.

3. GET ORGANIZED Copy and complete the graphic organizer. In each cell, write the formula for finding the indicated value for a regular convex polygon with n sides.

	Interior Angles	Exterior Angles
Sum of Angle Measures		
One Angle Measure		

Power Presentations with PowerPoint®

Additional Examples

Example 5

Ann is making paper stars for party decorations. What is the measure of ∠1? **72°**

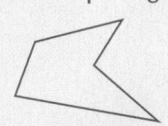

Also available on transparency

INTERVENTION
Questioning Strategies

EXAMPLE **5**

• What happens to the measure of each exterior angle as the number of sides of a regular polygon increases?

---

3 Close

Summarize

Review the naming of polygons, as shown on page 382. Discuss the difference between irregular and regular polygons, and concave and convex polygons. To review the Polygon Angle Sum Theorem and the Polygon Exterior Angle Sum Theorem, draw a regular pentagon and show how to find its interior and exterior angle measures. **108° and 72°**

ONGOING ASSESSMENT
and INTERVENTION

Diagnose Before the Lesson
6-1 Warm Up, TE p. 382

Monitor During the Lesson
Check It Out! Exercises, SE pp. 382–385
Questioning Strategies, TE pp. 383–385

Assess After the Lesson
6-1 Lesson Quiz, TE p. 388
Alternative Assessment, TE p. 388

Answers to Think and Discuss

1. Possible answers:
   Concave pentagon   Convex pentagon

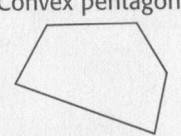

   A concave polygon seems to "cave in" or have a dent. A convex polygon does not have a dent.

2. Since the polygon is not reg., you cannot assume that each of the ext. ∡ has the same measure.

3. See p. A5.

6-1 Exercises

6-1 Exercises

go.hrw.com/Geo/TX
Homework Help Online
KEYWORD: MG7 6-1
Parent Resources Online
KEYWORD: MG7 Parent

Assignment Guide

Assign *Guided Practice* exercises as necessary.

If you finished Examples **1–3**
 Basic 16–24, 29, 30, 35–38, 46–50
 Average 16–24, 29, 30, 35–38, 44, 46–50
 Advanced 16–24, 29, 30, 35–38, 44, 46–50, 56, 57

If you finished Examples **1–5**
 Basic 16–31, 32–42 even, 43, 45–50, 53–55, 60–67
 Average 16–46, 51–56, 60–67
 Advanced 16–42, 44, 45, 51–67

Homework Quick Check
Quickly check key concepts.
Exercises: 16, 20, 24, 26, 28, 30, 36

Answers

1. Possible answer: If a polygon is equil., all its sides are ≅, but all its ∡ are not necessarily ≅. For a polygon to be reg., all its sides must be ≅, and all its ∡ must be ≅.

9. m∠A = m∠D = 81°; m∠B = 108°; m∠C = m∠E = 135°

⬥TAKS Practice

Grades 9–11	Exercises
Obj. 1	63–65
Obj. 2	29–42, 45, 55–57
Obj. 5	60–62
Obj. 6	29–42, 45, 54–57, 66, 67

GUIDED PRACTICE

1. **Vocabulary** Explain why an equilateral polygon is not necessarily a *regular* polygon.

SEE EXAMPLE 1
p. 382

Tell whether each outlined shape is a polygon. If it is a polygon, name it by the number of its sides.

2.
polygon, decagon

3.
not a polygon

4.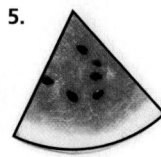
polygon, quadrilateral

5.
not a polygon

SEE EXAMPLE 2
p. 383

Tell whether each polygon is regular or irregular. Tell whether it is concave or convex.

6. regular, convex

7. irregular, concave

8. irregular, convex

SEE EXAMPLE 3
p. 384

9. Find the measure of each interior angle of pentagon *ABCDE*.

10. Find the measure of each interior angle of a regular dodecagon. **150°**

11. Find the sum of the interior angle measures of a convex 20-gon. **3240°**

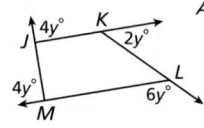

SEE EXAMPLE 4
p. 384

12. Find the value of *y* in polygon *JKLM*. **y = 22.5**

13. Find the measure of each exterior angle of a regular pentagon. **72°**

SEE EXAMPLE 5
p. 385

Safety Use the photograph of the traffic sign for Exercises 14 and 15.

14. Name the polygon by the number of its sides. **pentagon**

15. In the polygon, ∠P, ∠R, and ∠T are right angles, and ∠Q ≅ ∠S. What are m∠Q and m∠S?
 m∠Q = m∠S = 135°

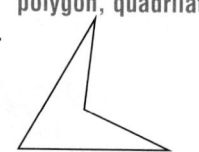

PRACTICE AND PROBLEM SOLVING

Independent Practice

For Exercises	See Example
16–18	1
19–21	2
22–24	3
25–26	4
27–28	5

TEKS ⬥ TAKS
Skills Practice p. S14
Application Practice p. S33

Tell whether each figure is a polygon. If it is a polygon, name it by the number of its sides.

16. polygon, hexagon

17. not a polygon

18. polygon, quadrilateral

Tell whether each polygon is regular or irregular. Tell whether it is concave or convex.

19. irregular, concave

20. regular, convex

21. irregular, convex

6-1 READING STRATEGIES

Triangle Quadrilateral Pentagon Hexagon Heptagon Octagon Nonagon Decagon Dodecagon

Diagonal
Vertex
Side

1. How many sides does a pentagon have? ___ five

2. Give some examples of pentagons in real life.
 Sample answer: pedestrian crossing street signs

3. How many vertices does a quadrilateral have? ___ four

4. How does the number of vertices of a polygon compare to the number of sides of the same polygon?
 There is an equal number of sides and vertices in polygons.

5. What is the name of a polygon with eight sides? ___ octagon

6. How many diagonals can be drawn from one vertex of a hexagon? ___ three

concave—any part of a diagonal contains points in the exterior of the polygon
convex—no diagonal contains points in the exterior of the polygon
Draw an example of each polygon.

7. convex heptagon
 Sample answer:

8. concave quadrilateral
 Sample answer:

6-1 RETEACH

The parts of a polygon are named on the quadrilateral below.

Number of Sides	Polygon
3	triangle
4	quadrilateral
5	pentagon
6	hexagon
7	heptagon
8	octagon
9	nonagon
10	decagon
n	*n*-gon

diagonal
side
vertex

You can name a polygon by the number of its sides.
A **regular polygon** has all sides congruent and all angles congruent. A polygon is **convex** if all its diagonals lie in the interior of the polygon. A polygon is **concave** if all or part of a diagonal lies outside the polygon.

Types of Polygons

regular, convex	irregular, convex	irregular, concave

Tell whether each figure is a polygon. If it is a polygon, name it by the number of its sides.

1. polygon; pentagon

2. polygon; heptagon

3. not a polygon

Tell whether each polygon is regular or irregular. Tell whether it is concave or convex.

4. irregular; convex

5. regular; convex

6. irregular; concave

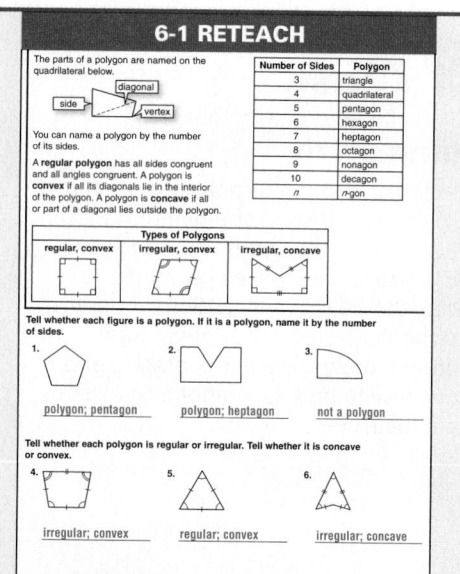

22. Find the measure of each interior angle of quadrilateral *RSTV*.

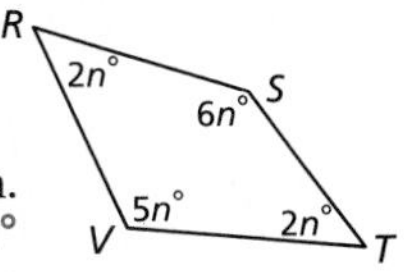

23. Find the measure of each interior angle of a regular 18-gon. **160°**

24. Find the sum of the interior angle measures of a convex heptagon. **900°**

25. Find the measure of each exterior angle of a regular nonagon. **40°**

26. A pentagon has exterior angle measures of $5a°$, $4a°$, $10a°$, $3a°$, and $8a°$. Find the value of a. **12**

Crafts The folds on the lid of the gift box form a regular hexagon. Find each measure.

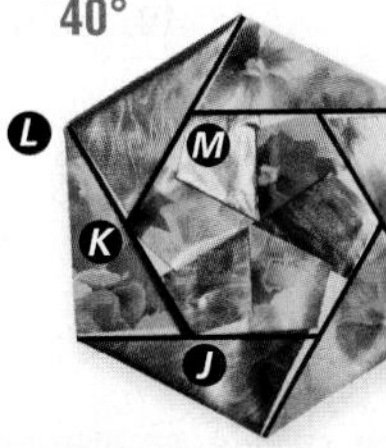

27. m∠*JKM* **120°**

28. m∠*MKL* **60°**

Algebra Find the value of x in each figure.

29. 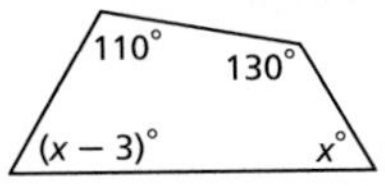

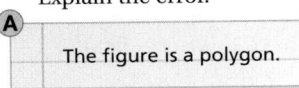

61.5

30. 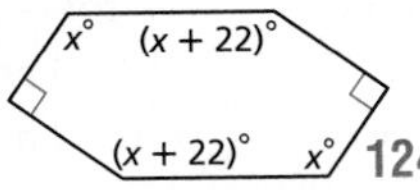

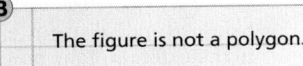

124

31. 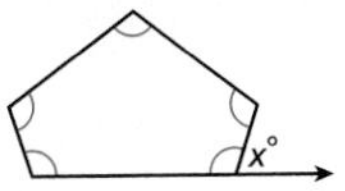

72

Find the number of sides a regular polygon must have to meet each condition.

32. Each interior angle measure equals each exterior angle measure. **4**

33. Each interior angle measure is four times the measure of each exterior angle. **10**

34. Each exterior angle measure is one eighth the measure of each interior angle. **18**

Name the convex polygon whose interior angle measures have each given sum.

35. 540° **pentagon** 36. 900° **heptagon** 37. 1800° **dodecagon** 38. 2520° **16-gon**

Multi-Step **An exterior angle measure of a regular polygon is given. Find the number of its sides and the measure of each interior angle.**

39. 120° **3; 60°** 40. 72° **5; 108°** 41. 36° **10; 144°** 42. 24° **15; 156°**

43. **///ERROR ANALYSIS///** Which conclusion is incorrect? Explain the error.

A The figure is a polygon.

B The figure is not a polygon.

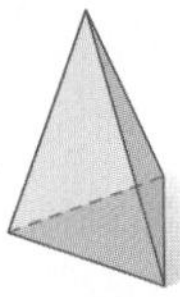

44. **Estimation** Graph the polygon formed by the points $A(-2, -6)$, $B(-4, -1)$, $C(-1, 2)$, $D(4, 0)$, and $E(3, -5)$. Estimate the measure of each interior angle. Make a conjecture about whether the polygon is equiangular. Now measure each interior angle with a protractor. Was your conjecture correct?

MULTI-STEP TAKS PREP

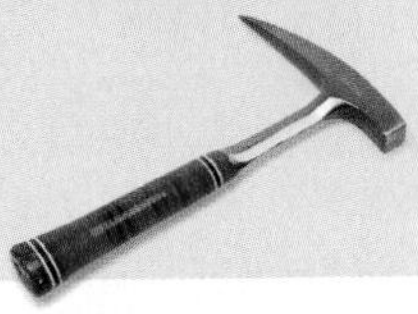

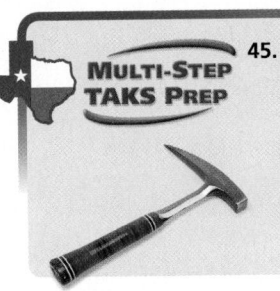

45. This problem will prepare you for the Multi-Step TAKS Prep on page 406.
In this quartz crystal, m∠A = 95°, m∠B = 125°, m∠E = m∠D = 130°, and ∠C ≅ ∠F ≅ ∠G. **heptagon**
a. Name polygon *ABCDEFG* by the number of sides.
b. What is the sum of the interior angle measures of *ABCDEFG*? **900°**
c. Find m∠F. **140°**

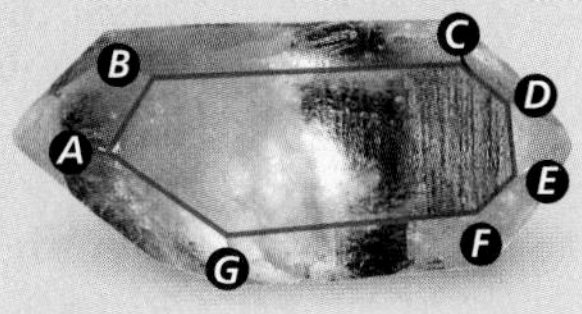

COMMON ERROR ALERT

If a diagram is not provided, suggest that students draw the polygon themselves. In **Exercises 39–42,** point out that the word *regular* is necessary to solve these problems.

MULTI-STEP TAKS PREP **Exercise 45** involves classifying polygons in crystals and finding interior angle measures. This exercise prepares students for the Multi-Step TAKS Prep on page 406.

Answers

22. m∠R = m∠T = 48°; m∠S = 144°; m∠V = 120°

43. A; possible answer: this is not a plane figure, so it cannot be a polygon.

44. 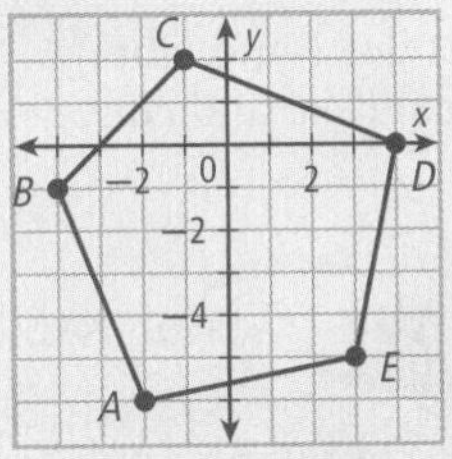

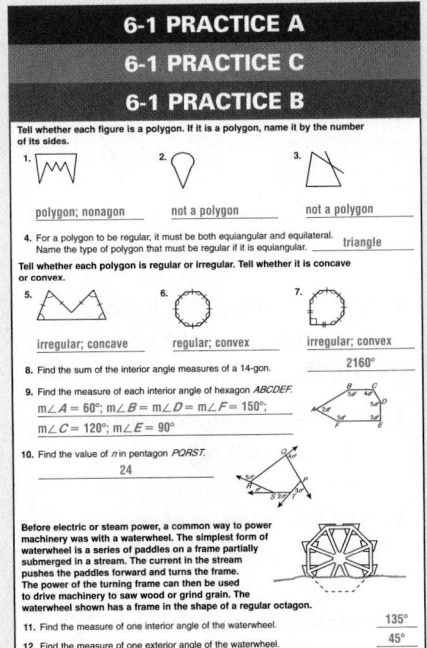

Check students' estimates; possible answer: the pentagon is not equiangular; m∠A = 100°; m∠B = 113°; m∠C = 113°; m∠D = 101°; m∠E = 113°; yes, the pentagon is not equiangular.

6-1 PROBLEM SOLVING

1. A campground site is in the shape of a convex quadrilateral. Three sides of the campground form two right angles. The third interior angle measures 10° less than the fourth angle. Find the measure of each interior angle.
90°, 90°, 85°, 95°

2. A pentagon has two exterior angles that measure (3*x*)°, two exterior angles that measure (2*x* + 22)°, and an exterior angle that measures (*x* + 41)°. If all of these angles have different vertices, what are the measures of the exterior angles of the pentagon?
75°, 75°, 72°, 72°, 66°

3. The top view of a hexagonal greenhouse is shown at right. What is the measure of ∠*PQR*, the acute angle formed by the house and the greenhouse?
54°

Choose the best answer.

4. A figure is an equiangular 18-gon. What is the measure of each exterior angle of the polygon?
A 10° B 18° **C 20°** D 36°

5. Three interior angles of a convex heptagon measure 125°, and two of the interior angles measure 143°. Which are possible measures for the other two interior angles of the heptagon?
F 48° and 48° G 39° and 100° H 100° and 116° **J 89° and 150°**

6. Find the measure of ∠*RKL*.
A 34° **B 68°** C 86° D 148°

7. What is the measure of ∠*GCD*?
F 123° G 116° H 73° J 29°

6-1 CHALLENGE

In the exercises on this page, you will explore a fascinating branch of mathematics that is called *dissection theory*.

1. Carefully trace the four figures at right onto a sheet of paper. Cut them out. Arrange the figures so that together they form a square. Sketch the arrangement in the blank space at right.

When you **dissect** a geometric figure, you cut it into two or more parts. The puzzle pieces in Exercise 1 were formed by dissecting a square into four congruent polygons. The figures at right show three other dissections.

2. Show four additional ways to dissect a square into four congruent polygons. (The polygons may be either convex or concave.)
Answers will vary.

3. Show four ways to dissect an equilateral triangle into three congruent polygons.
Answers will vary.

4. Show four ways to dissect a regular pentagon into five congruent polygons.
Answers will vary.

5. Describe a general technique for dissecting any regular *n*-gon into *n* congruent polygons.
Descriptions will vary.

6. The figure at right is a 4-by-4 grid of squares. Making cuts only along the grid lines, find all possible ways to dissect the grid into two congruent parts. Sketch your dissections on a separate sheet of paper.
There are six possible dissections.

6-1 PRACTICE A
6-1 PRACTICE C
6-1 PRACTICE B

Tell whether each figure is a polygon. If it is a polygon, name it by the number of its sides.

1. polygon; nonagon 2. not a polygon 3. not a polygon

4. For a polygon to be regular, it must be both equiangular and equilateral. Name the type of polygon that must be regular if it is equiangular. triangle

Tell whether each polygon is regular or irregular. Tell whether it is concave or convex.

5. irregular; concave 6. regular; convex 7. irregular; convex

8. Find the sum of the interior angle measures of a 14-gon. 2160°

9. Find the measure of each interior angle of hexagon *ABCDEF*.
m∠*A* = 60°; m∠*B* = m∠*D* = m∠*F* = 150°;
m∠*C* = 120°; m∠*E* = 90°

10. Find the value of *n* in pentagon *PQRST*.
24

Before electric or steam power, a common way to power machinery was with a waterwheel. The simplest form of waterwheel is a series of paddles on a frame partially submerged in a stream. The current in the stream pushes the paddles forward and turns the frame. The power of the turning frame can then be used to drive machinery to saw wood or grind grain. The waterwheel shown has a frame in the shape of a regular octagon.

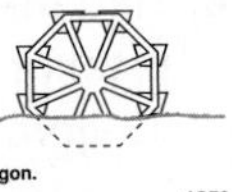

11. Find the measure of one interior angle of the waterwheel. 135°

12. Find the measure of one exterior angle of the waterwheel. 45°

Answers

47. Possible answer:

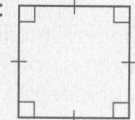

48. Possible answer:

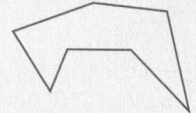

✎ **Journal**

Have students draw and label examples of concave and convex polygons.

✎ **ALTERNATIVE ASSESSMENT**

Have students cut out two polygons and name them based on the number of sides. Then have students cut out a convex pentagon. Have them find the sum of its interior and exterior angle measures. Have students use a protractor to verify their sums.

Power Presentations
with PowerPoint®

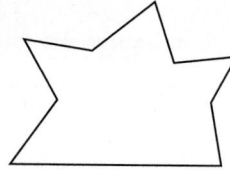

6-1 Lesson Quiz

1. Name the polygon by the number of its sides. Then tell whether the polygon is regular or irregular, concave or convex.

nonagon; irregular; concave

2. Find the sum of the interior angle measures of a convex 11-gon. 1620°

3. Find the measure of each interior angle of a regular 18-gon. 160°

4. Find the measure of each exterior angle of a regular 15-gon. 24°

Also available on transparency

388 Chapter 6

---

46. The perimeter of a regular polygon is 45 inches. The length of one side is 7.5 inches. Name the polygon by the number of its sides. **hexagon**

Draw an example of each figure.

47. a regular quadrilateral
48. an irregular concave heptagon
49. an irregular convex pentagon
50. an equilateral polygon that is not equiangular

51. **Write About It** Use the terms from the lesson to describe the figure as specifically as possible.

52. **Critical Thinking** What geometric figure does a regular polygon begin to resemble as the number of sides increases?
    circle

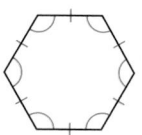

53. Which terms describe the figure shown?
    I. quadrilateral   II. concave   III. regular
    (A) I only   (C) I and II
    (B) II only   (D) I and III

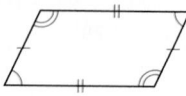

54. Which statement is NOT true about a regular 16-gon?
    (F) It is a convex polygon.
    (G) It has 16 congruent sides.
    (H) The sum of the interior angle measures is 2880°.
    (J) The sum of the exterior angles, one at each vertex, is 360°.

55. In polygon ABCD, m∠A = 49°, m∠B = 107°, and m∠C = 2m∠D. What is m∠C?
    (A) 24°   (B) 68°   (C) 102°   (D) 136°

CHALLENGE AND EXTEND

56. The interior angle measures of a convex pentagon are consecutive multiples of 4. Find the measure of each interior angle. **100°; 104°; 108°; 112°; 116°**

57. Polygon PQRST is a regular pentagon. Find the values of x, y, and z.
    x = 36; y = 36; z = 72

58. **Multi-Step** Polygon ABCDEFGHJK is a regular decagon. Sides $\overline{AB}$ and $\overline{DE}$ are extended so that they meet at point L in the exterior of the polygon. Find m∠BLD. **72°**

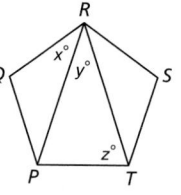

59. **Critical Thinking** Does the Polygon Angle Sum Theorem work for concave polygons? Draw a sketch to support your answer.
    Yes, if you allow for ∠ measures greater than 180°.

SPIRAL REVIEW

Solve by factoring. (Previous course)

60. $x^2 + 3x - 10 = 0$
    $x = -5$ or $x = 2$

61. $x^2 - x - 12 = 0$
    $x = -3$ or $x = 4$

62. $x^2 - 12x = -35$
    $x = 5$ or $x = 7$

The lengths of two sides of a triangle are given. Find the range of possible lengths for the third side. (Lesson 5-5)

63. 4, 4 $0 < x < 8$
64. 6, 12 $6 < x < 18$
65. 3, 7 $4 < x < 10$

Find each side length for a 30°-60°-90° triangle. (Lesson 5-8)

66. the length of the hypotenuse when the length of the shorter leg is 6 **12**

67. the length of the longer leg when the length of the hypotenuse is 10 $5\sqrt{3}$

Answers

49. Possible answer:

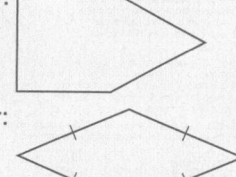

50. Possible answer:

51. The figure has 6 sides, so it is a hexagon. The 6 sides are ≅, so the hexagon is equilateral. The 6 ∠ are ≅, so the hexagon is equiangular. Since the hexagon is equilateral and equiangular, it is regular. No diagonal contains points in the exterior, so it is convex.

59. Possible answer:

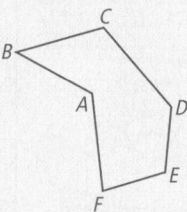

m∠A + m∠B + m∠C + m∠D + m∠E + m∠F = 720°

Relations and Functions

Algebra

Many numeric relationships in geometry can be represented by algebraic relations. These relations may or may not be functions, depending on their domain and range.

See Skills Bank page S61

A *relation* is a set of ordered pairs. All the first coordinates in the set of ordered pairs are the *domain* of the relation. All the second coordinates are the *range* of the relation.

A *function* is a type of relation that pairs each element in the domain with exactly one element in the range.

Example

Give the domain and range of the relation $y = \dfrac{6}{x-6}$. Tell whether the relation is a function.

Step 1 Make a table of values for the relation.

x	−6	0	5	6	7	12
y	−0.5	−1	−6	Undefined	6	1

Step 2 Plot the points and connect them with smooth curves.

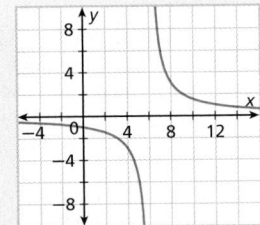

Step 3 Identify the domain and range.
Since y is undefined at $x = 6$, the domain of the relation is the set of all real numbers except 6. Since there is no x-value such that $y = 0$, the range of the relation is the set of all real numbers except 0.

Step 4 Determine whether the relation is a function.
From the graph, you can see that only one y-value exists for each x-value, so the relation is a function.

Try This  TAKS Grades 9–11 Obj. 2

Give the domain and range of each relation. Tell whether the relation is a function.

1. $y = (x - 2)180$
2. $y = 360$
3. $y = \dfrac{(x-2)180}{x}$
4. $y = \dfrac{360}{x}$
5. $x = 3y - 10$
6. $x^2 + y^2 = 9$
7. $x = -2$
8. $y = x^2 + 4$
9. $-x + 8y = 5$

Answers to *Try This*

1. D: all real numbers; R: all real numbers; function
2. D: all real numbers; R: 360; function
3. D: all real numbers except 0; R: all real numbers except 180; function
4. D: all real numbers except 0; R: all real numbers except 0; function
5. D: all real numbers; R: all real numbers; function
6. D: $-3 \le x \le 3$; R: $-3 \le y \le 3$; not a function
7. D: −2; R: all real numbers; not a function
8. D: all real numbers; R: $y \ge 4$; function
9. D: all real numbers; R: all real numbers; function

Organizer

See Skills Bank page S61

Pacing:
Traditional $\frac{1}{2}$ day
Block $\frac{1}{4}$ day

Objective: Apply the polygon formulas learned in Lesson 6-1 to identifying relations, functions, domain, and range.

 **Online Edition**

Teach

Remember

Students compare relations and functions and review the concepts of domain and range.

INTERVENTION ◄═══► For additional review and practice on relations and functions, see Skills Bank page S61.

Teaching Tip **Visual** In the example, $x = 6$ and $y = 0$ are both asymptotes. Remind students that an asymptote is a line the graph approaches as the absolute value of the variable increases.

Close

Assess

Ask students to use domain and range to explain whether the relation $y = \dfrac{-5x + 9}{3}$ is a function.
D: all real numbers; R: all real numbers; function

 TAKS *On Track for TAKS* connects TAKS objectives across the grade levels.

Grades 9–11
Obj. 2 Properties and Attributes of Functions A.2.B identify the mathematical domains and ranges and determine reasonable domain and range values for given situations, both continuous and discrete

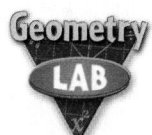
Pacing:
Traditional $\frac{1}{2}$ day
Block $\frac{1}{4}$ day

Objective: Explore properties of parallelograms.

Materials: index cards, patty paper, ruler

Online Edition

Countdown to TAKS Week 13

Teach

Discuss

Point out to students that if they have drawn their parallelograms correctly, each overlay involves a simple translation of ▱QRST.

Alternative Approach

Provide students with cutouts of congruent parallelograms to use.

Close

Key Concept

The opposite sides and opposite angles of a parallelogram are congruent. Consecutive angles are supplementary, and the diagonals bisect each other.

Assessment

Journal Have students summarize the relationships they discovered about parallelograms.

 Geometry TEKS

G.2 Geometric structure*
(B) make conjectures about … polygons … and determine the validity …

G.3 Geometric structure*
(B) construct and justify statements about geometric figures …

G.9 Congruence and the geometry of size*
(B) formulate and test conjectures about … polygons … based on explorations and concrete models

G.10 Congruence and the geometry of size*
(A) use congruence transformations to make conjectures and justify properties of geometric figures …

* Knowledge and Skills See p. 378.

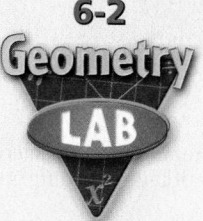

6-2

Geometry LAB

Use with Lesson 6-2

Explore Properties of Parallelograms

In this lab you will investigate the relationships among the angles and sides of a special type of quadrilateral called a *parallelogram*. You will need to apply the Transitive Property of Congruence. That is, if figure $A \cong$ figure B and figure $B \cong$ figure C, then figure $A \cong$ figure C.

 TEKS G.9.B Congruence and the geometry of size: formulate and test conjectures about … polygons … based on explorations and concrete models. Also G.2.B, G.3.B, G.10.A

Activity

1 Use opposite sides of an index card to draw a set of parallel lines on a piece of patty paper. Then use opposite sides of a ruler to draw a second set of parallel lines that intersects the first. Label the points of intersection A, B, C, and D, in that order. Quadrilateral $ABCD$ has two pairs of parallel sides. It is a *parallelogram*. **Check students' work.**

2 Place a second piece of patty paper over the first and trace $ABCD$. Label the points that correspond to A, B, C, and D as Q, R, S, and T, in that order. The parallelograms $ABCD$ and $QRST$ are congruent. Name all the pairs of congruent corresponding sides and angles.

3 Lay $ABCD$ over $QRST$ so that $\overline{AB}$ overlays $\overline{ST}$. What do you notice about their lengths? What does this tell you about $\overline{AB}$ and $\overline{CD}$? Now move $ABCD$ so that $\overline{DA}$ overlays $\overline{RS}$. What do you notice about their lengths? What does this tell you about $\overline{DA}$ and $\overline{BC}$?
$AB = ST$; $\overline{AB} \cong \overline{CD}$; $DA = RS$; $\overline{DA} \cong \overline{BC}$

4 Lay $ABCD$ over $QRST$ so that $\angle A$ overlays $\angle S$. What do you notice about their measures? What does this tell you about $\angle A$ and $\angle C$? Now move $ABCD$ so that $\angle B$ overlays $\angle T$. What do you notice about their measures? What does this tell you about $\angle B$ and $\angle D$?
$m\angle A = m\angle S$; $\angle A \cong \angle C$; $m\angle B = m\angle T$; $\angle B \cong \angle D$

5 Arrange the pieces of patty paper so that $\overline{RS}$ overlays $\overline{AD}$. What do you notice about $\overline{QR}$ and $\overline{AB}$? What does this tell you about $\angle A$ and $\angle R$? What can you conclude about $\angle A$ and $\angle B$?

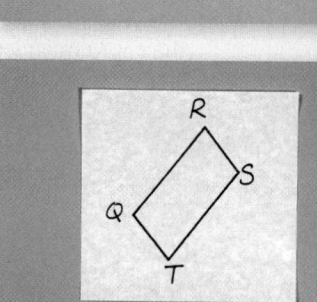

6 Draw diagonals $\overline{AC}$ and $\overline{BD}$. Fold $ABCD$ so that A matches C, making a crease. Unfold the paper and fold it again so that B matches D, making another crease. What do you notice about the creases? What can you conclude about the diagonals?
The creases intersect at the same pt. where $\overline{AC}$ and $\overline{BD}$ intersect. So the diags. intersect at the mdpt. of each, and therefore the diags. bisect each other.

Try This

1. Repeat the above steps with a different parallelogram. Do you get the same results? **Check students' work. They should obtain the same results.**

2. Make a Conjecture How do you think the sides of a parallelogram are related to each other? the angles? the diagonals? Write your conjectures as conditional statements.

Answers to *Activity*

2. $\overline{QR} \cong \overline{AB}$; $\overline{RS} \cong \overline{BC}$; $\overline{ST} \cong \overline{CD}$; $\overline{TQ} \cong \overline{DA}$;
$\angle Q \cong \angle A$; $\angle R \cong \angle B$; $\angle S \cong \angle C$;
$\angle T \cong \angle D$

5. $\overline{QR}$ and $\overline{AB}$ are collinear. $\angle A$ and $\angle R$ form a lin. pair, so $\angle A$ is supp. to $\angle R$. Since $\angle R \cong \angle B$, $\angle A$ is supp. to $\angle B$.

Answers to *Try This*

2. Possible answers: If a quad. is a ▱, then its opp. sides are ≅. If a quad. is a ▱, then its opp. ∡ are ≅. If a quad. is a ▱, then its cons. ∡ are supp. If a quad. is a ▱, then its diags. intersect at their mdpts.

6-2 Properties of Parallelograms

TEKS G.3.B Geometric structure: construct and justify statements about geometric figures and their properties. Also G.2.B, G.3.E, G.7.A, G.7.B, G.7.C, G.10.B

Objectives
Prove and apply properties of parallelograms.

Use properties of parallelograms to solve problems.

Vocabulary
parallelogram

Who uses this?
Race car designers can use a parallelogram-shaped linkage to keep the wheels of the car vertical on uneven surfaces. (See Example 1.)

Any polygon with four sides is a quadrilateral. However, some quadrilaterals have special properties. These *special quadrilaterals* are given their own names.

Helpful Hint
Opposite sides of a quadrilateral do not share a vertex. Opposite angles do not share a side.

A quadrilateral with two pairs of parallel sides is a **parallelogram**. To write the name of a parallelogram, you use the symbol ▱.

Parallelogram $ABCD$
▱$ABCD$

$\overline{AB} \parallel \overline{CD}, \overline{BC} \parallel \overline{DA}$

Know it! Note

Theorem 6-2-1 | **Properties of Parallelograms**

THEOREM	HYPOTHESIS	CONCLUSION
If a quadrilateral is a parallelogram, then its opposite sides are congruent. (▱ → opp. sides ≅)		$\overline{AB} \cong \overline{CD}$ $\overline{BC} \cong \overline{DA}$

PROOF | **Theorem 6-2-1**

Given: $JKLM$ is a parallelogram.
Prove: $\overline{JK} \cong \overline{LM}, \overline{KL} \cong \overline{MJ}$

Proof:

Statements	Reasons
1. $JKLM$ is a parallelogram.	1. Given
2. $\overline{JK} \parallel \overline{LM}, \overline{KL} \parallel \overline{MJ}$	2. Def. of ▱
3. $\angle 1 \cong \angle 2, \angle 3 \cong \angle 4$	3. Alt. Int. ∠ Thm.
4. $\overline{JL} \cong \overline{JL}$	4. Reflex. Prop. of ≅
5. $\triangle JKL \cong \triangle LMJ$	5. ASA *Steps 3, 4*
6. $\overline{JK} \cong \overline{LM}, \overline{KL} \cong \overline{MJ}$	6. CPCTC

1 Introduce

EXPLORATION

6-2 Properties of Parallelograms

A *parallelogram* is a quadrilateral with two pairs of parallel sides. Use geometry software to explore the properties of parallelograms.

1. Draw a line and a point not on the line.	2. Use the Construct menu to draw a line through the point that is parallel to the first line.
3. Repeat Steps 1 and 2 to draw another pair of parallel lines.	4. Construct the intersections of the lines. Label the points of intersection A, B, C, and D.

5. Measure the angles of parallelogram *ABCD*. What do you notice? Drag the vertices of *ABCD* to see if the same relationships hold for parallelograms with different shapes.

6. Measure the sides of parallelogram *ABCD*. What do you

Motivate

Draw two parallel lines cut by two parallel transversals. Explain that the resulting figure is a parallelogram. Ask students to locate examples of parallelograms in the classroom, such as the wall, the tile on the floor, or the door.

Explorations and answers are provided in the *Explorations* binder.

6-2 Organizer

Pacing: Traditional 1 day
Block $\frac{1}{2}$ day

Objectives: Prove and apply properties of parallelograms.

Use properties of parallelograms to solve problems.

PREMIER **Online Edition**
Tutorial Videos

Countdown to TAKS Week 13

Power Presentations
with PowerPoint®

Warm Up
Find the value of each variable.

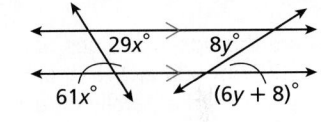

1. x 2
2. y 4
3. z 18

Also available on transparency

Math Humor

Q: What do you call an urgent message sent across a parallel network?

A: A parallelogram.

Geometry TEKS

G.2 Geometric structure*
(B) … determine the validity of … conjectures [about polygons] …

G.3 Geometric structure*
(B) construct and justify statements about geometric figures …

G.7 Dimensionality and the geometry of location*
(B) use slopes and equations of lines to investigate … relationships …

G.10 Congruence and the geometry of size*
(B) … apply triangle congruence relationships
Also G.3.E, G.7.A, G.7.C

* Knowledge and Skills See p. 378.

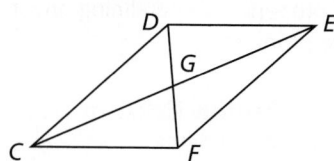

Example 1

In ▱*CDEF*, *DE* = 74 mm, *DG* = 31 mm, and m∠*FCD* = 42°. Find each measure.

A. *CF*   74 mm

B. m∠*EFC*   138°

C. *DF*   62 mm

INTERVENTION ◀▶
Questioning Strategies

EXAMPLE 1

• How are the opposite sides of a parallelogram related? How are the diagonals of a parallelogram related?

Teaching Tip   **Diversity** Explain that a *tangram* (MK) is an ancient Chinese puzzle made up of seven polygons that fit together in a square. It always includes a parallelogram as one piece. Point out that the key to solving the puzzle is often the correct placement of the parallelogram.

Know it!
.Note

Theorems   Properties of Parallelograms

	THEOREM	HYPOTHESIS	CONCLUSION
6-2-2	If a quadrilateral is a parallelogram, then its opposite angles are congruent. (▱ → opp. ∠ ≅)		∠*A* ≅ ∠*C* ∠*B* ≅ ∠*D*
6-2-3	If a quadrilateral is a parallelogram, then its consecutive angles are supplementary. (▱ → cons. ∠ supp.)		m∠*A* + m∠*B* = 180° m∠*B* + m∠*C* = 180° m∠*C* + m∠*D* = 180° m∠*D* + m∠*A* = 180°
6-2-4	If a quadrilateral is a parallelogram, then its diagonals bisect each other. (▱ → diags. bisect each other)		$\overline{AZ} \cong \overline{CZ}$ $\overline{BZ} \cong \overline{DZ}$

You will prove Theorems 6-2-3 and 6-2-4 in Exercises 45 and 44.

EXAMPLE 1   *Racing Application*

The diagram shows the parallelogram-shaped linkage that joins the frame of a race car to one wheel of the car. In ▱*PQRS*, *QR* = 48 cm, *RT* = 30 cm, and m∠*QPS* = 73°. Find each measure.

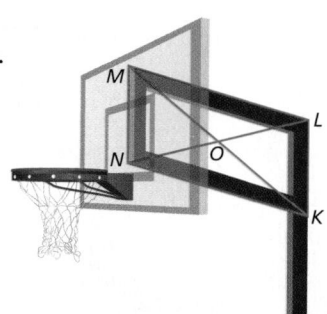

A *PS*
$\overline{PS} \cong \overline{QR}$ ▱ → opp. sides ≅
PS = *QR*   Def. of ≅ segs.
PS = 48 cm   Substitute 48 for *QR*.

B m∠*PQR*
m∠*PQR* + m∠*QPS* = 180°   ▱ → cons. ∠ supp.
m∠*PQR* + 73 = 180   Substitute 73 for m∠*QPS*.
m∠*PQR* = 107°   Subtract 73 from both sides.

C *PT*
$\overline{PT} \cong \overline{RT}$ ▱ → diags. bisect each other
PT = *RT*   Def. of ≅ segs.
PT = 30 cm   Substitute 30 for *RT*.

CHECK IT OUT!   In ▱*KLMN*, *LM* = 28 in., *LN* = 26 in., and m∠*LKN* = 74°. Find each measure.
1a. *KN* 28 in.
1b. m∠*NML* 74°
1c. *LO* 13 in.

---

2 Teach

Guided Instruction

Review the relationships among angle pairs formed by parallel lines and a transversal. As you discuss the four theorems in the lesson, explain that their proofs use CPCTC or these angle pairs.

Reaching All Learners
Through Visual Cues

Have students draw three parallelograms. Then have them use colored pencils to mark the pairs of congruent sides on one parallelogram, the pairs of congruent angles on the second parallelogram, and the pairs of supplementary angles on the third parallelogram.

EXAMPLE **2** **Using Properties of Parallelograms to Find Measures**

ABCD is a parallelogram. Find each measure.

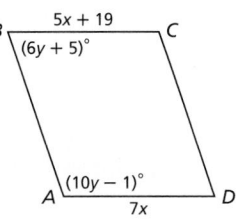

A *AD*

$\overline{AD} \cong \overline{BC}$	☐ → opp. sides ≅
$AD = BC$	Def. of ≅ segs.
$7x = 5x + 19$	Substitute the given values.
$2x = 19$	Subtract 5x from both sides.
$x = 9.5$	Divide both sides by 2.

$AD = 7x = 7(9.5) = 66.5$

B m∠*B*

$m\angle A + m\angle B = 180°$	☐ → cons. ∠ supp.
$(10y - 1) + (6y + 5) = 180$	Substitute the given values.
$16y + 4 = 180$	Combine like terms.
$16y = 176$	Subtract 4 from both sides.
$y = 11$	Divide both sides by 16.

$m\angle B = (6y + 5)° = [6(11) + 5]° = 71°$

 *EFGH* is a parallelogram.
Find each measure.

2a. *JG* **12**
2b. *FH* **18**

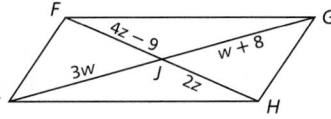

EXAMPLE **3** **Parallelograms in the Coordinate Plane**

Three vertices of ☐*ABCD* are $A(1, -2)$, $B(-2, 3)$,
and $D(5, -1)$. Find the coordinates of vertex *C*.

Since *ABCD* is a parallelogram, both pairs of
opposite sides must be parallel.

Step 1 Graph the given points.

Step 2 Find the slope of $\overline{AB}$ by counting
the units from *A* to *B*.
The rise from −2 to 3 is 5.
The run from 1 to −2 is −3.

Step 3 Start at *D* and count the same
number of units.
A rise of 5 from −1 is 4.
A run of −3 from 5 is 2. Label $(2, 4)$ as vertex *C*.

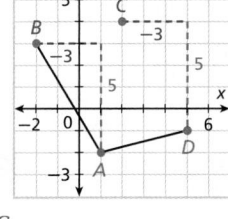

Step 4 Use the slope formula to verify that $\overline{BC} \parallel \overline{AD}$.

$$\text{slope of } \overline{BC} = \frac{4 - 3}{2 - (-2)} = \frac{1}{4}$$

$$\text{slope of } \overline{AD} = \frac{-1 - (-2)}{5 - 1} = \frac{1}{4}$$

The coordinates of vertex *C* are $(2, 4)$.

 **3.** Three vertices of ☐*PQRS* are $P(-3, -2)$, $Q(-1, 4)$, and $S(5, 0)$.
Find the coordinates of vertex *R*. **(7, 6)**

> **Remember!**
>
> When you are
> drawing a figure in
> the coordinate plane,
> the name *ABCD*
> gives the order of
> the vertices.

COMMON ERROR
/// **ALERT** \\\

Advise students to pay close attention to the markings on a diagram,
especially when writing a proof.
Explain that a quadrilateral with only
one set of parallel lines is not necessarily a parallelogram.

Power Presentations
with PowerPoint®

Additional Examples

Example **2**

WXYZ is a parallelogram. Find
each measure.

A. *YZ* 52

B. m∠*Z* 65°

Example **3**

Three vertices of ☐*JKLM* are
$J(3, -8)$, $K(-2, 2)$, and $L(2, 6)$.
Find the coordinates of vertex *M*.
$(7, -4)$

Also available on transparency

INTERVENTION ◄►
Questioning Strategies

EXAMPLE **2**

• How are algebra and the definition of supplementary angles used
to find the angle measure in this
example?

EXAMPLE **3**

• How are the slopes of the sides of
a parallelogram related?

6-2 Properties of Parallelograms **393**

Lesson 6-2 **393**

Example 4

A. Use the figure in Example 4A to write a two-column proof.
Given: *ABCD* is a parallelogram.
Prove: △*AEB* ≅ △*CED*

1. *ABCD* is a □. (Given)
2. $\overline{AB} \cong \overline{CD}$ (□ → opp. sides ≅)
3. $\overline{AE} \cong \overline{CE}, \overline{BE} \cong \overline{DE}$ (□ → diags. bisect each other)
4. △*AEB* ≅ △*CED* (SSS)

B. Use the figure in Example 4B to write a two-column proof.
Given: *GHJN* and *JKLM* are parallelograms. *H* and *M* are collinear. *N* and *K* are collinear.
Prove: ∠*H* ≅ ∠*M*

1. *GHJN* and *JKLM* are ⑤. (Given)
2. ∠*H* and ∠*HJN* are supp.; ∠*M* and ∠*MJK* are supp. (□ → cons. ⦞ supp.)
3. ∠*HJN* ≅ ∠*MJK* (Vert. ⦞ Thm.)
4. ∠*H* ≅ ∠*M* (≅ Supps. Thm.)

Also available on transparency

INTERVENTION ◄►
Questioning Strategies

EXAMPLE 4

• Can you think of another way to prove the same result in each example? Explain.

Using Properties of Parallelograms in a Proof

Write a two-column proof.

A Theorem 6-2-2
Given: *ABCD* is a parallelogram.
Prove: ∠*BAD* ≅ ∠*DCB*, ∠*ABC* ≅ ∠*CDA*
Proof:

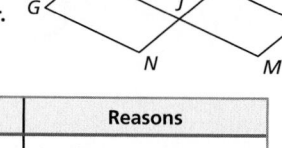

Statements	Reasons
1. *ABCD* is a parallelogram.	1. Given
2. $\overline{AB} \cong \overline{CD}, \overline{DA} \cong \overline{BC}$	2. □ → opp. sides ≅
3. $\overline{BD} \cong \overline{BD}$	3. Reflex. Prop. of ≅
4. △*BAD* ≅ △*DCB*	4. SSS *Steps 2, 3*
5. ∠*BAD* ≅ ∠*DCB*	5. CPCTC
6. $\overline{AC} \cong \overline{AC}$	6. Reflex. Prop. of ≅
7. △*ABC* ≅ △*CDA*	7. SSS *Steps 2, 6*
8. ∠*ABC* ≅ ∠*CDA*	8. CPCTC

B **Given:** *GHJN* and *JKLM* are parallelograms. *H* and *M* are collinear. *N* and *K* are collinear.
Prove: ∠*G* ≅ ∠*L*
Proof:

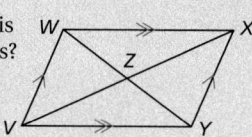

Statements	Reasons
1. *GHJN* and *JKLM* are parallelograms.	1. Given
2. ∠*HJN* ≅ ∠*G*, ∠*MJK* ≅ ∠*L*	2. □ → opp. ⦞ ≅
3. ∠*HJN* ≅ ∠*MJK*	3. Vert. ⦞ Thm.
4. ∠*G* ≅ ∠*L*	4. Trans. Prop. of ≅

 **CHECK IT OUT!**

4. Use the figure in Example 4B to write a two-column proof.
Given: *GHJN* and *JKLM* are parallelograms.
H and *M* are collinear. *N* and *K* are collinear.
Prove: ∠*N* ≅ ∠*K*

---

4. 1. *GHJN* and *JKLM* are ⑤. (Given)
2. ∠*N* and ∠*HJN* are supp. ∠*K* and ∠*MJK* are supp. (□ → cons. ⦞ supp.)
3. ∠*HJN* ≅ ∠*MJK* (Vert. ⦞ Thm.)
4. ∠*N* ≅ ∠*K* (≅ Supps. Thm.)

 **Know it!**
.Note

THINK AND DISCUSS

1. The measure of one angle of a parallelogram is 71°. What are the measures of the other angles?

2. In □*VWXY*, *VW* = 21, and *WY* = 36. Find as many other measures as you can. Justify your answers.

3. **GET ORGANIZED** Copy and complete the graphic organizer. In each cell, draw a figure with markings that represents the given property.

Properties of Parallelograms				
Opp. sides ∥	Opp. sides ≅	Opp. ⦞ ≅	Cons. ⦞ supp.	Diags. bisect each other

---

3 Close

Summarize

Review the five properties of parallelograms covered in the lesson.

• Opposite sides are parallel.
• Opposite sides are congruent.
• Opposite angles are congruent.
• Consecutive angles are supplementary.
• Diagonals bisect each other.

Draw a sketch on the board to illustrate each property.

ONGOING ASSESSMENT

and INTERVENTION ◄►

Diagnose **Before** the Lesson
6-2 Warm Up, TE p. 391

Monitor **During** the Lesson
Check It Out! Exercises, SE pp. 392–394
Questioning Strategies, TE pp. 392–394

Assess **After** the Lesson
6-2 Lesson Quiz, TE p. 397
Alternative Assessment, TE p. 397

Answers to *Think and Discuss*

1. The measure of the opp. ∠ is 71°. The measure of each cons. ∠ is 109°.

2. *XY* = 21, *WZ* = 18, and *YZ* = 18. Possible answer: Since *VWXY* is a □, its opp. sides are ≅. So *XY* = *VW* = 21. *WY* is one of its diags., and by Thm. 6-2-4, the other diag. bisects it, so *WZ* = *YZ* = $\frac{1}{2}$(*WY*) = 18.

3. See p. A5.

6-2 Exercises

go.hrw.com/Geo/TX
Homework Help Online
KEYWORD: MG7 6-2
Parent Resources Online
KEYWORD: MG7 Parent

GUIDED PRACTICE

1. Only 1 pair of sides are ∥. By def., a ▱ has 2 pairs of ∥ sides.

Vocabulary Apply the vocabulary from this lesson to answer each question.

1. Explain why the figure at right is NOT a *parallelogram*.

2. Draw ▱*PQRS*. Name the opposite sides and opposite angles.

SEE EXAMPLE 1
p. 392

Safety The handrail is made from congruent parallelograms. In ▱*ABCD*, *AB* = 17.5, *DE* = 18, and m∠*BCD* = 110°. Find each measure.

3. *BD* 36
4. *CD* 17.5
5. *BE* 18
6. m∠*ABC* 70°
7. m∠*ADC* 70°
8. m∠*DAB* 110°

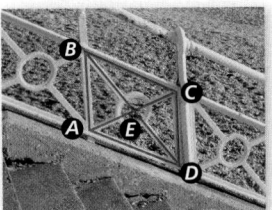

SEE EXAMPLE 2
p. 393

JKLM is a parallelogram. Find each measure.

9. *JK* 24.5
10. *LM* 24.5
11. m∠*L* 51°
12. m∠*M* 129°

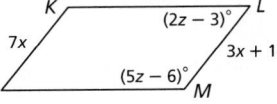

SEE EXAMPLE 3
p. 393

13. **Multi-Step** Three vertices of ▱*DFGH* are $D(-9, 4)$, $F(-1, 5)$, and $G(2, 0)$. Find the coordinates of vertex *H*. $(-6, -1)$

SEE EXAMPLE 4
p. 394

14. Write a two-column proof.
 Given: *PSTV* is a parallelogram. $\overline{PQ} \cong \overline{RQ}$
 Prove: ∠*STV* ≅ ∠*R*

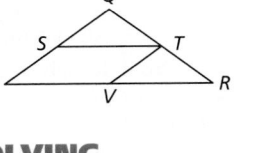

PRACTICE AND PROBLEM SOLVING

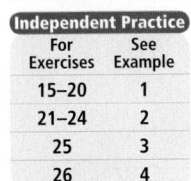

Independent Practice	
For Exercises	See Example
15–20	1
21–24	2
25	3
26	4

TEKS ⇒ TAKS

Skills Practice p. S14
Application Practice p. S33

Shipping Cranes can be used to load cargo onto ships. In ▱*JKLM*, *JL* = 165.8, *JK* = 110, and m∠*JML* = 50°. Find the measure of each part of the crane.

15. *JN* 82.9
16. *LM* 110
17. *LN* 82.9
18. m∠*JKL* 50°
19. m∠*KLM* 130°
20. m∠*MJK* 130°

WXYZ is a parallelogram. Find each measure.

21. *WV* 10
22. *YW* 20
23. *XZ* 28
24. *ZV* 14

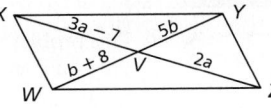

25. **Multi-Step** Three vertices of ▱*PRTV* are $P(-4, -4)$, $R(-10, 0)$, and $V(5, -1)$. Find the coordinates of vertex *T*. $(-1, 3)$

26. Write a two-column proof.
 Given: *ABCD* and *AFGH* are parallelograms.
 Prove: ∠*C* ≅ ∠*G*

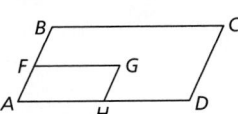

Answers

2. Possible answer:

opposite sides: $\overline{PQ}$ and $\overline{RS}$, $\overline{QR}$ and $\overline{SP}$
opposite angles: ∠*P* and ∠*R*, ∠*Q* and ∠*S*

14. 1. *PSTV* is a ▱. $\overline{PQ} \cong \overline{RQ}$ (Given)
 2. ∠*STV* ≅ ∠*P* (▱ → opp. ∡ ≅)
 3. ∠*P* ≅ ∠*R* (Isosc. △ Thm.)
 4. ∠*STV* ≅ ∠*R* (Trans. Prop. of ≅)

26. 1. *ABCD* and *AFGH* are ▱. (Given)
 2. ∠*C* ≅ ∠*A*, ∠*A* ≅ ∠*G*
 (▱ → opp. ∡ ≅)
 3. ∠*C* ≅ ∠*G* (Trans. Prop. of ≅)

6-2 Exercises

Assignment Guide

Assign *Guided Practice* exercises as necessary.

If you finished Examples **1–2**
 Basic 15–24, 27–30, 32–42 even
 Average 15–24, 27–31, 32–40 even, 41–43, 46, 47
 Advanced 15–24, 27–31, 32–40 even, 41–43, 46, 47, 56

If you finished Examples **1–4**
 Basic 15–30, 32–40, 42, 46, 48, 51–53, 58–66
 Average 15–26, 29, 30, 32–40 even, 41–54, 58–66
 Advanced 15–31, 32–42 even, 44–66

Homework Quick Check
Quickly check key concepts.
Exercises: 16, 22, 25, 26, 32, 42

Teaching Tip

Critical Thinking For **Exercise 25,** explain that while there are 3 points that would complete the parallelogram, only one point (−1, 3) completes ▱*PRTV*. Challenge students to find the other two points that would form a parallelogram if the order of the vertices were not important. (11, −5) and (−19, −3)

⬦ TAKS Practice

Grades 9–11	Exercises
Obj. 2	27–30, 48, 51, 56, 58, 59, 64–66
Obj. 4	46, 47
Obj. 6	41–43, 64–66
Obj. 7	54, 55

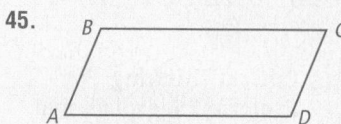
Answers

27. $PQ = QR = RS = SP = 21$

28. $PQ = RS = 10.5; QR = SP = 31.5$

29. $PQ = RS = 17.5; QR = SP = 24.5$

30. $PQ = RS = 6; QR = SP = 36$

31b. ∠2 is supp. to ∠1 (▱ → cons. ∡ supp.); ∠4 is supp. to ∠1 (▱ → cons. ∡ supp.); ∠5 is supp. to ∠1(▱ → cons. ∡ supp.); ∠7 is supp. to ∠1 (Subst.)

45.

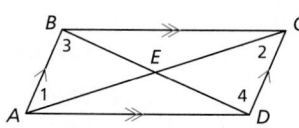

Given: *ABCD* is a ▱.
Prove: ∠A and ∠B are supp. ∠B and ∠C are supp. ∠C and ∠D are supp. ∠D and ∠A are supp.

1. *ABCD* is a ▱. (Given)
2. $\overline{AB} \parallel \overline{CD}, \overline{BC} \parallel \overline{DA}$ (Def. of ▱)
3. ∠A and ∠B are supp. ∠B and ∠C are supp. ∠C and ∠D are supp. ∠D and ∠A are supp. (Same-Side Int. ∡ Thm.)

49, 50, 56, 57. See p. A21.

31a. ∠3 ≅ ∠1 (Corr. ∡ Post.); ∠6 ≅ ∠1 (▱ → opp. ∡ ≅); ∠8 ≅ ∠1 (▱ → opp. ∡ ≅)

32. ∠RKM (▱ → opp. ∡ ≅)

33. ∠KMP (▱ → opp. ∡ ≅)

34. $\overline{RT}$ (▱ → diags. bisect each other)

35. $\overline{KM}$ (▱ → opp. sides ≅)

36. $\overline{RK}$ (Def. of ▱)

37. $\overline{RP}$ (Def. of ▱)

38. ∠RKP (Alt. Int. ∡ Thm.)

39. ∠RTP (Vert. ∡ Thm.)

41. $x = 119$; $y = 61$; $z = 119$

42. $x = 90$; $y = 37$; $z = 53$

43. $x = 24$; $y = 50$; $z = 50$

44d. opp. sides of a ▱ are ≅
e. ASA
f. CPCTC

31a. ∠3 ≅ ∠1 **x²y Algebra** The perimeter of ▱*PQRS* is 84. Find the length of each side of ▱*PQRS* under the given conditions.

27. $PQ = QR$ 28. $QR = 3(RS)$ 29. $RS = SP - 7$ 30. $SP = RS^2$

31. **Cars** To repair a large truck, a mechanic might use a *parallelogram lift*. In the lift, $\overline{FG} \cong \overline{GH} \cong \overline{LK} \cong \overline{KJ}$, and $\overline{FL} \cong \overline{GK} \cong \overline{HJ}$.

a. Which angles are congruent to ∠1? Justify your answer.

b. What is the relationship between ∠1 and each of the remaining labeled angles? Justify your answer.

Complete each statement about ▱*KMPR*. Justify your answer.

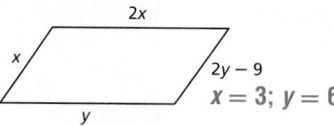

32. ∠MPR ≅ __?__   33. ∠PRK ≅ __?__   34. $\overline{MT}$ ≅ __?__

35. $\overline{PR}$ ≅ __?__   36. $\overline{MP} \parallel$ __?__   37. $\overline{MK} \parallel$ __?__

38. ∠MPK ≅ __?__   39. ∠MTK ≅ __?__   40. m∠MKR + m∠PRK = __?__
180° (▱ → cons. ∡ supp.)

Find the values of *x*, *y*, and *z* in each parallelogram.

41.   42.   43.

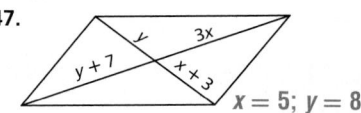

44. Complete the paragraph proof of Theorem 6-2-4 by filling in the blanks.

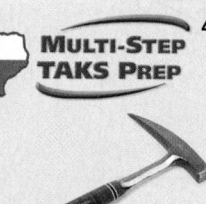

Given: *ABCD* is a parallelogram.
Prove: $\overline{AC}$ and $\overline{BD}$ bisect each other at *E*.

Proof: It is given that *ABCD* is a parallelogram. By the definition of a parallelogram, $\overline{AB} \parallel$ **a.** __?CD__. By the Alternate Interior Angles Theorem, ∠1 ≅ **b.** __?∠2__, and ∠3 ≅ **c.** __?∠4__. $\overline{AB} \cong \overline{CD}$ because **d.** __?__. This means that △ABE ≅ △CDE by **e.** __?__. So by **f.** __?__, $\overline{AE} \cong \overline{CE}$, and $\overline{BE} \cong \overline{DE}$. Therefore $\overline{AC}$ and $\overline{BD}$ bisect each other at *E* by the definition of **g.** __?__. **bisect**

45. Write a two-column proof of Theorem 6-2-3: If a quadrilateral is a parallelogram, then its consecutive angles are supplementary.

x²y Algebra Find the values of *x* and *y* in each parallelogram.

46.   47.

2x, x, 2y − 9, y
$x = 3; y = 6$

y, 3x, y + 7, x + 3
$x = 5; y = 8$

48. **MULTI-STEP TAKS PREP** This problem will prepare you for the Multi-Step TAKS Prep on page 406.

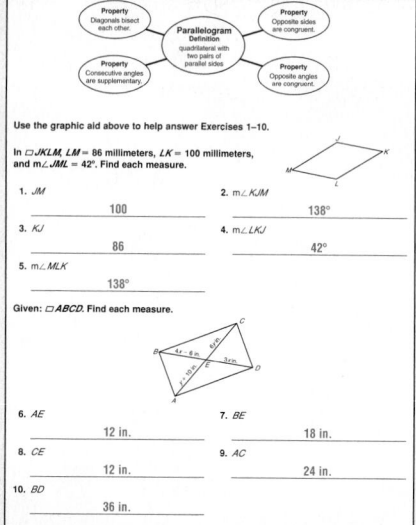

In this calcite crystal, the face *ABCD* is a parallelogram.

a. In ▱*ABCD*, m∠B = $(6x + 12)°$, and m∠D = $(9x - 33)°$. Find m∠B. **102°**

b. Find m∠A and m∠C. Which theorem or theorems did you use to find these angle measures?
78° (▱ → cons. ∡ supp.)

6-2 PRACTICE A
6-2 PRACTICE C
6-2 PRACTICE B

A gurney is a wheeled cot or stretcher used in hospitals. Many gurneys are made so that the base will fold up for easy storage in an ambulance. When partially folded, the base forms a parallelogram. In ▱*STUV*, *VU* = 91 centimeters, *UW* = 108.8 centimeters, and m∠ *TSV* = 57°. Find each measure.

1. *SW*   2. *TS*   3. *US*
108.8 cm   91 cm   217.6 cm

4. m∠ *SVU*   5. m∠ *STU*   6. m∠ *TUV*
123°   123°   57°

JKLM is a parallelogram. Find each measure.

7. m∠*L*   8. m∠*K*   9. *MJ*
117°   63°   71

VWXY is a parallelogram. Find each measure.

10. *VX*   11. *XZ*
21   10.5

12. *ZW*   13. *WY*
15   30

14. Three vertices of ▱*ABCD* are B(−3, 3), C(2, 7), and D(5, 1). Find the coordinates of vertex *A*.   (0, −3)

Write a two-column proof.
15. Given: *DEFG* is a parallelogram.
Prove: m∠*DHG* = m∠*EDH* + m∠*FGH*   Possible answer:

Statements	Reasons
1. *DEFG* is a parallelogram.	1. Given
2. m∠*EDG* = m∠*EDH* + m∠*GDH*, m∠*FGD* = m∠*FGH* + m∠*DGH*	2. Angle Add. Post.
3. m∠*EDG* + m∠*FGD* = 180°	3. ▱ → cons. ∡ supp.
4. m∠*EDH* + m∠*GDH* + m∠*FGH* + m∠*DGH* = 180°	4. Subst. (Steps 2, 3)
5. m∠*GDH* + m∠*DGH* + m∠*DHG* = 180°	5. Triangle Sum Thm.
6. m∠*GDH* + m∠*DGH* + m∠*DHG* = m∠*EDH* + m∠*GDH* + m∠*FGH* + m∠*DGH*	6. Trans. Prop. of =
7. m∠*DHG* = m∠*EDH* + m∠*FGH*	7. Subtr. Prop. of =

6-2 READING STRATEGIES

Property: Diagonals bisect each other.
Property: Opposite sides are congruent.
Parallelogram Definition quadrilateral with two pairs of parallel sides
Property: Consecutive angles are supplementary.
Property: Opposite angles are congruent.

Use the graphic aid above to help answer Exercises 1–10.

In ▱*JKLM*, *LM* = 86 millimeters, *LK* = 100 millimeters, and m∠*JML* = 42°. Find each measure.

1. *JM*   2. m∠*KJM*
100   138°

3. *KJ*   4. m∠*LKJ*
86   42°

5. m∠*MLK*
138°

Given: ▱*ABCD*. Find each measure.

6. *AE*   7. *BE*
12 in.   18 in.

8. *CE*   9. *AC*
12 in.   24 in.

10. *BD*
36 in.

6-2 RETEACH

A parallelogram is a quadrilateral with two pairs of parallel sides. All parallelograms, such as ▱*FGHJ*, have the following properties.

Properties of Parallelograms

$\overline{FG} \cong \overline{HJ}$, $\overline{GH} \cong \overline{JF}$	∠F ≅ ∠H, ∠G ≅ ∠J
Opposite sides are congruent.	Opposite angles are congruent.
m∠F + m∠G = 180°, m∠G + m∠H = 180°, m∠H + m∠J = 180°, m∠J + m∠F = 180°	$\overline{FP} \cong \overline{HP}$, $\overline{GP} \cong \overline{JP}$
Consecutive angles are supplementary.	The diagonals bisect each other.

Find each measure.

1. *AB*   2. m∠*D*
10 cm   70°

Find each measure in ▱*LMNP*.

3. *ML*   4. *LP*
12 m   10 m

5. m∠*LPM*   6. *LN*
53°   18 m

7. m∠*MLN*   8. *QN*
32°   9 m

49. Critical Thinking Draw any parallelogram. Draw a second parallelogram whose corresponding sides are congruent to the sides of the first parallelogram but whose corresponding angles are not congruent to the angles of the first.

    a. Is there an SSSS congruence postulate for parallelograms? Explain. no

    b. Remember the meaning of triangle rigidity. Is a parallelogram rigid? Explain. no

 50. Write About It Explain why every parallelogram is a quadrilateral but every quadrilateral is not necessarily a parallelogram.

 **TEST PREP**

51. What is the value of x in $\square PQRS$?

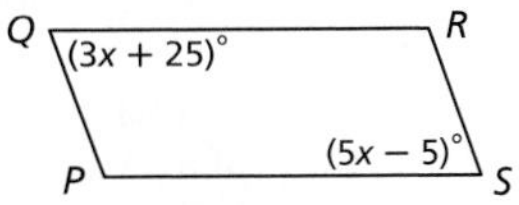

    Ⓐ 15   Ⓒ 30

    Ⓑ 20   Ⓓ 70

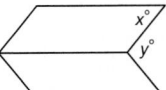

52. The diagonals of $\square JKLM$ intersect at Z. Which statement is true?

    Ⓕ $JL = KM$ Ⓖ $JL = \frac{1}{2}KM$ Ⓗ $JL = \frac{1}{2}JZ$ Ⓙ $JL = 2JZ$

53. Gridded Response In $\square ABCD$, $BC = 8.2$, and $CD = 5$. What is the perimeter of $\square ABCD$? 26.4

CHALLENGE AND EXTEND

The coordinates of three vertices of a parallelogram are given. Give the coordinates for all possible locations of the fourth vertex.

54. (12, 0), (−4, 0), (4, 10)

55. (2, 4), (4, −6), (−6, −2)

54. $(0, 5), (4, 0), (8, 5)$ **55.** $(-2, 1), (3, -1), (-1, -4)$

56. The feathers on an arrow form two congruent parallelograms that share a common side. Each parallelogram is the reflection of the other across the line they share. Show that $y = 2x$.

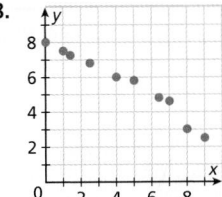

57. Prove that the bisectors of two consecutive angles of a parallelogram are perpendicular.

SPIRAL REVIEW

Describe the correlation shown in each scatter plot as positive, negative, or no correlation. *(Previous course)*

58.

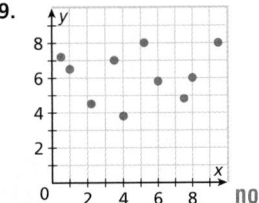 negative correlation

59.

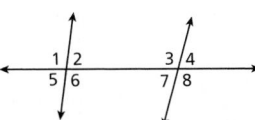 no correlation

Classify each angle pair. *(Lesson 3-1)*

60. alt. int. ∠

61. alt. ext. ∠

60. $\angle 2$ and $\angle 7$ **61.** $\angle 5$ and $\angle 4$

62. $\angle 6$ and $\angle 7$ same-side int. ∠   **63.** $\angle 1$ and $\angle 3$ corr. ∠

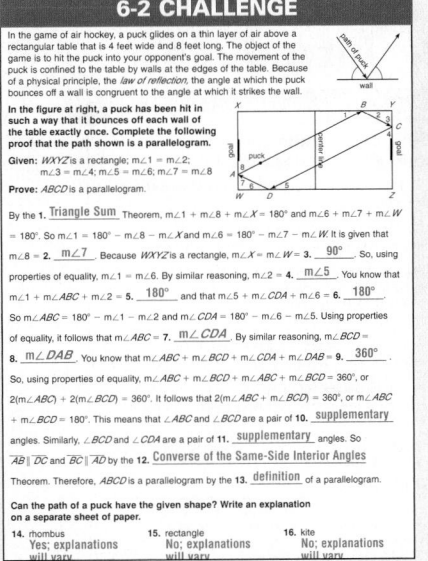

An interior angle measure of a regular polygon is given. Find the number of sides and the measure of each exterior angle. *(Lesson 6-1)*

64. 120° 6 sides; 60°   **65.** 135° 8 sides; 45°   **66.** 156° 15 sides; 24°

6-2 PROBLEM SOLVING

Use the diagram for Exercises 1 and 2. The wall frames on the staircase wall form parallelograms *ABCD* and *EFGH*.

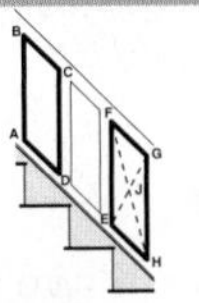

1. In $\square ABCD$, the measure of $\angle A$ is three times the measure of $\angle B$. What are the measures of $\angle C$ and $\angle D$?

m$\angle C$ = 135°; m$\angle D$ = 45°

2. In $\square EFGH$, $FH = 5x$ inches, $EG = (2x + 4)$ inches, and $JG = 8$ inches. What is the length of JH?

15 in.

3. The diagram shows a section of the support structure of a roller coaster. In $\square JKLM$, $JK = (3z − 0.9)$ feet, and $LM = (z + 2.7)$ feet. Find JK.

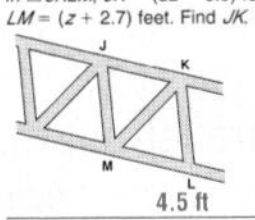

4.5 ft

4. In $\square TUVW$, part of a ceramic tile pattern, m$\angle TUV = (8x + 1)°$ and m$\angle UVW = (12x + 19)°$. Find m$\angle TUV$.

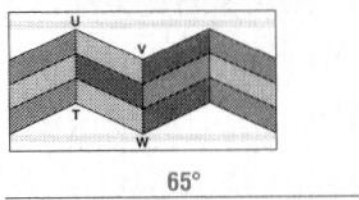

65°

Choose the best answer.

5. What is the measure of $\angle Z$ in parallelogram *WXYZ*? 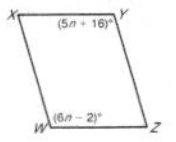
    A 18°
    Ⓑ 74°
    C 106°
    D 108°

6. The perimeter of $\square CDEF$ is 54 centimeters. Find the length of $\overline{FC}$ if $\overline{DE}$ is 5 centimeters longer than $\overline{EF}$.
    F 11 cm
    G 14 cm
    Ⓗ 16 cm
    J 44 cm

7. In $\square PQRS$, $QT = 7x$, $TS = 2x + 2.5$, $RT = 2y$, and $TP = y + 3$. Find the perimeter of $\triangle PTS$. 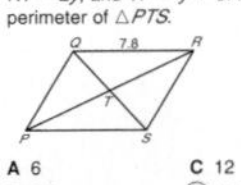
    A 6   C 12
    B 9.5   Ⓓ 17.3

6-2 CHALLENGE

In the game of air hockey, a puck glides on a thin layer of air above a rectangular table that is 4 feet wide and 8 feet long. The object of the game is to hit the puck into your opponent's goal. The movement of the puck is confined to the table by walls at the edges of the table. Because of a physical principle, the *law of reflection*, the angle at which the puck bounces off a wall is congruent to the angle at which it strikes the wall.

In the figure at right, a puck has been hit in such a way that it bounces off each wall of the table exactly once. Complete the following proof that the path shown is a parallelogram.

Given: *WXYZ* is a rectangle; m$\angle 1 = $ m$\angle 2$;
    m$\angle 3 = $ m$\angle 4$; m$\angle 5 = $ m$\angle 6$; m$\angle 7 = $ m$\angle 8$

Prove: *ABCD* is a parallelogram.

By the **1.** Triangle Sum Theorem, m$\angle 1 + $ m$\angle 8 + $ m$\angle X = 180°$ and m$\angle 6 + $ m$\angle 7 + $ m$\angle W$
= 180°. So m$\angle 1 = 180° − $ m$\angle 8 − $ m$\angle X$ and m$\angle 6 = 180° − $ m$\angle 7 − $ m$\angle W$. It is given that

m$\angle 8 = $ **2.** m$\angle 7$. Because *WXYZ* is a rectangle, m$\angle X = $ m$\angle W = $ **3.** 90° . So, using

properties of equality, m$\angle 1 = $ m$\angle 6$. By similar reasoning, m$\angle X = $ m$\angle W = $ **4.** m$\angle 5$. You know that

m$\angle 1 + $ m$\angle ABC + $ m$\angle 2 = $ **5.** 180° and that m$\angle 5 + $ m$\angle CDA = $ m$\angle 6 = $ **6.** 180°.

So m$\angle ABC = 180° − $ m$\angle 1 − $ m$\angle 2$ and m$\angle CDA = 180° − $ m$\angle 6 − $ m$\angle 5$. Using properties

of equality, it follows that m$\angle ABC = $ **7.** m$\angle CDA$. By similar reasoning, m$\angle BCD = $

8. m$\angle DAB$. You know that m$\angle ABC + $ m$\angle BCD + $ m$\angle CDA + $ m$\angle DAB = $ **9.** 360° .

So, using properties of equality, m$\angle ABC + $ m$\angle BCD + $ m$\angle ABC + $ m$\angle BCD = 360°$, or

2(m$\angle ABC$) + 2(m$\angle BCD$) = 360°. It follows that 2(m$\angle ABC + $ m$\angle BCD$) = 360°, or m$\angle ABC$

+ m$\angle BCD = 180°$. This means that $\angle ABC$ and $\angle BCD$ are a pair of **10.** supplementary

angles. Similarly, $\angle BCD$ and $\angle CDA$ are a pair of **11.** supplementary angles. So

$\overline{AB} \parallel \overline{DC}$ and $\overline{BC} \parallel \overline{AD}$ by the **12.** Converse of the Same-Side Interior Angles

Theorem. Therefore, *ABCD* is a parallelogram by the **13.** definition of a parallelogram.

Can the path of a puck have the given shape? Write an explanation on a separate sheet of paper.

14. rhombus
    Yes; explanations will vary.

15. rectangle
    No; explanations will vary.

16. kite
    No; explanations will vary.

✎ *Journal*

Ask students to describe how they remember which parts of a parallelogram are congruent and which parts are supplementary.

ALTERNATIVE ASSESSMENT

Have students draw a parallelogram and write algebraic expressions for a pair of congruent sides and a pair of supplementary angles. Have students exchange papers and solve for the measures of the labeled sides and all four angles.

Power Presentations with PowerPoint®

✓ **6-2 Lesson Quiz**

In $\square PNWL$, $NW = 12$, $PM = 9$, and m$\angle WLP = 144°$. Find each measure.

1. PW 18   **2.** m$\angle PNW$ 144°

QRST is a parallelogram. Find each measure.

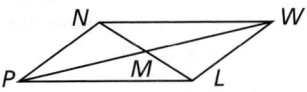

3. TQ 28   **4.** m$\angle T$ 71°

5. Three vertices of $\square ABCD$ are $A(2, -6)$, $B(-1, 2)$, and $C(5, 3)$. Find the coordinates of vertex D. $(8, -5)$

6. Write a two-column proof.
    Given: *RSTU* is a parallelogram.
    Prove: $\triangle RSU \cong \triangle TUS$

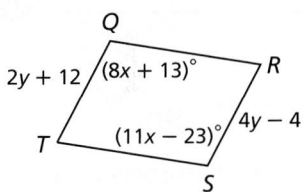

    1. *RSTU* is a $\square$. (Given)
    2. $\overline{RU} \cong \overline{TS}$, $\overline{RS} \cong \overline{UT}$ ($\square \rightarrow$ opp. sides $\cong$)
    3. $\angle R \cong \angle T$ ($\square \rightarrow$ opp. $\angle$ $\cong$)
    4. $\triangle RSU \cong \triangle TUS$ (SAS)

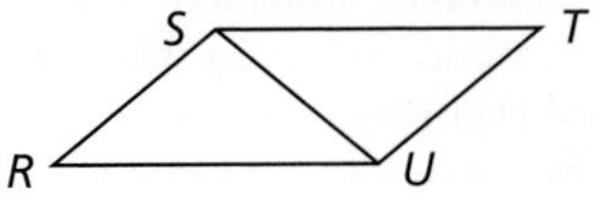

Also available on transparency

Objective: Prove that a given quadrilateral is a parallelogram.

Geometry Lab
In *Texas Lab Manual*

Online Edition
Tutorial Videos

Countdown to TAKS Week 13

Power Presentations
with PowerPoint®

Warm Up

Justify each statement.

1. $\overline{QR} \cong \overline{QR}$ Reflex. Prop. of $\cong$

2. $\ell \parallel m$ Conv. of the Alt. Int. ∡ Thm.

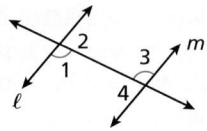

Evaluate each expression for $x = 12$ and $y = 8.5$.

3. $2x + 7$ 31

4. $16x - 9$ 183

5. $(8y + 5)°$ 73°

Also available on transparency

Math Humor

Q: Did you hear about the quadrilateral who wanted to be a parallelogram?

A: Yes, his opposite angles weren't quite up to par.

Geometry TEKS

G.2 Geometric structure*
(A) use constructions to explore attributes of geometric figures ...
(B) ... determine the validity of ... conjectures [about polygons] ...

G.3 Geometric structure*
(B) construct and justify statements about geometric figures ...
(E) use deductive reasoning ...

G.7 Dimensionality and the geometry of location*
(A) use ... coordinate systems ...
(B) use slopes and equations of lines to investigate ... relationships ...
(C) ... use ... length, slope, ...

* Knowledge and Skills See p. 378.

6-3 Conditions for Parallelograms

TEKS G.3.B Geometric structure: construct and justify statements about geometric figures and their properties. Also G.2.A, G.2.B, G.3.E, G.7.A, G.7.B, G.7.C

Objective
Prove that a given quadrilateral is a parallelogram.

Who uses this?
A bird watcher can use a *parallelogram mount* to adjust the height of a pair of binoculars without changing the viewing angle. (See Example 4.)

You have learned to identify the properties of a parallelogram. Now you will be given the properties of a quadrilateral and will have to tell if the quadrilateral is a parallelogram. To do this, you can use the definition of a parallelogram or the conditions below.

Know it!
Note

Remember!
In the converse of a theorem, the hypothesis and conclusion are exchanged.

Theorems   Conditions for Parallelograms

THEOREM	EXAMPLE
6-3-1 If one pair of opposite sides of a quadrilateral are parallel and congruent, then the quadrilateral is a parallelogram. (quad. with pair of opp. sides $\parallel$ and $\cong \rightarrow \square$)	
6-3-2 If both pairs of opposite sides of a quadrilateral are congruent, then the quadrilateral is a parallelogram. (quad. with opp. sides $\cong \rightarrow \square$)	
6-3-3 If both pairs of opposite angles of a quadrilateral are congruent, then the quadrilateral is a parallelogram. (quad. with opp. ∡ $\cong \rightarrow \square$)	

You will prove Theorems 6-3-2 and 6-3-3 in Exercises 26 and 29.

PROOF   Theorem 6-3-1

Given: $\overline{KL} \parallel \overline{MJ}$, $\overline{KL} \cong \overline{MJ}$
Prove: *JKLM* is a parallelogram.

Proof:
It is given that $\overline{KL} \cong \overline{MJ}$. Since $\overline{KL} \parallel \overline{MJ}$, $\angle 1 \cong \angle 2$ by the Alternate Interior Angles Theorem. By the Reflexive Property of Congruence, $\overline{JL} \cong \overline{JL}$. So $\triangle JKL \cong \triangle LMJ$ by SAS. By CPCTC, $\angle 3 \cong \angle 4$, and $\overline{JK} \parallel \overline{LM}$ by the Converse of the Alternate Interior Angles Theorem. Since the opposite sides of *JKLM* are parallel, *JKLM* is a parallelogram by definition.

---

1 Introduce

EXPLORATION

6-3 Conditions for Parallelograms

For this Exploration you will need scissors, a ruler, and several chenille stems.

1. Cut two stems so that they are different lengths. Mark the midpoint of each stem.

2. Place the stems on a sheet of paper. Cross the stems so they intersect at their midpoints. Mark a point on the paper at each endpoint of the stems.

3. Remove the stems and connect the points to form a quadrilateral. What type of quadrilateral does it appear to be?

4. Repeat the process, but arrange the stems so that they intersect at their midpoints at a different angle. Do you get the same result?

5. Repeat Steps 1–4, using stems of different lengths. Do you get the same results?

THINK AND DISCUSS

6. **Explain** how you can use your observations to make a conjecture about quadrilaterals whose diagonals bisect each other.

Motivate

Have students cut two short strips of equal length and two long strips of equal length out of heavy paper. Punch holes through the ends of each and use brads to make a parallelogram. Ask students if they think the figure is always a parallelogram, no matter how it is moved. Explain that they will explore this concept in this lesson.

Explorations and answers are provided in the *Explorations* binder.

The two theorems below can also be used to show that a given quadrilateral is a parallelogram.

Theorems | **Conditions for Parallelograms**

THEOREM	EXAMPLE
6-3-4 If an angle of a quadrilateral is supplementary to both of its consecutive angles, then the quadrilateral is a parallelogram. (quad. with ∠ supp. to cons. ⟂ → ▱)	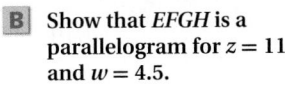
6-3-5 If the diagonals of a quadrilateral bisect each other, then the quadrilateral is a parallelogram. (quad. with diags. bisecting each other → ▱)	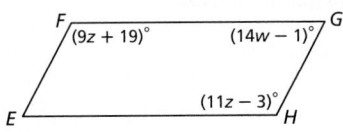

You will prove Theorems 6-3-4 and 6-3-5 in Exercises 27 and 30.

EXAMPLE 1   **Verifying Figures are Parallelograms**

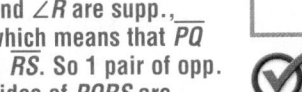

A Show that *ABCD* is a parallelogram for $x = 7$ and $y = 4$.

Step 1 Find *BC* and *DA*.

| $BC = x + 14$ | *Given* | $DA = 3x$ |
| $BC = 7 + 14 = 21$ | *Substitute and simplify.* | $DA = 3x = 3(7) = 21$ |

Step 2 Find *AB* and *CD*.

| $AB = 5y - 4$ | *Given* | $CD = 2y + 8$ |
| $AB = 5(4) - 4 = 16$ | *Substitute and simplify.* | $CD = 2(4) + 8 = 16$ |

Since $BC = DA$ and $AB = CD$, *ABCD* is a parallelogram by Theorem 6-3-2.

B Show that *EFGH* is a parallelogram for $z = 11$ and $w = 4.5$.

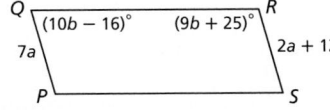

$m\angle F = (9z + 19)^\circ$	*Given*
$m\angle F = [9(11) + 19]^\circ = 118^\circ$	*Substitute 11 for z and simplify.*
$m\angle H = (11z - 3)^\circ$	*Given*
$m\angle H = [11(11) - 3]^\circ = 118^\circ$	*Substitute 11 for z and simplify.*
$m\angle G = (14w - 1)^\circ$	*Given*
$m\angle G = [14(4.5) - 1]^\circ = 62^\circ$	*Substitute 4.5 for w and simplify.*

Since $118^\circ + 62^\circ = 180^\circ$, ∠*G* is supplementary to both ∠*F* and ∠*H*. *EFGH* is a parallelogram by Theorem 6-3-4.

1. $PQ = RS = 16.8$, so $\overline{PQ} \cong \overline{RS}$. $m\angle Q = 74^\circ$, and $m\angle R = 106^\circ$, so ∠*Q* and ∠*R* are supp., which means that $\overline{PQ} \parallel \overline{RS}$. So 1 pair of opp. sides of *PQRS* are ∥ and ≅. By Thm. 6-3-1, *PQRS* is a ▱.

CHECK IT OUT!
1. Show that *PQRS* is a parallelogram for $a = 2.4$ and $b = 9$.

2 Teach

Guided Instruction

Review the properties of a parallelogram. Explain that students will now work with the converse situation; they will determine if a quadrilateral with certain properties is a parallelogram.

Teaching Tip **Reading Math** Encourage students to pay close attention to the key words in each theorem, such as *opposite, parallel,* and *congruent.* Have them write the theorems and highlight these key words.

ENGLISH LANGUAGE LEARNERS

Reaching All Learners
Through Kinesthetic Experience

Have students use raw spaghetti to demonstrate the theorems in the lesson. For example, ask them to try to form a parallelogram with opposite sides that are congruent but not parallel, or vice versa. This should emphasize that in Theorem 6-3-1, the same pair of opposite sides must be congruent *and* parallel.

When students are proving that a figure in the coordinate plane is a parallelogram, advise them to plot the points first so that the order of the vertices will be obvious. This will prevent them from confusing the diagonals with the sides.

Power Presentations
with PowerPoint®

Additional Examples

Example 1

A. Show that *JKLM* is a parallelogram for $a = 3$ and $b = 9$.

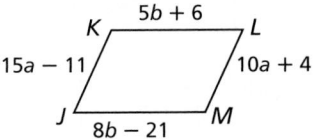

$JK = LM = 34$, and $KL = JM = 51$, so *JKLM* is a ▱ by Thm. 6-3-2.

B. Show that *PQRS* is a parallelogram for $x = 10$ and $y = 6.5$.

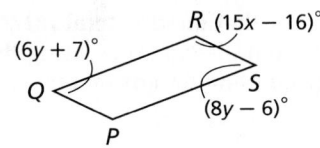

$m\angle Q = m\angle S = 46^\circ$; $m\angle R = 134^\circ$. Since $134^\circ + 46^\circ = 180^\circ$, ∠*R* is supp. to ∠*Q* and ∠*S*. *PQRS* is a ▱ by Thm. 6-3-4.

Also available on transparency

INTERVENTION
Questioning Strategies

EXAMPLE 1

• How is Theorem 6-3-2 used to show that the given quadrilateral is a parallelogram in Example 1A?

• How is Theorem 6-3-4 used to show that the given quadrilateral is a parallelogram in Example 1B?

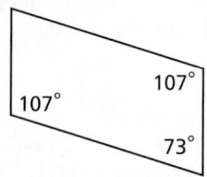

Additional Examples

Example 2

Determine if each quadrilateral must be a parallelogram. Justify your answer.

A.

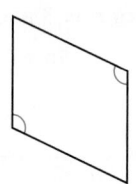

107°
107°
73°

Yes; the 73° ∠ is supp. to both of its cons. ∠. By Thm. 6-3-4, the quad. is a ▱.

B.

No; 1 pair of opp. ∠ are ≅. The other pair are not. The conditions for a ▱ are not met.

Example 3

Show that quadrilateral JKLM is a parallelogram by using the given definition or theorem.

A. $J(-1, -6)$, $K(-4, -1)$, $L(4, 5)$, $M(7, 0)$; definition of parallelogram Slope of $\overline{JK}$ = slope of $\overline{LM} = -\frac{5}{3}$; slope of $\overline{KL}$ = slope of $\overline{MJ} = \frac{3}{4}$; both pairs of opp. sides are ∥, so JKLM is a ▱ by def.

B. $A(2, 3)$, $B(6, 2)$, $C(5, 0)$, $D(1, 1)$; Theorem 6-3-1 Slope of $\overline{DA}$ = slope of $\overline{BC}$ = 2; $DA = BC = \sqrt{5}$; so $\overline{DA} \parallel \overline{BC}$ and $\overline{DA} \cong \overline{BC}$. By Thm. 6-3-1, ABCD is a ▱.

Also available on transparency

INTERVENTION ◀■▶
Questioning Strategies

EXAMPLE 2

• What conditions must a quadrilateral satisfy to be a parallelogram? Explain.

EXAMPLE 3

• How can you use the diagonals to show that a quadrilateral in the coordinate plane is a parallelogram?

 E X A M P L E 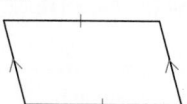 **Applying Conditions for Parallelograms**

Determine if each quadrilateral must be a parallelogram. Justify your answer.

 A

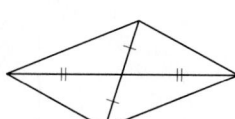 B

No. One pair of opposite sides are parallel. A different pair of opposite sides are congruent. The conditions for a parallelogram are not met.

Yes. The diagonals bisect each other. By Theorem 6-3-5, the quadrilateral is a parallelogram.

2a. Yes; possible answer: the diag. of the quad. forms 2 △. 2 ∠ of 1 △ are ≅ to 2 ∠ of the other, so the third pair of ∠ are ≅ by the Third ∠ Thm. So both pairs of opp. ∠ of the quad. are ≅. By Thm. 6-3-3, the quad. is a ▱.

2b. No; 2 pairs of cons. sides are ≅. None of the sets of conditions for a ▱ are met.

CHECK IT OUT! Determine if each quadrilateral must be a parallelogram. Justify your answer.

2a. 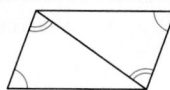   **2b.**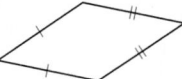

E X A M P L E 3 **Proving Parallelograms in the Coordinate Plane**

Show that quadrilateral ABCD is a parallelogram by using the given definition or theorem.

A $A(-3, 2)$, $B(-2, 7)$, $C(2, 4)$, $D(1, -1)$; definition of parallelogram

Find the slopes of both pairs of opposite sides.

$$\text{slope of } \overline{AB} = \frac{7 - 2}{-2 - (-3)} = \frac{5}{1} = 5$$

$$\text{slope of } \overline{CD} = \frac{-1 - 4}{1 - 2} = \frac{-5}{-1} = 5$$

$$\text{slope of } \overline{BC} = \frac{4 - 7}{2 - (-2)} = \frac{-3}{4} = -\frac{3}{4}$$

$$\text{slope of } \overline{DA} = \frac{2 - (-1)}{-3 - 1} = \frac{3}{-4} = -\frac{3}{4}$$

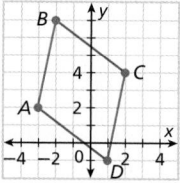

Since both pairs of opposite sides are parallel, ABCD is a parallelogram by definition.

B $F(-4, -2)$, $G(-2, 2)$, $H(4, 3)$, $J(2, -1)$; Theorem 6-3-1

Find the slopes and lengths of one pair of opposite sides.

$$\text{slope of } \overline{GH} = \frac{3 - 2}{4 - (-2)} = \frac{1}{6}$$

$$\text{slope of } \overline{JF} = \frac{-2 - (-1)}{-4 - 2} = \frac{-1}{-6} = \frac{1}{6}$$

$$GH = \sqrt{[4 - (-2)]^2 + (3 - 2)^2} = \sqrt{37}$$

$$JF = \sqrt{(-4 - 2)^2 + [-2 - (-1)]^2} = \sqrt{37}$$

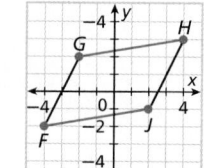

$\overline{GH}$ and $\overline{JF}$ have the same slope, so $\overline{GH} \parallel \overline{JF}$. Since $GH = JF$, $\overline{GH} \cong \overline{JF}$. So by Theorem 6-3-1, FGHJ is a parallelogram.

Helpful Hint

To say that a quadrilateral is a parallelogram *by definition*, you must show that both pairs of opposite sides are parallel.

CHECK IT OUT!
3. Use the definition of a parallelogram to show that the quadrilateral with vertices $K(-3, 0)$, $L(-5, 7)$, $M(3, 5)$, and $N(5, -2)$ is a parallelogram.

You have learned several ways to determine whether a quadrilateral is a parallelogram. You can use the given information about a figure to decide which condition is best to apply.

<table>
<tr><th colspan="2">Conditions for Parallelograms</th></tr>
<tr><td colspan="2">Both pairs of opposite sides are parallel. (definition)</td></tr>
<tr><td colspan="2">One pair of opposite sides are parallel and congruent. (Theorem 6-3-1)</td></tr>
<tr><td colspan="2">Both pairs of opposite sides are congruent. (Theorem 6-3-2)</td></tr>
<tr><td colspan="2">Both pairs of opposite angles are congruent. (Theorem 6-3-3)</td></tr>
<tr><td colspan="2">One angle is supplementary to both of its consecutive angles. (Theorem 6-3-4)</td></tr>
<tr><td colspan="2">The diagonals bisect each other. (Theorem 6-3-5)</td></tr>
</table>

Helpful Hint

To show that a quadrilateral is a parallelogram, you only have to show that it satisfies one of these sets of conditions.

EXAMPLE 4 **Bird-Watching Application**

In the parallelogram mount, there are bolts at P, Q, R, and S such that $PQ = RS$ and $QR = SP$. The frame $PQRS$ moves when you raise or lower the binoculars. Why is $PQRS$ always a parallelogram?

When you move the binoculars, the angle measures change, but PQ, QR, RS, and SP stay the same. So it is always true that $PQ = RS$ and $QR = SP$. Since both pairs of opposite sides of the quadrilateral are congruent, $PQRS$ is always a parallelogram.

 **TEXAS LINK**
Bird-Watching

The westernmost bald eagle nest in Texas is 9 miles north of Llano, where a family of bald eagles can be seen from the side of the highway during their winter nesting season.

 **CHECK IT OUT!**
4. The frame is attached to the tripod at points A and B such that $AB = RS$ and $BR = SA$. So $ABRS$ is also a parallelogram. How does this ensure that the angle of the binoculars stays the same?

THINK AND DISCUSS

1. What do all the theorems in this lesson have in common?
2. How are the theorems in this lesson different from the theorems in Lesson 6-2?
3. **GET ORGANIZED** Copy and complete the graphic organizer. In each box, write one of the six conditions for a parallelogram. Then sketch a parallelogram and label it to show how it meets the condition.

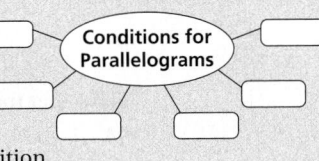

Conditions for Parallelograms

6-3 Conditions for Parallelograms **401**

Power Presentations
with PowerPoint®

Additional Examples

Example 4

The legs of a keyboard tray are connected by a bolt at their midpoints, which allows the tray to be raised or lowered. Why is $PQRS$ always a parallelogram?

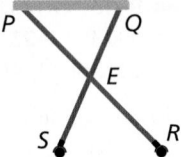

Since the bolt is at the mdpt. of both legs, $PE = ER$ and $SE = EQ$. So the diags. of $PQRS$ bisect each other, and by Thm. 6-3-5, $PQRS$ is a $\square$.

Also available on transparency

INTERVENTION
Questioning Strategies

EXAMPLE 4

- How could you prove that the opposite angles of $PQRS$ are congruent?
- Why are parallelograms useful in mechanical structures?

Answers to Check It Out!

3. Possible answer: slope of $\overline{KL}$ = slope of $\overline{MN}$ = $-\frac{7}{2}$; slope of $\overline{LM}$ = slope of $\overline{NK}$ = $-\frac{1}{4}$; both pairs of opp. sides have the same slope, so $\overline{KL} \parallel \overline{MN}$ and $\overline{LM} \parallel \overline{NK}$; by def., $KLMN$ is a $\square$.

4. Possible answer: Since $ABRS$ is a $\square$, it is always true that $\overline{AB} \parallel \overline{RS}$. Since $\overline{AB}$ stays vert., $\overline{RS}$ also remains vert. no matter how the frame is adjusted. Therefore the viewing $\angle$ never changes.

---

3 Close

Summarize

Ask students the following: "A pair of opposite angles in a quadrilateral each measure 103°. Can you conclude that this quadrilateral is a parallelogram? Explain why or draw a counterexample." No, since only 1 pair of opp. $\angle$ are $\cong$. Possible counterexample:

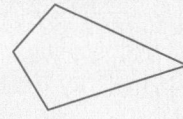

ONGOING ASSESSMENT
and INTERVENTION

Diagnose Before the Lesson
6-3 Warm Up, TE p. 398

Monitor During the Lesson
Check It Out! Exercises, SE pp. 399–401
Questioning Strategies, TE pp. 399–401

Assess After the Lesson
6-3 Lesson Quiz, TE p. 405
Alternative Assessment, TE p. 405

Answers to Think and Discuss

1. Possible answer: The conclusion of each thm. is "The quad. is a $\square$."

2. Possible answer: In Lesson 6-2, "A quad. is a $\square$" is the hypothesis of each thm. rather than the conclusion.

3. See p. A5.

Lesson 6-3 **401**

6-3 **Exercises**

6-3 **Exercises**

go.hrw.com/Geo/TX
Homework Help Online
KEYWORD: MG7 6-3
Parent Resources Online
KEYWORD: MG7 Parent

Assignment Guide

Assign *Guided Practice* exercises as necessary.

If you finished Examples **1–2**
  Basic 9–13, 17–20, 26, 27
  Average 9–13, 17–23, 26, 29
  Advanced 9–13, 17–23, 25–27, 29, 30, 33, 40

If you finished Examples **1–4**
  Basic 9–20, 26, 27, 34–37, 41–49
  Average 9–23, 24–32 even, 33–38, 41–49
  Advanced 9–16, 18, 20–49

Homework Quick Check
Quickly check key concepts.
Exercises: 10, 12, 14, 16, 18, 20

Answers

1. $FJ = HJ = 10$, so $\overline{FJ} \cong \overline{HJ}$. Thus $\overline{EG}$ bisects $\overline{FH}$. $EJ = GJ = 18$, so $\overline{EJ} \cong \overline{GJ}$. Thus $\overline{FH}$ bisects $\overline{EG}$. So the diags. of *EFGH* bisect each other. By Thm. 6-3-5, *EFGH* is a ▱.

2. $m\angle L = m\angle Q = 106°$, and $m\angle P = 74°$. So $\angle P$ is supp. to $\angle L$ and to $\angle Q$. So 1 ∠ of *KLPQ* is supp. to both of its cons. ∡. By Thm. 6-3-4, *KLPQ* is a ▱.

3. Both pairs of opp. ∡ of the quad. are ≅. By Thm. 6-3-3, the quad. is a ▱.

4. 1 pair of opp. sides of the quad. are ≅. 1 diag. is bisected by the other diag. None of the conditions for a ▱ are met.

▼TAKS Practice

Grades 9–11	Exercises
Obj. 2	20–23, 41–43, 46–49
Obj. 6	25
Obj. 7	36, 37, 39

GUIDED PRACTICE

SEE EXAMPLE **1**
p. 399

1. Show that *EFGH* is a parallelogram for $s = 5$ and $t = 6$.

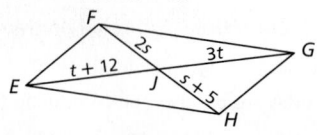

2. Show that *KLPQ* is a parallelogram for $m = 14$ and $n = 12.5$.

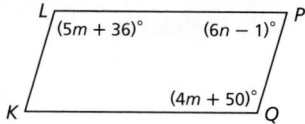

SEE EXAMPLE **2**
p. 400

Determine if each quadrilateral must be a parallelogram. Justify your answer.

3.  yes

4. 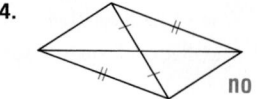 no

5. 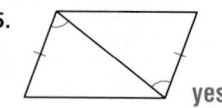 yes

SEE EXAMPLE **3**
p. 400

Show that the quadrilateral with the given vertices is a parallelogram.

6. $W(-5, -2)$, $X(-3, 3)$, $Y(3, 5)$, $Z(1, 0)$

7. $R(-1, -5)$, $S(-2, -1)$, $T(4, -1)$, $U(5, -5)$

SEE EXAMPLE **4**
p. 401

8. **Navigation** A parallel rule can be used to plot a course on a navigation chart. The tool is made of two rulers connected at hinges to two congruent crossbars $\overline{AD}$ and $\overline{BC}$. You place the edge of one ruler on your desired course and then move the second ruler over the compass rose on the chart to read the bearing for your course. If $\overline{AD} \parallel \overline{BC}$, why is $\overline{AB}$ always parallel to $\overline{CD}$?

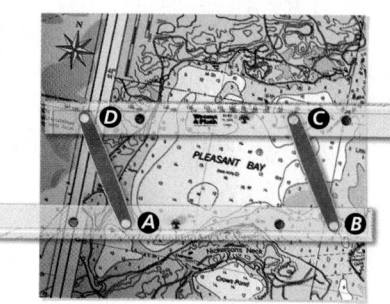

PRACTICE AND PROBLEM SOLVING

Independent Practice
For Exercises	See Example
9–10	1
11–13	2
14–15	3
16	4

TEKS ✈ TAKS
Skills Practice p. S14
Application Practice p. S33

9. Show that *BCGH* is a parallelogram for $x = 3.2$ and $y = 7$.

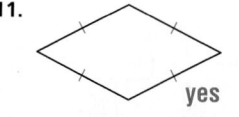

10. Show that *TUVW* is a parallelogram for $a = 19.5$ and $b = 22$.

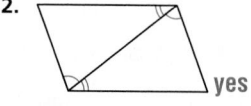

Determine if each quadrilateral must be a parallelogram. Justify your answer.

11. 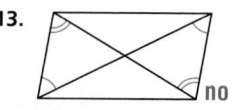 yes

12. 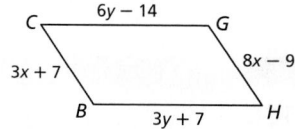 yes

13. 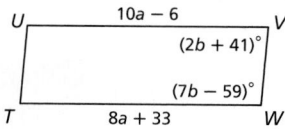 no

Show that the quadrilateral with the given vertices is a parallelogram.

14. $J(-1, 0)$, $K(-3, 7)$, $L(2, 6)$, $M(4, -1)$

15. $P(-8, -4)$, $Q(-5, 1)$, $R(1, -5)$, $S(-2, -10)$

5. Possible answer: A pair of alt. int. ∡ are ≅, so 1 pair of opp. sides are ∥. The same pair of opp. sides are ≅. By Thm. 6-3-1, the quad. is a ▱.

6. Possible answer: slope of $\overline{WX}$ = slope of $\overline{YZ} = \frac{5}{2}$; slope of $\overline{XY}$ = slope of $\overline{ZW} = \frac{1}{3}$; both pairs of opp. sides have the same slope, so $\overline{WX} \parallel \overline{YZ}$, and $\overline{XY} \parallel \overline{ZW}$; by def., *WXYZ* is a ▱.

7. Possible answer: slope of $\overline{ST}$ = slope of $\overline{UR} = 0$; $\overline{ST}$ and $\overline{UR}$ have the same slope, so $\overline{ST} \parallel \overline{UR}$; $ST = UR = 6$; 1 pair of opp. sides are ∥ and ≅; by Thm. 6-3-1, *RSTU* is a ▱.

8. Possible answer: $\overline{BC}$ and $\overline{AD}$ are opp. sides of quad. *ABCD*. It is given that $\overline{AD} \parallel \overline{BC}$ and $\overline{AD} \cong \overline{BC}$. By Thm. 6-3-1, if 1 pair of opp. sides of a quad. are ∥ and ≅, then the quad. is a ▱. So *ABCD* is a ▱. By the def. of a ▱, both pairs of opp. sides are ∥, so $\overline{AB}$ is always ∥ to $\overline{CD}$.

9. $BC = GH = 16.6$, so $\overline{BC} \cong \overline{GH}$. $CG = HB = 28$, so $\overline{CG} \cong \overline{HB}$. Since both pairs of opp. sides of *BCGH* are ≅, *BCGH* is a ▱ by Thm. 6-3-2.

10. $UV = WT = 189$, so $\overline{UV} \cong \overline{WT}$. $m\angle V = 85°$, and $m\angle W = 95°$, so $\angle V$ is supp. to $\angle W$. Therefore $\overline{UV} \parallel \overline{WT}$. By Thm. 6-3-1, *TUVW* is a ▱.

18. No; you are only given the measures of the 4 ∡ formed by the intersecting diags. of the quad. None of the sets of conditions for a ▱ are met.

19. Yes; the diags. of the quad. bisect each other. By Thm. 6-3-5, the quad. is a ▱.

16. Design The toolbox has cantilever trays that pull away from the box so that you can reach the items beneath them. Two congruent brackets connect each tray to the box. Given that $AD = BC$, how do the brackets $\overline{AB}$ and $\overline{CD}$ keep the tray horizontal?

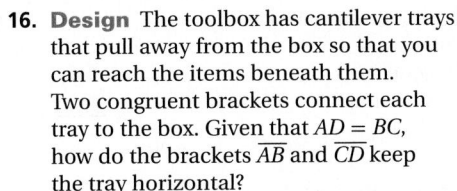

Determine if each quadrilateral must be a parallelogram. Justify your answer.

17. 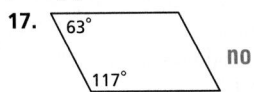 no   **18.** 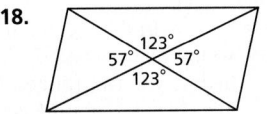   **19.**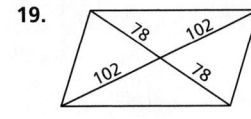

x/y Algebra Find the values of a and b that would make the quadrilateral a parallelogram.

20.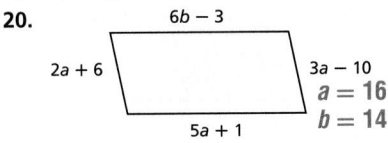

21. 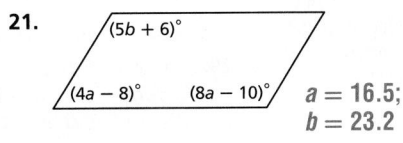 $a = 16.5$; $b = 23.2$

20. $a = 16$; $b = 14$

22. 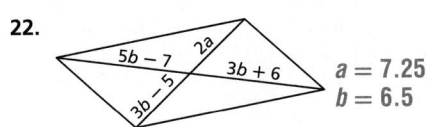 $a = 7.25$; $b = 6.5$

23. 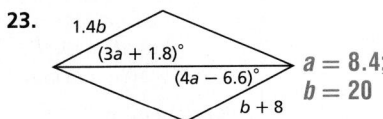 $a = 8.4$; $b = 20$

24. Critical Thinking Draw a quadrilateral that has congruent diagonals but is not a parallelogram. What can you conclude about using congruent diagonals as a condition for a parallelogram?

25. Possible answer: The red and green △ are isosc. rt. △, so the measure of each acute ∠ of the △ is 45°. Each of the smaller ∡ of the yellow stripe is comp. to 1 of the acute ∡ of the rt. △, so the measure of each of the smaller ∡ of the yellow stripe is 90° − 45° = 45°. Each of the larger ∡ of the yellow stripe is supp. to 1 of the acute ∡ of the rt. △, so the measure of each of the larger ∡ of the yellow stripe is 180° − 45° = 135°. So the yellow stripe is a quad. in which both pairs of opp. ∡ are ≅. By Thm. 6-3-3, the shape of the yellow stripe is a ▱.

25. Social Studies The angles at the corners of the flag of the Republic of the Congo are right angles. The red and green triangles are congruent isosceles right triangles. Why is the shape of the yellow stripe a parallelogram?

26. Complete the two-column proof of Theorem 6-3-2 by filling in the blanks.

Given: $\overline{AB} \cong \overline{CD}$, $\overline{BC} \cong \overline{DA}$

Prove: $ABCD$ is a parallelogram.

Proof:

Statements	Reasons
1. $\overline{AB} \cong \overline{CD}$, $\overline{BC} \cong \overline{DA}$	1. Given
2. $\overline{BD} \cong \overline{BD}$	2. a. __?__
3. $\triangle DAB \cong$ **b.** __?__ $\triangle BCD$	3. c. __?__ SSS
4. $\angle 1 \cong$ **d.** __?__ , $\angle 4 \cong$ **e.** __?__	4. CPCTC
5. $\overline{AB} \parallel \overline{CD}$, $\overline{BC} \parallel \overline{DA}$ **d.** $\angle 3$	5. f. __?__
6. $ABCD$ is a parallelogram. **e.** $\angle 2$	6. g. __?__ Def. of ▱

a. Reflex. Prop. of ≅

f. Conv. of Alt. Int. ∡ Thm.

6-3 Conditions for Parallelograms   **403**

Answers

11. All the sides are ≅ to each other. So both pairs of opp. sides are ≅. By Thm. 6-3-2, the quad. is a ▱.

12. Each pair of ≅ ∡ is a pair of alt. int. ∡. So both pairs of opp. sides of the quad. are ∥. The quad. is a ▱ by def.

13. Each pair of ≅ ∡ is a pair of alt. int. ∡. Each pair indicates that the same set of opp. sides of the quad. are ∥. If only 1 set of opp. sides are ∥, you cannot conclude that the quad. is a ▱.

14. Possible answer: slope of $\overline{JK}$ = slope of $\overline{LM} = -\frac{7}{2}$; slope of $\overline{KL}$ = slope of $\overline{MJ} = -\frac{1}{5}$; both pairs of opp. sides have the same slope, so $\overline{JK} \parallel \overline{LM}$ and $\overline{KL} \parallel \overline{MJ}$; by def., $JKLM$ is a ▱.

15. Possible answer: slope of $\overline{PQ}$ = slope of $\overline{RS} = \frac{5}{3}$; $\overline{PQ}$ and $\overline{RS}$ have the same slope, so $\overline{PQ} \parallel \overline{RS}$; $PQ = RS = \sqrt{34}$; 1 pair of opp. sides are ∥ and ≅; by Thm. 6-3-1, $PQRS$ is a ▱.

Teaching Tip   **Auditory** For **Exercises 11–13** and **17–19,** ask students to state the properties represented by each diagram. Then state the six conditions for parallelograms and have the students decide if any of these are met.

Answers

16. Possible answer: The brackets are always the same length, so it is always true that $AB = CD$. The bolts are always the same distance apart, so it is always true that $BC = DA$. By Thm. 6-3-2, $ABCD$ is always a ▱. The side $\overline{AD}$ stays horiz. no matter how you move the tray. Since $\overline{BC} \parallel \overline{AD}$, $\overline{BC}$ stays horiz. Since $\overline{BC}$ holds the tray in position, the tray will stay horiz. no matter how it is moved.

17. The given ∠ measures only indicate that 1 ∠ of the quad. is supp. to 1 of its cons. ∡. By Thm. 6-3-4, you must know that 1 ∠ is supp. to both of its cons. ∡ in order to conclude that the quad. is a ▱.

24. Possible answer:

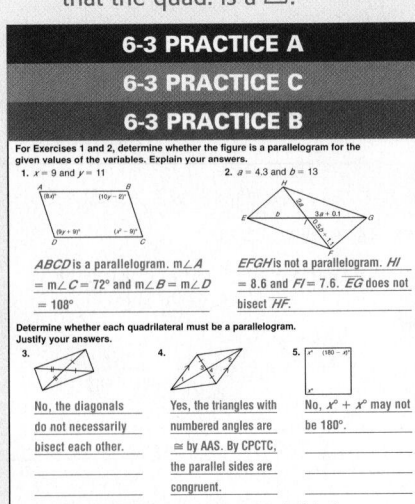

If the diags. of a quad. are ≅, you cannot necessarily conclude that the quad. is a ▱.

6-3 PRACTICE A

6-3 PRACTICE C

6-3 PRACTICE B

For Exercises 1 and 2, determine whether the figure is a parallelogram for the given values of the variables. Explain your answers.

1. $x = 9$ and $y = 11$ **2.** $a = 4.3$ and $b = 13$

$ABCD$ is a parallelogram. m∠A = m∠C = 72° and m∠B = m∠D = 108°

$EFGH$ is not a parallelogram. HI = 8.6 and FI = 7.6. $\overline{EG}$ does not bisect $\overline{HF}$.

Determine whether each quadrilateral must be a parallelogram. Justify your answers.

3. No, the diagonals do not necessarily bisect each other.

4. Yes, the triangles with numbered angles are ≅ by AAS. By CPCTC, the parallel sides are congruent.

5. No, $x° + x°$ may not be 180°.

Use the given method to determine whether the quadrilateral with the given vertices is a parallelogram.

6. Find the slopes of all four sides: $J(-4, -1)$, $K(-7, -4)$, $L(2, -10)$, $M(5, -7)$

$JKLM$ is a parallelogram.

7. Find the lengths of all four sides: $P(2, 2)$, $Q(1, -3)$, $R(-4, 2)$, $S(-3, 7)$

$PQRS$ is a parallelogram.

8. Find the slopes and lengths of one pair of opposite sides:

$T(\frac{3}{2}, -2)$, $U(\frac{3}{2}, 4)$, $V(-\frac{1}{2}, 0)$, $W(-\frac{1}{2}, -6)$

$TUVW$ is a parallelogram.

Lesson 6-3   **403**

MULTI-STEP TAKS PREP **Exercise 34** involves determining if a given quadrilateral is a parallelogram. This exercise prepares students for the Multi-Step TAKS Prep on page 406.

Answers

28. Given: *ABCD* is a ▱. *E* is the mdpt. of $\overline{AB}$, and *F* is the mdpt. of $\overline{DC}$.
Prove: *AEFD* and *EBCF* are ▱.
Proof: Since *ABCD* is a ▱, $\overline{AB} \parallel \overline{CD}$, so $\overline{AE} \parallel \overline{DF}$ and $\overline{EB} \parallel \overline{FC}$. Since opp. sides of a ▱ are ≅, $\overline{AB} \cong \overline{DC}$. It is given that *E* is the mdpt. of $\overline{AB}$ and *F* is the mdpt. of $\overline{DC}$. Because these two segs. are ≅, it follows that $\overline{AE} \cong \overline{EB} \cong \overline{DF} \cong \overline{FC}$. Since $\overline{AE} \parallel \overline{DF}$ and $\overline{AE} \cong \overline{DF}$, *AEFD* is a ▱. Similarly, *EBCF* is a ▱.

29. Possible answer:
1. $\angle E \cong \angle G$, $\angle F \cong \angle H$ (Given)
2. $m\angle E = m\angle G$, $m\angle F = m\angle H$ (Def. of ≅ ∡)
3. $m\angle E + m\angle F + m\angle G + m\angle H = 360°$ (Polygon Sum Thm.)
4. $m\angle E + m\angle F + m\angle E + m\angle F = 360°$, $m\angle E + m\angle H + m\angle E + m\angle H = 360°$ (Subst.)
5. $2m\angle E + 2m\angle F = 360°$, $2m\angle E + 2m\angle H = 360°$ (Distrib. Prop.)
6. $m\angle E + m\angle F = 180°$, $m\angle E + m\angle H = 180°$ (Div. Prop. of =)
7. $\angle E$ is supp. to $\angle F$. $\angle E$ is supp. to $\angle H$. (Def. of supp. ∡)
8. $\overline{EF} \parallel \overline{GH}$, $\overline{FG} \parallel \overline{HE}$ (Conv. of Same-Side Int. ∡ Thm.)
9. *EFGH* is a ▱. (Def. of ▱)

30. 1. $\overline{JL}$ and $\overline{KM}$ bisect each other. (Given)
2. $\overline{JN} \cong \overline{LN}$, $\overline{KN} \cong \overline{MN}$ (Def. of bisect)
3. $\angle JNK \cong \angle LNM$, $\angle KNL \cong \angle MNJ$ (Vert. ∡ Thm.)
4. $\triangle JNK \cong \triangle LNM$, $\triangle KNL \cong \triangle MNJ$ (SAS)
5. $\angle JKN \cong \angle LMN$, $\angle KLN \cong \angle MJN$ (CPCTC)
6. $\overline{JK} \parallel \overline{LM}$, $\overline{KL} \parallel \overline{MJ}$ (Conv. of Alt. Int. ∡ Thm.)
7. *JKLM* is a ▱. (Def. of ▱)

31–33. See p. A21.

34b. Since $\angle S$ and $\angle R$ are supp., $\overline{PS} \parallel \overline{QR}$. Thus *PQRS* is a ▱ by Thm. 6-3-1.
c. Draw $\overline{PR}$. $\angle QPR \cong \angle SRP$ (Alt. Int. ∡ Thm.), and $\overline{PR} \cong \overline{PR}$ (Reflex. Prop. of ≅). So $\triangle QPR \cong \triangle SRP$ by AAS, and $\overline{PQ} \cong \overline{SR}$ (CPCTC). Since $\overline{PQ} \parallel \overline{SR}$ and $\overline{PQ} \cong \overline{SR}$, *PQRS* is a ▱ by Thm. 6-3-1.

37, 38, 40–43, 45. See p. A22.

a. $\angle Q$ **b.** $\angle S$
c. $\overline{SP}$ **d.** $\overline{RS}$
e. ▱

LINK
Measurement
Ancient balance scales had one beam that moved on a single hinge. The stress on the hinge often made the scale imprecise.

27. Complete the paragraph proof of Theorem 6-3-4 by filling in the blanks.
Given: $\angle P$ is supplementary to $\angle Q$.
$\angle P$ is supplementary to $\angle S$.
Prove: *PQRS* is a parallelogram.

Proof:
It is given that $\angle P$ is supplementary to **a.** ___?___ and **b.** ___?___ . By the Converse of the Same-Side Interior Angles Theorem, $\overline{QR} \parallel$ **c.** ___?___ and $\overline{PQ} \parallel$ **d.** ___?___ . So *PQRS* is a parallelogram by the definition of **e.** ___?___ .

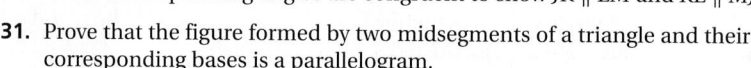

28. Measurement In the eighteenth century, Gilles Personne de Roberval designed a scale with two beams and two hinges. In ▱*ABCD*, *E* is the midpoint of $\overline{AB}$, and *F* is the midpoint of $\overline{CD}$. Write a paragraph proof that *AEFD* and *EBCF* are parallelograms.

Prove each theorem.

29. Theorem 6-3-3
Given: $\angle E \cong \angle G$, $\angle F \cong \angle H$
Prove: *EFGH* is a parallelogram.
Plan: Show that the sum of the interior angles of *EFGH* is 360°. Then apply properties of equality to show that $m\angle E + m\angle F = 180°$ and $m\angle E + m\angle H = 180°$. Then you can conclude that $\overline{EF} \parallel \overline{GH}$ and $\overline{FG} \parallel \overline{HE}$.

30. Theorem 6-3-5
Given: $\overline{JL}$ and $\overline{KM}$ bisect each other.
Prove: *JKLM* is a parallelogram.
Plan: Show that $\triangle JNK \cong \triangle LNM$ and $\triangle KNL \cong \triangle MNJ$. Then use the fact that the corresponding angles are congruent to show $\overline{JK} \parallel \overline{LM}$ and $\overline{KL} \parallel \overline{MJ}$.

31. Prove that the figure formed by two midsegments of a triangle and their corresponding bases is a parallelogram.

32. Write About It Use the theorems from Lessons 6-2 and 6-3 to write three biconditional statements about parallelograms.

33. Construction Explain how you can construct a parallelogram based on the conditions of Theorem 6-3-1. Use your method to construct a parallelogram.

MULTI-STEP TAKS PREP

34. This problem will prepare you for the Multi-Step TAKS Prep on page 406.

A geologist made the following observations while examining this amethyst crystal. Tell whether each set of observations allows the geologist to conclude that *PQRS* is a parallelogram. If so, explain why.
a. $\overline{PQ} \cong \overline{SR}$, and $\overline{PS} \parallel \overline{QR}$. **no**
b. $\angle S$ and $\angle R$ are supplementary, and $\overline{PS} \cong \overline{QR}$.
c. $\angle S \cong \angle Q$, and $\overline{PQ} \parallel \overline{SR}$. **yes**

yes

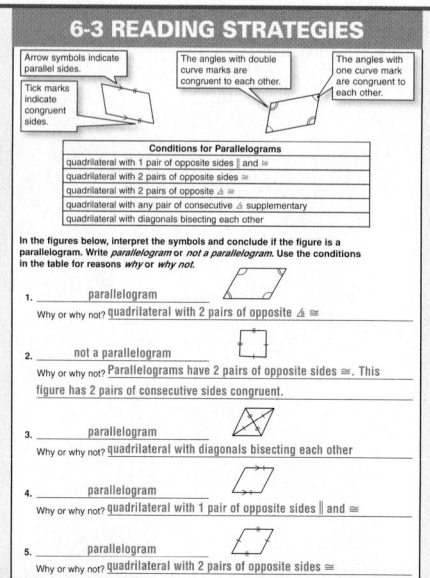

404 Chapter 6 Polygons and Quadrilaterals

6-3 READING STRATEGIES

Arrow symbols indicate parallel sides.
Tick marks indicate congruent sides.
The angles with double curve marks are congruent to each other.
The angles with one curve mark are congruent to each other.

Conditions for Parallelograms
quadrilateral with 1 pair of opposite sides ∥ and ≅
quadrilateral with 2 pairs of opposite sides ≅
quadrilateral with 2 pairs of opposite ∡ ≅
quadrilateral with any pair of consecutive ∡ supplementary
quadrilateral with diagonals bisecting each other

In the figures below, interpret the symbols and conclude if the figure is a parallelogram. Write *parallelogram* or *not a parallelogram*. Use the conditions in the table for reasons *why* or *why not*.

1. ___parallelogram___
Why or why not? quadrilateral with 2 pairs of opposite ∡ ≅

2. ___not a parallelogram___
Why or why not? Parallelograms have 2 pairs of opposite sides ≅. This figure has 2 pairs of consecutive sides congruent.

3. ___parallelogram___
Why or why not? quadrilateral with diagonals bisecting each other

4. ___parallelogram___
Why or why not? quadrilateral with 1 pair of opposite sides ∥ and ≅

5. ___parallelogram___
Why or why not? quadrilateral with 2 pairs of opposite sides ≅

6-3 RETEACH

You can use the following conditions to determine whether a quadrilateral such as *PQRS* is a parallelogram.

Conditions for Parallelograms

$QR \parallel SP$ $QR \cong SP$	$QR \cong SP$ $PQ \cong RS$
If one pair of opposite sides is ∥ and ≅, then *PQRS* is a parallelogram.	If both pairs of opposite sides are ≅, then *PQRS* is a parallelogram.
$\angle P \cong \angle R$ $\angle Q \cong \angle S$	$PT \cong RT$ $QT \cong ST$
If both pairs of opposite angles are ≅, then *PQRS* is a parallelogram.	If the diagonals bisect each other, then *PQRS* is a parallelogram.

A quadrilateral is also a parallelogram if one of the angles is supplementary to both of its consecutive angles.
$65° + 115° = 180°$, so $\angle A$ is supplementary to $\angle B$ and $\angle D$.
Therefore, *ABCD* is a parallelogram.

Show that each quadrilateral is a parallelogram for the given values. Explain.

1. Given: $x = 9$ and $y = 4$

$QR = ST = 12$; $RS = TQ = 16$; both pairs of opp. sides are ≅.

2. Given: $w = 3$ and $z = 31$

$DE = FC = 10$; $m\angle E = 118°$ and $m\angle F = 62°$, so $\angle E$, $\angle F$ are supp. and $\overline{DE} \parallel \overline{FC}$; one pair of opposite sides are ∥ and ≅.

404 Chapter 6

35. What additional information would allow you to conclude that *WXYZ* is a parallelogram?

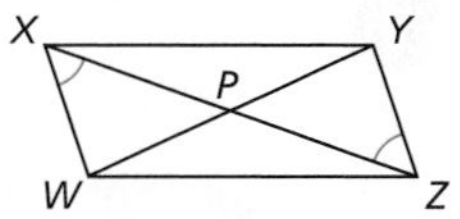

Ⓐ $\overline{XY} \cong \overline{ZW}$ Ⓒ $\overline{WY} \cong \overline{WZ}$

Ⓑ $\overline{WX} \cong \overline{YZ}$ Ⓓ $\angle XWY \cong \angle ZYW$

36. Which could be the coordinates of the fourth vertex of $\square ABCD$ with $A(-1, -1)$, $B(1, 3)$, and $C(6, 1)$?

Ⓕ $D(8, 5)$ Ⓖ $D(4, -3)$ Ⓗ $D(13, 3)$ Ⓘ $D(3, 7)$

37. Short Response The vertices of quadrilateral *RSTV* are $R(-5, 0)$, $S(-1, 3)$, $T(5, 1)$, and $V(2, -2)$. Is *RSTV* a parallelogram? Justify your answer. no

CHALLENGE AND EXTEND

 38. Write About It As the upper platform of the movable staircase is raised and lowered, the height of each step changes. How does the upper platform remain parallel to the ground?

$(3, 1); (-6, -3.5)$ **39. Multi-Step** The diagonals of a parallelogram intersect at $(-2, 1.5)$. Two vertices are located at $(-7, 2)$ and $(2, 6.5)$. Find the coordinates of the other two vertices.

40. Given: *D* is the midpoint of $\overline{AC}$, and *E* is the midpoint of $\overline{BC}$.

Prove: $\overline{DE} \parallel \overline{AB}$, $DE = \frac{1}{2}AB$

(*Hint:* Extend $\overline{DE}$ to form $\overline{DF}$ so that $\overline{EF} \cong \overline{DE}$. Then show that *DFBA* is a parallelogram.)

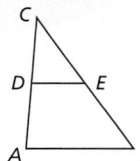

SPIRAL REVIEW

Complete a table of values for each function. Use the domain $\{-5, -2, 0, 0.5\}$. (*Previous course*)

41. $f(x) = 7x - 3$ **42.** $f(x) = \dfrac{x + 2}{2}$ **43.** $f(x) = 3x^2 + 2$

Use SAS to explain why each pair of triangles are congruent. (*Lesson 4-4*)

44. $\triangle ABD \cong \triangle CDB$ **45.** $\triangle TUW \cong \triangle VUW$

44. It is given that $\overline{BC} \cong \overline{DA}$ and that $\angle DBC \cong \angle BDA$. By the Reflex. Prop. of $\cong$, $\overline{DB} \cong \overline{DB}$. Therefore, $\triangle ABD \cong \triangle CDB$ by SAS.

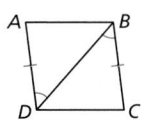

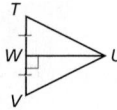

For $\square JKLM$, find each measure. (*Lesson 6-2*)

46. *NM* 14   **47.** *LM* 12

48. *JL* 16   **49.** *JK* 12

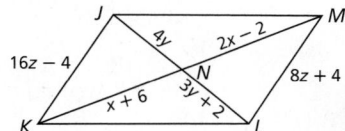

Right margin

Journal

Have students describe how to use the measures of the sides of a quadrilateral to determine if it is a parallelogram.

ALTERNATIVE ASSESSMENT

Have pairs of students use straws or spaghetti to create parallelograms by using three different methods (e.g., opposite sides are congruent, or diagonals bisect each other). Have students use the theorems from the lesson to explain why each construction is valid.

Power Presentations with PowerPoint®

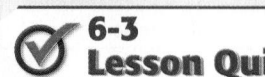

6-3 Lesson Quiz

1. Show that *JKLM* is a parallelogram for $a = 4$ and $b = 5$.

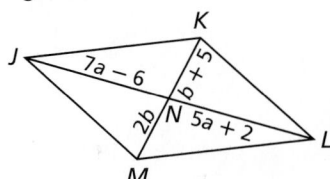

$JN = LN = 22$; $KN = MN = 10$; so *JKLM* is a $\square$ by Thm. 6-3-5.

2. Determine if *QWRT* must be a parallelogram. Justify your answer.

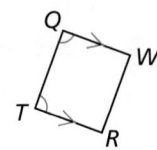

No; 1 pair of cons. $\angle$ are $\cong$, and 1 pair of opp. sides are $\parallel$. The conditions for a $\square$ are not met.

3. Show that the quadrilateral with vertices $E(-1, 5)$, $F(2, 4)$, $G(0, -3)$, and $H(-3, -2)$ is a parallelogram. Slope of $\overline{EF}$ = slope of $\overline{GH}$ = $-\frac{1}{3}$; $EF = GH = \sqrt{10}$; since 1 pair of opp. sides are $\parallel$ and $\cong$, *EFGH* is a $\square$ by Thm. 6-3-1.

Also available on transparency

Bottom panels

6-3 PROBLEM SOLVING

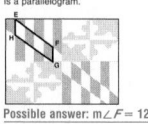

Use the diagram for Exercises 1 and 2. A *pantograph* is a drawing instrument used to magnify figures.

1. If you drag the point at *P* so that the angle measures change, will *LMNP* continue to be a parallelogram? Explain.

Yes; both pairs of opposite sides of quadrilateral *LMNP* remain congruent, so *LMNP* is always a $\square$.

2. If you drag the point at *P* so that m∠*LMN* = 56°, what will be the measure of ∠*QLP*?

56°

3. In the state flag of Maryland, m∠*G* = 60° and m∠*H* = 120°. Name one more condition that would allow you to conclude that *EFGH* is a parallelogram.

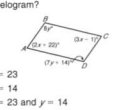

Possible answer: m∠*F* = 120°

4. The graphs of $y = 2x$, $y = 2x - 5$, and $y = -x$ in the coordinate plane contain three sides of a quadrilateral. Give an equation of a line whose graph contains a segment that can complete the quadrilateral to form a parallelogram. Explain.

Possible answer: $y = -x + 1$; both pairs of opposite sides have the same slope, so they are parallel.

Choose the best answer.

5. For which value of *n* is *QRST* a parallelogram?

A 15.5
B 20.6
C 22
D 25

6. Under what conditions must *ABCD* be a parallelogram?

F $x = 23$
G $y = 14$
H $x = 23$ and $y = 14$
J $x = 14$ and $y = 23$

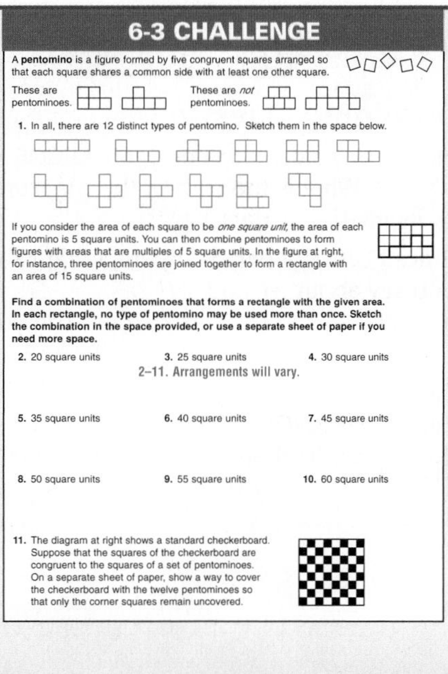

6-3 CHALLENGE

A *pentomino* is a figure formed by five congruent squares arranged so that each square shares a common side with at least one other square.

These are pentominoes.   These are *not* pentominoes.

1. In all, there are 12 distinct types of pentomino. Sketch them in the space below.

If you consider the area of each square to be *one square unit*, the area of each pentomino is 5 square units. You can then combine pentominoes to form figures with areas that are multiples of 5 square units. In the figure at right, for instance, three pentominoes are joined together to form a rectangle with an area of 15 square units.

Find a combination of pentominoes that forms a rectangle with the given area. In each rectangle, no type of pentomino may be used more than once. Sketch the combination in the space provided, or use a separate sheet of paper if you need more space.

2. 20 square units   3. 25 square units   4. 30 square units

2–11. Arrangements will vary.

5. 35 square units   6. 40 square units   7. 45 square units

8. 50 square units   9. 55 square units   10. 60 square units

11. The diagram at right shows a standard checkerboard. Suppose that the squares of the checkerboard are congruent to the squares of a set of pentominoes. On a separate sheet of paper, show a way to cover the checkerboard with the twelve pentominoes so that only the corner squares remain uncovered.

MULTI-STEP TAKS PREP

Organizer

Objective: Assess students' ability to apply concepts and skills in Lessons 6-1 through 6-3 in a real-world format.

PREMIER **Online Edition**

Resources

 Geometry Assessments
www.mathtekstoolkit.org

Problem	Text Reference
1	Lesson 6-1
2	Lesson 6-2
3	Lesson 6-3

Answers

2. 85°; since *FGHJ* is a ▱, ∠F and ∠J are supp. So 9x − 13 + 7x + 1 = 180, and x = 12. Thus m∠J = (7)12 + 1 = 85°. Opp. ∠ are ≅, so m∠G = 85°.

Polygons and Parallelograms

Crystal Clear A crystal is a mineral formation that has polygonal faces. Geologists classify crystals based on the types of polygons that the faces form.

1. What type of polygon is *ABCDE* in the fluorite crystal? Given that $\overline{AE} \parallel \overline{CD}$, m∠B = 120°, m∠E = 65°, and ∠C ≅ ∠D, find m∠A. **pentagon; 125°**

2. The pink crystals are called rhodochrosite. The face *FGHJ* is a parallelogram. Given that m∠F = (9x − 13)° and m∠J = (7x + 1)°, find m∠G. Explain how you found this angle measure.

3. While studying the amazonite crystal, a geologist found that $\overline{MN} \cong \overline{QP}$ and ∠NQP ≅ ∠QNM. Can the geologist conclude that *MNPQ* is a parallelogram? Why or why not? Justify your answer.

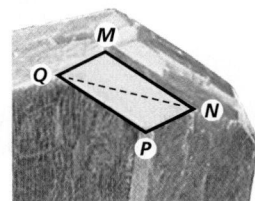

3. Yes; ∠NQP ≅ ∠QNM, so $\overline{MN} \parallel \overline{QP}$ by the Conv. of the Alt. Int. ∠ Thm. So *MNPQ* is a ▱ by Thm. 6-3-1.

⭠TAKS *Practice*

Grades 9–11	Problems
Obj. 2	1, 2
Obj. 6	1, 2
Obj. 10	2

INTERVENTION ⬅ ➡

Scaffolding Questions

1. How many sides does polygon *ABCDE* have? 5 What is the sum of the measures of its interior angles? **540°**

2. Since *FGHJ* is a parallelogram, what can you say about ∠F and ∠J? ∠F and ∠J are supp. Once you know m∠J, how can you find m∠G? ∠J and ∠G are ≅, so m∠G = m∠J.

3. Given that ∠NQP ≅ ∠QNM , what can you conclude about $\overline{MN}$ and $\overline{QP}$? Explain. They are ∥ by the Conv. of the Alt. Int. ∠ Thm.

Extension

In **Problem 3**, suppose that $\overline{MN} \cong \overline{QP}$ and $\overline{MQ} \parallel \overline{NP}$. Can you conclude that *MNPQ* is a parallelogram? If so, explain why. If not, draw a counterexample. no

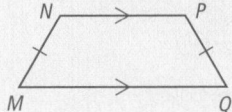

READY TO GO ON?

SECTION 6A

Quiz for Lessons 6-1 Through 6-3

6-1 Properties and Attributes of Polygons

Tell whether each figure is a polygon. If it is a polygon, name it by the number of its sides.

1. 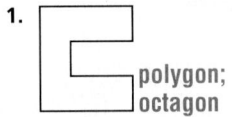 polygon; octagon

2. 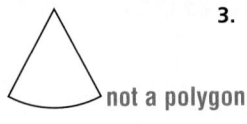 not a polygon

3. 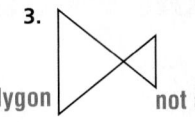 not a polygon

4. 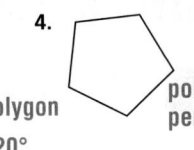 polygon; pentagon

5. Find the sum of the interior angle measures of a convex 16-gon. 2520°

6. The surface of a trampoline is in the shape of a regular hexagon. Find the measure of each interior angle of the trampoline. 120°

7. A park in the shape of quadrilateral *PQRS* is bordered by four sidewalks. Find the measure of each exterior angle of the park.

8. Find the measure of each exterior angle of a regular decagon. 36°

7. 126°; 72°; 63°; 99°

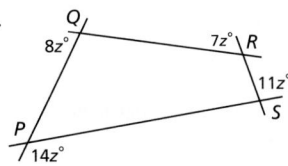

6-2 Properties of Parallelograms

A pantograph is used to copy drawings. Its legs form a parallelogram. In ▱*JKLM*, *LM* = 17 cm, *KN* = 13.5 cm, and m∠*KJM* = 102°. Find each measure.

9. *KM* 27 cm **10.** *KJ* 17 cm **11.** *MN* 13.5 cm

12. m∠*JKL* 78° **13.** m∠*JML* 78° **14.** m∠*KLM* 102°

15. Three vertices of ▱*ABCD* are *A*(−3, 1), *B*(5, 7), and *C*(6, 2). Find the coordinates of vertex *D*. (−2, −4)

WXYZ is a parallelogram. Find each measure.

16. *WX* 11 **17.** *YZ* 11

18. m∠*X* 81° **19.** m∠*W* 99°

X (5a − 39)° Y
6b − 7   10b − 19
(3a + 27)°
W   Z

6-3 Conditions for Parallelograms

20. Show that *RSTV* is a parallelogram for *x* = 6 and *y* = 4.5.

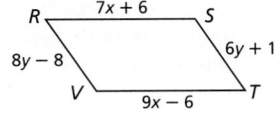
R 7x + 6 S
8y − 8   6y + 1
V 9x − 6 T

21. Show that *GHJK* is a parallelogram for *m* = 12 and *n* = 9.5.

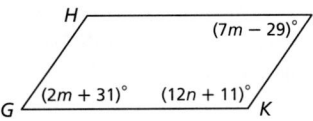
H   (7m − 29)° J
(2m + 31)° (12n + 11)°
G   K

Determine if each quadrilateral must be a parallelogram. Justify your answer.

22.  yes

23. 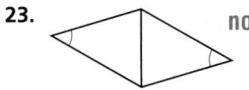 no

24. 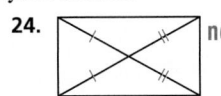 no

25. Show that a quadrilateral with vertices *C*(−9, 4), *D*(−4, 8), *E*(2, 6), and *F*(−3, 2) is a parallelogram.

SECTION 6A

READY TO GO ON?

Organizer

Objective: Assess students' mastery of concepts and skills in Lessons 6-1 through 6-3.

Resources

Assessment Resources
  Section 6A Quiz

Test & Practice Generator
One-Stop Planner®

INTERVENTION

Resources

Ready to Go On? Intervention and Enrichment Worksheets

Ready to Go On? CD-ROM

Ready to Go On? Online

my.hrw.com

Answers
20–25. See p. A22.

READY TO GO ON?
Diagnose and Prescribe

NO INTERVENE

YES ENRICH

READY TO GO ON? Intervention, Section 6A			
Ready to Go On? Intervention	**Worksheets**	**CD-ROM**	**Online**
Lesson 6-1	6-1 Intervention	Activity 6-1	Diagnose and Prescribe Online
Lesson 6-2	6-2 Intervention	Activity 6-2	
Lesson 6-3	6-3 Intervention	Activity 6-3	

READY TO GO ON? Enrichment, Section 6A

Worksheets
CD-ROM
Online

Other Special Quadrilaterals

 ## One-Minute Section Planner

Lesson	Lab Resources	Materials
Lesson 6-4 Properties of Special Parallelograms • Prove and apply properties of rectangles, rhombuses, and squares. • Use properties of rectangles, rhombuses, and squares to solve problems. ☑ Exit Level TAKS ☑ ACT ☐ SAT ☐ SAT Subject Tests	**Texas Lab Manual** 6-4 Geometry Lab	**Optional** toothpicks, compass (MK), straightedge (MK), magazine photos of rectangles, rhombuses, and squares, paper strips, brads, construction paper, scissors, protractor (MK), ruler (MK)
6-5 Technology Lab Predict Conditions for Special Parallelograms • Use geometry software to predict the conditions for rectangles, rhombuses, and squares. ☐ Exit Level TAKS ☐ ACT ☐ SAT ☐ SAT Subject Tests		**Required** geometry software
Lesson 6-5 Conditions for Special Parallelograms • Prove that a given quadrilateral is a rectangle, rhombus, or square. ☐ Exit Level TAKS ☑ ACT ☐ SAT ☐ SAT Subject Tests	**Texas Lab Manual** 6-5 Geometry Lab	**Optional** compass (MK), straightedge (MK)
6-6 Technology Lab Explore Isosceles Trapezoids • Use geometry software to investigate the properties and conditions of an isosceles trapezoid. ☐ Exit Level TAKS ☑ ACT ☑ SAT ☑ SAT Subject Tests		**Required** geometry software
Lesson 6-6 Properties of Kites and Trapezoids • Use properties of kites to solve problems. • Use properties of trapezoids to solve problems. ☑ Exit Level TAKS ☑ ACT ☑ SAT ☑ SAT Subject Tests	**Texas Lab Manual** 6-6 Geometry Lab 6-6 Technology Lab	**Optional** patty paper, compass (MK), straightedge (MK), geometry software, colored pencils, protractor (MK)

MK = *Manipulatives Kit*

Section Overview

Rectangles, Rhombuses, and Squares

Lessons 6-4, 6-5

 Why? Professionals such as engineers and architects use rectangles, rhombuses, and squares for structural purposes.

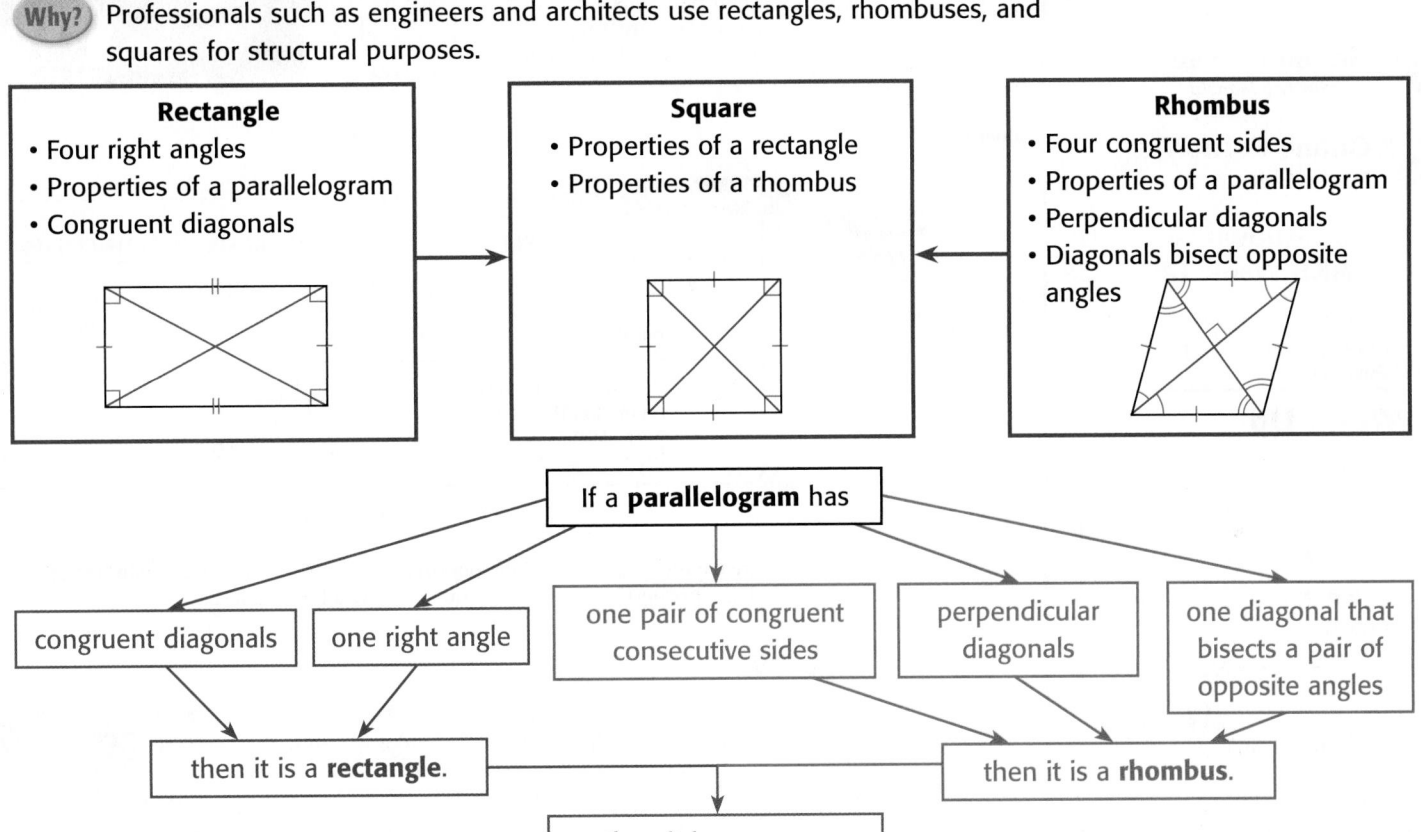

Rectangle
- Four right angles
- Properties of a parallelogram
- Congruent diagonals

Square
- Properties of a rectangle
- Properties of a rhombus

Rhombus
- Four congruent sides
- Properties of a parallelogram
- Perpendicular diagonals
- Diagonals bisect opposite angles

If a **parallelogram** has

congruent diagonals | one right angle | one pair of congruent consecutive sides | perpendicular diagonals | one diagonal that bisects a pair of opposite angles

then it is a **rectangle**.

then it is a **rhombus**.

then it is a **square**.

Kites and Trapezoids

Lesson 6-6

 Why? Kites and trapezoids can be used to solve geometric problems.

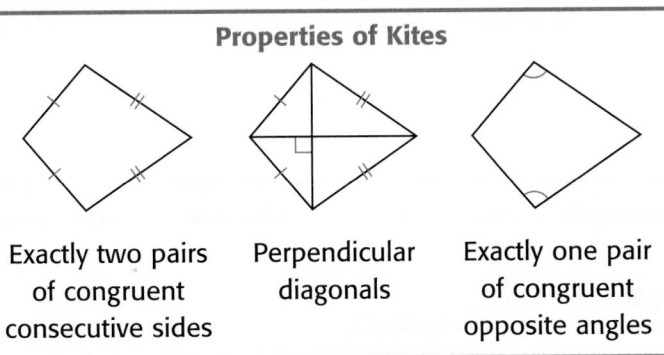

Properties of Kites

Exactly two pairs of congruent consecutive sides | Perpendicular diagonals | Exactly one pair of congruent opposite angles

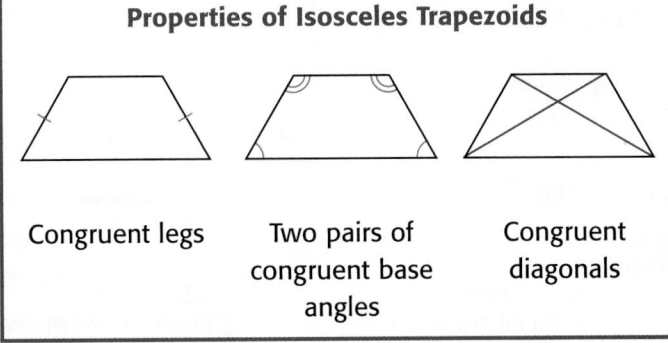

Properties of Isosceles Trapezoids

Congruent legs | Two pairs of congruent base angles | Congruent diagonals

Trapezoid Midsegment Theorem

The **midsegment** of a trapezoid is parallel to each base, and its length is $\frac{1}{2}$ the sum of the lengths of the bases.

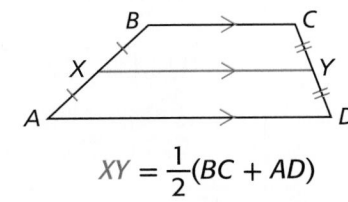

$$XY = \frac{1}{2}(BC + AD)$$

Objectives: Prove and apply properties of rectangles, rhombuses, and squares.

Use properties of rectangles, rhombuses, and squares to solve problems.

Geometry Lab
In *Texas Lab Manual*

Online Edition
Tutorial Videos

Countdown to TAKS Week 14

Power Presentations
with PowerPoint®

Warm Up

Solve for *x*.

1. $16x - 3 = 12x + 13$ 4

2. $2x - 4 = 90$ 47

***ABCD* is a parallelogram. Find each measure.**

B ——————— C
$(16x - 4)°$
$5y - 1$ $2y + 8$
$(14x + 34)°$
A ——————— D

3. *CD*   14   **4.** m∠C   104°

Also available on transparency

Math Humor

Q: What did the rhombus say to the square?

A: Lean on me, friend!

⭐ Geometry TEKS

G.2 Geometric structure*
(A) use constructions to explore attributes of geometric figures …
(B) … determine the validity of … conjectures [about polygons]

G.3 Geometric structure*
(B) construct and justify statements about geometric figures …

G.7 Dimensionality and the geometry of location*
(B) use slopes and equations of lines to investigate … relationships …
Also G.3.E, G.7.A, G.7.C

* Knowledge and Skills See p. 378.

6-4 Properties of Special Parallelograms

⭐ TEKS G.3.B Geometric structure: construct and justify statements about geometric figures …. Also G.2.A, G.2.B, G.3.E, G.7.A, G.7.B, G.7.C

Objectives
Prove and apply properties of rectangles, rhombuses, and squares.

Use properties of rectangles, rhombuses, and squares to solve problems.

Vocabulary
rectangle
rhombus
square

Who uses this?
Artists who work with stained glass can use properties of rectangles to cut materials to the correct sizes.

A second type of special quadrilateral is a *rectangle*. A **rectangle** is a quadrilateral with four right angles.

B ———— C
A ———— D
Rectangle *ABCD*

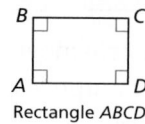
Theorems **Properties of Rectangles**

THEOREM	HYPOTHESIS	CONCLUSION
6-4-1 If a quadrilateral is a rectangle, then it is a parallelogram. (rect. → ▱)	B □ C / A □ D	*ABCD* is a parallelogram.
6-4-2 If a parallelogram is a rectangle, then its diagonals are congruent. (rect. → diags. ≅)	B ⊠ C / A ⊠ D	$\overline{AC} \cong \overline{BD}$

You will prove Theorems 6-4-1 and 6-4-2 in Exercises 38 and 35.

Since a rectangle is a parallelogram by Theorem 6-4-1, a rectangle "inherits" all the properties of parallelograms that you learned in Lesson 6-2.

EXAMPLE 1 *Craft Application*

An artist connects stained glass pieces with lead strips. In this rectangular window, the strips are cut so that $FG = 14$ in. and $FH = 20$ in. Find JG.

$\overline{EG} \cong \overline{FH}$ Rect. → diags. ≅
$EG = FH = 20$ Def. of ≅ segs.
$JG = \frac{1}{2}EG$ ▱ → diags. bisect each other
$JG = \frac{1}{2}(20) = 10$ in.   Substitute and simplify.

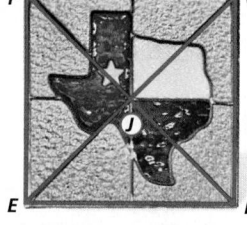
F   G
E   H
J

CHECK IT OUT! **Carpentry** The rectangular gate has diagonal braces. Find each length.

1a. *HJ*
48 in.

1b. *HK*
61.6 in.

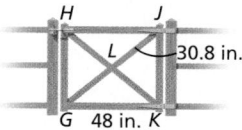
H   J
L   30.8 in.
G 48 in. K

1 Introduce

EXPLORATION
6-4 Properties of Special Parallelograms

A *rhombus* is a quadrilateral with four congruent sides. Use toothpicks to explore properties of rhombuses.

1. Arrange four congruent toothpicks to form a quadrilateral. Since the toothpicks are congruent, the quadrilateral is a rhombus.

2. Form different rhombuses by changing the angles between the toothpicks. What do you notice about the opposite sides of every rhombus you make? What can you conclude?

3. Use toothpicks to form a rhombus on a sheet of paper. Mark the vertices on the paper and remove the toothpicks. Connect the vertices to draw the rhombus and its diagonals. What do you notice about the angle of intersection of the diagonals?

4. Repeat Step 3 with a different rhombus. Do you get the same result?

THINK AND DISCUSS

5. Explain how you can use your findings to state a conjecture about the diagonals of a rhombus.

Motivate

Look through magazines or books to find pictures of rectangles, rhombuses, and squares. Group the pictures based on the type of figure. Then show the pictures to the class and ask students to describe the identifying characteristics of each type of figure.

Explorations and answers are provided in the *Explorations* binder.

A *rhombus* is another special quadrilateral. A **rhombus** is a quadrilateral with four congruent sides.

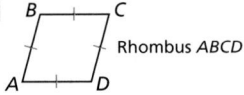
Rhombus *ABCD*

Know it!
.Note

Theorems (Properties of Rhombuses)

THEOREM	HYPOTHESIS	CONCLUSION
6-4-3 If a quadrilateral is a rhombus, then it is a parallelogram. (rhombus → ▱)	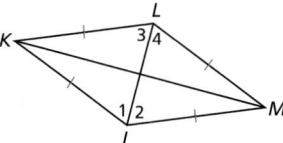	*ABCD* is a parallelogram.
6-4-4 If a parallelogram is a rhombus, then its diagonals are perpendicular. (rhombus → diags. ⊥)		$\overline{AC} \perp \overline{BD}$
6-4-5 If a parallelogram is a rhombus, then each diagonal bisects a pair of opposite angles. (rhombus → each diag. bisects opp. ⦟)		$\angle 1 \cong \angle 2$ $\angle 3 \cong \angle 4$ $\angle 5 \cong \angle 6$ $\angle 7 \cong \angle 8$

You will prove Theorems 6-4-3 and 6-4-4 in Exercises 34 and 37.

PROOF

Theorem 6-4-5

Given: *JKLM* is a rhombus.
Prove: $\overline{JL}$ bisects $\angle KJM$ and $\angle KLM$.
$\overline{KM}$ bisects $\angle JKL$ and $\angle JML$.

Proof:
Since *JKLM* is a rhombus, $\overline{JK} \cong \overline{JM}$, and $\overline{KL} \cong \overline{ML}$ by the definition of a rhombus. By the Reflexive Property of Congruence, $\overline{JL} \cong \overline{JL}$. Thus $\triangle JKL \cong \triangle JML$ by SSS. Then $\angle 1 \cong \angle 2$, and $\angle 3 \cong \angle 4$ by CPCTC. So $\overline{JL}$ bisects $\angle KJM$ and $\angle KLM$ by the definition of an angle bisector. By similar reasoning, $\overline{KM}$ bisects $\angle JKL$ and $\angle JML$.

Like a rectangle, a rhombus is a parallelogram. So you can apply the properties of parallelograms to rhombuses.

EXAMPLE 2 **Using Properties of Rhombuses to Find Measures**

RSTV is a rhombus. Find each measure.

**Algebra**

A *VT*

$ST = SR$	*Def. of rhombus*
$4x + 7 = 9x - 11$	*Substitute the given values.*
$18 = 5x$	*Subtract 4x from both sides and add 11 to both sides.*
$3.6 = x$	*Divide both sides by 5.*
$VT = ST$	*Def. of rhombus*
$VT = 4x + 7$	*Substitute 4x + 7 for ST.*
$VT = 4(3.6) + 7 = 21.4$	*Substitute 3.6 for x and simplify.*

6-4 Properties of Special Parallelograms **409**

Additional Examples

Example 1

A woodworker constructs a rectangular picture frame so that *JK* = 50 cm and *JL* = 86 cm. Find *HM*.   43 cm

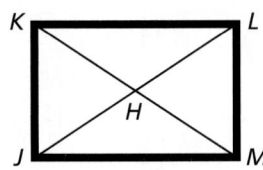

Example 2

TVWX is a rhombus. Find each measure.

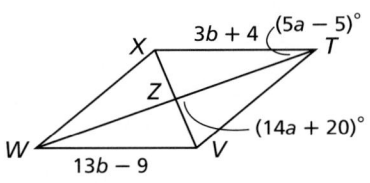

A. *TV*   7.9

B. m∠*VTZ*   20°

Also available on transparency

INTERVENTION ◀▪▶
Questioning Strategies

EXAMPLE 1

• In a rectangle, how do you know that $\frac{1}{2}$ of one diagonal is congruent to $\frac{1}{2}$ of the other diagonal?

EXAMPLE 2

• What type of angles do the diagonals of a rhombus form?

Reading Math Remind students that the sides and angles marked in the figure are not necessarily the ones asked for in the problem. Have students copy the figure and circle the length or measure they are asked to find as soon as they read the problem.

**Teach**

Guided Instruction

Review the properties of parallelograms from Lesson 6-2. Then discuss the properties of rectangles and rhombuses. Point out that these figures are also parallelograms. Explain that a square has all the properties of a parallelogram, a rectangle, and a rhombus.

Teaching Tip **Kinesthetic** Have students make a physical model of a parallelogram with paper strips and brads. Ask them to adjust the model until it is a rectangle and then measure its diagonals.

Reaching All Learners

Through Modeling

Divide students into groups. Have each group cut out models of a rectangle, a rhombus, and a square from construction paper. Then have students use a protractor (MK) and a ruler (MK) to verify the properties in Theorems 6-4-1 through 6-4-5.

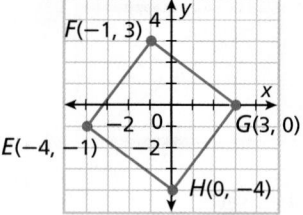
Example 3

Show that the diagonals of square *EFGH* are congruent perpendicular bisectors of each other.

$EG = FH = \sqrt{50}$, so $\overline{EG} \cong \overline{FH}$. Slope of $\overline{EG} = \frac{1}{7}$, and slope of $\overline{FH} = -7$, so $\overline{EG} \perp \overline{FH}$. $\left(-\frac{1}{2}, -\frac{1}{2}\right)$ is the midpoint of $\overline{EG}$ and $\overline{FH}$, so $\overline{EG}$ and $\overline{FH}$ bisect each other. Thus the diags. of *EFGH* are $\cong \perp$ bisectors of each other.

Also available on transparency

INTERVENTION ◄═►
Questioning Strategies

EXAMPLE **3**

• Does the order in which you show that the diagonals are congruent, are perpendicular, and share a midpoint matter?

• How does showing that the diagonals have the same midpoint prove that they bisect each other?

---

3. $SV = TW = \sqrt{122}$, so $\overline{SV} \cong \overline{TW}$.
Slope of $\overline{SV} = \frac{1}{11}$, and slope of $\overline{TW} = -11$, so $\overline{SV} \perp \overline{TW}$. The coordinates of the mdpt. of $\overline{SV}$ and $\overline{TW}$ are $\left(\frac{1}{2}, -\frac{7}{2}\right)$, so $\overline{SV}$ and $\overline{TW}$ bisect each other. So the diags. of *STVW* are $\cong \perp$ bisectors of each other.

RSTV is a rhombus. Find each measure.

 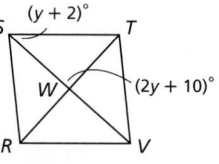

B m∠*WSR*

m∠*SWT* = 90°	*Rhombus → diags.* ⊥
$2y + 10 = 90$	*Substitute 2y + 10 for m∠SWT.*
$y = 40$	*Subtract 10 from both sides and divide both sides by 2.*
m∠*WSR* = m∠*TSW*	*Rhombus → each diag. bisects opp.* ∡
m∠*WSR* = $(y + 2)°$	*Substitute y + 2 for m∠TSW.*
m∠*WSR* = $(40 + 2)° = 42°$	*Substitute 40 for y and simplify.*

 *CDFG* is a rhombus. Find each measure.

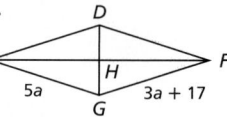

2a. *CD* **42.5**

2b. m∠*GCH* if m∠*GCD* = $(b + 3)°$ and m∠*CDF* = $(6b - 40)°$ **17°**

Helpful Hint

Rectangles, rhombuses, and squares are sometimes referred to as *special parallelograms.*

A **square** is a quadrilateral with four right angles and four congruent sides. In the exercises, you will show that a square is a parallelogram, a rectangle, and a rhombus. So a square has the properties of all three.

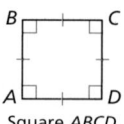

Square *ABCD*

EXAMPLE 3 **Verifying Properties of Squares**

Show that the diagonals of square *ABCD* are congruent perpendicular bisectors of each other.

Step 1 Show that $\overline{AC}$ and $\overline{BD}$ are congruent.

$$AC = \sqrt{[2 - (-1)]^2 + (7 - 0)^2} = \sqrt{58}$$

$$BD = \sqrt{[4 - (-3)]^2 + (2 - 5)^2} = \sqrt{58}$$

Since $AC = BD$, $\overline{AC} \cong \overline{BD}$.

Step 2 Show that $\overline{AC}$ and $\overline{BD}$ are perpendicular.

slope of $\overline{AC} = \dfrac{7 - 0}{2 - (-1)} = \dfrac{7}{3}$

slope of $\overline{BD} = \dfrac{2 - 5}{4 - (-3)} = \dfrac{-3}{7} = -\dfrac{3}{7}$

Since $\left(\dfrac{7}{3}\right)\left(-\dfrac{3}{7}\right) = -1$, $\overline{AC} \perp \overline{BD}$.

Step 3 Show that $\overline{AC}$ and $\overline{BD}$ bisect each other.

mdpt. of $\overline{AC}$: $\left(\dfrac{-1 + 2}{2}, \dfrac{0 + 7}{2}\right) = \left(\dfrac{1}{2}, \dfrac{7}{2}\right)$

mdpt. of $\overline{BD}$: $\left(\dfrac{-3 + 4}{2}, \dfrac{5 + 2}{2}\right) = \left(\dfrac{1}{2}, \dfrac{7}{2}\right)$

Since $\overline{AC}$ and $\overline{BD}$ have the same midpoint, they bisect each other. The diagonals are congruent perpendicular bisectors of each other.

 **3.** The vertices of square *STVW* are $S(-5, -4)$, $T(0, 2)$, $V(6, -3)$, and $W(1, -9)$. Show that the diagonals of square *STVW* are congruent perpendicular bisectors of each other.

Teaching Tip

Critical Thinking Ask students the following: Suppose the equations $y = 2x + 5$ and $4y + x = 8$ represent the lines containing the diagonals of a quadrilateral. Can this quadrilateral be a square? No, the slopes of these lines $\left(2 \text{ and } -\dfrac{1}{4}\right)$ are not opposite reciprocals, so the diagonals are not perpendicular.

To remember the properties of rectangles, rhombuses, and squares, I start with a **square**, which has all the properties of the others.

To get a **rectangle** that is not a square, I stretch the square in one direction. Its diagonals are still congruent, but they are no longer perpendicular.

To get a **rhombus** that is not a square, I go back to the square and slide the top in one direction. Its diagonals are still perpendicular and bisect the opposite angles, but they aren't congruent.

EXAMPLE 4 Using Properties of Special Parallelograms in Proofs

Given: *EFGH* is a rectangle. *J* is the midpoint of $\overline{EH}$.
Prove: △*FJG* is isosceles.

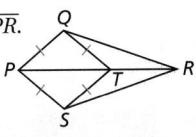

Proof:

Statements	Reasons
1. *EFGH* is a rectangle. *J* is the midpoint of $\overline{EH}$.	1. Given
2. ∠*E* and ∠*H* are right angles.	2. Def. of rect.
3. ∠*E* ≅ ∠*H*	3. Rt. ∠ ≅ Thm.
4. *EFGH* is a parallelogram.	4. Rect. → ▱
5. $\overline{EF}$ ≅ $\overline{HG}$	5. ▱ → opp. sides ≅
6. $\overline{EJ}$ ≅ $\overline{HJ}$	6. Def. of mdpt.
7. △*FJE* ≅ △*GJH*	7. SAS Steps 3, 5, 6
8. $\overline{FJ}$ ≅ $\overline{GJ}$	8. CPCTC
9. △*FJG* is isosceles.	9. Def. of isosc. △

4. Possible answer:
1. *PQTS* is a rhombus. (Given)
2. $\overline{PT}$ bisects ∠*QPS*. (Rhombus → each diag. bisects opp. ∠)
3. ∠*QPR* ≅ ∠*SPR* (Def. of ∠ bisector)
4. $\overline{PQ}$ ≅ $\overline{PS}$ (Def. of rhombus)
5. $\overline{PR}$ ≅ $\overline{PR}$ (Reflex. Prop. of ≅)
6. △*QPR* ≅ △*SPR* (SAS)
7. $\overline{RQ}$ ≅ $\overline{RS}$ (CPCTC)

 **CHECK IT OUT!**

4. **Given:** *PQTS* is a rhombus with diagonal $\overline{PR}$.
   Prove: $\overline{RQ}$ ≅ $\overline{RS}$

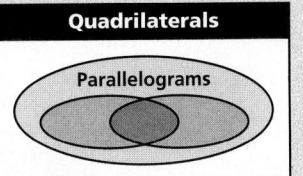

THINK AND DISCUSS

1. Which theorem means "The diagonals of a rectangle are congruent"? Why do you think the theorem is written as a conditional?

2. What properties of a rhombus are the same as the properties of all parallelograms? What special properties does a rhombus have?

 3. **GET ORGANIZED** Copy and complete the graphic organizer. Write the missing terms in the three unlabeled sections. Then write a definition of each term.

Quadrilaterals
Parallelograms

 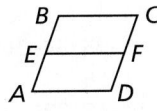
6-4 Properties of Special Parallelograms **411**

Lesson 6-4 **411**

6-4 **Exercises**

6-4 **Exercises**

go.hrw.com/Geo/TX
Homework Help Online
KEYWORD: MG7 6-4
Parent Resources Online
KEYWORD: MG7 Parent

Assignment Guide

Assign *Guided Practice* exercises as necessary.

If you finished Examples **1–2**
  Basic 10–15, 18–21, 24–30 even, 40–42
  Average 10–15, 18–30 even, 40–42, 51
  Advanced 10–15, 18–30 even, 33, 40–42, 48, 51

If you finished Examples **1–4**
  Basic 10–23, 24–28 even, 29, 31, 34–36, 40–42, 44–47, 52–56
  Average 10–28, 34–36, 39–48, 51–56
  Advanced 10–19, 22–32 even, 33, 35–56

Homework Quick Check
Quickly check key concepts.
Exercises: 10, 14, 16, 17, 22, 24

Answers

8. $JL = KM = \sqrt{74}$, so $\overline{JL} \cong \overline{KM}$. Slope of $\overline{JL} = \frac{7}{5}$, and slope of $\overline{KM} = -\frac{5}{7}$, so $\overline{JL} \perp \overline{KM}$. The coordinates of the mdpt. of $\overline{JL}$ and $\overline{KM}$ are $\left(-\frac{1}{2}, -\frac{3}{2}\right)$, so $\overline{JL}$ and $\overline{KM}$ bisect each other. So the diags. of *JKLM* are $\cong \perp$ bisectors of each other.

⬥TAKS Practice

Grades 9–11	Exercises
Obj. 2	45
Obj. 5	48
Obj. 6	18–23, 47
Obj. 7	36
Obj. 8	40–42
Obj. 9	52
Obj. 10	51, 52

GUIDED PRACTICE

1. **Vocabulary** What is another name for an *equilateral quadrilateral*? an *equiangular quadrilateral*? a *regular quadrilateral*?
  rhombus; rectangle; square

SEE EXAMPLE **1**
p. 408

Engineering The braces of the bridge support lie along the diagonals of rectangle *PQRS*. $RS = 160$ ft, and $QS = 380$ ft. Find each length.

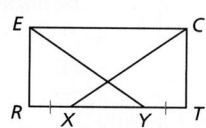

2. *TQ* **190 ft**
3. *PQ* **160 ft**
4. *ST* **190 ft**
5. *PR* **380 ft**

SEE EXAMPLE **2**
p. 409

ABCD is a rhombus. Find each measure.
6. *AB* $32\frac{1}{3}$
7. m∠*ABC* **122°**

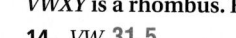

SEE EXAMPLE **3**
p. 410

8. **Multi-Step** The vertices of square *JKLM* are $J(-3, -5)$, $K(-4, 1)$, $L(2, 2)$, and $M(3, -4)$. Show that the diagonals of square *JKLM* are congruent perpendicular bisectors of each other.

SEE EXAMPLE **4**
p. 411

9. **Given:** *RECT* is a rectangle. $\overline{RX} \cong \overline{TY}$
  Prove: $\triangle REY \cong \triangle TCX$

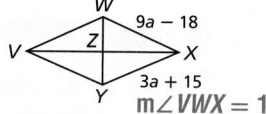

PRACTICE AND PROBLEM SOLVING

Independent Practice	
For Exercises	See Example
10–13	1
14–15	2
16	3
17	4

TEKS ⬥ **TAKS**

Skills Practice p. S15
Application Practice p. S33

Carpentry A carpenter measures the diagonals of a piece of wood. In rectangle *JKLM*, $JM = 25$ in., and $JP = 14\frac{1}{2}$ in. Find each length.

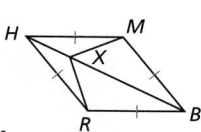

10. *JL* **29**
11. *KL* **25**
12. *KM* **29**
13. *MP* $14\frac{1}{2}$

VWXY is a rhombus. Find each measure.

14. *VW* **31.5**
15. m∠*VWX* and m∠*WYX* if m∠*WVY* = $(4b + 10)°$ and m∠*XZW* = $(10b - 5)°$
  m∠*VWX* = 132°; m∠*WYX* = 66°

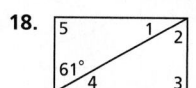

16. **Multi-Step** The vertices of square *PQRS* are $P(-4, 0)$, $Q(4, 3)$, $R(7, -5)$, and $S(-1, -8)$. Show that the diagonals of square *PQRS* are congruent perpendicular bisectors of each other.

17. **Given:** *RHMB* is a rhombus with diagonal $\overline{HB}$.
  Prove: ∠*HMX* ≅ ∠*HRX*

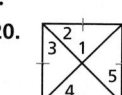

Find the measures of the numbered angles in each rectangle.

18. m∠1 = 29°;
m∠2 = 61°;
m∠3 = 90°;
m∠4 = 29°;
m∠5 = 90°.

19. m∠1 = 54°;
m∠2 = 36°;
m∠3 = 54°;
m∠4 = 108°;
m∠5 = 72°

18. [figure with 61°]
19. [figure with 36°]
20. [figure]

6-4 PRACTICE A

Match each figure with the letter of one of the vocabulary terms. Use each term once.

1. **B**
2. **C**
3. **A**

A. rectangle
B. rhombus
C. square

Fill in the blanks to complete each theorem.
4. If a parallelogram is a rhombus, then its diagonals are **perpendicular**.
5. If a parallelogram is a rectangle, then its diagonals are **congruent**.
6. If a quadrilateral is a rectangle, then it is a **parallelogram**.
7. If a parallelogram is a rhombus, then each diagonal **bisects** a pair of opposite angles.
8. If a quadrilateral is a rhombus, then it is a **parallelogram**.

The part of a ruler shown is a rectangle with $AB = 3$ inches and $BD = 3\frac{1}{4}$ inches. Find each length.
9. *DC* = **3 inches**
10. *AC* = **$3\frac{1}{4}$ inches**

Use the phrases and theorems from the Word Bank to complete this two-column proof.

Word Bank:
Alternate Interior ∠ Thm.
GHIJ is a parallelogram.
Trans. Prop. of ≅
∠2 ≅ ∠3

11. **Given:** *GHIJ* is a rhombus.
Prove: ∠1 ≅ ∠3

Statements	Reasons
1. *GHIJ* is a rhombus.	1. Given
2. **a.** *GHIJ* is a parallelogram.	2. rhomb. → ▱
3. $\overline{GH} \parallel \overline{JI}$	3. ▱ → opp. sides ∥
4. ∠1 ≅ ∠2	4. **b.** Alternate Interior ∠ Thm.
5. **c.** ∠2 ≅ ∠3	5. rhomb. → each diag. bisects opp. ∠s
6. ∠1 ≅ ∠3	6. **d.** Trans. Prop. of ≅

6-4 PRACTICE B

Tell whether each figure must be a rectangle, rhombus, or square based on the information given. Use the most specific name possible.
1. **rectangle**
2. **square**
3. **rhombus**

A modern artist's sculpture has rectangular faces. The face shown here is 9 feet long and 4 feet wide. Find each measure in simplest radical form. (*Hint:* Use the Pythagorean Theorem.)
4. *DC* = **9 feet**
5. *AD* = **4 feet**
6. *DB* = **$\sqrt{97}$ feet**
7. *AE* = **$\frac{\sqrt{97}}{2}$ feet**

VWXY is a rhombus. Find each measure.
8. *XY* = **36**
9. m∠*YVW* = **107°**
10. m∠*VYX* = **73°**
11. m∠*XYZ* = **36.5°**

12. The vertices of square *JKLM* are $J(-2, 4)$, $K(-3, -1)$, $L(2, -2)$, and $M(3, 3)$. Find each of the following to show that the diagonals of square *JKLM* are congruent perpendicular bisectors of each other.
$JL = 2\sqrt{13}$
$KM = 2\sqrt{13}$
slope of $\overline{JL} = -\frac{3}{2}$
slope of $\overline{KM} = \frac{2}{3}$
midpoint of $\overline{JL} = ($ **0** , **1** $)$
midpoint of $\overline{KM} = ($ **0** , **1** $)$

Write a paragraph proof.
13. **Given:** *ABCD* is a rectangle.
Prove: ∠*EDC* ≅ ∠*ECD*

Possible answer: *ABCD* is a rectangle, so $\overline{AC}$ is congruent to $\overline{BD}$. Because *ABCD* is a rectangle, it is also a parallelogram. Because *ABCD* is a parallelogram, its diagonals bisect each other. By the definition of bisector, $EC = \frac{1}{2}AC$ and $ED = \frac{1}{2}BD$. But by the definition of congruent segments, $AC = BD$. So substitution and the Transitive Property of Equality show that $EC = ED$. Because $EC = ED$, $\triangle ECD$ is an isosceles triangle. The base angles of an isosceles triangle are congruent, so ∠*EDC* ≅ ∠*ECD*.

Find the measures of the numbered angles in each rhombus.

21.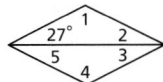
27° 1 2
5 3
4

22.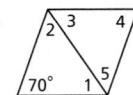
2 3 4
70° 1 5

23.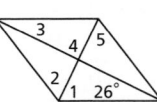
3 4 5
2 1 26°

Tell whether each statement is sometimes, always, or never true.
(*Hint:* Refer to your graphic organizer for this lesson.)

24. A rectangle is a parallelogram. **A**

25. A rhombus is a square. **S**

26. A parallelogram is a rhombus. **S**

27. A rhombus is a rectangle. **S**

28. A square is a rhombus. **A**

29. A rectangle is a quadrilateral. **A**

30. A square is a rectangle. **A**

31. A rectangle is a square. **S**

32. **Critical Thinking** A triangle is equilateral if and only if the triangle is equiangular. Can you make a similar statement about a quadrilateral? Explain your answer.

History

33. **History** There are five shapes of clay tiles in this tile mosaic from the ruins of Pompeii.
   a. Make a sketch of each shape of tile and tell whether the shape is a polygon.
   b. Name each polygon by its number of sides. Does each shape appear to be regular or irregular?
   c. Do any of the shapes appear to be special parallelograms? If so, identify them by name.
   d. Find the measure of each interior angle of the center polygon. **120°**

Pompeii was located in what is today southern Italy. In C.E. 79, Mount Vesuvius erupted and buried Pompeii in volcanic ash. The ruins have been excavated and provide a glimpse into life in ancient Rome.

34. You cannot use Thm. 6-2-1 to justify the final statement because you do not know that *JKLM* is a ▱. That is what is being proven. Instead, Thm. 6-3-2 states that if both pairs of opp. sides of a quad. are ≅, then the quad. is a ▱. So *JKLM* is a ▱ by Thm. 6-3-2.

34. **/// ERROR ANALYSIS ///** Find and correct the error in this proof of Theorem 6-4-3.
   Given: *JKLM* is a rhombus.
   Prove: *JKLM* is a parallelogram.

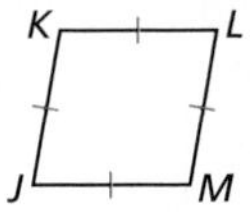

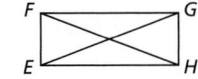
K L
J M

   Proof:
   It is given that *JKLM* is a rhombus. So by the definition of a rhombus, $\overline{JK} \cong \overline{LM}$, and $\overline{KL} \cong \overline{MJ}$. Theorem 6-2-1 states that if a quadrilateral is a parallelogram, then its opposite sides are congruent. So *JKLM* is a parallelogram by Theorem 6-2-1.

35. Complete the two-column proof of Theorem 6-4-2 by filling in the blanks.
   Given: *EFGH* is a rectangle.
   Prove: $\overline{FH} \cong \overline{GE}$

F G
E H

   Proof:

Statements	Reasons
1. *EFGH* is a rectangle.	1. Given
2. *EFGH* is a parallelogram.	2. a. ___?___ Rect. → ▱
3. $\overline{EF} \cong$ b. ___?___ $\overline{HG}$	3. ▱ → opp. sides ≅
4. $\overline{EH} \cong \overline{EH}$	4. c. ___?___ Reflex. Prop. of ≅
5. ∠*FEH* and ∠*GHE* are right angles.	5. d. ___?___ Def. of rect.
6. ∠*FEH* ≅ e. ___?___ ∠*GHE*	6. Rt. ∠ ≅ Thm.
7. △*FEH* ≅ △*GHE*	7. f. ___?___ SAS
8. $\overline{FH} \cong \overline{GE}$	8. g. ___?___ CPCTC

6-4 Properties of Special Parallelograms **413**

6-4 PRACTICE C

For Exercises 1–5, give your answers in simplest radical form.

1. Find the length of the diagonals of a rectangle with sides of lengths *a* and *b*. $\sqrt{a^2 + b^2}$

2. Find the length of the diagonals of a square with sides of length *a*. $\sqrt{2}\,a$

3. Find the length of the sides of a square with diagonals of length *a*. $\frac{\sqrt{2}}{2}a$

4. Find the length of the sides of a rhombus with diagonals of lengths *a* and *b*. $\frac{\sqrt{a^2 + b^2}}{2}$

5. Find the length of a rectangle with width *x* and a diagonal of length 2*x*. $\sqrt{3}\,x$

6. Find the measures of the angles in the triangles formed by one diagonal of the rectangle in Exercise 5.   30°-60°-90°

The figure shows a kind of quadrilateral called a *kite*. A kite is a quadrilateral with exactly two pairs of congruent consecutive sides. Use the figure to write paragraph proofs for Exercises 7 and 8.

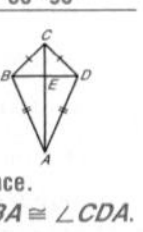

7. Prove: ∠*CBA* ≅ ∠*CDA*
   Possible answer: It is given that $\overline{CB} \cong \overline{CD}$ and $\overline{AB} \cong \overline{AD}$. $\overline{CA}$ is congruent to $\overline{CA}$ by the Reflexive Property of Congruence. Thus △*ABC* is congruent to △*ADC* by SSS. By CPCTC, ∠*CBA* ≅ ∠*CDA*.

8. Prove: $\overline{AC}$ is the perpendicular bisector of $\overline{BD}$.
   Possible answer: It is given that $\overline{CB} \cong \overline{CD}$ and $\overline{AB} \cong \overline{AD}$. So *C* and *A* are on the perpendicular bisector of $\overline{BD}$ by the Conv. of the Perpendicular Bisector Thm. So, since two points determine a line, $\overline{AC}$ is the perpendicular bisector of $\overline{BD}$.

For Exercises 9–11, name all the types of quadrilaterals (kite, parallelogram, rectangle, rhombus, or square) that satisfy the given conditions.

9. The diagonals bisect each other.
   parallelogram, rectangle, rhombus, square

10. The diagonals are perpendicular.
    kite, rhombus, square

11. The diagonals are congruent.
    rectangle, square

33a. 1. △ Polygon
     2. ▭ Polygon
     3. ⬡ Polygon
     4. ◇ Polygon
     5. ⬠ Not a polygon

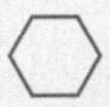

   b. 1. triangle; reg.
      2. quad.; reg.
      3. hexagon; reg.
      4. quad.; irregular

   c. Shape 2 appears to be a square. Shape 4 appears to be a rhombus.

COMMON ERROR ALERT

Some students may have difficulty determining whether a statement is *sometimes* or *always* true in **Exercises 24–31.** Suggest that they rewrite each sentence as a conditional statement before trying to assess its truth value.

Teaching Tip   **Social Studies Link** The tile mosaic in **Exercise 33** was used as a street sign in ancient Pompeii. Explain that when written histories do not exist, archaeologists work with the ruins and remains of ancient cultures to learn how these people lived.

Answers

9. Possible answer:
   1. *RECT* is a rect. $\overline{RX} \cong \overline{TY}$ (Given)
   2. $\overline{XY} \cong \overline{XY}$ (Reflex. Prop. of ≅)
   3. *RX* = *TY*, *XY* = *XY* (Def. of ≅ segs.)
   4. *RX* + *XY* = *TY* + *XY* (Add. Prop. of =)
   5. *RX* + *XY* = *RY*, *TY* + *XY* = *TX* (Seg. Add. Post.)
   6. *RY* = *TX* (Subst.)
   7. $\overline{RY} \cong \overline{TX}$ (Def. of ≅ segs.)
   8. ∠*R* and ∠*T* are rt. ∠. (Def. of rect.)
   9. ∠*R* ≅ ∠*T* (Rt. ∠ ≅ Thm.)
   10. *RECT* is a ▱. (Rect. → ▱)
   11. $\overline{RE} \cong \overline{TC}$ (▱ → opp. sides ≅)
   12. △*REY* ≅ △*TCX* (SAS)

16. *PR* = *QS* = $\sqrt{146}$, so $\overline{PR} \cong \overline{QS}$. Slope of $\overline{PR} = -\frac{5}{11}$, and slope of $\overline{QS} = \frac{11}{5}$, so $\overline{PR} \perp \overline{QS}$. The coordinates of the mdpt. of $\overline{PR}$ and $\overline{QS}$ are $\left(\frac{3}{2}, -\frac{5}{2}\right)$, so $\overline{PR}$ and $\overline{QS}$ bisect each other. So the diags. of *PQRS* are ≅ ⊥ bisectors of each other.

17. Possible answer:
    1. *RHMB* is a rhombus. $\overline{HB}$ is a diag. of *RHMB*. (Given)
    2. $\overline{MH} \cong \overline{RH}$ (Def. of rhombus)
    3. $\overline{HB}$ bisects ∠*RHM*. (Rhombus → each diag. bisects opp. ∠)
    4. ∠*MHX* ≅ ∠*RHX* (Def. of ∠ bisector)
    5. $\overline{HX} \cong \overline{HX}$ (Reflex. Prop. of ≅)
    6. △*MHX* ≅ △*RHX* (SAS)
    7. ∠*HMX* ≅ ∠*HRX* (CPCTC)

20. m∠1 = 90°; m∠2 = 45°; m∠3 = 45°; m∠4 = 45°; m∠5 = 45°

21. m∠1 = 126°; m∠2 = 27°; m∠3 = 27°; m∠4 = 126°; m∠5 = 27°

22. m∠1 = 55°; m∠2 = 55°; m∠3 = 55°; m∠4 = 70°; m∠5 = 55°

23. m∠1 = 64°; m∠2 = 64°; m∠3 = 26°; m∠4 = 90°; m∠5 = 64°

32. See p. A22.

36. This problem will prepare you for the Multi-Step TAKS Prep on page 436.

The organizers of a fair plan to fence off a plot of land given by the coordinates A(2, 4), B(4, 2), C(−1, −3), and D(−3, −1).

a. Find the slope of each side of quadrilateral ABCD. slope of $\overline{AB}$ = slope of $\overline{CD}$ = −1; slope of $\overline{BC}$ = slope of $\overline{DA}$ = 1

b. What type of quadrilateral is formed by the fences? Justify your answer.

c. The organizers plan to build a straight path connecting A and C and another path connecting B and D. Explain why these two paths will have the same length. By Thm. 6-4-2, the diags. of a rect. are ≅.

36b. Rect.; adj. sides are ⊥.

37. Use this plan to write a proof of Theorem 6-4-4.

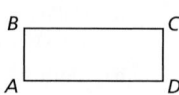

Given: VWXY is a rhombus.

Prove: $\overline{VX} \perp \overline{WY}$

Plan: Use the definition of a rhombus and the properties of parallelograms to show that △WZX ≅ △YZX. Then use CPCTC to show that ∠WZX and ∠YZX are right angles.

38. Write a paragraph proof of Theorem 6-4-1.

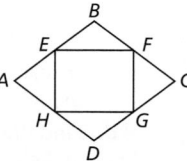

Given: ABCD is a rectangle.

Prove: ABCD is a parallelogram.

39. Write a two-column proof.

Given: ABCD is a rhombus. E, F, G, and H are the midpoints of the sides.

Prove: EFGH is a parallelogram.

Multi-Step Find the perimeter and area of each figure. Round to the nearest hundredth, if necessary.

40.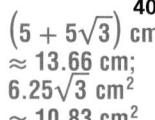

$(5 + 5\sqrt{3})$ cm
≈ **13.66 cm**;
$6.25\sqrt{3}$ cm²
≈ **10.83 cm²**

41.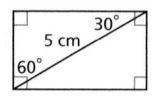

$28\sqrt{2}$ in. ≈ **39.60 in.**; **98 in²**

42.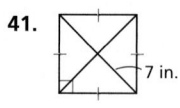

20 cm; 24 cm²

43. Write About It Explain why each of these conditional statements is true.
a. If a quadrilateral is a square, then it is a parallelogram.
b. If a quadrilateral is a square, then it is a rectangle.
c. If a quadrilateral is a square, then it is a rhombus.

44. Write About It List the properties that a square "inherits" because it is (1) a parallelogram, (2) a rectangle, and (3) a rhombus.

45. Which expression represents the measure of ∠J in rhombus JKLM?

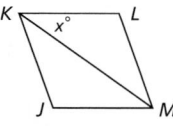

Ⓐ x° Ⓒ (180 − x)°
Ⓑ 2x° Ⓓ (180 − 2x)°

46. Short Response The diagonals of rectangle QRST intersect at point P. If QR = 1.8 cm, QP = 1.5 cm, and QT = 2.4 cm, find the perimeter of △RST. Explain how you found your answer.

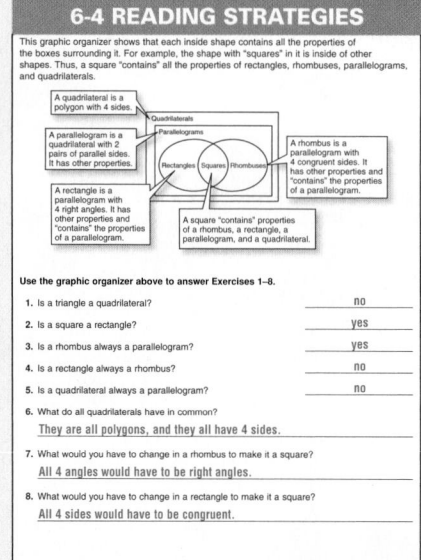

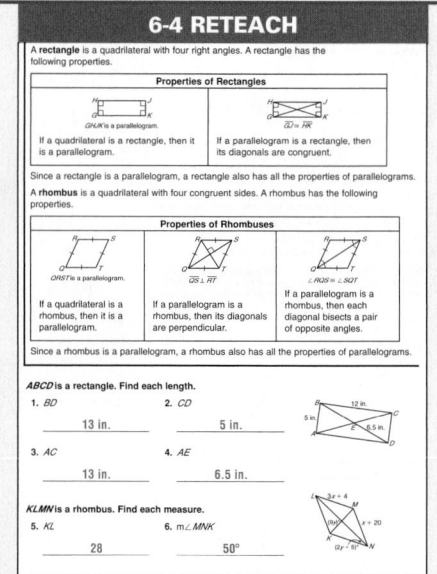

47. Which statement is NOT true of a rectangle?

  F Both pairs of opposite sides are congruent and parallel.

  G Both pairs of opposite angles are congruent and supplementary.

  (H) All pairs of consecutive sides are congruent and perpendicular.

  (J) All pairs of consecutive angles are congruent and supplementary.

CHALLENGE AND EXTEND

48. Algebra Find the value of x in the rhombus.
$x = 5$ or $x = -5.25$

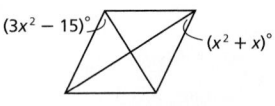
$(3x^2 - 15)°$ $(x^2 + x)°$

49. Prove that the segment joining the midpoints of two consecutive sides of a rhombus is perpendicular to one diagonal and parallel to the other.

50. Extend the definition of a triangle midsegment to write a definition for the midsegment of a rectangle. Prove that a midsegment of a rectangle divides the rectangle into two congruent rectangles.

51. The figure is formed by joining eleven congruent squares. How many rectangles are in the figure?

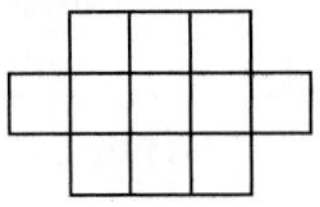

SPIRAL REVIEW

51. 45
(11 1-by-1's,
8 1-by-2's,
5 1-by-3's,
2 1-by-4's,
1 1-by-5,
6 2-by-1's,
4 2-by-2's,
2 2-by-3's,
3 3-by-1's,
2 3-by-2's,
1 3-by-3)

52. The cost c of a taxi ride is given by $c = 2 + 1.8(m - 1)$, where m is the length of the trip in miles. Mr. Hatch takes a 6-mile taxi ride. How much change should he get if he pays with a \$20 bill and leaves a 10% tip? *(Previous course)* \$7.90

Determine if each conditional is true. If false, give a counterexample. *(Lesson 2-2)*

53. If a number is divisible by −3, then it is divisible by 3. **T**

54. If the diameter of a circle is doubled, then the area of the circle will double. **F**

Determine if each quadrilateral must be a parallelogram. Justify your answer. *(Lesson 6-3)*

55.  No; none of the conditions for a ▱ are met.

56. 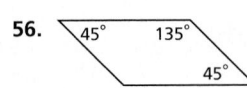 45°   135°   45°
Yes; 1 ∠ is supp. to both of its cons. ∠, so the quad. is a ▱.

Construction Rhombus

Check students' constructions.

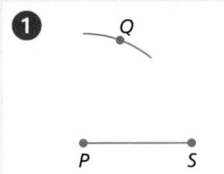 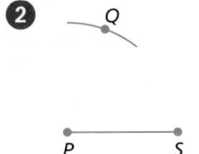 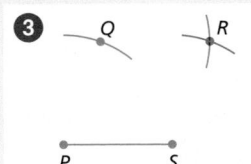 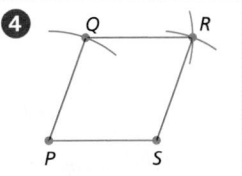

Draw $\overline{PS}$. Set the compass to the length of $\overline{PS}$. Place the compass point at P and draw an arc above $\overline{PS}$. Label a point Q on the arc.

Place the compass point at Q and draw an arc to the right of Q.

Place the compass point at S and draw an arc that intersects the arc drawn from Q. Label the point of intersection R.

Draw $\overline{PQ}$, $\overline{QR}$, and $\overline{RS}$.

6-4 PROBLEM SOLVING

Use the diagram for Exercises 1 and 2.
The soccer goalposts determine rectangle *ABCD*.

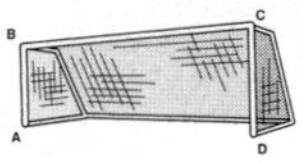

1. The distance between goalposts, *BC*, is three times the distance from the top of the goalpost to the ground. If the perimeter of *ABCD* is $21\frac{1}{3}$ yards, what is the length of *BC*?

8 yd

2. The distance from *B* to *D* is approximately $(x + 10)$ feet, and the distance from *A* to *C* is approximately $(2x - 5.3)$ feet. What is the approximate distance from *A* to *C*?

25.3 ft

3. *MNPQ* is a rhombus. The measure of ∠*MRQ* is $(13t − 1)°$, and the measure of ∠*PQR* is $(7t + 4)°$. What is the measure of ∠*PQM*?

106°

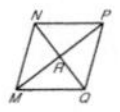

4. The *scissor lift* forms rhombus *PQRS* with $PQ = (7b − 5)$ meters and $QR = (2b − 0.5)$ meters. If *S* is the midpoint of *RT*, what is the length of *RT*?

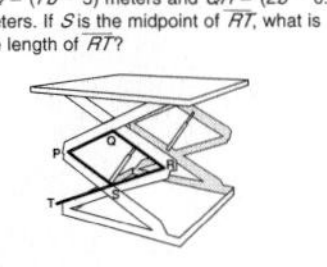

2.6 m

5. The diagram shows the lid of a rectangular case that holds 80 CDs. What are the dimensions of the case?

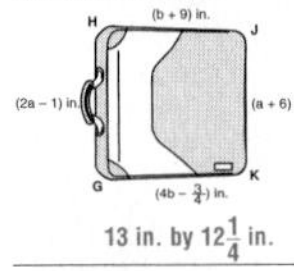

13 in. by $12\frac{1}{4}$ in.

Choose the best answer.

6. What is the measure of ∠1 in the rectangle?

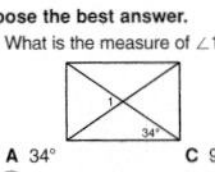

A 34°   C 90°
B 68°   D 146°

7. A square graphed on the coordinate plane has a diagonal with endpoints *E*(2, 3) and *F*(0, −3). What are the coordinates of the endpoints of the other diagonal?

F (4, −1) and (−2, 1)
G (4, 0) and (−2, 1)
H (4, −1) and (−3, 1)
J (3, −1) and (−2, 1)

6-4 CHALLENGE

The figure at right shows a Chinese puzzle called the *tangram*. No one is certain how old the puzzle is, but it was unquestionably one of the most popular puzzles of the nineteenth century. The seven puzzle pieces are called tans. To make your own tans, fold a large square sheet of paper in half four times as shown below. Unfold the paper, draw the segments shown, then cut along the segments.

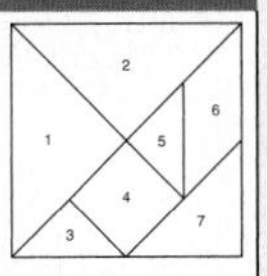

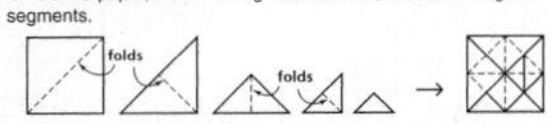

Some or all of the tans can be arranged to form special types of quadrilaterals. For instance, the figure at right shows how tans 1, 3, 5, 6, and 7 can be arranged to form a trapezoid.

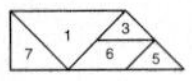

Complete the table below by arranging the given number of tans to form each figure. If it is not possible to make the figure, enter an *X* in the table.

Number of tans	Square	Rectangle (not square)	Isosceles trapezoid	Trapezoid (not isosceles)	Rhombus (not square)	Parallelogram (not rhombus or rectangle)
1. 2		X			X	
2. 3					X	
3. 4					X	
4. 5					X	
5. 6	X				X	X
6. 7					X	

7. Tangram puzzles arise from the countless silhouettes of people, animals, and objects that can be formed by arrangements of the tans. Find an arrangement of the tans that forms the silhouette of a bird, as shown at right. Sketch your answer on a separate sheet of paper.

Journal
Have students describe the properties of a rectangle and a rhombus, and then have them draw and label examples of each type of figure.

ALTERNATIVE ASSESSMENT
Have students draw and label diagrams to represent the hypothesis and conclusion of each theorem in the lesson.

Power Presentations with PowerPoint®

6-4 Lesson Quiz

A slab of concrete is poured with diagonal spacers. In rectangle *CNRT*, *CN* = 35 ft, and *NT* = 58 ft. Find each length.

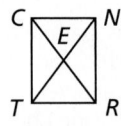

1. *TR*   35 ft   **2.** *CE*   29 ft

PQRS is a rhombus. Find each measure.

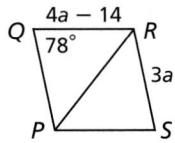
$4a - 14$ 78° $3a$

3. *QP*   42   **4.** m∠*QRP*   51°

5. The vertices of square *ABCD* are *A*(1, 3), *B*(3, 2), *C*(4, 4), and *D*(2, 5). Show that its diagonals are congruent perpendicular bisectors of each other. $AC = BD = \sqrt{10}$, so $\overline{AC} \cong \overline{BD}$. Slope of $\overline{AC} = \frac{1}{3}$, and slope of $\overline{BD} = -3$, so $\overline{AC} \perp \overline{BD}$. (2.5, 3.5) is the mdpt. of $\overline{AC}$ and $\overline{BD}$, so $\overline{AC}$ and $\overline{BD}$ bisect each other.

6. Given: *ABCD* is a rhombus.
Prove: $\triangle ABE \cong \triangle CDF$

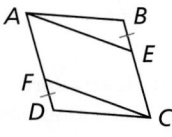

1. *ABCD* is a rhombus. (Given)
2. $\overline{AB} \cong \overline{CD}$ (Def. of rhombus)
3. *ABCD* is a ▱ (Rhombus → ▱)
4. ∠*B* ≅ ∠*D* (▱ → opp. ∠ ≅)
5. $\overline{DF} \cong \overline{BE}$ (Given)
6. $\triangle ABE \cong \triangle CDF$ (SAS)

Also available on transparency

Pacing:
Traditional 1 day
Block $\frac{1}{2}$ day

Objective: Use geometry
software to predict the conditions
for rectangles, rhombuses, and
squares.

Materials: geometry software

PREMIER **Online Edition**
TechKeys

**Countdown to
TAKS Week 14**

Teach

Discuss

Guide students through the construction of the parallelogram given
in **Steps 1** and **2**. Then ask students
to predict the answers to the questions in the activities before they
follow each subsequent instruction.
Have students refer to their journals
or graphic organizers if they need to
review the properties of each special
parallelogram.

 Geometry TEKS

G.2 Geometric structure*
(A) use constructions to explore
attributes of geometric figures and to
make conjectures about geometric
relationships
(B) make conjectures about …
polygons … and determine the
validity …

G.3 Geometric structure*
(B) construct and justify statements
about geometric figures and their
properties

**G.9 Congruence and the geometry
of size***
(B) formulate and test conjectures
about the properties and attributes of
polygons and their component parts
based on explorations and concrete
models

* Knowledge and Skills See p. 378.

6-5

Technology **LAB**
Predict Conditions for Special Parallelograms

In this lab, you will use geometry software to predict the conditions that are
sufficient to prove that a parallelogram is a rectangle, rhombus, or square.

Use with Lesson 6-5

 TEKS G.2.A Geometric structure: use constructions to
explore attributes of geometric figures and to make
conjectures about geometric relationships. Also G.2.B,
G.3.B, G.9.B

go.hrw.com/Geo/TX
Lab Resources Online
KEYWORD: MG7 Lab6

Activity 1

1. Construct $\overline{AB}$ and $\overline{AD}$ with a common endpoint A.
Construct a line through D parallel to $\overline{AB}$.
Construct a line through B parallel to $\overline{AD}$.
Check students' work.

2. Construct point C at the intersection of the
two lines. Hide the lines and construct $\overline{BC}$
and $\overline{CD}$ to complete the parallelogram.
Check students' work.

3. Measure the four sides and angles of the
parallelogram. **Check students' work.**

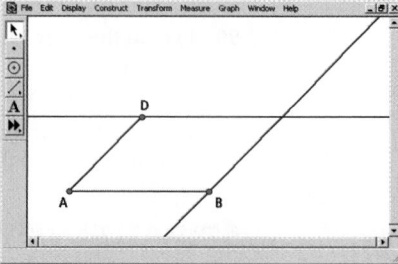

4. Move A so that m$\angle ABC = 90°$. What type of
special parallelogram results? **rect.**

5. Move A so that m$\angle ABC \neq 90°$. **Check students' work.**

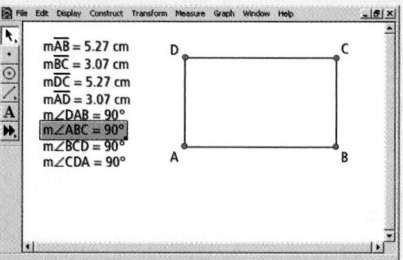

6. Construct $\overline{AC}$ and $\overline{BD}$ and measure their lengths.
Move A so that $AC = BD$. What type of special
parallelogram results? **rect.**

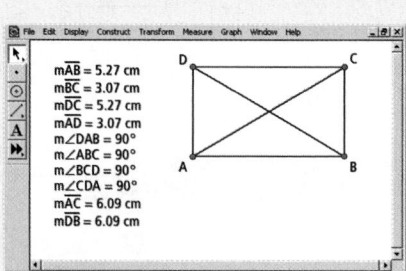

Try This

Both pairs of opp. sides are ‖, so *ABCD* is a ▱ by def.
1. How does the method of constructing *ABCD* in Steps 1 and 2 guarantee
that the quadrilateral is a parallelogram?

2. **Make a Conjecture** What are two conditions for a rectangle?
Write your conjectures as conditional statements. **Possible answers: If a ▱ has a rt. ∠,
then it is a rect. If a ▱ has ≅ diags.,
then it is a rect.**

416 Chapter 6 Polygons and Quadrilaterals

Activity 2

1 Use the parallelogram you constructed in Activity 1. Move *A* so that *AB* = *BC*. What type of special parallelogram results? **rhombus**

2 Move *A* so that *AB* ≠ *BC*. **Check students' work.**

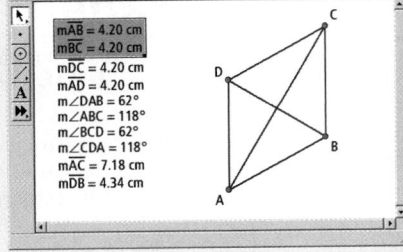

3 Label the intersection of the diagonals as *E*. Measure ∠*AEB*. **Check students' work.**

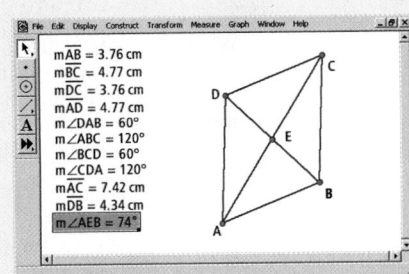

4 Move *A* so that m∠*AEB* = 90°. What type of special parallelogram results? **rhombus**

5 Move *A* so that m∠*AEB* ≠ 90°. **Check students' work.**

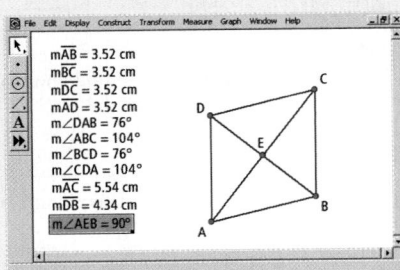

6 Measure ∠*ABD* and ∠*CBD*. Move *A* so that m∠*ABD* = m∠*CBD*. What type of special parallelogram results? **rhombus**

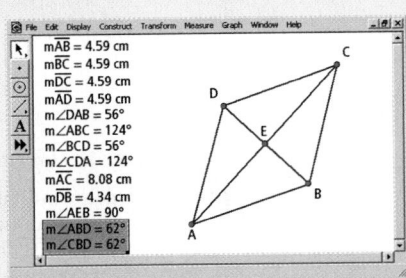

Try This

3. Make a Conjecture What are three conditions for a rhombus? Write your conjectures as conditional statements.

4. Make a Conjecture A square is both a rectangle and a rhombus. What conditions do you think must hold for a parallelogram to be a square?

Close

Key Concept

By manipulating the side lengths and angle measures in a parallelogram, you can discover the conditions for a rectangle, rhombus, or square.

Assessment

Journal Have students summarize the conditions for a rectangle, rhombus, and square.

Answers to *Try This*

3. Possible answers: If a pair of cons. sides of a ▱ are ≅, then the ▱ is a rhombus. If the diags. of a ▱ are ⊥, then the ▱ is a rhombus. If a diag. of a ▱ bisects opp. ∡, then the ▱ is a rhombus.

4. Possible answers: If a ▱ is a rect. and a rhombus, then the ▱ is a square.

Objective: Prove that a given quadrilateral is a rectangle, rhombus, or square.

Geometry Lab
In *Texas Lab Manual*

Online Edition
Tutorial Videos, Interactivity

Countdown to TAKS Week 14

Power Presentations with PowerPoint®

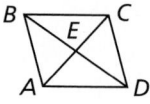

Warm Up

1. Find *AB* for *A*(−3, 5) and *B*(1, 2).   5

2. Find the slope of $\overline{JK}$ for *J*(−4, 4) and *K*(3, −3).   −1

***ABCD* is a parallelogram. Justify each statement.**

3. ∠*ABC* ≅ ∠*CDA*   ▱ → opp.
   ∠ ≅

4. ∠*AEB* ≅ ∠*CED*   Vert. ∠ Thm.

Also available on transparency

Math Humor

Parent: Your geometry teacher thinks you need extra homework.
Student: Tell her I want proof!

⭐ Geometry TEKS

G.2 Geometric structure*
(A) use constructions to explore attributes of geometric figures …
(B) … determine the validity of … conjectures [about polygons]

G.3 Geometric structure*
(B) construct and justify statements about geometric figures …
(E) use deductive reasoning …

G.7 Dimensionality and the geometry of location*
(A) use … coordinate systems …
(B) use slopes and equations of lines to investigate … relationships …
(C) … use formulas involving length, slope, and midpoint

* Knowledge and Skills See p. 378.

418 Chapter 6

⭐ **TEKS G.3.B** Geometric structure: construct and justify statements about geometric figures and their properties. Also G.2.A, G.2.B, G.3.E, G.7.A, G.7.B, G.7.C

Objective
Prove that a given quadrilateral is a rectangle, rhombus, or square.

Who uses this?
Building contractors and carpenters can use the conditions for rectangles to make sure the frame for a house has the correct shape.

When you are given a parallelogram with certain properties, you can use the theorems below to determine whether the parallelogram is a rectangle.

Know it! **.Note**

Theorems **Conditions for Rectangles**

THEOREM	EXAMPLE
6-5-1 If one angle of a parallelogram is a right angle, then the parallelogram is a rectangle. (▱ with one rt. ∠ → rect.)	*diagram: B C A D with right angle at A*
6-5-2 If the diagonals of a parallelogram are congruent, then the parallelogram is a rectangle. (▱ with diags. ≅ → rect.)	*diagram: B C A D with diagonals* $\overline{AC} \cong \overline{BD}$

You will prove Theorems 6-5-1 and 6-5-2 in Exercises 31 and 28.

EXAMPLE 1 *Carpentry Application*

A contractor built a wood frame for the side of a house so that $\overline{XY} \cong \overline{WZ}$ and $\overline{XW} \cong \overline{YZ}$. Using a tape measure, the contractor found that *XZ* = *WY*. Why must the frame be a rectangle?

Both pairs of opposite sides of *WXYZ* are congruent, so *WXYZ* is a parallelogram. Since *XZ* = *WY*, the diagonals of ▱*WXYZ* are congruent. Therefore the frame is a rectangle by Theorem 6-5-2.

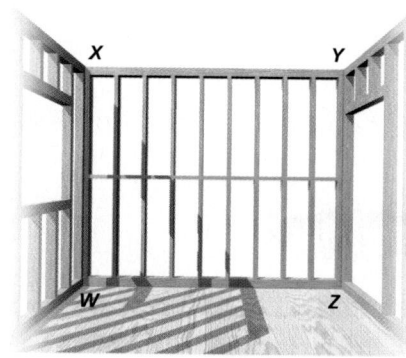

418 Chapter 6 Polygons and Quadrilaterals

---

1 Introduce

EXPLORATION

6-5 **Conditions for Special Parallelograms**

Recall that if the diagonals of a quadrilateral bisect each other, then the quadrilateral is a parallelogram.

1. The figures show quadrilaterals with diagonals that bisect each other, so the quadrilaterals are parallelograms. The diagonals are also perpendicular. What type of parallelograms do *ABCD*, *EFGH*, and *JKLM* appear to be?

2. The figures show three more quadrilaterals with diagonals that bisect each other. Their diagonals are also congruent to each other. What type of parallelograms do *NPQR*, *STUV*, and *WXYZ* appear to be?

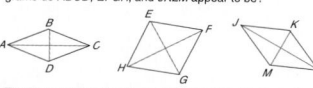

3. Based on the above, describe some conditions that allow you to conclude that a parallelogram is a rhombus or a rectangle.

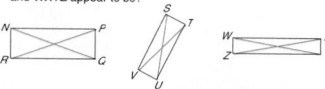

Motivate

Remind students that in the previous lesson they were introduced to the properties of rectangles, rhombuses, and squares. Explain that in this lesson, they will be given a quadrilateral and will learn what conditions can be used to classify it as a rectangle, rhombus, or square.

Explorations and answers are provided in the *Explorations* binder.

1. A carpenter's square can be used to test that an angle is a right angle. How could the contractor use a carpenter's square to check that the frame is a rectangle?

Below are some conditions you can use to determine whether a parallelogram is a rhombus.

Caution! //////

In order to apply Theorems 6-5-1 through 6-5-5, the quadrilateral must be a parallelogram.

Theorems (Conditions for Rhombuses)

THEOREM		EXAMPLE
6-5-3	If one pair of consecutive sides of a parallelogram are congruent, then the parallelogram is a rhombus. (□ with one pair cons. sides ≅ → rhombus)	
6-5-4	If the diagonals of a parallelogram are perpendicular, then the parallelogram is a rhombus. (□ with diags. ⊥ → rhombus)	
6-5-5	If one diagonal of a parallelogram bisects a pair of opposite angles, then the parallelogram is a rhombus. (□ with diag. bisecting opp. ⩘ → rhombus)	

You will prove Theorems 6-5-3 and 6-5-4 in Exercises 32 and 30.

PROOF **Theorem 6-5-5**

Given: *JKLM* is a parallelogram.
$\overline{JL}$ bisects ∠*KJM* and ∠*KLM*.
Prove: *JKLM* is a rhombus.
Proof:

Statements	Reasons
1. *JKLM* is a parallelogram. $\overline{JL}$ bisects ∠*KJM* and ∠*KLM*.	1. Given
2. ∠1 ≅ ∠2, ∠3 ≅ ∠4	2. Def. of ∠ bisector
3. $\overline{JL} ≅ \overline{JL}$	3. Reflex. Prop. of ≅
4. △*JKL* ≅ △*JML*	4. ASA *Steps 2, 3*
5. $\overline{JK} ≅ \overline{JM}$	5. CPCTC
6. *JKLM* is a rhombus.	6. □ with one pair cons. sides ≅ → rhombus

To prove that a given quadrilateral is a square, it is sufficient to show that the figure is both a rectangle and a rhombus. You will explain why this is true in Exercise 43.

2 Teach

Guided Instruction

Review the conditions for rectangles, rhombuses, and squares. In particular, if a parallelogram

- has one right angle, it is a rectangle.
- has congruent diagonals, it is a rectangle.
- has congruent consecutive sides, it is a rhombus.
- has perpendicular diagonals, it is a rhombus.
- is a rectangle and a rhombus, it is a square.

 Reaching All Learners
Through Communication

Have a student list aloud four words, one of which does not fit with the other three. Have another student identify which word does not belong and explain to the class why. For example, the first student might say, "rhombus, rectangle, square, equilateral triangle." A possible response is that the rectangle does not belong because it does not necessarily have all congruent sides.

Additional Examples

Example 1

A manufacturer builds a mold for a desktop so that $\overline{AB} ≅ \overline{CD}$, $\overline{BC} ≅ \overline{DA}$, and m∠*ABC* = 90°. Why must *ABCD* be a rectangle?

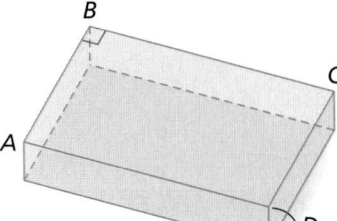

Both pairs of opp. sides of *ABCD* are ≅, so *ABCD* is a □. Since m∠*ABC* = 90°, 1 ∠ of □*ABCD* is a rt. ∠. *ABCD* is a rect. by Thm. 6-5-1.

Also available on transparency

INTERVENTION ◀▬▶
Questioning Strategies

EXAMPLE **1**

- Is a four-sided object with congruent opposite sides always a rectangle? Explain.
- How do you know when you have enough information to classify an object as a rectangle?

 Critical Thinking Some math textbooks define a rectangle as a parallelogram with one right angle. Point out to students that this definition is equivalent to "a quadrilateral with four right angles," because of Theorems 6-4-1 and 6-5-1.

 Auditory Call on students to read each theorem aloud. Then ask them to explain the theorem in their own words. Challenge students to come up with unique ways to explain the theorems. **ENGLISH LANGUAGE LEARNERS**

Answers to *Check It Out!*

1. Both pairs of opp. sides of *WXYZ* are ≅, so *WXYZ* is a □. The contractor can use the carpenter's square to see if 1 ∠ of *WXYZ* is a rt. ∠. If 1 ∠ is a rt. ∠, then by Thm. 6-5-1 the frame is a rect.

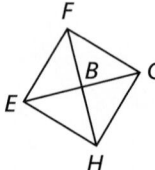

Example 2

Determine if the conclusion is valid. If not, tell what additional information is needed to make it valid.

A. Given: $\overline{EF} \cong \overline{FG}$, $\overline{EG} \perp \overline{FH}$

Conclusion: *EFGH* is a rhombus.

Not valid. You must first know that *EFGH* is a ▱.

B. Given: $\overline{EB} \cong \overline{BG}$, $\overline{FB} \cong \overline{BH}$, $\overline{EG} \cong \overline{FH}$, $\triangle EBF \cong \triangle EBH$

Conclusion: *EFGH* is a square.

valid

Example 3

Use the diagonals to determine whether a parallelogram with the given vertices is a rectangle, rhombus, or square. Give all the names that apply.

A. $P(-1, 4)$, $Q(2, 6)$, $R(4, 3)$, $S(1, 1)$ rect., rhombus, square

B. $W(0, 1)$, $X(4, 2)$, $Y(3, -2)$, $Z(-1, -3)$ rhombus

Also available on transparency

INTERVENTION ◄═►
Questioning Strategies

EXAMPLE **2**

• How do you determine what additional information is needed to make a conclusion valid?

• Can there be more than one way to demonstrate that a conclusion is valid? Explain.

EXAMPLE **3**

• How can you use the diagonals of a parallelogram to classify a figure as a rectangle, rhombus, or square?

Remember!

You can also prove that a given quadrilateral is a rectangle, rhombus, or square by using the definitions of the special quadrilaterals.

2. Not valid; by Thm. 6-5-1, if 1 ∠ of a ▱ is a rt. ∠, then the ▱ is a rect. To apply this thm., you need to know that *ABCD* is a ▱.

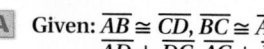

EXAMPLE 2 **Applying Conditions for Special Parallelograms**

Determine if the conclusion is valid. If not, tell what additional information is needed to make it valid.

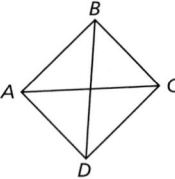

A Given: $\overline{AB} \cong \overline{CD}$, $\overline{BC} \cong \overline{AD}$, $\overline{AD} \perp \overline{DC}$, $\overline{AC} \perp \overline{BD}$

Conclusion: *ABCD* is a square.

Step 1 Determine if *ABCD* is a parallelogram.

$\overline{AB} \cong \overline{CD}$, $\overline{BC} \cong \overline{AD}$ *Given*

ABCD is a parallelogram.   *Quad. with opp. sides ≅ → ▱*

Step 2 Determine if *ABCD* is a rectangle.

$\overline{AD} \perp \overline{DC}$, so $\angle ADC$ is a right angle.   *Def. of ⊥*

ABCD is a rectangle.   *▱ with one rt. ∠ → rect.*

Step 3 Determine if *ABCD* is a rhombus.

$\overline{AC} \perp \overline{BD}$ *Given*

ABCD is a rhombus.   *▱ with diags. ⊥ → rhombus*

Step 4 Determine if *ABCD* is a square.

Since *ABCD* is a rectangle and a rhombus, it has four right angles and four congruent sides. So *ABCD* is a square by definition. The conclusion is valid.

B Given: $\overline{AB} \cong \overline{BC}$

Conclusion: *ABCD* is a rhombus.

The conclusion is not valid. By Theorem 6-5-3, if one pair of consecutive sides of a parallelogram are congruent, then the parallelogram is a rhombus. To apply this theorem, you must first know that *ABCD* is a parallelogram.

CHECK IT OUT! **2.** Determine if the conclusion is valid. If not, tell what additional information is needed to make it valid.
Given: $\angle ABC$ is a right angle.
Conclusion: *ABCD* is a rectangle.

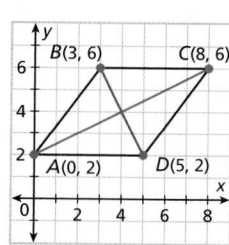

EXAMPLE 3 **Identifying Special Parallelograms in the Coordinate Plane**

Use the diagonals to determine whether a parallelogram with the given vertices is a rectangle, rhombus, or square. Give all the names that apply.

A $A(0, 2)$, $B(3, 6)$, $C(8, 6)$, $D(5, 2)$

Step 1 Graph ▱*ABCD*.

Step 2 Determine if *ABCD* is a rectangle.

$AC = \sqrt{(8 - 0)^2 + (6 - 2)^2}$
$= \sqrt{80} = 4\sqrt{5}$

$BD = \sqrt{(5 - 3)^2 + (2 - 6)^2}$
$= \sqrt{20} = 2\sqrt{5}$

Since $4\sqrt{5} \neq 2\sqrt{5}$, *ABCD* is not a rectangle. Thus *ABCD* is not a square.

Step 3 Determine if $ABCD$ is a rhombus.

slope of $\overline{AC} = \dfrac{6-2}{8-0} = \dfrac{1}{2}$ slope of $\overline{BD} = \dfrac{2-6}{5-3} = -2$

Since $\left(\dfrac{1}{2}\right)(-2) = -1$, $\overline{AC} \perp \overline{BD}$. $ABCD$ is a rhombus.

 $E(-4, -1)$, $F(-3, 2)$, $G(3, 0)$, $H(2, -3)$

Step 1 Graph $\square EFGH$.

Step 2 Determine if $EFGH$ is a rectangle.

$EG = \sqrt{[3-(-4)]^2 + [0-(-1)]^2}$

$\quad = \sqrt{50} = 5\sqrt{2}$

$FH = \sqrt{[2-(-3)]^2 + (-3-2)^2}$

$\quad = \sqrt{50} = 5\sqrt{2}$

Since $5\sqrt{2} = 5\sqrt{2}$, the diagonals are congruent.
$EFGH$ is a rectangle.

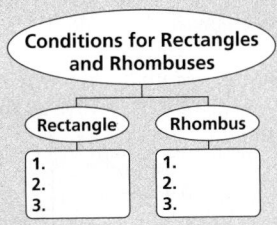

Step 3 Determine if $EFGH$ is a rhombus.

slope of $\overline{EG} = \dfrac{0-(-1)}{3-(-4)} = \dfrac{1}{7}$

slope of $\overline{FH} = \dfrac{-3-2}{2-(-3)} = \dfrac{-5}{5} = -1$

Since $\left(\dfrac{1}{7}\right)(-1) \neq -1$, $\overline{EG} \not\perp \overline{FH}$.

So $EFGH$ is a not a rhombus and cannot be a square.

CHECK IT OUT! Use the diagonals to determine whether a parallelogram with the given vertices is a rectangle, rhombus, or square. Give all the names that apply.

3a. $K(-5, -1)$, $L(-2, 4)$, $M(3, 1)$, $N(0, -4)$ rect., rhombus, square
3b. $P(-4, 6)$, $Q(2, 5)$, $R(3, -1)$, $S(-3, 0)$ rhombus

THINK AND DISCUSS

1. What special parallelogram is formed when the diagonals of a parallelogram are congruent? when the diagonals are perpendicular? when the diagonals are both congruent and perpendicular?

2. Draw a figure that shows why this statement is not necessarily true: If one angle of a quadrilateral is a right angle, then the quadrilateral is a rectangle.

3. A rectangle can also be defined as a parallelogram with a right angle. Explain why this definition is accurate.

4. **GET ORGANIZED** Copy and complete the graphic organizer. In each box, write at least three conditions for the given parallelogram.

Conditions for Rectangles and Rhombuses

Rectangle
1.
2.
3.

Rhombus
1.
2.
3.

3 Close

Summarize

Ask students to classify the figure below.

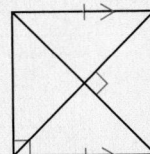

1 pair of opp. sides are $\cong$ and $\parallel$, so it is a $\square$. It has 1 rt. $\angle$, so it is a rect. Its diags. are $\perp$, so it is a rhombus. Since it is a rect. and a rhombus, it is also a square.

ONGOING ASSESSMENT
and INTERVENTION

Diagnose Before the Lesson
6-5 Warm Up, TE p. 418

Monitor During the Lesson
Check It Out! Exercises, SE pp. 419–421
Questioning Strategies, TE pp. 419–420

Assess After the Lesson
6-5 Lesson Quiz, TE p. 425
Alternative Assessment, TE p. 425

Answers to *Think and Discuss*

1. rect.; rhombus; square

2. Possible answer:

3. If a quad. is a rect., then it is a $\square$. If a $\square$ has 1 rt. $\angle$, then it is a rect. Thus these defs. are equivalent.

4. See p. A6.

6-5 **Exercises**

6-5 **Exercises**

go.hrw.com/Geo/TX
Homework Help Online
KEYWORD: MG7 6-5
Parent Resources Online
KEYWORD: MG7 Parent

Assignment Guide

Assign *Guided Practice* exercises as necessary.

If you finished Examples **1–3**
Basic 6–17, 19, 20, 22,
28–30, 33, 35, 39–41,
45–52
Average 6–10, 12–16 even, 17,
18, 20–24, 26–29, 31,
33, 35–41, 44–52
Advanced 6–10, 12–24 even,
25–27, 29–52

Homework Quick Check
Quickly check key concepts.
Exercises: 6, 8, 10, 12, 20, 22

Answers

1. Possible answer: If *WXYZ* is both a rhombus and a rect., then it is a square. All 4 sides of *WXYZ* are ≅, so *WXYZ* is a rhombus. A rhombus is a ▱. If the diags. of a ▱ are ≅, then by Thm. 6-5-2 the ▱ is a rect. So the club members can measure the diags., and if they are equal, *WXYZ* is both a rhombus and a rect. Therefore it is a square.

2. By Thm. 6-5-2, if the diags. of a ▱ are ≅, then the ▱ is a rect. To apply this thm., you need to know that *ABCD* is a ▱.

6. Both pairs of opp. sides of *PQRS* are ≅, so *PQRS* is a ▱. Since *PZ = QZ* and *RZ = SZ*, it follows that *PR = QS* by the Segment Addition Postulate. Thus $\overline{PR} \cong \overline{QS}$. So the diags. of ▱*PQRS* are ≅. The frame is a rect. by Thm. 6-5-2.

⬇ TAKS Practice

GUIDED PRACTICE

SEE EXAMPLE **1**
p. 418

1. **Gardening** A city garden club is planting a square garden. They drive pegs into the ground at each corner and tie strings between each pair. The pegs are spaced so that $\overline{WX} \cong \overline{XY} \cong \overline{YZ} \cong \overline{ZW}$. How can the garden club use the diagonal strings to verify that the garden is a square?

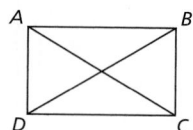

SEE EXAMPLE **2**
p. 420

Determine if the conclusion is valid. If not, tell what additional information is needed to make it valid.

2. Given: $\overline{AC} \cong \overline{BD}$
Conclusion: *ABCD* is a rectangle. **not valid**

3. Given: $\overline{AB} \parallel \overline{CD}$, $\overline{AB} \cong \overline{CD}$, $\overline{AB} \perp \overline{BC}$
Conclusion: *ABCD* is a rectangle. **valid**

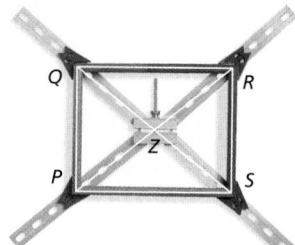

SEE EXAMPLE **3**
p. 420

Multi-Step Use the diagonals to determine whether a parallelogram with the given vertices is a rectangle, rhombus, or square. Give all the names that apply.

4. $P(-5, 2)$, $Q(4, 5)$, $R(6, -1)$, $S(-3, -4)$ **rect.**

5. $W(-6, 0)$, $X(1, 4)$, $Y(2, -4)$, $Z(-5, -8)$ **rhombus**

PRACTICE AND PROBLEM SOLVING

6. **Crafts** A framer uses a clamp to hold together the pieces of a picture frame. The pieces are cut so that $\overline{PQ} \cong \overline{RS}$ and $\overline{QR} \cong \overline{SP}$. The clamp is adjusted so that *PZ*, *QZ*, *RZ*, and *SZ* are all equal. Why must the frame be a rectangle?

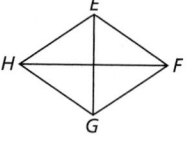

Determine if the conclusion is valid. If not, tell what additional information is needed to make it valid.

7. Given: $\overline{EG}$ and $\overline{FH}$ bisect each other. $\overline{EG} \perp \overline{FH}$
Conclusion: *EFGH* is a rhombus. **valid**

8. Given: $\overline{FH}$ bisects ∠*EFG* and ∠*EHG*.
Conclusion: *EFGH* is a rhombus.

8. Not valid; by Thm. 6-5-5, if 1 diag. of a ▱ bisects a pair of opp. ∡, then the ▱ is a rhombus. To apply this thm., you need to know that *EFGH* is a ▱.

Multi-Step Use the diagonals to determine whether a parallelogram with the given vertices is a rectangle, rhombus, or square. Give all the names that apply.

9. $A(-10, 4)$, $B(-2, 10)$, $C(4, 2)$, $D(-4, -4)$ **square, rect., rhombus**

10. $J(-9, -7)$, $K(-4, -2)$, $L(3, -3)$, $M(-2, -8)$ **rhombus**

Tell whether each quadrilateral is a parallelogram, rectangle, rhombus, or square. Give all the names that apply.

11. 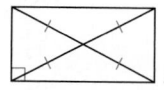 ▱, rect.

12. 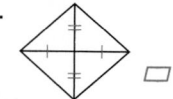 ▱

13.  ▱, rect., rhombus, square

6-5 READING STRATEGIES

Theorem	Example
If one angle of a parallelogram is a right angle, then the parallelogram is a rectangle.	
If the diagonals of a parallelogram are congruent, then the parallelogram is a rectangle.	
If one pair of consecutive sides of a parallelogram is congruent, then the parallelogram is a rhombus.	
If the diagonals of a parallelogram are perpendicular, then the parallelogram is a rhombus.	
If one diagonal of a parallelogram bisects a pair of opposite angles, then the parallelogram is a rhombus.	
If a parallelogram is both a rectangle and a rhombus, then the parallelogram is a square.	

In the table below, write the name of the quadrilateral that BEST matches the information that is checked. Choose from the following list:
rectangle   rhombus   square

Quadrilateral that BEST matches the information	Parallelogram with one right angle	Parallelogram with a diagonal that bisects a pair of opposite angles	Parallelogram with congruent diagonals	Parallelogram with one pair of congruent consecutive sides	Parallelogram with perpendicular diagonals
1. rectangle	x				
2. rhombus		x			
3. square	x	x			
4. rectangle			x		
5. square			x	x	
6. rhombus				x	
7. rhombus					x

6-5 RETEACH

You can use the following conditions to determine whether a parallelogram is a rectangle.

If one angle is a right angle, then ▱*JKLM* is a rectangle.	If the diagonals are congruent, then ▱*JKLM* is a rectangle. $\overline{JL} \cong \overline{KM}$

You can use the following conditions to determine whether a parallelogram is a rhombus.

If one pair of consecutive sides are congruent, then ▱*TUVW* is a rhombus.	If the diagonals are perpendicular, then ▱*TUVW* is a rhombus.	If one diagonal bisects a pair of opposite angles, then ▱*TUVW* is a rhombus.

Determine whether the conclusion is valid. If not, tell what additional information is needed to make it valid.

1. *EFGH* is a rectangle.

valid

2. *MPQR* is a rhombus.

Not valid; need to know that *MPQR* is a ▱.

For Exercises 3 and 4, use the figure to determine whether the conclusion is valid. If not, tell what additional information is needed to make it valid.

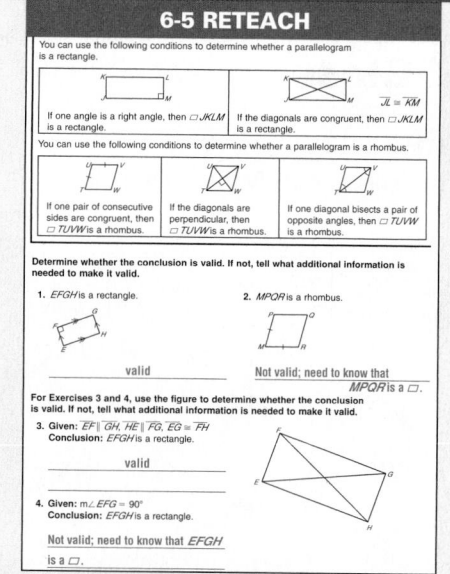

3. Given: $\overline{EF} \cong \overline{GH}$, $\overline{HE} \cong \overline{FG}$, $\overline{EG} \cong \overline{FH}$
Conclusion: *EFGH* is a rectangle.

valid

4. Given: m∠*EFG* = 90°
Conclusion: *EFGH* is a rectangle.

Not valid; need to know that *EFGH* is a ▱.

Tell whether each quadrilateral is a parallelogram, rectangle, rhombus, or square. Give all the names that apply.

14.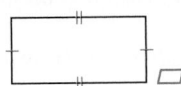

15. 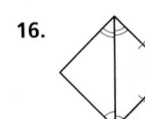 ☐, rect., rhombus, square

16. 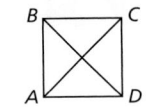 ☐, rhombus

17. B; possible answer: it is given that *ABCD* is a ☐. *AC* and *BD* are its diags. By Thm. 6-5-2, if the diags. of a ☐ are ≅, you can conclude that the ☐ is a rect. There is not enough information to conclude that *ABCD* is a square.

17. ///ERROR ANALYSIS/// In ☐*ABCD*, $\overline{AC} \cong \overline{BD}$. Which conclusion is incorrect? Explain the error.

Ⓐ ABCD is a rectangle.

Ⓑ ABCD is a square.

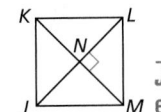

Give one characteristic of the diagonals of each figure that would make the conclusion valid.

18. Conclusion: *JKLM* is a rhombus.

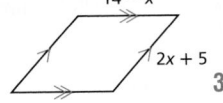 *JL* and *KM* bisect each other.

19. Conclusion: *PQRS* is a square.

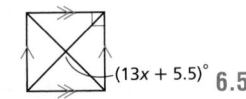 $\overline{PR} \cong \overline{QS}$

The coordinates of three vertices of ☐*ABCD* are given. Find the coordinates of *D* so that the given type of figure is formed.

20. (−5, 4)

21. (2, 6)

22. (−4, −2)

23. (−2, −2)

20. $A(4, -2), B(-5, -2), C(4, 4)$; rectangle
21. $A(-5, 5), B(0, 0), C(7, 1)$; rhombus
22. $A(0, 2), B(4, -2), C(0, -6)$; square
23. $A(2, 1), B(-1, 5), C(-5, 2)$; square

Find the value of *x* that makes each parallelogram the given type.

24. rectangle

$(5x - 3)°$ 18.6

25. rhombus

$14 - x$, $2x + 5$, 3

26. square

$(13x + 5.5)°$ 6.5

27. Rhombus; since the diags. bisect each other, the quad. is a ☐. Since the diags. of the ☐ are ⊥, the quad. is a rhombus.

27. Critical Thinking The diagonals of a quadrilateral are perpendicular bisectors of each other. What is the best name for this quadrilateral? Explain your answer.

28. Complete the two-column proof of Theorem 6-5-2 by filling in the blanks.

Given: *EFGH* is a parallelogram.
$\overline{EG} \cong \overline{HF}$
Prove: *EFGH* is a rectangle.

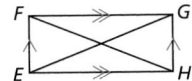

Proof:

Statements	Reasons
1. *EFGH* is a parallelogram. $\overline{EG} \cong \overline{HF}$	1. Given
2. $\overline{EF} \cong \overline{HG}$	2. a. ___?___ ☐ → opp. sides ≅
3. b. ___?___ $\overline{EH} \cong \overline{EH}$	3. Reflex. Prop. of ≅
4. △*EFH* ≅ △*HGE*	4. c. ___?___ SSS
5. ∠*FEH* ≅ d. ___?___ ∠*GHE*	5. e. ___?___ CPCTC
6. ∠*FEH* and ∠*GHE* are supplementary.	6. f. ___?___ ☐ → cons. ∠ supp.
7. g. ___?___ ∠*FEH* and ∠*GHE* are rt. ∠.	7. ≅ ∠ supp. → rt. ∠
8. *EFGH* is a rectangle.	8. h. ___?___ h. ☐ with 1 rt. ∠ → rect.

Teaching Tip

Communicating Math
When students work **Exercises 18 and 19,** encourage them to write a complete statement of the given information and then compare it with the theorems in the lesson.

6-5 PRACTICE A

6-5 PRACTICE C

6-5 PRACTICE B

1. On the National Mall in Washington, D.C., a reflecting pool lies between the Lincoln Memorial and the World War II Memorial. The pool has two 2300-foot-long sides and two 150-foot-long sides. Tell what additional information you need to know in order to determine whether the reflecting pool is a rectangle. (*Hint:* Remember that you have to show it is a parallelogram first.)

Possible answer: To know that the reflecting pool is a parallelogram, the congruent sides must be opposite each other. If this is true, then knowing that one angle in the pool is a right angle or that the diagonals are congruent proves that the pool is a rectangle.

Use the figure for Exercises 2–5. Determine whether each conclusion is valid. If not, tell what additional information is needed to make it valid.

2. **Given:** $\overline{AC}$ and $\overline{BD}$ bisect each other. $\overline{AC} \cong \overline{BD}$
   Conclusion: *ABCD* is a square.
   Not valid; possible answer: you need to know that $\overline{AC} \perp \overline{BD}$.

3. **Given:** $\overline{AC} \perp \overline{BD}, \overline{AB} \cong \overline{BC}$
   Conclusion: *ABCD* is a rhombus. Not valid;
   possible answer: you need to know that $\overline{AC}$ and $\overline{BD}$ bisect each other.

4. **Given:** $\overline{AB} \cong \overline{DC}, \overline{AD} \cong \overline{BC}, m\angle ADB = m\angle ABD = 45°$
   Conclusion: *ABCD* is a square.
   valid

5. **Given:** $\overline{AB} \parallel \overline{DC}, \overline{AD} \cong \overline{BC}, \overline{AC} \cong \overline{BD}$
   Conclusion: *ABCD* is a rectangle.
   Not valid; possible answer: you need to know that $\overline{AD} \parallel \overline{BC}$.

Find the lengths and slopes of the diagonals to determine whether a parallelogram with the given vertices is a rectangle, rhombus, or square. Give all names that apply.

6. $E(-2, -4), F(0, -1), G(-3, 1), H(-5, -2)$ rectangle, rhombus, square
   $EG = \sqrt{26}$ $FH = \sqrt{26}$
   slope of $\overline{EG} = -5$ slope of $\overline{FH} = \frac{1}{5}$

7. $P(-1, 3), Q(-2, 5), R(0, 4), S(1, 2)$ rhombus
   $PR = \sqrt{2}$ $QS = 3\sqrt{2}$
   slope of $\overline{PR} = 1$ slope of $\overline{QS} = -1$

6-5 PROBLEM SOLVING

1. An amusement park has a rectangular observation deck with walkways above the bungee jumping and sky jumping. The distance from the center of the deck to points *E, F, G,* and *H* is 15 meters. Explain why *EFGH* must be a rectangle.

Diagonals bisect each other, so the quad. is a ☐. The diagonals are ≅, so *EFGH* is a rect. because ☐ with diags. ≅ → rect.

2. In the mosaic, $\overline{AB} \parallel \overline{CD}$ and $\overline{BC} \parallel \overline{DA}$. If *AB* = 4 inches and *BC* = 4 inches, can you conclude that *ABCD* is a square? Explain.

No; from the given information, you can conclude only that *ABCD* is a rhombus.

Choose the best answer.

4. The vertices of a parallelogram are *M*(0, −4), *P*(6, −1), *Q*(4, 3), and *R*(−2, 0). Classify the parallelogram as specifically as possible.
   Ⓐ rectangle only
   B square
   C rhombus only
   D quadrilateral

6. In parallelogram *KLMN*, $m\angle L = (4w + 5)°$. Choose the value of *w* that makes *KLMN* a rectangle.
   A 90   C 43.75
   B 85   Ⓓ 21.25

3. If $\overline{TV} \cong \overline{US}$, explain why the basketball backboard must be a rectangle.

Both pairs of opposite sides are ≅, so *STUV* is a ☐. *STUV* is a rectangle because ☐ with diags. → rect.

5. Choose the best description for the quadrilateral.
   Ⓕ parallelogram
   G parallelogram and rectangle
   H parallelogram and rhombus
   J parallelogram and square

7. The coordinates of three vertices of quadrilateral *ABCD* are *A*(3, −1), *B*(10, 0), and *C*(5, 5). For which coordinates of *D* will the quadrilateral be a rhombus?
   F (−1, 4)   H (−1, 3)
   Ⓖ (−2, 4)   J (−2, 3)

6-5 CHALLENGE

If each vertex of a polygon lies on a circle, the polygon is said to be *inscribed* in that circle. It is possible to make compass-and-straightedge constructions of several types of regular polygons by inscribing them in circles.

To construct a regular pentagon, do Exercises 1–6 in order.

1. In the circle at right, point *O* is the center. Draw a diameter and label it $\overline{XY}$. (A diameter of a circle is a segment that has its endpoints on the circle and that passes through the center of the circle.)

2. Construct the perpendicular bisector of $\overline{XY}$. Label the points where it intersects the circle *A* and *Z*.

3. Bisect $\overline{OY}$. Label the midpoint *M*.

4. Place the compass point on *M* and the pencil on *A*. Draw an arc that intersects $\overline{XO}$. Label the intersection *N*.

5. Set the compass equal to the distance *AN*. Start at point *A* and mark five congruent arcs on the circle. Label the points of intersection *A, B, C, D,* and *E*, in that order.

6. Draw $\overline{AB}, \overline{BC}, \overline{CD}, \overline{DE},$ and $\overline{EA}$. *ABCDE* is a regular pentagon.

7. a. If Exercises 1–6 have been done correctly, what should be true of the measures of the sides and angles of pentagon *ABCDE*?
   The measure of each angle should be 108°. All the sides should be congruent.
   b. Use a ruler, a protractor, and your answer to part **a** to check your construction.
   Results will vary.

8. Using the regular pentagon construction as a basis, devise a way to construct a regular decagon. Show your construction on a separate sheet of paper. In Exercises 1–5, draw line segments; bisect angles; label intersecting points; draw line segments.

9. Regular polygon constructions can be the starting point for many attractive designs. Below are some designs that are derived from pentagons and regular decagons. Choose one of these designs. Use a compass and straightedge to re-create the design on a separate sheet of paper.

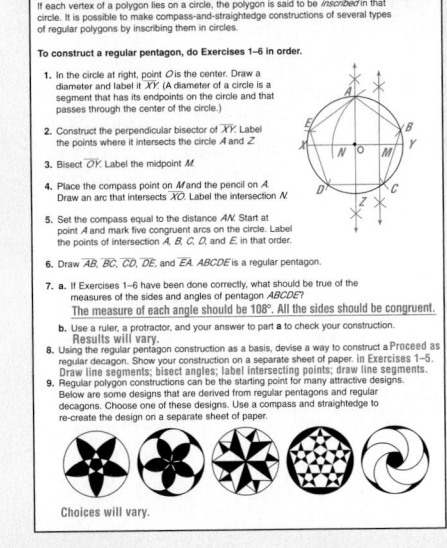

Choices will vary.

involves identifying special parallelograms in the coordinate plane. This exercise prepares students for the Multi-Step TAKS Prep on page 436.

Answers

29a. slope of $\overline{AB}$ = slope of $\overline{CD}$ = $-\frac{1}{3}$; slope of $\overline{AD}$ = slope of $\overline{CB} = -3$

b. Slope of $\overline{AC} = -1$; slope of $\overline{BD} = 1$; the slopes are negative reciprocals of each other, so $\overline{AC} \perp \overline{BD}$.

c. *ABCD* is a rhombus, since it is a ▱ and its diags. are ⊥ (Thm. 6-5-4).

31. Possible answer:
1. *ABCD* is a ▱. ∠*A* is a rt. ∠. (Given)
2. m∠*A* = 90° (Def. of rt. ∠)
3. ∠*A* and ∠*B* are supp. (▱ → cons. ▵ supp.)
4. m∠*A* + m∠*B* = 180° (Def. of supp. ▵)
5. 90° + m∠*B* = 180° (Subst.)
6. m∠*B* = 90° (Subtr. Prop. of =)
7. ∠*C* ≅ ∠*A*, ∠*D* ≅ ∠*B* (▱ → opp. ▵ ≅)
8. m∠*C* = m∠*A*, m∠*D* = m∠*B* (Def. of ≅ ▵)
9. m∠*C* = 90°, m∠*D* = 90° (Trans. Prop. of =)
10. ∠*B*, ∠*C*, and ∠*D* are rt. ▵. (Def. of rt. ∠)
11. *ABCD* is a rect. (Def. of rect.)

32. Possible answer: It is given that $\overline{JK} \cong \overline{KL}$. Since opp. sides of a ▱ are ≅, $\overline{JK} \cong \overline{LM}$, and $\overline{KL} \cong \overline{MJ}$. By the Trans. Prop. of ≅, $\overline{JK} \cong \overline{MJ}$. So $\overline{JK}$ is ≅ to each of the other 3 sides of *JKLM*. Therefore *JKLM* is a rhombus by def.

33a.

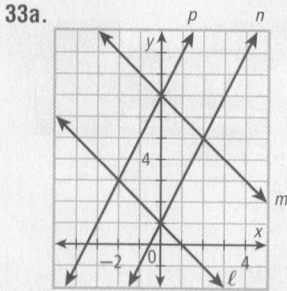

34. Possible answer:
1. *FHJN* and *GLMF* are ▱. $\overline{FG} \cong \overline{FN}$ (Given)
2. $\overline{FH} \parallel \overline{NJ}$, $\overline{GL} \parallel \overline{FM}$ (Def. of ▱)
3. *FGKN* is a ▱. (Def. of ▱)
4. *FGKN* is a rhombus. (▱ with 1 pair cons. sides ≅ → rhombus)

29. This problem will prepare you for the Multi-Step TAKS Prep on page 436.

A state fair takes place on a plot of land given by the coordinates $A(-2, 3)$, $B(1, 2)$, $C(2, -1)$, and $D(-1, 0)$.

a. Show that the opposite sides of quadrilateral *ABCD* are parallel.

b. A straight path connects *A* and *C*, and another path connects *B* and *D*. Use slopes to prove that these two paths are perpendicular.

c. What can you conclude about *ABCD*? Explain your answer.

30. Complete the paragraph proof of Theorem 6-5-4 by filling in the blanks.

Given: *PQRS* is a parallelogram. $\overline{PR} \perp \overline{QS}$
Prove: *PQRS* is a rhombus.

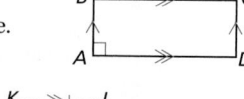

Proof:
It is given that *PQRS* is a parallelogram. The diagonals of a parallelogram bisect each other, so $\overline{PT} \cong$ **a.** ___?___ . By the Reflexive Property of Congruence, $\overline{QT} \cong$ **b.** ___?___ . It is given that $\overline{PR} \perp \overline{QS}$, so ∠*QTP* and ∠*QTR* are right angles by the definition of **c.** ___?___ . Then ∠*QTP* ≅ ∠*QTR* by the **d.** ___?___ . So △*QTP* ≅ △*QTR* by **e.** ___?___ , and $\overline{QP} \cong$ **f.** ___?___ , by CPCTC. By Theorem 6-5-3, if one pair of consecutive sides of a parallelogram are congruent, then the parallelogram is a **g.** ___?___ . Therefore *PQRS* is rhombus.

a. $\overline{RT}$
b. $\overline{QT}$
c. ⊥ lines
d. Rt. ∠ ≅ Thm.
e. SAS
f. $\overline{QR}$
g. rhombus

31. Write a two-column proof of Theorem 6-5-1.

Given: *ABCD* is a parallelogram. ∠*A* is a right angle.
Prove: *ABCD* is a rectangle.

32. Write a paragraph proof of Theorem 6-5-3.

Given: *JKLM* is a parallelogram. $\overline{JK} \cong \overline{KL}$
Prove: *JKLM* is a rhombus.

33. **Algebra** Four lines are represented by the equations below.

$\ell: y = -x + 1$ $m: y = -x + 7$ $n: y = 2x + 1$ $p: y = 2x + 7$

a. Graph the four lines in the coordinate plane.

b. Classify the quadrilateral formed by the lines. ▱

c. **What if...?** Suppose the slopes of lines *n* and *p* change to 1. Reclassify the quadrilateral. **square**

34. Write a two-column proof.

Given: *FHJN* and *GLMF* are parallelograms. $\overline{FG} \cong \overline{FN}$
Prove: *FGKN* is a rhombus.

35. **Write About It** Use Theorems 6-4-2 and 6-5-2 to write a biconditional statement about rectangles. Use Theorems 6-4-4 and 6-5-4 to write a biconditional statement about rhombuses. Can you combine Theorems 6-4-5 and 6-5-5 to write a biconditional statement? Explain your answer.

36–38.
Check students' work. Answers will vary.

Construction Use the diagonals to construct each figure. Then use the theorems from this lesson to explain why your method works.

36. rectangle   **37.** rhombus   **38.** square

---

35. A ▱ is a rect. if and only if its diags. are ≅; a ▱ is a rhombus if and only if its diags. are ⊥; no; possible answer: Thms. 6-4-5 and 6-5-5 are not converses. The conclusion of the conditional in Thm. 6-4-5 refers to both diags. of a ▱. The hypothesis of the conditional in Thm. 6-5-5 refers to only 1 diag. of a ▱.

41b. m∠*JKM* = m∠*LMK*, so $\overline{JK} \parallel \overline{LM}$. Since both pairs of opp. sides are ∥, *JKLM* is a ▱.

c. There is not enough information to determine if the diags. are ≅ or if the ▱ has a rt. ∠.

d. m∠*KNL* = 90°, so the diags. are ⊥, and *JKLM* is a rhombus.

42. Possible answer:
1. $\overline{AC} \cong \overline{DF}$, $\overline{AB} \cong \overline{DE}$, $\overline{AB} \perp \overline{BC}$, $\overline{DE} \perp \overline{EF}$, $\overline{BE} \perp \overline{EF}$, $\overline{BC} \parallel \overline{EF}$ (Given)
2. m∠*ABC* = 90°, m∠*DEF* = 90°, m∠*BEF* = 90° (Def. of ⊥)
3. ∠*ABC*, ∠*DEF*, and ∠*BEF* are rt. ▵. (Def. of rt. ∠)
4. △*ABC* and △*DEF* are rt. ▵. (Def. of rt. △)
5. △*ABC* ≅ △*DEF* (HL)
6. $\overline{BC} \cong \overline{EF}$ (CPCTC)
7. *EBCF* is a ▱. (Quad. with pair of opp. sides ≅ and ∥ → ▱)
8. *EBCF* is a rect. (▱ with 1 rt. ∠ → rect.)

39. In ▱*PQRS*, $\overline{PR}$ and $\overline{QS}$ intersect at *T*. What additional information is needed to conclude that *PQRS* is a rectangle?

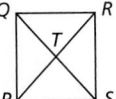

Ⓐ $\overline{PT} \cong \overline{QT}$ Ⓒ $\overline{PT} \perp \overline{QT}$

Ⓑ $\overline{PT} \cong \overline{RT}$ Ⓓ $\overline{PT}$ bisects ∠*QPS*.

40. Which of the following is the best name for figure *WXYZ* with vertices *W*(−3, 1), *X*(1, 5), *Y*(8, −2), and *Z*(4, −6)?

Ⓕ Parallelogram   Ⓖ Rectangle   Ⓗ Rhombus   Ⓙ Square

41. Extended Response $15x = 13x + 12; x = 6$

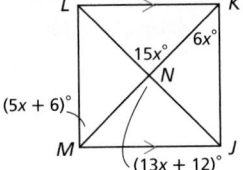

a. Write and solve an equation to find the value of *x*.

b. Is *JKLM* a parallelogram? Explain. **yes**

c. Is *JKLM* a rectangle? Explain. **not necessarily**

d. Is *JKLM* a rhombus? Explain. **yes**

CHALLENGE AND EXTEND

42. Given: $\overline{AC} \cong \overline{DF}$, $\overline{AB} \cong \overline{DE}$, $\overline{AB} \perp \overline{BC}$, $\overline{DE} \perp \overline{EF}$, $\overline{BE} \perp \overline{EF}$, $\overline{BC} \parallel \overline{EF}$

Prove: *EBCF* is a rectangle.

43. Critical Thinking Consider the following statement: If a quadrilateral is a rectangle and a rhombus, then it is a square.

a. Explain why the statement is true.

b. If a quadrilateral is a rectangle, is it necessary to show that all four sides are congruent in order to conclude that it is a square? Explain. **no**

c. If a quadrilateral is a rhombus, is it necessary to show that all four angles are right angles in order to conclude that it is a square? Explain. **no**

44. The diags. of the ▱ are ⊥, so it is a rhombus.

44. Cars As you turn the crank of a car jack, the platform that supports the car raises. Use the diagonals of the parallelogram to explain whether the jack forms a rectangle, rhombus, or square.

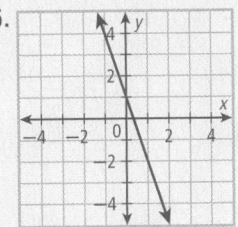

SPIRAL REVIEW

Sketch the graph of each function. State whether the function is linear or nonlinear. *(Previous course)*

45. $y = -3x + 1$
   linear

46. $y = x^2 - 4$
   nonlinear

47. $y = 3$
   linear

Find the perimeter of each figure. Round to the nearest tenth. *(Lesson 5-7)*

48. 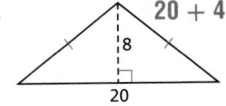 $20 + 4\sqrt{41} \approx 45.6$

49. 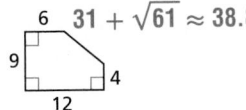 6 $31 + \sqrt{61} \approx 38.8$

Find the value of each variable that would make the quadrilateral a parallelogram. *(Lesson 6-3)*

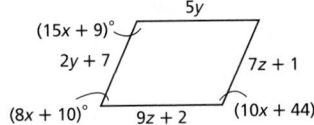

50. *x* **7**   **51.** *y* **4**   **52.** *z* **2**

43a. Possible answer: If a quad. is a rect., then it has 4 rt. ∡. If a quad. is a rhombus, then it has 4 ≅ sides. By def., a quad. with 4 ≅ sides and 4 rt. ∡ is a square. Therefore the statement is true.

b. Possible answer: If a quad. is a rect., then it is a ▱. By Thm. 6-5-3, if 1 pair of cons. sides of a ▱ are ≅, then the ▱ is a rhombus. So if 1 pair of cons. sides of a rect. are ≅, it is a rhombus. If a quad. is a rect. and a rhombus, then it is a square.

c. Possible answer: If a quad. is a rhombus, then it is a ▱. By Thm. 6-5-1, if 1 ∠ of a ▱ is a rt. ∠, then the ▱ is a rect. So if 1 ∠ of a rhombus is a rt. ∠, it is a rect. If a quad. is a rhombus and a rect., then it is a square.

45.

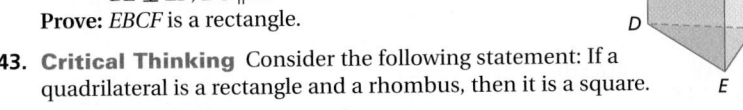

46, 47. For graphs, see p. A23.

 **TEST PREP DOCTOR** ➕ If students have difficulty with **Exercise 39**, point out that *PQRS* is a parallelogram and that the diagonals of a parallelogram bisect each other. Tell students who chose **C** that they can conclude that *PQRS* is a rhombus, but not a rectangle.

Journal

Have students draw a graphic organizer showing the relationship between a parallelogram, rectangle, rhombus, and square.

ALTERNATIVE ASSESSMENT

Have each student draw three parallelograms and mark some given characteristics on each. Have students exchange papers and explain whether each figure is a rectangle, rhombus, square, or none of these.

Power Presentations with PowerPoint®

 **6-5 Lesson Quiz**

1. Given that $AB = BC = CD = DA$, what additional information is needed to conclude that *ABCD* is a square?
$\overline{AC} \cong \overline{BD}$

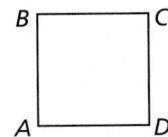

2. Determine if the conclusion is valid. If not, tell what additional information is needed to make it valid.

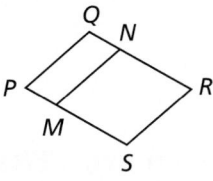

Given: *PQRS* and *PQNM* are ▱. $\overline{MN} \cong \overline{NR}$
Conclusion: *MNRS* is a rhombus.   **valid**

3. Use the diagonals to determine whether a parallelogram with vertices *A*(2, 7), *B*(7, 9), *C*(5, 4), and *D*(0, 2) is a rectangle, rhombus, or square. Give all the names that apply.
$AC \neq BD$, so *ABCD* is not a rect. or a square. The slope of $AC = -1$, and the slope of $BD = 1$, so $\overline{AC} \perp \overline{BD}$. *ABCD* is a rhombus.

Also available on transparency

Pacing:
Traditional 1 day
Block $\frac{1}{2}$ day

Objective: Use geometry software to investigate the properties and conditions of an isosceles trapezoid.

Materials: geometry software

Online Edition
TechKeys

Countdown to TAKS Week 14

Teach

Discuss

After **Activity 1, Step 5,** ask students to compare m∠ACD and m∠BDC. Explain to students that in order to prove that a trapezoid is isosceles, you only have to show that one pair of base angles is congruent. Ask students to discuss why the other pair is necessarily congruent.

Close

Key Concept

An isosceles trapezoid has congruent pairs of base angles and congruent diagonals.

Assessment

Journal Have students describe the properties they discovered about isosceles trapezoids.

 Geometry TEKS

G.2 Geometric structure*
(A) use constructions to explore attributes of geometric figures and to make conjectures about geometric relationships
(B) make conjectures about ... polygons ... and determine the validity ...

G.3 Geometric structure*
(B) construct and justify statements about geometric figures ...

G.9 Congruence and the geometry of size*
(B) formulate and test conjectures about ... polygons and their component parts based on explorations and concrete models

* Knowledge and Skills See p. 378.

Technology LAB

Explore Isosceles Trapezoids

In this lab you will investigate the properties and conditions of an *isosceles trapezoid*. A *trapezoid* is a quadrilateral with one pair of parallel sides, called *bases*. The sides that are not parallel are called *legs*. In an isosceles trapezoid, the legs are congruent.

Use with Lesson 6-6

 TEKS G.2.A Geometric structure: use constructions to explore attributes of geometric figures and to make conjectures about geometric relationships. Also G.2.B, G.3.B, G.9.B

go.hrw.com/Geo/TX
Lab Resources Online
KEYWORD: MG7 Lab6

Activity 1

① Draw $\overline{AB}$ and a point C not on $\overline{AB}$. Construct a parallel line ℓ through C. **Check students' work.**

② Draw point D on line ℓ. Construct $\overline{AC}$ and $\overline{BD}$. **Check students' work.**

③ Measure AC, BD, ∠CAB, ∠ABD, ∠ACD, and ∠CDB. **Check students' work.**

④ Move D until AC = BD. What do you notice about m∠CAB and m∠ABD? What do you notice about m∠ACD and m∠CDB? **m∠CAB = m∠ABD; m∠ACD = m∠CDB**

⑤ Move D so that AC ≠ BD. Now move D so that m∠CAB = m∠ABD. What do you notice about AC and BD? **AC = BD**

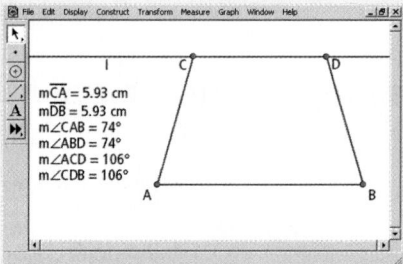

Try This

Possible answer: If a trap. is isosc., then its base ∠ are ≅.

1. **Make a Conjecture** What is true about the base angles of an isosceles trapezoid? Write your conjecture as a conditional statement.

2. **Make a Conjecture** How can the base angles of a trapezoid be used to determine if the trapezoid is isosceles? Write your conjecture as a conditional statement. **Possible answer: If 1 pair of base ∠ of a trap. are ≅, then the trap. is isosc.**

Activity 2

① Construct $\overline{AD}$ and $\overline{CB}$. **Check students' work.**

② Measure AD and CB. **Check students' work.**

③ Move D until AC = BD. What do you notice about AD and CB? **AD = CB**

④ Move D so that AC ≠ BD. Now move D so that AD = BC. What do you notice about AC and BD? **AC = BD**

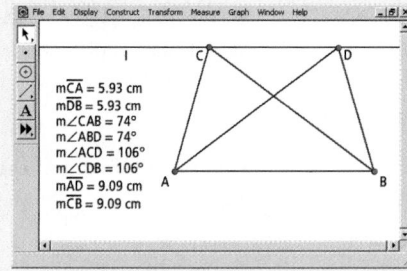

Try This

Possible answer: If a trap. is isosc., then its diags. are ≅.

3. **Make a Conjecture** What is true about the diagonals of an isosceles trapezoid? Write your conjecture as a conditional statement.

4. **Make a Conjecture** How can the diagonals of a trapezoid be used to determine if the trapezoid is isosceles? Write your conjecture as a conditional statement. **Possible answer: If the diags. of a trap. are ≅, then the trap. is isosc.**

Properties of Kites and Trapezoids

TEKS G.3.B Geometric structure: construct and justify statements about geometric figures and their properties. Also G.2.A, G.2.B, G.3.E, G.7.A, G.7.B, G.7.C

Objectives
Use properties of kites to solve problems.

Use properties of trapezoids to solve problems.

Vocabulary
kite
trapezoid
base of a trapezoid
leg of a trapezoid
base angle of a trapezoid
isosceles trapezoid
midsegment of a
 trapezoid

Why learn this?

The design of a simple kite flown at the beach shares the properties of the geometric figure called a *kite*.

A **kite** is a quadrilateral with exactly two pairs of congruent consecutive sides.

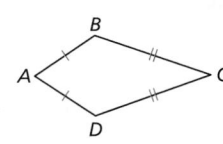

Kite *ABCD*

Theorems | **Properties of Kites**

	THEOREM	HYPOTHESIS	CONCLUSION
6-6-1	If a quadrilateral is a kite, then its diagonals are perpendicular. (kite → diags. ⊥)		$\overline{AC} \perp \overline{BD}$
6-6-2	If a quadrilateral is a kite, then exactly one pair of opposite angles are congruent. (kite → one pair opp. ⦞ ≅)		$\angle B \cong \angle D$ $\angle A \not\cong \angle C$

You will prove Theorem 6-6-1 in Exercise 39.

PROOF | **Theorem 6-6-2**

Given: *JKLM* is a kite with $\overline{JK} \cong \overline{JM}$ and $\overline{KL} \cong \overline{ML}$.
Prove: $\angle K \cong \angle M$, $\angle KJM \not\cong \angle KLM$

Proof:
Step 1 Prove $\angle K \cong \angle M$.
 It is given that $\overline{JK} \cong \overline{JM}$ and $\overline{KL} \cong \overline{ML}$. By the Reflexive Property of Congruence, $\overline{JL} \cong \overline{JL}$. This means that $\triangle JKL \cong \triangle JML$ by SSS. So $\angle K \cong \angle M$ by CPCTC.

Step 2 Prove $\angle KJM \not\cong \angle KLM$.
 If $\angle KJM \cong \angle KLM$, then both pairs of opposite angles of *JKLM* are congruent. This would mean that *JKLM* is a parallelogram. But this contradicts the given fact that *JKLM* is a kite. Therefore $\angle KJM \not\cong \angle KLM$.

Pacing: Traditional 1 day
 Block $\frac{1}{2}$ day
Objectives: Use properties of kites to solve problems.

Use properties of trapezoids to solve problems.

 Geometry Lab
In *Texas Lab Manual*

 Online Edition
Tutorial Videos

 Countdown to TAKS Week 14

Power Presentations
with PowerPoint®

 Warm Up

Solve for x.

1. $x^2 + 38 = 3x^2 - 12$ 5 or −5

2. $137 + x = 180$ 43

3. $42 = \frac{1}{4}(12 + x)$ 156

4. Find *FE*. $6\sqrt{11}$ in.

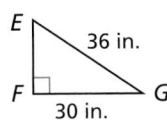

E
36 in.
F
30 in.
G

Also available on transparency

Math Humor

Q: Do geometry teachers have any special talents?

A: I hear they can fly kites well.

⭐ **Geometry TEKS**

G.2 Geometric structure*
(A) use constructions to explore attributes of geometric figures …
(B) … determine the validity of … conjectures [about polygons]

G.3 Geometric structure*
(B) construct and justify statements about geometric figures …
(E) use deductive reasoning …

G.7 Dimensionality and the geometry of location*
(A) use … coordinate systems …
(B) use slopes and equations of lines to investigate … relationships …
(C) … use formulas involving length, slope, and midpoint

* Knowledge and Skills See p. 378.

---

1 Introduce

EXPLORATION

6-6 **Properties of Kites and Trapezoids**

A *kite* is a quadrilateral with exactly two pairs of congruent consecutive sides.

1. Draw three noncollinear points A, B, and C on a piece of patty paper so that $AB \neq AC$. Then draw $\overline{AB}$ and $\overline{AC}$.	2. Fold the paper so that the fold passes through points B and C. Use the point of a pencil to make a small hole through point A.
3. Unfold the paper. Label the hole across from point A as point D.	4. Draw $\overline{BD}$ and $\overline{CD}$. What type of quadrilateral is *ABDC*?

5. Draw the diagonals of quadrilateral *ABDC*. Do they bisect each other? Are they perpendicular?

6. Repeat the process starting with a new set of points. Do you get the same results?

THINK AND DISCUSS
7. Explain how to use your findings to make a conjecture about

Motivate

Challenge students to draw a counterexample for these statements.
 A quadrilateral with one pair of consecutive congruent sides is a rhombus. A quadrilateral with congruent diagonals is a rectangle.
Then draw a kite and an isosceles trapezoid for students. Explain that they will learn the properties of these quadrilaterals in this lesson.

Explorations and answers are provided in the *Explorations* binder.

Additional Examples

Example 1

Lucy is framing a kite with wooden dowels. She uses two dowels that measure 18 cm, one dowel that measures 30 cm, and two dowels that measure 27 cm. To complete the kite, she needs a dowel to place along $\overline{KL}$. She has a dowel that is 36 cm long. About how much wood will she have left over after cutting the last dowel? ≈ 3.6 cm

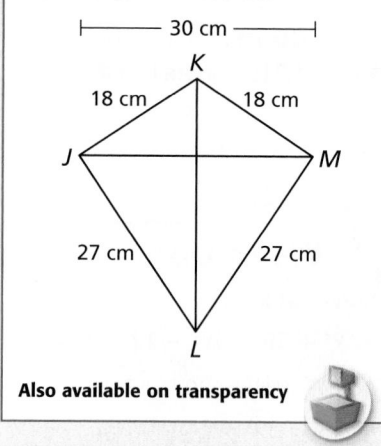

Also available on transparency

INTERVENTION ◀▶
Questioning Strategies

EXAMPLE 1

• What kind of triangles do the diagonals of a kite form? Are any of these triangles congruent? Explain.

about 191.2 in.;
3 packages

EXAMPLE 1

PROBLEM SOLVING

Problem-Solving Application

Alicia is using a pattern to make a kite. She has made the frame of the kite by placing wooden sticks along the diagonals. She also has cut four triangular pieces of fabric and has attached them to the frame. To finish the kite, Alicia must cover the outer edges with a cloth binding. There are 2 yards of binding in one package. What is the total amount of binding needed to cover the edges of the kite? How many packages of binding must Alicia buy?

1 **Understand the Problem**

The **answer** has two parts.
• the total length of binding Alicia needs
• the number of packages of binding Alicia must buy

2 **Make a Plan**

The diagonals of a kite are perpendicular, so the four triangles are right triangles. Use the Pythagorean Theorem and the properties of kites to find the unknown side lengths. Add these lengths to find the perimeter of the kite.

3 **Solve**

$$PQ = \sqrt{16^2 + 13^2} \qquad \textit{Pyth. Thm.}$$
$$= \sqrt{425} = 5\sqrt{17} \text{ in.}$$
$$RQ = PQ = 5\sqrt{17} \text{ in.} \qquad \overline{PQ} \cong \overline{RQ}$$
$$PS = \sqrt{16^2 + 22^2} \qquad \textit{Pyth. Thm.}$$
$$= \sqrt{740} = 2\sqrt{185} \text{ in.}$$
$$RS = PS = 2\sqrt{185} \text{ in.} \qquad \overline{RS} \cong \overline{PS}$$

perimeter of $PQRS = 5\sqrt{17} + 5\sqrt{17} + 2\sqrt{185} + 2\sqrt{185} \approx 95.6$ in.

Alicia needs approximately 95.6 inches of binding.
One package of binding contains 2 yards, or 72 inches.

$$\frac{95.6}{72} \approx 1.3 \text{ packages of binding}$$

In order to have enough, Alicia must buy 2 packages of binding.

4 **Look Back**

To estimate the perimeter, change the side lengths into decimals and round. $5\sqrt{17} \approx 21$, and $2\sqrt{185} \approx 27$. The perimeter of the kite is approximately $2(21) + 2(27) = 96$. So 95.6 is a reasonable answer.

CHECK IT OUT!

1. **What if...?** Daryl is going to make a kite by doubling all the measures in the kite above. What is the total amount of binding needed to cover the edges of his kite? How many packages of binding must Daryl buy?

---

2 Teach

Guided Instruction

Draw a kite and an isosceles trapezoid on the board. As you discuss the properties of each type of figure, label the diagrams accordingly. For kites, include that their diagonals are perpendicular and that they have one pair of congruent opposite angles. For isosceles trapezoids, include that each pair of base angles is congruent and that the diagonals are congruent.

Reaching All Learners
Through Multiple Representations

Have students make a table of the properties of kites and trapezoids. Have them list the properties of each in their own words and draw a diagram to represent each. Then have students compare different types of quadrilaterals. For example, ask "How are kites and squares alike?" Possible answer: Both are quadrilaterals, and both have perpendicular diagonals. "How are trapezoids and parallelograms alike?" Possible answer: Both have a pair of parallel sides.

EXAMPLE 2

Using Properties of Kites

In kite *EFGH*, m∠*FEJ* = 25°, and m∠*FGJ* = 57°.
Find each measure.

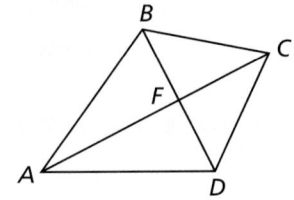

A m∠*GFJ*

m∠*FJG* = 90°	*Kite → diags. ⊥*
m∠*GFJ* + m∠*FGJ* = 90	*Acute ⊾ of rt. △ are comp.*
m∠*GFJ* + 57 = 90	*Substitute 57 for m∠FGJ.*
m∠*GFJ* = 33°	*Subtract 57 from both sides.*

B m∠*JFE*

△*FJE* is also a right triangle, so m∠*JFE* + m∠*FEJ* = 90°. By substituting 25° for m∠*FEJ*, you find that m∠*JFE* = 65°.

C m∠*GHE*

∠*GHE* ≅ ∠*GFE*	*Kite → one pair opp. ⊾ ≅*
m∠*GHE* = m∠*GFE*	*Def. of ≅ ⊾*
m∠*GFE* = m∠*GFJ* + m∠*JFE*	*∠ Add. Post.*
m∠*GHE* = 33° + 65° = 98°	*Substitute.*

 **CHECK IT OUT!** In kite *PQRS*, m∠*PQR* = 78°, and m∠*TRS* = 59°. Find each measure.

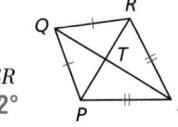

2a. m∠*QRT*	2b. m∠*QPS*	2c. m∠*PSR*
51°	110°	62°

A **trapezoid** is a quadrilateral with exactly one pair of parallel sides. Each of the parallel sides is called a **base**. The nonparallel sides are called **legs**. **Base angles** of a trapezoid are two consecutive angles whose common side is a base.

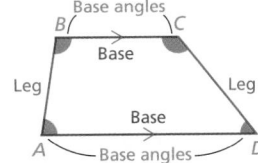

If the legs of a trapezoid are congruent, the trapezoid is an **isosceles trapezoid**. The following theorems state the properties of an isosceles trapezoid.

Know it! .Note

Theorems (**Isosceles Trapezoids**)

	THEOREM	DIAGRAM	EXAMPLE
6-6-3	If a quadrilateral is an isosceles trapezoid, then each pair of base angles are congruent. (isosc. trap. → base ⊾ ≅)		∠*A* ≅ ∠*D* ∠*B* ≅ ∠*C*
6-6-4	If a trapezoid has one pair of congruent base angles, then the trapezoid is isosceles. (trap. with pair base ⊾ ≅ → isosc. trap.)		*ABCD* is isosceles.
6-6-5	A trapezoid is isosceles if and only if its diagonals are congruent. (isosc. trap. ↔ diags. ≅)		$\overline{AC} \cong \overline{DB}$ ↔ *ABCD* is isosceles.

Remember!

Theorem 6-6-5 is a biconditional statement. So it is true both "forward" and "backward."

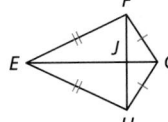 **Power Presentations with PowerPoint®**

Additional Examples

Example 2

In kite *ABCD*, m∠*DAB* = 54°, and m∠*CDF* = 52°. Find each measure.

A. m∠*BCD*   76°

B. m∠*ABC*   115°

C. m∠*FDA*   63°

Also available on transparency

INTERVENTION
Questioning Strategies

EXAMPLE 2

• How do you use the properties of a kite to find the measures of its angles?

 Teaching Tip **Technology** Have students use geometry software to draw the figures in some of the examples. This will allow them to check their answers.

Example 3

A. Find m∠A.   80°

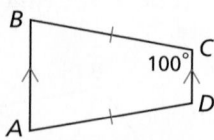

B. $KB = 21.9$, and $MF = 32.7$.
Find FB.   10.8

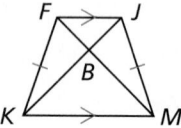

Example 4

A. Find the value of a so that
$PQRS$ is isosceles.   9 or −9

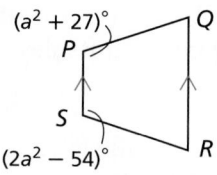

B. $AD = 12x - 11$, and $BC = 9x - 2$. Find the value of x so that $ABCD$ is isosceles.   3

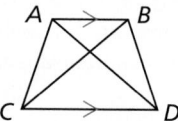

INTERVENTION ◄━►
Questioning Strategies

EXAMPLE 3

• If you are trying to find the length of one part of a diagonal of an isosceles trapezoid, what information do you need?

• Can the bases of a trapezoid be congruent? Explain.

EXAMPLE 4

• What is the relationship between base angles in an isosceles trapezoid?

EXAMPLE 3 **Using Properties of Isosceles Trapezoids**

A Find m∠Y.

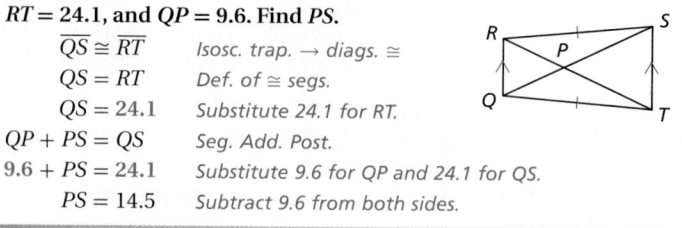

$m\angle W + m\angle X = 180°$	Same-Side Int. ∠ Thm.
$117 + m\angle X = 180$	Substitute 117 for m∠W.
$m\angle X = 63°$	Subtract 117 from both sides.
$\angle Y \cong \angle X$	Isosc. trap. → base ∠ ≅
$m\angle Y = m\angle X$	Def. of ≅ ∠
$m\angle Y = 63°$	Substitute 63 for m∠X.

B $RT = 24.1$, and $QP = 9.6$. Find PS.

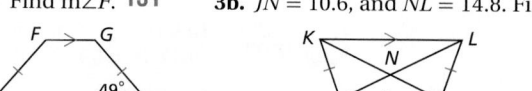

$\overline{QS} \cong \overline{RT}$	Isosc. trap. → diags. ≅
$QS = RT$	Def. of ≅ segs.
$QS = 24.1$	Substitute 24.1 for RT.
$QP + PS = QS$	Seg. Add. Post.
$9.6 + PS = 24.1$	Substitute 9.6 for QP and 24.1 for QS.
$PS = 14.5$	Subtract 9.6 from both sides.

CHECK IT OUT!
3a. Find m∠F. **131°**   **3b.** $JN = 10.6$, and $NL = 14.8$. Find KM.
25.4

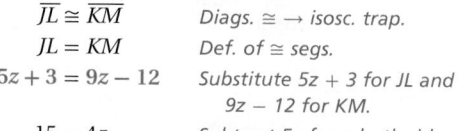

EXAMPLE 4 **Applying Conditions for Isosceles Trapezoids**

x^2y **Algebra**

A Find the value of y so that $EFGH$ is isosceles.

$\angle E \cong \angle H$	Trap. with pair base ∠ ≅ → isosc. trap.
$m\angle E = m\angle H$	Def. of ≅ ∠
$2y^2 - 25 = y^2 + 24$	Substitute $2y^2 - 25$ for m∠E and $y^2 + 24$ for m∠H.
$y^2 = 49$	Subtract y^2 from both sides and add 25 to both sides.
$y = 7$ or $y = -7$	Find the square root of both sides.

B $JL = 5z + 3$, and $KM = 9z - 12$. Find the value of z so that $JKLM$ is isosceles.

$\overline{JL} \cong \overline{KM}$	Diags. ≅ → isosc. trap.
$JL = KM$	Def. of ≅ segs.
$5z + 3 = 9z - 12$	Substitute $5z + 3$ for JL and $9z - 12$ for KM.
$15 = 4z$	Subtract 5z from both sides and add 12 to both sides.
$3.75 = z$	Divide both sides by 4.

CHECK IT OUT!
4. Find the value of x so that $PQST$ is isosceles.
$x = 4$ or $x = -4$

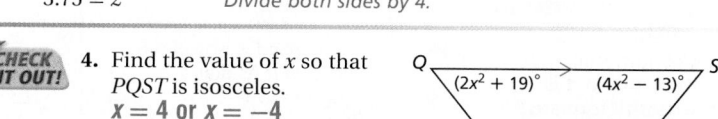

Teaching Tip **Algebra** In **Example 4A**, some students might think the value of the variable cannot be negative, since they are working with positive angles. Point out that since the variable is squared, the angle measure is positive.

The **midsegment of a trapezoid** is the segment whose endpoints are the midpoints of the legs. In Lesson 5-1, you studied the Triangle Midsegment Theorem. The Trapezoid Midsegment Theorem is similar to it.

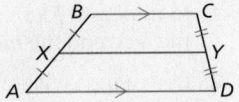
Midsegment

Know it!
.Note

Theorem 6-6-6 | **Trapezoid Midsegment Theorem**

The midsegment of a trapezoid is parallel to each base, and its length is one half the sum of the lengths of the bases.

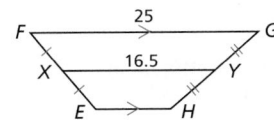

$\overline{XY} \parallel \overline{BC}, \overline{XY} \parallel \overline{AD}$

$XY = \frac{1}{2}(BC + AD)$

You will prove the Trapezoid Midsegment Theorem in Exercise 46.

EXAMPLE **5** | **Finding Lengths Using Midsegments**

Find *ST*.

$MN = \frac{1}{2}(ST + RU)$ *Trap. Midsegment Thm.*

$31 = \frac{1}{2}(ST + 38)$ *Substitute the given values.*

$62 = ST + 38$ *Multiply both sides by 2.*

$24 = ST$ *Subtract 38 from both sides.*

CHECK IT OUT!

5. Find *EH*.
8

THINK AND DISCUSS

1. Is it possible for the legs of a trapezoid to be parallel? Explain.

2. How is the midsegment of a trapezoid similar to a midsegment of a triangle? How is it different?

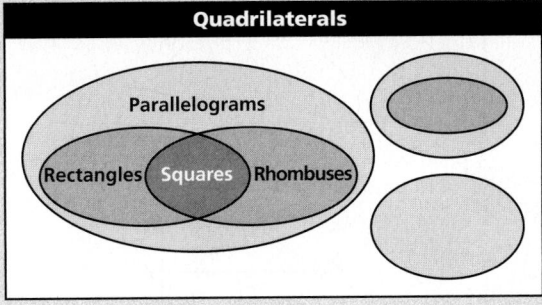

3. GET ORGANIZED Copy and complete the graphic organizer. Write the missing terms in the unlabeled sections. Then write a definition of each term. (*Hint:* This completes the Venn diagram you started in Lesson 6-4.)

Quadrilaterals

Parallelograms

Rectangles   Squares   Rhombuses

6-6 Properties of Kites and Trapezoids   **431**

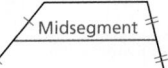
Power Presentations
with PowerPoint®

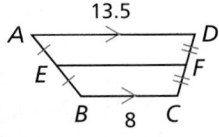
Additional Examples

Example **5**

Find *EF*.   10.75

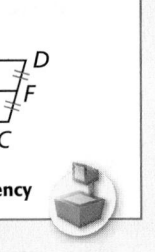

Also available on transparency

INTERVENTION ◄►
Questioning Strategies

EXAMPLE **5**

• In the formula for the length of the midsegment, how do you know which segment lengths to substitute where?

Teaching Tip

Reading Math Tell students that the midsegment of a trapezoid can also be called a *median*.

ENGLISH LANGUAGE LEARNERS

Teaching Tip

Critical Thinking Ask students the following: If $y = x + 2$ and $y = x + 6$ represent the lines containing the parallel sides of a trapezoid, what equation represents the line containing the midsegment? $y = x + 4$

---

3 Close

Summarize

Review the properties of kites and trapezoids and the difference between a trapezoid and an isosceles trapezoid. Review the Trapezoid Midsegment Theorem, and remind students that the midsegment of a trapezoid is the segment whose endpoints are the midpoints of the legs.

ONGOING ASSESSMENT

and INTERVENTION ◄►

Diagnose Before the Lesson
6-6 Warm Up, TE p. 427

Monitor During the Lesson
Check It Out! Exercises, SE pp. 428–431
Questioning Strategies, TE pp. 428–431

Assess After the Lesson
6-6 Lesson Quiz, TE p. 435
Alternative Assessment, TE p. 435

Answers to *Think and Discuss*

1. No; possible answer: if the legs are ∥, then the trap. has 2 pairs of ∥ sides. By def., the figure would be a ▱, not a trap.

2. Possible answer: Similarities: The endpoints of both are the mdpts. of 2 sides. Both are ∥ to another side. Differences: A △ has 3 midsegments, while a trap. has just 1. To find the length of a midsegment of a △, you find half the measure of just 1 side; to find the length of the midsegment of a trap., you must average the lengths of 2 sides.

3. See p. A6.

go.hrw.com/Geo/TX
Homework Help Online
KEYWORD: MG7 6-6
Parent Resources Online
KEYWORD: MG7 Parent

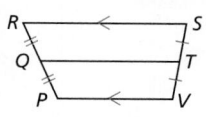

Assignment Guide

Assign *Guided Practice* exercises as necessary.

If you finished Examples **1–2**
Basic 13–16, 24, 25, 28, 29, 31
Average 13–16, 24, 25, 28, 29, 31, 37, 38
Advanced 13–16, 24, 25, 28, 29, 31, 37–39

If you finished Examples **1–5**
Basic 13–34, 40–42, 45, 47–49, 52–56
Average 13–23, 24–32 even, 33–36, 38–42 even, 43–45, 47–49, 52–56
Advanced 13–23, 28–32 even, 33, 35–42, 44–56

Homework Quick Check
Quickly check key concepts.
Exercises: 13, 14, 18, 20, 22, 28, 32

Answers
2. Possible answer: In a ▱, 2 pairs of opp. sides are ≅. In a kite, exactly 2 distinct pairs of cons. sides are ≅.

TAKS Practice

Grades 9–11	Exercises
Obj. 1	53, 54
Obj. 2	31, 32, 34, 35, 51
Obj. 5	36
Obj. 6	27–32, 37, 44
Obj. 7	26, 33, 40–43, 46, 55, 56
Obj. 9	52
Obj. 10	37, 52

GUIDED PRACTICE

Vocabulary Apply the vocabulary from this lesson to answer each question.

bases: $\overline{RS}$ and $\overline{PV}$;
legs: $\overline{PR}$ and $\overline{VS}$;
midsegment: $\overline{QT}$

1. In trapezoid *PRSV*, name the *bases*, the *legs*, and the *midsegment*.

2. Both a parallelogram and a *kite* have two pairs of congruent sides. How are the congruent sides of a kite different from the congruent sides of a parallelogram?

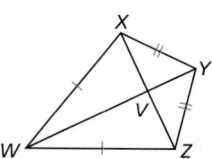

SEE EXAMPLE 1
p. 428

3. **Crafts** The edges of the kite-shaped glass in the sun catcher are sealed with lead strips. *JH*, *KH*, and *LH* are 2.75 inches, and *MH* is 5.5 inches. How much lead is needed to seal the edges of the sun catcher? If the craftsperson has two 3-foot lengths of lead, how many sun catchers can be sealed?
about 20.1 in.; 3 sun catchers

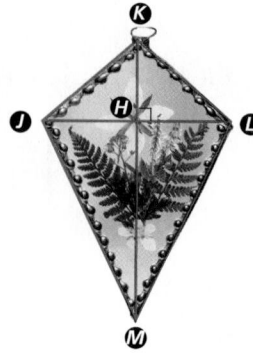

SEE EXAMPLE 2
p. 429

In kite *WXYZ*, m∠*WXY* = 104°, and m∠*VYZ* = 49°. Find each measure.

4. m∠*VZY* **41°**

5. m∠*VXW* **63°**

6. m∠*XWZ* **54°**

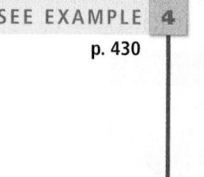

SEE EXAMPLE 3
p. 430

7. Find m∠*A*. **106°**

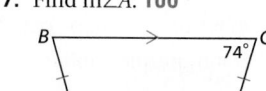

8. *RW* = 17.7, and *SV* = 23.3.
Find *TW*.
5.6

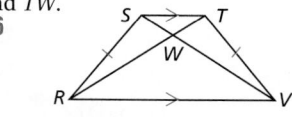

SEE EXAMPLE 4
p. 430

9. Find the value of *z* so that *EFGH* is isosceles. **2 or −2**

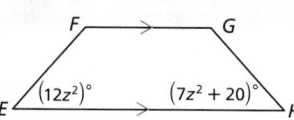

10. *MQ* = 7*y* − 6, and *LP* = 4*y* + 11.
Find the value of *y* so that *LMPQ* is isosceles.
$$\frac{17}{3} = 5\frac{2}{3}$$

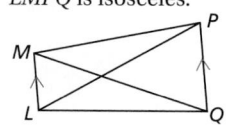

SEE EXAMPLE 5
p. 431

11. Find *QR*. **14**

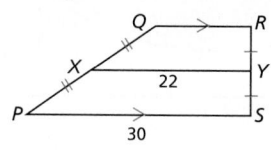

12. Find *AZ*. **9.5**

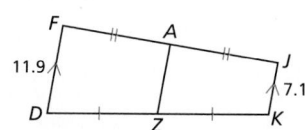

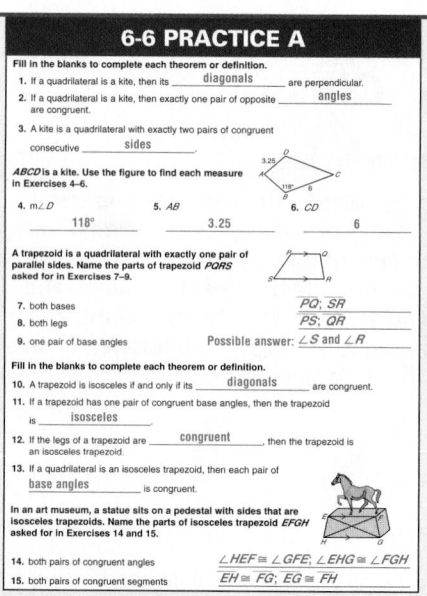

PRACTICE AND PROBLEM SOLVING

Independent Practice

For Exercises	See Example
13	1
14–16	2
17–18	3
19–20	4
21–22	5

TEKS ● TAKS

Skills Practice p. S15
Application Practice p. S33

13. Design Each square section in the iron railing contains four small kites. The figure shows the dimensions of one kite. What length of iron is needed to outline one small kite? How much iron is needed to outline one complete section, including the square?
about 56.6 in.; about 418.3 in.

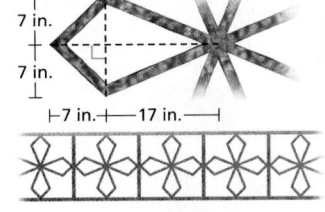
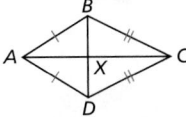

In kite $ABCD$, m$\angle DAX = 32°$, and m$\angle XDC = 64°$.
Find each measure.

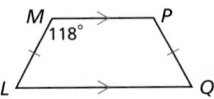

14. m$\angle XDA$ **58°** **15.** m$\angle ABC$ **122°** **16.** m$\angle BCD$ **52°**

17. Find m$\angle Q$. **62°**

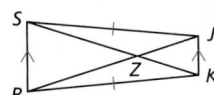

18. $SZ = 62.6$, and $KZ = 34$. Find RJ. **96.6**

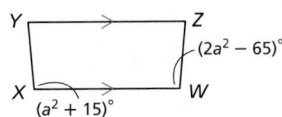

19. Algebra Find the value of a so that $XYZW$ is isosceles. Give your answer as a simplified radical. $\pm 4\sqrt{5}$

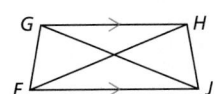

20. Algebra $GJ = 4x - 1$, and $FH = 9x - 15$. Find the value of x so that $FGHJ$ is isosceles. **2.8**

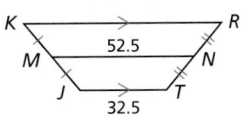

21. Find PQ. **3.6**

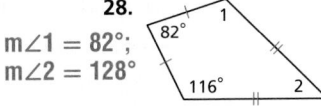

22. Find KR. **72.5**

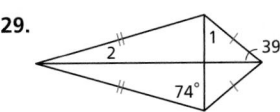

Tell whether each statement is sometimes, always, or never true.

23. The opposite angles of a trapezoid are supplementary. **S**

24. The opposite angles of a kite are supplementary. **S**

25. A pair of consecutive angles in a kite are supplementary. **N**

26. Estimation Hal is building a trapezoid-shaped frame for a flower bed. The lumber costs $1.29 per foot. Based on Hal's sketch, estimate the cost of the lumber. (*Hint:* Find the angle measures in the triangle formed by the dashed line.)
Possible answer: about $55

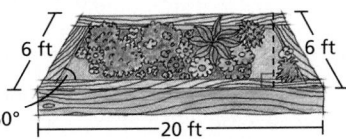

Find the measure of each numbered angle.

28. m$\angle 1 = 116°$; m$\angle 2 = 46°$

29. m$\angle 1 = 51°$; m$\angle 2 = 16°$

30. m$\angle 1 = 112°$; m$\angle 2 = 40°$

27.

28. m$\angle 1 = 82°$; m$\angle 2 = 128°$

29.

30.

31. m$\angle 1 = 120°$

32. m$\angle 1 = 117°$

6-6 PRACTICE B

In kite $ABCD$, m$\angle BAC = 35°$ and m$\angle BCD = 44°$.
For Exercises 1–3, find each measure.

1. m$\angle ABD$ **55°** **2.** m$\angle DCA$ **22°** **3.** m$\angle ABC$ **123°**

4. Find the area of $\triangle EFG$. **60 unit²**

5. Find m$\angle Z$ **98°** **6.** $KM = 7.5$, and $NM = 2.6$. Find LN. **4.9**

7. Find the value of n so that $PQRS$ is isosceles. $n = 11.5$

8. Find the value of x so that $EFGH$ is isosceles. $x = 12$ or -12

9. $BD = 7a - 0.5$, and $AC = 5a + 2.3$. Find the value of a so that $ABCD$ is isosceles. $a = 1.4$

10. $QS = 8z²$, and $RT = 6z² + 38$. Find the value of z so that $QRST$ is isosceles. $z = \sqrt{19}$ or $-\sqrt{19}$

Use the figure for Exercises 11 and 12. The figure shows a *ziggurat*. A ziggurat is a stepped, flat-topped pyramid that was used as a temple by ancient peoples of Mesopotamia. The dashed lines show that a ziggurat has sides roughly in the shape of a trapezoid.

11. Each "step" in the ziggurat has equal height. Give the vocabulary term for MN. trapezoid midsegment

12. The bottom of the ziggurat is 27.3 meters long, and the top of the ziggurat is 11.6 meters long. Find MN. **19.45 m**

6-6 PRACTICE C

Use the figure of kite $ABCD$ for Exercises 1–3.

1. The figure shows kite $ABCD$. Find a formula for the area of a kite in terms of the diagonals AC and BD.
Area $= \frac{1}{2}(AC)(BD)$

2. Suppose you are given BA, AC, and ED. Tell whether it is possible to find the area of $ABCD$. Explain your answer. **Yes; possible answer: the length of AE is half the length of AC; and BE may be found from BA and AE by using the Pythagorean Theorem. BD is the sum of BE and ED. The area is $\frac{1}{2}(AC)(BD)$.**

3. Suppose you are given BA, DA, and BD. Tell whether it is possible to find the area of $ABCD$ (with what you have learned so far in this geometry class). Explain your answer.
No; possible answer: there is no way to use the Pythagorean Theorem to find the length of AE, and thus AC, with the information provided.

Use the figure of trapezoid $PQRS$ for Exercise 4.

4. Write a paragraph proof.
Given: $PQ \parallel SR$, $QU \perp SR$, $PT \perp SR$
Prove: $POUT$ is a rectangle. **Possible answer: It is given that QU is perpendicular to SR and PT is perpendicular to SR, so $\angle PTU$ and $\angle QUT$ are right angles. It is also given that PQ is parallel to SR, so the same-side interior angles $\angle PTU$ and $\angle TPQ$ are supplementary, as are $\angle QUT$ and $\angle PQU$. An angle supplementary to a right angle must be a right angle, so $\angle TPQ$ and $\angle PQU$ are right angles. All four interior angles of $PQUT$ are right angles, so $POUT$ is a rectangle by the definition of a rectangle.**

Write a paragraph proof.

5. Given: Isosceles trapezoid $JKLM$
Prove: $\triangle JNM$ is isosceles.
Possible answer: It is given that $JKLM$ is an isosceles trapezoid, so $JK \cong ML$ and $KL \parallel JM$. Base angles in an isosceles trapezoid are congruent, so $\angle J \cong \angle M$. Corresponding angles are equal, so $\angle NKL \cong \angle J$ and $\angle NLK \cong \angle M$. By the Transitive Property of Congruence, $\angle NKL \cong \angle NLK$. $\angle NKL$ and $\angle NLK$ are the base angles of $\triangle NKL$, so it is an isosceles triangle. Thus $NK \cong NL$. By the Segment Addition Postulate, $JN = JK + NK$ and $MN = ML + NL$. By the Addition Property of Equality and the definition of congruent segments, $JN = MN$. Because JN and MN have the same length, they are congruent. So $\triangle JNM$ is isosceles.

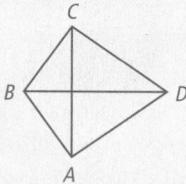

33. This problem will prepare you for the Multi-Step TAKS Prep on page 436.
The boundary of a fairground is a quadrilateral with vertices at $E(-1, 3)$, $F(3, 4)$, $G(2, 0)$, and $H(-3, -2)$.
  a. Use the Distance Formula to show that $EFGH$ is a kite.
  b. The organizers need to know the angle measure at each vertex. Given that m∠H = 46° and m∠F = 62°, find m∠E and m∠G.

 Algebra Find the length of the midsegment of each trapezoid.

34.  15   **35.** 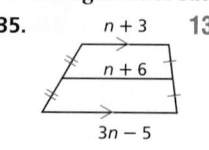 13   **36.** 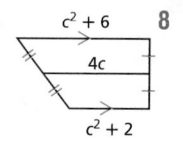 8

Mechanics

The Peaucellier cell, invented in 1864, converts circular motion into linear motion. This type of linkage was supposedly used in the fans that ventilated the Houses of Parliament in London prior to the invention of electric fans.

37. Mechanics A *Peaucellier cell* is made of seven rods connected by joints at the labeled points. $AQBP$ is a rhombus, and $\overline{OA} \cong \overline{OB}$. As P moves along a circular path, Q moves along a linear path. In the position shown, m∠AQB = 72°, and m∠AOB = 28°. What are m∠PAQ, m∠OAQ, and m∠OBP?

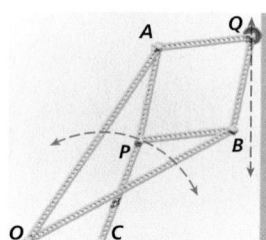

38. Prove that one diagonal of a kite bisects a pair of opposite angles and the other diagonal.

39. Prove Theorem 6-6-1: If a quadrilateral is a kite, then its diagonals are perpendicular.

Multi-Step Give the best name for a quadrilateral with the given vertices.
40. $(-4, -1)$, $(-4, 6)$, $(2, 6)$, $(2, -4)$ trap.   **41.** $(-5, 2)$, $(-5, 6)$, $(-1, 6)$, $(2, -1)$ kite
42. $(-2, -2)$, $(1, 7)$, $(4, 4)$, $(1, -5)$ ▱   **43.** $(-4, -3)$, $(0, 3)$, $(4, 3)$, $(8, -3)$ isosc. trap.

44. Carpentry The window frame is a regular octagon. It is made from eight pieces of wood shaped like congruent isosceles trapezoids. What are m∠A, m∠B, m∠C, and m∠D?

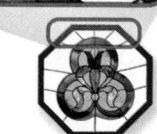
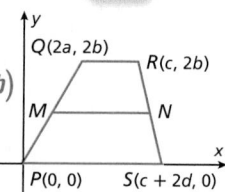

45. Write About It Compare an isosceles trapezoid to a trapezoid that is not isosceles. What properties do the figures have in common? What properties does one have that the other does not?

46d. $QR = c - 2a$; $PS = c + 2d$; $MN = c + d - a$; $c + d - a = \frac{1}{2}(c + 2d + c - 2a)$, so $MN = \frac{1}{2}(PS + QR)$.

46. Use coordinates to verify the Trapezoid Midsegment Theorem.
  a. M is the midpoint of $\overline{QP}$. What are its coordinates? (a, b)
  b. N is the midpoint of $\overline{RS}$. What are its coordinates? $(c + d, b)$
  c. Find the slopes of $\overline{QR}$, $\overline{PS}$, and $\overline{MN}$. What can you conclude? The slopes equal 0, so all 3 segs. are ∥.
  d. Find QR, PS, and MN. Show that $MN = \frac{1}{2}(PS + QR)$.

47. In trapezoid $PQRS$, what could be the lengths of $\overline{QR}$ and $\overline{PS}$?
  Ⓐ 6 and 10   Ⓒ 8 and 32
  Ⓑ 6 and 26   Ⓓ 10 and 24

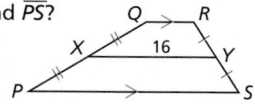

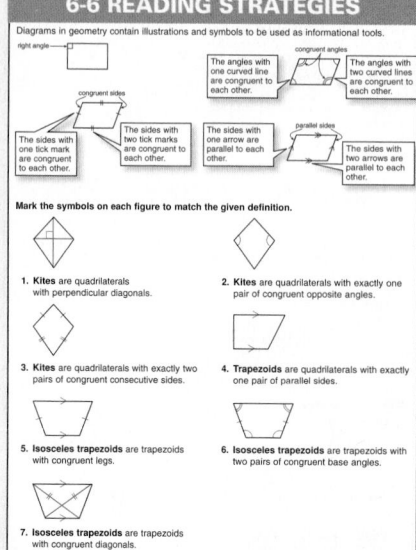
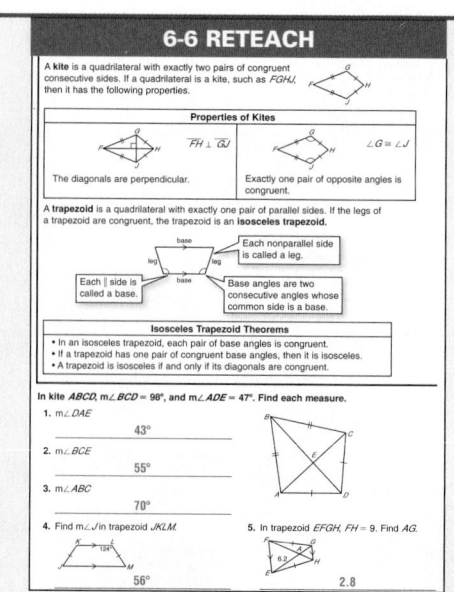

48. Which statement is never true for a kite?

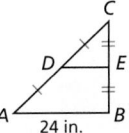

    F The diagonals are perpendicular.

    G One pair of opposite angles are congruent.

    (H) One pair of opposite sides are parallel.

    J Two pairs of consecutive sides are congruent.

49. Gridded Response What is the length of the midsegment of trapezoid *ADEB* in inches? **18**

CHALLENGE AND EXTEND

50. Write a two-column proof. (*Hint:* If there is a line and a point not on the line, then there is exactly one line through the point perpendicular to the given line. Use this fact to draw auxiliary lines $\overline{UX}$ and $\overline{VY}$ so that $\overline{UX} \perp \overline{WZ}$ and $\overline{VY} \perp \overline{WZ}$.)

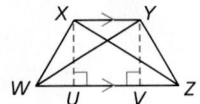

Given: *WXYZ* is a trapezoid with $\overline{XZ} \cong \overline{YW}$.
Prove: *WXYZ* is an isosceles trapezoid.

51. The perimeter of isosceles trapezoid *ABCD* is 27.4 inches. If $BC = 2(AB)$, find *AD*, *AB*, *BC*, and *CD*.
$AD = 7.08$ in.; $AB = CD = 5.08$ in.; $BC = 10.16$ in.

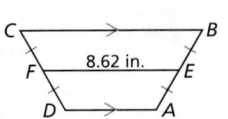

SPIRAL REVIEW

52. An empty pool is being filled with water. After 10 hours, 20% of the pool is full. If the pool is filled at a constant rate, what fraction of the pool will be full after 25 hours? *(Previous course)* $\frac{1}{2}$

Write and solve an inequality for *x*. *(Lesson 3-4)*

53.

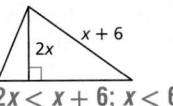

$2x < x + 6;\ x < 6$

54.

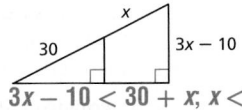

$3x - 10 < 30 + x,\ x < 20$

Tell whether a parallelogram with the given vertices is a rectangle, rhombus, or square. Give all the names that apply. *(Lesson 6-5)*

55. $(-3, 1), (-1, 3), (1, 1),$ and $(-1, -1)$
    rect., rhombus, square

56. $(1, 1), (4, 5), (4, 0),$ and $(1, -4)$
    rhombus

Construction   **Kite**

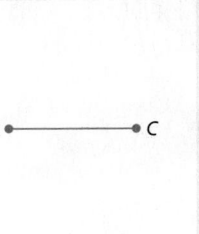   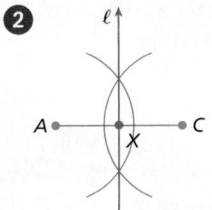   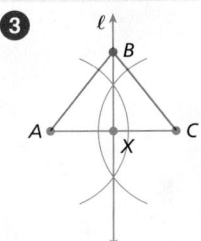 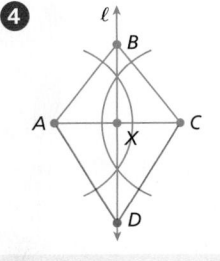

① Draw a segment $\overline{AC}$.

② Construct line ℓ as the perpendicular bisector of $\overline{AC}$. Label the intersection as *X*.

③ Draw a point *B* on ℓ above $\overline{AC}$. Draw $\overline{AB}$ and $\overline{CB}$.

④ Draw a point *D* on ℓ below $\overline{AC}$ so that $DX \neq BX$. Draw $\overline{AD}$ and $\overline{CD}$.

1. Critical Thinking How would you modify the construction above so that *ABCD* is a concave kite?

6-6 Properties of Kites and Trapezoids   **435**

6-6 PROBLEM SOLVING

Use the figure of the kite for Exercises 1 and 2.

1. What is *AD* to the nearest tenth?
    23.1

2. What is the perimeter of the kite to the nearest tenth?
    74.0

3. In kite *STUV*, m∠*TUW* = 35° and m∠*WSV* = 21°. What is the measure of ∠*UVS*?
    124°

4. A car window is in the shape of a trapezoid. When the window is halfway down, the top is $\overline{KL}$, the midsegment of *FGHJ*. If *KL* = 23 inches, what is *GH*?
    18 in.

Choose the best answer.

5. Trapezoid *PQRS* has base angles that measure $(9r + 21)°$ and $(15r - 21)°$. Find the value of *r* so that *PQRS* is isosceles.
  A 3
  B 5
  Ⓒ 7
  D 14

6. In kite *KLMN*, find the measure of ∠*M*.
  F 100.5° H 122°
  G 101° J 130°

7. In the design, eight isosceles trapezoids surround a regular octagon. What is the measure of ∠*B* in trapezoid *ABCD*?
  A 35°
  Ⓑ 45°
  C 55°
  D 65°

6-6 CHALLENGE

A **dart** is another type of geometric figure. Examples of darts are shown in the table.

Darts	Not Darts

1. Based on your observations of the figures in the table, write a definition of the term *dart*.
  Possible answer: A dart is a concave quadrilateral with exactly two pairs of congruent consecutive sides.

2. Describe the similarities and differences between the properties of darts and kites.
  Darts and kites both have exactly two pairs of congruent consecutive sides. Darts are concave, and kites are convex.

3. Find the values of *x* and *y* so that *GHJK* is a dart.
  $x = 11;\ y = 2$

4. Make a conjecture about the line that contains the diagonal from the tip to the vertex of the tail of a dart and the diagonal that joins the fin angles.
  Possible answer: The lines are perpendicular. The line containing the first diagonal bisects the diagonal that joins the fin angles.

5. Make a conjecture about the two triangles formed by the tip-to-tail diagonal.
  Possible answer: The triangles are congruent and obtuse.

6. Write a paragraph proof.
  Given: *ABCD* is a dart with $\overline{AB} \cong \overline{AD}$ and $\overline{BC} \cong \overline{DC}$.
  Prove: ∠*B* ≅ ∠*D*
  Possible answer: It is given that $\overline{AB} \cong \overline{AD}$ and $\overline{BC} \cong \overline{DC}$. By the Reflex. Prop. of ≅, $\overline{AC} \cong \overline{AC}$. This means that $\triangle ABC \cong \triangle ADC$ by SSS. So ∠*B* ≅ ∠*D* by CPCTC.

✎ *Journal*

Have students draw an isosceles trapezoid. Have them label the angle measures in terms of *x* and write a justification for each measure.

ALTERNATIVE ASSESSMENT

Have students construct a kite and an isosceles trapezoid. Have them measure one angle in each figure and then use the properties in the lesson to find the other three angle measures.

Power Presentations
  with PowerPoint®

6-6
✓ Lesson Quiz

1. Erin is making a kite based on the pattern below. About how much binding does Erin need to cover the edges of the kite?
  about 191.2 in.

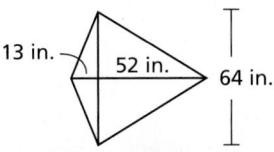

In kite *HJKL*, m∠*KLP* = 72°, and m∠*HJP* = 49.5°. Find each measure.

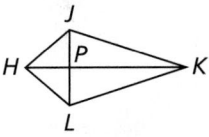

2. m∠*LHJ*   81°   **3.** m∠*PKL*   18°

Use the diagram for Items 4 and 5.

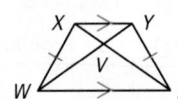

4. m∠*WZY* = 61°. Find m∠*WXY*.
  119°

5. *XV* = 4.6, and *WY* = 14.2. Find *VZ*.   9.6

6. Find *LP*.   18

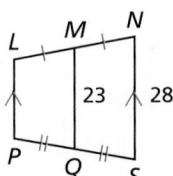

Also available on transparency

Lesson 6-6   **435**

Organizer

Objective: Assess students' ability to apply concepts and skills in Lessons 6-4 through 6-6 in a real-world format.

 Online Edition

Resources

 Geometry Assessments
www.mathtekstoolkit.org

Problem	Text Reference
1	Lesson 6-4
2	Lesson 6-3
3	Lesson 6-5
4	Lesson 6-6
5	Lesson 6-6

Answers

1. By the Distance Formula, $AB = BC = CD = DA = 4\sqrt{5}$. Since the 4 sides of $ABCD$ are $\cong$, $ABCD$ is a rhombus. $\overline{AC}$ and $\overline{BD}$ are the diags. of the rhombus, so by Thm. 6-4-4, $\overline{AC} \perp \overline{BD}$.

2. Slope of $\overline{SP}$ = slope of $\overline{RQ}$ = 1, and slope of $\overline{SR}$ = slope of $\overline{PQ}$ = −1, so opp. sides are ∥, and $PQRS$ is a ▱ by def.

3. See p. A23.

🔻 TAKS Practice

Grades 9–11	Problems
Obj. 6	5
Obj. 7	1–5
Obj. 10	2–4

Other Special Quadrilaterals

A Fair Arrangement The organizers of a county fair are using a coordinate plane to plan the layout of the fairground. The fence that surrounds the fairground will have vertices at $A(-1, 4)$, $B(7, 8)$, $C(3, 0)$, and $D(-5, -4)$.

1. The organizers consider creating two straight paths through the fairground: one from point A to point C and another from point B to point D. Use a theorem from Lesson 6-4 to prove that these paths would be perpendicular.

2. The organizers instead decide to put an entry gate at the midpoint of each side of the fence, as shown. They plan to create straight paths that connect the gates. Show that the paths $\overline{PQ}$, $\overline{QR}$, $\overline{RS}$, and $\overline{SP}$ form a parallelogram.

3. Use the paths $\overline{PR}$ and $\overline{SQ}$ to tell whether $\square PQRS$ is a rhombus, rectangle, or square.

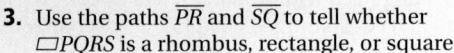

4. One section of the fair will contain all the rides and games. The organizers will fence off this area within the fairground by using the existing fences along $\overline{AB}$ and $\overline{BC}$ and adding fences along $\overline{AE}$ and $\overline{CE}$, where E has coordinates $(-1, 0)$. What type of quadrilateral will be formed by these four fences? **kite**

5. To construct the fences, the organizers need to know the angle measures at each vertex. Given that m$\angle B = 37°$, find the measures of the other angles in quadrilateral $ABCE$. m$\angle E = 90°$; m$\angle BAE = $ m$\angle BCE = 116.5°$

INTERVENTION

Scaffolding Questions

1. What type of quadrilateral is $ABCD$? rhombus What is true about its diagonals? They are ⊥.

2–3. How do $\overline{PR}$ and $\overline{SQ}$ relate to $\square PQRS$? They are diags. of $PQRS$. How can you show that $\overline{PR} \cong \overline{SQ}$? Use the Distance Formula to find PR and SQ. What can you conclude about a parallelogram with congruent diagonals? The ▱ is a rect.

4–5. Which sides of $ABCE$ are congruent? $\overline{AE} \cong \overline{CE}$; $\overline{AB} \cong \overline{BC}$ Which angles of $ABCE$ must be congruent? $\angle BAE \cong \angle BCE$

Extension

Suppose the coordinates of B are $(3, 4)$, with P, Q, R, and S as the midpoints of the sides of $ABCD$. Classify the quadrilaterals $ABCD$, $PQRS$, and $ABCE$. kite; rectangle; square

Quiz for Lessons 6-4 Through 6-6

✓ **6-4** **Properties of Special Parallelograms**

The flag of Jamaica is a rectangle with stripes along the diagonals.
In rectangle *QRST*, *QS* = 80.5, and *RS* = 36. Find each length.

1. *SP* **40.25**   2. *QT* **36**   3. *TR* **80.5**   4. *TP* **40.25**

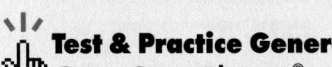

GHJK is a rhombus. Find each measure.

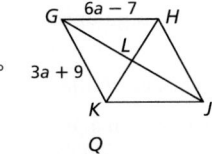

5. *HJ* **25**
6. m∠*HJG* and m∠*GHJ* if m∠*JLH* = $(4b - 6)°$
   and m∠*JKH* = $(2b + 11)°$
   m∠*HJG* = **31°**; m∠*GHJ* = **118°**
7. **Given:** *QSTV* is a rhombus. $\overline{PT} \cong \overline{RT}$
   Prove: $\overline{PQ} \cong \overline{RQ}$

✓ **6-5** **Conditions for Special Parallelograms**

Determine if the conclusion is valid. If not, tell what additional information
is needed to make it valid.

8. **Given:** $\overline{AC} \perp \overline{BD}$ **not valid**
   Conclusion: *ABCD* is a rhombus.
9. **Given:** $\overline{AB} \cong \overline{CD}, \overline{AC} \cong \overline{BD}, \overline{AB} \parallel \overline{CD}$
   Conclusion: *ABCD* is a rectangle. **valid**

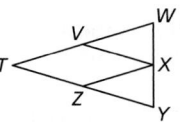

Use the diagonals to determine whether a parallelogram with the given vertices is a
rectangle, rhombus, or square. Give all the names that apply. **rect., rhombus, square**

10. $W(-2, 2), X(1, 5), Y(7, -1), Z(4, -4)$ **rect.**   11. $M(-4, 5), N(1, 7), P(3, 2), Q(-2, 0)$

12. **Given:** $\overline{VX}$ and $\overline{ZX}$ are midsegments of △*TWY*. $\overline{TW} \cong \overline{TY}$
    Prove: *TVXZ* is a rhombus.

✓ **6-6** **Properties of Kites and Trapezoids**

In kite *EFGH*, m∠*FHG* = 68°, and m∠*FEH* = 62°. Find each measure.

13. m∠*FEJ* **31°**   14. m∠*EHJ* **59°**

15. m∠*FGJ* **22°**   16. m∠*EHG* **127°**

17. Find m∠*R*. **103°**   18. *YZ* = 34.2, and *VX* = 53.4. Find *WZ*. **19.2**

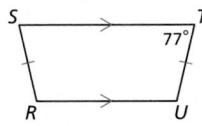
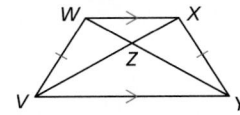

19. A dulcimer is a trapezoid-shaped stringed instrument.
    The bases are 43 in. and 23 in. long. If a string is
    attached at the midpoint of each leg of the trapezoid,
    how long is the string? **33 in.**

SECTION
6B

READY TO GO ON?

Organizer

Objective: Assess students'
mastery of concepts and skills in
Lessons 6-4 through 6-6.

Resources

Assessment Resources
   Section 6B Quiz

Test & Practice Generator
One-Stop Planner®

INTERVENTION ◆═══▶

Resources

Ready to Go On?
Intervention and
Enrichment Worksheets

Ready to Go On? CD-ROM

Ready to Go On? Online

my.hrw.com

Answers

7, 8, 12. See p. A23.

READY TO GO ON?
Diagnose and Prescribe

NO
INTERVENE

YES
ENRICH

READY TO GO ON? Intervention, Section 6B			
Ready to Go On? **Intervention**	**Worksheets**	**CD-ROM**	**Online**
✓ Lesson 6-4	6-4 Intervention	Activity 6-4	
✓ Lesson 6-5	6-5 Intervention	Activity 6-5	Diagnose and Prescribe Online
✓ Lesson 6-6	6-6 Intervention	Activity 6-6	

READY TO GO ON?
Enrichment, Section 6B

Worksheets
CD-ROM
Online

Organizer

Objective: Help students organize and review key concepts and skills presented in Chapter 6.

Online Edition
Multilingual Glossary

Resources

PuzzlePro
One-Stop Planner®

Multilingual Glossary Online
go.hrw.com/Geo/TX
KEYWORD: MG7 Glossary

Lesson Tutorial Videos
CD-ROM

Test & Practice Generator
One-Stop Planner®

Answers

1. vertex of a polygon
2. convex
3. rhombus
4. base of a trapezoid
5. not a polygon
6. polygon; △
7. polygon; dodecagon
8. irregular; concave
9. irregular; convex
10. reg.; convex
11. 1800°
12. 162°
13. 90°
14. m∠A = m∠D = 144°; m∠B = m∠E = 126°; m∠C = m∠F = 90°

Know it!
Note
For a complete list of the postulates and theorems in this chapter, see p. S82.

Vocabulary

base of a trapezoid 429
base angle of a trapezoid 429
concave 383
convex 383
diagonal 382
isosceles trapezoid 429

kite 427
leg of a trapezoid 429
midsegment of a trapezoid . . 431
parallelogram 391
rectangle 408
regular polygon 382

rhombus 409
side of a polygon 382
square 410
trapezoid 429
vertex of a polygon 382

Complete the sentences below with vocabulary words from the list above.

1. The common endpoint of two sides of a polygon is a(n) ___?___ .

2. A polygon is ___?___ if no diagonal contains points in the exterior.

3. A(n) ___?___ is a quadrilateral with four congruent sides.

4. Each of the parallel sides of a trapezoid is called a(n) ___?___ .

6-1 Properties and Attributes of Polygons *(pp. 382–388)*

 TEKS G.2.B, G.3.B, G.4.A, G.5.A, G.5.B, G.7.A

EXAMPLES

■ Tell whether the figure is a polygon. If it is a polygon, name it by the number of its sides.

 The figure is a closed plane figure made of segments that intersect only at their endpoints, so it is a polygon. It has six sides, so it is a hexagon.

■ Tell whether the polygon is regular or irregular. Tell whether it is concave or convex.

 The polygon is equilateral, but it is not equiangular. So it is not regular. No diagonal contains points in the exterior, so it is convex.

Find each measure.

■ the sum of the interior angle measures of a convex 11-gon

$(n - 2)180°$ *Polygon ∠ Sum Thm.*
$(11 - 2)180° = 1620°$ *Substitute 11 for n.*

■ the measure of each exterior angle of a regular pentagon

sum of ext. ∡ = 360°   *Polygon Ext. ∠ SumThm.*

measure of one ext. ∠ = $\frac{360°}{5} = 72°$

EXERCISES

Tell whether each figure is a polygon. If it is a polygon, name it by the number of its sides.

5.    6. △   7.

Tell whether each polygon is regular or irregular. Tell whether it is concave or convex.

8.    9.   10. ⬡

Find each measure.

11. the sum of the interior angle measures of a convex dodecagon

12. the measure of each interior angle of a regular 20-gon

13. the measure of each exterior angle of a regular quadrilateral

14. the measure of each interior angle of hexagon *ABCDEF*

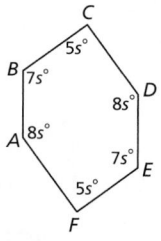

6-2 Properties of Parallelograms (pp. 391–397)

TEKS G.2.B, G.3.B, G.3.E, G.7.A, G.7.B, G.7.C, G.10.B

EXAMPLES

■ In $\square PQRS$, $m\angle RSP = 99°$, $PQ = 19.8$, and $RT = 12.3$. Find PT.

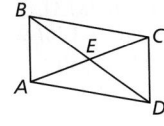

$\overline{PT} \cong \overline{RT}$	$\square \to$ diags. bisect each other
$PT = RT$	Def. of $\cong$ segs.
$PT = 12.3$	Substitute 12.3 for RT.

JKLM is a parallelogram. Find each measure.

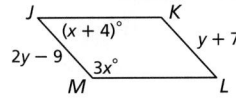

■ LK

$\overline{JM} \cong \overline{LK}$	$\square \to$ opp. sides $\cong$
$JM = LK$	Def. of $\cong$ segs.
$2y - 9 = y + 7$	Substitute the given values.
$y = 16$	Solve for y.
$LK = 16 + 7 = 23$	

■ $m\angle M$

$m\angle J + m\angle M = 180°$	$\square \to$ cons. $\angle$ supp.
$(x + 4) + 3x = 180$	Substitute the given values.
$x = 44$	Solve for x.
$m\angle M = 3(44) = 132°$	

EXERCISES

In $\square ABCD$, $m\angle ABC = 79°$, $BC = 62.4$, and $BD = 75$. Find each measure.

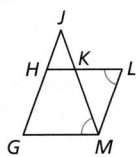

15. BE **16.** AD

17. ED **18.** $m\angle CDA$

19. $m\angle BCD$ **20.** $m\angle DAB$

WXYZ is a parallelogram. Find each measure.

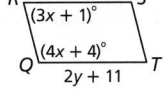

21. WX **22.** YZ

23. $m\angle W$ **24.** $m\angle X$

25. $m\angle Y$ **26.** $m\angle Z$

27. Three vertices of $\square RSTV$ are $R(-8, 1)$, $S(2, 3)$, and $V(-4, -7)$. Find the coordinates of vertex T.

28. Write a two-column proof.
Given: GHLM is a parallelogram.
$\angle L \cong \angle JMG$
Prove: $\triangle GJM$ is isosceles.

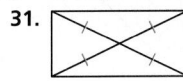

6-3 Conditions for Parallelograms (pp. 398–405)

TEKS G.2.A, G.2.B, G.3.B, G.3.E, G.7.A, G.7.B, G.7.C

EXAMPLES

■ Show that *MNPQ* is a parallelogram for $a = 6$ and $b = 1.6$.

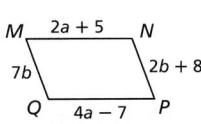

$MN = 2a + 5$	$QP = 4a - 7$
$MN = 2(6) + 5 = 17$	$QP = 4(6) - 7 = 17$
$MQ = 7b$	$NP = 2b + 8$
$MQ = 7(1.6) = 11.2$	$NP = 2(1.6) + 8 = 11.2$

Since its opposite sides are congruent, *MNPQ* is a parallelogram.

■ Determine if the quadrilateral must be a parallelogram. Justify your answer.

No. One pair of opposite angles are congruent, and one pair of consecutive sides are congruent. None of the conditions for a parallelogram are met.

EXERCISES

Show that the quadrilateral is a parallelogram for the given values of the variables.

29. $m = 13$, $n = 27$ **30.** $x = 25$, $y = 7$

Determine if the quadrilateral must be a parallelogram. Justify your answer.

31.   **32.**

33. Show that the quadrilateral with vertices $B(-4, 3)$, $D(6, 5)$, $F(7, -1)$, and $H(-3, -3)$ is a parallelogram.

Study Guide: Review **439**

Answers

15. 37.5
16. 62.4
17. 37.5
18. 79°
19. 101°
20. 101°
21. 9.5
22. 9.5
23. 54°
24. 126°
25. 54°
26. 126°
27. $T(6, -5)$
28. 1. GHLM is a $\square$. $\angle L \cong \angle JMG$ (Given)
2. $\angle G \cong \angle L$ ($\square \to$ opp. $\angle$ $\cong$)
3. $\angle G \cong \angle JMG$ (Trans. Prop. of $\cong$)
4. $\overline{GJ} \cong \overline{MJ}$ (Conv. of Isosc. $\triangle$ Thm.)
5. $\triangle GJM$ is isosc. (Def. of isosc. $\triangle$)
29. $m\angle A = m\angle E = 63°$; $m\angle G = 117°$; since $117° + 63° = 180°$, $\angle G$ is supp. to $\angle A$ and to $\angle E$. So 1 $\angle$ of ACEG is supp. to both of its cons. $\angle$. By Thm. 6-3-4, ACEG is a $\square$.
30. $RS = QT = 25$, so $\overline{RS} \cong \overline{QT}$. $m\angle R = 76°$, $m\angle Q = 104°$, and $m\angle R + m\angle Q = 180°$, so $\angle R$ is supp. to $\angle Q$. Since $\angle R$ and $\angle Q$ are a pair of same-side int. $\angle$, and they are supp., $\overline{RS} \parallel \overline{QT}$. So 1 pair of opp. sides of QRST are $\parallel$ and $\cong$. By Thm. 6-3-1, QRST is a $\square$.
31. Yes; the diags. of the quad. bisect each other. By Thm. 6-3-5, the quad. is a $\square$.
32. No; a pair of alt. int. $\angle$ are $\cong$, so 1 pair of opp. sides are $\parallel$. A different pair of opp. sides are $\cong$. None of the conditions for a $\square$ are met.
33. slope of $\overline{BD}$ = slope of $\overline{FH}$ = $\frac{1}{5}$; slope of $\overline{BH}$ = slope of $\overline{DF}$ = -6; both pairs of opp. sides have the same slope, so $\overline{BD} \parallel \overline{FH}$ and $\overline{BH} \parallel \overline{DF}$; by def., BDFH is a $\square$.

Study Guide: Review **439**

34. 18
35. 39.6
36. 39.6
37. 19.8
38. 25.5
39. 10.5
40. 25.5
41. 21
42. 41°
43. 49°
44. 82°
45. 98°
46. m∠1 = 57°; m∠2 = 66°; m∠3 = 33°; m∠4 = 114°; m∠5 = 57°
47. m∠1 = 37°; m∠2 = 53°; m∠3 = 90°; m∠4 = 37°; m∠5 = 53°
48. $RT = SU = 2\sqrt{10}$, so $\overline{RT} \cong \overline{SU}$. Slope of $\overline{RT} = -3$, and slope of $\overline{SU} = \frac{1}{3}$, so $\overline{RT} \perp \overline{SU}$. The coordinates of the mdpt. of $\overline{RT}$ and $\overline{SU}$ are $(-4, -3)$, so $\overline{RT}$ and $\overline{SU}$ bisect each other. So the diags. of *RSTU* are $\cong \perp$ bisectors of each other.
49. $EG = FH = 3\sqrt{2}$, so $\overline{EG} \cong \overline{FH}$. Slope of $\overline{EG} = -1$, and slope of $\overline{FH} = 1$, so $\overline{EG} \perp \overline{FH}$. The coordinates of the mdpt. of $\overline{EG}$ and $\overline{FH}$ are $\left(\frac{7}{2}, -\frac{1}{2}\right)$, so $\overline{EG}$ and $\overline{FH}$ bisect each other. So the diags. of *EFGH* are $\cong \perp$ bisectors of each other.
50. Not valid; by Thm. 6-5-2, if the diags. of a ▱ are $\cong$, then the ▱ is a rect. By Thm. 6-5-4, if the diags. of a ▱ are $\perp$, then the ▱ is a rhombus. If a ▱ is both a rect. and a rhombus, then the ▱ is a square. To apply this chain of reasoning, you must first know that *EFRS* is a ▱.
51. valid
52. valid

Properties of Special Parallelograms *(pp. 408–415)*    TEKS G.2.A, G.2.B, G.3.B, G.3.E, G.7.A, G.7.B, G.7.C

EXAMPLES

In rectangle *JKLM*, $KM = 52.8$, and $JM = 45.6$. Find each length.

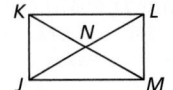

- *KL*

    JKLM is a ▱.   Rect. → ▱
    $KL = JM = 45.6$ ▱ → opp. sides $\cong$

- *NL*

    $JL = KM = 52.8$ Rect. → diags. $\cong$
    $NL = \frac{1}{2}JL = 26.4$ ▱ → diags. bisect each other

- *PQRS* is a rhombus. Find m∠*QPR*, given that m∠*QTR* = $(6y + 6)°$ and m∠*SPR* = $3y°$.

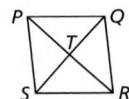

    m∠*QTR* = 90°   Rhombus → diags. $\perp$
    $6y + 6 = 90$ Substitute the given value.
    $y = 14$ Solve for y.
    m∠*QPR* = m∠*SPR*   Rhombus → each diag. bisects opp. ∠
    m∠*QPR* = $3(14)° = 42°$

- The vertices of square *ABCD* are $A(5, 0)$, $B(2, 4)$, $C(-2, 1)$, and $D(1, -3)$. Show that the diagonals of square *ABCD* are congruent perpendicular bisectors of each other.

    $AC = BD = 5\sqrt{2}$ Diags. are $\cong$.
    slope of $\overline{AC} = -\frac{1}{7}$ Product of slopes is -1,
    slope of $\overline{BD} = 7$ so diags. are $\perp$.
    mdpt. of $\overline{AC}$
      = mdpt. of $\overline{BD} = \left(\frac{3}{2}, \frac{1}{2}\right)$ Diags. bisect each other.

EXERCISES

In rectangle *ABCD*, $CD = 18$, and $CE = 19.8$. Find each length.

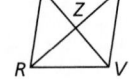

34. *AB*   35. *AC*
36. *BD*   37. *BE*

In rhombus *WXYZ*, $WX = 7a + 1$, $WZ = 9a - 6$, and $VZ = 3a$. Find each measure.

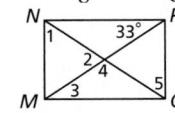

38. *WZ*   39. *XV*
40. *XY*   41. *XZ*

In rhombus *RSTV*, m∠*TZV* = $(8n + 18)°$, and m∠*SRV* = $(9n + 1)°$. Find each measure.

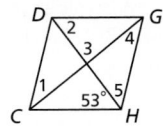

42. m∠*TRS*   43. m∠*RSV*
44. m∠*STV*   45. m∠*TVR*

Find the measures of the numbered angles in each figure.

46. rectangle *MNPQ*   47. rhombus *CDGH*

Show that the diagonals of the square with the given vertices are congruent perpendicular bisectors of each other.

48. $R(-5, 0)$, $S(-1, -2)$, $T(-3, -6)$, and $U(-7, -4)$
49. $E(2, 1)$, $F(5, 1)$, $G(5, -2)$, and $H(2, -2)$

Conditions for Special Parallelograms *(pp. 418–425)*    TEKS G.2.A, G.2.B, G.3.B, G.3.E, G.7.A, G.7.B, G.7.C

EXAMPLES

- Determine if the conclusion is valid. If not, tell what additional information is needed to make it valid.

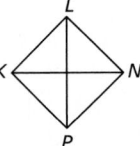

    Given: $\overline{LP} \perp \overline{KN}$
    Conclusion: *KLNP* is a rhombus.

    The conclusion is not valid. If the diagonals of a parallelogram are perpendicular, then the parallelogram is a rhombus. To apply this theorem, you must first know that *KLNP* is a parallelogram.

EXERCISES

Determine if the conclusion is valid. If not, tell what additional information is needed to make it valid.

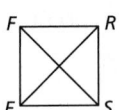

50. Given: $\overline{ER} \perp \overline{FS}$, $\overline{ER} \cong \overline{FS}$
    Conclusion: *EFRS* is a square.

51. Given: $\overline{ER}$ and $\overline{FS}$ bisect each other.
    $\overline{ER} \cong \overline{FS}$
    Conclusion: *EFRS* is a rectangle.

52. Given: $\overline{EF} \parallel \overline{RS}$, $\overline{FR} \parallel \overline{ES}$, $\overline{EF} \cong \overline{ES}$
    Conclusion: *EFRS* is a rhombus.

- Use the diagonals to tell whether a parallelogram with vertices $P(-5, 3)$, $Q(0, 1)$, $R(2, -4)$, and $S(-3, -2)$ is a rectangle, rhombus, or square. Give all the names that apply.

$PR = \sqrt{98} = 7\sqrt{2}$ *Distance Formula*
$QS = \sqrt{18} = 3\sqrt{2}$ *Distance Formula*

Since $PR \neq QS$, $PQRS$ is not a rectangle and not a square.

slope of $\overline{PR} = \dfrac{7}{-7} = -1$ *Slope Formula*

slope of $\overline{QS} = \dfrac{3}{3} = 1$ *Slope Formula*

Since the product of the slopes is -1, the diagonals are perpendicular. $PQRS$ is a rhombus.

Use the diagonals to tell whether a parallelogram with the given vertices is a rectangle, rhombus, or square. Give all the names that apply.

53. $B(-3, 0)$, $F(-2, 7)$, $J(5, 8)$, $N(4, 1)$

54. $D(-4, -3)$, $H(5, 6)$, $L(8, 3)$, $P(-1, -6)$

55. $Q(-8, -2)$, $T(-6, 8)$, $W(4, 6)$, $Z(2, -4)$

6-6 Properties of Kites and Trapezoids *(pp. 427–435)*

⭐ TEKS G.2.A, G.2.B, G.3.B, G.3.E, G.7.A, G.7.B, G.7.C

EXAMPLES

- In kite $PQRS$, $m\angle SRT = 24°$, and $m\angle TSP = 53°$. Find $m\angle SPT$.

$\triangle PTS$ is a right triangle.   *Kite → diags. ⊥*
$m\angle SPT + m\angle TSP = 90°$ *Acute ∡ of rt. △ are comp.*

$m\angle SPT + 53 = 90$ *Substitute 53 for $m\angle TSP$.*
$m\angle SPT = 37°$ *Subtract 53 from both sides.*

- Find $m\angle D$.

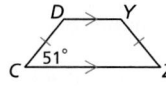

$m\angle C + m\angle D = 180°$ *Same-Side Int. ∡ Thm.*
$51 + m\angle D = 180$ *Substitute 51 for $m\angle C$.*
$m\angle D = 129°$ *Subtract.*

- In trapezoid $HJLN$, $JP = 32.5$, and $HL = 50$. Find PN.

$\overline{JN} \cong \overline{HL}$ *Isosc. trap. → diags. ≅*
$JN = HL = 50$ *Def. of ≅ segs.*
$JP + PN = JN$ *Seg. Add. Post.*
$32.5 + PN = 50$ *Substitute.*
$PN = 17.5$ *Subtract 32.5 from both sides.*

- Find WZ.

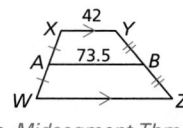

$AB = \dfrac{1}{2}(XY + WZ)$ *Trap. Midsegment Thm.*
$73.5 = \dfrac{1}{2}(42 + WZ)$ *Substitute.*
$147 = 42 + WZ$ *Multiply both sides by 2.*
$105 = WZ$ *Solve for WZ.*

EXERCISES

In kite $WXYZ$, $m\angle VXY = 58°$, and $m\angle ZWX = 50°$.
Find each measure.

56. $m\angle XYZ$ **57.** $m\angle ZWV$

58. $m\angle VZW$ **59.** $m\angle WZY$

Find each measure.

60. $m\angle R$ and $m\angle S$ **61.** BZ if $ZH = 70$ and $EK = 121.6$

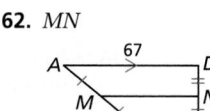

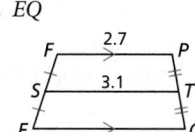

62. MN **63.** EQ

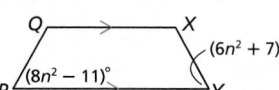

64. Find the value of n so that $PQXY$ is isosceles.

Give the best name for a quadrilateral whose vertices have the given coordinates.

65. $(-4, 5)$, $(-1, 8)$, $(5, 5)$, $(-1, 2)$

66. $(1, 4)$, $(5, 4)$, $(5, -4)$, $(1, -1)$

67. $(-6, -1)$, $(-4, 2)$, $(0, 2)$, $(2, -1)$

Organizer

Objective: Assess students' mastery of concepts and skills in Chapter 6.

 Online Edition

Resources

 Assessment Resources

Chapter 6 Tests

• Free Response (Levels A, B, C)

• Multiple Choice (Levels A, B, C)

• Performance Assessment

 IDEA Works! CD-ROM

Modified Chapter 6 Test

 **Test & Practice Generator One-Stop Planner®**

TAKS Practice

Grades 9–11	Items
Obj. 2	3–5, 7, 13
Obj. 6	3–5
Obj. 7	8, 11, 16, 17
Obj. 10	3, 20

Tell whether each figure is a polygon. If it is a polygon, name it by the number of its sides.

1. 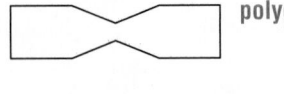 not a polygon
2. 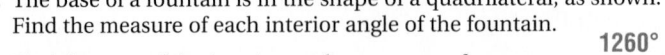 polygon; decagon

3. The base of a fountain is in the shape of a quadrilateral, as shown. Find the measure of each interior angle of the fountain.

4. Find the sum of the interior angle measures of a convex nonagon. **1260°**

5. Find the measure of each exterior angle of a regular 15-gon. **24°**

3. $m\angle A = 96°$; $m\angle B = 112°$; $m\angle C = 64°$; $m\angle D = 88°$

6. In ▱EFGH, EH = 28, HZ = 9, and FH = 18; m∠EHG = 145°. Find FH and m∠FEH. m∠FEH = 35°

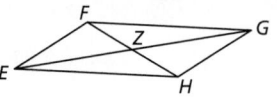

7. JKLM is a parallelogram. Find KL and m∠L. **KL = 17; m∠L = 52°**

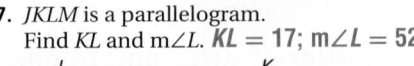

8. Three vertices of ▱PQRS are $P(-2, -3)$, $R(7, 5)$, and $S(6, 1)$. Find the coordinates of Q. **(−1, 1)**

9. Show that WXYZ is a parallelogram for $a = 4$ and $b = 3$.

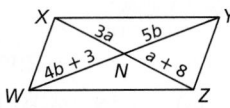

10. Determine if CDGH must be a parallelogram. Justify your answer.

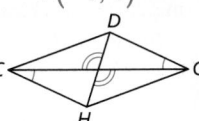

11. Show that a quadrilateral with vertices $K(-7, -3)$, $L(2, 0)$, $S(5, -4)$, and $T(-4, -7)$ is a parallelogram.

12. In rectangle PLCM, LC = 19, and LM = 23. Find PT and PM. **PT = 11.5; PM = 19**

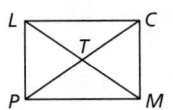

13. In rhombus EHKN, $m\angle NQK = (7z + 6)°$, and $m\angle ENQ = (5z + 1)°$. Find m∠HEQ and m∠EHK. **m∠HEQ = 29°; m∠EHK = 122°**

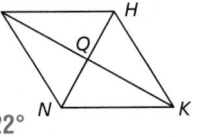

Determine if the conclusion is valid. If not, tell what additional information is needed to make it valid.

14. Given: $\overline{NP} \cong \overline{PQ} \cong \overline{QM} \cong \overline{MN}$ Conclusion: MNPQ is a square. **not valid**

15. Given: $\overline{NP} \cong \overline{MQ}$, $\overline{NM} \cong \overline{PQ}$, $\overline{NQ} \cong \overline{MP}$ Conclusion: MNPQ is a rectangle. **valid**

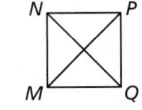

Use the diagonals to determine whether a parallelogram with the given vertices is a rectangle, rhombus, or square. Give all the names that apply.

16. $A(-5, 7)$, $C(3, 6)$, $E(7, -1)$, $G(-1, 0)$ **rhombus**

17. $P(4, 1)$, $Q(3, 4)$, $R(-3, 2)$, $S(-2, -1)$ **rect.**

18. m∠JFR = 43°, and m∠JNB = 68°. Find m∠FBN. **103°**

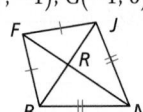

19. PV = 61.1, and YS = 24.7. Find MY. **36.4**

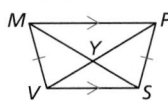

20. Find HR. **27 in.**

24 in.

Answers

9. XN = ZN = 12, so $\overline{XN} \cong \overline{ZN}$. Thus $\overline{WY}$ bisects $\overline{XZ}$. WN = YN = 15, so $\overline{WN} \cong \overline{YN}$. Thus $\overline{XZ}$ bisects $\overline{WY}$. The diags. of WXYZ bisect each other. By Thm. 6-3-5, WXYZ is a ▱.

10. No; 1 pair of opp. sides of the quad. are ∥. A pair of vert. ∡ formed by the diags. are ≅. None of the conditions for a ▱ are met.

11. Possible answer: slope of $\overline{KL}$ = slope of $\overline{ST} = \frac{1}{3}$; slope of $\overline{KT}$ = slope of $\overline{LS} = -\frac{4}{3}$; both pairs of opp. sides have the same slope, so $\overline{KL} \parallel \overline{ST}$ and $\overline{KT} \parallel \overline{LS}$; by def., KLST is a ▱.

14. Possible answer: MNPQ is a rhombus by def. because its 4 sides are ≅. To show that MNPQ is a square, you need to know that MNPQ is also a rect.

COLLEGE ENTRANCE EXAM PRACTICE

FOCUS ON SAT

The scores for each SAT section range from 200 to 800. Your score is calculated by subtracting a fraction for each incorrect multiple-choice answer from the total number of correct answers. No points are deducted for incorrect grid-in answers or items you left blank.

 **HOT TIP!**

If you have time, go back through each section of the test and check as many of your answers as possible. Try to use a different method of solving the problem than you used the first time.

You may want to time yourself as you take this practice test. It should take you about 6 minutes to complete.

1. Given the quadrilateral below, what value of x would allow you to conclude that the figure is a parallelogram?

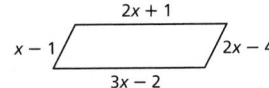

(A) -2

(B) 0

(C) 1

(D) 2

(E) 3

2. In the figure below, if $ABCD$ is a rectangle, what type of triangle must $\triangle ABE$ be?

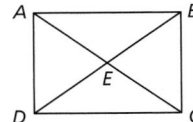

(A) Equilateral

(B) Right

(C) Equiangular

(D) Isosceles

(E) Scalene

3. Which of the following terms best describes the figure below?

(A) Rhombus

(B) Trapezoid

(C) Quadrilateral

(D) Square

(E) Parallelogram

4. Three vertices of $\square MNPQ$ are $M(3, 1)$, $N(0, 6)$, and $P(4, 7)$. Which of the following could be the coordinates of vertex Q?

(A) $(7, 0)$

(B) $(-1, 1)$

(C) $(7, 2)$

(D) $(11, 3)$

(E) $(9, 4)$

5. If $ABCDE$ is a regular pentagon, what is the measure of $\angle C$?

(A) $45°$

(B) $60°$

(C) $90°$

(D) $108°$

(E) $120°$

Organizer

Objective: Provide practice for college entrance exams such as the SAT.

PREMIER **Online Edition**

Resources

📎 *College Entrance Exam Practice*

Questions on the SAT represent the following math strands:

Number and Operation, 30–32%

Algebra and Functions, 28–32%

Geometry and Measurement, 27–30%

Data Analysis, Statistics, and Probability, 10–12%

Items on this page focus on:

• Geometry and Measurement

Text References:

Item	1	2	3	4	5
Lesson	6-3	6-4	6-6	6-2	6-1

TEST PREP DOCTOR ✚

1. Students who chose **A** may have set the lengths of adjacent sides equal to each other. Remind students that any quadrilateral in which both pairs of opposite sides are congruent must be a parallelogram.

2. Students who chose **B** may be thinking of the properties of a rhombus, in which the diagonals are perpendicular. Remind students that the diagonals of a rectangle bisect each other, and ask students what that means about the sides of $\triangle ABE$.

3. Students who did not choose **B** should review the vocabulary from this chapter. Ask students to review their graphic organizer from page 431, which shows the relationships between the quadrilaterals studied in this chapter.

4. Students who chose **A** or **E** may have found the correct slopes but applied them incorrectly. Suggest that students graph the points in the coordinate plane to make sure they understand their relative locations.

5. Remind students that the sum of the measures of the interior angles of a convex polygon with n sides is $(n - 2)180$ and that a pentagon has 5 sides.

TAKS TACKLER
Standardized Test Strategies

Organizer

Objective: Provide opportunities to learn and practice common test-taking strategies.

 Online Edition

Resources

 TAKS Prep Workbook

 TAKS Prep CD-ROM

 TAKS Practice Online

go.hrw.com/Geo/TX
KEYWORD: MG7 TestPrep

TAKS PREP DOCTOR This TAKS Tackler focuses on using logic and estimation to eliminate answer choices to multiple-choice test items. While this strategy may not always give students the specific answer, it may save students time by eliminating some of the choices. Encourage students to read a multiple-choice test item carefully. Then, before they begin to solve the problem, have them determine if any of the answer choices can be eliminated.

Multiple Choice: Eliminate Answer Choices

For some multiple-choice test items, you can eliminate one or more of the answer choices without having to do many calculations. Use estimation or logic to help you decide which answer choices can be eliminated.

EXAMPLE 1

What is the value of *x* in the figure?

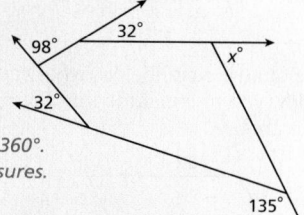

(A) 3°   (C) 83°

(B) 63°   (D) 153°

The sum of the exterior angle measures of a convex polygon is 360°. By rounding, you can estimate the sum of the given angle measures.

$100° + 30° + 140° + 30° = 300°$

If x = 153°, the sum of the angle measures would be far greater than 360°. So eliminate D.

If x = 3°, the sum would be far less than 360°. So eliminate A.

From your estimate, it seems likely that the correct choice is B, 63°. Confirm that this is correct by doing the actual calculation.

$98° + 32° + 63° + 135° + 32° = 360°$

The correct answer is B, 63°.

EXAMPLE 2

What is m∠B in the isosceles trapezoid?

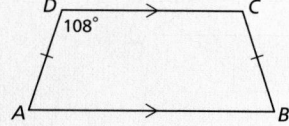

(F) 216°   (H) 72°

(G) 108°   (J) 58°

Base angles of an isosceles trapezoid are congruent. Since ∠D and ∠B are not a pair of base angles, their measures are not equal. Eliminate G, 108°.

∠D and ∠C are base angles, so m∠C = 108°. ∠B and ∠C are same-side interior angles formed by parallel lines. So they are supplementary angles. Therefore the measure of angle B cannot be greater than 180°. You can eliminate F.

$m∠B = 180° - 108° = 72°$

The correct answer is H, 72°.

Read each test item and answer the questions that follow.

Item A

The diagonals of rectangle *MNPQ* intersect at *S*. If *MN* = 4.1 meters, *MS* = 2.35 meters, and *MQ* = 2.3 meters, what is the area of △*MPQ* to the nearest tenth?

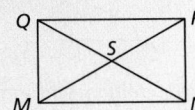

- (A) 4.7 square meters
- (B) 5.4 meters
- (C) 9.4 square meters
- (D) 12.8 meters

1. Are there any answer choices you can eliminate immediately? If so, which choices and why?

2. Describe how to use estimation to eliminate at least one more answer choice.

Item B

What is the sum of the interior angles of a convex hexagon?

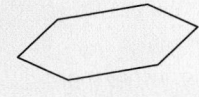

- (F) 180°
- (G) 500°
- (H) 720°
- (J) 1080°

3. Can any of the answer choices be eliminated immediately? If so, which choices and why?

4. How can you use the fact that 500 is not a multiple of 180 to eliminate choice G?

5. A student answered this problem with J. Explain the mistake the student made.

Item C

In isoseceles trapezoid *ABCD*, *AC* = 18.2, and *DG* = 6.3. What is *GB*?

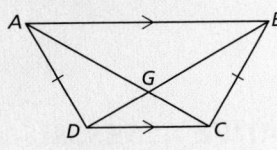

- (A) 24.5
- (B) 11.9
- (C) 6.3
- (D) 2.9

6. Will the measure of $\overline{GB}$ be more than, less than, or equal to the measure of $\overline{AC}$? What answer choices can you eliminate and why?

7. Explain how to use estimation to answer this problem.

Item D

In trapezoid *LMNP*, $\overline{XY}$ = 25 feet. What are two possible lengths for $\overline{LM}$ and $\overline{PN}$?

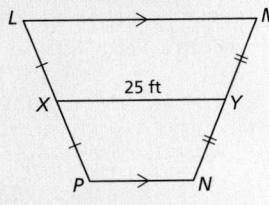

25 ft

- (F) 18 feet and 32 feet
- (G) 49 feet and 2 feet
- (H) 10 feet and 15 feet
- (J) 7 inches and 43 inches

8. Which answer choice can you eliminate immediately? Why?

9. A student used logic to eliminate choice H. Do you agree with the student's decision? Explain.

10. A student used estimation and answered this problem with G. Explain the mistake the student made.

Answers

Possible answers:

1. Yes; **B** and **D**; the units are incorrect.

2. Use the formula for the area of a △ and substitute 4 for the height and 2 for the base: $A = \frac{1}{2}bh = \frac{1}{2}(4)(2) = 4$. Eliminate **C** because it is much greater than 4.

3. Yes; **F**; 180° is the sum of the int. ∡ of a △, and because a hexagon has 3 more sides than a △, the sum of its int. ∡ must be much greater than 180°.

4. The sum of the int. ∡ of a convex polygon must be a multiple of 180°. Because 500 is not a multiple of 180, it can be eliminated.

5. The student did not subtract 2 from the number of sides before multiplying by 180.

6. Less than; **A** can be eliminated because 24.5 > 18.2.

7. Use compatible numbers and subtract: 18 − 6 = 12. *GB* is about 12, so select **B** as the answer.

8. **J**; the units are incorrect.

9. Yes; the midsegment of a trap. has a measure less than that of the longest base and greater than that of the shortest base. Because 10 and 15 are both less than 25, it cannot be the correct answer.

10. The student used numbers compatible with 50 and 0: $\frac{1}{2}(50 + 0) = 25$. However, the student should have checked the answer, because $\frac{1}{2}(49 + 2) = 25.5 \neq 25$.

Answers to Test Items

A. A
B. H
C. B
D. F

⬆**TAKS Practice**

Grades 9–11	Items
Obj. 2	B
Obj. 6	B–D
Obj. 8	A

Organizer

Objective: Provide review and practice for Chapters 1–6 and standardized tests.

 PREMIER **Online Edition**

Resources

Assessment Resources
Chapter 6 Cumulative Test

TAKS Prep Workbook

TAKS Prep CD-ROM

TAKS Practice Online
go.hrw.com/Geo/TX
KEYWORD: MG7 TestPrep

TAKS PREP DOCTOR For **Item 1,** students who chose **B** used the given angle measures as the interior angle measures. Students who chose **C** found the value of *x*. Students who chose **D** found the smallest exterior angle measure.

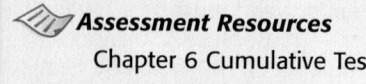 **TAKS Practice**

Grades 9–11	Items
Obj. 2	1, 5, 12, 14–16
Obj. 3	4
Obj. 6	5, 12, 14, 16
Obj. 7	10, 13
Obj. 8	11
Obj. 10	15

CUMULATIVE ASSESSMENT, CHAPTERS 1–6

Multiple Choice

1. The exterior angles of a triangle have measures of $(x + 10)°$, $(2x + 20)°$, and $3x°$. What is the measure of the smallest interior angle of the triangle?

   Ⓐ 15° Ⓒ 55°
   Ⓑ 35° Ⓓ 65°

2. If a plant is a monocot, then its leaves have parallel veins. If a plant is an orchid, then it is a monocot. A Mexican vanilla plant is an orchid. Based on this information, which conclusion is NOT valid?

   Ⓕ The leaves of a Mexican vanilla plant have parallel veins.
   Ⓖ A Mexican vanilla plant is a monocot.
   Ⓗ All orchids have leaves with parallel veins.
   Ⓙ All monocots are orchids.

3. If $\triangle ABC \cong \triangle PQR$ and $\triangle RPQ \cong \triangle XYZ$, which of the following angles is congruent to $\angle CAB$?

   Ⓐ $\angle QRP$ Ⓒ $\angle YXZ$
   Ⓑ $\angle XZY$ Ⓓ $\angle XYZ$

4. Which line coincides with the line $2y + 3x = 4$?

   Ⓕ $3y + 2x = 4$
   Ⓖ $y = \frac{2}{3}x + 2$
   Ⓗ a line through $(-1, 1)$ and $(2, 3)$
   Ⓙ a line through $(0, 2)$ and $(4, -4)$

5. What is the value of *x* in polygon *ABCDEF*?

   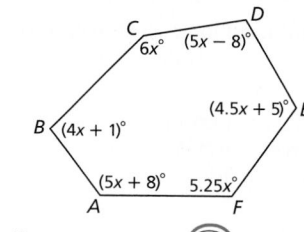

   Ⓐ 12 Ⓒ 24
   Ⓑ 18 Ⓓ 36

Use the figure below for Items 6 and 7.

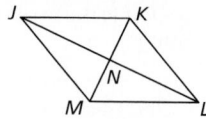

6. If $\overline{JK} \parallel \overline{ML}$, what additional information do you need to prove that quadrilateral *JKLM* is a parallelogram?

   Ⓕ $\overline{JM} \cong \overline{KL}$
   Ⓖ $\overline{MN} \cong \overline{LN}$
   Ⓗ $\angle MLK$ and $\angle LKJ$ are right angles.
   Ⓙ $\angle JML$ and $\angle KLM$ are supplementary.

7. Given that *JKLM* is a parallelogram and that $m\angle KLN = 25°$, $m\angle JMN = 65°$, and $m\angle JML = 130°$, which term best describes quadrilateral *JKLM*?

   Ⓐ Rectangle
   Ⓑ Rhombus
   Ⓒ Square
   Ⓓ Trapezoid

8. For two lines and a transversal, $\angle 1$ and $\angle 2$ are same-side interior angles, $\angle 2$ and $\angle 3$ are vertical angles, and $\angle 3$ and $\angle 4$ are alternate exterior angles. Which classification best describes the angle pair $\angle 2$ and $\angle 4$?

   Ⓕ Adjacent angles
   Ⓖ Alternate interior angles
   Ⓗ Corresponding angles
   Ⓙ Vertical angles

9. For $\triangle ABC$ and $\triangle DEF$, $\angle A \cong \angle F$, and $\overline{AC} \cong \overline{EF}$. Which of the following would allow you to conclude that these triangles are congruent by AAS?

   Ⓐ $\angle ABC \cong \angle EDF$
   Ⓑ $\angle ACB \cong \angle EDF$
   Ⓒ $\angle BAC \cong \angle FDE$
   Ⓓ $\angle CBA \cong \angle FED$

10. The vertices of ▱*ABCD* are *A*(1, 4), *B*(4, *y*), *C*(3, −2), and *D*(0, −3). What is the value of *y*?

 Ⓕ 3   Ⓗ 5
 Ⓖ 4   Ⓙ 6

11. Quadrilateral *RSTU* is a kite. What is the length of $\overline{RV}$?

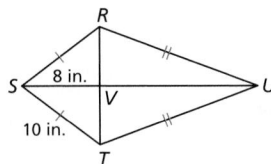

 Ⓐ 4 inches   Ⓒ 6 inches
 Ⓑ 5 inches   Ⓓ 13 inches

12. What is the measure of each interior angle in a regular dodecagon?

 Ⓕ 30°   Ⓗ 150°
 Ⓖ 144°   Ⓙ 162°

13. The coordinates of the vertices of quadrilateral *RSTU* are *R*(1, 3), *S*(2, 7), *T*(10, 5), and *U*(9, 1). Which term best describes quadrilateral *RSTU*?

 Ⓐ Parallelogram   Ⓒ Rhombus
 Ⓑ Rectangle   Ⓓ Trapezoid

 Mixed numbers cannot be entered into the grid for gridded-response questions. For example, if you get an answer of $7\frac{1}{4}$, you must grid either 7.25 or $\frac{29}{4}$.

Gridded Response

14. If quadrilateral *MNPQ* is a parallelogram, what is the value of *x*? **36**

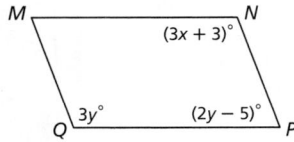

15. What is the greatest number of line segments determined by six coplanar points when no three are collinear? **15**

16. Quadrilateral *RSTU* is a rectangle with diagonals $\overline{RT}$ and $\overline{SU}$. If *RT* = 4*a* + 2 and *SU* = 6*a* − 25, what is the value of *a*? **13.5**

Short Response

17. In △*ABC*, *AE* = 9*x* − 11.25, and *AF* = *x* + 4.

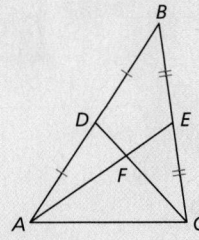

 a. Find the value of *x*. Show your work and explain how you found your answer.

 b. If $\overline{DF} \cong \overline{EF}$, show that △*AFD* ≅ △*CFE*. State any theorems or postulates used.

18. Consider quadrilateral *ABCD*.

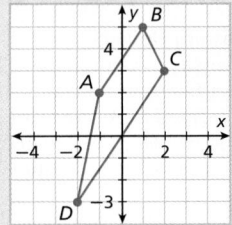

 a. Show that *ABCD* is a trapezoid. Justify your answer.

 b. What are the coordinates for the endpoints of the midsegment of trapezoid *ABCD*?

19. Suppose that ∠*M* is complementary to ∠*N* and ∠*N* is complementary to ∠*P*. Explain why the measurements of these three angles cannot be the angle measurements of a triangle.

Extended Response

20. Given △*ABC* and △*XYZ*, suppose that $\overline{AB} \cong \overline{XY}$ and $\overline{BC} \cong \overline{YZ}$.

 a. If *AB* = 5, *BC* = 6, *AC* = 8, and m∠*B* < m∠*Y*, explain why △*XYZ* is obtuse. Justify your reasoning and state any theorems or postulates used.

 b. If *AB* = 3, *BC* = 5, *AC* = 5, and m∠*B* > m∠*Y*, find the length of $\overline{XZ}$ so that △*XYZ* is a right triangle. Justify your reasoning and state any theorems or postulates used.

 c. If *AB* = 8 and *BC* = 4, find the range of possible values for the length of $\overline{AC}$. Justify your answer.

Short-Response Rubric

Items 17–19

2 Points = The student's answer is an accurate and complete execution of the task or tasks.

1 Point = The student's answer contains attributes of an appropriate response but is flawed.

0 Points = The student's answer contains no attributes of an appropriate response.

Extended-Response Rubric

Item 20

4 Points = The student correctly finds *XZ* and the range for *AC*. Explanations are complete, and work demonstrates a thorough understanding of concepts related to triangle inequality theorems.

3 Points = The student's answers are correct, but explanations may contain minor flaws. Work demonstrates an understanding of major concepts related to triangle inequality theorems.

2 Points = The student answers correctly, but explanations are missing or incomplete. Work demonstrates a limited understanding of triangle inequality theorems.

1 Point = The student answers incorrectly but makes a reasonable attempt to show work.

0 Points = The student answers incorrectly and does not attempt all parts of the problem.

Answers

17a. By the Centroid Thm., $\frac{2}{3}(9x - 11.25)$ = *x* + 4. So 6*x* − 7.5 = *x* + 4, −11.5 = −5*x*, and *x* = 2.3.

 b. Possible answer: By the Centroid Thm., $FC = \frac{2}{3}DC$. It is given that $\overline{DF} \cong \overline{EF}$, so *DF* = *EF*. From part **a**, *EF* = 3.15, and *AF* = 6.3. So *DF* = 3.15. *FC* = $\frac{2}{3}(DF + FC) = \frac{2}{3}(3.15 + FC)$, so *FC* = 6.3. Thus *AF* = *FC*, and $\overline{AF} \cong \overline{FC}$. ∠*DFA* ≅ ∠*EFC* by the Vert. ∠ Thm. Thus △*AFD* ≅ △*CFE* by SAS.

18a. Slope of $\overline{AB} = \frac{3}{2}$, and slope of $\overline{CD} = \frac{3}{2}$, so $\overline{AB} \parallel \overline{CD}$. Slope of $\overline{BC} = -2$, and slope of $\overline{AD} = 5$. So $\overline{BC}$ is not ∥ to $\overline{AC}$. *ABCD* is a trap. by def.

 b. $\left(-1\frac{1}{2}, -\frac{1}{2}\right), \left(1\frac{1}{2}, 4\right)$

19. ∠*M* ≅ ∠*P* by the ≅ Comps. Thm., and thus m∠*M* = m∠*P*. Also, m∠*N* = 90° − m∠*P* by the def. of comp. ∠. If these ∠ were ∠ of a △, m∠*M* + m∠*N* + m∠*P* = 180° by the △ Sum Thm. By subst., m∠*P* + (90° − m∠*P*) + m∠*P* = 180°. Thus, m∠*P* = 90°. But m∠*P* < 90° because ∠*N* is comp. to ∠*P*. So there is a contradiction, and therefore, these ∠ cannot be the ∠ of a △.

20a. Since m∠*B* < m∠*Y*, $\overline{AB} \cong \overline{XY}$, and $\overline{BC} \cong \overline{YZ}$, it follows by the Hinge Thm. that *XZ* > *AC* = 8. Since 64 > 25 + 36, △*ABC* is obtuse by the Pyth. Inequals. Thm. Since the longer side lies opp. the greater ∠, ∠*B* is the largest ∠ in △*ABC*. Since △*ABC* is obtuse, ∠*B* must be obtuse. Since m∠*B* < m∠*Y*, m∠*Y* must also be obtuse, so △*XYZ* is obtuse.

 b. Since m∠*B* > m∠*Y*, $\overline{AB} \cong \overline{XY}$, and $\overline{BC} \cong \overline{YZ}$, it follows by the Hinge Thm. that *XZ* < *AC* = 5. So the hyp. of △*XYZ* would be $\overline{YZ}$, the longest side. According to the Pyth. Thm., $XY^2 + XZ^2 = YZ^2$, $3^2 + XZ^2 = 5^2$, $XZ^2 = 25 − 9 = 16$, and *XZ* = 4.

 c. 4 < *AC* < 12. By the △ Inequal. Thm., *AB* + *AC* > *BC*. By subst. 8 + *AC* > 4. This is true when *AC* > 0. *AB* + *BC* > *AC*, so 8 + 4 = 12 > *AC*. Also, *AC* + *BC* > *AB*, so *AC* + 4 > 8, and *AC* > 4.

Problem Solving on Location

Organizer

Objective: Choose appropriate problem-solving strategies and use them with skills from Chapters 5 and 6 to solve real-world problems.

 Online Edition

Southwestern University

Reading Strategies

Have students read **Problem 2** aloud. Ask the class to identify what information in the problem is unnecessary to solve it. the names of the room and the building Explain that a *rotunda* is an architectural term for a domed, round building but that this definition is not needed to solve the problem.

Using Data For **Problem 4,** ask students to identify the right angles in *ABCD*. ∠A, ∠ABE, ∠E, ∠ADC, ∠CDG, ∠CFG, ∠CFE, ∠DCF, and ∠G Ask students which postulates or theorems they used to find the other angle measures in *ABCD*. Possible answers: ∠ Add. Post., Lin. Pair Post., Polygon ∠ Sum Thm., Conv. of the Same-Side Int. ∡ Thm.

TAKS *Problem Solving on Location* focuses on TAKS objectives involving the underlying mathematical processes.

Grades 9–11
Obj. 10 Mathematical processes and tools 8.14.A, 8.14.B, 8.14.C; 8.15.A; 8.16.A, 8.16.B

Problem Solving on Location

TEXAS

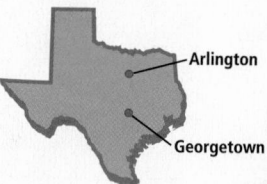

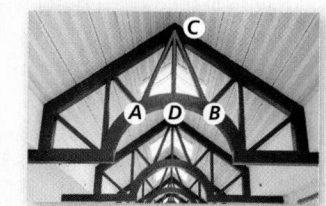

Southwestern University

Southwestern University, a nationally recognized liberal arts university in Georgetown, Texas, is Texas's oldest university. Southwestern was officially chartered in 1875 but was formed from the resources of four existing schools—Rutersville College (chartered in 1840), Wesleyan College (chartered in 1844), McKenzie College (chartered in 1848), and Soule University (chartered in 1856).

Choose one or more strategies to solve each problem.

1. The trusses that line the ceiling of the McCombs Campus Center are made of triangular shapes. The center shape resembles an equilateral triangle. If the side $\overline{AC}$ of the triangle is 42 inches long, about how tall is the center truss $\overline{CD}$? Round to the nearest inch. **36 in.**

2. The floor of the Rockwell Rotunda in the McCombs Campus Center is in the shape of a regular octagon. What is the measure of each interior angle of the rotunda floor? **135°**

3. Each section of the stained-glass window is made of five polygonal shapes. Name each polygon by the number of its sides. Tell whether each polygon appears to be regular or irregular, and concave or convex. Identify which of the five polygons appear to be special quadrilaterals.

4. Square *ABEG* at the center of the marble fireplace is composed of three shapes— a smaller square *DCFG* and two congruent quadrilaterals *ABCD* and *EBCF*. Find the angle measures in *ABCD*, and explain why *ABCD* must be a trapezoid.

Problem-Solving Focus

For **Problem 3,** ask students which problem-solving strategy might be helpful, and have them explain how they would apply the strategy. Possible answer: Make an organized list. Draw a separate diagram for each of the five shapes in the section of glass. Then name and classify each shape from the individual diagrams.

Discuss different strategies that could be used to solve **Problem 3.** Some students might make an organized list or a table of the shapes. Other students might copy the section of glass and outline the shapes rather than redrawing them.

Answers

3. △: convex, irregular; quad.: convex, irregular, rect.; quad.: convex, irregular, ▱; quad.: convex, irregular, ▱; pentagon: convex, irregular

4. Possible answer: Since *ABEG* and *DCFG* are squares, ∠A, ∠CDG, and ∠ABE are rt. ∡ and measure 90°. So ∠ADC is also a rt. ∠ by the Lin. Pair Post., so m∠ADC = 90°. Since *ABCD* ≅ *EBCF*, ∠ABC ≅ ∠EBC. So each of these ∡ measures 45°. By the Polygon ∠ Sum Thm., m∠BCD = 135°. By the Conv. of the Same-Side Int. ∡ Thm, $\overline{AB} \parallel \overline{CD}$. Since m∠ABC ≠ m∠BCD, $\overline{AD} \nparallel \overline{BC}$. So *ABCD* is a trapezoid by def.

Titan

When it opened in April 2001 at Six Flags Over Texas in Arlington, Titan became the tallest roller coaster in Texas and the third tallest in the world. Titan trains travel up to 85 mi/h and cover over 5312 feet of track. The first hill features a 255-foot drop at a 65° angle into a dark, 120-foot-long tunnel!

Choose one or more strategies to solve each problem.

17 mi/h

1. If a Titan train takes 3 minutes and 30 seconds to travel the entire track, what is the roller coaster's average speed in miles per hour?

2. If a Titan train travels through the tunnel at its maximum speed, about how long does it take the train to pass through the tunnel? Round to the nearest hundredth of a second. **0.96 s**

3. Titan has three trains, each of which holds 30 passengers. If the roller coaster can accommodate 1600 passengers per hour, about how many trains run each hour? **about 53 trains**

The figure below shows the structure of the first hill of Titan. For 4–6, use the figure.

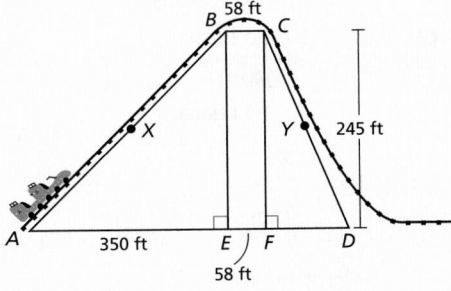

4. Titan reaches its maximum height at the top of the first hill. The ascent covers a horizontal distance *AE* of about 350 feet. What is the length of the ascent $\overline{AB}$ to the nearest foot? **427 ft**

5. The length of the descent $\overline{CD}$ is about 270 feet. What is *FD* to the nearest foot? **113 ft**

6. Event organizers plan to hang a banner across the first hill of Titan from *X* to *Y*, where *X* is the midpoint of $\overline{AB}$ and *Y* is the midpoint of $\overline{CD}$. What is the width of the banner to the nearest foot? **290 ft**

Problem Solving Strategies

Draw a Diagram
Make a Model
Guess and Test
Work Backward
Find a Pattern
Make a Table
Solve a Simpler Problem
Use Logical Reasoning
Use a Venn Diagram
Make an Organized List

Titan

Reading Strategies

ENGLISH LANGUAGE LEARNERS

Make sure that students understand what the words *ascent* and *descent* mean. If students are unfamiliar with the terms, ask them if they can guess their meanings from context clues in the problems.

Using Data For **Problems 4–6**, have students identify the segments in the figure that represent the ascent and descent. $\overline{AB}$; $\overline{CD}$ Ask students to identify two right triangles in the figure. $\triangle AEB$ and $\triangle CFD$

Problem-Solving Focus

For **Problems 1** and **2**, focus on the final step of the problem-solving process: **(4) Look Back.** In particular, ask students whether their answers seem reasonable. Based on their experiences with roller coasters, do the average speed and the amount of time for the tunnel seem realistic? If not, encourage students to check their work for errors.

CHAPTER 7

Similarity

Section 7A
Similarity Relationships

7-1 **Ratio and Proportion**
7-1 **Technology Lab** Explore the Golden Ratio
7-2 **Ratios in Similar Polygons**
7-3 **Technology Lab** Predict Triangle Similarity Relationships
7-3 **Triangle Similarity: AA, SSS, and SAS**

Section 7B
Applying Similarity

7-4 **Technology Lab** Investigate Angle Bisectors of a Triangle
7-4 **Applying Properties of Similar Triangles**
7-5 **Using Proportional Relationships**
7-6 **Dilations and Similarity in the Coordinate Plane**
On Track for TAKS Direct Variation

Pacing Guide for 45-Minute Classes

Chapter 7

Countdown to TAKS Weeks 15, 16

DAY 1	DAY 2	DAY 3	DAY 4	DAY 5
7-1 Lesson	7-1 Technology Lab	7-2 Lesson	7-3 Technology Lab	7-3 Lesson
DAY 6	**DAY 7**	**DAY 8**	**DAY 9**	**DAY 10**
7-3 Lesson	Multi-Step TAKS Prep Ready to Go On?	7-4 Technology Lab 7-4 Lesson	7-4 Lesson	7-5 Lesson
DAY 11	**DAY 12**	**DAY 13**	**DAY 14**	**DAY 15**
7-6 Lesson	7-6 Lesson On Track for TAKS	Multi-Step TAKS Prep Ready to Go On?	Chapter 7 Review	Chapter 7 Test

Pacing Guide for 90-Minute Classes

Chapter 7

DAY 1	DAY 2	DAY 3	DAY 4	DAY 5
7-1 Lesson 7-1 Technology Lab	7-2 Lesson 7-3 Technology Lab	7-3 Lesson	Multi-Step TAKS Prep Ready to Go On? 7-4 Technology Lab 7-4 Lesson	7-4 Lesson 7-5 Lesson
DAY 6	**DAY 7**	**DAY 8**		
7-6 Lesson On Track for TAKS	Multi-Step TAKS Prep Ready to Go On? Chapter 7 Review	Chapter 7 Test 8-1 Lesson		

ONGOING ASSESSMENT and INTERVENTION

	DIAGNOSE	PRESCRIBE

Assess Prior Knowledge

Before Chapter 7

Diagnose readiness for the chapter.
Are You Ready? SE p. 451

Prescribe intervention.
Are You Ready? Intervention Skills 10, 12, 27, 36

Formative Assessment

Before Every Lesson

Diagnose readiness for the lesson.
Warm Up TE, every lesson

Prescribe intervention.
Skills Bank SE pp. S50–S81
Reteach CRB, Ch. 1–7

During Every Lesson

Diagnose understanding of lesson concepts.
Check It Out! SE, every example
Think and Discuss SE, every lesson
Write About It SE, every lesson
Journal TE, every lesson

Prescribe intervention.
Questioning Strategies TE, every example
Reading Strategies CRB, every lesson
Success for ELL pp. 85–96

After Every Lesson

Diagnose mastery of lesson concepts.
Lesson Quiz TE, every lesson
Alternative Assessment TE, every lesson
Test Prep SE, every lesson
Test and Practice Generator

Prescribe intervention.
Reteach CRB, every lesson
Problem Solving CRB, every lesson
Test Prep Doctor TE, every lesson
Homework Help Online

Before Chapter 7 Testing

Diagnose mastery of concepts in the chapter.
Ready to Go On? SE pp. 479, 503
Multi-Step TAKS Prep SE pp. 478, 502
Section Quizzes AR pp. 125–126
Test and Practice Generator

Prescribe intervention.
Ready to Go On? Intervention pp. 92–108
Scaffolding Questions TE pp. 478, 502

Before High Stakes Testing

Diagnose mastery of benchmark concepts.
Ready for TAKS? Benchmark Tests
College Entrance Exam Practice SE p. 509
TAKS Prep SE pp. 512–513
TAKS Prep CD-ROM

Prescribe intervention.
Ready for TAKS? Intervention
College Entrance Exam Practice
TAKS Prep Workbook

Summative Assessment

After Chapter 7

Check mastery of chapter concepts.
Multiple-Choice Tests (Forms A, B, C)
Free-Response Tests (Forms A, B, C)
Performance Assessment AR pp. 127–140
Test and Practice Generator

Prescribe intervention.
Reteach CRB, every lesson
Lesson Tutorial Videos Chapter 7

Check mastery of benchmark concepts.
TAKS Tests
College Entrance Exams

Prescribe intervention.
TAKS Prep Workbook
College Entrance Exam Practice

CHAPTER 7

Supporting the Teacher

Chapter 7 Resource Book

Practice A, B, C
pp. 3–5, 11–13, 19–21, 27–29, 35–37, 43–45

Reading Strategies ELL
pp. 10, 18, 26, 34, 42, 50

Reteach
pp. 6–7, 14–15, 22–23, 30–31, 38–39, 46–47

Problem Solving
pp. 9, 17, 25, 33, 41, 49

Challenge
pp. 8, 16, 24, 32, 40, 48

Parent Letter   pp. 1–2

Transparencies

Lesson Transparencies, Volume 3 .... Chapter 7
• Warm Ups
• Teaching Transparencies
• Additional Examples
• Lesson Quizzes

Alternate Openers: Explorations ....pp. 43–48

Countdown to TAKS ....pp. 29–32

Know-It Notebook .... Chapter 7
• Graphic Organizers
• Key Concepts
• Vocabulary
• Chapter Review
• Big Ideas
• Postulates
• Theorems

Teacher Tools

Power Presentations®
Complete PowerPoint® presentations for Chapter 7 lessons

Lesson Tutorial Videos®
Holt authors Ed Burger and Freddie Renfro present tutorials to support the Chapter 7 lessons.

One-Stop Planner®
Easy access to all Chapter 7 resources and assessments, as well as software for lesson planning, test generation, and puzzle creation

IDEA Works!®
Key Chapter 7 resources and assessments modified to address special learning needs

Lesson Plans..pp. 43–48

Solutions Key ....p. 493

Geometry Posters...................................... Chapter 7

TechKeys   **Lab Resources**

Project Teacher Support   **Parent Resources**

Workbooks

Homework and Practice Workbook
Teacher's Guide ....pp. 43–48

Know-It Notebook
Teacher's Guide ....pp. 95–108

Problem Solving Workbook
Teacher's Guide ....pp. 43–48

TAKS Prep Workbook
Teacher's Guide

Technology Highlights for the Teacher

 Power Presentations
Dynamic presentations to engage students. Complete PowerPoint® presentations for every lesson in Chapter 7.

One-Stop Planner
Easy access to Chapter 7 resources and assessments. Includes lesson-planning, test-generation, and puzzle-creation software.

 Premier Online Edition
Chapter 7 includes Tutorial Videos, Lesson Activities, Lesson Quizzes, Homework Help, and Chapter Project.

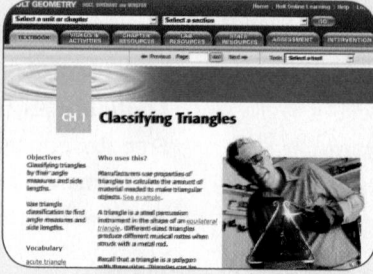

KEY: **SE** = Student Edition   **TE** = Teacher's Edition   English Language Learners   Spanish version available   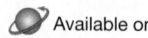 Available online   Available on CD-ROM

Reaching All Learners

Resources for All Learners

Texas Lab Manual	Chapter 7
Homework and Practice Workbook	pp. 43–48
Know-It Notebook	pp. 95–108
Problem Solving Workbook	pp. 43–48

DEVELOPING LEARNERS

Practice A	CRB, every lesson
Reteach	CRB, every lesson
Inclusion	TE pp. 456, 463, 471, 473, 491
Questioning Strategies	TE, every example
Modified Chapter 7 Resources	*IDEA Works!*
Homework Help Online	

ON-LEVEL LEARNERS

Practice B	CRB, every lesson
Multiple Representations	TE p. 489
Modeling	TE p. 497

ADVANCED LEARNERS

Practice C	CRB, every lesson
Challenge	CRB, every lesson
Reading and Writing Math EXTENSION	TE p. 453
Multi-Step TAKS Prep EXTENSION	TE pp. 478, 502
Critical Thinking	TE pp. 482, 485, 494, 496

English Language Learners

ENGLISH LANGUAGE LEARNERS

Are You Ready? Vocabulary	SE p. 452
Vocabulary Connections	SE p. 453
Lesson Vocabulary	SE, every lesson
Vocabulary Exercises	SE, every exercise set
Vocabulary Review	SE p. 504
English Language Learners	TE pp. 464, 483, 496
Reading Strategies	CRB, every lesson
Success for English Language Learners	pp. 85–96
Multilingual Glossary	

Reaching All Learners Through...

Kinesthetic Experience	TE pp. 455, 466, 473, 482, 496
Inclusion	TE pp. 456, 463, 471, 473, 491
Visual Cues	TE pp. 458, 466, 471, 492, 501
Concrete Manipulatives	TE p. 463
Critical Thinking	TE pp. 482, 485, 494, 496
Cooperative Learning	TE p. 489
Auditory Cues	TE p. 490
Multiple Representations	TE p. 497
Test Prep Doctor	TE pp. 459, 467, 477, 487 493, 500, 509, 510, 512
Common Error Alerts	TE pp. 463, 473, 475, 483, 485, 489, 493, 499
Scaffolding Questions	TE pp. 478, 502

Technology Highlights for Reaching All Learners

Lesson Tutorial Videos

Starring Holt authors Ed Burger and Freddie Renfro! Live tutorials to support every lesson in Chapter 7.

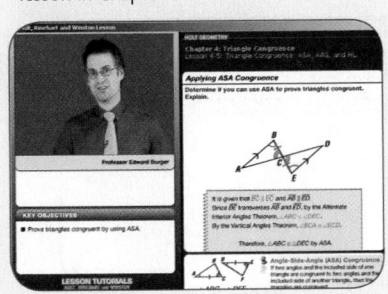

Multilingual Glossary

Searchable glossary includes definitions in English, Spanish, Vietnamese, Chinese, Hmong, Korean, and 4 other languages.

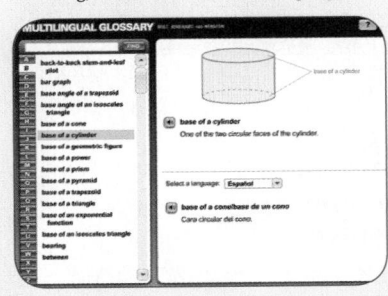

Online Interactivities

Interactive tutorials provide visually engaging alternative opportunities to learn concepts and master skills.

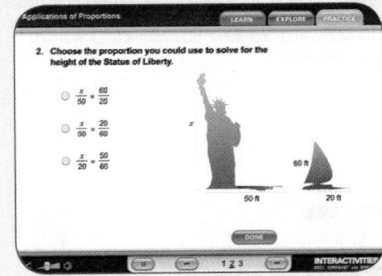

KEY: **SE** = *Student Edition* **TE** = *Teacher's Edition* **CRB** = *Chapter Resource Book*  Spanish version available   Available online Available on CD-ROM

Ongoing Assessment

Assessing Prior Knowledge

Determine whether students have the prerequisite concepts and skills for success in Chapter 7.

Are You Ready? .... SE p. 451
Warm Up .... TE, every lesson

Test Preparation

Provide practice and review for Chapter 7 and standardized tests.

Multi-Step TAKS Prep .... SE pp. 478, 502
Study Guide: Review .... SE pp. 504–507
TAKS Tackler .... SE pp. 510–511
TAKS Prep .... SE pp. 512–513
College Entrance Exam Practice .... SE p. 509
Countdown to TAKS **Transparencies** ...... pp. 29–32
Ready for TAKS?
TAKS Workbook
TAKS Prep **CD-ROM**
IDEA Works!

Alternative Assessment

Assess students' understanding of Chapter 7 concepts and combined problem-solving skills.

Chapter 7 Project .... SE p. 450
Alternative Assessment .... TE, every lesson
Performance Assessment .... AR pp. 139–140
Portfolio Assessment .... AR p. xxxiv

Daily Assessment

Provide formative assessment for each day of Chapter 7.

Questioning Strategies .... TE, every example
Think and Discuss .... SE, every lesson
Check It Out! Exercises .... SE, every example
Write About It .... SE, every lesson
Journal .... TE, every lesson
Lesson Quiz .... TE, every lesson
Alternative Assessment .... TE, every lesson
Modified Lesson Quizzes .... *IDEA Works!*

Weekly Assessment

Provide formative assessment for each week of Chapter 7.

Multi-Step TAKS Prep .... SE pp. 478, 502
Ready to Go On? .... SE pp. 479, 503
Cumulative Assessment .... SE pp. 512–513
Test and Practice Generator SPANISH ..*One-Stop Planner*

Formal Assessment

Provide summative assessment of Chapter 7 mastery.

Section Quizzes .... AR pp. 125–126
Chapter 7 Test .... SE p. 508
Chapter Test (Levels A, B, C) .... AR pp. 127–138
　　　　• Multiple Choice　• Free Response
Cumulative Test .... AR pp. 141–144
Test and Practice Generator SPANISH ..*One-Stop Planner*
Modified Chapter 7 Test .... *IDEA Works!*

Technology Highlights for Ongoing Assessment

Are You Ready?
Automatically assess readiness and prescribe intervention for Chapter 7 prerequisite skills.

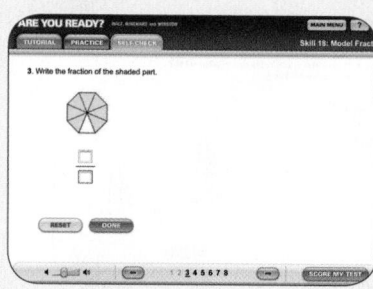

Ready to Go On? SPANISH
Automatically assess understanding of and prescribe intervention for Sections 7A and 7B.

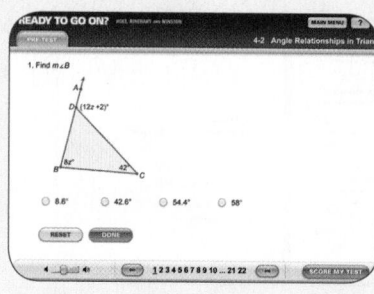

Ready for TAKS SPANISH
Automatically assess proficiency with and provide intervention for TAKS objectives. Grade 6 through Exit Level.

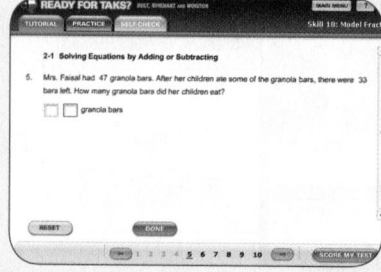

KEY:　**SE** = *Student Edition*　**TE** = *Teacher's Edition*　**AR** = Assessment Resources　SPANISH Spanish version available　Available online　Available on CD-ROM

CHAPTER
7

Formal Assessment

Three levels (A, B, C) of multiple-choice and free-response chapter tests are available in the *Assessment Resources.*

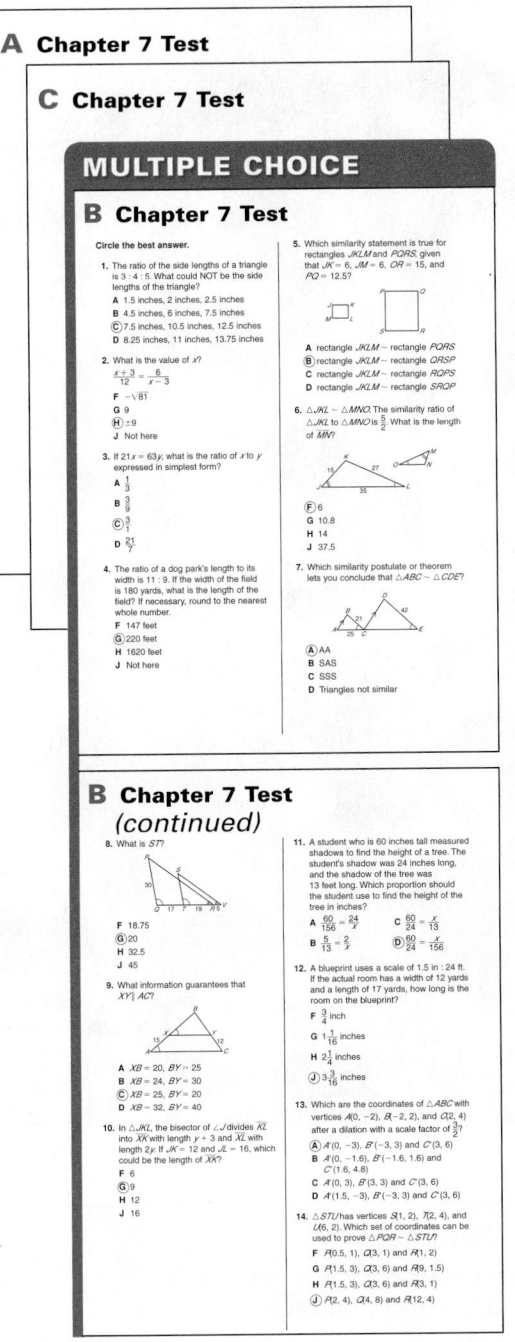

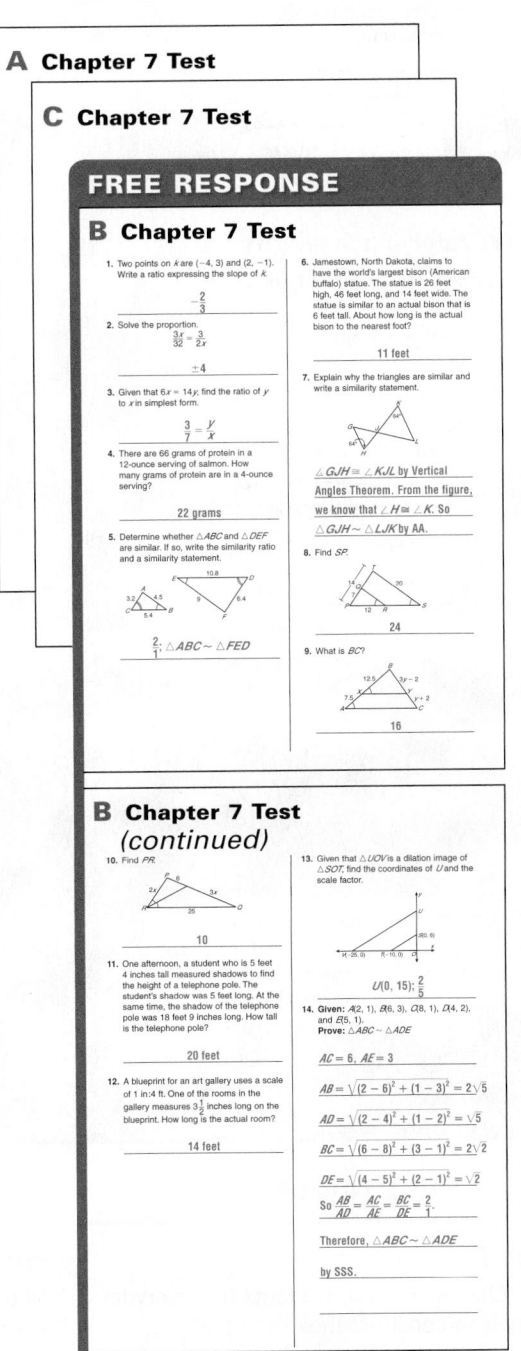

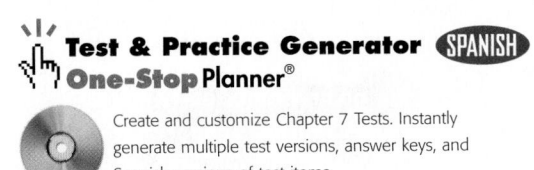

Test & Practice Generator SPANISH
One-Stop Planner®

Create and customize Chapter 7 Tests. Instantly
generate multiple test versions, answer keys, and
Spanish versions of test items.

SECTION **7A**
Similarity Relationships

 On page 478, students apply similarity concepts to solve real-world problems. They use ratios, proportions, and similar triangles to model building a set for a video project.

Exercises designed to prepare students for success on the Multi-Step TAKS Prep can be found on pages 458, 466, and 476.

SECTION **7B**
Applying Similarity

 On page 502, students apply ratios, proportions, and similar triangles to model a real-world design situation.

Exercises designed to prepare students for success on the Multi-Step TAKS Prep can be found on pages 486, 492, and 499.

7A Similarity Relationships

7-1 Ratio and Proportion
Lab Explore the Golden Ratio
7-2 Ratios in Similar Polygons
Lab Predict Triangle Similarity Relationships
7-3 Triangle Similarity: AA, SSS, and SAS

MULTI-STEP TAKS PREP

7B Applying Similarity

Lab Investigate Angle Bisectors of a Triangle
7-4 Applying Properties of Similar Triangles
7-5 Using Proportional Relationships
7-6 Dilations and Similarity in the Coordinate Plane

MULTI-STEP TAKS PREP

go.hrw.com/Geo/TX
Chapter Project Online
KEYWORD: MG7 ChProj

The Lighthouse Rock is located in Palo Duro Canyon or "the Grand Canyon of Texas."

About the Project

Close Encounters

In the Chapter Project, students use everyday materials to construct their own pinhole camera. Then they use similar triangles, ratios, and proportions to understand the mathematics behind the pinhole camera.

Project Resources

All project resources for teachers and students are provided online.

Materials:
- empty coffee can, hammer, nail, cardboard, tape, pin, waxed paper, scissors, rubber band
- meterstick or tape measure

go.hrw.com/Geo/TX
Project Teacher Support
KEYWORD: MG7 ProjectTS

Geometry in Texas

The unusually shaped Lighthouse Rock is a well known landmark at Palo Duro Canyon State Park. You can use the information in this chapter to find the height of this rock formation which towers several hundred feet above the rim of the canyon.

ARE YOU READY?

✓ Vocabulary

Match each term on the left with a definition on the right.

1. side of a polygon **E**
2. denominator **F**
3. numerator **B**
4. vertex of a polygon **D**
5. vertical angles **A**

A. two nonadjacent angles formed by two intersecting lines

B. the top number of a fraction, which tells how many parts of a whole are being considered

C. a point that corresponds to one and only one number

D. the intersection of two sides of a polygon

E. one of the segments that form a polygon

F. the bottom number of a fraction, which tells how many equal parts are in the whole

✓ Simplify Fractions

Write each fraction in simplest form.

6. $\frac{16}{20}$ **$\frac{4}{5}$**
7. $\frac{14}{21}$ **$\frac{2}{3}$**
8. $\frac{33}{121}$ **$\frac{3}{11}$**
9. $\frac{56}{80}$ **$\frac{7}{10}$**

✓ Ratios

Use the table to write each ratio in simplest form.

10. jazz CDs to country CDs **3 to 4**
11. hip-hop CDs to jazz CDs **17 to 9**
12. rock CDs to total CDs **9 to 28**
13. total CDs to country CDs **14 to 3**

Ryan's CD Collection	
Rock	36
Jazz	18
Hip-hop	34
Country	24

✓ Identify Polygons

Determine whether each figure is a polygon. If so, name it by the number of sides.

14. 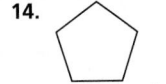 yes; pentagon
15.  yes; hexagon
16.  no
17.  yes; octagon

✓ Find Perimeter

Find the perimeter of each figure.

18. rectangle *PQRS* **25 ft**
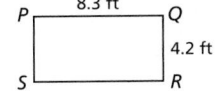

19. regular hexagon *ABCDEF* **180 cm**
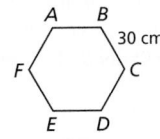

20. rhombus *JKLM* **45.6 m**
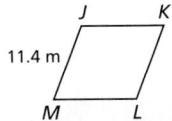

21. regular pentagon *UVWXY* **19.5 in.**
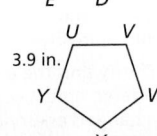

Similarity 451

ARE YOU READY?

Organizer

Objective: Assess students' understanding of prerequisite skills.

Prerequisite Skills

Simplify Fractions
Ratios
Identify Polygons
Find Perimeter

Assessing Prior Knowledge

INTERVENTION

Diagnose and Prescribe

Use this page to determine whether intervention is necessary or whether enrichment is appropriate.

Resources

 Are You Ready? Intervention and Enrichment Worksheets

 Are You Ready? CD-ROM

 Are You Ready? Online

my.hrw.com

ARE YOU READY?
Diagnose and Prescribe

 NO INTERVENE

 YES ENRICH

✓ Prerequisite Skill	✍ Worksheets	💿 CD-ROM	🌐 Online
✓ Simply Fractions	Skill 10	Activity 10	
✓ Ratios	Skill 12	Activity 12	Diagnose and Prescribe Online
✓ Identify Polygons	Skill 27	Activity 27	
✓ Find Perimeter	Skill 36	Activity 36	

ARE YOU READY? Intervention, Chapter 7

ARE YOU READY? Enrichment, Chapter 7
✍ Worksheets
💿 CD-ROM
🌐 Online

Organizer

Objective: Help students organize the new concepts they will learn in Chapter 7.

Online Edition
Multilingual Glossary

Resources

PuzzlePro
One-Stop Planner®

Multilingual Glossary Online
go.hrw.com/Geo/TX
KEYWORD: MG7 Glossary

Answers to Vocabulary Connections

1. One figure is an enlargement (or reduction) of the other.

2. A scale drawing is a drawing that represents an enlargement or reduction of an object.

3. The word *similar* means "alike." Similar polygons are polygons that have the same shape.

4. Possible answer: win/loss ratio, and the aspect ratio of a television screen; both involve a comparison of one quantity to another by means of division.

CHAPTER
7 Study Guide: Preview

Key Vocabulary/Vocabulario

dilation	dilatación
proportion	proporción
ratio	razón
scale	escala
scale drawing	dibujo a escala
scale factor	factor de escala
similar	semejante
similar polygons	polígonos semejantes
similarity ratio	razón de semejanza

Vocabulary Connections

To become familiar with some of the vocabulary terms in the chapter, consider the following. You may refer to the chapter, the glossary, or a dictionary if you like.

1. When an eye doctor dilates your eyes, the pupils become enlarged. What might it mean for one geometric figure to be a **dilation** of another figure?

2. A blueprint is a scale drawing of a building. What do you think is the definition of a **scale drawing**?

3. What does the word *similar* mean in everyday language? What do you think the term **similar polygons** means?

4. Bike riders often talk about gear ratios. Give examples of situations where the word **ratio** is used. What do these examples have in common?

Geometry TEKS

Geometry TEKS	Les. 7-1	7-2 Tech. Lab	Les. 7-2	7-3 Tech. Lab	Les. 7-3	7-4 Tech. Lab	Les. 7-4	Les. 7-5	Les. 7-6
G.1.B Geometric structure* recognize the historical development of geometric systems and know mathematics is developed for a variety of purposes								★	
G.2.A Geometric structure* use constructions to explore attributes of geometric figures and to make conjectures about geometric relationships				★		★	★		
G.3.B Geometric structure* construct and justify statements about geometric figures and their properties				★		★	★		
G.5.B Geometric patterns* use numeric and geometric patterns to make generalizations about geometric properties, including properties of polygons, ratios in similar figures ...	★	★	★		★	★	★		
G.9.B Congruence and the geometry of size* formulate and test conjectures about the properties and attributes of polygons ... based on explorations and concrete models				★	★	★	★		★
G.11.A Similarity and the geometry of shape* use and extend similarity properties and transformations to explore and justify conjectures about geometric figures.			★	★	★		★	★	★
G.11.B Similarity and the geometry of shape* use ratios to solve problems involving similar figures	★		★		★		★	★	
G.11.D Similarity and the geometry of shape* describe the effect on perimeter, area ... when one or more dimensions of a figure are changed and apply this idea in solving problems								★	

* Knowledge and skills are written out completely on pages TX28–TX35.

Geometry TEKS—Knowledge and Skills

G.1 Geometric structure The student understands the structure of, and relationships within, an axiomatic system.

G.2 Geometric structure The student analyzes geometric relationships in order to make and verify conjectures.

G.3 Geometric structure The student applies logical reasoning to justify and prove mathematical statements.

G.5 Geometric patterns The student uses a variety of representations to describe geometric relationships and solve problems.

G.7 Dimensionality and the geometry of location The student understands that coordinate systems provide convenient and efficient ways of representing geometric figures and uses them accordingly.

G.9 Congruence and the geometry of size The student analyzes properties and describes relationships in geometric figures.

G.11 Similarity and the geometry of shape The student applies the concepts of similarity to justify properties of figures and solve problems.

Reading Strategy: Read and Understand the Problem

Many of the concepts you are learning are used in real-world situations. Throughout the text, there are examples and exercises that are real-world word problems. Listed below are strategies for solving word problems.

Problem Solving Strategies

- Read slowly and carefully. Determine what information is given and what you are asked to find.
- If a diagram is provided, read the labels and make sure that you understand the information. If you do not, resketch and relabel the diagram so it makes sense to you. If a diagram is not provided, make a quick sketch and label it.
- Use the given information to set up and solve the problem.
- Decide whether your answer makes sense.

From Lesson 6-1: Look at how the Polygon Exterior Angle Theorem is used in photography.

Photography Application

The aperture of the camera shown is formed by ten blades. The blades overlap to form a regular decagon. What is the measure of $\angle CBD$?

Step	Procedure	Result
Understand the Problem	• List the **important information**. • The **answer** will be the measure of $\angle CBD$.	$\angle CBD$ is one of the exterior angles of the regular decagon formed by the apeture.
Make a Plan	• A **diagram** is provided, and it is labeled accurately.	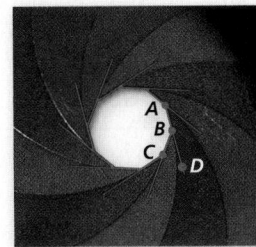
Solve	• You can use the **Polygon Exterior Angle Theorem**. Then divide to find the measure of **one** of the exterior angles.	$m\angle CBD = \dfrac{360°}{10} = 36°$
Look Back	• The **answer** is reasonable since a decagon has 10 exterior angles.	$10(36°) = 360°$

 **Try This**

Use the problem-solving strategies for the following problem.

1. A painter's scaffold is constructed so that the braces lie along the diagonals of rectangle *PQRS*. Given $RS = 28$ and $QS = 85$, find *QT*.

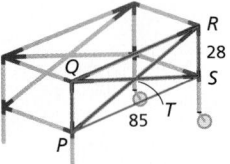

TAKS Objectives

Grades 9–11

Obj. 1 Functional Relationships A.1.C, A.1.D

Obj. 2 Properties and Attributes of Functions A.4.A

Obj. 3 Linear Functions A.6.G

Obj. 6 Geometric Relationships and Spatial Reasoning 8.6.A, 8.6.B, 8.7.D, G.5.B

Obj. 7 Two- and Three-Dimensional Representations 8.7.B

Obj. 8 Measurement 8.9.B, 8.10.A, G.11.A, G.11.B

Obj. 9 Percents, Proportions, Probability, and Statistics 8.3.B

Obj. 10 Mathematical Processes and Tools 8.14.A, 8.14.B, 8.14.C

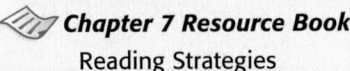
Organizer

Objective: Help students apply strategies to understand and retain key concepts.

PREMIER **Online Edition**

Resources

Chapter 7 Resource Book
Reading Strategies

Study Strategy: Identify Important Information in Real-World Problems

Discuss Students benefit from a planned approach to problem-solving. Real-world problems are often in the form of word problems. It is easy to make mistakes by misinterpreting the given information.

Extend As students work through Chapter 7, encourage them to apply the problem-solving method. Ask them to list the important information when they begin a problem. Help them identify what information they are given and what information they need to solve the problem. Remind them that some of the given information is stated in words and other information is given in the diagram, such as right angles and parallel lines.

Answers to *Try This*

1. (1) The answer will be the measure of $\overline{QT}$. *PQRS* is a rect. with diags. $\overline{RP}$ and $\overline{QS}$.

(2) A diagram is provided, which gives extra information. You need only the length of diag. $\overline{QS}$. Divide *QS* by 2 to find *QT*.

(3) The diags. of a rect. bisect each other. So $QT = \frac{1}{2}QS$. $QT = \frac{1}{2}(85) = 42.5$

(4) The answer is reasonable, since $2(42.5) = 85$.

Similarity Relationships

One-Minute Section Planner

Lesson	Lab Resources	Materials
Lesson 7-1 Ratio and Proportion • Write and simplify ratios. • Use proportions to solve problems. ☑ Exit Level TAKS ☐ ACT ☑ SAT ☑ SAT Subject Tests		**Optional** scale models (e.g., road map, globe, blueprint, replica of building or other structure), rulers (MK)
7-2 Technology Lab Explore the Golden Ratio • Use geometry software to explore the golden ratio and the golden rectangle. ☐ Exit Level TAKS ☐ ACT ☐ SAT ☐ SAT Subject Tests		**Required** rulers (MK), geometry software
Lesson 7-2 Ratios in Similar Polygons • Identify similar polygons. • Apply properties of similar polygons to solve problems. ☑ Exit Level TAKS ☐ ACT ☑ SAT ☐ SAT Subject Tests	*Texas Lab Manual* 7-2 Geometry Lab	**Optional** pattern blocks (MK), transparency sheets, rulers (MK), graph paper, protractor (MK)
7-3 Technology Lab Predict Triangle Similarity Relationships • Use geometry software to find ways to determine that triangles are similar. ☐ Exit Level TAKS ☐ ACT ☐ SAT ☐ SAT Subject Tests		**Required** geometry software
Lesson 7-3 Triangle Similarity: AA, SAS, SAS • Prove certain triangles are similar by using AA, SSS, and SAS. • Use triangle similarity to solve problems. ☑ Exit Level TAKS ☐ ACT ☐ SAT ☐ SAT Subject Tests		**Optional** colored pencils, highlighters, tangrams (MK), protractor (MK)

MK = *Manipulatives Kit*

Section Overview

Ratio and Proportion

Lesson 7-1

 Ratio and proportions are the basis for proportional reasoning, which is necessary in a variety of real-world situations.

A **ratio** compares two numbers by division. a to b, $a:b$, or $\frac{a}{b}$, with $b \neq 0$.

A **proportion** is an equation stating that two ratios are equal.
$$\frac{a}{b} = \frac{c}{d}$$

Cross Products Property

If $\frac{a}{b} = \frac{c}{d}$, then $ad = bc$

Properties of Proportions

$$\frac{a}{b} = \frac{c}{d} \Leftrightarrow \frac{b}{a} = \frac{d}{c} \Leftrightarrow \frac{a}{c} = \frac{b}{d}$$

The ratio of the angle measures in a triangle is $7:8:15$.
$$7x + 8x + 15x = 180$$
$$30x = 180$$
$$x = 6$$

The angle measures are as follows:
$$7x = 42° \qquad 8x = 48° \qquad 15x = 90°$$

Given $\frac{9}{x} = \frac{54}{66}$, use the Cross Products Property to find x.
$$9(66) = 54x$$
$$54x = 594$$
$$x = 11$$

Ratios in Similar Polygons and Triangle Similarity

Lessons 7-2, 7-3

 Similar polygons are used in building models of real objects and in the design of bridges and towers.

Similar Polygons
- Corresponding angles are congruent.
- Corresponding sides are proportional.

quadrilateral $ABCD \sim$ quadrilateral $EFGH$

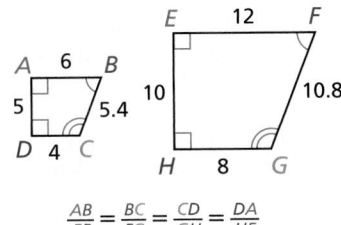

$$\frac{AB}{EF} = \frac{BC}{FG} = \frac{CD}{GH} = \frac{DA}{HE}$$

Similarity ratio $\quad \dfrac{6}{12} = \dfrac{5.4}{10.8} = \dfrac{4}{8} = \dfrac{5}{10} = \dfrac{1}{2}$

Properties of Similarity

Reflexive $\triangle ABC \sim \triangle ABC$

Symmetric   If $\triangle ABC \sim \triangle DEF$, then $\triangle DEF \sim \triangle ABC$.

Transitive   If $\triangle ABC \sim \triangle DEF$ and $\triangle DEF \sim \triangle XYZ$, then $\triangle ABC \sim \triangle XYZ$.

Triangle Similarity

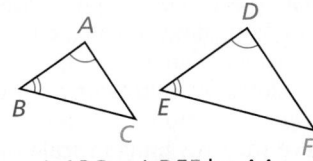

$\triangle ABC \sim \triangle DEF$ by AA $\sim$

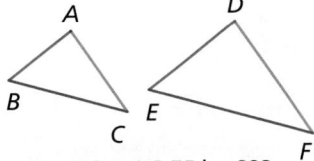

$\triangle ABC \sim \triangle DEF$ by SSS $\sim$

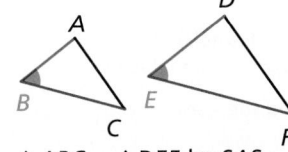

$\triangle ABC \sim \triangle DEF$ by SAS $\sim$

Objectives: Write and simplify ratios.

Use proportions to solve problems.

Online Edition
Tutorial Videos

Countdown to TAKS Week 15

Power Presentations
with PowerPoint®

Warm Up

Find the slope of the line through each pair of points.

1. $(1, 5)$ and $(3, 9)$ 2

2. $(-6, 4)$ and $(6, -2)$ $-\frac{1}{2}$

Solve each equation.

3. $4x + 5x + 6x = 45$ $x = 3$

4. $(x - 5)^2 = 81$ $x = 14$ or $x = -4$

5. Write $\frac{16}{24}$ in simplest form. $\frac{2}{3}$

Also available on transparency

Q: Who invented fractions?

A: Henry the $\frac{1}{8}$!

Geometry TEKS

G.5 Geometric patterns*
(B) use numeric and geometric patterns to make generalizations about geometric properties, including ... ratios in similar figures ...

G.7 Dimensionality and the geometry of location*
(B) use slopes ... to investigate geometric relationships, including parallel lines, ... and special segments of triangles ...
(C) develop and use formulas involving length, slope, and midpoint

G.11 Similarity and the geometry of shape*
(B) use ratios to solve problems involving similar figures

* Knowledge and Skills See p. 452

7-1 Ratio and Proportion

TEKS G.11.B Similarity and the geometry of shape: use ratios to solve problems involving similar figures. Also G.5.B, G.7.B, G.7.C

Objectives
Write and simplify ratios.
Use proportions to solve problems.

Vocabulary
ratio
proportion
extremes
means
cross products

Who uses this?
Filmmakers use ratios and proportions when creating special effects. (See Example 5.)

The *Lord of the Rings* movies transport viewers to the fantasy world of Middle Earth. Many scenes feature vast fortresses, sprawling cities, and bottomless mines. To film these images, the moviemakers used *ratios* to help them build highly detailed miniature models.

A **ratio** compares two numbers by division. The ratio of two numbers a and b can be written as a to b, $a:b$, or $\frac{a}{b}$, where $b \neq 0$. For example, the ratios 1 to 2, $1:2$, and $\frac{1}{2}$ all represent the same comparison.

EXAMPLE 1 Writing Ratios

Write a ratio expressing the slope of ℓ.

Remember!
In a ratio, the denominator of the fraction cannot be zero because division by zero is undefined.

$$\text{Slope} = \frac{\text{rise}}{\text{run}} = \frac{y_2 - y_1}{x_2 - x_1}$$

$$= \frac{3 - (-1)}{4 - (-2)} \quad \text{Substitute the given values.}$$

$$= \frac{4}{6} = \frac{2}{3} \quad \text{Simplify.}$$

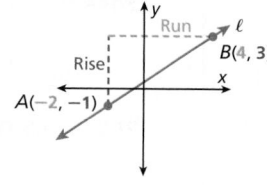

CHECK IT OUT! 1. Given that two points on m are $C(-2, 3)$ and $D(6, 5)$, write a ratio expressing the slope of m. $\frac{1}{4}$

A ratio can involve more than two numbers. For the rectangle, the ratio of the side lengths may be written as $3:7:3:7$.

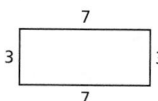

EXAMPLE 2 Using Ratios

The ratio of the side lengths of a quadrilateral is $2:3:5:7$, and its perimeter is 85 ft. What is the length of the longest side?

Let the side lengths be $2x$, $3x$, $5x$, and $7x$. Then $2x + 3x + 5x + 7x = 85$. After like terms are combined, $17x = 85$. So $x = 5$. The length of the longest side is $7x = 7(5) = 35$ ft.

CHECK IT OUT! 2. The ratio of the angle measures in a triangle is $1:6:13$. What is the measure of each angle? **9°; 54°; 117°**

---

1 Introduce

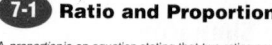

EXPLORATION

7-1 Ratio and Proportion

A *proportion* is an equation stating that two ratios are equal.
1. Use the numbers 1, 3, 4, and 12 to write a proportion. Write one number in each square.

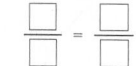

2. There are other ways to use these numbers to fill in the squares. Write as many different proportions as possible.

3. Use the same numbers to write an equation by filling in the circles.

○ • ○ = ○ • ○

4. All of the equations that you wrote in Steps 1–3 are equivalent. Write the proportion $\frac{a}{b} = \frac{c}{d}$ in as many equivalent forms as you can.

THINK AND DISCUSS
5. **Discuss** whether the proportion $\frac{a}{b} = \frac{c}{d}$ is equivalent to $\frac{a}{c} = \frac{b}{d}$. Give an example using numbers to support your

Motivate

Bring in several items that are scale models, including a two-dimensional and a three-dimensional object. These might consist of a road map for your state, a globe, a blueprint for a house or a school in your district, and a replica of a famous building. Ask students what these *scale models* have in common. same proportions as the original Have students bring in scale models from their art or design classes to present to the class.

Explorations and answers are provided in the *Explorations* binder.

A **proportion** is an equation stating that two ratios are equal. In the proportion $\frac{a}{b} = \frac{c}{d}$, the values a and d are the **extremes**. The values b and c are the **means**. When the proportion is written as $a:b = c:d$, the extremes are in the first and last positions. The means are in the two middle positions.

In Algebra 1 you learned the Cross Products Property. The product of the extremes ad and the product of the means bc are called the **cross products**.

Cross Products Property

In a proportion, if $\frac{a}{b} = \frac{c}{d}$ and b and $d \neq 0$, then $ad = bc$.

$$\frac{a}{b} \diagdown \frac{c}{d}$$

$$ad = bc$$

EXAMPLE 3 **Solving Proportions**

Solve each proportion.

A $\frac{5}{y} = \frac{45}{63}$

$5(63) = y(45)$ *Cross Products Prop.*

$315 = 45y$ *Simplify.*

$y = 7$ *Divide both sides by 45.*

B $\frac{x+2}{6} = \frac{24}{x+2}$

$(x+2)^2 = 6(24)$ *Cross Products Prop.*

$(x+2)^2 = 144$ *Simplify.*

$x + 2 = \pm 12$ *Find the square root of both sides.*

$x + 2 = 12$ or $x + 2 = -12$ *Rewrite as two eqns.*

$x = 10$ or $x = -14$ *Subtract 2 from both sides.*

 Solve each proportion.

3a. $\frac{3}{8} = \frac{x}{56}$ 21   **3b.** $\frac{2y}{9} = \frac{8}{4y}$ ± 3

3c. $\frac{d}{3} = \frac{6}{2}$ 9   **3d.** $\frac{x+3}{4} = \frac{9}{x+3}$ 3 or -9

The following table shows equivalent forms of the Cross Products Property.

Properties of Proportions

ALGEBRA	NUMBERS
The proportion $\frac{a}{b} = \frac{c}{d}$ is equivalent to the following:	The proportion $\frac{1}{3} = \frac{2}{6}$ is equivalent to the following:
$ad = bc$	$1(6) = 3(2)$
$\frac{b}{a} = \frac{d}{c}$	$\frac{3}{1} = \frac{6}{2}$
$\frac{a}{c} = \frac{b}{d}$	$\frac{1}{2} = \frac{3}{6}$

Example 1

Write a ratio expressing the slope of ℓ. $-\frac{5}{3}$

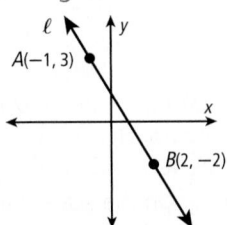

Example 2

The ratio of the side lengths of a triangle is $4:7:5$, and its perimeter is 96 cm. What is the length of the shortest side?   24 cm

Example 3

Solve each proportion.

A. $\frac{7}{x} = \frac{56}{72}$ $x = 9$

B. $\frac{z-4}{5} = \frac{20}{z-4}$ $z = 14$ or $z = -6$

Also available on transparency

INTERVENTION ◄►
Questioning Strategies

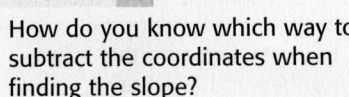

EXAMPLE **1**

• How do you know which way to subtract the coordinates when finding the slope?

EXAMPLE **2**

• If the ratio of the side lengths of a quadrilateral is $1:1:1:1$, what kind of special quadrilateral is it?

• How do you use a ratio of side lengths to write an algebraic expression for perimeter?

EXAMPLE **3**

• How can you solve an equation when the variable expression is squared?

• How can you check your solution to a proportion?

---

2 Teach

Guided Instruction

Explain that a ratio compares two numbers by division. Show why a proportion is an equation that states that two ratios are equal and uses the Cross Products Property to solve. Review the properties of proportions and discuss how to use the properties to solve equations.

Teaching Tip   **Algebra** Show students that once the Cross Products Property has been applied, the result is either a linear or a simple quadratic equation that they can solve algebraically.

Reaching All Learners

Through Kinesthetic Experience

Explain to students that the scale on a map gives the ratio of the map distance to the actual distance. Students should use a ruler to measure the distance between two cities. Then estimate the distance between the cities. Emphasize the importance of making accurate measurements and using the correct scale. Rulers can be found in the Manipulatives Kit (MK).

INTERVENTION ◄►
Questioning Strategies

EXAMPLE 4

- Did you expect the result of Example 4 to be the reciprocal? Explain.

EXAMPLE 5

- How is algebra used in this application of ratio and proportion?

Teaching Tip

Inclusion If students make errors in writing proportions in problem-solving applications, show them that it may be easier to write the proportion in words first, and then place the numbers in the ratios.

EXAMPLE 4 **Using Properties of Proportions**

Given that $4x = 10y$, find the ratio of x to y in simplest form.

$$4x = 10y$$
$$\frac{x}{y} = \frac{10}{4} \qquad \textit{Divide both sides by 4y.}$$
$$\frac{x}{y} = \frac{5}{2} \qquad \textit{Simplify.}$$

Reading Math
Since x comes before y in the sentence, x will be in the numerator of the fraction.

 **4.** Given that $16s = 20t$, find the ratio $t:s$ in simplest form. $4:5$

EXAMPLE 5 *Problem-Solving Application*

PROBLEM SOLVING

During the filming of *The Lord of the Rings*, the special-effects team built a model of Sauron's tower with a height of 8 m and a width of 6 m. If the width of the full-size tower is 996 m, what is its height?

1 **Understand the Problem**

The **answer** will be the height of the tower.

2 **Make a Plan**

Let x be the height of the tower. Write a proportion that compares the ratios of the height to the width.

$$\frac{\text{height of model tower}}{\text{width of model tower}} = \frac{\text{height of full-size tower}}{\text{width of full-size tower}}$$

$$\frac{8}{6} = \frac{x}{996}$$

3 **Solve**

$$\frac{8}{6} = \frac{x}{996}$$
$$6x = 8(996) \qquad \textit{Cross Products Prop.}$$
$$6x = 7968 \qquad \textit{Simplify.}$$
$$x = 1328 \qquad \textit{Divide both sides by 6.}$$

The height of the full-size tower is 1328 m.

4 **Look Back**

Check the answer in the original problem. The ratio of the height to the width of the model is $8:6$, or $4:3$. The ratio of the height to the width of the tower is $1328:996$. In simplest form, this ratio is also $4:3$. So the ratios are equal, and the answer is correct.

 5. What if...? Suppose the special-effects team made a different model with a height of 9.2 m and a width of 6 m. What is the height of the actual tower? 1527.2 m

---

3 **Close**

Summarize

To summarize the lesson, lead a discussion based on these questions: "What is the difference between a ratio and a proportion?" Possible answer: A ratio is an expression that compares two quantities, while a proportion is an equation that states that two ratios are equal. "What method can be used to solve any proportion?" Possible answer: Use the Cross Products Property to write an equation, which may be linear or quadratic. Then solve the resulting equation.

ONGOING ASSESSMENT
and **INTERVENTION** ◄►

Diagnose Before the Lesson
7-1 Warm Up, TE p. 454

Monitor During the Lesson
Check It Out! Exercises, SE pp. 454–456
Questioning Strategies, TE pp. 455–456

Assess After the Lesson
7-1 Lesson Quiz, TE p. 459
Alternative Assessment, TE p. 459

Answers to *Think and Discuss*

1. No; the ratio 6:7 is less than 1; the ratio 7:6 is greater than 1.

2. She can see if the cross products are =. Since 3(28) = 7(12), the ratios do form a proportion. Therefore the ratios are = and the fractions are equivalent.

3. See p. A6.

THINK AND DISCUSS

1. Is the ratio 6:7 the same ratio as 7:6? Why or why not?

2. Susan wants to know if the fractions $\frac{3}{7}$ and $\frac{12}{28}$ are equivalent. Explain how she can use the properties of proportions to find out.

 *Know it! Note*

3. **GET ORGANIZED** Copy and complete the graphic organizer. In the boxes, write the definition of a proportion, the properties of proportions, and examples and nonexamples of a proportion.

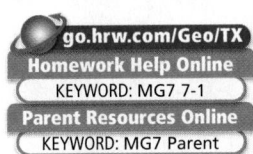

Definition	Properties
Proportion	
Examples	Nonexamples

7-1 Exercises

go.hrw.com/Geo/TX
Homework Help Online
KEYWORD: MG7 7-1
Parent Resources Online
KEYWORD: MG7 Parent

7-1 Exercises

GUIDED PRACTICE

Vocabulary Apply the vocabulary from this lesson to answer each question.

1. Name the means and extremes in the proportion $\frac{1}{3} = \frac{2}{6}$. **means: 3 and 2; extremes: 1 and 6**

2. Write the cross products for the proportion $\frac{s}{t} = \frac{u}{v}$. ***sv; tu***

SEE EXAMPLE **1**
p. 454

Write a ratio expressing the slope of each line.

3. ℓ $\frac{1}{2}$ 4. m $\frac{1}{1}$ 5. n $-\frac{2}{3}$

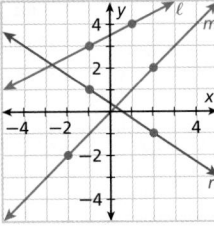

SEE EXAMPLE **2**
p. 454

6. The ratio of the side lengths of a quadrilateral is 2:4:5:7, and its perimeter is 36 m. What is the length of the shortest side? **4 m**

7. The ratio of the angle measures in a triangle is 5:12:19. What is the measure of the largest angle? **95°**

SEE EXAMPLE **3**
p. 455

Solve each proportion.

8. $\frac{x}{2} = \frac{40}{16}$ **5**

9. $\frac{7}{y} = \frac{21}{27}$ **9**

10. $\frac{6}{58} = \frac{t}{29}$ **3**

11. $\frac{y}{3} = \frac{27}{y}$ **±9**

12. $\frac{16}{x-1} = \frac{x-1}{4}$ **9 or −7**

13. $\frac{x^2}{18} = \frac{x}{6}$ **0 or 3**

SEE EXAMPLE **4**
p. 456

14. Given that $2a = 8b$, find the ratio of a to b in simplest form. **4 to 1**

15. Given that $6x = 27y$, find the ratio $y:x$ in simplest form. **2:9**

SEE EXAMPLE **5**
p. 456

16. **Architecture** The Arkansas State Capitol Building is a smaller version of the U.S. Capitol Building. The U.S. Capitol is 752 ft long and 288 ft tall. The Arkansas State Capitol is 564 ft long. What is the height of the Arkansas State Capitol? **216 ft**

7-1 Ratio and Proportion **457**

Assignment Guide

Assign *Guided Practice* exercises as necessary.

If you finished Examples **1–3**
   Basic 17–27, 34–38
   Average 17–27, 34–38, 40, 47
Advanced 17–27, 34–37, 41, 51

If you finished Examples **1–5**
   Basic 17–32, 35–40
          42–47, 52–59
   Average 17–30, 32–36, 39–48, 51–59
Advanced 17–33, 37–59

Homework Quick Check
Quickly check key concepts.
Exercises: 18, 20, 26, 28, 30, 32

⬧TAKS Practice

Grades 9–11	Exercises
Obj. 1	39, 42, 46
Obj. 2	31–33, 39, 42, 46, 48, 52–54
Obj. 6	39, 41, 42, 44, 46, 48
Obj. 7	35–37, 39
Obj. 8	39, 41, 42, 46, 48
Obj. 9	39, 41, 42, 44, 46, 48
Obj. 10	34, 39, 42, 44, 46

PRACTICE AND PROBLEM SOLVING

Independent Practice

For Exercises	See Example
17–19	1
20–21	2
22–27	3
28–29	4
30	5

TEKS TAKS

Skills Practice p. S16
Application Practice p. S34

Write a ratio expressing the slope of each line.

17. ℓ $\dfrac{3}{1}$ **18.** m $\dfrac{-1}{1}$ **19.** n $\dfrac{3}{2}$

20. The ratio of the side lengths of an isosceles triangle is $4:4:7$, and its perimeter is 52.5 cm. What is the length of the base of the triangle? **24.5 cm**

21. The ratio of the angle measures in a parallelogram is $2:3:2:3$. What is the measure of each angle?
72°; 108°; 72°; 108°

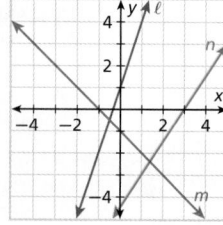

Solve each proportion.

22. $\dfrac{6}{8} = \dfrac{9}{y}$ **12**   **23.** $\dfrac{x}{14} = \dfrac{50}{35}$ **20**   **24.** $\dfrac{z}{12} = \dfrac{3}{8}$ **4.5**

25. $\dfrac{2m + 2}{3} = \dfrac{12}{2m + 2}$ **2 or −4**   **26.** $\dfrac{5y}{16} = \dfrac{125}{y}$ **±20**   **27.** $\dfrac{x + 2}{12} = \dfrac{5}{x - 2}$ **±8**

28. Given that $5y = 25x$, find the ratio of x to y in simplest form. $\dfrac{1}{5}$

29. Given that $35b = 21c$, find the ratio $b:c$ in simplest form. **3:5**

Travel

For more than 50 years, Madurodam has been Holland's smallest city. The canal houses, market, airplanes, and windmills are all replicated on a 1:25 scale.

Source: madurodam.nl

30. **Travel** Madurodam is a park in the Netherlands that contains a complete Dutch city built entirely of miniature models. One of the models of a windmill is 1.2 m tall and 0.8 m wide. The width of the actual windmill is 20 m. What is its height? **30 m**

Given that $\dfrac{a}{b} = \dfrac{5}{7}$, complete each of the following equations.

31. $7a = $ **32.** $\dfrac{b}{a} = \dfrac{7}{5}$ **33.** $\dfrac{a}{5} = \dfrac{b}{7}$
         $5b$

34. **Sports** During the 2003 NFL season, the Dallas Cowboys won 10 of their 16 regular-season games. What is their ratio of wins to losses in simplest form? **5:3**

Write a ratio expressing the slope of the line through each pair of points.

35. $(-6, -4)$ and $(21, 5)$ $\dfrac{1}{3}$ **36.** $(16, -5)$ and $(6, 1)$ $-\dfrac{3}{5}$

37. $\left(6\dfrac{1}{2}, -2\right)$ and $\left(4, 5\dfrac{1}{2}\right)$ **−3**   **38.** $(-6, 1)$ and $(-2, 0)$ $-\dfrac{1}{4}$

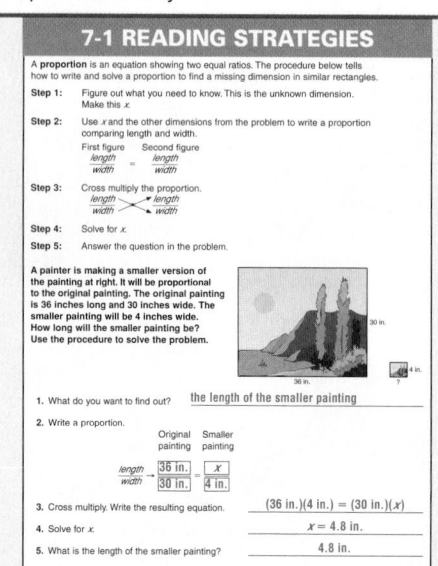

MULTI-STEP TAKS PREP

39. This problem will prepare you for the Multi-Step TAKS Prep on page 478.
A claymation film is shot on a set that is a scale model of an actual city. On the set, a skyscraper is 1.25 in. wide and 15 in. tall. The actual skyscraper is 800 ft tall.
  a. Write a proportion that you can use to find the width of the actual skyscraper.
  b. Solve the proportion from part **a.** What is the width of the actual skyscraper?

a. $\dfrac{1.25 \text{ in.}}{15 \text{ in.}} = \dfrac{x \text{ in.}}{9600 \text{ in.}}$ **b.** $x = 800$ in., or 66 ft 8 in.

40. Critical Thinking The ratio of the lengths of a quadrilateral's consecutive sides is $2:5:2:5$. The ratio of the lengths of the quadrilateral's diagonals is $1:1$. What type of quadrilateral is this? Explain.

41. Multi-Step One square has sides 6 cm long. Another has sides 9 cm long. Find the ratio of the areas of the squares. $\dfrac{4}{9}$

42. Photography A photo shop makes prints of photographs in a variety of sizes. Every print has a length-to-width ratio of $5:3.5$ regardless of its size. A customer wants a print that is 20 in. long. What is the width of this print? **14 in.**

43. Write About It What is the difference between a ratio and a proportion?

44. An 18-inch stick breaks into three pieces. The ratio of the lengths of the pieces is $1:4:5$. Which of these is NOT a length of one of the pieces?

Ⓐ 1.8 inches   Ⓑ 3.6 inches   Ⓒ 7.2 inches   Ⓓ 9 inches

45. Which of the following is equivalent to $\dfrac{3}{5} = \dfrac{x}{y}$?

Ⓕ $\dfrac{3}{y} = \dfrac{5}{x}$ Ⓖ $3x = 5y$ Ⓗ $\dfrac{x}{3} = \dfrac{y}{5}$ Ⓙ $3(5) = xy$

46. A recipe for salad dressing calls for oil and vinegar in a ratio of 5 parts oil to 2 parts vinegar. If you use $1\frac{1}{4}$ cups of oil, how many cups of vinegar will you need?

Ⓐ $\dfrac{1}{2}$ Ⓑ $\dfrac{5}{8}$ Ⓒ $2\frac{1}{2}$ Ⓓ $6\frac{1}{4}$

47. Short Response Explain how to solve the proportion $\dfrac{36}{72} = \dfrac{15}{x}$ for x. Tell what you must assume about x in order to solve the proportion.

CHALLENGE AND EXTEND

48. The ratio of the perimeter of rectangle $ABCD$ to the perimeter of rectangle $EFGH$ is $4:7$. Find x. **10**

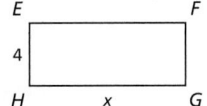

49. Explain why $\dfrac{a}{b} = \dfrac{c}{d}$ and $\dfrac{a+b}{b} = \dfrac{c+d}{d}$ are equivalent proportions.

50. Probability The numbers 1, 2, 3, and 6 are randomly placed in these four boxes: 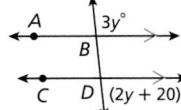. What is the probability that the two ratios will form a proportion? $\dfrac{1}{3}$

51. Express the ratio $\dfrac{x^2 + 9x + 18}{x^2 - 36}$ in simplest form. $\dfrac{x+3}{x-6}$, where $x \neq \pm 6$

SPIRAL REVIEW

Complete each ordered pair so that it is a solution to $y - 6x = -3$. *(Previous course)*

52. $(0, \blacksquare)$ **−3**   **53.** $(\blacksquare, 3)$ **1**   **54.** $(-4, \blacksquare)$ **−27**

Find each angle measure. *(Lesson 3-2)*

55. $m\angle ABD$ **96°**   **56.** $m\angle CDB$ **84°**

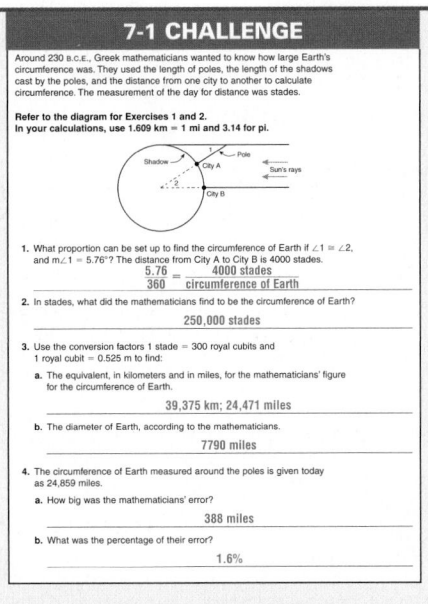

Each set of numbers represents the side lengths of a triangle. Classify each triangle as acute, right, or obtuse. *(Lesson 5-7)*

57. 5, 8, 9 **acute**   **58.** 8, 15, 20 **obtuse**   **59.** 7, 24, 25 **right**

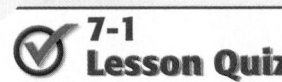

Pacing:
Traditional 1 day
Block $\frac{1}{2}$ day

Objective: Use geometry software to explore the golden ratio and the golden rectangle.

Materials: geometry software

PREMIER
Online Edition
TechKeys

Countdown to TAKS Week 15

Teach

Discuss

Throughout history, the golden ratio has been said to appear in many works of art, in paintings, and in architecture. It also appears in the structures of some plants. Explain to students that they will be using geometry software to explore the golden ratio. Since the value of the golden ratio is $\frac{1+\sqrt{5}}{2} \approx 1.618$ you may want to review irrational numbers and their decimal approximations.

 Geometry TEKS

G.1 Geometric structure*

(A) develop an awareness of the structure of a mathematical system, connecting definitions, postulates, …

G.2 Geometric structure*

(B) make conjectures about angles, lines, polygons, … and determine the validity of the conjectures, choosing from a variety of approaches …

G.5 Geometric patterns*

(A) use numeric and geometric patterns to develop algebraic expressions representing geometric properties

(B) use numeric and geometric patterns to make generalizations about geometric properties … ratios in similar figures …

***Knowledge and Skills** See p. 452

7-2

Technology **Explore the Golden Ratio**
LAB

Use with Lesson 7-2

In about 300 B.C.E., Euclid showed in his book *Elements* how to calculate the *golden ratio*. It is claimed that this ratio was used in many works of art and architecture to produce rectangles of pleasing proportions. The *golden ratio* also appears in the natural world and it is said even in the human face. If the ratio of a rectangle's length to its width is equal to the golden ratio, it is called a *golden rectangle*.

 TEKS G.5.B Geometric patterns: use numeric and geometric patterns to make generalizations about geometric properties … ratios in similar figures ….
Also G.1.A, G.2.B, G.5.A

go.hrw.com/Geo/TX
Lab Resources Online
KEYWORD: MG7 Lab7

Activity 1

❶ Construct a segment and label its endpoints A and B. Place P on the segment so that $\overline{AP}$ is longer than $\overline{PB}$. What are AP, PB, and AB? What is the ratio of AP to PB and the ratio of AB to AP? Drag P along the segment until the ratios are equal. What is the value of the equal ratios to the nearest hundredth?
Check students' work. The equal ratios have the approximate value of 1.62.

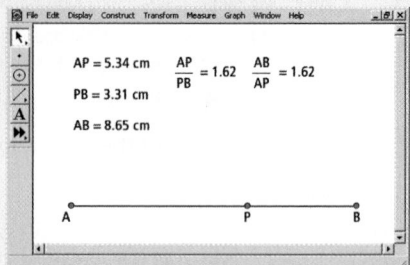

❷ Construct a *golden rectangle* beginning with a square. Create $\overline{AB}$. Then construct a circle with its center at A and a radius of $\overline{AB}$. Construct a line perpendicular to $\overline{AB}$ through A. Where the circle and the perpendicular line intersect, label the point D. Construct perpendicular lines through B and D and label their intersection C. Hide the lines and the circle, leaving only the segments to complete the square.

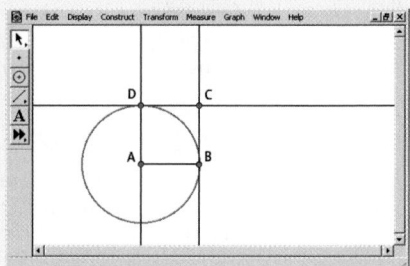

❸ Find the midpoint of $\overline{AB}$ and label it M. Create a segment from M to C. Construct a circle with its center at M and radius of $\overline{MC}$. Construct a ray with endpoint A through B. Where the circle and the ray intersect, label the point E. Create a line through E that is perpendicular to $\overrightarrow{AB}$. Show the previously hidden line through D and C. Label the point of intersection of these two lines F. Hide the lines and circle and create segments to complete golden rectangle $AEFD$.

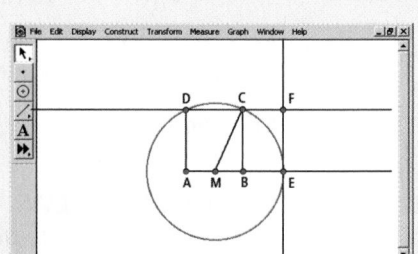

❹ Measure $\overline{AE}$, $\overline{EF}$, and $\overline{BE}$. Find the ratio of AE to EF and the ratio of EF to BE. Compare these ratios to those found in Step 1. What do you notice? **The ratios have the same value as the ratios is step 1.**

Try This

1. Adjust your construction from Step 2 so that the side of the original square is 2 units long. Use the Pythagorean Theorem to find the length of $\overline{MC}$. Calculate the length of $\overline{AE}$. Write the ratio of AE to EF as a fraction and as a decimal rounded to the nearest thousandth.

2. Find the length of $\overline{BE}$ in your construction from Step 3. Write the ratio of EF to BE as a fraction and as a decimal rounded to the nearest thousandth. Compare your results to those from Try This Problem 1. What do you notice?

3. Each number in the Fibonacci sequence $(1, 1, 2, 3, 5, 8, 13 \dots)$ is created by adding the two preceding numbers together. That is, $1 + 1 = 2$, $1 + 2 = 3$, $2 + 3 = 5$, and so on. Investigate the ratios of the numbers in the sequence by finding the quotients. $\frac{1}{1} = 1$, $\frac{2}{1} = 2$, $\frac{3}{2} = 1.5$, $\frac{5}{3} = 1.\overline{666}$, $\frac{8}{5} = 1.6$, and so on. What do you notice as you continue to find the quotients? **The quotients have values that approach 1.618.**

Tell why each of the following is an example of the appearance of the Fibonacci sequence in nature.

4.

There are $1 + 1 = 2$ rabbits.

5.

There are $8 + 13 = 21$ petals on the daisy.

Determine whether each picture is an example of an application of the golden rectangle. Measure the length and the width of each and decide whether the ratio of the length to the width is approximately the golden ratio.

6.

5.4 cm

4 cm

no; $\frac{5.4}{4} \approx 1.4$

7.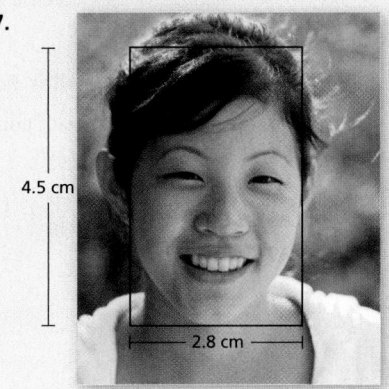

4.5 cm

2.8 cm

yes; $\frac{4.5}{2.8} \approx 1.6$

Close

Key Concept

The golden ratio is a ratio between lengths of line segments that is revealed in many different ways, both in the natural world and in man-made objects. Rectangular objects are called golden rectangles if the ratio of their length to their width is a certain proportion.

Assessment

Journal Have students create their own drawing using golden rectangles. Then explain how they know it is an example of a golden rectangle.

Answers to *Try This*

1. If the side length of the square is 2 units, then $MB = 1$ unit, and $BC = 2$ units. $\overline{MC}$ is the hyp. of the rt. $\triangle$ formed by $\overline{MB}$ and $\overline{BC}$. By the Pyth. Thm., $\overline{MC}$ has length $\sqrt{5}$ units. $\overline{AE}$ has length $\sqrt{5} + 1$ units. $\frac{AE}{EF} = \frac{\sqrt{5}+1}{2} \approx 1.618$.

2. BE has length $\sqrt{5} - 1$ units. $\frac{BE}{EF} = \frac{\sqrt{5}-1}{2} \approx 0.618$. The sign of the numerator in this fraction is different from that of the fraction in Try This **Problem 1.**

Objectives: Identify similar polygons.

Apply properties of similar polygons to solve problems.

 Geometry Lab
In *Texas Lab Manual*

 Online Edition
Tutorial Videos, Interactivity

 Countdown to TAKS Week 15

Power Presentations
with PowerPoint®

Warm Up

1. If $\triangle QRS \cong \triangle ZYX$, identify the pairs of congruent angles and the pairs of congruent sides.
$\angle Q \cong \angle Z; \angle R \cong \angle Y; \angle S \cong \angle X; \overline{QR} \cong \overline{ZY}; \overline{RS} \cong \overline{YX}; \overline{QS} \cong \overline{ZX}$

Solve each proportion.

2. $\dfrac{2}{x-3} = \dfrac{8}{3x-3}$ $x = 9$

3. $\dfrac{x-6}{42} = \dfrac{2x-14}{77}$ $x = 18$

Also available on transparency

Math Humor

Q: What does the zero say to the eight?

A: Nice belt!

Geometry TEKS

G.5 Geometric patterns*
(B) use numeric and geometric patterns to make generalizations about geometric properties, including properties of polygons, ratios in similar figures …

G.11 Similarity and the geometry of shape*
(A) use and extend similarity properties and transformations to explore and justify conjectures about geometric figures
(B) use ratios to solve problems involving similar figures

* Knowledge and Skills See p. 452

7-2 Ratios in Similar Polygons

 TEKS G.5.B Geometric patterns: use … geometric patterns to make generalizations about ratios in similar figures …

Objectives
Identify similar polygons.

Apply properties of similar polygons to solve problems.

Vocabulary
similar
similar polygons
similarity ratio

 Also G.11.A, G.11.B

Why learn this?
Similar polygons are used to build models of actual objects. (See Example 3.)

Figures that are **similar** (~) have the same shape but not necessarily the same size.

$\triangle 1$ is similar to $\triangle 2(\triangle 1 \sim \triangle 2)$. $\triangle 1$ is not similar to $\triangle 3(\triangle 1 \nsim \triangle 3)$.

 Know it! Note

Similar Polygons

DEFINITION	DIAGRAM	STATEMENTS
Two polygons are **similar polygons** if and only if their corresponding angles are congruent and their corresponding sides are proportional.	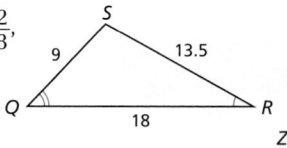 $ABCD \sim EFGH$	$\angle A \cong \angle E$ $\angle B \cong \angle F$ $\angle C \cong \angle G$ $\angle D \cong \angle H$ $\frac{AB}{EF} = \frac{BC}{FG} = \frac{CD}{GH} = \frac{DA}{HE} = \frac{1}{2}$

EXAMPLE 1 **Describing Similar Polygons**

Identify the pairs of congruent angles and corresponding sides.

$\angle Z \cong \angle R$ and $\angle Y \cong \angle Q$. By the Third Angles Theorem, $\angle X \cong \angle S$.

$\dfrac{XY}{SQ} = \dfrac{6}{9} = \dfrac{2}{3}, \dfrac{YZ}{QR} = \dfrac{12}{18} = \dfrac{2}{3},$

$\dfrac{XZ}{SR} = \dfrac{9}{13.5} = \dfrac{2}{3}$

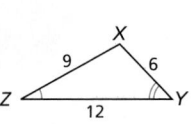

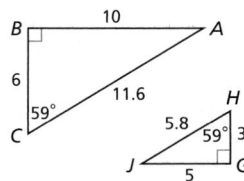 **CHECK IT OUT!**

1. Identify the pairs of congruent angles and corresponding sides.
$\angle A \cong \angle J; \angle B \cong \angle G; \angle C \cong \angle H;$
$\dfrac{AB}{JG} = \dfrac{BC}{GH} = \dfrac{AC}{JH} = 2$

---

1 Introduce

EXPLORATION

7-2 Ratios in Similar Polygons

Figures that are *similar* have the same shape but not necessarily the same size. Use graph paper to explore similar figures.

1. Copy $\triangle ABC$ on a piece of graph paper.

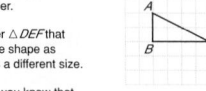

2. Draw another $\triangle DEF$ that has the same shape as $\triangle ABC$ but is a different size.

3. Explain how you know that $\triangle DEF$ has the same shape as $\triangle ABC$.

4. Use a protractor to measure the angles of $\triangle ABC$ and $\triangle DEF$. What do you notice?

5. How do the side lengths of $\triangle ABC$ and $\triangle DEF$ compare?

6. Complete the following conjecture: Two polygons are similar polygons if and only if their corresponding angles are __?__ and their corresponding sides are __?__.

THINK AND DISCUSS

7. Discuss whether the two rectangles are similar. Explain why or why not.

Motivate

Draw three or more similar triangles, each a different size and color, on separate transparencies. Show on the overhead that by superimposing the triangles so that the angles coincide, all the triangles have three pairs of congruent angles. Explain to students that they will learn how to determine if polygons are similar by identifying corresponding congruent angles and comparing corresponding side lengths.

Explorations and answers are provided in the *Explorations* binder.

A **similarity ratio** is the ratio of the lengths of the corresponding sides of two similar polygons. The similarity ratio of $\triangle ABC$ to $\triangle DEF$ is $\frac{3}{6}$, or $\frac{1}{2}$. The similarity ratio of $\triangle DEF$ to $\triangle ABC$ is $\frac{6}{3}$, or 2.

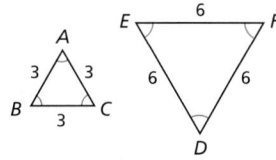

EXAMPLE 2 **Identifying Similar Polygons**

Determine whether the polygons are similar. If so, write the similarity ratio and a similarity statement.

A rectangles $PQRS$ and $TUVW$

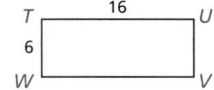

Step 1 Identify pairs of congruent angles.

$\angle P \cong \angle T$, $\angle Q \cong \angle U$, $\angle R \cong \angle V$, and $\angle S \cong \angle W$ *All ∠ of a rect. are rt. ∠ and are ≅.*

Step 2 Compare corresponding sides.

$$\frac{PQ}{TU} = \frac{12}{16} = \frac{3}{4}, \quad \frac{PS}{TW} = \frac{4}{6} = \frac{2}{3}$$

Since corresponding sides are not proportional, the rectangles are not similar.

B $\triangle ABC$ and $\triangle DEF$

Step 1 Identify pairs of congruent angles.

$\angle A \cong \angle D$, $\angle B \cong \angle E$ *Given*

$\angle C \cong \angle F$ *Third ∠ Thm.*

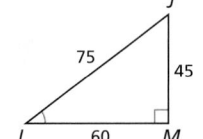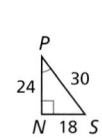

Step 2 Compare corresponding sides.

$$\frac{AB}{DE} = \frac{20}{15} = \frac{4}{3}, \quad \frac{BC}{EF} = \frac{24}{18} = \frac{4}{3}, \quad \frac{AC}{DF} = \frac{16}{12} = \frac{4}{3}$$

Thus the similarity ratio is $\frac{4}{3}$, and $\triangle ABC \sim \triangle DEF$.

CHECK IT OUT!

2. Determine if $\triangle JLM \sim \triangle NPS$. If so, write the similarity ratio and a similarity statement.

yes; $\frac{5}{2}$; $\triangle LMJ \sim \triangle PNS$

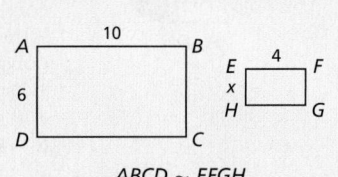

Student to Student   **Proportions with Similar Figures**

Anna Woods
Westwood High School

When I set up a proportion, I make sure each ratio compares the figures in the same order. To find x, I wrote $\frac{10}{4} = \frac{6}{x}$. This will work because the first ratio compares the lengths starting with rectangle ABCD. The second ratio compares the widths, also starting with rectangle ABCD.

$ABCD \sim EFGH$

7-2 Ratios in Similar Polygons   **463**

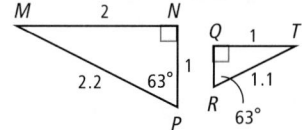
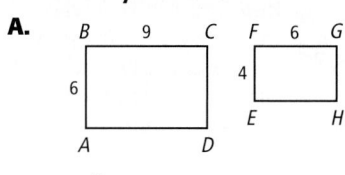

2 Teach

Guided Instruction

Review how to identify corresponding angles and corresponding sides of congruent polygons. Compare and contrast the definitions of similar and congruent. Show students how to use similarity ratios to find the unknown lengths of corresponding sides in similar polygons.

 Inclusion Remind students that when polygons are named in the problem, the order of the vertices can help identify corresponding sides and vertices.

Reaching All Learners

Through Concrete Manipulatives

Have students work with pattern blocks (MK) to explore the concept of similarity. Students can work in pairs, with one student creating a block design and the other creating a figure that is similar, but not congruent, to the first one. For more sets of pattern blocks, there are websites that feature "virtual pattern blocks," allowing students to select, combine, and rearrange blocks on a computer screen.

Lesson 7-2   **463**

Power Presentations
with PowerPoint®

Additional Examples

Example 3

Find the length of the model to the nearest tenth of a centimeter.

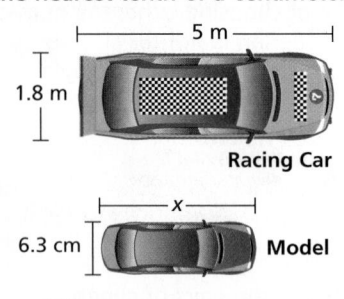

Racing Car

Model

$x \approx 17.5$ cm

Also available on transparency

INTERVENTION ◄─►
Questioning Strategies

EXAMPLE 3

• When solving a proportion about a scale model, do you need to use the same units for the dimensions of the original object and the scale model?

Teaching Tip | **Reading Math** Review the difference between $\triangle QRS \cong \triangle ZYX$ and $\triangle QRS \sim \triangle ZYX$. Have students practice reading similarity statements and identifying the corresponding parts. For example, $\triangle QRS \sim \triangle ZYX$ means that triangle QRS is similar to triangle ZYX. Q corresponds to Z, R corresponds to Y, and S corresponds to X.

EXAMPLE **3** **Hobby Application**

A Railbox boxcar can be used to transport auto parts. If the length of the actual boxcar is 50 ft, find the width of the actual boxcar to the nearest tenth of a foot.

Let x be the width of the actual boxcar in feet. The rectangular model of a boxcar is similar to the rectangular boxcar, so the corresponding lengths are proportional.

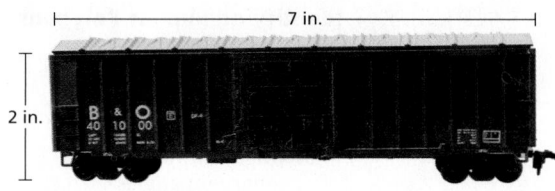

Helpful Hint

When you work with proportions, be sure the ratios compare corresponding measures.

$$\frac{\text{length of boxcar}}{\text{length of model}} = \frac{\text{width of boxcar}}{\text{width of model}}$$

$$\frac{50}{7} = \frac{x}{2}$$

$7x = (50)(2)$ *Cross Products Prop.*

$7x = 100$ *Simplify.*

$x \approx 14.3$ *Divide both sides by 7.*

The width of the model is approximately 14.3 ft.

 **CHECK IT OUT!**   **3.** A boxcar has the dimensions shown. A model of the boxcar is 1.25 in. wide. Find the length of the model to the nearest inch.

5 in.

36.25 ft

9 ft | Boxcar

x in.

Model | 1.25 in.

THINK AND DISCUSS

1. If you combine the symbol for similarity with the equal sign, what symbol is formed?

2. The similarity ratio of rectangle $ABCD$ to rectangle $EFGH$ is $\frac{1}{9}$. How do the side lengths of rectangle $ABCD$ compare to the corresponding side lengths of rectangle $EFGH$?

3. What shape(s) are always similar?

 **Know it! Note**

4. **GET ORGANIZED** Copy and complete the graphic organizer. Write the definition of similar polygons, and a similarity statement. Then draw examples and nonexamples of similar polygons.

Definition	Similarity statement
	Similar Polygons
Examples	Nonexamples

---

3 Close

Summarize

Review the concepts of similarity, same shape; and congruence, same shape and same size. Point out that only when the similarity ratio is 1:1 are similar polygons congruent. Write proportions comparing corresponding sides for $\triangle ABC \sim \triangle DEF$ $\left(\frac{AB}{DE} = \frac{AC}{DF} = \frac{BC}{EF}\right)$, and identify the congruent angles ($\angle A \cong \angle D$, $\angle B \cong \angle E$, $\angle C \cong \angle F$).

ONGOING ASSESSMENT

and INTERVENTION ◄─►

Diagnose Before the Lesson
7-2 Warm Up, TE p. 462

Monitor During the Lesson
Check It Out! Exercises, SE pp. 462–464
Questioning Strategies, TE pp. 463–464

Assess After the Lesson
7-2 Lesson Quiz, TE p. 467
Alternative Assessment, TE p. 467

Answers to *Think and Discuss*

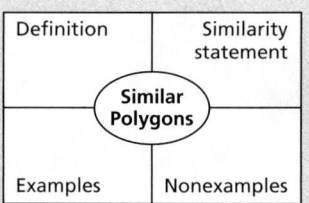

1. $\cong$

2. The sides of rect. *EFGH* are 9 times as long as the corr. sides of rect. *ABCD*.

3. Possible answers: reg. polygons of the same type; ⊚

4. See p. A6.

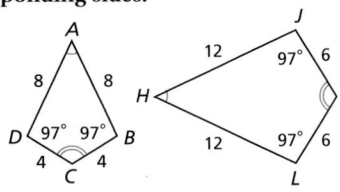

go.hrw.com/Geo/TX
Homework Help Online
KEYWORD: MG7 7-2
Parent Resources Online
KEYWORD: MG7 Parent

GUIDED PRACTICE

1. **Vocabulary** Give an example of similar figures in your classroom.
Possible answer: students' desks

SEE EXAMPLE **1**
p. 462

Identify the pairs of congruent angles and corresponding sides.

2.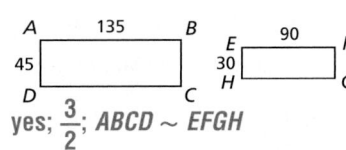

3.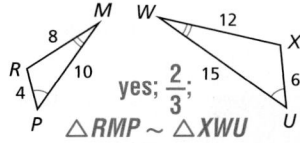

SEE EXAMPLE **2**
p. 463

Multi-Step Determine whether the polygons are similar. If so, write the similarity ratio and a similarity statement.

4. rectangles *ABCD* and *EFGH*

yes; $\frac{3}{2}$; *ABCD* ~ *EFGH*

5. △*RMP* and △*UWX*

yes; $\frac{2}{3}$; △*RMP* ~ △*XWU*

SEE EXAMPLE **3**
p. 464

6. **Art** The town of Goodland, Kansas, claims that it has one of the world's largest easels. It holds an enlargement of a van Gogh painting that is 24 ft wide. The original painting is 58 cm wide and 73 cm tall. If the reproduction is similar to the original, what is the height of the reproduction to the nearest foot? **30 ft**

PRACTICE AND PROBLEM SOLVING

Independent Practice

For Exercises	See Example
7–8	1
9–10	2
11	3

TEKS ⚹ **TAKS**

Skills Practice p. S16
Application Practice p. S34

Identify the pairs of congruent angles and corresponding sides.

7.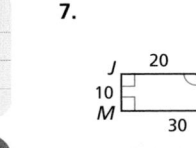

8.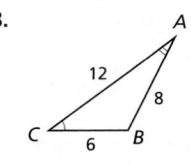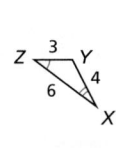

Multi-Step Determine whether the polygons are similar. If so, write the similarity ratio and a similarity statement.

9. △*RSQ* and △*UXZ*

9. yes; $\frac{7}{8}$; △*RSQ* ~ △*UZX*

10. rectangles *ABCD* and *JKLM*

no

7-2 Ratios in Similar Polygons **465**

Assignment Guide

Assign *Guided Practice* exercises as necessary.

If you finished Examples **1–3**
Basic 7–17, 19–21, 25–29, 34–40
Average 7–15, 18–20, 22–30, 34–40
Advanced 7–11, 12–20 even, 21–40

Homework Quick Check
Quickly check key concepts.
Exercises: 8, 10, 11, 14, 20

Answers

2. $\angle M \cong \angle U$; $\angle N \cong \angle V$; $\angle P \cong \angle W$; $\frac{MN}{UV} = \frac{NP}{VW} = \frac{PM}{WU} = \frac{1}{2}$

3. $\angle A \cong \angle H$; $\angle B \cong \angle J$; $\angle C \cong \angle K$; $\angle D \cong \angle L$; $\frac{AB}{HJ} = \frac{BC}{JK} = \frac{CD}{KL}$
$= \frac{DA}{LH} = \frac{2}{3}$

7. $\angle J \cong \angle S$; $\angle K \cong \angle T$; $\angle L \cong \angle U$; $\angle M \cong \angle V$; $\frac{JK}{ST} = \frac{KL}{TU} = \frac{LM}{UV}$
$= \frac{MJ}{VS} = \frac{5}{6}$

8. $\angle A \cong \angle X$; $\angle B \cong \angle Y$; $\angle C \cong \angle Z$; $\frac{AB}{XY} = \frac{BC}{YZ} = \frac{CA}{ZX} = 2$

🌟 **TAKS Practice**

Grades 9–11	Exercises
Obj. 1	19, 20, 21, 24, 26–28, 30, 32, 33
Obj. 2	19, 20, 24, 26–28, 30, 33
Obj. 6	12, 19, 20, 23, 24, 27, 28, 30, 33, 35–37
Obj. 7	24, 26, 30, 32
Obj. 8	12, 19, 20, 23, 24, 26–28, 30, 33, 35–37
Obj. 9	12, 19, 20, 23, 24, 26–28, 30, 33
Obj. 10	24, 26, 30, 34

Teacher to Teacher

Corresponding vertices in similar figures are usually named in alphabetical order. However, this could enable a student to solve problems using only the letters' order instead of the desired geometric reasons. Think about naming figures by beginning the sequence of letters at different corresponding vertices.

Roger Fuller
Grand Prairie, TX

11. Hobbies The ratio of the model car's dimensions to the actual car's dimensions is $\frac{1}{56}$. The model has a length of 3 in. What is the length of the actual car? **14 ft**

12. Square $ABCD$ has an area of 4 m². Square $PQRS$ has an area of 36 m². What is the similarity ratio of square $ABCD$ to square $PQRS$? What is the similarity ratio of square $PQRS$ to square $ABCD$? $\frac{1}{3}$; $\frac{3}{1}$

Tell whether each statement is sometimes, always, or never true.

13. Two right triangles are similar. **S**

14. Two squares are similar. **A**

15. A parallelogram and a trapezoid are similar. **N**

16. If two polygons are congruent, they are also similar. **A**

17. If two polygons are similar, they are also congruent. **S**

18. Critical Thinking Explain why any two regular polygons having the same number of sides are similar. **By def. of reg. polygons, the corr. int. ∠ are ≅, and the side lengths are ≅ and proportional. So any 2 reg. polygons with the same number of sides are ∼.**

Find the value of x.

19. $ABCD \sim EFGH$ **5**

20. $\triangle MNP \sim \triangle XYZ$ **15**

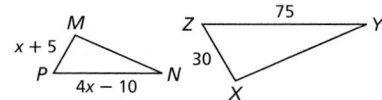

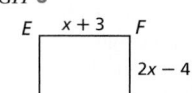

LINK

Monument

The height of the Statue of Liberty from the foundation of the pedestal to the torch is 305 ft. Her index finger measures 8 ft, and the fingernail is 13 in. by 10 in.

Source: libertystatepark.org

21. Estimation The Statue of Liberty's hand is 16.4 ft long. Assume that your own body is similar to that of the Statue of Liberty and estimate the length of the Statue of Liberty's nose. (*Hint:* Use a ruler to measure your own hand and nose. Then set up a proportion.) **Possible answer: 4.5 ft**

22. Write the definition of similar polygons as two conditional statements.

23. $\square JKLM \sim \square NOPQ$. If $m\angle K = 75°$, name two 75° angles in $\square NOPQ$. **∠O; ∠Q**

24. A dining room is 18 ft long and 14 ft wide. On a blueprint for the house, the dining room is 3.5 in. long. To the nearest tenth of an inch, what is the width of the dining room on the blueprint? **2.7 in.**

25. Write About It Two similar polygons have a similarity ratio of 1 : 1. What can you say about the two polygons? Explain.

MULTI-STEP TAKS PREP

26. This problem will prepare you for the Multi-Step TAKS Prep on page 478.

A stage set consists of a painted backdrop with some wooden flats in front of it. One of the flats shows a tree that has a similarity ratio of $\frac{1}{2}$ to an actual tree. To give an illusion of distance, the backdrop includes a small painted tree that has a similarity ratio of $\frac{1}{10}$ to the tree on the flat.

  a. The tree on the backdrop is 0.9 ft tall. What is the height of the tree on the flat? **9 ft**

  b. What is the height of the actual tree? **18 ft**

  c. Find the similarity ratio of the tree on the backdrop to the actual tree. $\frac{1}{20}$

7-2 PRACTICE A

7-2 PRACTICE C

7-2 PRACTICE B

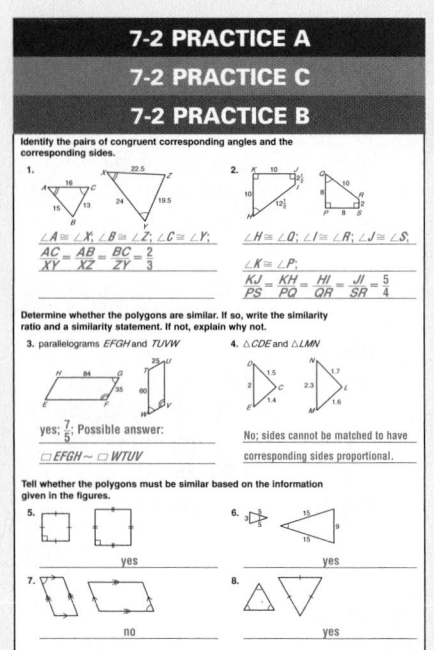

7-2 READING STRATEGIES

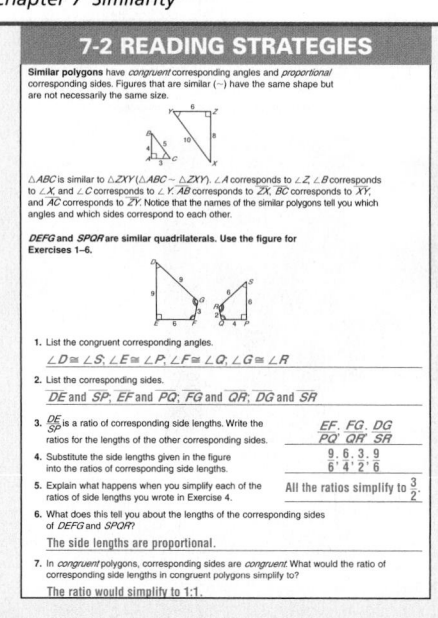

7-2 RETEACH

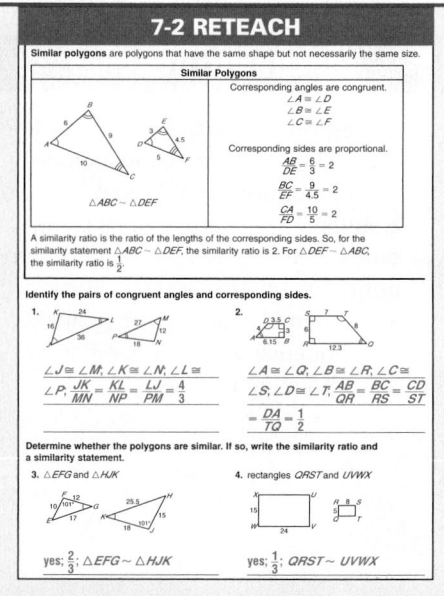

27. Which value of *y* makes the two rectangles similar?

   (A) 3   (C) 25.2

   (B) 8.2   (D) 28.8

28. △*CGL* ~ △*MPS*. The similarity ratio of △*CGL* to △*MPS* is $\frac{5}{2}$. What is the length of $\overline{PS}$?

   (F) 8   (H) 50

   (G) 12   (J) 75

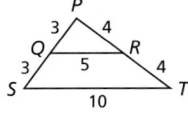

29. Short Response Explain why 1.5, 2.5, 3.5 and 6, 10, 12 cannot be corresponding sides of similar triangles.

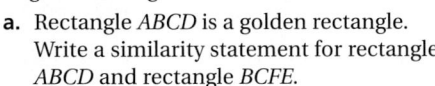
The ratios of the sides are not the same; $\frac{12}{3.5} = \frac{24}{7}$; $\frac{10}{2.5} = 4$; $\frac{6}{1.5} = 4$.

CHALLENGE AND EXTEND

30. Architecture An architect is designing a building that is 200 ft long and 140 ft wide. She builds a model so that the similarity ratio of the model to the building is $\frac{1}{500}$. What is the length and width of the model in inches? **4.8 in. long; 3.36 in. wide**

31. Write a paragraph proof.

   Given: $\overline{QR} \parallel \overline{ST}$

   Prove: △*PQR* ~ △*PST*

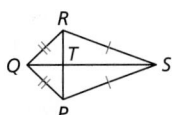

32. In the figure, *D* is the midpoint of $\overline{AC}$.

   a. Find *AC*, *DC*, and *DB*.

   b. Use your results from part **a** to help you explain why △*ABC* ~ △*CDB*.

33. A golden rectangle has the following property: If a square is cut from one end of the rectangle, the rectangle that remains is similar to the original rectangle.

33a. rect. *ABCD* ~ rect. *BCFE*

b. $\frac{\ell}{1} = \frac{1}{\ell - 1}$

c. $\ell = \frac{1 + \sqrt{5}}{2}$

d. $\ell \approx 1.6$

   a. Rectangle *ABCD* is a golden rectangle. Write a similarity statement for rectangle *ABCD* and rectangle *BCFE*.

   b. Write a proportion using the corresponding sides of these rectangles.

   c. Solve the proportion for ℓ. (*Hint:* Use the Quadratic Formula.)

   d. The value of ℓ is known as the golden ratio. Use a calculator to find ℓ to the nearest tenth.

SPIRAL REVIEW

34. There are four runners in a 200-meter race. Assuming there are no ties, in how many different orders can the runners finish the race? (*Previous course*) **24**

In kite *PQRS*, $\overline{PS} \cong \overline{RS}$, $\overline{QR} \cong \overline{QP}$, m∠*QPT* = 45°, and m∠*RST* = 20°. Find each angle measure. (*Lesson 6-6*)

35. m∠*QTR* **90°**   **36.** m∠*PST* **20°**   **37.** m∠*TPS* **70°**

Complete each of the following equations, given that $\frac{x}{4} = \frac{y}{10}$. (*Lesson 7-1*)

38. $10x = \blacksquare$ $4y$ **39.** $\frac{10}{y} = \blacksquare$ $\frac{4}{x}$ **40.** $\frac{x}{y} = \blacksquare$ $\frac{4}{10}$, or $\frac{2}{5}$

Journal

Ask students to explain what a scale on a map means, how it is used, and how it is related to the concept of a similarity ratio.

ALTERNATIVE ASSESSMENT

Have students draw an obtuse triangle, measure its angles and sides, and write the measurements on the triangle. Ask them to draw two more triangles similar to the original, using similarity ratios of $\frac{2}{1}$ and $\frac{1}{2}$. Then calculate what the side lengths of the new triangles should be, and compare these to the results they get by measuring.

Power Presentations with PowerPoint®

7-2 Lesson Quiz

1. Determine whether the polygons are similar. If so, write the similarity ratio and a similarity statement. no

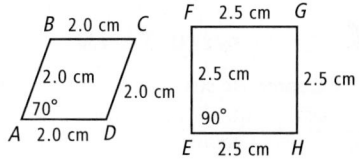

2. The ratio of a model sailboat's dimensions to the actual boat's dimensions is $\frac{1}{30}$. If the length of the model is 10 inches, what is the length of the actual sailboat in feet? **25 ft**

3. Tell whether the following statement is *sometimes*, *always*, or *never* true. Two equilateral triangles are similar. Always

Also available on transparency

7-2 PROBLEM SOLVING

1. *EFGH* ~ *JKLM*. What is the value of *x*?

2. The ratio of a model scale die cast motorcycle is 1:18. The model is $5\frac{1}{4}$ inches long. What is the length of the actual motorcycle in feet and inches?
7 ft 10.5 in.

3. A diagram of a new competition swimming pool is shown. If the width of the pool is 25 meters, find the length of the actual pool.

4. Rectangle A has side lengths 16.4 centimeters and 10.8 centimeters. Rectangle B has side lengths 10.25 centimeters and 6.75 centimeters. Determine whether the rectangles are similar. If so, write the similarity ratio.
yes; $\frac{8}{5}$

Choose the best answer.

5. A pet store has various sizes of guinea pig cages. A diagram of the top view of one of the cages is shown. What are possible dimensions of this cage?

  A 28 in. by 24 in. **C** 30 in. by 24 in.
  B 28 in. by 18 in. **D** 30 in. by 18 in.

6. A gymnasium is 96 feet long and 75 feet wide. On a blueprint, the gymnasium is 5.5 inches long. To the nearest tenth of an inch, what is the width of the gymnasium on the blueprint?
  F 3.7 in.   **H** 7.0 in.
  G 4.3 in.   **J** 13.6 in.

7. △*QRS* ~ △*TUV*. Find the value of *y*.

  A 3.6   **C** 19
  B 5.5   **D** 33

8. △*ABC* has side lengths 14, 8, and 10.4. What are possible side lengths of △*DEF* if △*ABC* ~ △*DEF*?
  F 28, 20, 20.8
  G 35, 16, 20.8
  H 28, 20, 26
  J 35, 20, 26

Answers

31. Since $\overline{QR} \parallel \overline{ST}$, ∠*PQR* ≅ ∠*PST*, and ∠*PRQ* ≅ ∠*PTS* by the Alt. Int. ∠ Thm. ∠*P* ≅ ∠*P* by the Reflex. Prop. of ≅. Thus the corr. ∠ of △*PQR* and △*PST* are ≅. It is easy to see that *PS* = 6 and *PT* = 8, so $\frac{PQ}{PS} = \frac{PR}{PT} = \frac{QR}{ST} = \frac{1}{2}$. Therefore △*PQR* ~ △*PST* by the def. of ~ polygons.

32a. *AC* = $\sqrt{2}$, *DC* = *BD* = $\frac{\sqrt{2}}{2}$

  b. By the Isosc. △ Thm., ∠*A* ≅ ∠*C*, so m∠*A* = m∠*C* = 45°. Also ∠*DBC* ≅ ∠*C*, so m∠*DBC* = 45°. Thus the corr. ∠ of △*ABC* and △*BDC* are ≅. $\frac{AB}{BD} = \frac{BC}{DC} = \frac{AC}{BC} = \sqrt{2}$. By the def. of similarity, △*ABC* ~ △*CDB*.

Pacing:
Traditional 1 day
Block $\frac{1}{2}$ day

Objective: Use geometry
software to find ways to determine
that triangles are similar.

Materials: geometry software

Online Edition
TechKeys

**Countdown to
TAKS Week 15**

Teach

Discuss

Review with students that SAS, ASA,
and SSS guarantee congruent triangles, and explain that in this lab,
students will be using geometry software to discover if there are similar
conditions that guarantee similar triangles. Also review the definitions of
similar and *congruent* triangles and
make sure that students understand
how these two concepts differ.

 Geometry TEKS

G.2 Geometric structure*
(A) use constructions to explore
attributes of geometric figures and
to make conjectures ...

G.3 Geometric structure*
(B) construct and justify statements
about geometric figures ...

**G.9 Congruence and the geometry
of size***
(B) formulate and test conjectures
about the properties and attributes of
polygons ... based on explorations ...

**G.11 Similarity and the geometry
of shape***
(A) use and extend similarity
properties and transformations to
explore and justify conjectures ...

* Knowledge and Skills See p. 452

**7-3
Technology
LAB**

Use with Lesson 7-3

Predict Triangle
Similarity Relationships

In Chapter 4, you found shortcuts for determining that two triangles
are congruent. Now you will use geometry software to find ways to
determine that triangles are similar.

 TEKS G.11.A Similarity and the geometry of
shape: use and extend similarity properties and
transformations to explore and justify conjectures
about geometric figures. Also G.2.A, G.3.B, G.9.B

go.hrw.com/Geo/TX
Lab Resources Online
KEYWORD: MG7 Lab7

Activity 1

1. Construct △*ABC*. Construct $\overline{DE}$ longer than
any of the sides of △*ABC*. Rotate $\overline{DE}$ around
D by rotation ∠*BAC*. Rotate $\overline{DE}$ around *E* by
rotation ∠*ABC*. Label the intersection point of
the two rotated segments as *F*.

2. Measure angles to confirm that ∠*BAC* ≅ ∠*EDF*
and ∠*ABC* ≅ ∠*DEF*. Drag a vertex of △*ABC*
or an endpoint of $\overline{DE}$ to show that the two
triangles have two pairs of congruent angles.

3. Measure the side lengths of both triangles.
Divide each side length of △*ABC* by the
corresponding side length of △*DEF*.
Compare the resulting ratios. What do you notice? **The ratios of corr. side lengths are =.**

Try This

1. What theorem guarantees that the third pair of angles in the triangles are also
congruent? **△ Sum Thm.**

2. Will the ratios of corresponding sides found in Step 3 always be equal? Drag
a vertex of △*ABC* or an endpoint of $\overline{DE}$ to investigate this question. State a
conjecture based on your results. **Yes; in ~ △, corr. sides are proportional.**

Activity 2

1. Construct a new △*ABC*. Create *P* in the
interior of the triangle. Create △*DEF* by
enlarging △*ABC* around *P* by a multiple
of 2 using the Dilation command. Drag *P*
outside of △*ABC* to separate the triangles.

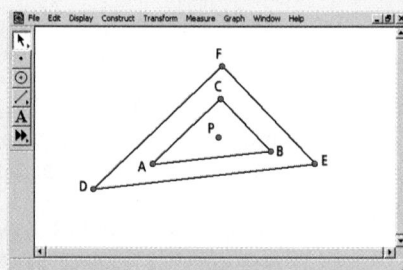

2 Measure the side lengths of △DEF to confirm that each side is twice as long as the corresponding side of △ABC. Drag a vertex of △ABC to verify that this relationship is true.

3 Measure the angles of both triangles. What do you notice? **Corr. ∠ are ≅.**

3. Did the construction of the triangles with three pairs of sides in the same ratio guarantee that the corresponding angles would be congruent? State a conjecture based on these results. **Yes; if 2 △ have their corr. sides in the same ratio, then the △ are ~.**

4. Compare your conjecture to the SSS Congruence Theorem from Chapter 4. How are they similar and how are they different?
They are similar in that both allow you to conclude that corr. ∠ are ≅. They are different in that the conjecture suggests that △ with corr. sides in the same ratio have the same shape, but the SSS ≅ Thm. allows you to conclude that the △ have both the same shape and the same size.

Activity 3

1 Construct a different △ABC. Create P in the interior of the triangle. Expand $\overline{AB}$ and $\overline{AC}$ around P by a multiple of 2 using the Dilation command. Create an angle congruent to ∠BAC with sides that are each twice as long as $\overline{AB}$ and $\overline{AC}$.

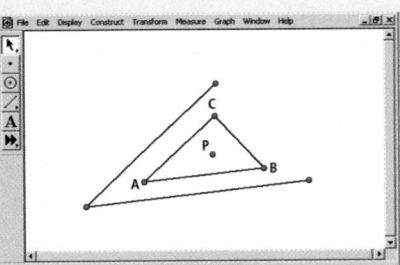

2 Use a segment to create the third side of a new triangle and label it △DEF. Drag P outside of △ABC to separate the triangles.

3 Measure each side length and determine the relationship between corresponding sides of △ABC and △DEF. **The ratio of the corr. sides of △ABC and △DEF are proportional.**

4 Measure the angles of both triangles. What do you notice? **The corr. ∠ of the △ are ≅.**

Try This

5. Tell whether △ABC is similar to △DEF. Explain your reasoning. **Yes; corr. sides are proportional and corr. ∠ are ≅.**

6. Write a conjecture based on the activity. What congruency theorem is related to your conjecture?
If △ have 2 pairs of corr. sides in proportion and the included ∠ are ≅, then the △ are ~. This is related to the SAS ≅ Thm.

Close

Key Concept

Triangles can be proved similar by AA, SSS, and SAS, where corresponding angles are congruent and pairs of corresponding sides are proportional.

Assessment

Journal Have students compare and contrast the conditions that guarantee similar triangles with those that guarantee congruence.

Pacing: Traditional 2 days
Block 1 day

Objectives: Prove certain triangles are similar by using AA, SSS, and SAS.

Use triangle similarity to solve problems.

Online Edition
Tutorial Videos

Countdown to TAKS Week 15

Power Presentations
with PowerPoint®

Warm Up

Solve each proportion.

1. $\frac{6}{11} = \frac{8}{b}$ $b = \frac{44}{3}$ or $14\frac{2}{3}$

2. $\frac{5}{z} = \frac{z}{20}$ $z = \pm10$

3. $\frac{3}{10} = \frac{6}{x + 12}$ $x = 8$

4. If $\triangle QRS \sim \triangle XYZ$, identify the pairs of congruent angles and write 3 proportions using pairs of corresponding sides.

$\angle Q \cong \angle X$; $\angle R \cong \angle Y$;
$\angle S \cong \angle Z$; $\frac{QR}{XY} = \frac{RS}{YZ}$;
$\frac{RS}{YZ} = \frac{QS}{XZ}$; $\frac{QS}{XZ} = \frac{QR}{XY}$

Also available on transparency

Math Humor

Q: What do you call a fierce beast?
A: A line

Geometry TEKS

G.5 Geometric patterns*
(B) use numeric and geometric patterns to make generalizations about geometric properties, including ... ratios in similar figures ...

G.11 Similarity and the geometry of shape*
(A) use and extend similarity properties and transformations to explore and justify conjectures ...
(B) use ratios to solve problems involving similar figures

***Knowledge and Skills** See p. 452

7-3 # Triangle Similarity: AA, SSS, and SAS

TEKS G.11.B Similarity and the geometry of shape: use ratios to solve problems involving similar figures. Also G.5.B, G.11.A

Objectives
Prove certain triangles are similar by using AA, SSS, and SAS.

Use triangle similarity to solve problems.

Who uses this?
Engineers use similar triangles when designing buildings, such as the Pyramid Building in San Diego, California. (See Example 5.)

There are several ways to prove certain triangles are similar. The following postulate, as well as the SSS and SAS Similarity Theorems, will be used in proofs just as SSS, SAS, ASA, HL, and AAS were used to prove triangles congruent.

Know it!
.Note

Postulate 7-3-1 Angle-Angle (AA) Similarity

POSTULATE	HYPOTHESIS	CONCLUSION
If two angles of one triangle are congruent to two angles of another triangle, then the triangles are similar.		$\triangle ABC \sim \triangle DEF$

EXAMPLE 1 **Using the AA Similarity Postulate**

Explain why the triangles are similar and write a similarity statement.

Since $\overline{PT} \parallel \overline{SR}$, $\angle P \cong \angle R$, and $\angle T \cong \angle S$ by the Alternate Interior Angles Theorem. Therefore $\triangle PQT \sim \triangle RQS$ by AA $\sim$.

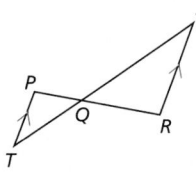

CHECK IT OUT!
1. Explain why the triangles are similar and write a similarity statement.

By the $\triangle$ Sum Thm., m$\angle C = 47°$, so $\angle C \cong \angle F$. $\angle B \cong \angle E$ by the Rt. $\angle \cong$ Thm. Therefore $\triangle ABC \sim \triangle DEF$ by AA $\sim$.

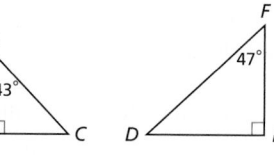

Know it!
.Note

Theorem 7-3-2 Side-Side-Side (SSS) Similarity

THEOREM	HYPOTHESIS	CONCLUSION
If the three sides of one triangle are proportional to the three corresponding sides of another triangle, then the triangles are similar.		$\triangle ABC \sim \triangle DEF$

You will prove Theorem 7-3-2 in Exercise 38.

---

1 # Introduce

EXPLORATION

7-3 **Triangle Similarity: AA, SSS, and SAS**

Explore a shortcut for proving that two triangles are similar.

1. Draw $\triangle ABC$ with the given measurements. (*Hint:* First draw $\overline{AB}$. Then use a protractor to draw $\angle A$ and $\angle B$ at each endpoint of $\overline{AB}$.)

$\triangle ABC$	
m$\angle A$	45°
m$\angle B$	60°

2. Draw $\triangle DEF$ with the given measurements so that $\triangle DEF$ is **NOT** congruent to $\triangle ABC$. (*Hint:* First draw $\overline{DE}$ so that $DE \neq AB$.)

$\triangle DEF$	
m$\angle D$	45°
m$\angle E$	60°

3. What can you say about $\angle C$ and $\angle F$? Why?

4. Measure the lengths of the sides of each triangle. Then calculate $\frac{AB}{DE}$, $\frac{BC}{EF}$, and $\frac{AC}{DF}$. What do you notice about these values?

5. What can you conclude about $\triangle ABC$ and $\triangle DEF$? Why?

6. Repeat Steps 1–5, choosing your own measures so that m$\angle A =$ m$\angle D$ and m$\angle B =$ m$\angle E$. Do you get the same results?

THINK AND DISCUSS

7. **Describe** a shortcut, based on your results, for showing that two triangles are similar.

8. **Explain** how you can use your shortcut

Motivate

Review the triangle congruence postulates SSS, SAS, and ASA. Point out that in this lesson, postulates and theorems will be used as shortcuts to prove that two triangles are similar. Given a set of tangrams (MK) or other objects, students should categorize and describe the pieces that are similar, and those that are congruent to each other.

Explorations and answers are provided in the *Explorations* binder.

Know it!
Note

Theorem 7-3-3	**Side-Angle-Side (SAS) Similarity**	
THEOREM	**HYPOTHESIS**	**CONCLUSION**
If two sides of one triangle are proportional to two sides of another triangle and their included angles are congruent, then the triangles are similar.	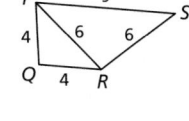 $\angle B \cong \angle E$	$\triangle ABC \sim \triangle DEF$

You will prove Theorem 7-3-3 in Exercise 39.

EXAMPLE 2 **Verifying Triangle Similarity**

Verify that the triangles are similar.

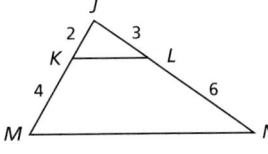

A △*PQR* and △*PRS*

$$\frac{PQ}{PR} = \frac{4}{6} = \frac{2}{3}, \frac{QR}{RS} = \frac{4}{6} = \frac{2}{3}, \frac{PR}{PS} = \frac{6}{9} = \frac{2}{3}$$

Therefore △*PQR* ~ △*PRS* by SSS ~.

B △*JKL* and △*JMN*

∠*J* ≅ ∠*J* by the Reflexive Property of ≅.

$$\frac{JK}{JM} = \frac{2}{6} = \frac{1}{3}, \frac{JL}{JN} = \frac{3}{9} = \frac{1}{3}$$

Therefore △*JKL* ~ △*JMN* by SAS ~.

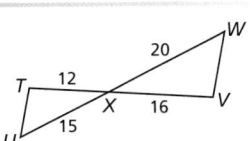

 **2.** Verify that △*TXU* ~ △*VXW*.
∠*TXU* ≅ ∠*VXW* by the Vert. ∡ Thm. $\frac{TX}{VX} = \frac{12}{16} = \frac{3}{4}$, and $\frac{XU}{XW} = \frac{15}{20} = \frac{3}{4}$. Therefore △*TXU* ~ △*VXW* by SAS ~.

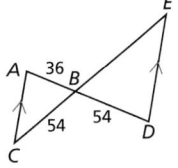

EXAMPLE 3 **Finding Lengths in Similar Triangles**

Explain why △*ABC* ~ △*DBE* and then find *BE*.

Step 1 Prove triangles are similar.
As shown $\overline{AC} \parallel \overline{ED}$, ∠*A* ≅ ∠*D*, and ∠*C* ≅ ∠*E* by the Alternate Interior Angles Theorem. Therefore △*ABC* ~ △*DBE* by AA ~.

Step 2 Find *BE*.

$\dfrac{AB}{DB} = \dfrac{BC}{BE}$	*Corr. sides are proportional.*
$\dfrac{36}{54} = \dfrac{54}{BE}$	*Substitute 36 for AB, 54 for DB, and 54 for BC.*
$36(BE) = 54^2$	*Cross Products Prop.*
$36(BE) = 2916$	*Simplify.*
$BE = 81$	*Divide both sides by 36.*

3. It is given that ∠*RSV* ≅ ∠*T*. By the Reflex. Prop. of ≅, ∠*R* ≅ ∠*R*. Therefore △*RSV* ~ △*RTU* by AA ~. *RT* = 15.

 **3.** Explain why △*RSV* ~ △*RTU* and then find *RT*.

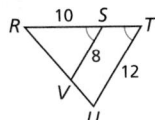

---

2 Teach

Guided Instruction

Introduce the AA Similarity Postulate and the SSS and SAS Similarity Theorems, illustrating each with an example. Remind students that in triangle similarity, they should identify sides that are *proportional*, rather than congruent. Finally, discuss the Properties of Similarity and give an example of each.

 Inclusion Remind students that similarity statements indicate corresponding parts in the same way as in congruence statements.

Reaching All Learners

Through Visual Cues

When working with similar triangles, some students have trouble identifying the corresponding sides. Point out that tick marks should not be used, because they imply congruent segments. Instead, encourage students to use different colored pencils or highlighters to mark the segments that make up each corresponding pair.

Additional Examples

Example 1

Explain why the triangles are similar and write a similarity statement.

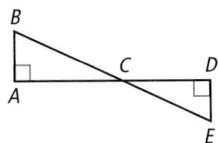

∠*A* ≅ ∠*D* by the Rt. ∠ ≅ Thm. ∠*ACB* ≅ ∠*DCE* by the Vert. ∡ Thm. Therefore △*ACB* ~ △*DEC* by AA ~.

Example 2

Verify that the triangles are similar.

A. △*PQR* and △*STU*

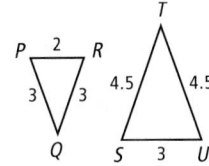

$\frac{PQ}{ST} = \frac{QR}{TU} = \frac{PR}{SU} = \frac{2}{3}$. Therefore △*PQR* ~ △*STU* by SSS ~.

B. △*DEF* and △*HJK*

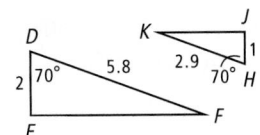

m∠*D* = m∠*H* = 70°, so ∠*D* ≅ ∠*H*. $\frac{DE}{JH} = \frac{2}{1}$ and $\frac{DF}{HK} = \frac{5.8}{2.9} = \frac{2}{1}$. Therefore △*DEF* ~ △*HJK* by SAS ~.

Example 3

Explain why △*ABE* ~ △*ACD*, and then find *CD*.

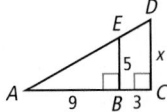

∠*A* ≅ ∠*A* by the Reflex. Prop. of ≅. ∠*ABE* ≅ ∠*ACD* by the Rt. ∠ ≅ Thm. Therefore △*ABE* ~ △*ACD* by AA ~. $CD = \frac{60}{9} = \frac{20}{3}$, or $6\frac{2}{3}$.

Also available on transparency

INTERVENTION ◀▶
Questioning Strategies

EXAMPLES **1–3**

• Why are ASA and AAS not similarity theorems?

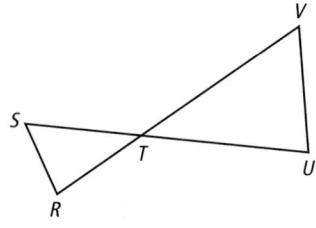

Example 4

Given: $3UT = 5RT$ and $3VT = 5ST$

Prove: $\triangle UVT \sim \triangle RST$

Proof:

1. $3UT = 5RT$ and $3VT = 5ST$ (Given)
2. $\dfrac{UT}{RT} = \dfrac{5}{3}$, $\dfrac{VT}{ST} = \dfrac{5}{3}$ (Div. Prop. of =)
3. $\dfrac{UT}{RT} = \dfrac{VT}{ST}$ (Trans. Prop. of =)
4. $\angle UTV \cong \angle RTS$ (Vert. $\angle$s. Thm.)
5. $\triangle UVT \sim \triangle RST$ (SAS $\sim$)

Example 5

Use the diagram in **Example 5** to find BC to the nearest tenth.

21.6 ft

Also available on transparency

INTERVENTION ◄─►
Questioning Strategies

EXAMPLE 4

- Can you use just two pairs of corresponding sides when proving triangles similar? Explain.

EXAMPLE 5

- How can the Triangle Midsegment Theorem be applied to find the lengths of some of the segments in the diagram in Example 5?

EXAMPLE 4 **Writing Proofs with Similar Triangles**

Given: A is the midpoint of $\overline{BC}$.
D is the midpoint of $\overline{BE}$.

Prove: $\triangle BDA \sim \triangle BEC$

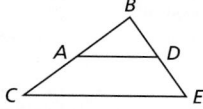

Proof:

Statements	Reasons
1. A is the mdpt. of $\overline{BC}$. D is the mdpt. of $\overline{BE}$.	1. Given
2. $\overline{BA} \cong \overline{AC}$, $\overline{BD} \cong \overline{DE}$	2. Def. of mdpt.
3. $BA = AC$, $BD = DE$	3. Def. of $\cong$ seg.
4. $BC = BA + AC$, $BE = BD + DE$	4. Seg. Add. Post.
5. $BC = BA + BA$, $BE = BD + BD$	5. Subst. Prop.
6. $BC = 2BA$, $BE = 2BD$	6. Simplify.
7. $\dfrac{BC}{BA} = 2$, $\dfrac{BE}{BD} = 2$	7. Div. Prop. of =
8. $\dfrac{BC}{BA} = \dfrac{BE}{BD}$	8. Trans. Prop. of =
9. $\angle B \cong \angle B$	9. Reflex. Prop. of $\cong$
10. $\triangle BDA \sim \triangle BEC$	10. SAS $\sim$ *Steps 8, 9*

4. 1. M is the mdpt. of $\overline{JK}$, N is the mdpt. of $\overline{KL}$, and P is the mdpt. of $\overline{JL}$. (Given)

2. $MP = \frac{1}{2}KL$, $MN = \frac{1}{2}JL$, $NP = \frac{1}{2}KJ$ ($\triangle$ Midsegs. Thm.)

3. $\dfrac{MP}{KL} = \dfrac{MN}{JL} = \dfrac{NP}{KJ} = \dfrac{1}{2}$ (Div. Prop. of =)

4. $\triangle JKL \sim \triangle NPM$ (SSS $\sim$ *Step 3*)

 **4.** **Given:** M is the midpoint of $\overline{JK}$. N is the midpoint of $\overline{KL}$, and P is the midpoint of $\overline{JL}$.

Prove: $\triangle JKL \sim \triangle NPM$
(*Hint:* Use the Triangle Midsegment Theorem and SSS $\sim$.)

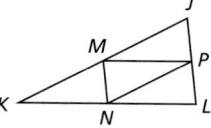

EXAMPLE 5 *Engineering Application*

The photo shows a gable roof. $\overline{AC} \parallel \overline{FG}$. Use similar triangles to prove $\triangle ABC \sim \triangle FBG$ and then find BF to the nearest tenth of a foot.

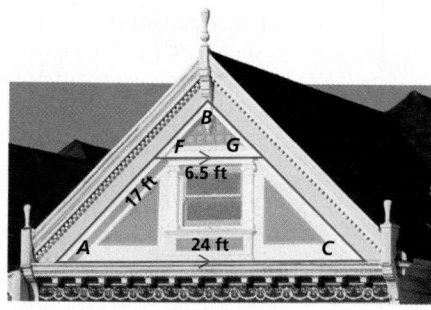

Step 1 Prove the triangles are similar.

$\overline{AC} \parallel \overline{FG}$	*Given*
$\angle BFG \cong \angle BAC$	*Corr. $\angle$s. Thm.*
$\angle B \cong \angle B$	*Reflex. Prop. of $\cong$*

Therefore $\triangle ABC \sim \triangle FBG$ by AA $\sim$.

Step 2 Find *BF*.

$$\frac{BA}{AC} = \frac{BF}{FG}$$ *Corr. sides are proportional.*

$$\frac{17}{24} = \frac{BF}{6.5}$$ *Substitute the given values.*

$$17(6.5) = 24(BF)$$ *Cross Products Prop.*

$$110.5 = 24(BF)$$ *Simplify.*

$$4.6 \text{ ft} \approx BF$$ *Divide both sides by 24.*

 **5. What if...?** If $AB = 4x$, $AC = 5x$, and $BF = 4$, find *FG*. 5

You learned in Chapter 2 that the Reflexive, Symmetric, and Transitive Properties of Equality have corresponding properties of congruence. These properties also hold true for similarity of triangles.

Know it! Note

Properties of Similarity

Reflexive Property of Similarity

△*ABC* ~ △*ABC* (Reflex. Prop. of ~)

Symmetric Property of Similarity

If △*ABC* ~ △*DEF*, then △*DEF* ~ △*ABC*. (Sym. Prop. of ~)

Transitive Property of Similarity

If △*ABC* ~ △*DEF* and △*DEF* ~ △*XYZ*, then △*ABC* ~ △*XYZ*. (Trans. Prop. of ~)

THINK AND DISCUSS

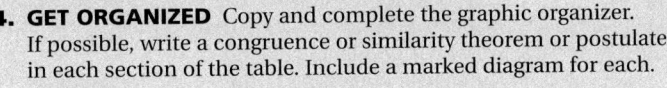

1. What additional information, if any, would you you need in order to show that △*ABC* ~ △*DEF* by the AA Similarity Postulate?

2. What additional information, if any, would you need in order to show that △*ABC* ~ △*DEF* by the SAS Similarity Theorem?

3. Do corresponding sides of similar triangles need to be proportional and congruent? Explain.

Know it! Note

4. GET ORGANIZED Copy and complete the graphic organizer. If possible, write a congruence or similarity theorem or postulate in each section of the table. Include a marked diagram for each.

	Congruence	Similarity
SSS		
SAS		
AA		

If you only need to know that two angles of two triangles are congruent in order to prove similarity, students might think you only need to know three angles of two quadrilaterals to do the same. Students will inaccurately compare the ratios of the sides as in SSS similarity for any *n*-gon. Use counterexamples to show that this is incorrect. Stress that triangles are a special case because they are rigid structures.

Teaching Tip — **Kinesthetic** Some students may have difficulty identifying corresponding sides in similar triangles because of the orientation of the figures. Show these students how they can copy one of the triangles onto a piece of paper, then cut it out and rotate it, so that the two triangles have the same orientation.

Teaching Tip — **Inclusion** When using the SSS and SAS Similarity Theorems, some students have difficulty matching up the corresponding sides. Tell these students to match up small to small sides, medium to medium sides, and large to large sides.

---

3 Close

Summarize

Review the three ways that students have learned to prove triangles similar: AA, SSS, and SAS. Go over how to find the lengths of missing sides in similar triangles. Review the Reflexive, Symmetric, and Transitive Properties of Similarity.

ONGOING ASSESSMENT

and INTERVENTION ⬅️➡️

Diagnose **Before** the Lesson
7-3 Warm Up, TE p. 470

Monitor **During** the Lesson
Check It Out! Exercises, SE pp. 470–473
Questioning Strategies, TE pp. 471–472

Assess **After** the Lesson
7-3 Lesson Quiz, TE p. 477
Alternative Assessment, TE p. 477

Answers to *Think and Discuss*

1. ∠*A* ≅ ∠*D* or ∠*C* ≅ ∠*F*

2. $\frac{BA}{ED} = \frac{3}{5}$

3. No; the corr. sides need to be proportional but not necessarily ≅ for the △ to be ~.

4. See p. A6.

go.hrw.com/Geo/TX
Homework Help Online
KEYWORD: MG7 7-3
Parent Resources Online
KEYWORD: MG7 Parent

Assignment Guide

Assign *Guided Practice* exercises as necessary.

If you finished Examples **1–3**
  Basic 11–16, 20–24, 31
  Average 11–16, 19–24, 27, 31
  Advanced 11–16, 20–24, 27, 31, 37, 40

If you finished Examples **1–5**
  Basic 11–19, 23–25, 32–37, 41–46
  Average 11–25, 29–37, 41–46
  Advanced 11–20, 23–28, 30, 31, 33–46

Homework Quick Check
Quickly check key concepts.
Exercises: 11, 12, 14, 16, 18, 23

Answers

1. By the △ Sum Thm., m∠A = 47°. So by the def. of ≅, ∠A ≅ ∠F, and ∠C ≅ ∠H. Therefore △ABC ~ △FGH by AA ~.

2. It is given that ∠P ≅ ∠T. ∠QST is a rt. ∠ by the Lin. Pair Thm., so ∠QST ≅ ∠RSP. Therefore △QST ~ △RSP by AA ~.

3. $\frac{DF}{JL} = \frac{DE}{JK} = \frac{EF}{KL} = \frac{1}{2}$, so △DEF ~ △JKL by SSS ~.

4. It is given that ∠NMP ≅ ∠RMQ. $\frac{MN}{MR} = \frac{MP}{MQ} = \frac{2}{3}$. Therefore △MNP ~ △MRQ by SAS ~.

5. It is given that ∠AED ≅ ∠ACB. ∠A ≅ ∠A by the Reflex. Prop. of ≅. Therefore △AED ~ △ACB by AA ~. AB = 10

6–8. See p. A23.

TAKS Practice

Grades 9–11	Exercises
Obj. 1	23, 24, 27, 34, 37, 41
Obj. 2	23, 24, 27, 34, 37, 41, 44–46
Obj. 6	23–25, 27, 34, 35, 37
Obj. 8	23–25, 27, 34, 35, 37
Obj. 10	25, 27, 41

GUIDED PRACTICE

SEE EXAMPLE 1
p. 470

Explain why the triangles are similar and write a similarity statement.

1.

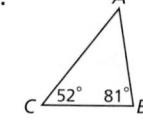

2.

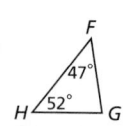

SEE EXAMPLE 2
p. 471

Verify that the triangles are similar.

3. △DEF and △JKL

4. △MNP and △MRQ

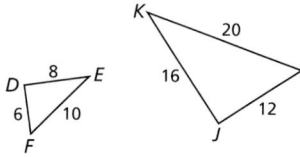

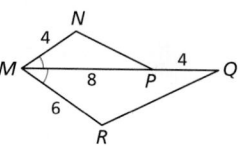

SEE EXAMPLE 3
p. 471

Multi-Step Explain why the triangles are similar and then find each length.

5. AB

6. WY

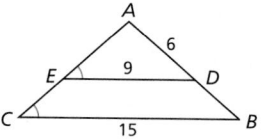

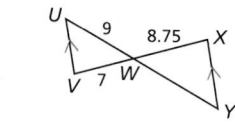

SEE EXAMPLE 4
p. 472

7. **Given:** $\overleftrightarrow{MN} \parallel \overline{KL}$
   Prove: △JMN ~ △JKL

8. **Given:** SQ = 2QP, TR = 2RP
   Prove: △PQR ~ △PST

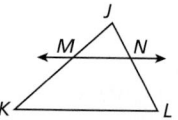

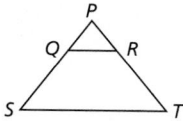

9. The coordinates of A, B, and C are A(0, 0), B(2, 6), and C(8, −2). What theorem or postulate justifies the statement △ABC ~ △DEF, if the coordinates of D and E are twice the coordinates of B and C? **SAS or SSS ~ Thm.**

SEE EXAMPLE 5
p. 472

10. **Surveying** In order to measure the distance AB across the meteorite crater, a surveyor at S locates points A, B, C, and D as shown. What is AB to the nearest meter? nearest kilometer? **1200 m, or 1.2 km**

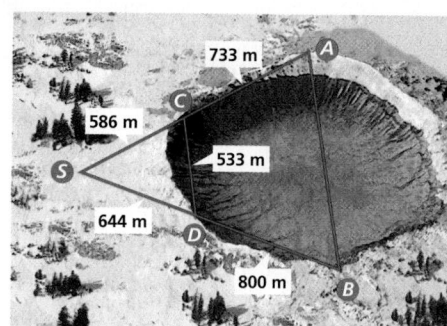

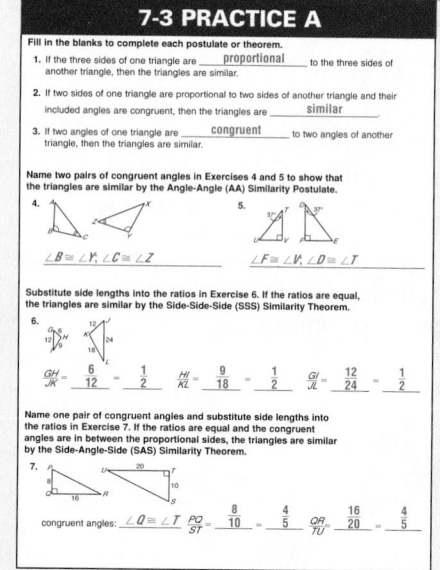

PRACTICE AND PROBLEM SOLVING

Explain why the triangles are similar and write a similarity statement.

11.

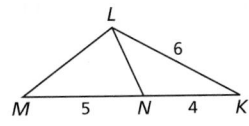

12.

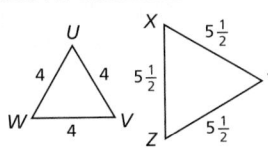

11. It is given that ∠GLH ≅ ∠K. ∠G ≅ ∠G by the Reflex. Prop. of ≅. Therefore △HLG ~ △JKG by AA ~.

12. By the Isosc. △ Thm., ∠C ≅ ∠B. By the △ Sum Thm. $m\angle C = m\angle B = 74°$. In the same way, $m\angle F = 74°$. So by the def. of ≅, ∠B ≅ ∠E and ∠C ≅ ∠F. Therefore △ABC ~ △DEF by AA ~.

13. ∠K ≅ ∠K by the Reflex. Prop. of ≅. $\frac{KL}{KN} = \frac{KM}{KL} = \frac{3}{2}$. Therefore △KLM ~ △KNL by SAS ~.

14. $\frac{UV}{XY} = \frac{VW}{YZ} = \frac{WU}{ZX} = \frac{8}{11}$. Therefore △UVW ~ △XYZ by SSS ~.

Verify that the given triangles are similar.

13. △KLM and △KNL

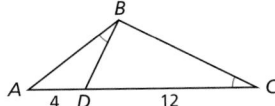

14. △UVW and △XYZ

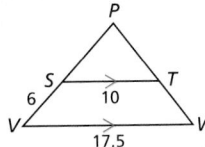

Multi-Step Explain why the triangles are similar and then find each length.

15. AB

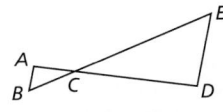

16. PS

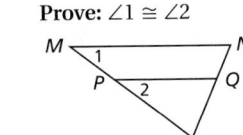

17. Given: CD = 3AC, CE = 3BC

  Prove: △ABC ~ △DEC

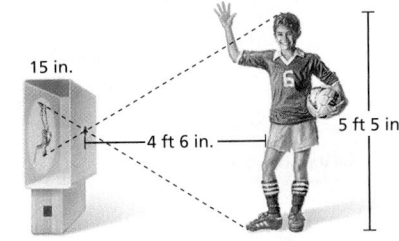

18. Given: $\frac{PR}{MR} = \frac{QR}{NR}$

  Prove: ∠1 ≅ ∠2

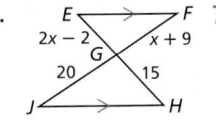

19. Photography The picture shows a person taking a pinhole photograph of himself. Light entering the opening reflects his image on the wall, forming similar triangles. What is the height of the image to the nearest tenth of an inch? **1.5 in.**

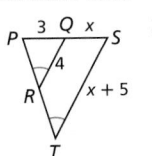

15 in.

4 ft 6 in.

5 ft 5 in.

Draw △JKL and △MNP. Determine if you can conclude that △JKL ~ △MNP based on the given information. If so, which postulate or theorem justifies your response?

20. ∠K ≅ ∠N, $\frac{JK}{MN} = \frac{KL}{NP}$
yes; SAS ~

21. $\frac{JK}{MN} = \frac{KL}{NP} = \frac{JL}{MP}$
yes; SSS ~

22. ∠J ≅ ∠M, $\frac{JL}{MP} = \frac{KL}{NP}$ **no**

Find the value of x.

23.

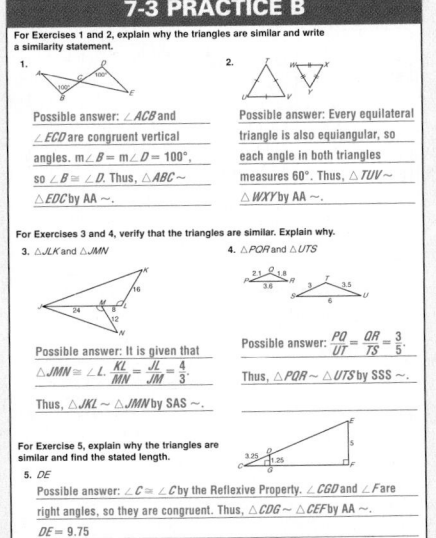

3

24.

E, F, G
2x − 2   x + 9
20   15
J   H

7

A common error in **Exercise 16** is to let $PS = x$ and then to write and solve the proportion $\frac{x}{6} = \frac{10}{17.5}$. Point out that 6 is not the length of a side of any triangle, so it cannot be used in the proportion. Encourage students to draw △PST and △PVW separately and then write the correct proportion, $\frac{x}{x+6} = \frac{10}{17.5}$.

Teaching Tip

Algebra In **Exercise 16**, remind students that in any proportion such as $\frac{x}{x+6} = \frac{10}{17.5}$, they should use parentheses to write the product as $10(x+6)$. Then use the Distributive Property to remove the parentheses.

Answers

15. It is given that ∠ABD ≅ ∠C. ∠A ≅ ∠A by the Reflex. Prop. of ≅. Therefore △ABD ~ △ACB by AA ~. AB = 8

16. Since $\overline{ST} \parallel \overline{VW}$, ∠PST ≅ ∠V by the Corr. ∡ Post. ∠P ≅ ∠P by the Reflex. Prop. of ≅. Therefore △PST ~ △PVW by AA ~. PS = 8

17. 1. CD = 3AC, CE = 3BC (Given)
  2. $\frac{CD}{AC} = 3$, $\frac{CE}{BC} = 3$ (Div. Prop. of =)
  3. ∠ACB ≅ ∠DCE (Vert. ∡ Thm.)
  4. △ABC ≅ △DEC (SAS ~ Steps 2, 3)

18. 1. $\frac{PR}{MR} = \frac{QR}{NR}$ (Given)
  2. ∠R ≅ ∠R (Reflex. Prop. of ≅)
  3. △PQR ~ △MNR (SAS ~ Steps 1, 2)
  4. ∠1 ≅ ∠2 (Def. of ~ ⧍)

involves determining which of three isosceles triangles are similar, and finding a similarity ratio. This exercise prepares students for the Multi-Step TAKS Prep on page 478.

Answers

26. Possible answer: Yes; if corr. ∡ are ≅ and corr. sides are proportional, △ABC ~ △XYZ.

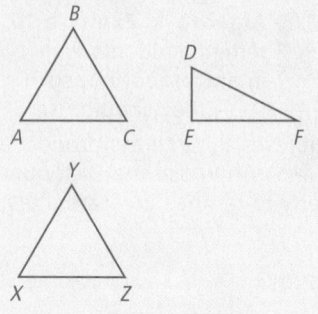

28. Since △ABC ~ △DEF, by the def. of ~ △, ∠A ≅ ∠D, and ∠B ≅ ∠E. Similarly, since △DEF ~ △XYZ, ∠D ≅ ∠X, and ∠E ≅ ∠Y. Thus by the Trans. Prop. of ≅, ∠A ≅ ∠X, and ∠B ≅ ∠Y. △ABC ~ △XYZ by AA ~.

29. Possible answer:

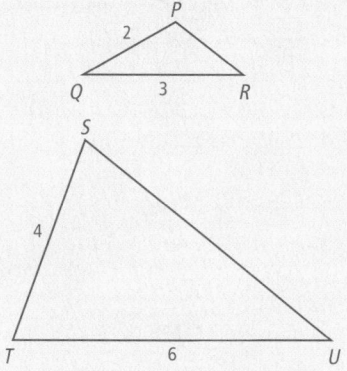

30. Since △KNJ is isosc. with vertex ∠N, $\overline{KN} \cong \overline{JN}$ by def. of an isosc. △. ∠NKJ ≅ ∠NJK by the Isosc. △ Thm. It is given that ∠H ≅ ∠L, so △GHJ ~ △MLK by AA ~.

31a. The △ are ~ by AA ~ if you assume that the camera is ∥ to the hurricane (that is, $\overline{YX} \parallel \overline{AB}$).

b. △YWZ ~ △BCZ, and △XWZ ~ △ACZ, also by AA ~.

c. 105 mi

33. Let the measure of the vertex ∡ be x°. Then by the Isosc. △ Thm., the base ∡ in each of the △ must measure $\left(\frac{180-x}{2}\right)°$. So the △ are ~ by AA ~.

25. This problem will prepare you for the Multi-Step TAKS Prep on page 478.

The set for an animated film includes three small triangles that represent pyramids.

a. Which pyramids are similar? Why?

b. What is the similarity ratio of the similar pyramids? $\frac{5}{4}$

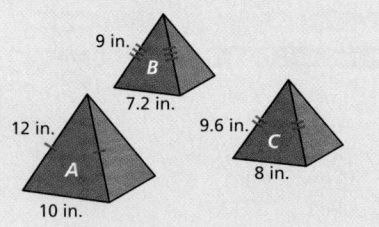

25a. Pyramids A and C are ~ because the ratios of their corr. sides lengths are =.

26. Critical Thinking △ABC is not similar to △DEF, and △DEF is not similar to △XYZ. Could △ABC be similar to △XYZ? Why or why not? Make a sketch to support your answer.

27. Recreation To play shuffleboard, two teams take turns sliding disks on a court. The dimensions of the scoring area for a standard shuffleboard court are shown. What are JK and MN? **2 ft; 4 ft**

28. Prove the Transitive Property of Similarity.
Given: △ABC ~ △DEF,
    △DEF ~ △XYZ
Prove: △ABC ~ △XYZ

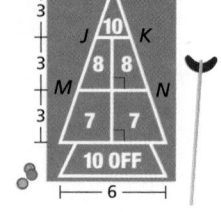

29. Draw and label △PQR and △STU such that $\frac{PQ}{ST} = \frac{QR}{TU}$ but △PQR is NOT similar to △STU.

30. Given: △KNJ is isosceles with ∠N as the vertex angle.
    ∠H ≅ ∠L
Prove: △GHJ ~ △MLK

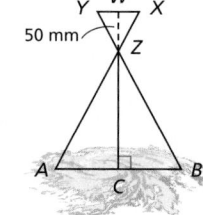

31. Meteorology Satellite photography makes it possible to measure the diameter of a hurricane. The figure shows that a camera's aperture YX is 35 mm and its focal length WZ is 50 mm. The satellite W holding the camera is 150 mi above the hurricane, centered at C.

a. Why is △XYZ ~ △ABZ? What assumption must you make about the position of the camera in order to make this conclusion?

b. What other triangles in the figure must be similar? Why?

c. Find the diameter AB of the hurricane.

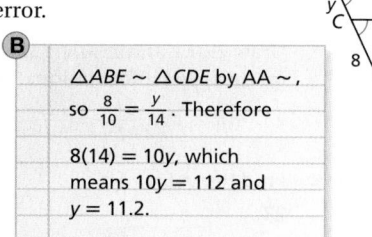

32. /// **ERROR ANALYSIS** /// Which solution for the value of y is incorrect? Explain the error.

32. Solution B is incorrect. The proportion should be $\frac{8}{10} = \frac{8+y}{14}$.

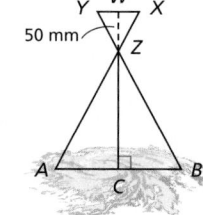

A	**B**
△ABE ~ △CDE by AA ~, so $\frac{14}{8+y} = \frac{10}{8}$. Then $10(8+y) = 8(14)$, or $80 + 10y = 112$. So $10y = 32$ and $y = 3.2$.	△ABE ~ △CDE by AA ~, so $\frac{8}{10} = \frac{y}{14}$. Therefore $8(14) = 10y$, which means $10y = 112$ and $y = 11.2$.

33. Write About It Two isosceles triangles have congruent vertex angles. Explain why the two triangles must be similar.

7-3 READING STRATEGIES

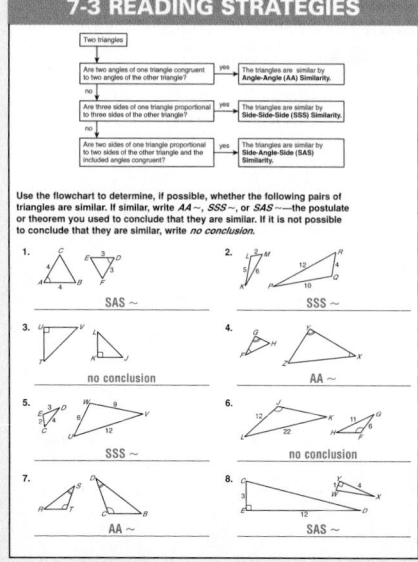

7-3 RETEACH

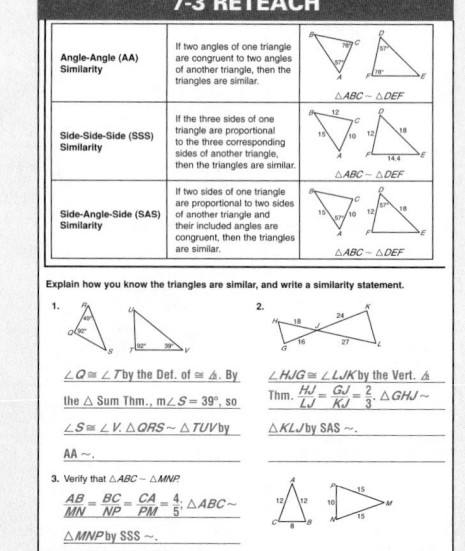